PROPERTIES OF ABSOLUTE VALUE

$|a| \geq 0$

$|a| = |-a|$

$|a - b| = |b - a|$

$|a^2| = |a|^2 = a^2$

MULTIPLICATION PATTERNS

$(a + b)^2 = a^2 + 2ab + b^2$

$(a - b)^2 = a^2 - 2ab + b^2$

$(a + b)(a - b) = a^2 - b^2$

$(a + b)^3 = a^3 + 3a^2b + 3ab^2 + b^3$

$(a - b)^3 = a^3 - 3a^2b + 3ab^2 - b^3$

$(a + b)^n = \binom{n}{0}a^n + \binom{n}{1}a^{n-1}b + \binom{n}{2}a^{n-2}b^2 + \cdots + \binom{n}{n}b^n$

PROPERTIES OF EXPONENTS AND RADICALS

$b^n \cdot b^m = b^{n+m}$ $\dfrac{b^n}{b^m} = b^{n-m}$

$(b^n)^m = b^{mn}$

$(ab)^n = a^n b^n$ $\sqrt[n]{ab} = \sqrt[n]{a}\sqrt[n]{b}$

$\left(\dfrac{a}{b}\right)^n = \dfrac{a^n}{b^n}$ $\sqrt[n]{\dfrac{a}{b}} = \dfrac{\sqrt[n]{a}}{\sqrt[n]{b}}$

EQUATIONS DETERMINING FUNCTIONS

Linear function: $f(x) = ax + b$

Quadratic function: $f(x) = ax^2 + bx + c$

Polynomial function: $f(x) = a_n x^n + a_{n-1}x^{n-1} + \cdots + a_1 x + a_0$

Rational function: $f(x) = \dfrac{g(x)}{h(x)}$,   where g and h are polynomial functions

Exponential function: $f(x) = b^x$,   where $b > 0$ and $b \neq 1$

Logarithmic function: $f(x) = \log_b x$,   where $b > 0$ and $b \neq 1$

INTERVAL

(a, ∞)	
$(-\infty, b)$	$\{x \mid x < b\}$
(a, b)	$\{x \mid a < x < b\}$
$[a, \infty)$	$\{x \mid x \geq a\}$
$(-\infty, b]$	$\{x \mid x \leq b\}$
$(a, b]$	$\{x \mid a < x \leq b\}$
$[a, b)$	$\{x \mid a \leq x < b\}$
$[a, b]$	$\{x \mid a \leq x \leq b\}$

PROPERTIES OF LOGARITHMS

$\log_b b = 1$

$\log_b 1 = 0$

$\log_b rs = \log_b r + \log_b s$

$\log_b\left(\dfrac{r}{s}\right) = \log_b r - \log_b s$

$\log_b r^p = p(\log_b r)$

FACTORING PATTERNS

$a^2 - b^2 = (a + b)(a - b)$

$a^3 - b^3 = (a - b)(a^2 + ab + b^2)$

$a^3 + b^3 = (a + b)(a^2 - ab + b^2)$

PRECALCULUS

THIRD EDITION

Jerome E. Kaufmann

PWS PUBLISHING COMPANY

I(T)P An International Thomson Publishing Company

Boston • Albany • Bonn • Cincinnati • Detroit • London • Madrid •
Melbourne • Mexico City • New York • Paris • San Francisco •
Singapore • Tokyo • Toronto • Washington

PWS PUBLISHING COMPANY
20 Park Plaza, Boston, Massachusetts 02116-4324

 This book is printed on recycled, acid-free paper.

I(T)P™

International Thomson Publishing
The trademark ITP is used under license.

For more information, contact:

PWS Publishing Co.
20 Park Plaza
Boston, MA 02116

International Thomson Publishing Europe
Berkshire House 168-173
High Holborn
London WC1V 7AA
England

Thomas Nelson Australia
102 Dodds Street
South Melbourne, 3205
Victoria, Australia

Nelson Canada
1120 Birchmount Road
Scarborough, Ontario
Canada M1K 5G4

International Thomson Editores
Campos Eliseos 385, Piso 7
Col. Polanco
11560 México D.F., Mexico

International Thomson Publishing GmbH
Königswinterer Strasse 418
53227 Bonn, Germany

International Thomson Publishing Asia
221 Henderson Road
#05-10 Henderson Building
Singapore 0315

International Thomson Publishing Japan
Hirakawacho Kyowa Building, 31
2-2-1 Hirakawacho
Chiyoda-ku, Tokyo 102
Japan

Library of Congress Cataloging-in-Publication Data
Kaufmann, Jerome E.
    Precalculus/Jerome E. Kaufmann.—3rd ed.
        p. cm.
    Includes index.
    ISBN 0-534-94362-4
    1. Algebra. 2. Trigonometry. 3. Geometry, Analytic.
    I. Title.
QA154.2.K375 1995
512'.1—dc20   94-39026
                                                                CIP

Photo Credits

Ch 1 (p. 2)—Flip Chalfant/The Image Bank;   *Ch 2 (p. 95)*—1988 Frank Whitney/The Image Bank;   *Ch 3 (p. 157)*—Daniel S. Brody/Stock, Boston;   *Ch 4 (p. 227)*—Louis H. Jawitz/The Image Bank;   *Ch 5 (p. 297)*—Barbara Alper/Stock, Boston;   *Ch 6 (p. 363)*—Fredrik D. Bodin/Stock, Boston;   *Ch 7 (p. 461)*—Michael Salas/The Image Bank;   *Ch 8 (p. 521)*—Fredrik D. Bodin/Stock, Boston;   *Ch 9 (p. 569)*—Joe McNally/The Image Bank;   *Ch 10 (p. 621)*—Murray Alcosser/The Image Bank;   *Ch 11 (p. 655)*—Fredrik D. Bodin/Stock, Boston

Sponsoring Editor: David Dietz
Assistant Editor: Mary Beckwith
Production Coordinator: Robine Andrau
Marketing Manager: Marianne C. P. Rutter
Manufacturing Coordinator: Marcia A. Locke
Production: Susan Graham

Interior/Cover Designer: Julia Gecha
Interior Illustrator: Network Graphics
Typesetter: York Graphic Services
Cover Photo: Nicholas Foster/The Image Bank
Cover Printer: New England Book Components
Text Printer: Quebecor Printing/Hawkins

Printed and bound in the United States of America
94 95 96 97 98 — 10 9 8 7 6 5 4 3 2 1

CONTENTS

7 TRIGONOMETRY AND PROBLEM SOLVING 460

8 TOPICS IN ANALYTIC GEOMETRY 520

9 CONIC SECTIONS 568

PREFACE

Precalculus, Third Edition, contains the basic concepts from algebra, trigonometry, and analytic geometry that are needed in subsequent mathematics courses, especially the calculus sequence. Four major ideas serve as unifying themes, namely, (1) solving equations and inequalities, (2) developing problem-solving techniques, (3) developing graphing techniques, and (4) developing an understanding of the concept of a function. These are the four vital areas for precalculus students.

Regarding the choice of topics and the method of presentation, I have kept an eye on the calculus courses that come later for many of these students. Note, for example, the simplification work with certain types of complex fractions (Section 1.4); the material of difference quotients (Section 3.1); the idea of finding two functions that can be used to make up a given composite function (Section 3.5); the work with rationalizing numerators instead of denominators (Section 4.1); the emphasis on the natural exponential and logarithmic functions (Sections 4.3 and 4.5); the formation of a good basis for the concept of a limit (Sections 5.4 and 5.5); and the inclusion of work with partial fractions (Section 5.6).

Furthermore, Chapter 8 contains several topics (vectors, polar coordinates, parametric equations, and 3-space coordinate geometry) that are necessary for calculus. A complete treatment of the conic sections is given in Chapter 9.

New in This Edition

1. **Graphics Calculator Examples**, incorporated throughout the text, enable students to experience the power of this technology as it is used to demonstrate the graphical approach to problem solving.

2. **Graphics Calculator Activities**, a new category of problems, were added to give students practice with graphics calculators. About half of the problem sets contain these problems with a total of approximately 650 new exercises. These exercises were designed to reinforce concepts already presented and lay the groundwork for concepts about to be discussed. They also ask students to predict shapes and locations of graphs based on earlier graphing experiences and to solve problems that are best expressed graphically with the aid of a graphics calculator. Through working these problems, students should become more familiar with the

capabilities and limitations of the graphics calculator. See, for example, Problem Sets 2.3, 2.4, 3.2, 3.3, 3.4, 4.3, 5.3, 6.4, and 8.4.

3. **Thoughts into Words**, another new category of problems, are designed to encourage students to express in written form their understanding of various mathematical ideas. About two-thirds of the problem sets contain these exercises. For example, see Problem Sets 1.1, 1.4, 1.5, 3.1, 5.3, 6.5, 7.2, 8.6, and 9.3.

4. All of the applications in examples and exercises have been labeled to help identify types of problems at a glance.

5. New **Cumulative Review Problem Sets** have been added at the end of Chapters 5 and 7.

6. A greater emphasis on developing specific problem-solving techniques has been incorporated in appropriate sections throughout the text. For example, see Sections 1.5 and 7.1.

7. New chapter introductions also emphasize the problem-solving facet of mathematics.

8. A new Section 3.4 introduces transformations—that is, translations, reflections, stretchings, and shrinkings—of some basic curves. These ideas are then used throughout the text when various functions are graphed.

9. A new Section 7.4 has been added. This section is a combination of the material on the ambiguous case in solving triangles from old Section 7.3 and some new material on area formulas.

10. Parts of Chapter 8 have been rewritten and reorganized. Parametric equations have been moved so as to precede the work on polar equations. Some graphing utilities use parametric equations to graph polar equations.

11. The material on solving systems of linear equations using the substitution and elimination-by-addition methods has been moved from Section 11.1 to Section 2.4. This allows us to use systems of equations as a problem-solving tool throughout the text.

Specific Comments About Some of the Chapters

1. Chapter 1, with the possible exception of the binomial theorem in Section 1.2 and complex numbers in Section 1.5, is a review of intermediate algebra. This material was written so that it can be reviewed with a minimum of instructor help.

2. Chapter 2 was written on the premise that even students at this level need more work with coordinate geometry concepts, especially graphing techniques, to form a basis for the function concept. The straight line and circle are covered extensively in this chapter so that Chapter 9 can be devoted to the parabola, ellipse, and hyperbola.

3. Chapters 3, 4, and 5 are tied together by the function concept. A straight-forward approach to the function concept is presented in Chapter 3. The entire chapter is devoted to functions without the need for the student to jump back and forth between functions and relations that are not functions. Chapter 4 presents a modern-day version of exponents and logarithms, with an emphasis on the natural exponential and logarithmic functions; the emphasis is on making the concepts and their applications understood, with the calculator used as a computational tool. Chapter 5 presents some of the highlights of the theory of equations without getting too bogged down in deductive details; we then concentrate on graphing polynomial and rational functions. We discuss partial fraction decomposition in the final section of Chapter 5.

4. The trigonometry material in Chapters 6 and 7 is organized specifically for this type of course. Chapter 6 contains the analytic part of trigonometry that is needed for calculus. The trigonometric functions are introduced via angles and this section is followed immediately by the unit circle interpretation. Thus all of the standard ways of interpreting the trigonometric functions are presented early in the chapter. Graphing is the key issue of Sections 6.3 and 6.4. Variations of all six basic trigonometric curves are covered in a carefully organized manner, which is consistent with the graphing discussions in the previous chapters. Problem solving is the focus of Chapter 7. Vectors are introduced in a geometric setting and then used to solve problems.

5. Chapter 8 contains several topics that are a prerequisite for the study of calculus. Sometimes they are introduced first in calculus; however, I personally feel that a brief introduction to these ideas prior to calculus is extremely valuable. Graphing is again the key issue with the introduction of polar coordinates, parametric equations, and 3-space coordinate geometry.

6. Chapter 9 contains the usual definition-oriented development of the conic sections. The translation formulas are developed and then used to produce standard equations for parabolas, ellipses, and hyperbolas. The rotation formulas are developed and used in Section 9.4.

7. Chapters 10 and 11 were written to provide the instructor with some flexibility as to choice of topics. Chapter 11 is devoted primarily to solving systems of linear equations using matrices and determinants.

Other Special Features of the Book

1. Many of the problem sets contain a special section entitled **Further Investigations**. (Most of these exercises are the Miscellaneous Problems of the previous edition.) These problems encompass a variety of ideas: Some of them are proofs, some exhibit alternative approaches to topics covered in

the text, and some bring in supplementary topics and relationships. All of them could be omitted without breaking the continuity pattern of the text.

2. There is a **Review Problem Set** at the end of each chapter. These sets are designed to help students pull together the ideas presented in the chapter. For example, in Chapter 9 each section presents a different conic section. Then the review problem set contains a mixture of conic sections for the students to identify and graph.

3. I tried to make the **Chapter Summary** truly useful from a student's viewpoint. There is no standard format for these chapter summaries. Instead, at the end of each chapter I asked myself the question "What is the most effective way of summarizing the big ideas of this chapter?" In Chapter 5, for example, it seemed natural to summarize in terms of the two main themes "solving polynomial equations" and "graphing polynomial and rational functions."

I made every effort to write this text in the same easy-to-read manner as my other books in this series. Some of the topics are by nature a little difficult; however, they can be presented in a way that is easy to understand without sacrificing mathematical integrity. I hope that I have accomplished this objective.

Supplements for Instructors

The following supplements are available to adopters of this text:

- An *Instructor's Answer Book* offers answers to all the exercises. Detailed solutions are provided for some of the more challenging problems.

- *Test Bank with Chapter Tests* may be photocopied by instructors and used by them to test their students. Answers to test questions are provided at the back of the book for the instructor only. There is one multiple-choice test and one short-answer test for each text chapter.

- *EXPTest,* a computerized test bank for IBM PCs and compatibles, contains hundreds of problems. Questions are multiple choice, true/false, and open-ended. Instructors can interact with the program by adding to existing questions and producing individual tests.

- *ExamBuilder,* a computerized test bank for the Macintosh, has features and questions similar to those of EXPTest.

- *Transparencies* Thirty-three full color acetates provide enlarged versions of illustrations that are similar to those found in the text.

Supplements for Students

- *Student's Solutions Manual* provides detailed solutions to about one-fourth of the text's exercises.

- *College Algebra and Trigonometry Explorations for the TI-81 and TI-82 Graphics Calculators* by Nancy Hyde, Broward Community College, is designed to complement the Kaufmann precalculus series of texts. The purpose of these explorations is to guide the student into discovering or reinforcing important mathematical concepts through visualization, computation, and programming. This book provides (1) an introduction to the TI-81 and TI-82 graphics calculators; (2) examples to be used in the classroom, in small groups, or by the student working independently; and (3) corresponding exercises. Each college algebra or trigonometry activity in the book includes a brief explanation, relevant graphics calculator techniques, and examples that show the graphical interpretation of the concept. The author demonstrates how these concepts can be explored graphically or how the graphical representation reinforces a concept.

- *Precalculus in Context: Functioning in the Real World* by Davis, Moran, and Murphy is a lab manual consisting of twelve projects that encourages students to explore precalculus concepts. Graphics calculators or computer graphing software are required to solve each experiment and its corresponding exercises.

- *Videotapes* are available to qualified adopters. Through the departmental or college audiovisual library, students can check out these videos and use them to review material when they need additional help.

- *INVESTIGATE,* tutorial software for the Macintosh and IBM PCs and compatibles, helps students review precalculus as needed. Questions are presented to the students with full mathematical notation and graphs. When students give incorrect answers, they are stepped through explanations of the problems to give immediate feedback and to correct misunderstandings. The program comes with a pop-up calculator, which instructors may disable at their discretion. INVESTIGATE may be set up to record individual students' grades and is fully network compatible. Operation of both the MS-DOS and Macintosh versions is identical, allowing easy training and use in labs having both types of computers.

- *Quick Reference Card* Packaged with this edition of the text is a new problem-solving tool—a formula card. This perforated card, found in the back of the book, will help students master key formulas, equations, and graphs in the course. By serving as a quick reference and minimizing the need for page turning, the formula card reduces the time spent on tedious tasks so that students can focus on the central concepts and principles of the course.

- *Student Edition of Theorist* is software for the Macintosh that combines powerful algebra and graphics capabilities with an intuitive, user-friendly interface. Once they purchase it, students will be able to make use of this software for this course as well as for future mathematics courses.

Acknowledgments

I would like to take this opportunity to thank the following people who served as reviewers for this text:

Alice Burstein
Middlesex Community Technical College

Parviz Khajeh-Khalili
Christopher Newport University

Edward L. Curtis
Wilkes Community College

Dr. C.J. Knickerbocker
St. Lawrence University

Martin Forrest
Louisiana State University

Judy McInerney
Sandhills Community College

Michele Goodro
Casper College

William J. Soeffing
Sioux Falls College

Mary Lou Hart
Brevard Community College

Dr. Jan Vandever
South Dakota State University

Dick Holliday
Rogue Community College

David C. Vella
Skidmore College.

I am very grateful to the staff of PWS, especially David Dietz and Mary Beckwith, for their continuous cooperation and assistance throughout this project. I would also like to express my sincere gratitude to Robine Andrau and to Susan Graham. They continue to make my life as an author so much easier by carrying out the details of production in a dedicated and caring way. My thanks go out to Joan and Stuart Thomas for all of their hard work on the creation and programming of questions for the computerized test banks and chapter tests.

Again, very special thanks are due to my wife, Arlene, who spends numerous hours typing and proofreading manuscripts, answer keys, and solutions manuals.

Jerome E. Kaufmann
Marble Falls, Texas

SOME BASIC CONCEPTS OF ALGEBRA

A good understanding of some basic algebraic concepts provides a sound basis for developing problem solving techniques. Furthermore, the development of many topics in trigonometry and analytic geometry depends upon this same algebraic foundation. Therefore, *be sure* that you can work effectively with the algebraic concepts we review in this first chapter.

We can use the equation $0.2(8) - 0.2x + x = 0.9(8)$ to determine the change of the mixture in a radiator from 20% antifreeze to 90% antifreeze. We would drain 7 liters of coolant from a radiator that holds 8 liters and replace them with pure antifreeze, which will change the protection against temperature from 12°F to −20°F.

1.1   SOME BASIC IDEAS

Many areas of mathematics use the concept of sets. A **set** is a collection of objects and the objects are called **elements** or **members** of the set. The use of capital letters to name sets, and set braces, { }, to enclose the elements or a description of the elements provides a convenient way to communicate about sets. For example, a set A consisting of the vowels of the alphabet can be represented as follows.

A = {vowels of the alphabet}	Word description
A = {a, e, i, o, u}	List or roster description
A = $\{x \mid x$ is a vowel$\}$	Set-builder notation

The **set-builder notation** combines the use of braces and the concept of a variable. The expression $\{x \mid x$ is a vowel$\}$ is read, *The set of all x such that x is a vowel.* The vertical line is read, *such that.* A set consisting of no elements is called the **empty** or **null set** and is written $\varnothing$.

Two sets are said to be **equal** if they contain exactly the same elements. For example, {1, 2, 3} = {2, 1, 3} because both sets contain exactly the same elements; the order in which the elements are listed is not important. A slash mark through an equality symbol denotes *not equal to.* Thus if A = {1, 2, 3} and B = {3, 6}, we can write $A \neq B$, which is read, *Set A is not equal to set B.*

Real Numbers

The following terminology is commonly used to classify different types of numbers.

{1, 2, 3, 4, . . . }	Natural numbers, counting numbers, positive integers
{0, 1, 2, 3, . . . }	Whole numbers, nonnegative integers
{ . . . , −3, −2, −1}	Negative integers
{ . . . , −3, −2, −1, 0}	Nonpositive integers
{ . . . , −2, −1, 0, 1, 2, . . . }	Integers

A **rational number** is defined as any number that can be expressed in the form $\frac{a}{b}$, where a and b are integers and b is not zero. The following are examples of rational numbers:

$\frac{2}{3}$,

$-\frac{3}{4}$,

6 because $6 = \frac{6}{1}$,

-4 because $-4 = \frac{-4}{1} = \frac{4}{-1}$,

0 because $0 = \frac{0}{1} = \frac{0}{2} = \frac{0}{3}$, etc.,

$.3$ because $.3 = \frac{3}{10}$,

$6\frac{1}{2}$ because $6\frac{1}{2} = \frac{13}{2}$

A rational number can also be defined in terms of a decimal representation. Before doing so, let's briefly review the different possibilities for decimal representations. Decimals can be classified as *terminating, repeating,* or *nonrepeating.* Here are some examples of each.

$$\begin{pmatrix} .3 \\ .46 \\ .789 \\ .2143 \end{pmatrix}$$ Terminating decimals

$$\begin{pmatrix} .3333 \ldots \\ .141414 \ldots \\ .712712712 \ldots \\ .24171717 \ldots \\ .9675283283283 \ldots \end{pmatrix}$$ Repeating decimals

$$\begin{pmatrix} .472195631 \ldots \\ .21411711191111 \ldots \\ .752389433215333 \ldots \end{pmatrix}$$ Nonrepeating decimals

A **repeating decimal** has a block of digits that repeats indefinitely. This repeating block of digits may be of any number of digits and may or may not begin immediately after the decimal point. A small horizontal bar is commonly used to indicate the repeat block. Thus, .3333 . . . can be expressed as $.\overline{3}$ and .24171717 . . . as $.24\overline{17}$.

In terms of decimals, a **rational number** is defined as a number that has either a terminating or a repeating decimal representation. The following examples illustrate some rational numbers written in $\dfrac{a}{b}$ form and in the equivalent decimal form.

$$\tfrac{3}{4} = .75, \qquad \tfrac{3}{11} = .\overline{27}, \qquad \tfrac{1}{8} = .125, \qquad \tfrac{1}{7} = .\overline{142857}, \qquad \tfrac{1}{3} = .\overline{3}$$

An **irrational number** is defined as a number that cannot be expressed in $\dfrac{a}{b}$ form, where a and b are integers and b is not zero. Furthermore, an irrational number has a nonrepeating decimal representation. The following are some examples of irrational numbers and a partial decimal representation for each.

$$\sqrt{2} = 1.414213562373095 \ldots$$

$$\sqrt{3} = 1.73205080756887 \ldots$$

$$\pi = 3.14159265358979 \ldots$$

The entire set of **real numbers** is composed of the rational numbers along with the irrationals. The following tree diagram can be used to summarize the various classifications of the real number system.

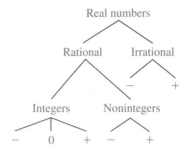

The concept of subset is convenient to explain at this time. A set A is a **subset** of another set B if and only if every element of A is also an element of B. For example, if $A = \{1, 2\}$ and $B = \{1, 2, 3\}$, then A is a subset of B (written $A \subseteq B$ and read, *A is a subset of B*). The slash mark can also be used here to denote negation. If $A = \{1, 2, 4, 6\}$ and $B = \{2, 3, 7\}$, we can say that *A is not a subset of B* by writing $A \nsubseteq B$. The following statements use the subset vocabulary and symbolism.

1. The set of whole numbers is a subset of the set of integers.

$$\{0, 1, 2, 3, \ldots\} \subseteq \{\ldots, -2, -1, 0, 1, 2, \ldots\}$$

2. The set of integers is a subset of the set of rational numbers.

$$\{\ldots, -2, -1, 0, 1, 2, \ldots\} \subseteq \{x \mid x \text{ is a rational number}\}$$

3. The set of rational numbers is a subset of the set of real numbers.

$$\{x \mid x \text{ is a rational number}\} \subseteq \{y \mid y \text{ is a real number}\}$$

As you work with the set of real numbers, the following properties will guide your study. Be sure that you understand these properties, for not only do they facilitate manipulations with real numbers, but they also serve as a basis for many algebraic computations. The letters a, b, and c represent real numbers.

Properties of Real Numbers

Closure properties	$a + b$ is a unique real number.
	ab is a unique real number.
Commutative properties	$a + b = b + a$
	$ab = ba$
Associative properties	$(a + b) + c = a + (b + c)$
	$(ab)c = a(bc)$
Identity properties	There exists a real number 0 such that $a + 0 = 0 + a = a$.
	There exists a real number 1 such that $a(1) = 1(a) = a$.

Inverse properties	For every real number a, there exists a unique real number $-a$, such that $a + (-a) = (-a) + a = 0$.
	For every nonzero real number a, there exists a unique real number $\dfrac{1}{a}$, such that $a\left(\dfrac{1}{a}\right) = \dfrac{1}{a}(a) = 1$.
Multiplication property of zero	$a(0) = 0(a) = 0$
Multiplication property of negative one	$a(-1) = -1(a) = -a$
Distributive property	$a(b + c) = ab + ac$

Algebraic Expressions

In algebra, the concept of a variable provides the basis for generalizing arithmetic ideas. For example, by using x and y to represent *any* two real numbers, the expression $x + y$ can be used to represent the indicated sum of *any* two real numbers. The x and y in such an expression are called variables and the phrase $x + y$ is called an algebraic expression.

Algebraic expressions such as

$$2x, \qquad 8xy, \qquad -3xy, \qquad -4abc, \qquad \text{and} \qquad z$$

are called terms. A term is an indicated product and may have any number of factors. The variables of a term are called literal factors and the numerical factor is called the numerical coefficient. Thus, in $8xy$, the x and y are literal factors and 8 is the numerical coefficient. Since $1(z) = z$, the numerical coefficient of the term z is understood to be 1. Terms having the same literal factors are called similar or like terms. The distributive property in the form $ba + ca = (b + c)a$ provides the basis for simplifying algebraic expressions by combining similar terms, as illustrated by the following example.

$$-6xy + 4xy = (-6 + 4)xy$$
$$= -2xy$$

Sometimes an algebraic expression can be simplified by using the distributive property to both remove parentheses and combine similar terms, as the next example illustrates.

$$-5(y + 3) - 2(y - 8) = -5(y) - 5(3) - 2(y) - 2(-8)$$
$$= -5y - 15 - 2y + 16$$
$$= -7y + 1$$

An algebraic expression takes on a numerical value whenever each variable in the expression is replaced by a real number. For example, if x is replaced by 2, y by -4, and z by -5, the algebraic expression $3xy - 4z$ becomes the numerical expression $3(2)(-4) - 4(-5)$, which equals -4. We say that $3xy - 4z$ has a value of -4 when x equals 2, y equals -4, and z equals -5. Finding the value of an algebraic expression when given certain values for the variables is often called **evaluating an algebraic expression**.

The following **order of operations** should be followed when simplifying numerical expressions.

1. Perform the operations inside the symbols of inclusion (parentheses and brackets) and above and below each fraction bar. Start with the innermost inclusion symbol.

2. Perform all multiplications and divisions in the order in which they appear, from left to right.

3. Perform all additions and subtractions in the order in which they appear, from left to right.

EXAMPLE 1

Evaluate $\dfrac{a - [4b - (2c + 1)]}{a - b}$ when $a = -8$, $b = -7$, and $c = 14$.

Solution

$$\frac{a - [4b - (2c + 1)]}{a - b} = \frac{-8 - [4(-7) - (2(14) + 1)]}{-8 - (-7)}$$

$$= \frac{-8 - [-28 - 29]}{-1}$$

$$= \frac{-8 - [-57]}{-1}$$

$$= \frac{49}{-1} = -49$$

You should also realize that first simplifying by combining similar terms can sometimes aid in the process of evaluating an algebraic expression. The next example illustrates this idea.

EXAMPLE 2

Evaluate $2(3x + 1) - 3(4x - 3)$ when $x = -5$.

Solution

$$2(3x + 1) - 3(4x - 3) = 6x + 2 - 12x + 9 = -6x + 11$$

Now substitute -5 for x to obtain

$$-6x + 11 = -6(-5) + 11$$
$$= 30 + 11$$
$$= 41.$$

Exponents

Positive integers are used as **exponents** to indicate repeated multiplication. For example, $4 \cdot 4 \cdot 4$ can be written 4^3, where the "raised 3" indicates that 4 is to be used as a factor three times. In general, if n is a positive integer and b is any real number, then

$$b^n = \underbrace{b \cdot b \cdot b \cdot \;\cdots\; \cdot b.}_{n \text{ factors of } b}$$

The number b is referred to as the **base** and n is called the **exponent**. The expression b^n can be read, *b to the nth power* or *the nth power of b*. The terms **squared** and **cubed** are commonly associated with exponents of 2 and 3, respectively. For example, b^2 is read, *b squared* and b^3 as *b cubed*. An exponent of 1 is usually not written, so b^1 is simply written b. The following examples illustrate the use of positive integers as exponents.

$$2^3 = 2 \cdot 2 \cdot 2 = 8, \qquad \left(\tfrac{1}{2}\right)^4 = \tfrac{1}{2} \cdot \tfrac{1}{2} \cdot \tfrac{1}{2} \cdot \tfrac{1}{2} = \tfrac{1}{16},$$
$$(-5)^2 = (-5)(-5) = 25, \qquad -5^2 = -(5 \cdot 5) = -25$$

We especially want to call your attention to the last two examples. Note that $(-5)^2$ means -5 is the base to be used as a factor twice. However, -5^2 means that 5 is the base and after it is squared, we take the opposite of that result.

If $b \neq 0$, the extension to using nonpositive integers as exponents is made by defining

$$b^0 = 1 \qquad \text{and} \qquad b^{-n} = \frac{1}{b^n}.$$

Thus, we can write

$$5^0 = 1, \qquad 2^{-4} = \frac{1}{2^4} = \frac{1}{16},$$

$$(-213)^0 = 1, \qquad \left(\frac{3}{4}\right)^{-2} = \frac{1}{\left(\frac{3}{4}\right)^2} = \frac{1}{\frac{9}{16}} = \frac{16}{9}.$$

The following property summarizes the basic rules to follow when working with exponents. We have included "name tags" for easy reference.

PROPERTY 1.1

If m and n are integers, and a and b are real numbers, with $b \neq 0$ whenever it appears in a denominator, then

1. $b^n \cdot b^m = b^{n+m}$ Product of two powers

2. $(b^n)^m = b^{mn}$ Power of a power

3. $(ab)^n = a^n b^n$ Power of a product

4. $\left(\dfrac{a}{b}\right)^n = \dfrac{a^n}{b^n}$ Power of a quotient

5. $\dfrac{b^n}{b^m} = b^{n-m}$ Quotient of two powers

Let's consider some examples that illustrate the various parts of Property 1.1.

EXAMPLE 3

Evaluate

a. $(2^{-1} \cdot 3^2)^{-1}$ **b.** $\left(\dfrac{2^{-3}}{3^{-2}}\right)^{-2}$

Solutions

a. $(2^{-1} \cdot 3^2)^{-1} = (2^{-1})^{-1}(3^2)^{-1}$ Power of a product

$\qquad\qquad\qquad = (2^1)(3^{-2})$ Power of a power

$\qquad\qquad\qquad = (2)\left(\dfrac{1}{3^2}\right)$

$\qquad\qquad\qquad = (2)\left(\tfrac{1}{9}\right)$

$\qquad\qquad\qquad = \dfrac{2}{9}$

b. $\left(\dfrac{2^{-3}}{3^{-2}}\right)^{-2} = \dfrac{(2^{-3})^{-2}}{(3^{-2})^{-2}}$ Power of a quotient

$\qquad\qquad\quad = \dfrac{2^6}{3^4}$ Power of a power

$\qquad\qquad\quad = \tfrac{64}{81}$

EXAMPLE 4

Find the indicated products and quotients and express your final results with positive integral exponents only.

a. $(3x^2 y^{-4})(4x^{-3}y)$ **b.** $\left(\dfrac{15x^{-1}y^2}{5xy^{-4}}\right)^{-1}$

Solutions

a. $(3x^2y^{-4})(4x^{-3}y) = 12x^{2+(-3)}y^{-4+1}$

$$= 12x^{-1}y^{-3}$$

$$= \frac{12}{xy^3}$$

b. $\left(\dfrac{15x^{-1}y^2}{5xy^{-4}}\right)^{-1} = (3x^{-1-1}y^{2-(-4)})^{-1}$

$$= (3x^{-2}y^6)^{-1}$$

$$= (3)^{-1}(x^{-2})^{-1}(y^6)^{-1}$$

$$= 3^{-1}x^2y^{-6}$$

$$= \frac{x^2}{3y^6}$$

EXAMPLE 5

Simplify $(4^{-1} - 3^{-2})^{-1}$.

Solution

$$(4^{-1} - 3^{-2})^{-1} = \left(\frac{1}{4} - \frac{1}{3^2}\right)^{-1}$$

$$= \left(\frac{1}{4} - \frac{1}{9}\right)^{-1}$$

$$= \left(\frac{9}{36} - \frac{4}{36}\right)^{-1}$$

$$= \left(\frac{5}{36}\right)^{-1} = \frac{1}{\left(\frac{5}{36}\right)^1} = \frac{36}{5}$$

Real Number Line and Absolute Value

It is often convenient to have a geometric representation of the set of real numbers in front of us, as in Figure 1.1. Such a representation, called the **real number line**, indicates a one-to-one correspondence between the set of real numbers and the points on a line. That is to say, to each real number there corresponds one and only one point on the line, and to each point on the line there corresponds one and only

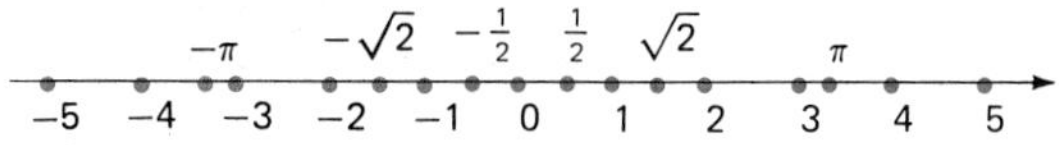

FIGURE 1.1

one real number. The number that corresponds to a particular point on the line is called the **coordinate** of the point.

Many operations, relations, properties, and concepts pertaining to real numbers can be given a geometric interpretation on the number line. For example, the addition problem $(-1) + (-2)$ can be interpreted on the number line as in Figure 1.2.

$$\overleftarrow{\quad}^{-2}$$
$$\overleftarrow{\quad}^{-1}$$

$$\begin{array}{ccccccc} + & + & + & + & + & + & + \\ -4 & -3 & -2 & -1 & 0 & 1 & 2 \end{array} \rightarrow \qquad (-1) + (-2) = -3$$

F I G U R E   1 . 2

The inequality relations also have a geometric interpretation. The statement $a > b$ (read, *a is greater than b*) means that a is to the right of b and the statement $c < d$ (read, *c is less than d*) means that c is to the left of d (Figure 1.3).

$$\begin{array}{cc} b & a \\ \bullet & \bullet \end{array} \rightarrow \qquad \begin{array}{cc} c & d \\ \bullet & \bullet \end{array} \rightarrow$$

F I G U R E   1 . 3

The property $-(-x) = x$ can be pictured on the number line in a sequence of steps as shown in Figure 1.4.

1. Choose a point that has a coordinate of x.

2. Locate its opposite (written as $-x$) on the other side of 0.

3. Locate the opposite of $-x$ (written as $-(-x)$) on the other side of 0.

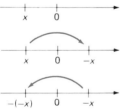

F I G U R E   1 . 4

Therefore we state that *the opposite of the opposite of any real number is the number itself* and we symbolically express this as $-(-x) = x$.

REMARK   The symbol -1 can be read, *negative one, negative of one, opposite of one,* or *additive inverse of one.* The opposite-of and additive-inverse-of terminology is especially meaningful when working with variables. For example, the symbol $-x$, read, *opposite of x* or *additive inverse of x* emphasizes an important issue. Since x can be any real number, $-x$ (opposite of x) can be zero, positive, or negative. If x is positive, then $-x$ is negative. If x is negative, then $-x$ is positive. If x is zero, then $-x$ is zero.

The concept of absolute value can be interpreted on the number line. Geometrically, the **absolute value** of any real number is the distance between the number

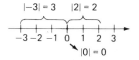

$|-3| = 3 \quad |2| = 2$

$|0| = 0$

FIGURE 1.5

and zero on the number line. For example, the absolute value of 2 is 2, the absolute value of -3 is 3, and the absolute value of 0 is 0 (Figure 1.5). Symbolically, absolute value is denoted with vertical bars. Thus we write $|2| = 2$, $|-3| = 3$, and $|0| = 0$. More formally, the concept of absolute value is defined as follows.

DEFINITION 1.1

For all real numbers a,

    1. If $a \geq 0$, then $|a| = a$

    2. If $a < 0$, then $|a| = -a$.

As a consequence of Definition 1.1, we can deduce the following properties pertaining to absolute value.

PROPERTY 1.2

If a and b are real numbers, then

    1. $|a| \geq 0$

    2. $|a| = |-a|$

    3. $|a - b| = |b - a|$

    4. $|a^2| = |a|^2 = a^2$.

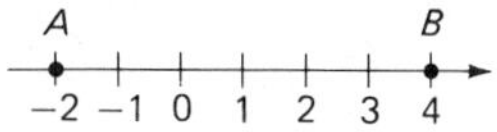

A B

$-2\ -1\ \ 0\ \ 1\ \ 2\ \ 3\ \ 4$

FIGURE 1.6

In Figure 1.6 we have indicated points A and B at -2 and 4, respectively. The distance between A and B is obviously 6 units and can be calculated by either using $|-2 - 4|$ or $|4 - (-2)|$. In general, if two points on a real number line have coordinates x_1 and x_2, the distance between the two points is determined by $|x_2 - x_1|$ or $|x_1 - x_2|$.

PROBLEM SET 1.1

Identify each of the following (Problems 1–10) as true or false.

1. Every rational number is a real number.

2. Every irrational number is a real number.

3. Every real number is a rational number.

4. If a number is real, then it is irrational.

5. Some irrational numbers are also rational numbers.

6. All integers are rational numbers.

7. The number zero is a rational number.

8. Zero is a positive integer.

9. Zero is a negative number.

10. All whole numbers are integers.

For Problems 11–20, use the following set designations.

$$N = \{x \mid x \text{ is a natural number}\}$$
$$W = \{x \mid x \text{ is a whole number}\}$$
$$I = \{x \mid x \text{ is an integer}\}$$
$$Q = \{x \mid x \text{ is a rational number}\}$$
$$H = \{x \mid x \text{ is an irrational number}\}$$
$$R = \{x \mid x \text{ is a real number}\}$$

Place $\subseteq$ or $\not\subseteq$ in each blank to make a true statement.

11. N_____R **12.** R_____N

13. N_____I **14.** I_____Q

15. H_____Q **16.** Q_____H

17. W_____I **18.** N_____W

19. I_____W **20.** I_____N

For Problems 21–34, evaluate each of the algebraic expressions for the given values of the variables.

21. $x - (2y + 3z)$, $x = -3, y = -4,$ and $z = 9$

22. $3a - [2b - (4c + 1)]$, $a = 4, b = 6,$ and $c = -8$

23. $\dfrac{-2x + 7y}{x - y}$, $x = -3$ and $y = -2$

24. $\dfrac{x - 3y + 2z}{2x - y}$, $x = 4, y = 9,$ and $z = -12$

25. $5x + 4y - 9y - 2y$, $x = 2$ and $y = -8$

26. $5a + 7b - 9a - 6b$, $a = -7$ and $b = 8$

27. $\left|\dfrac{x - y}{y - x}\right|$, $x = -6$ and $y = 13$

28. $\left|\dfrac{2a - 3b}{3b - 2a}\right|$, $a = -4$ and $b = -8$

29. $-4(2x - 1) - 5(3x + 7)$, $x = -1$

30. $5(a - 3) - 4(2a + 1) - 2(a - 4)$, $a = -3$

31. $2x^2 - 3xy - y^2$, $x = -1$ and $y = -2$

32. $3x^2 + 5xy - 2y^2$, $x = -2$ and $y = 3$

33. $-x^2 - 2y^2$, $x = -2$ and $y = -3$

34. $-x^2 - xy + y^2$, $x = -1$ and $y = 4$

35. Find the distance on the real number line between two points whose coordinates are as follows.

   a. 17 and 35   ***b.*** -14 and 12

   c. 18 and -21 ***d.*** -17 and -42

   e. -56 and -21 ***f.*** 0 and -37

36. Evaluate each of the following if x is a nonzero real number.

   a. $\dfrac{|x|}{x}$ ***b.*** $\dfrac{x}{|x|}$ ***c.*** $\dfrac{|-x|}{-x}$ ***d.*** $|x| - |-x|$

For Problems 37–66, evaluate each of the numerical expressions.

37. 2^{-3} **38.** 3^{-2}

39. -10^{-3} **40.** 10^{-4}

41. $\dfrac{1}{3^{-3}}$ **42.** $\dfrac{1}{2^{-5}}$

43. $\left(\frac{1}{2}\right)^{-2}$ **44.** $-\left(\frac{1}{3}\right)^{-2}$

45. $\left(-\frac{2}{3}\right)^{-3}$ **46.** $\left(\frac{5}{6}\right)^{-2}$

47. $\left(-\frac{1}{5}\right)^{0}$ **48.** $\dfrac{1}{\left(\frac{3}{5}\right)^{-2}}$

49. $\dfrac{1}{\left(\frac{4}{5}\right)^{-2}}$ **50.** $-\left(\frac{4}{5}\right)^{0}$

51. $2^5 \cdot 2^{-3}$ **52.** $3^{-2} \cdot 3^5$

53. $(3^{-2})^{-2}$ **54.** $[(-2)^{-1}]^{-3}$

55. $(3^{-1} \cdot 2^2)^{-1}$ **56.** $(2^3 \cdot 3^{-2})^{-2}$

57. $\left(\dfrac{2^{-2}}{5^{-1}}\right)^{-2}$ **58.** $\left(\dfrac{3^{-1}}{2^{-3}}\right)^{-2}$

59. $3^{-2} + 2^{-3}$ **60.** $2^{-3} + 5^{-1}$

61. $\left(\frac{2}{3}\right)^{-1} - \left(\frac{3}{4}\right)^{-1}$ **62.** $3^{-2} - 2^3$

63. $(2^{-4} + 3^{-1})^{-1}$ **64.** $(3^{-2} - 5^{-1})^{-1}$

65. $(2^{-1} - 3^{-2})^{-2}$ **66.** $(4^{-1} - 2^{-3})^{-2}$

For Problems 67–74, simplify each expression. Express final results without using zero or negative integers as exponents.

67. $(x^3y^{-4})^{-1}$ **68.** $(ab^2c^{-1})^{-3}$ **69.** $\left(\dfrac{y^4}{x^{-1}}\right)^{-3}$

70. $\left(\dfrac{x^{-2}}{y^3}\right)^{-2}$ **71.** $\left(\dfrac{2a^{-1}}{3b^{-2}}\right)^{-2}$ **72.** $\left(\dfrac{3x^2y}{4a^{-1}b^{-3}}\right)^{-1}$

73. $\dfrac{a^2b^{-3}}{a^{-1}b^{-2}}$ **74.** $\dfrac{x^{-1}y^{-2}}{x^3y^{-1}}$

For Problems 75–84, find the indicated products and quotients; express results using positive integral exponents only.

75. $(2x^{-1}y^2)(3x^{-2}y^{-3})$ **76.** $(4x^{-2}y^3)(-5x^3y^{-4})$

77. $(-6a^5y^{-4})(-a^{-7}y)$ **78.** $(-8a^{-4}b^{-5})(-6a^{-1}b^8)$

79. $\dfrac{24x^{-1}y^{-2}}{6x^{-4}y^3}$ **80.** $\dfrac{56xy^{-3}}{8x^2y^2}$

81. $\dfrac{-35a^3b^{-2}}{7a^5b^{-1}}$ **82.** $\dfrac{27a^{-4}b^{-5}}{-3a^{-2}b^{-4}}$

83. $\left(\dfrac{14x^{-2}y^{-4}}{7x^{-3}y^{-6}}\right)^{-2}$ **84.** $\left(\dfrac{24x^5y^{-3}}{-8x^6y^{-1}}\right)^{-3}$

For Problems 85–94, find each of the indicated products and quotients. Assume that all variables appearing as exponents represent integers.

85. $(3x^a)(4x^{2a+1})$ **86.** $(5x^{-a})(-6x^{3a-1})$

87. $(x^a)(x^{-a})$ **88.** $(-2y^{3b})(-4y^{b+1})$

89. $\dfrac{x^{3a}}{x^a}$ **90.** $\dfrac{4x^{2a+1}}{2x^{a-2}}$

91. $\dfrac{-24y^{5b+1}}{6y^{-b-1}}$ **92.** $(x^a)^{2b}(x^b)^a$

93. $\dfrac{(xy)^b}{y^b}$ **94.** $\dfrac{(2x^{2b})(-4x^{b+1})}{8x^{-b+2}}$

95. You should be able to do calculations like those in this problem set *with* and *without* a calculator. Be sure that you can do Problems 21–34 and Problems 37–66 with *your* calculator.

THOUGHTS into WORDS

96. How would you describe the difference between arithmetic and algebra?

97. Why is it important to have a good understanding of the basic properties of the real numbers as you study algebra?

98. How would you explain to someone why the product of x^2 and x^4 is x^6 and not x^8?

99. Explain how you would simplify $(3^{-1} \cdot 2^{-2})^{-1}$. How would you simplify $(3^{-1} + 2^{-2})^{-1}$?

1.2   POLYNOMIALS AND THE BINOMIAL THEOREM

Recall that algebraic expressions such as $5x$, $-6y^2$, $2x^{-1}y^{-2}$, $14a^2b$, $5x^{-4}$, and $-17ab^2c^3$ are called terms. Terms containing variables with only nonnegative integers as exponents are called **monomials**. Of the previously listed terms, $5x$, $-6y^2$, $14a^2b$, and $-17ab^2c^3$ are monomials. The **degree** of a monomial is the sum of the exponents of the literal factors. For example, $7xy$ is of degree 2, while $14a^2b$ is of degree 3, and $-17ab^2c^3$ is of degree 6. If the monomial contains only one variable, then the exponent of that variable is the degree of the monomial. For example, $5x^3$ is of degree 3 and $-8y^4$ is of degree 4. Any nonzero constant term, such as 8, is of degree zero.

A **polynomial** is a monomial or a finite sum of monomials. Thus,

$$4x^2, \qquad 3x^2 - 2x - 4, \qquad 7x^4 - 6x^3 + 5x^2 - 2x - 1,$$

$$3x^2y + 2y, \qquad \tfrac{1}{5}a^2 - \tfrac{2}{3}b^2, \qquad \text{and} \qquad 14$$

are examples of polynomials. In addition to calling a polynomial with one term a monomial, we also classify polynomials with two terms as **binomials**, and those with three terms as **trinomials**.

The **degree of a polynomial** is the degree of the term with the highest degree in the polynomial. The following examples illustrate some of this terminology.

The polynomial $4x^3y^4$ is a monomial in two variables of degree 7.

The polynomial $4x^2y - 2xy$ is a binomial in two variables of degree 3.

The polynomial $9x^2 - 7x - 1$ is a trinomial in one variable of degree 2.

Addition and Subtraction of Polynomials

Both adding and subtracting polynomials rely on the same properties. The commutative, associative, and distributive properties provide the basis for rearranging, regrouping, and combining similar terms. Consider the following addition problems.

$$
\begin{aligned}
(4x^2 + 5x + 1) + (7x^2 - 9x + 4) &= 4x^2 + 7x^2 + 5x - 9x + 1 + 4 \\
&= (4 + 7)x^2 + (5 - 9)x + (1 + 4) \\
&= 11x^2 - 4x + 5
\end{aligned}
$$

$$
\begin{aligned}
(5x - 3) + (3x + 2) + (8x + 6) &= 5x + 3x + 8x - 3 + 2 + 6 \\
&= (5 + 3 + 8)x + (-3 + 2 + 6) \\
&= 16x + 5
\end{aligned}
$$

The definition of subtraction as "adding the opposite" $(a - b = a + (-b))$ extends to polynomials in general. The opposite or additive inverse of a polynomial can be formed by taking the opposite of each term. For example, the opposite of $3x^2 - 7x + 1$ is $-3x^2 + 7x - 1$. Symbolically, this is expressed

$$-(3x^2 - 7x + 1) = -3x^2 + 7x - 1.$$

You can also think in terms of the property $-x = -1(x)$ and the distributive property. Therefore,

$$
\begin{aligned}
-(3x^2 - 7x + 1) &= -1(3x^2 - 7x + 1) \\
&= -3x^2 + 7x - 1.
\end{aligned}
$$

Now consider the following subtraction of polynomials.

$$
\begin{aligned}
(7x^2 - 2x - 4) - (3x^2 + 7x - 1) &= (7x^2 - 2x - 4) + (-3x^2 - 7x + 1) \\
&= (7x^2 - 3x^2) + (-2x - 7x) + (-4 + 1) \\
&= 4x^2 - 9x - 3
\end{aligned}
$$

Multiplying Polynomials

The distributive property is usually stated as $a(b + c) = ab + ac$, but it can be extended as follows.

$$a(b + c + d) = ab + ac + ad$$

$$a(b + c + d + e) = ab + ac + ad + ae$$

etc.

The commutative and associative properties, the properties of exponents, and the distributive property work together to form a basis for multiplying polynomials. The following example shows how to find the product of a monomial and a trinomial.

$$3x^2(2x^2 + 5x + 3) = 3x^2(2x^2) + 3x^2(5x) + 3x^2(3)$$
$$= 6x^4 + 15x^3 + 9x^2$$

In general, to find the product of two polynomials, multiply each term of the first polynomial times each term of the second polynomial and combine similar terms, as the next example illustrates.

$$(2x + 3)(3x^2 - 5x - 2) = 2x(3x^2 - 5x - 2) + 3(3x^2 - 5x - 2)$$
$$= 6x^3 - 10x^2 - 4x + 9x^2 - 15x - 6$$
$$= 6x^3 - x^2 - 19x - 6$$

In a previous algebra course you may have developed a shortcut for multiplying binomials, as illustrated by the following example.

$$(2x + 5)(3x - 2) = 6x^2 + 11x - 10$$

STEP 1   Multiply $(2x)(3x)$

STEP 2   Multiply $(2x)(-2)$ and $(5)(3x)$ and combine

STEP 3   Multiply $(5)(-2)$

REMARK   Shortcuts can be very helpful for certain manipulations in mathematics. [*A word of caution*: Do not lose the understanding of what you are doing. Make sure you can do the manipulation without the shortcut.]

Special Patterns

When multiplying binomials, some special patterns occur that you should learn to recognize. These patterns can be used to find products, and some of them are very useful later when factoring polynomials.

$$(a + b)^2 = a^2 + 2ab + b^2$$

$$(a - b)^2 = a^2 - 2ab + b^2$$

$$(a + b)(a - b) = a^2 - b^2$$

$$(a + b)^3 = a^3 + 3a^2b + 3ab^2 + b^3$$

$$(a - b)^3 = a^3 - 3a^2b + 3ab^2 - b^3$$

The following three examples illustrate the first three patterns, respectively.

$$(2x + 3)^2 = (2x)^2 + 2(2x)(3) + (3)^2$$
$$= 4x^2 + 12x + 9$$

$$(5x - 2)^2 = (5x)^2 - 2(5x)(2) + (2)^2$$
$$= 25x^2 - 20x + 4$$

$$(3x + 2y)(3x - 2y) = (3x)^2 - (2y)^2 = 9x^2 - 4y^2$$

In the first two examples, the resulting trinomial is called a **perfect-square trinomial**, which is the result of squaring a binomial. In the third example, the resulting binomial is called the **difference of two squares**. We will use both of these patterns again in the next section when factoring polynomials.

The cubing-of-binomial patterns are helpful primarily when multiplying. These patterns can shorten your work when cubing a binomial, as the next two examples illustrate.

$$(3x + 2)^3 = (3x)^3 + 3(3x)^2(2) + 3(3x)(2)^2 + (2)^3$$
$$= 27x^3 + 54x^2 + 36x + 8$$

$$(5x - 2y)^3 = (5x)^3 - 3(5x)^2(2y) + 3(5x)(2y)^2 - (2y)^3$$
$$= 125x^3 - 150x^2y + 60xy^2 - 8y^3$$

Keep in mind that these multiplying patterns are useful shortcuts; but if you forget them, simply revert to applying the distributive property.

Binomial Expansion Pattern

It is possible to write the expansion of $(a + b)^n$, where n is any positive integer, without showing all of the intermediate steps of multiplying and combining similar terms. To do this, let's observe some patterns in the following examples; each expansion can be verified by direct multiplication.

$$(a + b)^1 = a + b$$

$$(a + b)^2 = a^2 + 2ab + b^2$$

$$(a + b)^3 = a^3 + 3a^2b + 3ab^2 + b^3$$

$$(a + b)^4 = a^4 + 4a^3b + 6a^2b^2 + 4ab^3 + b^4$$

$$(a + b)^5 = a^5 + 5a^4b + 10a^3b^2 + 10a^2b^3 + 5ab^4 + b^5$$

First, note the patterns of the exponents for a and b on a term-by-term basis. The exponents of a begin with the exponent of the binomial and *decrease* by 1, term by term, until the last term, which has $a^0 = 1$. The exponents of b begin with zero ($b^0 = 1$) and *increase* by 1, term by term, until the last term, which contains b to the power of the original binomial. In other words, the variables in the expansion of $(a + b)^n$ have the pattern

$$a^n, \qquad a^{n-1}b, \qquad a^{n-2}b^2, \qquad \ldots, \qquad ab^{n-1}, \qquad b^n,$$

where for each term, the sum of the exponents of a and b is n.

Now let's consider the numerical coefficients of the terms of a binomial expansion. Before stating a formula that will yield these coefficients, we need to introduce the concept of **factorial notation**. If n is any positive integer, the symbol $n!$ (read, *n factorial*) is defined as follows.

$$n! = n(n - 1)(n - 2) \ldots 1$$

In other words, $n!$ is the product of the first n positive integers. For example,

$$1! = 1, \qquad 2! = 2 \cdot 1 = 2, \qquad 3! = 3 \cdot 2 \cdot 1 = 6, \qquad \text{and}$$
$$4! = 4 \cdot 3 \cdot 2 \cdot 1 = 24.$$

We also define $0! = 1$.

The numerical coefficients of the terms of a binomial expansion (often referred to as binomial coefficients) are denoted by $\binom{n}{k}$, where $k = 0, 1, 2, 3, \ldots, n$ and are given by the formula

$$\binom{n}{k} = \frac{n!}{k!(n - k)!}.$$

The symbol $\binom{n}{k}$ denotes the coefficient of the $(k + 1)$st term of the expansion of $(a + b)^n$. In other words, when $k = 0$, then $\binom{n}{0}$ denotes the coefficient of the first term; when $k = 1$, $\binom{n}{1}$ denotes the coefficient of the second term, and so on. The coefficients of the terms of the expansion of $(a + b)^5$ are $\binom{5}{0}$, $\binom{5}{1}$, $\binom{5}{2}$, $\binom{5}{3}$, $\binom{5}{4}$, and $\binom{5}{5}$, and are calculated by the formula as follows.

$$\binom{5}{0} = \frac{5!}{0!(5 - 0)!} = \frac{5!}{0!5!} = 1$$

$$\binom{5}{1} = \frac{5!}{1!(5-1)!} = \frac{5!}{1!4!} = 5$$

$$\binom{5}{2} = \frac{5!}{2!(5-2)!} = \frac{5!}{2!3!} = 10$$

$$\binom{5}{3} = \frac{5!}{3!(5-3)!} = \frac{5!}{3!2!} = 10$$

$$\binom{5}{4} = \frac{5!}{4!(5-4)!} = \frac{5!}{4!1!} = 5$$

$$\binom{5}{5} = \frac{5!}{5!(5-5)!} = \frac{5!}{5!0!} = 1$$

REMARK   To evaluate an expression such as $\frac{9!}{2!7!}$, you may find the following format helpful.

$$\frac{9!}{2!7!} = \frac{9 \cdot 8 \cdot 7!}{2!7!} = \frac{9 \cdot \overset{4}{\cancel{8}}}{\cancel{2} \cdot 1} = 36$$

A general expansion of $(a + b)^n$, often called the **binomial theorem**, can now be stated.

Binomial Theorem

For any binomial $(a + b)$ and any positive integer n,

$$(a + b)^n = \binom{n}{0}a^n + \binom{n}{1}a^{n-1}b + \binom{n}{2}a^{n-2}b^2 + \cdots + \binom{n}{n}b^n.$$

A formal proof of the binomial theorem requires mathematical induction, which is presented in Chapter 10. For now, let's simply illustrate how the binomial theorem can be used. Keep in mind that $\binom{n}{0} = 1$ and $\binom{n}{n} = 1$.

EXAMPLE I

Expand $(a + b)^6$.

Solution

$$(a + b)^6 = a^6 + \binom{6}{1}a^5b + \binom{6}{2}a^4b^2 + \binom{6}{3}a^3b^3 + \binom{6}{4}a^2b^4 + \binom{6}{5}ab^5 + b^6$$

$$= a^6 + 6a^5b + 15a^4b^2 + 20a^3b^3 + 15a^2b^4 + 6ab^5 + b^6$$

$\left(\tfrac{4}{0}\right)(2x)^4 + \left(\tfrac{4}{1}\right)(2x)^3(3y) + \left(\tfrac{4}{2}\right)(2x)^2(3y)^2 + \left(\tfrac{4}{3}\right)(2x)(3y)^3$

$\dfrac{4 \cdot 3 \cdot 2}{1(3 \cdot 2 \cdot 1)}$ $\dfrac{4 \cdot 3}{2}$ $+ \left(\tfrac{4}{4}\right)(3y)^4$

EXAMPLE 2

Expand $(2x + 3y)^4$.

Solution

$$(2x + 3y)^4 = (2x)^4 + \binom{4}{1}(2x)^3(3y)^1 + \binom{4}{2}(2x)^2(3y)^2 + \binom{4}{3}(2x)(3y)^3 + (3y)^4$$

$$= 16x^4 + 96x^3y + 216x^2y^2 + 216xy^3 + 81y^4 \qquad \blacksquare$$

EXAMPLE 3

Expand $(x - 2y^2)^5$.

Solution

We shall treat $(x - 2y^2)^5$ as $[x + (-2y^2)]^5$.

$$[x + (-2y^2)]^5 = x^5 + \binom{5}{1}x^4(-2y^2) + \binom{5}{2}x^3(-2y^2)^2 + \binom{5}{3}x^2(-2y^2)^3 + \binom{5}{4}x(-2y^2)^4 + (-2y^2)^5$$

$$= x^5 - 10x^4y^2 + 40x^3y^4 - 80x^2y^6 + 80xy^8 - 32y^{10} \qquad \blacksquare$$

Finding Specific Terms

Sometimes it is convenient to be able to find a specific term of a binomial expansion without writing out the entire expansion. For example, suppose that we want the 6th term of the expansion $(a + b)^{12}$. We can reason as follows.

> The 6th term will contain b^5. (Note in the binomial theorem that the *exponent of b is always one less than the number of the term*.) Since the sum of the exponents for a and b must be 12 (the exponent of the binomial), the 6th term will also contain a^7. The coefficient is $\binom{12}{5}$, where the 5 agrees with the exponent of b^5. Therefore, the 6th term is
> $$\binom{12}{5}a^7b^5 = 792a^7b^5.$$

EXAMPLE 4

Find the 4th term of $(3x + 2y)^7$.

Solution

The 4th term contains $(2y)^3$ and therefore also contains $(3x)^4$. The coefficient is $\binom{7}{3}$. Thus, the 4th term is

$$\binom{7}{3}(3x)^4(2y)^3 = 35(81x^4)(8y^3)$$

$$= 22{,}680x^4y^3. \qquad \blacksquare$$

EXAMPLE 5

Find the 6th term of $(2x - y^2)^8$.

Solution

First, let's treat $(2x - y^2)^8$ as $[2x + (-y^2)]^8$. The 6th term contains $(-y^2)^5$ and $(2x)^3$. The coefficient is $\binom{8}{5}$. Therefore, the 6th term is

$$\binom{8}{5}(2x)^3(-y^2)^5 = 56(8x^3)(-y^{10})$$

$$= -448x^3y^{10}.$$

PROBLEM SET 1.2

In Problems 1–8, perform the indicated additions and subtractions.

1. $(5x^2 - 7x - 2) + (9x^2 + 8x - 4)$

2. $(-9x^2 + 8x + 4) + (7x^2 - 5x - 3)$

3. $(14x^2 - x - 1) - (15x^2 + 3x + 8)$

4. $(-3x^2 + 2x + 4) - (4x^2 + 6x - 5)$

5. $(3x - 4) - (6x + 3) + (9x - 4)$

6. $(7a - 2) - (8a - 1) - (10a - 2)$

7. $(8x^2 - 6x - 2) + (x^2 - x - 1) - (3x^2 - 2x + 4)$

8. $(12x^2 + 7x - 2) - (3x^2 + 4x + 5) + (-4x^2 - 7x - 2)$

In Problems 9–50, find the indicated products. Remember the special patterns that were discussed in this section.

9. $3xy(4x^2y + 5xy^2)$

10. $-2ab^2(3a^2b - 4ab^3)$

11. $6a^3b^2(5ab - 4a^2b + 3ab^2)$

12. $-xy^4(5x^2y - 4xy^2 + 3x^2y^2)$

13. $(2x - 1)(3x + 2)$

14. $(4x + 3)(5x - 2)$

15. $(n - 7)(3n - 2)$

16. $(4n - 1)(n + 6)$

17. $(5n + 2)(4n - 7)$

18. $(2n + 5)(7n - 5)$

19. $(x + 2)(x - 4)(x + 3)$

20. $(x - 1)(x + 6)(x - 5)$

21. $(x - 1)(2x + 3)(3x - 2)$

22. $(2x + 5)(x - 4)(3x + 1)$

23. $(3t + 2)(2t^2 - t - 1)$

24. $(3t - 2)(2t^2 + 3t + 4)$

25. $(x^2 + 2x - 1)(x^2 + 6x + 4)$

26. $(x^2 - x + 4)(2x^2 - 3x - 1)$

27. $(x^2 - 5x - 2)^2$ **28.** $(-x^2 + x - 1)^2$

29. $(5x - 7)(5x + 7)$ **30.** $(3x + 4)(3x - 4)$

31. $(7 - 2x)(7 + 2x)$

32. $(9 - 2x)(9 + 2x)$

33. $(-2x + 4)(-2x - 4)$

34. $(-x - 2)(-x + 2)$

35. $(-3x + 2)(3x - 2)$

36. $(-4x - 5)(4x + 5)$

37. $(n + 2)(2n - 1)(n - 2)$

38. $(n - 3)(3n - 1)(n + 3)$

39. $(2t - 7)^2$ **40.** $(3t - 4)^2$

41. $(1 - 5x)^2$ **42.** $(2 + 3x)^2$

43. $(x + 4)^3$ **44.** $(x - 2)^3$

45. $(2x + 1)^3$ **46.** $(3x + 4)^3$

47. $(5x - 2y)^3$ **48.** $(2x - 3y)^3$

49. $(x - 2)(x + 4)^2$ **50.** $(2x + 1)(x - 3)^2$

For Problems 51–70, use the binomial theorem to help expand each of the following.

51. $(a + b)^7$ **52.** $(a + b)^8$

53. $(x - y)^6$ **54.** $(x - y)^5$

55. $(n - 1)^5$ **56.** $(n - 2)^5$

57. $(2n + 1)^4$ **58.** $(3n + 2)^4$

59. $(2a - b)^4$ **60.** $(3a - 2b)^4$

61. $(x^2 + y)^7$ **62.** $(x + 2y^2)^6$

63. $(2x^2 - y^2)^6$ **64.** $(3x^2 - y^2)^5$

65. $\left(2 + \dfrac{1}{n}\right)^5$ **66.** $\left(3 + \dfrac{2}{n}\right)^7$

67. $\left(1 - \dfrac{1}{n}\right)^8$ **68.** $\left(2 - \dfrac{1}{n}\right)^6$

69. $(-x + 2y)^4$ **70.** $(-x + 3y)^4$

For Problems 71–78, write the first four terms of each of the binomial expansions.

71. $(x + y)^{12}$ **72.** $(x + y)^{15}$

73. $(x^2 - 2y^3)^{14}$ **74.** $(x^3 - 3y^2)^{11}$

75. $\left(a + \dfrac{1}{n}\right)^9$ **76.** $\left(2 - \dfrac{1}{n}\right)^6$

77. $(-x + 2y)^{10}$ **78.** $(-a - b)^{14}$

For Problems 79–86, find the specified term of each of the following.

79. 4th term of $(x + y)^8$ **80.** 7th term of $(x + y)^{11}$

81. 5th term of $(x - y)^9$ **82.** 4th term of $(x - 2y)^6$

83. 8th term of $(x^2 + y^3)^{10}$

84. 9th term of $(a + b^3)^{12}$

85. 7th term of $\left(1 - \dfrac{1}{n}\right)^{15}$

86. 8th term of $\left(1 - \dfrac{1}{n}\right)^{13}$

87. Use the binomial theorem to help simplify each of the following.

  a. $\dfrac{(x + h)^3 - x^3}{h}$ **b.** $\dfrac{(x + h)^4 - x^4}{h}$

  c. $\dfrac{(x + h)^5 - x^5}{h}$

88. Describe how to multiply a binomial and a trinomial.

89. Explain the role of the distributive property when multiplying polynomials.

90. Describe how to find the term that contains x^8 in the expansion of $(x^2 + 2y^3)^7$ without determining the complete expansion.

1.3   FACTORING POLYNOMIALS

If a polynomial is equal to the product of other polynomials, then each polynomial in the product is called a **factor** of the original polynomial. For example, since $x^2 - 4$ can be expressed as $(x + 2)(x - 2)$, we say that $x + 2$ and $x - 2$ are factors of $x^2 - 4$. The process of expressing a polynomial as a product of polynomials is called **factoring**. In this section we will consider methods of factoring polynomials with integer coefficients.

In general, factoring is the reverse of multiplication; so we can use our knowledge of multiplication to help develop factoring techniques. For example, we previously used the distributive property to find the product of a monomial and a polynomial, as the next example illustrates.

$$3x(x + 4) = 3x(x) + 3x(4) = 3x^2 + 12x$$

For factoring purposes, the distributive property (now in the form $ab + ac = a(b + c)$) can be used to reverse the process. (The step in the dashed box can be done mentally.)

$$3x^2 + 12x = \boxed{3x(x) + 3x(4)} = 3x(x + 4)$$

Polynomials can be factored in a variety of ways. Consider some factorizations of $3x^2 + 12x$.

$$3x^2 + 12x = 3x(x + 4) \qquad \text{or} \qquad 3x^2 + 12x = 3(x^2 + 4x) \qquad \text{or}$$

$$3x^2 + 12x = x(3x + 12) \qquad \text{or} \qquad 3x^2 + 12x = \tfrac{1}{2}(6x^2 + 24x)$$

We are, however, primarily interested in the first of these factorization forms, which we shall refer to as the **completely factored form**. A polynomial with integral coefficients is in completely factored form if:

1. It is expressed as a product of polynomials with **integral coefficients**, and
2. No polynomial, other than a monomial, within the factored form can be further factored into polynomials with integral coefficients.

Do you see why the first of the factored forms of $3x^2 + 12x$ is said to be in completely factored form? In each of the other three forms, the polynomial inside the parentheses can be further factored. Furthermore, in the last form, $\tfrac{1}{2}(6x^2 + 24x)$, the condition of using only integers is violated.

This application of the distributive property is often referred to as **factoring out the highest common monomial factor**. The following examples further illustrate the process.

$$8ab - 18b = 2b(4a - 9)$$

$$30x^3 + 42x^4 - 24x^5 = 6x^3(5 + 7x - 4x^2)$$

Sometimes there may be a **common binomial factor** rather than a common monomial factor, as illustrated by the next two examples.

$$a^2(b + 1) + 2(b + 1) = (b + 1)(a^2 + 2)$$

$$x(x + 2) + 3(x + 2) = (x + 2)(x + 3)$$

It sometimes seems that a given polynomial exhibits no apparent common factor. Such is the case with $ab + 3a + bc + 3c$. However, by factoring a from the first two terms and c from the last two terms, we can proceed as follows.

$$ab + 3a + bc + 3c = a(b + 3) + c(b + 3)$$
$$= (b + 3)(a + c)$$

We refer to this process as **factoring by grouping**.

Difference of Two Squares

In Section 1.2 we called your attention to some special multiplication patterns. One of these patterns was the following:

$$(a + b)(a - b) = a^2 - b^2$$

This same pattern, viewed as a factoring pattern,

$$a^2 - b^2 = (a + b)(a - b)$$

is referred to as the **difference of two squares**. Applying the pattern is a fairly simple process, as the next example illustrates. Again, the step in the dashed box is usually performed mentally.

$$4x^2 - 25 = \lceil (2x)^2 - (5)^2 \rceil = (2x + 5)(2x - 5)$$

You must be careful not to assume an analogous factoring pattern for the **sum of two squares**; *it does not exist*. For example, $x^2 + 4$ is *not factorable using integers*. Sometimes the difference-of-two-squares pattern can be applied more than once.

$$16x^4 - 81y^4 = (4x^2 + 9y^2)(4x^2 - 9y^2)$$
$$= (4x^2 + 9y^2)(2x + 3y)(2x - 3y)$$

It may also happen that the squares are not just simple monomial squares.

$$(x + y)^2 - (2z - 3)^2 = [(x + y) + (2z - 3)][(x + y) - (2z - 3)]$$
$$= (x + y + 2z - 3)(x + y - 2z + 3)$$

Factoring Trinomials

Expressing a trinomial as the product of two binomials is one of the most common factoring techniques used in algebra. As we discussed before, to develop a factoring technique we first look at some multiplication patterns. Let's consider the product

$(x + a)(x + b)$, using the distributive property to show how each term of the resulting trinomial is formed.

$$(x + a)(x + b) = x(x + b) + a(x + b)$$
$$= x(x) + x(b) + a(x) + a(b)$$
$$= x^2 + (a + b)x + ab$$

Notice that the coefficient of the middle term is the *sum* of a and b and the last term is the *product* of a and b. These two relationships can be used to factor trinomials.

EXAMPLE 1

Factor $x^2 + 12x + 20$.

Solution

We need two integers whose sum is 12 and whose product is 20. The integers are 2 and 10, and we can complete the factoring as follows.

$$x^2 + 12x + 20 = (x + 2)(x + 10)$$ ▬▬▬

EXAMPLE 2

Factor $x^2 - 3x - 54$.

Solution

We need two integers whose sum is -3 and whose product is -54. The integers are -9 and 6, and we can complete the factoring as follows.

$$x^2 - 3x - 54 = (x - 9)(x + 6)$$ ▬▬▬

EXAMPLE 3

Factor $x^2 + 7x + 16$.

Solution

We need two integers whose sum is 7 and whose product is 16. The only possible pairs of factors of 16 are $1 \cdot 16$, $2 \cdot 8$, and $4 \cdot 4$. Since a sum of 7 is not produced by any of these pairs, the polynomial $x^2 + 7x + 16$ is *not factorable using integers*.

▬▬▬

Trinomials of the Form $ax^2 + bx + c$

Now let's consider factoring trinomials where the coefficient of the squared term is not one. First, let's illustrate an informal trial-and-error technique that works quite well for certain types of trinomials. This technique is based on our knowledge of multiplication of binomials.

EXAMPLE 4

Factor $3x^2 + 5x + 2$.

Solution

By looking at the first term, $3x^2$, and the positive signs of the other two terms, we know that the binomials are of the form

$$(x + \underline{})(3x + \underline{}).$$

Since the factors of the last term, 2, are 1 and 2, we have only the following two possibilities to try.

$$(x + 2)(3x + 1) \qquad \text{or} \qquad (x + 1)(3x + 2)$$

By checking the middle term formed in each of these products, we find that the second possibility yields the desired middle term of $5x$. Therefore,

$$3x^2 + 5x + 2 = (x + 1)(3x + 2).$$

EXAMPLE 5

Factor $8x^2 - 30x + 7$.

Solution

First, observe that the first term, $8x^2$, can be written as $2x \cdot 4x$ or $x \cdot 8x$. Secondly, since the middle term is negative and the last term is positive, we know that the binomials are of the form

$$(2x - \underline{})(4x - \underline{}) \qquad \text{or} \qquad (x - \underline{})(8x - \underline{}).$$

Thirdly, since the factors of the last term, 7, are 1 and 7, the following possibilities exist.

$$(2x - 1)(4x - 7) \qquad (2x - 7)(4x - 1)$$
$$(x - 1)(8x - 7) \qquad (x - 7)(8x - 1)$$

By checking the middle term formed in each of these products, we find that $(2x - 7)(4x - 1)$ produces the desired middle term of $-30x$. Therefore,

$$8x^2 - 30x + 7 = (2x - 7)(4x - 1).$$

EXAMPLE 6

Factor $5x^2 - 18x - 8$.

Solution

The first term, $5x^2$, can be written as $x \cdot 5x$. The last term, -8, can be written as $(-2)(4)$, $(2)(-4)$, $(-1)(8)$, or $(1)(-8)$. Therefore, we have the following possibilities to try.

$$(x - 2)(5x + 4) \qquad (x + 4)(5x - 2)$$
$$(x + 2)(5x - 4) \qquad (x - 4)(5x + 2)$$
$$(x - 1)(5x + 8) \qquad (x + 8)(5x - 1)$$
$$(x + 1)(5x - 8) \qquad (x - 8)(5x + 1)$$

By checking the middle terms, we find that $(x - 4)(5x + 2)$ yields the desired middle term of $-18x$. Thus,

$$5x^2 - 18x - 8 = (x - 4)(5x + 2).$$

EXAMPLE 7

Factor $4x^2 + 6x + 9$.

Solution

The first term, $4x^2$, and the positive signs of the middle and last terms indicate that the binomials are of the form

$$(x + \underline{\hspace{0.3cm}})(4x + \underline{\hspace{0.3cm}}) \quad \text{or} \quad (2x + \underline{\hspace{0.3cm}})(2x + \underline{\hspace{0.3cm}}).$$

Since the factors of the last term, 9, are 1 and 9 or 3 and 3, we have the following possibilities to try.

$$(x + 1)(4x + 9) \qquad (x + 9)(4x + 1)$$

$$(x + 3)(4x + 3) \qquad (2x + 1)(2x + 9)$$

$$(2x + 3)(2x + 3)$$

By trying all of these possibilities, we find that none of them yields a middle term of $6x$. Therefore, $4x^2 + 6x + 9$ is *not factorable using integers.*

Certainly as the number of possibilities increases, this trial-and-error technique for factoring becomes more tedious. The key idea is to organize your work so that you consider all possibilities. We have suggested one possible format in the previous examples. However, as you practice such problems, you may devise a format that works better for you. Whatever works best for you is the right approach.

There is another more systematic technique that you may wish to use with some trinomials. It is an extension of the technique we used earlier with trinomials where the coefficient of the squared term was one. To see the basis of this technique, consider the following general product.

$$(px + r)(qx + s) = px(qx) + px(s) + r(qx) + r(s)$$
$$= (pq)x^2 + ps(x) + rq(x) + rs$$
$$= (pq)x^2 + (ps + rq)x + rs$$

Notice that the product of the coefficient of x^2 and the constant term is $pqrs$. Likewise, the product of the two coefficients of x (ps and rq) is also $pqrs$. Therefore, the coefficient of x must be a sum of the form $ps + rq$, such that the product of the coefficient of x^2 and the constant term is $pqrs$. Let's see how this works in some specific examples.

EXAMPLE 8

Factor $6x^2 + 17x + 5$.

Solution

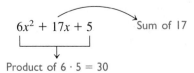

We need two integers whose sum is 17 and whose product is 30. The integers 2 and 15 satisfy these conditions. Therefore the middle term, $17x$, of the given trinomial can be expressed as $2x + 15x$ and we can proceed as follows.

$$6x^2 + 17x + 5 = 6x^2 + 2x + 15x + 5$$
$$= 2x(3x + 1) + 5(3x + 1)$$
$$= (3x + 1)(2x + 5)$$

E X A M P L E 9

Factor $5x^2 - 18x - 8$.

Solution

$5x^2 - 18x - 8$ Sum of -18

Product of $5(-8) = -40$

We need two integers whose sum is -18 and whose product is -40. The integers -20 and 2 satisfy these conditions. Therefore the middle term, $-18x$, of the trinomial can be written $-20x + 2x$ and we can factor as follows.

$$5x^2 - 18x - 8 = 5x^2 - 20x + 2x - 8$$
$$= 5x(x - 4) + 2(x - 4)$$
$$= (x - 4)(5x + 2)$$

E X A M P L E 10

Factor $24x^2 + 2x - 15$.

Solution

$24x^2 + 2x - 15$ Sum of 2

Product of $24(-15) = -360$

We need two integers whose sum is 2 and whose product is -360. To help find these integers, let's factor 360 into primes.

$$360 = 2 \cdot 2 \cdot 2 \cdot 3 \cdot 3 \cdot 5$$

Now by grouping these factors in various ways, we find that $2 \cdot 2 \cdot 5 = 20$ and $2 \cdot 3 \cdot 3 = 18$, so we can use the integers 20 and -18 to produce a sum of 2 and a product of -360. Therefore the middle term, $2x$, of the trinomial can be expressed as $20x - 18x$ and we can proceed as follows.

$$24x^2 + 2x - 15 = 24x^2 + 20x - 18x - 15$$
$$= 4x(6x + 5) - 3(6x + 5)$$
$$= (6x + 5)(4x - 3)$$

Sum and Difference of Two Cubes

Earlier in this section we discussed the difference-of-squares factoring pattern. We also pointed out that no analogous sum-of-squares pattern exists; that is to say, a polynomial such as $x^2 + 9$ is not factorable using integers. However, there do exist patterns for both the **sum and difference of two cubes**. These patterns are as follows.

$$a^3 + b^3 = (a + b)(a^2 - ab + b^2)$$
$$a^3 - b^3 = (a - b)(a^2 + ab + b^2)$$

Note how these patterns are used in the next three examples.

$$x^3 + 8 = (x)^3 + (2)^3 = (x + 2)(x^2 - 2x + 4)$$
$$8x^3 - 27y^3 = (2x)^3 - (3y)^3 = (2x - 3y)(4x^2 + 6xy + 9y^2)$$
$$8a^6 + 125b^3 = (2a^2)^3 + (5b)^3 = (2a^2 + 5b)(4a^4 - 10a^2b + 25b^2)$$

We want to leave you with one final word of caution: **Be sure to factor completely.** Sometimes more than one technique needs to be applied, or perhaps the same technique can be applied more than once. Furthermore, it is advisable to look for a highest common monomial factor first, and then to consider other techniques. Study the following examples very carefully.

$$3x^2 + 18x + 24 = 3(x^2 + 6x + 8) = 3(x + 4)(x + 2)$$
$$a^4 - 6a^2 - 27 = (a^2 - 9)(a^2 + 3) = (a + 3)(a - 3)(a^2 + 3)$$
$$3x^3 - 24y^3 = 3(x^3 - 8y^3) = 3(x - 2y)(x^2 + 2xy + 4y^2)$$

PROBLEM SET 1.3

Factor completely each of the following. Indicate any that are not factorable using integers.

1. $6xy - 8xy^2$

2. $4a^2b^2 + 12ab^3$

3. $x(z + 3) + y(z + 3)$

4. $5(x + y) + a(x + y)$

5. $9x^2 - 25$

6. $9x^2y^2 - 64$

7. $a^2 + 5a - 24$

8. $x^2 + 7x - 36$

9. $5n^2 + 18n - 8$

10. $4n^2 + 17n - 15$

11. $4x^2 + 9$

12. $9x^2 - 1$

13. $3x + 3y + ax + ay$

14. $ac + bc + a + b$

15. $(x + 4)^2 - y^2$

16. $x^2 - (y - 1)^2$

17. $12 - 7x - 12x^2$

18. $6 + 15x - 20x^2$

19. $8x^3 + 27y^3$

20. $x^3 - 1$

21. $x^4 - 7x^2 - 30$

22. $x^4 - 2x^2 - 24$

23. $21x^2 + 11xy - 2y^2$

24. $12x^2 - 28xy + 15y^2$

25. $3x^4y + 9x^2y - 84y$

26. $x^6 - x^2$

27. $2a^2 - 3bc - 2ab + 3ac$

28. $2a^2 - 5bc + 10ac - ab$

29. $3x^3 - 21x^2 + 144x$

30. $-2x^3 + 6x^2 + 14x$

31. $6n^2 + 3n - 20$

32. $4n^2 + 19n - 18$

33. $2x^4 - 11x^2 + 12$

34. $3x^4 - x^2 - 2$

35. $64x^3 - 27y^3$

36. $x^3 + 64$

37. $4n^3 + 32$

38. $5x^4 - 40x$

39. $10t^2 - 33t - 7$

40. $8y^2 + 22y - 21$

41. $4x^2 + 16$

42. $n^3 - 49n$

43. $12n^2 + 59n + 72$

44. $9a^2 - 42a + 49$

45. $18n^3 + 39n^2 - 15n$

46. $2n^3 + 6n^2 + 10n$

47. $3x^2 + x - 5$

48. $25t^2 - 100$

49. $8x^2 + 2xy - y^2$

50. $12x^2 + 7xy - 10y^2$

51. $16x^4 - 2x$

52. $-x - 27x^4$

53. $2x^4y - 26x^2y - 96y$

54. $3x^4y - 15x^2y - 108y$

55. $(a + b)^2 - (c + d)^2$

56. $(a - b)^2 - (c - d)^2$

57. $x^2 + 8x + 16 - y^2$

58. $4x^2 + 12x + 9 - y^2$

59. $x^2 - y^2 - 10y - 25$

60. $y^2 - x^2 + 16x - 64$

61. $x^3 + x^2y - x - y$

62. $x^3 - x^2y - 4x + 4y$

Factor each of the following and assume that all variables appearing as exponents represent integers.

63. $x^{2a} - 16$

64. $x^{4a} - 9$

65. $x^{3n} - y^{3n}$

66. $x^{3a} + y^{6a}$

67. $x^{2a} - 3x^a - 28$

68. $x^{2a} + 10x^a + 21$

69. $2x^{2n} + 7x^n - 30$

70. $3x^{2n} - 16x^n - 12$

71. $x^{4n} - y^{4n}$

72. $16x^{2a} + 24x^a + 9$

THOUGHTS into WORDS

73. Describe, in words, the pattern for factoring the sum of two cubes.

74. What does it mean to say that the polynomial $x^2 + 5x + 7$ is not factorable using integers?

75. What role does the distributive property play when factoring polynomials?

76. Explain how you would factor $x^2 + 60x + 864$.

FURTHER INVESTIGATIONS

77. Suppose that we want to factor $x^2 + 34x + 288$. We need to find two integers whose sum is 34 and whose product is 288. These numbers can be found as follows: Since we need a product of 288, let's consider the prime factorization of 288.

$$288 = 2^5 \cdot 3^2$$

Now we need to use five 2s and two 3s in the statement

$$(\quad) + (\quad) = 34.$$

Since 34 is divisible by 2 but not by 4, four factors of 2 must be in one number and one factor of 2 in the other number. Also, since 34 is not divisible by 3, both factors of 3 must be in the same number. These facts aid us in determining that

$$(2 \cdot 2 \cdot 2 \cdot 2) + (2 \cdot 3 \cdot 3) = 34.$$

In other words, the two numbers are 16 and 18. Thus we can complete the original factoring problem as follows.

$$x^2 + 34x + 288 = (x + 16)(x + 18)$$

Use this approach to factor each of the following.

a. $x^2 + 35x + 96$

b. $x^2 + 27x + 176$

c. $x^2 - 45x + 504$

d. $x^2 - 26x + 168$

e. $x^2 + 60x + 896$

f. $x^2 - 84x + 1728$

g. $32x^2 + 36x + 9$

h. $8x^2 + 58x + 27$

i. $16x^2 + 30x - 25$

j. $6x^2 + 7x - 24$

1.4   RATIONAL EXPRESSIONS

Indicated quotients of algebraic expressions are called **algebraic fractions**, or **fractional expressions**. The indicated quotient of two polynomials is called a **rational expression**. (This is analogous to defining a rational number as the indicated quotient of two integers.) The following are examples of rational expressions:

$$\frac{3x^2}{5}, \quad \frac{x-2}{x+3}, \quad \frac{x^2+5x-1}{x^2-9}, \quad \frac{xy^2+x^2y}{xy}, \quad \frac{a^3-3a^2-5a-1}{a^4+a^3+6}.$$

Because division by zero must be avoided, no values can be assigned to variables that will create a denominator of zero. Thus, the rational expression $\dfrac{x-2}{x+3}$ is meaningful for all real number values of x except $x = -3$. Rather than making restrictions for each individual expression, we will merely assume that **all denominators represent nonzero real numbers**

The basic properties of the real numbers can be used to work with rational expressions. For example, the property

$$\frac{a \cdot k}{b \cdot k} = \frac{a}{b},$$

which is used to reduce rational numbers, is also used to *simplify* rational expressions. Consider the following examples.

$$\frac{15xy}{25y} = \frac{3 \cdot \cancel{5} \cdot x \cdot \cancel{y}}{\cancel{5} \cdot 5 \cdot \cancel{y}} = \frac{3x}{5}, \qquad \frac{-9}{18x^2y} = -\frac{\overset{1}{\cancel{9}}}{\underset{2}{\cancel{18}x^2y}} = -\frac{1}{2x^2y}$$

Notice that slightly different formats were used in these two examples. In the first one we factored the coefficients into primes and then proceeded to simplify; however, in the second problem we simply divided a common factor of 9 out of both the numerator and the denominator. This is basically a format issue and depends upon your personal preference. Also notice that in the second example, we applied the property $\dfrac{-a}{b} = -\dfrac{a}{b}$. This is part of the general property that states

$$\frac{-a}{b} = \frac{a}{-b} = -\frac{a}{b}.$$

The factoring techniques discussed in the previous section can be used to factor numerators and denominators so that the property $(a \cdot k)/(b \cdot k) = a/b$ can be applied. Consider the following examples.

$$\frac{x^2+4x}{x^2-16} = \frac{x(\cancel{x+4})}{(x-4)(\cancel{x+4})} = \frac{x}{x-4}$$

$$\frac{5n^2+6n-8}{10n^2-3n-4} = \frac{(\cancel{5n-4})(n+2)}{(\cancel{5n-4})(2n+1)} = \frac{n+2}{2n+1}$$

$$\frac{x^3 + y^3}{x^2 + xy + 2x + 2y} = \frac{(x + y)(x^2 - xy + y^2)}{x(x + y) + 2(x + y)}$$

$$= \frac{\cancel{(x + y)}(x^2 - xy + y^2)}{\cancel{(x + y)}(x + 2)} = \frac{x^2 - xy + y^2}{x + 2}$$

$$\frac{6x^3y - 6xy}{x^3 + 5x^2 + 4x} = \frac{6xy(x^2 - 1)}{x(x^2 + 5x + 4)} = \frac{6xy\cancel{(x + 1)}(x - 1)}{\cancel{x(x + 1)}(x + 4)} = \frac{6y(x - 1)}{x + 4}$$

Note that in the last example, we left the numerator of the final fraction in factored form. This is often done if expressions other than monomials are involved. Either

$$\frac{6y(x - 1)}{x + 4} \qquad \text{or} \qquad \frac{6xy - 6y}{x + 4}$$

is an acceptable answer.

Remember that the quotient of any nonzero real number and its opposite is -1. For example, $6/-6 = -1$ and $-8/8 = -1$. Likewise, the indicated quotient of any polynomial and its opposite is equal to -1. For example,

$$\frac{a}{-a} = -1 \qquad \text{Because } a \text{ and } -a \text{ are opposites;}$$

$$\frac{a - b}{b - a} = -1 \qquad \text{Because } a - b \text{ and } b - a \text{ are opposites;}$$

$$\frac{x^2 - 4}{4 - x^2} = -1 \qquad \text{Because } x^2 - 4 \text{ and } 4 - x^2 \text{ are opposites.}$$

The next example illustrates the use of this idea when simplifying rational expressions.

$$\frac{4 - x^2}{x^2 + x - 6} = \frac{(2 + x)\boxed{(2 - x)}}{(x + 3)\boxed{(x - 2)}}$$

$$= (-1)\left(\frac{x + 2}{x + 3}\right) \qquad \frac{2 - x}{x - 2} = -1$$

$$= -\frac{x + 2}{x + 3} \qquad \text{or} \qquad \frac{-x - 2}{x + 3}$$

Multiplying and Dividing Rational Expressions

Multiplication of rational expressions is based on the following property:

$$\frac{a}{b} \cdot \frac{c}{d} = \frac{ac}{bd}.$$

In other words, we multiply numerators and we multiply denominators and express the final product in simplified form. Study the following examples carefully and pay special attention to the formats used to organize the computational work.

$$\frac{3x}{4y} \cdot \frac{8y^2}{9x} = \frac{\overset{2}{\cancel{3}} \cdot \overset{2}{\cancel{8}} \cdot \cancel{x} \cdot \overset{y}{\cancel{y^2}}}{\underset{3}{\cancel{4}} \cdot \cancel{9} \cdot \cancel{x} \cdot \cancel{y}} = \frac{2y}{3}$$

$$\frac{12x^2y}{-18xy} \cdot \frac{-24xy^2}{56y^3} = \frac{\overset{2}{\cancel{12}} \cdot \overset{8}{\cancel{24}} \cdot \overset{x^2}{\cancel{x^3}} \cdot y^3}{\underset{3}{\cancel{18}} \cdot \underset{7}{\cancel{56}} \cdot \cancel{x} \cdot \underset{y}{\cancel{y^4}}} = \frac{2x^2}{7y}$$

$$\frac{12x^2y}{-18xy} = -\frac{12x^2y}{18xy} \text{ and }$$

$$\frac{-24xy^2}{56y^3} = -\frac{24xy^2}{56y^3}$$

so the product is positive

$$\frac{y}{x^2 - 4} \cdot \frac{x + 2}{y^2} = \frac{\cancel{y}(\cancel{x + 2})}{\underset{y}{\cancel{y^2}}(\cancel{x + 2})(x - 2)} = \frac{1}{y(x - 2)}$$

$$\frac{x^2 - x}{x + 5} \cdot \frac{x^2 + 5x + 4}{x^4 - x^2} = \frac{\cancel{x}(\cancel{x - 1})(\cancel{x + 1})(x + 4)}{(x + 5)(\underset{x}{\cancel{x^2}})(\cancel{x + 1})(\cancel{x - 1})} = \frac{x + 4}{x(x + 5)}$$

To divide rational expressions we merely apply the following property.

$$\frac{a}{b} \div \frac{c}{d} = \frac{a}{b} \cdot \frac{d}{c} = \frac{ad}{bc}$$

That is to say, the quotient of two rational expressions is the product of the first expression times the reciprocal of the second. Consider the following examples.

$$\frac{16x^2y}{24xy^3} \div \frac{9xy}{8x^2y^2} = \frac{16x^2y}{24xy^3} \cdot \frac{8x^2y^2}{9xy} = \frac{16 \cdot \overset{x^2}{\cancel{8}} \cdot \overset{}{\cancel{x^4}} \cdot y^3}{\underset{3}{\cancel{24}} \cdot 9 \cdot \cancel{x^2} \cdot \underset{y}{\cancel{y^4}}} = \frac{16x^2}{27y}$$

$$\frac{3a^2 + 12}{3a^2 - 15a} \div \frac{a^4 - 16}{a^2 - 3a - 10} = \frac{3a^2 + 12}{3a^2 - 15a} \cdot \frac{a^2 - 3a - 10}{a^4 - 16}$$

$$= \frac{\cancel{3}(\cancel{a^2 + 4})(\cancel{a - 5})(\cancel{a + 2})}{\cancel{3}a(\cancel{a - 5})(\cancel{a^2 + 4})(\cancel{a + 2})(a - 2)}$$

$$= \frac{1}{a(a - 2)}$$

Adding and Subtracting Rational Expressions

The following two properties provide the basis for adding and subtracting rational expressions:

$$\frac{a}{b} + \frac{c}{b} = \frac{a + c}{b} \qquad\qquad \frac{a}{b} - \frac{c}{b} = \frac{a - c}{b}$$

These properties state that rational expressions with a common denominator can be added (or subtracted) by adding (or subtracting) the numerators and placing the result over the common denominator. Let's illustrate this idea.

$$\frac{8}{x-2} + \frac{3}{x-2} = \frac{8+3}{x-2} = \frac{11}{x-2}$$

$$\frac{9}{4y} - \frac{7}{4y} = \frac{9-7}{4y} = \frac{2}{4y} = \frac{1}{2y}$$

[Don't forget to simplify the final result.]

$$\frac{n^2}{n-1} - \frac{1}{n-1} = \frac{n^2-1}{n-1}$$

$$= \frac{(n+1)(n-1)}{n-1} = n+1$$

If we need to add or subtract rational expressions that do not have a common denominator, then we apply the property $a/b = (a \cdot k)/(b \cdot k)$ to obtain equivalent fractions with a common denominator. Study the next examples and pay special attention to the format we use to organize our work.

> **REMARK** Remember that the **least common multiple** of a set of whole numbers is the smallest nonzero whole number divisible by each of the numbers in the set. When we add or subtract rational numbers, the least common multiple of the denominators of those numbers is the **least common denominator (LCD)**. This concept of a least common denominator can be extended to include polynomials.

EXAMPLE 1   Add $\dfrac{x+2}{4} + \dfrac{3x+1}{3}$.

Solution

By inspection we see that the LCD is 12.

$$\frac{x+2}{4} + \frac{3x+1}{3} = \left(\frac{x+2}{4}\right)\left(\frac{3}{3}\right) + \left(\frac{3x+1}{3}\right)\left(\frac{4}{4}\right)$$

$$= \frac{3(x+2)}{12} + \frac{4(3x+1)}{12}$$

$$= \frac{3x+6+12x+4}{12} = \frac{15x+10}{12}$$

EXAMPLE 2

Perform the indicated operations.

$$\frac{x + 3}{10} + \frac{2x + 1}{15} - \frac{x - 2}{18}$$

Solution

If you cannot determine the LCD by inspection, then use the prime-factored forms of the denominators.

$$10 = 2 \cdot 5 \qquad 15 = 3 \cdot 5 \qquad 18 = 2 \cdot 3 \cdot 3$$

The LCD must contain one factor of 2, two factors of 3, and one factor of 5. Thus the LCD is $2 \cdot 3 \cdot 3 \cdot 5 = 90$.

$$\frac{x + 3}{10} + \frac{2x + 1}{15} - \frac{x - 2}{18} = \left(\frac{x + 3}{10}\right)\left(\frac{9}{9}\right) + \left(\frac{2x + 1}{15}\right)\left(\frac{6}{6}\right) - \left(\frac{x - 2}{18}\right)\left(\frac{5}{5}\right)$$

$$= \frac{9(x + 3)}{90} + \frac{6(2x + 1)}{90} - \frac{5(x - 2)}{90}$$

$$= \frac{9x + 27 + 12x + 6 - 5x + 10}{90}$$

$$= \frac{16x + 43}{90}$$

Having variables in the denominators does not create any serious difficulty; our approach remains the same. Study the following examples very carefully. In each problem notice the same basic procedure: (1) find the LCD; (2) change each fraction to an equivalent fraction having the LCD as its denominator; (3) add or subtract numerators and place this result over the LCD; and (4) look for possibilities to simplify the resulting fraction.

EXAMPLE 3

Add $\dfrac{3}{2x} + \dfrac{5}{3y}$.

Solution

Using an LCD of $6xy$, we can proceed as follows.

$$\frac{3}{2x} + \frac{5}{3y} = \left(\frac{3}{2x}\right)\left(\frac{3y}{3y}\right) + \left(\frac{5}{3y}\right)\left(\frac{2x}{2x}\right)$$

$$= \frac{9y}{6xy} + \frac{10x}{6xy}$$

$$= \frac{9y + 10x}{6xy}$$

EXAMPLE 4

Subtract $\dfrac{7}{12ab} - \dfrac{11}{15a^2}$.

Solution

We can factor the numerical coefficients of the denominators into primes to help find the LCD.

$$\left.\begin{array}{l} 12ab = 2 \cdot 2 \cdot 3 \cdot a \cdot b \\ 15a^2 = 3 \cdot 5 \cdot a^2 \end{array}\right\} \quad \text{LCD} = 2 \cdot 2 \cdot 3 \cdot 5 \cdot a^2 \cdot b = 60a^2b$$

$$\frac{7}{12ab} - \frac{11}{15a^2} = \left(\frac{7}{12ab}\right)\left(\frac{5a}{5a}\right) - \left(\frac{11}{15a^2}\right)\left(\frac{4b}{4b}\right)$$

$$= \frac{35a}{60a^2b} - \frac{44b}{60a^2b}$$

$$= \frac{35a - 44b}{60a^2b}$$

EXAMPLE 5

Add $\dfrac{8}{x^2 - 4x} + \dfrac{2}{x}$.

Solution

$$\left.\begin{array}{r} x^2 - 4x = x(x - 4) \\ x = x \end{array}\right\} \quad \text{LCD} = x(x - 4)$$

$$\frac{8}{x(x - 4)} + \frac{2}{x} = \frac{8}{x(x - 4)} + \left(\frac{2}{x}\right)\left(\frac{x - 4}{x - 4}\right)$$

$$= \frac{8}{x(x - 4)} + \frac{2(x - 4)}{x(x - 4)}$$

$$= \frac{8 + 2x - 8}{x(x - 4)}$$

$$= \frac{2\cancel{x}}{\cancel{x}(x - 4)}$$

$$= \frac{2}{x - 4}$$

EXAMPLE 6   Add $\dfrac{3n}{n^2 + 6n + 5} + \dfrac{4}{n^2 - 7n - 8}$.

Solution

$$\left.\begin{array}{l} n^2 + 6n + 5 = (n + 5)(n + 1) \\ n^2 - 7n - 8 = (n - 8)(n + 1) \end{array}\right\} \quad \text{LCD} = (n + 1)(n + 5)(n - 8)$$

$$\dfrac{3n}{n^2 + 6n + 5} + \dfrac{4}{n^2 - 7n - 8} = \left[\dfrac{3n}{(n + 5)(n + 1)}\right]\left(\dfrac{n - 8}{n - 8}\right) + \left[\dfrac{4}{(n - 8)(n + 1)}\right]\left(\dfrac{n + 5}{n + 5}\right)$$

$$= \dfrac{3n(n - 8)}{(n + 5)(n + 1)(n - 8)} + \dfrac{4(n + 5)}{(n + 5)(n + 1)(n - 8)}$$

$$= \dfrac{3n^2 - 24n + 4n + 20}{(n + 5)(n + 1)(n - 8)}$$

$$= \dfrac{3n^2 - 20n + 20}{(n + 5)(n + 1)(n - 8)}$$

Simplifying Complex Fractions

Fractional forms that contain rational expressions in the numerator and/or denominator are called **complex fractions**. The following examples illustrate some approaches to simplifying complex fractions.

EXAMPLE 7   Simplify $\dfrac{\dfrac{3}{x} + \dfrac{2}{y}}{\dfrac{5}{x} - \dfrac{6}{y^2}}$.

Solution A

By treating the numerator as the sum of two rational expressions and the denominator as the difference of two rational expressions, we can proceed as follows.

$$\dfrac{\dfrac{3}{x} + \dfrac{2}{y}}{\dfrac{5}{x} - \dfrac{6}{y^2}} = \dfrac{\left(\dfrac{3}{x}\right)\left(\dfrac{y}{y}\right) + \left(\dfrac{2}{y}\right)\left(\dfrac{x}{x}\right)}{\left(\dfrac{5}{x}\right)\left(\dfrac{y^2}{y^2}\right) - \left(\dfrac{6}{y^2}\right)\left(\dfrac{x}{x}\right)}$$

$$= \dfrac{\dfrac{3y}{xy} + \dfrac{2x}{xy}}{\dfrac{5y^2}{xy^2} - \dfrac{6x}{xy^2}} = \dfrac{\dfrac{3y + 2x}{xy}}{\dfrac{5y^2 - 6x}{xy^2}}$$

$$= \frac{3y + 2x}{xy} \cdot \frac{\overset{y}{\cancel{xy^2}}}{5y^2 - 6x}$$

$$= \frac{y(3y + 2x)}{5y^2 - 6x}$$

Solution B

The LCD of all four denominators (x, y, x, and y^2) is xy^2. Let's multiply the entire complex fraction by a form of 1, namely, $\dfrac{xy^2}{xy^2}$.

$$\frac{\dfrac{3}{x} + \dfrac{2}{y}}{\dfrac{5}{x} - \dfrac{6}{y^2}} = \left(\frac{\dfrac{3}{x} + \dfrac{2}{y}}{\dfrac{5}{x} - \dfrac{6}{y^2}} \right) \left(\frac{xy^2}{xy^2} \right)$$

$$= \frac{(xy^2)\left(\dfrac{3}{x}\right) + (xy^2)\left(\dfrac{2}{y}\right)}{(xy^2)\left(\dfrac{5}{x}\right) - (xy^2)\left(\dfrac{6}{y^2}\right)}$$

$$= \frac{\dfrac{3xy^2}{x} + \dfrac{2xy^2}{y}}{\dfrac{5xy^2}{x} - \dfrac{6xy^2}{y^2}}$$

$$= \frac{3y^2 + 2xy}{5y^2 - 6x} \quad \text{or} \quad \frac{y(3y + 2x)}{5y^2 - 6x} \qquad \blacksquare$$

Certainly either approach (Solution A or Solution B) will work with a problem such as Example 7. We suggest that you study Solution B very carefully. This approach works effectively with complex fractions when the LCD of all the denominators is easy to find. Let's consider another example that illustrates a type of complex fraction used in certain calculus problems.

EXAMPLE 8

Simplify $\dfrac{\dfrac{1}{x + h} - \dfrac{1}{x}}{h}$.

Solution

$$\frac{\dfrac{1}{x+h}-\dfrac{1}{x}}{\dfrac{h}{1}}=\left[\frac{x(x+h)}{x(x+h)}\right]\left[\frac{\dfrac{1}{x+h}-\dfrac{1}{x}}{\dfrac{h}{1}}\right]$$

$$=\frac{x(x+h)\left(\dfrac{1}{x+h}\right)-x(x+h)\left(\dfrac{1}{x}\right)}{x(x+h)(h)}$$

$$=\frac{x-(x+h)}{hx(x+h)}=\frac{x-x-h}{hx(x+h)}$$

$$=\frac{-h}{hx(x+h)}=-\frac{1}{x(x+h)}$$

The final example of this section illustrates another idea that we sometimes use when simplifying complex fractions.

E X A M P L E   9

Simplify $1-\dfrac{n}{1-\dfrac{1}{n}}$.

Solution

We first simplify the complex fraction by multiplying by n/n.

$$\frac{n}{1-\dfrac{1}{n}}\left(\frac{n}{n}\right)=\frac{n^2}{n-1}$$

Now we can perform the subtraction.

$$1-\frac{n^2}{n-1}=\left(\frac{n-1}{n-1}\right)\left(\frac{1}{1}\right)-\frac{n^2}{n-1}=\frac{n-1}{n-1}-\frac{n^2}{n-1}$$

$$=\frac{n-1-n^2}{n-1}\qquad\text{or}\qquad\frac{-n^2+n-1}{n-1}$$

P R O B L E M   S E T   1 . 4

Simplify each of the following rational expressions.

1. $\dfrac{14x^2y}{21xy}$ **2.** $\dfrac{-26xy^2}{65y}$ **3.** $\dfrac{-63xy^4}{-81x^2y}$ **4.** $\dfrac{x^2-y^2}{x^2+xy}$ **5.** $\dfrac{a^2+7a+12}{a^2-6a-27}$

6. $\dfrac{6x^2 + x - 15}{8x^2 - 10x - 3}$

7. $\dfrac{2x^3 + 3x^2 - 14x}{x^2y + 7xy - 18y}$

8. $\dfrac{3x - x^2}{x^2 - 9}$

9. $\dfrac{x^3 - y^3}{x^2 + xy - 2y^2}$

10. $\dfrac{ax - 3x + 2ay - 6y}{2ax - 6x + ay - 3y}$

11. $\dfrac{2y - 2xy}{x^2y - y}$

12. $\dfrac{16x^3y + 24x^2y^2 - 16xy^3}{24x^2y + 12xy^2 - 12y^3}$

Perform the following indicated operations involving rational expressions. Express final answers in simplest form.

13. $\dfrac{4x^2}{5y^2} \cdot \dfrac{15xy}{24x^2y^2}$

14. $\dfrac{5xy}{8y^2} \cdot \dfrac{18x^2y}{15}$

15. $\dfrac{-14xy^4}{18y^2} \cdot \dfrac{24x^2y^3}{35y^2}$

16. $\dfrac{6xy}{9y^4} \cdot \dfrac{30x^3y}{-48x}$

17. $\dfrac{7a^2b}{9ab^3} \div \dfrac{3a^4}{2a^2b^2}$

18. $\dfrac{9a^2c}{12bc^2} \div \dfrac{21ab}{14c^3}$

19. $\dfrac{5xy}{x + 6} \cdot \dfrac{x^2 - 36}{x^2 - 6x}$

20. $\dfrac{2a^2 + 6}{a^2 - a} \cdot \dfrac{a^3 - a^2}{8a - 4}$

21. $\dfrac{5a^2 + 20a}{a^3 - 2a^2} \cdot \dfrac{a^2 - a - 12}{a^2 - 16}$

22. $\dfrac{t^4 - 81}{t^2 - 6t + 9} \cdot \dfrac{6t^2 - 11t - 21}{5t^2 + 8t - 21}$

23. $\dfrac{x^2 + 5xy - 6y^2}{xy^2 - y^3} \cdot \dfrac{2x^2 + 15xy + 18y^2}{xy + 4y^2}$

24. $\dfrac{10n^2 + 21n - 10}{5n^2 + 33n - 14} \cdot \dfrac{2n^2 + 6n - 56}{2n^2 - 3n - 20}$

25. $\dfrac{9y^2}{x^2 + 12x + 36} \div \dfrac{12y}{x^2 + 6x}$

26. $\dfrac{x^2 - 4xy + 4y^2}{7xy^2} \div \dfrac{4x^2 - 3xy - 10y^2}{20x^2y + 25xy^2}$

27. $\dfrac{2x^2 + 3x}{2x^3 - 10x^2} \cdot \dfrac{x^2 - 8x + 15}{3x^3 - 27x} \div \dfrac{14x + 21}{x^2 - 6x - 27}$

28. $\dfrac{a^2 - 4ab + 4b^2}{6a^2 - 4ab} \cdot \dfrac{3a^2 + 5ab - 2b^2}{6a^2 + ab - b^2} \div \dfrac{a^2 - 4b^2}{8a + 4b}$

29. $\dfrac{x + 4}{6} + \dfrac{2x - 1}{4}$

30. $\dfrac{3n - 1}{9} - \dfrac{n + 2}{12}$

31. $\dfrac{x + 1}{4} + \dfrac{x - 3}{6} - \dfrac{x - 2}{8}$

32. $\dfrac{x - 2}{5} - \dfrac{x + 3}{6} + \dfrac{x + 1}{15}$

33. $\dfrac{7}{16a^2b} + \dfrac{3a}{20b^2}$

34. $\dfrac{5b}{24a^2} - \dfrac{11a}{32b}$

35. $\dfrac{1}{n^2} + \dfrac{3}{4n} - \dfrac{5}{6}$

36. $\dfrac{3}{n^2} - \dfrac{2}{5n} + \dfrac{4}{3}$

37. $\dfrac{3}{4x} + \dfrac{2}{3y} - 1$

38. $\dfrac{5}{6x} - \dfrac{3}{4y} + 2$

39. $\dfrac{3}{2x + 1} + \dfrac{2}{3x + 4}$

40. $\dfrac{5}{x - 1} - \dfrac{3}{2x - 3}$

41. $\dfrac{4x}{x^2 + 7x} + \dfrac{3}{x}$

42. $\dfrac{6}{x^2 + 8x} - \dfrac{3}{x}$

43. $\dfrac{4a - 4}{a^2 - 4} - \dfrac{3}{a + 2}$

44. $\dfrac{6a + 4}{a^2 - 1} - \dfrac{5}{a - 1}$

45. $\dfrac{3}{x+1} + \dfrac{x+5}{x^2-1} - \dfrac{3}{x-1}$

46. $\dfrac{5}{x} - \dfrac{5x-30}{x^2+6x} + \dfrac{x}{x+6}$

47. $\dfrac{5}{x^2+10x+21} + \dfrac{4}{x^2+12x+27}$

48. $\dfrac{8}{a^2-3a-18} - \dfrac{10}{a^2-7a-30}$

49. $\dfrac{5}{x^2-1} - \dfrac{2}{x^2+6x-16}$

50. $\dfrac{4}{x^2+2} - \dfrac{7}{x^2+x-12}$

51. $x - \dfrac{x^2}{x-1} + \dfrac{1}{x^2-1}$

52. $x - \dfrac{x^2}{x+7} - \dfrac{x}{x^2-49}$

53. $\dfrac{2n^2}{n^4-16} - \dfrac{n}{n^2-4} + \dfrac{1}{n+2}$

54. $\dfrac{n}{n^2+1} + \dfrac{n^2+3n}{n^4-1} - \dfrac{1}{n-1}$

55. $\dfrac{2x+1}{x^2-3x-4} + \dfrac{3x-2}{x^2+3x-28}$

56. $\dfrac{3x-4}{2x^2-9x-5} - \dfrac{2x-1}{3x^2-11x-20}$

57. Consider the addition problem $\dfrac{8}{x-2} + \dfrac{5}{2-x}$. Note that the denominators are opposites of each other. If the property $\dfrac{a}{-b} = -\dfrac{a}{b}$ is applied to the second fraction, we obtain $\dfrac{5}{2-x} = -\dfrac{5}{x-2}$. Thus we can proceed as follows.

$$\dfrac{8}{x-2} + \dfrac{5}{2-x} = \dfrac{8}{x-2} - \dfrac{5}{x-2} = \dfrac{8-5}{x-2}$$

$$= \dfrac{3}{x-2}$$

Use this approach to do the following problems.

a. $\dfrac{7}{x-1} + \dfrac{2}{1-x}$ **b.** $\dfrac{5}{2x-1} + \dfrac{8}{1-2x}$

c. $\dfrac{4}{a-3} - \dfrac{1}{3-a}$ **d.** $\dfrac{10}{a-9} - \dfrac{5}{9-a}$

e. $\dfrac{x^2}{x-1} - \dfrac{2x-3}{1-x}$ **f.** $\dfrac{x^2}{x-4} - \dfrac{3x-28}{4-x}$

Simplify each of the following complex fractions.

58. $\dfrac{\dfrac{2}{x} + \dfrac{7}{y}}{\dfrac{3}{x} - \dfrac{10}{y}}$ **59.** $\dfrac{\dfrac{5}{x^2} - \dfrac{3}{x}}{\dfrac{1}{y} + \dfrac{2}{y^2}}$

60. $\dfrac{\dfrac{1}{x} + 3}{\dfrac{2}{y} + 4}$ **61.** $\dfrac{1 + \dfrac{1}{x}}{1 - \dfrac{1}{x}}$

62. $\dfrac{3 - \dfrac{2}{n-4}}{5 + \dfrac{4}{n-4}}$ **63.** $\dfrac{1 - \dfrac{1}{n+1}}{1 + \dfrac{1}{n-1}}$

64. $\dfrac{\dfrac{2}{x-3} - \dfrac{3}{x+3}}{\dfrac{5}{x^2-9} - \dfrac{2}{x-3}}$ **65.** $\dfrac{\dfrac{-2}{x} - \dfrac{4}{x+2}}{\dfrac{3}{x^2+2x} + \dfrac{3}{x}}$

66. $\dfrac{\dfrac{-1}{y-2} + \dfrac{5}{x}}{\dfrac{3}{x} - \dfrac{4}{xy-2x}}$ **67.** $1 + \dfrac{x}{1 + \dfrac{1}{x}}$

68. $2 - \dfrac{x}{3 - \dfrac{2}{x}}$ **69.** $\dfrac{a}{\dfrac{1}{a} + 4} + 1$

70. $\dfrac{\dfrac{3a}{2 - \dfrac{1}{a}} - 1}{}$ **71.** $\dfrac{\dfrac{1}{(x+h)^2} - \dfrac{1}{x^2}}{h}$

72. $\dfrac{\dfrac{1}{(x+h)^3} - \dfrac{1}{x^3}}{h}$

73. $\dfrac{\dfrac{1}{x+h+1} - \dfrac{1}{x+1}}{h}$

75. $\dfrac{\dfrac{2}{2x+2h-1} - \dfrac{2}{2x-1}}{h}$

74. $\dfrac{\dfrac{3}{x+h} - \dfrac{3}{x}}{h}$

76. $\dfrac{\dfrac{3}{4x+4h+5} - \dfrac{3}{4x+5}}{h}$

THOUGHTS into WORDS

77. What role does factoring play when simplifying rational expressions?

78. Give a step-by-step description of how to add

$$\frac{5x+2}{8} + \frac{3x-7}{14}.$$

79. Look back at the two approaches shown in Example 7 to simplify a complex fraction. Which approach would you

use to simplify $\dfrac{\dfrac{3y}{4x} - \dfrac{2}{9x^2}}{\dfrac{5}{6xy} + \dfrac{7y}{18x^2}}$?

Which approach would you use to simplify $\dfrac{\dfrac{5}{9xy} + \dfrac{11}{18y}}{\dfrac{1}{6x} - \dfrac{3y}{42}}$? Explain the reason for your choice of approach for each problem.

80. Express the property $\dfrac{-a}{b} = \dfrac{a}{-b} = -\dfrac{a}{b}$ in words.

1.5   EQUATIONS AND PROBLEM SOLVING

An algebraic equation such as $5x + 2 = 12$ is neither true nor false as it stands; we sometimes refer to it as an open sentence. Each time that a number is substituted for x, the algebraic equation $5x + 2 = 12$ becomes a **numerical statement** that is either true or false. For example, if $x = 5$ then $5x + 2 = 12$ becomes $5(5) + 2 = 12$, which is a false statement. If $x = 2$, then $5x + 2 = 12$ becomes $5(2) + 2 = 12$, which is a true statement. **Solving an equation** refers to the process of finding the number (or numbers) that makes an algebraic equation a true numerical statement. Such numbers are called the **solutions** or **roots** of the equation and are said to **satisfy the equation**. The set of all solutions of an equation is called its **solution set** Thus $\{2\}$ is the solution set of $5x + 2 = 12$.

An equation that is satisfied by all numbers that can meaningfully replace the variable is called an **identity**. For example,

$$x^2 - 4 = (x+2)(x-2) \qquad \text{and} \qquad \frac{1}{x} + \frac{1}{2} = \frac{2+x}{2x}$$

are identities. In the last identity, x cannot equal zero; thus, the statement $1/x + \frac{1}{2} = (2+x)/2x$ is true for all real numbers except zero. An equation that is true for some but not all permissible values of the variable is called a **conditional equation**. Thus, the equation $5x + 2 = 12$ is a conditional equation.

Equivalent equations are equations that have the same solution set. The general procedure for solving an equation is to continue replacing the given equation with equivalent but simpler equations until an equation of the form *variable = constant* or *constant = variable* is obtained. Techniques for solving equations are centered around properties of equality. The following list summarizes some basic properties of equality.

P R O P E R T Y   1 . 3   *Properties of Equality*

For all real numbers a, b, and c

1. $a = a$ Reflexive property
2. If $a = b$, then $b = a$ Symmetric property
3. If $a = b$ and $b = c$, then $a = c$ Transitive property
4. If $a = b$, then a may be replaced by b, or b may be replaced by a, in any statement without changing the meaning of the statement   Substitution property
5. $a = b$ if and only if $a + c = b + c$ Addition property
6. $a = b$ if and only if $ac = bc$, where $c \neq 0$.   Multiplication property

---

Now let's consider how these properties of equality can be used to solve a variety of linear equations. A **linear equation** in the variable x is one that can be written in the form $ax + b = 0$, where a and b are real numbers and $a \neq 0$.

E X A M P L E   1

Solve $4(x - 2) - 3(x - 1) = 2(x + 6)$.

Solution

$$4(x - 2) - 3(x - 1) = 2(x + 6)$$
$$4x - 8 - 3x + 3 = 2x + 12$$
$$x - 5 = 2x + 12$$
$$-17 = x$$

 Check

$$4(x - 2) - 3(x - 1) = 2(x + 6)$$
$$4(-17 - 2) - 3(-17 - 1) \stackrel{?}{=} 2(-17 + 6)$$

$$4(-19) - 3(-18) \stackrel{?}{=} 2(-11)$$

$$-76 + 54 \stackrel{?}{=} -22$$

$$-22 = -22$$

The solution set is $\{-17\}$.

As you study our examples of solving equations, pay special attention to the steps shown in the solutions. Certainly, there are no rules regarding which steps should be performed mentally; this is an individual decision. We would suggest that you show enough steps so that the flow of the process is understood and that the chances of making careless computational errors are minimized. Furthermore, we shall discontinue showing the check for each problem, but remember that checking an answer is the only way of being sure of your result.

E X A M P L E   2   Solve $\dfrac{4x - 1}{10} - \dfrac{5x + 2}{4} = -3$.

Solution

$$\frac{4x - 1}{10} - \frac{5x + 2}{4} = -3$$

$$20\left(\frac{4x - 1}{10} - \frac{5x + 2}{4}\right) = 20(-3) \qquad \text{Multiply both sides by least common denominator (LCD)}$$

$$20\left(\frac{4x - 1}{10}\right) - 20\left(\frac{5x + 2}{4}\right) = -60$$

$$2(4x - 1) - 5(5x + 2) = -60$$

$$8x - 2 - 25x - 10 = -60$$

$$-17x - 12 = -60$$

$$-17x = -48$$

$$x = \frac{48}{17}$$

The solution set is $\left\{\frac{48}{17}\right\}$.

In Example 2, we multiplied both sides of the equation by the least common denominator in order to clear the equation of all fractions. Equations that have the variable in one or more of the denominators can be handled in much the same way, except we must **avoid any values of the variable that make a denominator zero**. Let's consider two examples to illustrate this idea.

EXAMPLE 3

Solve $\dfrac{65 - n}{n} = 4 + \dfrac{5}{n}$.

Solution

First, we need to realize that *n* **cannot equal zero**. Let's indicate this restriction so that we don't forget it; then we can proceed as follows.

$$\frac{65 - n}{n} = 4 + \frac{5}{n}, \qquad n \neq 0$$

$$n\left(\frac{65 - n}{n}\right) = n\left(4 + \frac{5}{n}\right)$$

$$65 - n = 4n + 5$$

$$60 = 5n$$

$$12 = n$$

The solution set is $\{12\}$.

EXAMPLE 4

Solve $\dfrac{a}{a - 2} + \dfrac{2}{3} = \dfrac{2}{a - 2}$.

Solution

$$\frac{a}{a - 2} + \frac{2}{3} = \frac{2}{a - 2}, \qquad a \neq 2$$

$$3(a - 2)\left(\frac{a}{a - 2} + \frac{2}{3}\right) = 3(a - 2)\left(\frac{2}{a - 2}\right)$$

$$3a + 2(a - 2) = 3(2)$$

$$3a + 2a - 4 = 6$$

$$5a = 10$$

$$a = 2$$

Because our initial restriction was $a \neq 2$, we conclude that this equation has no solution. The solution set is $\varnothing$.

When using a formula, it is sometimes convenient to change its form. For example, multiplying both sides of the formula $d = rt$ by $1/t$ produces the equivalent form $d/t = r$, which can be written as $r = d/t$. Likewise, multiplying both sides of $d = rt$ by $1/r$ produces another equivalent form $d/r = t$, which can be written as $t = d/r$. The following two examples further illustrate this process of obtaining equivalent forms of certain formulas.

EXAMPLE 5

If P dollars are invested at a simple rate of r percent per year, then the amount A accumulated after t years is given by the formula $A = P + Prt$. Solve this formula for P.

Solution

$$A = P + Prt$$

$$A = P(1 + rt) \qquad \text{Apply distributive property to right side}$$

$$\frac{A}{1 + rt} = P \qquad \text{Multiply both sides by } \frac{1}{1 + rt}$$

EXAMPLE 6

The area A of a trapezoid is given by the formula $A = \frac{1}{2}h(b_1 + b_2)$. Solve this equation for b_2.

Solution

$$A = \tfrac{1}{2}h(b_1 + b_2)$$

$$2A = h(b_1 + b_2) \qquad \text{Multiply both sides by 2}$$

$$2A = hb_1 + hb_2 \qquad \text{Apply distributive property to right side}$$

$$2A - hb_1 = hb_2 \qquad \text{Add } -hb_1 \text{ to both sides}$$

$$\frac{2A - hb_1}{h} = b_2 \qquad \text{Multiply both sides by } \frac{1}{h}$$

In Example 5 notice that the distributive property was used to change from $P + Prt$ to $P(1 + rt)$. However, in Example 6 the distributive property was used to change $h(b_1 + b_2)$ to $hb_1 + hb_2$. In both examples we isolated the term containing the variable being solved for so that an appropriate application of the multiplication property of equality would produce the desired result.

Problem Solving

Volumes have been written on the topic of problem solving, but certainly one of the best known sources is George Polya's book *How to Solve It*.* (It is true that this book was published almost 50 years ago, but Polya's insights into problem solving remain just as relevant in today's technology driven society.) In this book, Polya suggests the following four-phase plan for solving problems.

    1. *Understand the problem;*

    2. *Devise a plan* to solve the problem;

    3. *Carry out the plan* to solve the problem;

    4. *Look back* at the completed solution to review and discuss it.

---

*George Polya, *How to Solve It* (Princeton: Princeton University Press), 1945.

We shall comment briefly on each of the phases and offer some suggestions for using an algebraic approach to solve problems.

Understand the Problem   Read the problem carefully and make certain that you understand the meanings of all the words. Be especially alert for any technical terms used in the statement of the problem. Often it is helpful to sketch a figure, diagram, or chart to visualize and organize the conditions of the problem. Determine the known and unknown facts and if one of the previously mentioned pictorial devices is used, record these facts in the appropriate places of the diagram or chart.

Devise a Plan   This is the key part of the four-phase plan. It is sometimes referred to as the *analysis* of the problem. There are numerous strategies and techniques used to solve problems. We shall discuss some of these strategies at various places throughout this text; however, at this time we offer the following general suggestions.

1. Choose a meaningful variable to represent an unknown quantity in the problem (perhaps t if time is an unknown quantity) and represent any other unknowns in terms of that variable.

2. Look for a *guideline* that can be used to set up an equation. A guideline might be a formula such as $A = P + Prt$ from Example 7, or a statement of a relationship such as *the sum of the two numbers is 28*. Sometimes a relationship suggested by a pictorial device can be used as a guideline for setting up the equation. Also, be alert to the possibility that this *new* problem might really be an *old* problem in a new setting, possibly stated in different vocabulary.

3. Form an equation that contains the variable so that the conditions of the guideline are translated from English into algebra.

Carry Out the Plan   This phase is sometimes referred to as the *synthesis* of the plan. If phase two has been successfully completed, then carrying out the plan may simply be a matter of solving the equation and doing any further computations to answer all of the questions in the problem. Confidence in your plan creates a better working atmosphere for carrying it out. It is also in this phase that the calculator may become a valuable tool; the type of data and the amount of complexity involved in the computations are two factors that can influence your decision to use one.

Look Back   This is an important but often overlooked part of problem solving. The following list of questions suggests some things for you to consider in this phase.

1. Is your answer to the problem a *reasonable* answer?

2. Have you *checked* your answer by substituting it back into the conditions stated in the problem?

3. Looking back over your solution, do you now see another plan that could be used to solve the problem?

4. Do you see a way of generalizing your procedure for this problem that could be used to solve other problems of this type?

5. Do you now see that this problem is closely related to another problem that you have previously solved?

6. Have you "tucked away for future reference" the technique used to solve this problem?

Looking back over the solution of a newly solved problem can lay important groundwork for solving problems in the future.

Keep the previous suggestions in mind as we tackle some word problems. Perhaps it would also be helpful for you to attempt to solve these problems on your own before looking at our approach.

P R O B L E M 1

Students in a class   There are 51 students in a certain class. The number of females is 5 less than three times the number of males. Find the number of females and the number of males in the class.

Solution

Let m represent the number of males; then $3m - 5$ represents the number of females. Since the total number of students is 51, we can use the guideline *number of males plus number of females equals the total number of students* to help set up the equation.

$$m + (3m - 5) = 51$$

$$4m - 5 = 51$$

$$4m = 56$$

$$m = 14$$

Therefore, there are 14 males and $3(14) - 5 = 37$ females. ▬▬▬

P R O B L E M 2

Determining rates of bicycle riders   Domenica and Javier start from the same location at the same time and ride their bicycles in opposite directions for 4 hours, at which time they are 140 miles apart. If Domenica rides 3 miles per hour faster than Javier, find the rate of each rider.

Solution

Let r represent Javier's rate; then $r + 3$ represents Domenica's rate. Sketching a diagram may help in our analysis (Figure 1.7). Use the fact that the total distance is 140 miles as a guideline, and use the formula $d = rt$.

Distance Domenica rides + Distance Javier rides = 140
$$4(r + 3) \quad + \quad 4r \quad = 140$$

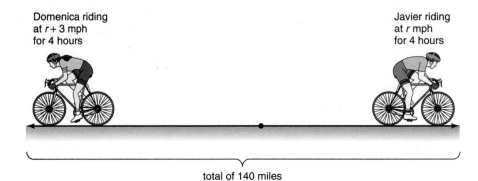

Domenica riding
at $r + 3$ mph
for 4 hours

Javier riding
at r mph
for 4 hours

total of 140 miles

FIGURE   1.7

Solving this equation yields Javier's rate.

$$4r + 12 + 4r = 140$$

$$8r = 128$$

$$r = 16$$

Thus, Javier rides at 16 miles per hour and Domenica at $16 + 3 = 19$ miles per hour.

REMARK   Don't forget that to check a word problem we must check our potential answers back into the statement of the problem. Thus, for Problem 2, if Javier rides for 4 hours at 16 miles per hour, he will travel $4(16) = 64$ miles. Likewise, if Domenica rides for 4 hours at 19 miles per hour, she will travel $4(19) = 76$ miles. Together they will travel $64 + 76 = 140$ miles and our answers are correct.

REMARK   Often an important part of the problem solving process is the sketching of a meaningful figure that can be used to record the given information and help in the analysis of the problem. Our sketches were done by professional artists for aesthetic purposes. Your sketches can be very roughly drawn as long as they depict the situation in a way that helps you analyze the problem.

PROBLEM 3

Investments at different rates   A man invests $8000, part of it at 11% and the remainder at 12%. His total yearly interest from the two investments is $930. How much did he invest at each rate?

Solution

Let x represent the amount invested at 11%. Then $8000 - x$ represents the amount invested at 12%. The following guideline can be used.

Interest earned   Interest earned   Total amount

from 11%   +   from 12%   =   of interest

investment   investment   earned

↓   ↓   ↓

$$(11\%)(x) \quad + (12\%)(8000 - x) = \quad \$930$$

Solving this equation yields

$$(11\%)(x) + (12\%)(8000 - x) = 930$$

$$.11x + .12(8000 - x) = 930$$

$$11x + 12(8000 - x) = 93000 \qquad \text{Multiply both sides by 100}$$

$$11x + 96000 - 12x = 93000$$

$$-x + 96000 = 93000$$

$$-x = -3000$$

$$x = 3000$$

Therefore, $8000 - x = 5000$. $3000 was invested at 11% and $5000 at 12%.

PROBLEM 4

Adding pure acid to a solution   How many milliliters of pure acid must be added to 50 milliliters of a 40% acid solution to obtain a 50% acid solution?

Solution

Sometimes making an *estimate* and then checking that estimate may help determine a guideline to use to solve the problem. Suppose that for this problem we estimate that it would take 8 milliliters of pure acid. To check this estimate let's add the 8 milliliters to the $.4(50) = 20$ milliliters of pure acid in the 40% solution to obtain $8 + 20 = 28$ milliliters of pure acid in the final solution. Thus, the final solution of $50 + 8 = 58$ milliliters would contain 28 milliliters of pure acid or it would be approximately a 48% acid solution. So our estimate of 8 milliliters is a little too small, but by checking it we have indicated a guideline that can be used to set up an equation. That is to say, *the amount of pure acid to start with plus the amount of pure acid to be added equals the amount of pure acid in the final solution.* If we let *a* represent the amount of pure acid to be added, we can set up and solve the following equation.

$\begin{pmatrix} \text{Pure acid to} \\ \text{start with} \end{pmatrix} + \begin{pmatrix} \text{Pure acid} \\ \text{added} \end{pmatrix} = \begin{pmatrix} \text{Pure acid in} \\ \text{final solution} \end{pmatrix}$

↓   ↓   ↓

$(40\%)(50) \quad + \quad 100\% \; a \quad = \quad 50\%(50 + a)$

Solving this equation we obtain the amount of acid we must add.

$$.4(50) + a = .5(50 + a)$$

$$4(50) + 10a = 5(50 + a)$$

$$200 + 10a = 250 + 5a$$

$$5a = 50$$

$$a = 10$$

We need to add 10 milliliters of pure acid. (Be sure to check this answer.)

P R O B L E M   S E T   1 . 5

Solve each of the following equations.

1. $4(2x - 1) = 3(3x + 2)$

2. $5x - 4(x - 6) = -11$

3. $-3(2t - 5) = 2(4t + 7)$

4. $3(2t - 1) - 2(5t + 1) = 4(3t + 4)$

5. $-(3x - 1) + (2x + 3) = -4 + 3(x - 1)$

6. $-2(y - 4) - (3y - 1) = -2 + 5(y + 1)$

7. $(x - 3)(x - 1) - x(x + 2) = 7$

8. $(3n + 4)(n - 2) - 3n(n + 3) = 3$

9. $(2y + 1)(3y - 2) - (6y - 1)(y + 4) = -20y$

10. $(4t - 3)(t + 2) - (2t + 3)^2 = -1$

11. $\dfrac{4y}{5} - 7 = \dfrac{y}{10}$

12. $\dfrac{y}{5} - 2 = \dfrac{y}{2} + 1$

13. $\dfrac{2x - 5}{6} - \dfrac{3x - 4}{8} = 0$

14. $\dfrac{n - 3}{2} - \dfrac{4n - 1}{6} = \dfrac{2}{3}$

15. $\dfrac{2t + 3}{6} - \dfrac{t - 9}{4} = 5$

16. $\dfrac{2x + 7}{9} - 4 = \dfrac{x - 7}{12}$

17. $\dfrac{3y - 1}{8} + y - 2 = \dfrac{y + 4}{4}$

18. $n + \dfrac{2n - 3}{9} - 2 = \dfrac{2n + 1}{3}$

19. $\dfrac{5}{x} + \dfrac{1}{3} = \dfrac{8}{x}$

20. $\dfrac{5}{3n} - \dfrac{1}{9} = \dfrac{1}{n}$

21. $\dfrac{1}{3n} + \dfrac{1}{2n} = \dfrac{1}{4}$

22. $\dfrac{1}{x} - \dfrac{3}{2x} = \dfrac{1}{5}$

23. $\dfrac{35 - x}{x} = 7 + \dfrac{3}{x}$

24. $\dfrac{n}{46 - n} = 5 + \dfrac{4}{46 - n}$

25. $\dfrac{n}{n + 1} + 3 = \dfrac{4}{n + 1}$

26. $\dfrac{a}{a + 5} - 2 = \dfrac{3a}{a + 5}$

27. $\dfrac{3x}{2x - 1} - 4 = \dfrac{x}{2x - 1}$

28. $\dfrac{x}{x - 8} - 4 = \dfrac{8}{x - 8}$

29. $\dfrac{3}{x + 3} - \dfrac{1}{x - 2} = \dfrac{5}{2x + 6}$

30. $\dfrac{6}{x + 3} + \dfrac{20}{x^2 + x - 6} = \dfrac{5}{x - 2}$

31. $\dfrac{n}{n - 3} - \dfrac{3}{2} = \dfrac{3}{n - 3}$

32. $\dfrac{4}{x - 2} + \dfrac{x}{x + 1} = \dfrac{x^2 - 2}{x^2 - x - 2}$

33. $.09x + .1(700 - x) = 67$

34. $.08x + .09(950 - x) = 81$

35. $.8(t - 2) = .5(9t + 10)$

36. $.3(2n - 5) = 11 - .65n$

37. $.92 + .9(x - .3) = 2x - 5.95$

38. $.5(3x + .7) = 20.6$

For Problems 39–44, solve each formula for the indicated variable.

39. $A = \dfrac{1}{2}h(b_1 + b_2)$ for b_1 Area of a trapezoid

40. $C = \dfrac{5}{9}(F - 32)$ for F Fahrenheit to Celsius

41. $V = C\left(1 - \dfrac{T}{N}\right)$ for T Linear depreciation

42. $I = kl(T - t)$ for T Expansion allowance in highway construction

43. $\dfrac{1}{R_n} = \dfrac{1}{R_1} + \dfrac{1}{R_2}$ for R_n Resistance in parallel circuit design

44. $f = \dfrac{1}{\dfrac{1}{a} + \dfrac{1}{b}}$ for b Focal length of a camera lens

APPLIED PROBLEMS

Solve each of the following problems by setting up and solving an appropriate algebraic equation.

45. *Consecutive integers*   The sum of three consecutive integers is 21 larger than twice the smallest integer. Find the integers.

46. *Consecutive even integers*   Find three consecutive even integers such that if the largest integer is subtracted from four times the smallest, the result is 6 more than twice the middle integer.

47. *Consecutive integers*   Find three consecutive integers such that the product of the two largest is 20 more than the square of the smallest integer.

48. *Consecutive integers*   Find four consecutive integers such that the product of the two largest is 46 more than the product of the two smallest integers.

49. *Average of salaries*   The average of the salaries of Kelly, Renee, and Nina is $20,000 a year. If Kelly earns $4000 less than Renee and Nina's salary is two-thirds of Renee's salary, find the salary of each person.

50. *Hourly pay*   Barry is paid double his salary for each hour worked over 40 hours in a week. Last week he worked 47 hours and earned $378. What is his normal hourly rate?

51. *Coin collection*   Greg had 80 coins consisting of pennies, nickels, and dimes. The number of nickels was five more than one-third the number of pennies and the number of dimes was one less than one-fourth the number of pennies. How many coins of each kind did he have?

52. *Coin collection*   Rita has a collection of 105 coins consisting of nickels, dimes, and quarters. The number of dimes is five more than one-third the number of nickels, and the number of quarters is twice the number of dimes. How many coins of each kind does she have?

53. *Relationships between ages*   The sum of the present ages of Eric and his father is 58 years. In ten years his father will be twice as old as Eric will be at that time. Find their present ages.

54. *Relationship between ages*   Brad is presently six years older than Pedro. Five years ago, Pedro's age was three-fourths of Brad's age at that time. Find the present ages of Brad and Pedro.

55. *Coin collection*   Robin has a collection of nickels, dimes, and quarters worth $38.50. She has ten more dimes than nickels and twice as many quarters as dimes. How many coins of each kind does she have?

56. *Coin collection*   A collection of 70 coins consisting of dimes, quarters, and half-dollars has a value of $17.75. There are three times as many quarters as dimes. Find the number of each kind of coin.

57. *Investments*   A certain amount of money is invested at 8% and $1500 more than that amount is invested at 9%. The annual interest from the 9% investment exceeds the annual interest from the 8% investment by $160. How much is invested at each rate?

58. *Investments*   A total of $5500 was invested, part of it at 9% and the remainder at 10%. If the total yearly interest amounted to $530, how much was invested at each rate?

59. *Investments*   A sum of $3500 is split between two investments, one paying 9% yearly interest and the other 11%. If the return on the 11% investment exceeds the return on the 9% investment by $85 per year, how much is invested at each rate?

60. *Investments*   Celia invested $2500 at 11% yearly interest. How much must she invest at 12% so that the interest from both investments totals $695?

61. *Area of a rectangle*   The length of a rectangle is 4 centimeters more than its width. If the width is increased by 2 centimeters and the length increased by 3 centimeters, a new rectangle is formed that has an area of 44 square centimeters more than the area of the original rectangle. Find the dimensions of the original rectangle.

62. *Dimensions of a picture*   The length of a picture without its border is 7 inches less than twice its width. If the border is 1 inch wide and its area is 62 square inches, what are the dimensions of the picture alone?

63. *Determining times of cars*   Jill starts at city A and travels toward city B at 50 miles per hour. At the same time, Russ starts at city B and travels on the same highway toward city A at 52 miles per hour. How long will it take before they meet if the two cities are 459 miles apart?

64. *Determining rates of cars*   Two cars, which are 510 miles apart and whose speeds differ by 6 miles per hour, are moving toward each other. If they meet in 5 hours, find the speed of each car.

65. *Determining times of joggers*   A jogger who can run an 8-minute mile starts one-half of a mile ahead of a jogger who can run a 6-minute mile. How long will it take the faster jogger to catch the slower jogger?

66. *Determining rates of airplanes*   An airplane travels 2050 miles in the same time that a car travels 260 miles. If the rate of the plane is 358 miles per hour greater than the rate of the car, find the rate of the plane.

67. *Adding pure alcohol*   A container has 6 liters of a 40% alcohol solution in it. How much pure alcohol should be added to raise it to a 60% solution?

68. *Adding pure acid*   How many liters of a 60% acid solution must be added to 14 liters of a 10% acid solution to produce a 25% acid solution?

69. *Mixing alcohol solutions*   One solution contains 50% alcohol and another solution contains 80% alcohol. How many liters of each solution should be mixed to produce 10.5 liters of a 70% alcohol solution?

70. *Replacing antifreeze*   A 10-quart radiator contains a 40% antifreeze solution. How much of the solution needs to be drained out and replaced with pure antifreeze in order to raise the solution to 70% antifreeze?

THOUGHTS into WORDS

71. How could you defend the statement that the equation $x + 1 = x + 2$ has no real number solutions?

72. What does the phrase ''declare a variable'' mean when solving a word problem?

73. Why must potential answers to word problems be checked back into the original statement of the problem?

FURTHER INVESTIGATIONS

74. Verify that for any three consecutive integers, the sum of the smallest and largest is equal to twice the middle integer.

75. Verify that no four consecutive integers can be found such that the product of the smallest and largest is equal to the product of the other two integers.

1.6 COMPLEX NUMBERS

There are some very simple equations that do not have solutions within the set of real numbers. For example, the equation $x^2 + 1 = 0$ has no solutions among the real numbers. Therefore, to be able to solve such equations, we need to extend the real number system. In this section we will introduce a set of numbers that contains some numbers whose squares are negative real numbers. Then, in the next section and in Chapter 5, we will see that this set of numbers, called the **complex numbers**, provides solutions not only for equations such as $x^2 + 1 = 0$, but also for any polynomial equation in general. Let's begin by defining a number i such that

$$i^2 = -1.$$

The number i is not a real number and is often called the **imaginary unit**, but the number i^2 is the real number -1. The imaginary unit i is used to define a complex number as follows.

DEFINITION 1.2

A **complex number** is any number that can be expressed in the form

$a + bi$, where a and b are real numbers.

The form $a + bi$ is called the **standard form** of a complex number. The real number a is called the **real part** of the complex number, and the real number b is called the **imaginary part**. (Note that b is a real number even though it is called the imaginary part.) Each of the following represents a complex number.

$6 + 2i$ It is expressed in the form $a + bi$. Traditionally, complex numbers for which $a \neq 0$ and $b \neq 0$ are called **imaginary numbers**.

$5 - 3i$ It can be written as $5 + (-3i)$ even though the form $5 - 3i$ is often used.

$-8 + i\sqrt{2}$ It can be written as $-8 + \sqrt{2}i$. It is easy to mistake $\sqrt{2}i$ for $\sqrt{2i}$. Thus, we commonly write $i\sqrt{2}$ instead of $\sqrt{2}i$ to avoid any difficulties with the radical sign.

$-9i$ It can be written as $0 + (-9i)$. Complex numbers such as $-9i$, for which $a = 0$ and $b \neq 0$, traditionally are called **pure imaginary numbers**.

5 It can be written as $5 + 0i$.

The set of real numbers is a subset of the set of complex numbers. The following diagram indicates the organizational format of the complex number system.

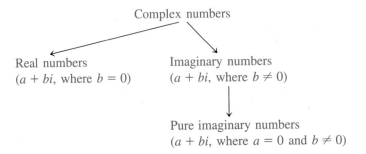

Two complex numbers $a + bi$ and $c + di$ are said to be **equal** if and only if $a = c$ and $b = d$. In other words, two complex numbers are equal if and only if their real parts are equal and their imaginary parts are equal.

Adding and Subtracting Complex Numbers

The following definition provides the basis for adding complex numbers.

$$(a + bi) + (c + di) = (a + c) + (b + d)i$$

Thus, we can add complex numbers by adding their real parts and adding their imaginary parts.

$$(-6 + 4i) + (8 - 7i) = (-6 + 8) + (4 - 7)i = 2 - 3i$$

$$\left(\tfrac{1}{2} + \tfrac{3}{4}i\right) + \left(\tfrac{2}{3} + \tfrac{1}{5}i\right) = \left(\tfrac{1}{2} + \tfrac{2}{3}\right) + \left(\tfrac{3}{4} + \tfrac{1}{5}\right)i = \tfrac{7}{6} + \tfrac{19}{20}i$$

The set of complex numbers is *closed with respect to addition*; that is, the sum of two complex numbers is a complex number. Furthermore, the commutative and associative properties of addition hold true for all complex numbers. The additive identity element is $0 + 0i$, or simply the real number 0. The additive inverse of $a + bi$ is $-a - bi$ because $(a + bi) + (-a - bi) = 0$. Therefore, to subtract $c + di$ from $a + bi$, we add the additive inverse of $c + di$.

$$(a + bi) - (c + di) = (a - c) + (b - d)i.$$

The following examples illustrate the subtraction of complex numbers.

$$(9 + 8i) - (5 + 3i) = (9 - 5) + (8 - 3)i = 4 + 5i$$

$$(3 - 2i) - (4 - 10i) = (3 - 4) + [-2 - (-10)]i = -1 + 8i$$

Multiplying and Dividing Complex Numbers

Since $i^2 = -1$, the number i is a square root of -1; so we write $i = \sqrt{-1}$. It should also be evident that $-i$ is a square root of -1 because

$$(-i)^2 = (-i)(-i) = i^2 = -1.$$

Therefore, in the set of complex numbers, -1 has two square roots, namely, i and $-i$. This is symbolically expressed as

$$i = \sqrt{-1} \qquad \text{and} \qquad -i = -\sqrt{-1}.$$

Let's extend the definition so that in the set of complex numbers, every negative real number has two square roots. For any positive number b,

$$(i\sqrt{b})^2 = i^2(b) = -1(b) = -b.$$

Therefore, let's denote the **principal square root** of $-b$ by $\sqrt{-b}$ and define it to be

$$\sqrt{-b} = i\sqrt{b},$$

where b is any positive real number. In other words, the principal square root of any negative number can be represented as the product of a real number and the imaginary unit i. Consider the following examples.

$$\sqrt{-4} = i\sqrt{4} = 2i$$

$$\sqrt{-17} = i\sqrt{17}$$

$$\sqrt{-24} = i\sqrt{24} = i\sqrt{4}\sqrt{6} = 2i\sqrt{6}$$

We should also observe that $-\sqrt{-b}$, where $b > 0$, is a square root of $-b$ because

$$(-\sqrt{-b})^2 = (-i\sqrt{b})^2 = i^2(b) = -b.$$

Thus, in the set of complex numbers, $-b$ (where $b > 0$) has two square roots, $i\sqrt{b}$ and $-i\sqrt{b}$. These are expressed as

$$\sqrt{-b} = i\sqrt{b} \qquad \text{and} \qquad -\sqrt{-b} = -i\sqrt{b}.$$

We must be careful with the use of the symbol $\sqrt{-b}$. Some properties that are true in the set of real numbers involving the square root symbol do not hold true if the square root symbol does not represent a real number. For example, $\sqrt{a}\sqrt{b} = \sqrt{ab}$ *does not hold true* if a and b are both negative numbers.

$$\text{Correct:} \qquad \sqrt{-4}\sqrt{-9} = (2i)(3i) = 6i^2 = -6$$

$$\text{Incorrect:} \qquad \sqrt{-4}\sqrt{-9} = \sqrt{36} = 6$$

To avoid difficulty with this idea, you should rewrite all expressions of the form $\sqrt{-b}$, where $b > 0$, in the form $i\sqrt{b}$ *before* doing any computations, as the following examples illustrate.

$$\sqrt{-2}\sqrt{-8} = (i\sqrt{2})(i\sqrt{8}) = i^2\sqrt{16} = (-1)(4) = -4$$

$$\sqrt{-6}\sqrt{-8} = (i\sqrt{6})(i\sqrt{8}) = i^2\sqrt{48} = (-1)\sqrt{16}\sqrt{3} = -4\sqrt{3}$$

$$\frac{\sqrt{-48}}{\sqrt{12}} = \frac{i\sqrt{48}}{\sqrt{12}} = i\sqrt{\frac{48}{12}} = i\sqrt{4} = 2i$$

From the facts $i = \sqrt{-1}$ and $i^2 = -1$, we see that

$$i^3 = i^2 \cdot i = -1(i) = -i \qquad \text{and} \qquad i^4 = i^2 \cdot i^2 = (-1)(-1) = 1.$$

Thus, any power of i greater than four can be expressed as $\pm i$ or ± 1. For example,

$$i^{17} = i^{16} \cdot i = (i^4)^4 \cdot i = (1)^4 \cdot i = i \qquad \text{and}$$

$$i^{34} = i^{32} \cdot i^2 = (i^4)^8 \cdot i^2 = (1)^8(-1) = -1.$$

Since complex numbers have a binomial form, we can find the product of two complex numbers in the same way that we find the product of two binomials. Then, by replacing i^2 with -1, we can simplify and express the final product in the standard form of a complex number. Consider the following examples.

$$\begin{aligned}
(2 + 3i)(4 + 5i) &= 2(4 + 5i) + 3i(4 + 5i) \\
&= 8 + 10i + 12i + 15i^2 \\
&= 8 + 22i + 15(-1) \\
&= -7 + 22i
\end{aligned}$$

$$\begin{aligned}
(5 + 3i)(5 - 3i) &= 5(5 - 3i) + 3i(5 - 3i) \\
&= 25 - 15i + 15i - 9i^2 \\
&= 25 - 9(-1) = 34
\end{aligned}$$

The latter example illustrates an important idea. The complex numbers $5 + 3i$ and $5 - 3i$ are called **conjugates** of each other. In general, the two complex numbers $a + bi$ and $a - bi$ are called conjugates of each other and their product is a real number.

$$\begin{aligned}
(a + bi)(a - bi) &= a(a - bi) + bi(a - bi) \\
&= a^2 - abi + abi - b^2i^2 \\
&= a^2 - b^2(-1) \\
&= a^2 + b^2
\end{aligned}$$

Conjugates are used to simplify an expression such as $3i/(5 + 2i)$, which indicates *the quotient of two complex numbers*. To eliminate i from the denominator and to change the indicated quotient to the standard form of a complex number, we can multiply both the numerator and denominator by the conjugate of the denominator.

$$\begin{aligned}
\frac{3i}{5 + 2i} &= \frac{3i}{5 + 2i} \cdot \frac{5 - 2i}{5 - 2i} \\
&= \frac{15i - 6i^2}{25 - 4i^2} \\
&= \frac{15i - 6(-1)}{25 - 4(-1)}
\end{aligned}$$

$$= \frac{6 + 15i}{29}$$

$$= \frac{6}{29} + \frac{15}{29}i$$

If the denominator is a pure imaginary number, then we can also change to standard form by choosing a multiplier other than the conjugate of the denominator. Our last example of this section illustrates this idea.

$$\frac{4 - 5i}{2i} = \frac{4 - 5i}{2i} \cdot \frac{i}{i}$$

$$= \frac{(4 - 5i)(i)}{(2i)(i)}$$

$$= \frac{4i - 5i^2}{2i^2}$$

$$= \frac{4i - 5(-1)}{2(-1)}$$

$$= \frac{5 + 4i}{-2}$$

$$= -\tfrac{5}{2} - 2i$$

PROBLEM SET 1.6

Add or subtract as indicated.

1. $(5 + 2i) + (8 + 6i)$

2. $(-9 + 3i) + (4 + 5i)$

3. $(8 + 6i) - (5 + 2i)$

4. $(-6 + 4i) - (4 + 6i)$

5. $(-7 - 3i) + (-4 + 4i)$

6. $(6 - 7i) - (7 - 6i)$

7. $(-2 - 3i) - (-1 - i)$

8. $\left(\frac{1}{3} + \frac{2}{5}i\right) + \left(\frac{1}{2} + \frac{1}{4}i\right)$

9. $\left(-\frac{3}{4} - \frac{1}{4}i\right) + \left(\frac{3}{5} + \frac{2}{3}i\right)$

10. $\left(\frac{5}{8} + \frac{1}{2}i\right) - \left(\frac{7}{8} + \frac{1}{5}i\right)$

11. $\left(\frac{3}{10} - \frac{3}{4}i\right) - \left(-\frac{2}{5} + \frac{1}{6}i\right)$

12. $(4 + i\sqrt{3}) + (-6 - 2i\sqrt{3})$

13. $(5 + 3i) + (7 - 2i) + (-8 - i)$

14. $(5 - 7i) - (6 - 2i) - (-1 - 2i)$

Write each of the following in terms of i and simplify. For example, $\sqrt{-20} = i\sqrt{20} = i\sqrt{4}\sqrt{5} = 2i\sqrt{5}$.

15. $\sqrt{-9}$ **16.** $\sqrt{-49}$ **17.** $\sqrt{-19}$

18. $\sqrt{-31}$ **19.** $\sqrt{-\dfrac{4}{9}}$ **20.** $\sqrt{-\dfrac{25}{36}}$

21. $\sqrt{-8}$ **22.** $\sqrt{-18}$ **23.** $\sqrt{-27}$

24. $\sqrt{-32}$ **25.** $\sqrt{-54}$ **26.** $\sqrt{-40}$

27. $3\sqrt{-36}$ **28.** $5\sqrt{-64}$ **29.** $4\sqrt{-18}$

30. $6\sqrt{-8}$

Write each of the following in terms of i, perform the indicated operations, and simplify. For example,

$$\sqrt{-9}\sqrt{-16} = (i\sqrt{9})(i\sqrt{16}) = (3i)(4i)$$
$$= 12i^2$$
$$= 12(-1)$$
$$= -12$$

31. $\sqrt{-4}\sqrt{-16}$ **32.** $\sqrt{-25}\sqrt{-9}$

33. $\sqrt{-2}\sqrt{-3}$ **34.** $\sqrt{-3}\sqrt{-7}$

35. $\sqrt{-5}\sqrt{-4}$ **36.** $\sqrt{-7}\sqrt{-9}$

37. $\sqrt{-6}\sqrt{-10}$ **38.** $\sqrt{-2}\sqrt{-12}$

39. $\sqrt{-8}\sqrt{-7}$ **40.** $\sqrt{-12}\sqrt{-5}$

41. $\dfrac{\sqrt{-36}}{\sqrt{-4}}$ **42.** $\dfrac{\sqrt{-64}}{\sqrt{-16}}$

43. $\dfrac{\sqrt{-54}}{\sqrt{-9}}$ **44.** $\dfrac{\sqrt{-18}}{\sqrt{-3}}$

Find each of the following products and express answers in standard form.

45. $(3i)(7i)$ **46.** $(-5i)(8i)$

47. $(4i)(3 - 2i)$ **48.** $(5i)(2 + 6i)$

49. $(3 + 2i)(4 + 6i)$ **50.** $(7 + 3i)(8 + 4i)$

51. $(4 + 5i)(2 - 9i)$ **52.** $(1 + i)(2 - i)$

53. $(-2 - 3i)(4 + 6i)$

54. $(-3 - 7i)(2 + 10i)$

55. $(6 - 4i)(-1 - 2i)$ **56.** $(7 - 3i)(-2 - 8i)$

57. $(3 + 4i)^2$ **58.** $(4 - 2i)^2$

59. $(-1 - 2i)^2$ **60.** $(-2 + 5i)^2$

61. $(8 - 7i)(8 + 7i)$ **62.** $(5 + 3i)(5 - 3i)$

63. $(-2 + 3i)(-2 - 3i)$

64. $(-6 - 7i)(-6 + 7i)$

Find each of the following quotients and express your answers in standard form.

65. $\dfrac{4i}{3 - 2i}$ **66.** $\dfrac{3i}{6 + 2i}$

67. $\dfrac{2 + 3i}{3i}$ **68.** $\dfrac{3 - 5i}{4i}$

69. $\dfrac{3}{2i}$ **70.** $\dfrac{7}{4i}$

71. $\dfrac{3 + 2i}{4 + 5i}$ **72.** $\dfrac{2 + 5i}{3 + 7i}$

73. $\dfrac{4 + 7i}{2 - 3i}$ **74.** $\dfrac{3 + 9i}{4 - i}$

75. $\dfrac{3 - 7i}{-2 + 4i}$ **76.** $\dfrac{4 - 10i}{-3 + 7i}$

77. $\dfrac{-1 - i}{-2 - 3i}$ **78.** $\dfrac{-4 + 9i}{-3 - 6i}$

FURTHER INVESTIGATIONS

Use the binomial theorem to expand Problems 79–84. Express the final result in the standard form of a complex number.

79. $(1 + i)^3$ **80.** $(2 - i)^4$ **81.** $(2 - 2i)^5$

82. $(1 - i)^6$ **83.** $(2 + i)^7$ **84.** $(-1 - i)^8$

85. Using $a + bi$ and $c + di$ to represent any two complex numbers, verify each of the following properties.

a. The conjugate of the sum of two complex numbers is equal to the sum of the conjugates of the two numbers.

b. The conjugate of the product of two complex numbers is equal to the product of the conjugates of the numbers.

1.7 QUADRATIC EQUATIONS AND PROBLEM SOLVING

A **quadratic equation** in the variable x is defined as any equation that can be written in the form

$$ax^2 + bx + c = 0,$$

where a, b, and c are real numbers and $a \neq 0$. The form $ax^2 + bx + c = 0$ is called the **standard form** of a quadratic equation. The choice of x for the variable is arbitrary. An equation such as $3t^2 + 5t - 4 = 0$ is a quadratic equation in the variable t.

Quadratic equations, for which the polynomial $ax^2 + bx + c$ is factorable, can be solved by applying the following property.

PROPERTY 1.4

$$ab = 0 \quad \text{if and only if } a = 0 \text{ or } b = 0.$$

The following example illustrates the use of Property 1.4.

EXAMPLE 1

Solve $6x^2 + x - 12 = 0$.

Solution

$$6x^2 + x - 12 = 0$$

$$(2x + 3)(3x - 4) = 0$$

$$2x + 3 = 0 \qquad \text{or} \qquad 3x - 4 = 0$$

$$2x = -3 \qquad \text{or} \qquad 3x = 4$$

$$x = -\frac{3}{2} \qquad \text{or} \qquad x = \frac{4}{3}$$

The solution set is $\left\{-\frac{3}{2}, \frac{4}{3}\right\}$.

Now suppose that we want to solve $x^2 = k$, where k is any real number. We can proceed as follows.

$$x^2 = k$$

$$x^2 - k = 0$$

$$(x + \sqrt{k})(x - \sqrt{k}) = 0$$

$$x + \sqrt{k} = 0 \qquad \text{or} \qquad x - \sqrt{k} = 0$$

$$x = -\sqrt{k} \qquad \text{or} \qquad x = \sqrt{k}$$

Therefore, we can state the following property for any real number k.

PROPERTY 1.5

The solution set of $x^2 = k$ is $\{-\sqrt{k}, \sqrt{k}\}$, which can also be written $\{\pm\sqrt{k}\}$.

Propety 1.5, along with our knowledge of the square root, makes it very easy to solve quadratic equations of the form $x^2 = k$.

EXAMPLE 2

Solve each of the following.

a. $(3n - 1)^2 = 32$ **b.** $(y + 2)^2 = -24$

Solutions

a. $(3n - 1)^2 = 32$

$$3n - 1 = \pm\sqrt{32} = \pm 4\sqrt{2}$$

$$3n - 1 = 4\sqrt{2} \qquad \text{or} \qquad 3n - 1 = -4\sqrt{2}$$

$$3n = 1 + 4\sqrt{2} \qquad \text{or} \qquad 3n = 1 - 4\sqrt{2}$$

$$n = \frac{1 + 4\sqrt{2}}{3} \qquad \text{or} \qquad n = \frac{1 - 4\sqrt{2}}{3}$$

The solution set is $\left\{\dfrac{1 \pm 4\sqrt{2}}{3}\right\}$.

b. $(y + 2)^2 = -24$

$$y + 2 = \pm\sqrt{-24} = \pm 2i\sqrt{6}$$

$$y + 2 = 2i\sqrt{6} \qquad \text{or} \qquad y + 2 = -2i\sqrt{6}$$

$$y = -2 + 2i\sqrt{6} \qquad \text{or} \qquad y = -2 - 2i\sqrt{6}$$

The solution set is $\{-2 \pm 2i\sqrt{6}\}$.

Completing the Square

In each of the following examples, the trinomial on the right side of the identity is called a **perfect-square trinomial** and it is the result of squaring the binomial on the left side.

$$(x + 5)^2 = x^2 + 10x + 25 \qquad (x - 7)^2 = x^2 - 14x + 49$$

$$(x + 9)^2 = x^2 + 18x + 81 \qquad (x - 12)^2 = x^2 - 24x + 144$$

Notice that in each of the perfect-square trinomials, the **constant term is equal to the square of one-half of the coefficient of the x-term**. This relationship allows us to form a perfect-square trinomial by adding a proper constant term. For example, suppose that we want to form a perfect-square trinomial from $x^2 + 8x$. Since $\frac{1}{2}(8) = 4$ and $4^2 = 16$, the perfect-square trinomial is $x^2 + 8x + 16$. Now let's use this idea to help solve a quadratic equation.

E X A M P L E 3

Solve $x^2 + 8x - 2 = 0$.

Solution

$$x^2 + 8x - 2 = 0$$

$$x^2 + 8x + \underline{\hspace{1cm}} = 2$$

$$x^2 + 8x + 16 = 2 + 16 \qquad \text{Add 16 to left side to form a perfect-}$$
$$\text{square trinomial; 16 has to be added}$$
$$\text{to right side.}$$

$$(x + 4)^2 = 18$$

$$x + 4 = \pm\sqrt{18} = \pm 3\sqrt{2}$$

$$x = -4 \pm 3\sqrt{2}$$

The solution set is $\{-4 \pm 3\sqrt{2}\}$. ━━━━━

We have been using a relationship for a perfect-square trinomial that states, *the constant term is equal to the square of one-half of the coefficient of the x-term.* This relationship holds only if the coefficient of x^2 is 1. Thus, a slight adjustment needs to be made when we are solving quadratic equations having a coefficient of x^2 other than 1. The next example shows how to make this adjustment.

E X A M P L E 4

Solve $2x^2 + 6x - 3 = 0$.

Solution

$$2x^2 + 6x - 3 = 0$$

$$2x^2 + 6x = 3$$

$$x^2 + 3x = \frac{3}{2} \qquad \text{Multiply both sides by } \frac{1}{2}$$

$$x^2 + 3x + \frac{9}{4} = \frac{3}{2} + \frac{9}{4} \qquad \text{Add } \frac{9}{4} \text{ to both sides}$$

$$\left(x + \frac{3}{2}\right)^2 = \frac{15}{4}$$

$$x + \frac{3}{2} = \pm\frac{\sqrt{15}}{2}$$

$$x = -\frac{3}{2} \pm \frac{\sqrt{15}}{2} = \frac{-3 \pm \sqrt{15}}{2}$$

The solution set is $\left\{ \dfrac{-3 \pm \sqrt{15}}{2} \right\}$.

Quadratic Formula

The process used in Examples 3 and 4 is called **completing the square**. It can be used to solve *any* quadratic equation. If we use this process of completing the square to solve the general quadratic equation $ax^2 + bx + c = 0$, we obtain a formula known as the **quadratic formula**. The details are as follows.

$$ax^2 + bx + c = 0, \qquad a \neq 0$$

$$ax^2 + bx = -c$$

$$x^2 + \frac{b}{a}x = -\frac{c}{a} \qquad \text{Multiply both sides by } \frac{1}{a}$$

$$x^2 + \frac{b}{a}x + \frac{b^2}{4a^2} = -\frac{c}{a} + \frac{b^2}{4a^2} \qquad \text{Complete the square by adding } \frac{b^2}{4a^2}$$
$$\text{to both sides}$$

$$\left(x + \frac{b}{2a} \right)^2 = \frac{b^2 - 4ac}{4a^2} \qquad \text{Combine the right side into a single fraction}$$

$$x + \frac{b}{2a} = \pm\sqrt{\frac{b^2 - 4ac}{4a^2}}$$

$$x + \frac{b}{2a} = \pm\frac{\sqrt{b^2 - 4ac}}{\sqrt{4a^2}}$$

$$x + \frac{b}{2a} = \pm\frac{\sqrt{b^2 - 4ac}}{2a} \qquad \sqrt{4a^2} = |2a| \text{ but } 2a \text{ can be used}$$
$$\text{because of the use of } \pm$$

$$x = -\frac{b}{2a} \pm \frac{\sqrt{b^2 - 4ac}}{2a} = \frac{-b \pm \sqrt{b^2 - 4ac}}{2a}$$

Thus, we can state the quadratic formula as follows.

Quadratic Formula

If $a \neq 0$, then the solutions (roots) of the quadratic equation $ax^2 + bx + c = 0$ are given by

$$x = \frac{-b \pm \sqrt{b^2 - 4ac}}{2a}.$$

The quadratic formula can be used to solve any quadratic equation by expressing the equation in the standard form $ax^2 + bx + c = 0$, and substituting the values for a, b, and c into the formula. Let's consider an example.

EXAMPLE 5

Solve $t^2 - 2t = -4$.

Solution

The quadratic formula is usually stated in terms of the variable x, but again the choice of variable is arbitrary. The given equation needs to be changed to standard form.

$$t^2 - 2t = -4$$

$$t^2 - 2t + 4 = 0$$

Now we can substitute 1 for a, -2 for b, and 4 for c into the quadratic formula.

$$t = \frac{-(-2) \pm \sqrt{(-2)^2 - 4(1)(4)}}{2(1)}$$

$$= \frac{2 \pm \sqrt{-12}}{2}$$

$$= \frac{2 \pm 2i\sqrt{3}}{2}$$

$$= 1 \pm i\sqrt{3}$$

The solution set is $\{1 \pm i\sqrt{3}\}$.

Observe that different kinds of solutions are obtained depending upon the radicand $(b^2 - 4ac)$ inside the radical in the quadratic formula. The number, $b^2 - 4ac$, is called the **discriminant** of the quadratic equation. It can be used to determine the nature of the solutions as follows.

1. If $b^2 - 4ac > 0$, the equation has two unequal real solutions.

2. If $b^2 - 4ac = 0$, the equation has one real solution.

3. If $b^2 - 4ac < 0$, the equation has two complex but nonreal solutions.

The following examples illustrate each of these situations. (You may want to solve the equations completely to verify our conclusions.)

EQUATION	DISCRIMINANT	NATURE OF SOLUTIONS
$4x^2 - 7x - 1 = 0$	$\begin{aligned} b^2 - 4ac &= (-7)^2 - 4(4)(-1) \\ &= 49 + 16 \\ &= 65 \end{aligned}$	Two real solutions
$4x^2 + 12x + 9 = 0$	$\begin{aligned} b^2 - 4ac &= (12)^2 - 4(4)(9) \\ &= 144 - 144 \\ &= 0 \end{aligned}$	One real solution
$5x^2 + 2x + 1 = 0$	$\begin{aligned} b^2 - 4ac &= (2)^2 - 4(5)(1) \\ &= 4 - 20 \\ &= -16 \end{aligned}$	Two complex solutions

There is another useful relationship involving the solutions of a quadratic equation and the numbers a, b, and c of the general form $ax^2 + bx + c = 0$. Suppose that we let x_1 and x_2 be the two roots generated by the quadratic formula. (If $b^2 - 4ac = 0$, then $x_1 = x_2$ and the "one-solution situation" can be thought of as two equal solutions.) Thus, we have

$$x_1 = \frac{-b + \sqrt{b^2 - 4ac}}{2a} \quad \text{and} \quad x_2 = \frac{-b - \sqrt{b^2 - 4ac}}{2a}.$$

Now let's consider the sum and product of the two roots.

$$\text{Sum:} \quad x_1 + x_2 = \frac{-b + \sqrt{b^2 - 4ac}}{2a} + \frac{-b - \sqrt{b^2 - 4ac}}{2a}$$

$$= \frac{-2b}{2a} = -\frac{b}{a}$$

$$\text{Product:} \quad (x_1)(x_2) = \left(\frac{-b + \sqrt{b^2 - 4ac}}{2a} \right) \left(\frac{-b - \sqrt{b^2 - 4ac}}{2a} \right)$$

$$= \frac{b^2 - (b^2 - 4ac)}{4a^2}$$

$$= \frac{b^2 - b^2 + 4ac}{4a^2}$$

$$= \frac{4ac}{4a^2} = \frac{c}{a}$$

These relationships provide another way of checking potential solutions when solving quadratic equations. We will illustrate this point in a moment.

Solving Quadratic Equations: Which Method?

Which method should be used to solve a particular quadratic equation? There is no definite answer to that question; it depends upon the type of equation and your personal preference. However, it is to your advantage to be able to use all three techniques and to know the strengths and weaknesses of each technique. In the next two examples we will give our reasons for choosing a specific technique.

E X A M P L E 6

Solve $x^2 - 4x - 192 = 0$.

Solution

The size of the constant term makes the factoring approach a little cumbersome for this problem. However, since the coefficient of the x^2-term is 1 and the coefficient of the x-term is even, the method of completing the square should work effectively.

$$x^2 - 4x - 192 = 0$$
$$x^2 - 4x = 192$$
$$x^2 - 4x + 4 = 192 + 4$$
$$(x - 2)^2 = 196$$
$$x - 2 = \pm\sqrt{196}$$
$$x - 2 = \pm14.$$

$$x - 2 = 14 \quad \text{or} \quad x - 2 = -14$$
$$x = 16 \quad \text{or} \quad x = -12$$

 Check

Sum of roots: $16 + (-12) = 4$ and $-\dfrac{b}{a} = -\left(\dfrac{-4}{1}\right) = 4$

Product of roots: $(16)(-12) = -192$ and $\dfrac{c}{a} = \dfrac{-192}{1} = -192$

The solution set is $\{-12, 16\}$.

E X A M P L E 7

Solve $2x^2 - x + 3 = 0$.

Solution

It would be reasonable first to try factoring the polynomial $2x^2 - x + 3$. Unfortunately, it is not factorable using integers; thus we must solve the equation by completing the square or by using the quadratic formula. Since the coefficient of the x^2-term is not 1, let's avoid completing the square and use the formula instead.

$$x = \frac{-b \pm \sqrt{b^2 - 4ac}}{2a}$$

$$= \frac{-(-1) \pm \sqrt{(-1)^2 - 4(2)(3)}}{2(2)}$$

$$= \frac{1 \pm \sqrt{-23}}{4}$$

$$= \frac{1 \pm i\sqrt{23}}{4}$$

 Check

Sum of roots: $\qquad \frac{1 + i\sqrt{23}}{4} + \frac{1 - i\sqrt{23}}{4} = \frac{2}{4} = \frac{1}{2}$ and

$$-\frac{b}{a} = -\frac{-1}{2} = \frac{1}{2}$$

Product of roots: $\qquad \left(\frac{1 + i\sqrt{23}}{4}\right)\left(\frac{1 - i\sqrt{23}}{4}\right) = \frac{1 - 23i^2}{16}$

$$= \frac{1 + 23}{16} = \frac{24}{16} = \frac{3}{2} \text{ and } \frac{c}{a} = \frac{3}{2}$$

The solution set is $\left\{\dfrac{1 \pm i\sqrt{23}}{4}\right\}$.

Equations of Quadratic Form

An equation such as $x^4 + 5x^2 - 36 = 0$ is not a quadratic equation. However, if we let $u = x^2$, then $u^2 = x^4$ and substituting u for x^2 and u^2 for x^4 in $x^4 + 5x^2 - 36 = 0$ produces the quadratic equation $u^2 + 5u - 36 = 0$. In general, an equation in the variable x is said to be of **quadratic form** if it can be written in the form $au^2 + bu + c = 0$, where $a \neq 0$ and u is some algebraic expression in x. We have two basic approaches to solving equations of quadratic form, as illustrated by the next two examples.

EXAMPLE 8

Solve $15x^{-2} - 11x^{-1} - 12 = 0$.

Solution

Let $u = x^{-1}$; then $u^2 = x^{-2}$ and the given equation can be written as $15u^2 - 11u - 12 = 0$. Solving this equation yields

$$15u^2 - 11u - 12 = 0$$

$$(5u + 3)(3u - 4) = 0$$

$$5u + 3 = 0 \qquad \text{or} \qquad 3u - 4 = 0$$

$$5u = -3 \qquad \text{or} \qquad 3u = 4$$

$$u = -\tfrac{3}{5} \qquad \text{or} \qquad u = \tfrac{4}{3}$$

Now substituting x^{-1} back for u, we have

$$x^{-1} = -\frac{3}{5} \quad \text{or} \quad x^{-1} = \frac{4}{3}$$

from which we obtain

$$\frac{1}{x} = \frac{-3}{5} \quad \text{or} \quad \frac{1}{x} = \frac{4}{3}$$

$$-3x = 5 \quad \text{or} \quad 4x = 3$$

$$x = -\frac{5}{3} \quad \text{or} \quad x = \frac{3}{4}.$$

The solution set is $\left\{-\frac{5}{3}, \frac{3}{4}\right\}$.

EXAMPLE 9

Solve $x^4 + 5x^2 - 36 = 0$.

Solution

$$x^4 + 5x^2 - 36 = 0$$

$$(x^2 + 9)(x^2 - 4) = 0$$

$$x^2 + 9 = 0 \quad \text{or} \quad x^2 - 4 = 0$$

$$x^2 = -9 \quad \text{or} \quad x^2 = 4$$

$$x = \pm 3i \quad \text{or} \quad x = \pm 2$$

The solution set is $\{\pm 3i, \pm 2\}$.

Notice that in Example 8 we made a substitution (u for x^{-1}) to change the original equation to a quadratic equation in terms of the variable u. Then after solving for u, we substituted x^{-1} for u to obtain the solutions of the original equation. However, in Example 9 we factored the given polynomial and proceeded without changing to a quadratic equation. The approach you choose may depend upon the complexity of the given equation.

Back to Problem Solving

The ability to solve quadratic equations provides that much more problem solving power. Let's consider two problems that translate into quadratic equations.

PROBLEM I

Arrangement of chairs   A room contains 120 chairs. The number of chairs per row is 1 less than twice the number of rows. Find the number of rows and the number of chairs per row.

Solution

Let r represent the number of rows. Then $2r - 1$ represents the number of chairs per row. The statement of the problem implies a formation of chairs for which the total number of chairs equals the number of rows times the number of chairs per row. Therefore, we can proceed as follows.

$$(\text{Number of rows}) \text{ times} \left(\begin{array}{c}\text{Number of}\\ \text{chairs per row}\end{array}\right) = \left(\begin{array}{c}\text{Total number}\\ \text{of chairs}\end{array}\right)$$

$$r(2r - 1) = 120$$

Solving this equation yields

$$2r^2 - r = 120$$

$$2r^2 - r - 120 = 0$$

$$(2r + 15)(r - 8) = 0$$

$$2r + 15 = 0 \qquad \text{or} \qquad r - 8 = 0$$

$$2r = -15 \qquad \text{or} \qquad r = 8$$

$$r = -\tfrac{15}{2} \qquad \text{or} \qquad r = 8.$$

The solution $-\tfrac{15}{2}$ must be disregarded, so there are 8 rows and $2(8) - 1 = 15$ chairs per row.

PROBLEM 2

Riding a bicycle versus riding a moped   To travel 60 miles, it takes Sue, riding a moped, 2 hours less than it takes Ann, riding a bicycle, to travel 50 miles. Sue travels 10 miles per hour faster than Ann. Find the time and rate of each girl's ride.

Solution

Let t represent Ann's time; then $t - 2$ represents Sue's time. We can record the information in this problem in a table. The fact that "Sue travels 10 miles per hour faster than Ann" can be used as a guideline.

	DISTANCE	TIME	$r = \dfrac{d}{t}$
Ann	50	t	$\dfrac{50}{t}$
Sue	60	$t-2$	$\dfrac{60}{t-2}$

$$\underset{\substack{\uparrow \\ \dfrac{60}{t-2}}}{\text{Sue's rate}} \quad \underset{\substack{\uparrow \\ =}}{\text{equals}} \quad \underset{\substack{\text{Ann's rate} \\ \text{plus 10} \\ \uparrow \\ \dfrac{50}{t} + 10}}{}$$

Solving this equation yields

$$t(t-2)\left(\frac{60}{t-2}\right) = t(t-2)\left(\frac{50}{t} + 10\right), \qquad t \neq 0,\ t \neq 2$$

$$60t = 50(t-2) + 10t(t-2)$$

$$60t = 50t - 100 + 10t^2 - 20t$$

$$0 = 10t^2 - 30t - 100$$

$$0 = t^2 - 3t - 10$$

$$0 = (t-5)(t+2)$$

$$t - 5 = 0 \qquad \text{or} \qquad t + 2 = 0$$

$$t = 5 \qquad \text{or} \qquad t = -2.$$

The solution -2 must be disregarded. Therefore, Ann rides for 5 hours at $\frac{50}{5} = 10$ miles per hour and Sue rides for $5 - 2 = 3$ hours at $\frac{60}{3} = 20$ miles per hour.

REMARK In Section 1.5 we solved a uniform motion problem with the aid of a simple line diagram that indicated a distance relationship. Here we used a table to record and organize the pertinent information of a uniform motion problem. Our objective is to show the various approaches so that you can decide what works best for you.

There is another class of problems commonly referred to as *work problems*, or sometimes as *rate-time problems*. For example, if a certain machine produces 120 items in 10 minutes, then we say that it is working at a rate of $\frac{120}{10} = 12$ items per minute. Likewise, if a person can do a certain job in 5 hours, then assuming a constant rate of work, that person is working at a rate of $\frac{1}{5}$ of the job per hour. In general, if Q is the quantity of something done in t units of time, then the rate is given by $r = Q/t$. The rate is stated in terms of *so much quantity per unit of time*. The uniform motion problems discussed earlier are a special kind of rate-time problems for which the *quantity* is distance. Likewise, the use of tables to organize information, as we illustrated with a motion problem, is a convenient aid for other rate-time problems. Let's consider some problems.

PROBLEM 3

Delivering papers It takes Amy twice as long to deliver papers as it does Nancy. How long would it take each girl by herself if they can deliver the papers together in 40 minutes?

Solution

Let m represent the number of minutes that it takes Nancy by herself. Then $2m$ represents Amy's time by herself. Thus, the information can be organized as in the table. (Notice that the quantity is 1; there is 1 job to be done.) Since their combined rate is $\frac{1}{40}$, we can solve the following equation.

$$\frac{1}{m} + \frac{1}{2m} = \frac{1}{40}$$

$$40m\left(\frac{1}{m} + \frac{1}{2m}\right) = 40m\left(\frac{1}{40}\right)$$

$$40 + 20 = m$$

$$60 = m$$

	QUANTITY	TIME	RATE
Nancy	1	m	$\dfrac{1}{m}$
Amy	1	$2m$	$\dfrac{1}{2m}$

Therefore, Nancy can deliver the papers by herself in 60 minutes and Amy can deliver them by herself in $2(60) = 120$ minutes.

Our final example of this section illustrates another approach that some people find meaningful for rate-time problems. This approach represents the fractional parts of a job. For example, if a person can do a certain job in 7 hours, then at the end of 3 hours he has finished $\frac{3}{7}$ of the job (again, a constant rate of work is assumed). At the end of 5 hours he has finished $\frac{5}{7}$ of the job and, in general, at the end of h hours he has finished $\frac{h}{7}$ of the job.

PROBLEM 4

Mowing a lawn   Walt can mow a lawn in 50 minutes and his son, Mike, can mow the same lawn in 40 minutes. One day Mike started to mow the lawn by himself and worked for 10 minutes. Then Walt joined him with another mower and they finished the lawn. How long did it take them to finish mowing the lawn after Walt started to help?

Solution

Let m represent the number of minutes that it takes them to finish the mowing after Walt starts to help. Since Mike has been mowing for 10 minutes, he has done $\frac{10}{40}$ or $\frac{1}{4}$ of the lawn before Walt starts. Thus, there is $\frac{3}{4}$ of the lawn yet to mow. The following guideline can be used to set up an equation.

$$\begin{pmatrix} \text{Fractional part of the} \\ \text{remaining three-fourths} \\ \text{of the lawn that Mike} \\ \text{will mow in } m \text{ minutes} \end{pmatrix} + \begin{pmatrix} \text{Fractional part of the} \\ \text{remaining three-fourths} \\ \text{of the lawn that Walt} \\ \text{will mow in } m \text{ minutes} \end{pmatrix} = \frac{3}{4}$$

$$\frac{m}{40} + \frac{m}{50} = \frac{3}{4}$$

Solving this equation yields

$$200\left(\frac{m}{40} + \frac{m}{50}\right) = 200\left(\frac{3}{4}\right)$$

$$5m + 4m = 150$$

$$9m = 150$$

$$m = \frac{150}{9} = \frac{50}{3}.$$

They should finish the lawn in $16\frac{2}{3}$ minutes.

As you tackle word problems throughout this text, keep in mind that our primary objective is to expand your repertoire of problem solving techniques. In the examples, we are sharing some of our ideas for solving problems, but don't hesitate to use your own ingenuity. Furthermore, don't become discouraged—all of us have difficulty with some problems. Give it your best shot.

PROBLEM SET 1.7

Solve each of the following quadratic equations by using the method that seems most appropriate to you.

1. $x^2 - 3x - 28 = 0$

2. $x^2 - 4x - 12 = 0$

3. $3x^2 + 5x = 12$

4. $2x^2 - 13x = -6$

5. $(2n + 1)^2 = 20$

6. $3(4n - 1)^2 + 1 = 16$

7. $n^2 + 10n = 2$

8. $n^2 + 6n = 1$

9. $2t^2 + 12t - 5 = 0$

10. $3p^2 + 12p - 2 = 0$

11. $(x - 2)^2 = -4$

12. $(x - 3)^2 = -9$

13. $x^2 - 2x = 288$

14. $x^2 + 4x = 221$

15. $15n^2 + 19n - 10 = 0$

16. $24x^2 + 23x - 12 = 0$

17. $n^2 - 3n + 7 = 0$

18. $n^2 - 5n + 8 = 0$

19. $2t^2 - 3t + 7 = 0$

20. $3n^2 - 2n + 5 = 0$

21. $2a^2 - 6a + 1 = 0$

22. $2x^2 + 3x - 1 = 0$

23. $8x^2 = 3 - 10x$

24. $18x^2 = 39x - 20$

25. $2x^2 = 3x$

26. $3n^2 = 3n$

27. $25x^2 - 30x + 9 = 0$

28. $16x^2 + 56x + 49 = 0$

29. $2x^2 - 4x - 3 = 0$

30. $3x^2 - 2x - 4 = 0$

For Problems 31–40, find the discriminant of each quadratic equation and determine whether the equation has (1) two complex but nonreal solutions, (2) one real solution, or (3) two unequal real solutions.

31. $4x^2 + 20x + 25 = 0$

32. $x^2 + 4x + 7 = 0$

33. $n^2 - 18n + 81 = 0$

34. $36n^2 - 31n + 3 = 0$

35. $2t^2 + 5t + 7 = 0$

36. $16t^2 = 40t - 25$

37. $6x^2 = 4x + 7$

38. $5x^2 - 2x - 4 = 0$

39. $x^2 + 48 = 0$

40. $5x^2 - 7x = 0$

Solve each of the following equations.

41. $\dfrac{a}{a + 2} + \dfrac{3}{a + 4} = \dfrac{14}{a^2 + 6a + 8}$

42. $\dfrac{3}{x + 1} + \dfrac{2}{x + 3} = 2$

43. $\dfrac{-2}{3x+2} + \dfrac{x-1}{9x^2-4} = \dfrac{3}{12x-8}$

44. $\dfrac{-1}{2x-5} + \dfrac{2x-4}{4x^2-25} = \dfrac{5}{6x+15}$

45. $\dfrac{n}{2n-3} + \dfrac{1}{n-3} = \dfrac{n^2-n-3}{2n^2-9n+9}$

46. $\dfrac{3}{x-2} + \dfrac{5}{x+3} = \dfrac{8x-1}{x^2+x-6}$

47. $\dfrac{x+1}{2x^2+7x-4} - \dfrac{x}{2x^2-7x+3} = \dfrac{1}{x^2+x-12}$

48. $\dfrac{2n}{6n^2+7n-3} - \dfrac{n-3}{3n^2+11n-4} = \dfrac{5}{2n^2+11n+12}$

49. $\dfrac{3y}{y^2+y-6} + \dfrac{2}{y^2+4y+3} = \dfrac{y}{y^2-y-2}$

50. $\dfrac{3y+1}{3y^2-4y-4} + \dfrac{9}{9y^2-4} = \dfrac{2y-2}{3y^2-8y+4}$

51. $x^4 - 5x^2 + 4 = 0$

52. $x^4 - 25x^2 + 144 = 0$

53. $2n^4 - 9n^2 + 4 = 0$

54. $3n^4 - 4n^2 + 1 = 0$

55. $x^4 - 2x^2 - 35 = 0$

56. $2x^4 + 5x^2 - 12 = 0$

57. $x^4 - 4x^2 + 1 = 0$

58. $x^4 - 8x^2 + 11 = 0$

59. $x^{-2} + 4x^{-1} - 12 = 0$

60. $12t^{-2} - 17t^{-1} - 5 = 0$

61. $2x^{-4} - x^{-2} - 3 = 0$

62. $3x^{-4} + 8x^{-2} - 16 = 0$

63. $(x^2 + 3x)^2 - 3(x^2 + 3x) - 4 = 0$

64. $(x^2 + x)^2 - 8(x^2 + x) + 12 = 0$

For Problems 65–70, solve each equation and express solutions to the nearest hundredth.

65. $x^4 - 3x^2 + 1 = 0$

66. $x^4 - 5x^2 + 2 = 0$

67. $2x^4 - 7x^2 + 2 = 0$

68. $3x^4 - 9x^2 + 1 = 0$

69. $x^4 - 100x^2 + 2304 = 0$

70. $4x^4 - 373x^2 + 3969 = 0$

APPLIED PROBLEMS

Set up an equation and solve each of the following problems.

71. *Apple orchard*   An apple orchard contains 126 trees. The number of trees in each row is four less than twice the number of rows. Find the number of rows and the number of trees per row.

72. *Reciprocal relationship*   The sum of a number and its reciprocal is $\frac{10}{3}$. Find the number.

73. *Rates of trains*   To travel 300 miles, it takes a freight train 2 hours more than it does an express train to travel 280 miles. The rate of the express train is 20 miles per hour greater than the rate of the freight train. Find the rates of both trains.

74. *Bicycle trip*   Rita rode her bicycle into the country at a speed of 20 miles per hour and returned along the same route at 15 miles per hour. If the round trip took 5 hours and 50 minutes, how far out did she ride?

75. *Filling a tank*   One pipe can fill a tank in 4 hours and another pipe can fill the tank in 6 hours. How long will it take to fill the tank if both pipes are used?

76. *Painting a shed*   Lolita and Doug working together can paint a shed in 3 hours and 20 minutes. If Doug can paint the shed by himself in 10 hours, how long would it take Lolita to paint the shed by herself?

77. *Filling a tank*   An inlet pipe can fill a tank in 10 minutes. A drain can empty the tank in 12 minutes. If the tank is empty and both the pipe and drain are open, how long will it take before the tank overflows?

78. *Overhauling an engine*   Mark can overhaul an engine in 20 hours and Phil can do the same job by himself in 30 hours. If they both work together for a time and then Mark finishes the job by himself in 5 hours, how long did they work together?

79. *Assembling a bookcase*   Pat and Mike working together can assemble a bookcase in 6 minutes. It takes Mike, working by himself, 9 minutes longer than it takes Pat working by himself to assemble the bookcase. How long does it take each, working alone, to do the job?

80. *Rate of typing*   Amelia can type 600 words in 5 minutes less time than it takes Paul to type 600 words. If Amelia types at a rate of 20 words per minute more than Paul types, find the rate of each.

81. *Purchasing golf balls*   Angie bought some golf balls for $14. If each ball had cost $.25 less, she could have purchased 1 more ball for the same amount of money. How many golf balls did Angie buy?

82. *Work contract*   A new labor contract provides for an increase of $1 per hour and a reduction of 5 hours in the work week. A worker who receives $320 per week under the old contract would receive $315 per week under the new contract. How long was the work week under the old contract?

83. *Painting a house*   Todd contracted to paint a house for $480. It took him 4 hours longer than he had anticipated so he earned $.50 per hour less than he originally calculated. How long had he anticipated that it would take him to paint the house?

84. *Right triangle*   One leg of a right triangle is 4 inches longer than the other leg. If the length of the hypotenuse is 20 inches, find the length of each leg.

85. *Right triangle*   The sum of the lengths of the two legs of a right triangle is 34 meters. If the length of the hypotenuse is 26 meters, find the length of each leg.

86. *Right triangle*   The lengths of the three sides of a right triangle are consecutive even integers. Find the length of each side.

87. *Area of a rectangle*   The perimeter of a rectangle is 44 inches and its area is 112 square inches. Find the length and width of the rectangle.

88. *Dimensions of a page*   A page of a magazine contains 70 square inches of type. The height of a page is twice the width. If the margin around the type is to be 2 inches uniformly, what are the dimensions of the page?

89. *Area of a rectangle*   The length of a rectangle is 4 meters more than twice its width. If the area of the rectangle is 126 square meters, find its length and width.

90. *Area of a triangle*   The length of one side of a triangle is 3 centimeters less than twice the length of the altitude to that side. If the area of the triangle is 52 square centimeters, find the length of a side and the length of the altitude to that side.

91. *Determining the width of a sidewalk*   A rectangular plot of ground measuring 12 meters by 20 meters is surrounded by a sidewalk of uniform width. The area of the sidewalk is 68 square meters. Find the width of the walk.

92. *Sum of areas of two squares*   A piece of wire 60 inches long is cut into two pieces and then each piece is bent into the shape of a square. If the sum of the areas of the two squares is 117 square inches, find the length of each piece of wire.

93. *Forming a box*   A rectangular piece of cardboard is 4 inches longer than it is wide. From each of its corners a square piece 2 inches on a side is cut out. The flaps are then turned up to form an open box, having a volume of 42 cubic inches. Find the length and width of the original piece of cardboard.

THOUGHTS into WORDS

94. Explain how you would solve $(x - 3)(x + 4) = 0$ and also how you would solve $(x - 3)(x + 4) = 8$.

95. Explain the process of "completing the square" to solve a quadratic equation.

96. Explain how to use the quadratic formula to solve $3x = x^2 - 2$.

97. How would you solve the equation $x^2 - 4x = 252$? Explain your choice of the method that you would use.

98. Discuss any new ideas relative to problem solving that you have acquired in this course.

1.8   INEQUALITIES AND ABSOLUTE VALUE

Algebraic inequalities contain one or more variables. The following are examples of algebraic inequalities.

$$x + 4 > 8 \qquad 3x + 2y \leq 4$$

$$(x - 2)(x + 4) \geq 0 \qquad x^2 + y^2 + z^2 \leq 16$$

An algebraic inequality such as $x + 4 > 8$ is neither true nor false as it stands; it is called an **open sentence**. For each numerical value substituted for x, the algebraic inequality $x + 4 > 8$ becomes a numerical statement of inequality that is true or false. For example, if $x = -3$, then $x + 4 > 8$ becomes $-3 + 4 > 8$, which is false. If $x = 5$, then $x + 4 > 8$ becomes $5 + 4 > 8$, which is true. **Solving an algebraic inequality** refers to the process of finding the numbers that make it a true numerical statement. Such numbers are called the *solutions* of the inequality and are said to *satisfy* it.

The general process for solving inequalities closely parallels that for solving equations. We continue to replace the given inequality with equivalent but simpler inequalities until the solution set is obvious. The following properties provide the basis for producing equivalent inequalities.

Addition Property of Inequality

For all real numbers a, b, and c,

$$a > b \quad \text{if and only if } a + c > b + c.$$

Multiplication Property of Inequality

a. For all real numbers a, b, and c, *with $c > 0$,*

$$a > b \quad \text{if and only if } ac > bc.$$

b. For all real numbers a, b, and c, *with $c < 0$,*

$$a > b \quad \text{if and only if } ac < bc.$$

Similar properties exist for the relation $<$. For example, $a < b$ if and only if $a + c < b + c$. Furthermore, pay special attention to part (b) of the multiplication property of inequality. If you multiply both sides of an inequality by a negative number, the inequality symbol must be reversed. For example, if you multiply both sides of $3 < 5$ by -2, the equivalent inequality $-2(3) > -2(5)$ is produced.

EXAMPLE 1

Solve $3(2x - 1) < 8x - 7$.

Solution

$$3(2x - 1) < 8x - 7$$

$$6x - 3 < 8x - 7 \qquad \text{Apply distributive property to left side}$$

$$-2x - 3 < -7 \qquad \text{Add } -8x \text{ to both sides}$$

$$-2x < -4 \qquad \text{Add 3 to both sides}$$

$$-\tfrac{1}{2}(-2x) > -\tfrac{1}{2}(-4) \qquad \text{Multiply both sides by } -\tfrac{1}{2}, \text{ which reverses the inequality}$$

$$x > 2$$

The solution set is $\{x \mid x > 2\}$.

FIGURE 1.8

A graph of the solution set $\{x \mid x > 2\}$ in Example 1 is shown in Figure 1.8. The parenthesis indicates that 2 does not belong to the solution set.

It is also convenient to express solution sets of inequalities using **interval notation**. For example, the symbol $(2, \infty)$ refers to the interval of real numbers greater than 2. As on the graph in Figure 1.8, the left-hand parenthesis indicates that 2 is not to be included. The infinity symbol, ∞, along with the right-hand parenthesis, indicates that there is no right-hand endpoint. Following is a list of interval notations along with the sets and graphs that they represent. Notice the use of brackets to include endpoints. Also recall that the notation $a < x < b$ is a compact way of expressing that "x is greater than a and x is less than b." From now on, we will express solution sets of inequalities using interval notation (Figure 1.9).

TYPE OF INTERVAL	SET	INTERVAL NOTATION	GRAPH (FIGURE 1.9)
Open interval	$\{x \mid x > a\}$	(a, ∞)	
	$\{x \mid a < x < b\}$	(a, b)	
	$\{x \mid x < b\}$	$(-\infty, b)$	
Half-open interval	$\{x \mid x \geq a\}$	$[a, \infty)$	
	$\{x \mid a < x \leq b\}$	$(a, b]$	
	$\{x \mid a \leq x < b\}$	$[a, b)$	
	$\{x \mid x \leq b\}$	$(-\infty, b]$	
Closed interval	$\{x \mid a \leq x \leq b\}$	$[a, b]$	

EXAMPLE 2

Solve $\dfrac{x-4}{6} - \dfrac{x-2}{9} \le \dfrac{5}{18}$.

Solution

$$\frac{x-4}{6} - \frac{x-2}{9} \le \frac{5}{18}$$

$$18\left(\frac{x-4}{6} - \frac{x-2}{9}\right) \le 18\left(\frac{5}{18}\right) \qquad \text{Multiply both sides by LCD}$$

$$18\left(\frac{x-4}{6}\right) - 18\left(\frac{x-2}{9}\right) \le 18\left(\frac{5}{18}\right)$$

$$3(x-4) - 2(x-2) \le 5$$

$$3x - 12 - 2x + 4 \le 5$$

$$x - 8 \le 5$$

$$x \le 13$$

The solution set is $(-\infty, 13]$.

EXAMPLE 3

Solve $-2 < \dfrac{3x+2}{2} < 7$.

Solution

$$-2 < \frac{3x+2}{2} < 7$$

$$2(-2) < 2\left(\frac{3x+2}{2}\right) < 2(7) \qquad \text{Multiply through by 2}$$

$$-4 < 3x + 2 < 14$$

$$-6 < 3x < 12$$

$$-2 < x < 4$$

The solution set is $(-2, 4)$.

Quadratic Inequalities

The equation $ax^2 + bx + c = 0$ has been referred to as the standard form of a quadratic equation in one variable. Similarly, the form $ax^2 + bx + c < 0$ is used to represent a **quadratic inequality**. (The symbol $<$ can be replaced by $>$, $\le$, or $\ge$ to produce other forms of quadratic inequalities.)

The number line becomes a useful tool for analyzing quadratic inequalities. Let's consider some examples to illustrate the procedure.

EXAMPLE 4

Solve $x^2 + x - 6 < 0$.

Solution

First, let's factor the polynomial.

$$x^2 + x - 6 < 0$$

$$(x + 3)(x - 2) < 0$$

Next, let's locate the values for which the product $(x + 3)(x - 2)$ is equal to zero. These numbers, often referred to as **critical numbers**, are -3 and 2, and they divide the number line into the three intervals $(-\infty, -3)$, $(-3, 2)$, and $(2, \infty)$ as shown in Figure 1.10. We can choose a **test number** from each of these intervals and deter-

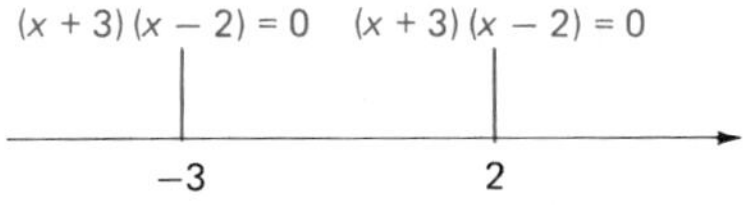

$(x + 3)(x - 2) = 0 \quad (x + 3)(x - 2) = 0$

$$\overline{||} \longrightarrow$$
$$-32$$

FIGURE   1.10

mine how it affects the signs of the factors $(x + 3)$ and $(x - 2)$, and consequently, how it affects the sign of the product of the two factors. This information is organized in Figure 1.11 where we used the test numbers -4, 0, and 3.

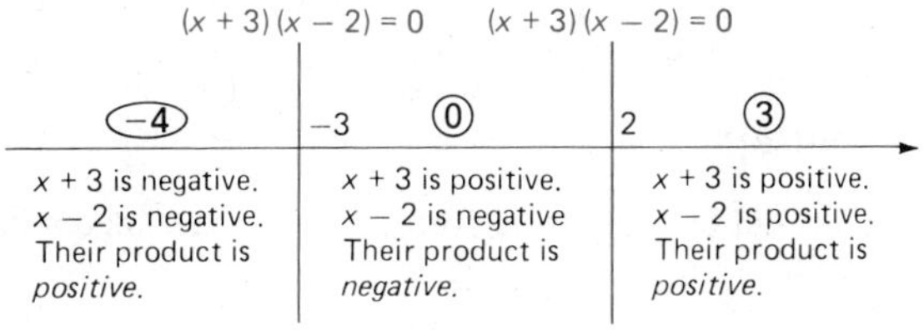

$(x + 3)(x - 2) = 0 \qquad (x + 3)(x - 2) = 0$

$\textcircled{-4}$	$-3\textcircled{0}$	$2\textcircled{3}$
$x + 3$ is negative. $x - 2$ is negative. Their product is *positive*.	$x + 3$ is positive. $x - 2$ is negative Their product is *negative*.	$x + 3$ is positive. $x - 2$ is positive. Their product is *positive*.

FIGURE   1.11

Therefore, the given inequality $x^2 + x - 6 < 0$ is satisfied by the numbers between -3 and 2. That is, the solution set is the open interval $(-3, 2)$.

Inequalities Involving Quotients

The same type of number line analysis can be used for indicated quotients as well as for indicated products. In other words, inequalities, such as $\dfrac{x - 2}{x + 3} > 0$, can be solved very effectively using the same basic approach that we used with quadratic inequalities. Let's consider two examples.

EXAMPLE 5

Solve $\dfrac{x - 2}{x + 3} > 0$.

Solution

First, indicate that at $x = 2$ the quotient $\dfrac{x - 2}{x + 3}$ equals zero and at $x = -3$ the quotient is undefined. The critical numbers -3 and 2 divide the number line into three intervals. Then using a test number from each interval (such as -4, 1, and 3), we can observe the sign behavior of the quotient $\dfrac{x - 2}{x + 3}$ (Figure 1.12).

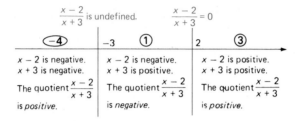

F I G U R E   1 . 1 2

Using the concept of set union*, the solution set can be expressed as $(-\infty, -3) \cup (2, \infty)$.

E X A M P L E 6

Solve $\dfrac{x + 2}{x + 4} \leq 3$.

Solution

First, let's change the form of the given inequality.

$$\frac{x + 2}{x + 4} \leq 3$$

$$\frac{x + 2}{x + 4} - 3 \leq 0$$

$$\frac{x + 2 - 3(x + 4)}{x + 4} \leq 0$$

$$\frac{x + 2 - 3x - 12}{x + 4} \leq 0$$

$$\frac{-2x - 10}{x + 4} \leq 0$$

Now we can proceed as before. If $x = -5$, then the quotient $\dfrac{-2x - 10}{x + 4}$ equals zero and if $x = -4$, the quotient is undefined. Then using test numbers such as -6, $-4\frac{1}{2}$,

---

*The union of sets A and B, written as $A \cup B$, is defined as $A \cup B = \{x \mid x \in A \ or \ x \in B\}$.

and -3 we can study the sign behavior of the quotient $\dfrac{-2x - 10}{x + 4}$ (Figure 1.13).

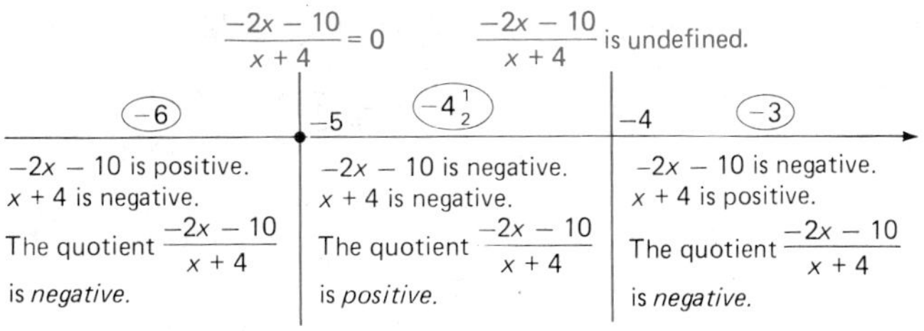

$$\frac{-2x - 10}{x + 4} = 0 \qquad \frac{-2x - 10}{x + 4} \text{ is undefined.}$$

| $\boxed{-6}$ | -5 | $\boxed{-4\frac{1}{2}}$ | -4 | $\boxed{-3}$ |

$-2x - 10$ is positive.
$x + 4$ is negative.

The quotient $\dfrac{-2x - 10}{x + 4}$

is *negative*.

$-2x - 10$ is negative.
$x + 4$ is negative.

The quotient $\dfrac{-2x - 10}{x + 4}$

is *positive*.

$-2x - 10$ is negative.
$x + 4$ is positive.

The quotient $\dfrac{-2x - 10}{x + 4}$

is *negative*.

FIGURE 1.13

Therefore, the solution set for $\dfrac{x + 2}{x + 4} \le 3$ is $(-\infty, -5] \cup (-4, \infty)$.

Equations and Inequalities Involving Absolute Value

In Section 1.1 we defined the absolute value of a real number by

$$|a| = \begin{cases} a, & \text{if } a \ge 0 \\ -a, & \text{if } a < 0. \end{cases}$$

We also interpreted the absolute value of any real number to be the distance between the number and zero on the number line. For example, $|6| = 6$ because the distance between 6 and 0 is 6 units. Likewise, $|-9| = 9$ because the distance between -9 and 0 is 9 units.

Both the definition and the number line interpretation of absolute value provide ways of analyzing a variety of equations and inequalities involving absolute value. For example, suppose that we need to solve the equation $|x| = 4$. In terms of distance on the number line, the equation $|x| = 4$ means that we are looking for numbers that are four units away from zero. Thus, x must be 4 or -4. From the definition viewpoint, we could proceed as follows.

If $x \ge 0$, then $|x| = x$ and the equation $|x| = 4$ becomes $x = 4$.

If $x < 0$, then $|x| = -x$ and the equation $|x| = 4$ becomes $-x = 4$, which is equivalent to $x = -4$.

With either approach we see that the solution set for $|x| = 4$ is $\{-4, 4\}$.

The following general property should seem reasonable from the distance interpretation and can be verified using the definition of absolute value.

PROPERTY 1.6

For any real number $k > 0$.

$$\text{if } |x| = k \quad \text{then } x = k \text{ or } x = -k.$$

Use the definition of absolute value, to verify Property 1.6 and reason as follows.

If $x \geq 0$, then $|x| = x$ and the equation $|x| = k$ becomes $x = k$.

If $x < 0$, then $|x| = -x$ and the equation $|x| = k$ becomes $-x = k$, which is equivalent to $x = -k$.

Therefore, the equation $|x| = k$ is equivalent to $x = k$ or $x = -k$. Now let's use Property 1.6 to solve an equation of the form $|ax + b| = k$.

EXAMPLE 7

Solve $|3x - 2| = 7$.

Solution

$$|3x - 2| = 7$$

$$3x - 2 = 7 \quad \text{or} \quad 3x - 2 = -7$$

$$3x = 9 \quad \text{or} \quad 3x = -5$$

$$x = 3 \quad \text{or} \quad x = -\tfrac{5}{3}$$

The solution set is $\left\{-\tfrac{5}{3}, 3\right\}$.

The distance interpretation for absolute value also provides a good basis for solving some inequalities. For example, to solve $|x| < 4$, we know that the distance between x and 0 must be less than four units. In other words, x is to be less than four units away from zero. Thus, $|x| < 4$ is equivalent to $-4 < x < 4$ and the solution set is the interval $(-4, 4)$. We will have you use the definition of absolute value and verify the following general property in the next set of exercises.

PROPERTY 1.7

For any real number $k > 0$,

$$\text{if } |x| < k, \quad \text{then } -k < x < k.$$

E X A M P L E   8

Solve $|2x + 1| < 5$.

Solution

$$|2x + 1| < 5$$
$$-5 < 2x + 1 < 5$$
$$-6 < 2x < 4$$
$$-3 < \ x < 2$$

The solution set is $(-3, 2)$.

Now suppose that we want to solve $|x| > 4$. The distance between x and 0 is to be more than 4 units; in other words, x is to be more than 4 units away from zero. Therefore, $|x| > 4$ is equivalent to $x < -4$ or $x > 4$ and the solution set is $(-\infty, -4) \cup (4, \infty)$. The following general property can be verified by using the definition of absolute value.

P R O P E R T Y   1 . 8

For any real number $k > 0$.
   if $|x| > k$,   then $x < -k$ or $x > k$.

E X A M P L E   9

Solve $|4x - 3| > 9$.

Solution

$$|4x - 3| > 9.$$

$4x - 3 < -9$	or	$4x - 3 > 9$
$4x < -6$	or	$4x > 12$
$x < -\frac{6}{4}$	or	$x > 3$
$x < -\frac{3}{2}$	or	$x > 3$

The solution set is $\left(-\infty, -\frac{3}{2}\right) \cup (3, \infty)$.

Properties 1.6, 1.7, and 1.8 provide a sound basis for solving many equations and inequalities involving absolute value. However, if at any time you become doubtful as to which property applies, don't forget the definition and the distance interpretation for absolute value. Furthermore, there are some equations and inequalities where the properties do not apply. Let's consider one such example.

EXAMPLE 10

Solve the equation $|3x - 1| = |x + 4|$.

Solution

We could solve this equation by applying the definition of absolute value to both expressions; however, let's approach it in a less formal way. For the two numbers, $3x - 1$ and $x + 4$, to have the same absolute value they must be equal or they must be opposites of each other. Therefore, the equation $|3x - 1| = |x + 4|$ is equivalent to $3x - 1 = x + 4$ or $3x - 1 = -(x + 4)$, which can be solved as follows.

$$3x - 1 = x + 4 \qquad \text{or} \qquad 3x - 1 = -(x + 4)$$
$$2x = 5 \qquad \text{or} \qquad 3x - 1 = -x - 4$$
$$x = \tfrac{5}{2} \qquad \text{or} \qquad 4x = -3$$
$$x = \tfrac{5}{2} \qquad \text{or} \qquad x = -\tfrac{3}{4}$$

The solution set is $\left\{-\tfrac{3}{4}, \tfrac{5}{2}\right\}$.   ▬▬▬▬

We should also note that in Properties 1.6 through 1.8, k is a positive number. This is not a serious restriction because problems where k is nonpositive are easily solved as follows.

$\|x - 2\| = 0$	The solution set is $\{2\}$ because $x - 2$ has to equal zero.
$\|3x - 7\| = -4$	The solution set is $\varnothing$. For any real number, the absolute value of $3x - 7$ will always be nonnegative.
$\|2x - 1\| < -3$	The solution set is $\varnothing$. For any real number, the absolute value of $2x - 1$ will always be nonnegative.
$\|5x + 2\| > -4$	The solution set is $(-\infty, \infty)$. The absolute value of $5x + 2$, regardless of which real number is substituted for x, will always be greater than -4.

The number line approach along with Properties 1.7 and 1.8 provides a systematic way of solving absolute value inequalities that have the variable in the denominator of a fraction. Let's analyze one such problem.

EXAMPLE 11

Solve $\left|\dfrac{x - 2}{x + 3}\right| < 4$.

Solution

By Property 1.7 $\left|\dfrac{x - 2}{x + 3}\right| < 4$ becomes $-4 < \dfrac{x - 2}{x + 3} < 4$, which can be written as

$$\dfrac{x - 2}{x + 3} > -4 \quad \text{and} \quad \dfrac{x - 2}{x + 3} < 4.$$

Now let's solve each part of this "and" statement.

(a)   **(b)**

$$\frac{x-2}{x+3} > -4 \quad \text{and} \quad \frac{x-2}{x+3} < 4$$

$$\frac{x-2}{x+3} + 4 > 0 \quad \text{and} \quad \frac{x-2}{x+3} - 4 < 0$$

$$\frac{x-2+4(x+3)}{x+3} > 0 \quad \text{and} \quad \frac{x-2-4(x+3)}{x+3} < 0$$

$$\frac{x-2+4x+12}{x+3} > 0 \quad \text{and} \quad \frac{x-2-4x-12}{x+3} < 0$$

$$\frac{5x+10}{x+3} > 0 \quad \text{and} \quad \frac{-3x-14}{x+3} < 0$$

The solution set for each of these inequalities is as follows (Figure 1.14).

FIGURE 1.14

The intersection* of the above two solution sets is the following set (Figure 1.15).

FIGURE 1.15

Therefore, the solution set is $\left|\dfrac{x-2}{x+3}\right| < 4$ is $\left(-\infty, -\frac{14}{3}\right) \cup (-2, \infty)$.   ■

Yes, Example 11 is a little messy, but it does illustrate the weaving together of previously used techniques to solve a more complicated problem. Don't be in a hurry when doing such problems. First, analyze the general approach to be taken and then carry out the details in a neatly organized format to minimize your chances of making careless errors.

---

*The **intersection** of sets A and B, written $A \cap B$, is defined as $A \cap B = \{x \mid x \in A \text{ and } x \in B\}$.

PROBLEM SET 1.8

Solve each of the following inequalities. Express the solution sets using interval notation.

1. $6(2t - 5) - 2(4t - 1) \geq 0$

2. $3(2x + 1) - 2(2x + 5) < 5(3x - 2)$

3. $\dfrac{2}{3}x - \dfrac{3}{4} \leq \dfrac{1}{4}x + \dfrac{2}{3}$

4. $\dfrac{3}{5} - \dfrac{x}{2} \geq \dfrac{1}{2} + \dfrac{x}{5}$

5. $\dfrac{n + 2}{4} + \dfrac{n - 3}{8} < 1$

6. $\dfrac{2n + 1}{6} + \dfrac{3n - 1}{5} > \dfrac{2}{15}$

7. $\dfrac{x}{2} - \dfrac{x - 1}{5} \geq \dfrac{x + 2}{10} - 4$

8. $\dfrac{4x - 3}{6} - \dfrac{2x - 1}{12} < -2$

9. $.09x + .1(x + 200) > 77$

10. $.06x + .08(250 - x) \geq 19$

11. $0 < \dfrac{5x - 1}{3} < 2$

12. $-3 \leq \dfrac{4x + 3}{2} \leq 1$

13. $3 \geq \dfrac{7 - x}{2} \geq 1$

14. $-2 \leq \dfrac{5 - 3x}{4} \leq \dfrac{1}{2}$

15. $x^2 - 2x - 15 > 0$

16. $x^2 - 12x + 32 \geq 0$

17. $3t^2 + 11t - 4 > 0$

18. $2t^2 - 9t - 5 > 0$

19. $15x^2 - 26x + 8 \leq 0$

20. $6x^2 + 25x + 14 \leq 0$

21. $4x^2 - 4x + 1 > 0$

22. $9x^2 + 6x + 1 \leq 0$

23. $(x + 1)(x - 3) > (x + 1)(2x - 1)$

24. $(x - 2)(2x + 5) > (x - 2)(x - 3)$

25. $(x + 1)(x - 2) \geq (x - 4)(x + 6)$

26. $(2x - 1)(x + 4) \geq (2x + 1)(x - 3)$

27. $(x - 1)(x - 2)(x + 4) > 0$

28. $(x + 1)(x - 3)(x + 7) \geq 0$

29. $(x + 2)(2x - 1)(x - 5) \leq 0$

30. $(x - 3)(3x + 2)(x + 4) < 0$

31. $x^3 - 2x^2 - 24x \geq 0$

32. $x^3 + 2x^2 - 3x > 0$

33. $(x - 2)^2(x + 3) > 0$

34. $(x + 4)^2(x + 5) > 0$

35. $\dfrac{2x - 1}{x + 2} < 0$

36. $\dfrac{3x + 2}{x - 1} > 0$

37. $\dfrac{-x + 3}{3x - 1} \geq 0$

38. $\dfrac{-n - 2}{n + 4} < 0$

39. $\dfrac{x - 1}{x + 2} < 2$

40. $\dfrac{t - 1}{t - 5} \leq 2$

41. $\dfrac{t - 3}{t + 5} > 1$

42. $\dfrac{x + 2}{x + 7} < 1$

43. $\dfrac{1}{x - 2} < \dfrac{1}{x + 3}$

44. $\dfrac{2}{x + 1} > \dfrac{3}{x - 4}$

Solve each of the following equations.

45. $|2n - 1| = 7$

46. $|2n + 1| = 11$

47. $|-2x - 1| = 6$

48. $|-3x - 2| = 8$

49. $|7x - 1| = -4$ **50.** $|5x - 4| = -3$

51. $\left|\dfrac{3}{k-1}\right| = 4$ **52.** $\left|\dfrac{-2}{n+3}\right| = 5$

53. $|3x - 1| = |2x + 3|$ **54.** $|2x + 1| = |4x - 3|$

55. $|x - 2| = |x + 4|$ **56.** $|2x - 3| = |2x + 5|$

Solve each of the following inequalities expressing the solution sets in interval notation.

57. $|2x - 1| \le 7$ **58.** $|2x + 1| \ge 3$

59. $|3n + 2| > 9$ **60.** $|5n - 2| < 2$

61. $|4x - 3| < -5$ **62.** $|4x + 5| > -3$

63. $|-1 - x| \ge 8$ **64.** $|-2 - x| \le 5$

65. $\left|\dfrac{x+1}{x-2}\right| < 3$ **66.** $\left|\dfrac{x-1}{x-4}\right| < 2$

67. $\left|\dfrac{x-1}{x+3}\right| > 1$ **68.** $\left|\dfrac{x+4}{x-5}\right| \ge 3$

69. $\left|\dfrac{n+2}{n}\right| \ge 4$ **70.** $\left|\dfrac{t+6}{t-2}\right| < 1$

71. $\left|\dfrac{k}{2k-1}\right| \le 2$ **72.** $\left|\dfrac{k}{k+2}\right| > 4$

Solve each of the following problems by setting up and solving an appropriate inequality.

73. *Investments*   Felix has $1000 to invest. Suppose he invests $500 at 8% interest. At what rate must he invest the

other $500 so that the two investments yield more than $100 of yearly interest?

74. *Investments*   Suppose that Annette invests $700 at 9%. How much must she invest at 11% so that the total yearly interest from the two investments exceeds $162?

75. *Exam scores*   Rhonda had scores of 94, 84, 86, and 88 on her first four history exams of the semester. What score must she obtain on the 5th exam to have an average of 90 or better for the five exams?

76. *Heights of basketball players*   The average height of the two forwards and the center of a basketball team is 6 feet 8 inches. What must the average height of the two guards be so that the team average is at least 6 feet 4 inches?

77. *Temperature*   If the temperature for a 24-hour period ranged between 41°F and 59°F, inclusive, what was the range in Celsius degrees? $\left(\mathrm{F} = \frac{9}{5}\mathrm{C} + 32\right)$

78. *Temperature*   If the temperature for a 24-hour period ranged between −20°C and −5°C, inclusive, what was the range in Fahrenheit degrees? $\left(\mathrm{C} = \frac{5}{9}(\mathrm{F} - 32)\right)$

79. *Mental age versus chronological age*   A person's intelligence quotient (IQ) is found by dividing mental age (M), as indicated by standard tests, by the chronological age (C), and then multiplying this ratio by 100. The formula $\mathrm{IQ} = \frac{100\mathrm{M}}{\mathrm{C}}$ can be used. If the IQ range of a group of 11-year-olds is given by $80 \le \mathrm{IQ} \le 140$, find the mental-age range of this group.

80. *Car rental*   A car can be rented from agency A at $75 per day plus $.10 a mile or from agency B at $50 a day plus $.20 a mile. If the car is driven m miles, for what values of m does it cost less to rent from agency A?

THOUGHTS into WORDS

81. Explain how you would solve the inequality $(x - 1)^2(x + 2)^2 > 0$.

82. Explain how you would solve the inequality $\dfrac{x-2}{(x+1)^2} > 0$.

83. Explain how you would solve the inequality $|3x - 7| > -2$.

84. Why is $\frac{3}{2}$ the only solution for $|2x - 3| \le 0$?

85. Consider the following approach for solving the inequality in Example 2 of this section.

$$\frac{x+2}{x+4} \le 3$$

$$(x+4)\left(\frac{x+2}{x+4}\right) \le 3(x+4) \qquad \text{Multiply both sides by } x + 4.$$

$$x + 2 \leq 3x + 12$$

$$-2x \leq 10$$

$$x \geq -5$$

Obviously, the solution set that we obtain using this approach differs from what we obtained in the text. What is wrong with this approach? Can we make any adjustments so that this basic approach works?

FURTHER INVESTIGATIONS

86. Use the definition of absolute value and prove Property 1.7.

87. Prove Property 1.8.

For Problems 88–91, use the definition of absolute value to help find the solution sets. For example, $|x - 2| + |x + 1| = 7$ becomes

$$(x - 2) + (x + 1) = 7 \quad \text{if } x \geq 2,$$

$$-(x - 2) + (x + 1) = 7 \quad \text{if } -1 < x < 2,$$

$$-(x - 2) + [-(x + 1)] = 7 \quad \text{if } x \leq -1.$$

88. $|x - 2| + |x + 1| = 7$ **89.** $|x + 2| + |x - 4| = 6$

90. $|x + 3| < |x - 8|$ **91.** $|x - 1| > |x + 4|$

CHAPTER I SUMMARY

Chapter 1 can be summarized in terms of four large topics (1) basic algebraic ideas, (2) solving equations, (3) solving inequalities, and (4) problem solving.

Basic Algebraic Ideas

Be sure of the following key concepts from this chapter: Set, null set, equal sets, subset, natural numbers, whole numbers, integers, rational numbers, irrational numbers, real numbers, complex numbers, absolute value, similar terms, exponent, monomial, binomial, polynomial, degree of a polynomial, perfect-square trinomial, factoring polynomials, and conjugate of a complex number.

The following properties of the real numbers provide a basis for arithmetic and algebraic computation: Closure for addition and multiplication, commutativity for addition and multiplication, associativity for addition and multiplication, identity properties for addition and multiplication, inverse properties for addition and multiplication, multiplication property of zero, multiplication property of negative one, and distributive property.

The following properties of absolute value are useful.

1. $|a| \geq 0$

2. $|a| = |-a|$ *a and b are real numbers*

3. $|a - b| = |b - a|$

The following properties of exponents provide the basis for much of our computational work with polynomials.

1. $b^n \cdot b^m = b^{n+m}$

2. $(b^n)^m = b^{mn}$

3. $(ab)^n = a^n b^n$ m and n are integers and a and b are real numbers, except $b \neq 0$ whenever it appears in a denominator

4. $\left(\dfrac{a}{b}\right)^n = \dfrac{a^n}{b^n}$

5. $\dfrac{b^n}{b^m} = b^{n-m}$

The following product patterns are helpful to recognize when multiplying polynomials.

1. $(a + b)^2 = a^2 + 2ab + b^2$

2. $(a - b)^2 = a^2 - 2ab + b^2$

3. $(a + b)(a - b) = a^2 - b^2$

4. $(a + b)^3 = a^3 + 3a^2 b + 3ab^2 + b^3$

5. $(a - b)^3 = a^3 - 3a^2 b + 3ab^2 - b^3$

6. $(a + b)^n = \dbinom{n}{0} a^n + \dbinom{n}{1} a^{n-1} b + \dbinom{n}{2} a^{n-2} b^2 + \cdots + \dbinom{n}{n} b^n$

Be sure of the following factoring techniques.

1. Factoring out the highest common monomial factor

2. Factoring by grouping

3. Factoring a trinomial into the product of two binomials

4. Recognizing some basic factoring patterns, namely,

$$a^2 - b^2 = (a + b)(a - b)$$

$$a^3 + b^3 = (a + b)(a^2 - ab + b^2)$$

$$a^3 - b^3 = (a - b)(a^2 + ab + b^2).$$

Be sure that you can simplify, add, subtract, and multiply rational expressions and simplify complex fractions based on the following properties.

$$\frac{a \cdot k}{b \cdot k} = \frac{a}{b} \qquad\qquad \frac{a}{b} \cdot \frac{c}{d} = \frac{ac}{bd}$$

$$\frac{a}{b} + \frac{c}{b} = \frac{a + c}{b} \qquad\qquad \frac{a}{b} - \frac{c}{b} = \frac{a - c}{b}$$

Be sure that you can add, subtract, multiply, and divide complex numbers.

Solving Equations

The following properties are used extensively in the equation solving process.

1. $a = b$ if and only if $a + c = b + c$.   Addition property of equality

2. $a = b$ if and only if $ac = bc$, $c \neq 0$.   Multiplication property of equality

3. $ab = 0$ if and only if $a = 0$ or $b = 0$.

Quadratic equations can be solved by (1) factoring, (2) completing the square, or (3) using the quadratic formula.

The quadratic formula can be stated as $x = \dfrac{-b \pm \sqrt{b^2 - 4ac}}{2a}$.

The discriminant $(b^2 - 4ac)$ of a quadratic equation indicates the nature of the solutions of the equation.

1. If $b^2 - 4ac > 0$, the equation has two unequal real solutions.

2. If $b^2 - 4ac = 0$, the equation has one real solution.

3. If $b^2 - 4ac < 0$, the equation has two complex but nonreal solutions.

If x_1 and x_2 are solutions of a quadratic equation $ax^2 + bx + c = 0$, then **(1)** $x_1 + x_2 = -\dfrac{b}{a}$ and **(2)** $(x_1)(x_2) = \dfrac{c}{a}$. These relationships can be used to check potential solutions.

The property *if $|x| = k$, then $x = k$ or $x = -k(k > 0)$* is often helpful for solving equations involving absolute value.

Solving Inequalities

The following properties form a basis for solving inequalities.

Addition Property of Inequality

For all real numbers a, b, and c,

$a > b$ if and only if $a + c > b + c$.

Multiplication Property of Inequality

(a) For all real numbers a, b, and c, *with $c > 0$*,

$a > b$ if and only if $ac > bc$.

(b) For all real numbers a, b, and c, *with $c < 0$*,

$a > b$ if and only if $ac < bc$.

Quadratic inequalities such as $(x + 3)(x - 7) > 0$ can be solved by considering the sign behavior of the individual factors.

The following properties play an important role in solving inequalities that involve absolute value.

1. If $|x| < k$, where $k > 0$, then $-k < x < k$.

2. If $|x| > k$, where $k > 0$, then $x > k$ or $x < -k$.

Problem Solving

It would be helpful for you to reread pages 47–49. Some key problem solving suggestions are given on those pages.

CHAPTER 1 REVIEW PROBLEM SET

For Problems 1–10, evaluate each of the following.

1. 5^{-3}

2. -3^{-4}

3. $\left(\frac{3}{4}\right)^{-2}$

4. $\dfrac{1}{\left(\frac{1}{3}\right)^{-2}}$

5. $\left(-\frac{1}{4}\right)^{-2}$

6. $[(-2)^{-1}]^{-3}$

7. $\left(\dfrac{2^{-1}}{3^{-2}}\right)^{-1}$

8. $2^{-1} + 4^{-2}$

9. $(3^{-1} - 2^{-2})^{-2}$

10. $(4^{-1} + 3^{-1})^{-1}$

For Problems 11–14, find the indicated products and quotients; express your results using positive integral exponents only.

11. $(3x^{-2}y^{-1})(4x^4y^2)$

12. $(-2xy)(6x^{-1}y^6)$

13. $\left(\dfrac{-52x^{-1}y^2}{4x^2y}\right)^{-1}$

14. $\left(\dfrac{24a^{-1}b^{-3}}{12ab}\right)^{-2}$

For Problems 15–30, perform the indicated operations and simplify.

15. $(-7x - 3) + (5x - 2) + (6x + 4)$

16. $(12x + 5) - (7x - 4) - (8x + 1)$

17. $3(a - 2) - 2(3a + 5) + 3(5a - 1)$

18. $(4x - 7)(5x + 6)$

19. $(-3x + 2)(4x - 3)$

20. $(7x - 3)(-5x + 1)$

21. $(x + 4)(x^2 - 3x - 7)$

22. $(2x + 1)(3x^2 - 2x + 6)$

23. $(x^2 - 2x - 3)(x^2 + 4x + 5)$

24. $(2x^2 - x - 2)(x^2 + 6x - 4)$

25. $(5x - 3)^2$

26. $(3x + 7)^2$

27. $(2x - 1)^3$

28. $(3x + 5)^3$

29. $(x + 2)^6$

30. $(x - 2y)^5$

31. Find the 6th term of the expansion $(a + 1)^{11}$.

32. Find the 8th term of the expansion $\left(\frac{1}{2}a - b\right)^{10}$.

33. Find the middle term of the expansion $(x^2 - 2y)^8$.

34. Find the term that contains y^8 of the expansion $(x^3 - y^2)^{12}$.

For Problems 35–46, factor completely each of the polynomials. Indicate any that are not factorable using integers.

35. $9x^2 - 4y^2$

36. $3x^3 - 9x^2 - 120x$

37. $4x^2 + 20x + 25$

38. $(x - y)^2 - 9$

39. $x^2 - 2x - xy + 2y$

40. $64x^3 - 27y^3$

41. $15x^2 - 14x - 8$

42. $3x^3 + 36$

43. $2x^2 - x - 8$

44. $3x^3 + 24$

45. $x^4 - 13x^2 + 36$

46. $4x^2 - 4x + 1 - y^2$

For Problems 47–58, perform the indicated operations and express the resulting complex numbers in standard form.

47. $(-7 + 3i) + (-4 - 9i)$

48. $(2 - 10i) - (3 - 8i)$

49. $(-1 + 4i) - (-2 + 6i)$

50. $(3i)(-7i)$

51. $(2 - 5i)(3 + 4i)$

52. $(-3 - i)(6 - 7i)$

53. $(4 + 2i)(-4 - i)$

54. $(5 - 2i)(5 + 2i)$

55. $\dfrac{5}{3i}$

56. $\dfrac{2 + 3i}{3 - 4i}$

57. $\dfrac{-1 - 2i}{-2 + i}$

58. $\dfrac{-6i}{5 + 2i}$

For Problems 59–68, perform the indicated operations and express your answers in simplest form.

59. $\dfrac{8xy}{18x^2y} \cdot \dfrac{24xy^2}{16y^3}$

60. $\dfrac{-14a^2b^2}{6b^3} \div \dfrac{21a}{15ab}$

61. $\dfrac{x^2 + 3x - 4}{x^2 - 1} \cdot \dfrac{3x^2 + 8x + 5}{x^2 + 4x}$

62. $\dfrac{9x^2 - 6x + 1}{2x^2 + 8} \cdot \dfrac{8x + 20}{6x^2 + 13x - 5}$

63. $\dfrac{3x - 2}{4} + \dfrac{5x - 1}{3}$

64. $\dfrac{2x - 6}{5} - \dfrac{x + 4}{3}$

65. $\dfrac{3}{n^2} + \dfrac{4}{5n} - \dfrac{2}{n}$

66. $\dfrac{5}{x^2 + 7x} - \dfrac{3}{x}$

67. $\dfrac{3x}{x^2 - 6x - 40} + \dfrac{4}{x^2 - 16}$

68. $\dfrac{2}{x - 2} - \dfrac{2}{x + 2} - \dfrac{4}{x^3 - 4x}$

For Problems 69–71, simplify each of the complex fractions.

69. $\dfrac{\dfrac{3}{x} - \dfrac{2}{y}}{\dfrac{5}{x^2} + \dfrac{7}{y}}$

70. $\dfrac{3 - \dfrac{2}{x}}{4 + \dfrac{3}{x}}$

71. $\dfrac{\dfrac{3}{(x + h)^2} - \dfrac{3}{x^2}}{h}$

For Problems 72–88 solve each of the equations.

72. $2(3x - 1) - 3(x - 2) = 2(x - 5)$

73. $\dfrac{n - 1}{4} - \dfrac{2n + 3}{5} = 2$

74. $\dfrac{2}{x + 2} + \dfrac{5}{x - 4} = \dfrac{7}{2x - 8}$

75. $.07x + .12(550 - x) = 56$

76. $(3x - 1)^2 = 16$

77. $4x^2 - 29x + 30 = 0$

78. $x^2 - 6x + 10 = 0$

79. $n^2 + 4n = 396$

80. $15x^3 + x^2 - 2x = 0$

81. $\dfrac{t + 3}{t - 1} - \dfrac{2t + 3}{t - 5} = \dfrac{3 - t^2}{t^2 - 6t + 5}$

82. $\dfrac{5 - x}{2 - x} - \dfrac{3 - 2x}{2x} = 1$

83. $x^4 + 4x^2 - 45 = 0$

84. $2n^{-4} - 11n^{-2} + 5 = 0$

85. $\left(x - \dfrac{2}{x}\right)^2 + 4\left(x - \dfrac{2}{x}\right) = 5$

86. $|5x - 1| = 7$

87. $|2x + 5| = |3x - 7|$

88. $\left|\dfrac{-3}{n - 1}\right| = 4$

For Problems 89–106 solve each of the inequalities and express the solution sets in interval notation.

89. $3(2 - x) + 2(x - 4) > -2(x + 5)$

90. $\dfrac{3}{5}x - \dfrac{1}{3} \le \dfrac{2}{3}x + \dfrac{3}{4}$

91. $\dfrac{n - 1}{3} - \dfrac{2n + 1}{4} > \dfrac{1}{6}$

92. $.08x + .09(700 - x) \ge 59$

93. $-16 \leq 7x - 2 \leq 5$

94. $5 > \dfrac{3y + 4}{2} > 1$

95. $x^2 - 3x - 18 < 0$

96. $n^2 - 5n \geq 14$

97. $(x - 1)(x - 4)(x + 2) < 0$

98. $\dfrac{x + 4}{2x - 3} \leq 0$

99. $\dfrac{5n - 1}{n - 2} > 0$

100. $\dfrac{x - 1}{x + 3} \geq 2$

101. $\dfrac{t + 5}{t - 4} < 1$

102. $|4x - 3| > 5$

103. $|3x + 5| \leq 14$

104. $|-3 - 2x| < 6$

105. $\left| \dfrac{x - 1}{x} \right| > 2$

106. $\left| \dfrac{n + 1}{n + 2} \right| < 1$

APPLIED PROBLEMS

For Problems 107–120, solve each of the problems.

107. *Consecutive odd integers*   The sum of three consecutive odd integers is 31 less than four times the largest integer. Find the integers.

108. *Division algorithm*   The sum of two numbers is 74. If the larger is divided by the smaller, the quotient is 7 and the remainder is 2. Find the numbers.

109. *Area of a rectangle*   The perimeter of a rectangle is 38 centimeters and its area is 84 square centimeters. Find the dimensions of the rectangle.

110. *Coin collection*   A sum of money amounting to $13.55 consists of nickels, dimes, and quarters. There are three times as many dimes as nickels and three less quarters than dimes. How many coins of each denomination are there?

111. *Profit as percent of selling price*   A retailer has some shirts that cost him $14 each. He wants to sell them to make a profit of 30% of the selling price. What price should he charge for the shirts?

112. *Mixing chemicals*   How many gallons of a solution of glycerine and water containing 55% glycerine should be added to 15 gallons of a 20% solution to give a 40% solution?

113. *Age relationships*   The sum of the present ages of Rosie and her mother is 47 years. In 5 years, Rosie will be one-half as old as her mother at that time. Find the present ages of both Rosie and her mother.

114. *Investments*   Kelly invested $800, part of it at 9% and the remainder at 12%. Her total yearly interest from the two investments was $85.50. How much did she invest at each rate?

115. *Test scores*   Regina had scores of 93, 88, 89, and 95 on her first four math exams. What score must she get on the 5th exam to have an average of 92 or better for the five exams?

116. *Determining the time of day*   At how many minutes after 2 P.M. will the minute hand of a clock overtake the hour hand?

117. *Mowing a lawn*   Russ started to mow the lawn, a task that usually takes him 40 minutes. After he had been working for 15 minutes, his friend Jay came along with his mower and began to help Russ. Working together, they finished the lawn in 10 minutes. How long would it have taken Jay to mow the lawn by himself?

118. *Buying stocks*   Barry bought a number of shares of stock for $600. A week later the value of the stock increased $3 per share and he sold all but 10 shares and regained his original investment of $600. How many shares did he sell and at what price per share?

119. *Traveling time*   Larry drove 156 miles in one hour more than it took Mike to drive 108 miles. Mike drove at an average rate of 2 miles per hour faster than Larry. How fast did each one travel?

120. *Work rates*   It takes Bill 2 hours longer to do a certain job than it takes Cindy. They worked together for 2 hours; then Cindy left and Bill finished the job in 1 hour. How long would it take each of them to do the job alone?

COORDINATE GEOMETRY AND GRAPHING TECHNIQUES

In the previous chapter we used the concepts of a variable and an algebraic equation to solve a variety of problems—that is, these concepts provided the basis for connecting mathematics to the real world. In this chapter we will continue to use mathematics to solve problems, but we will also explore some connections between different facets of mathematics.

René Descartes, a French mathematician of the 17th century, was able to transform geometric problems into an algebraic setting and then use the tools of algebra to solve those problems. This merger of algebraic and geometric ideas is the foundation of a branch of mathematics called **analytic geometry**, today more commonly called **coordinate geometry**. Basically, there are two kinds of problems in coordinate geometry, namely, (1) given an algebraic equation, find its geometric graph, and (2) given a set of conditions pertaining to a geometric graph, find its algebraic equation. We will discuss problems of both types in this chapter.

A system of two linear equations in two variables can be used to approximate the effect of the jet stream on airline schedules.

2.1   COORDINATE GEOMETRY

Recall that the real number line (Figure 2.1) exhibits a one-to-one correspondence between the set of real numbers and the points on a line. That is to say, to each real number there corresponds one and only one point on the line, and to each point on the line there corresponds one and only one real number. The number that corresponds to a particular point on the line is called the **coordinate** of the point.

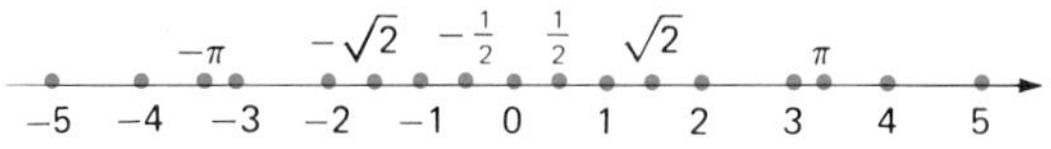

FIGURE 2.1

Suppose that on the number line we want to know the distance *from −2 to 6.* The "from-to" vocabulary implies a **directed distance** that can be found by $6 - (-2) = 8$ units. In other words, it is 8 units in a positive direction from −2 to 6. Likewise, the distance from 9 to −4 is $-4 - 9 = -13$; that is, 13 units in a negative direction. In general, if x_1 and x_2 are the coordinates of two points on the number line, then the distance *from x_1 to x_2* is given by $x_2 - x_1$ and the distance *from x_2 to x_1* is given by $x_1 - x_2$.

Now suppose that we want to find the distance *between −2 and 6.* The "between" vocabulary implies distance without regard to direction. Thus, the distance between −2 and 6 can be found by using either $|6 - (-2)| = 8$, or $|-2 - 6| = 8$. In general, if x_1 and x_2 are the coordinates of two points on the number line, the distance *between x_1 and x_2* can be found by using either $|x_2 - x_1|$ or $|x_1 - x_2|$.

Sometimes it is necessary to find the coordinate of a point located somewhere between two given points. For example, in Figure 2.2 suppose that we want to find the coordinate (x) of the point located two-thirds of the distance *from 2 to 8.* Since the total distance from 2 to 8 is $8 - 2 = 6$ units, we can start at 2 and move $\frac{2}{3}(6) = 4$ units toward 8. Thus,

$$x = 2 + \tfrac{2}{3}(6) = 2 + 4 = 6.$$

FIGURE 2.2

The following examples (Figures 2.3–2.5) further illustrate the process of finding the coordinate of a point somewhere between two given points. Problem (c) indicates that a general formula can be developed for this type of problem. However, it may be easier to remember the basic approach for doing such a problem rather than memorizing the formula.

As we saw in Chapter 1, the real number line provides a geometric model for graphing solutions of algebraic equations and inequalities *involving one variable.* For example, the solutions of $x > 2$ or $x \le -1$ are graphed in Figure 2.6.

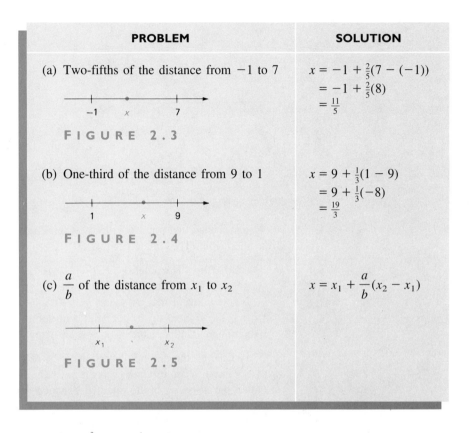

PROBLEM	SOLUTION
(a) Two-fifths of the distance from -1 to 7	$x = -1 + \frac{2}{5}(7 - (-1))$ $\quad = -1 + \frac{2}{5}(8)$ $\quad = \frac{11}{5}$
FIGURE 2.3	
(b) One-third of the distance from 9 to 1	$x = 9 + \frac{1}{3}(1 - 9)$ $\quad = 9 + \frac{1}{3}(-8)$ $\quad = \frac{19}{3}$
FIGURE 2.4	
(c) $\dfrac{a}{b}$ of the distance from x_1 to x_2	$x = x_1 + \dfrac{a}{b}(x_2 - x_1)$
FIGURE 2.5	

$$-4 \;\; -3 \;\; -2 \;\; -1 \;\; 0 \;\; 1 \;\; 2 \;\; 3 \;\; 4$$

FIGURE   2.6

Rectangular Coordinate System

To expand our work with coordinate geometry, we now consider two number lines: one vertical and one horizontal, perpendicular to each other at the point associated with zero on both lines (Figure 2.7). We refer to these number lines as the **horizontal and vertical axes**, or together as the **coordinate axes**. They partition the plane into four regions called **quadrants**. The quadrants are numbered counterclockwise from I through IV as indicated in Figure 2.7. The point of intersection of the two axes is called the **origin**.

It is now possible to set up a one-to-one correspondence between **ordered pairs** of real numbers and the points in a plane. To each ordered pair of real numbers there corresponds a unique point in the plane and to each point in the plane there corresponds a unique ordered pair of real numbers. We illustrated a part of this correspondence in Figure 2.8. The ordered pair $(3, 2)$ means that the point A is located 3 units to the right and two units up from the origin. The ordered pair

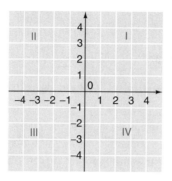

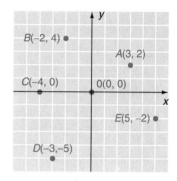

FIGURE 2.7   FIGURE 2.8

$(-3, -5)$ means that point D is located three units to the left and five units down from the origin. The ordered pair $(0, 0)$ is associated with the origin.

REMARK   The notation $(-2, 4)$ was used in Chapter 1 to indicate an interval of the real number line. Now we are using the same notation to indicate an ordered pair of real numbers. This "double meaning" should not be confusing; the context of the material will definitely indicate the particular usage. Throughout this chapter we will be using the ordered-pair interpretation.

In general, the real numbers a and b in the ordered pair (a, b) are associated with a point; they are referred to as the **coordinates of the point**. The first number, a, called the **abscissa** is the directed distance of the point from the vertical axis measured parallel to the horizontal axis. The second number, b, called the **ordinate** is the directed distance from the horizontal axis measured parallel to the vertical axis (Figure 2.9(a)). Thus, in the first quadrant all points have a positive abscissa and a positive ordinate. In the second quadrant all points have a negative abscissa and a positive ordinate. We have indicated the sign situations for all four quadrants in

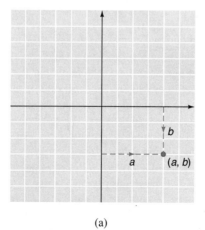

(a)

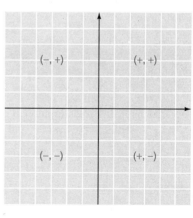

(b)

FIGURE 2.9

Figure 2.9(b). This system of associating points in a plane with pairs of real numbers is called the **rectangular coordinate system** or the **Cartesian coordinate system**.

Distance Between Two Points

As we work with the rectangular coordinate system, it is sometimes necessary to express the length of certain line segments. In other words, we need to be able to find the **distance between two points**. Let's first consider a specific example and then develop a general distance formula.

EXAMPLE 1

Find the distance between the points $A(2, 3)$ and $B(5, 7)$.

Solution

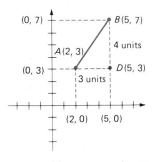

FIGURE 2.10

Let's plot the points and form a right triangle as indicated in Figure 2.10. Notice that the coordinates of point D are $(5, 3)$. Because $\overline{AD}$ is parallel to the horizontal axis, we have $AD = |5 - 2| = 3$ units. Likewise, $\overline{DB}$ is parallel to the vertical axis and therefore $DB = |7 - 3| = 4$ units.

Applying the Pythagorean theorem we obtain

$$(AB)^2 = (AD)^2 + (DB)^2$$
$$= 3^2 + 4^2$$
$$= 9 + 16$$
$$= 25,$$

thus,

$$AB = \sqrt{25} = 5 \text{ units.}$$

The approach used in Example 1 can be used to develop a general distance formula. However, before doing this let's make another notational agreement. For most problems in coordinate geometry it is customary to label the horizontal axis the x**-axis** and the vertical axis the y**-axis**. Then, ordered pairs representing points in the xy-plane are of the form (x, y); that is, x is the first coordinate and y is the second coordinate. Now let's develop a general distance formula.

Let $P_1(x_1, y_1)$ and $P_2(x_2, y_2)$ represent any two points in the xy-plane. Form a right triangle as indicated in Figure 2.11. The coordinates of the vertex of the right angle, point R, are (x_2, y_1). The length of $\overline{P_1 R}$ is $|x_2 - x_1|$ and the length of $\overline{RP_2}$ is $|y_2 - y_1|$. Letting d represent the length of $\overline{P_1 P_2}$ and applying the Pythagorean theorem, we obtain

$$d^2 = |x_2 - x_1|^2 + |y_2 - y_1|^2.$$

Since $|a|^2 = a^2$, the distance formula can be stated as

$$d = \sqrt{(x_2 - x_1)^2 + (y_2 - y_1)^2}.$$

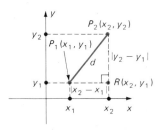

FIGURE 2.11

It makes no difference which point you call P_1 or P_2 when using the formula. Also, remember, if you forget the formula, don't panic, merely form a right triangle and apply the Pythagorean theorem as we did in Example 1.

Let's consider some examples illustrating the use of the distance formula.

E X A M P L E 2

Find the distance between $(-2, 5)$ and $(1, -1)$.

Solution

Let $(-2, 5)$ be P_1 and $(1, -1)$ be P_2. Using the distance formula, we obtain

$$
\begin{aligned}
d &= \sqrt{(x_2 - x_1)^2 + (y_2 - y_1)^2} \\
&= \sqrt{(1 - (-2))^2 + (-1 - 5)^2} \\
&= \sqrt{3^2 + (-6)^2} \\
&= \sqrt{9 + 36} \\
&= \sqrt{45} = 3\sqrt{5}.
\end{aligned}
$$

The distance between the two points is $3\sqrt{5}$ units.

In Example 2, notice the simplicity of the approach when using the distance formula. No diagram was needed; we merely plugged in the values and did the computation. However, many times a figure is helpful in the analysis of the problem, as we see in the next example.

E X A M P L E 3

Verify that the points $(-3, 6)$, $(3, 4)$, and $(1, -2)$ are vertices of an isosceles triangle. (An isosceles triangle has two sides of the same length.)

Solution

Let's plot the points and draw the triangle (Figure 2.12). Using the distance formula, the lengths d_1, d_2, and d_3 can be found as follows.

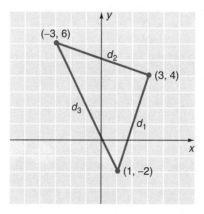

F I G U R E   2 . 12

$$d_1 = \sqrt{(3-1)^2 + (4-(-2))^2}$$
$$= \sqrt{4+36}$$
$$= \sqrt{40} = 2\sqrt{10}$$

$$d_2 = \sqrt{(-3-3)^2 + (6-4)^2}$$
$$= \sqrt{36+4}$$
$$= \sqrt{40} = 2\sqrt{10}$$

$$d_3 = \sqrt{(-3-1)^2 + (6-(-2))^2}$$
$$= \sqrt{16+64}$$
$$= \sqrt{80} = 4\sqrt{5}$$

Since $d_1 = d_2$, the triangle is an isosceles triangle.

Points of Division of a Line Segment

Earlier in this section we discussed the process of finding the coordinate of a point on a number line, located somewhere between two points on the line. This same type of problem can occur in the xy-plane and the approach used earlier can be extended to handle it. Let's consider an example.

E X A M P L E 4

Find the coordinates of the point that is two-thirds of the distance from $A(1, 2)$ to $B(7, 5)$.

Solution

In Figure 2.13 we plotted the given points and completed a figure to help with the analysis of the problem. To find the coordinates of point P we can proceed as follows. Point D is two-thirds of the distance from A to C because parallel lines cut off proportional segments on every transversal that intersects the lines. There-

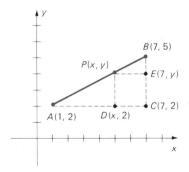

F I G U R E   2 . 13

fore, since $\overline{AC}$ is parallel to the x-axis, it can be treated as a segment of a number line as in Figure 2.14. Thus, we have

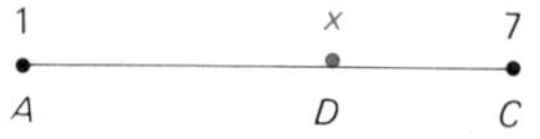

$$x = 1 + \tfrac{2}{3}(7 - 1) = 1 + \tfrac{2}{3}(6) = 5.$$

FIGURE 2.14

Similarly, $\overline{CB}$ is parallel to the y-axis; it can be treated as a segment of a number line as in Figure 2.15. Thus, we obtain

$$y = 2 + \tfrac{2}{3}(5 - 2) = 2 + \tfrac{2}{3}(3) = 4.$$

FIGURE 2.15

The point P has coordinates of $(5, 4)$.

The approach used in Example 4 can be generalized to find any point of division between two given points; that is, if $P_1(x_1, y_1)$ and $P_2(x_2, y_2)$ are two given points, then the coordinates of a point $P(x, y)$, which is located a/b of the distance from P_1 to P_2 are given by

$$x = x_1 + \frac{a}{b}(x_2 - x_1) \quad \text{and} \quad y = y_1 + \frac{a}{b}(y_2 - y_1).$$

Sometimes we need to find the midpoint of a line segment. Thus, in the previous equations the fraction a/b becomes $\tfrac{1}{2}$ and we obtain the following coordinates for the midpoint.

$$x = x_1 + \tfrac{1}{2}(x_2 - x_1) = x_1 + \tfrac{1}{2}x_2 - \tfrac{1}{2}x_1 = \tfrac{1}{2}x_1 + \tfrac{1}{2}x_2 = \tfrac{1}{2}(x_1 + x_2)$$

and

$$y = y_1 + \tfrac{1}{2}(y_2 - y_1) = y_1 + \tfrac{1}{2}y_2 - \tfrac{1}{2}y_1 = \tfrac{1}{2}y_1 + \tfrac{1}{2}y_2 = \tfrac{1}{2}(y_1 + y_2)$$

Therefore, the coordinates of the midpoint of a line segment determined by $P_1(x_1, y_1)$ and $P_2(x_2, y_2)$ are

Midpoint of a line segment

$$\left(\frac{x_1 + x_2}{2}, \frac{y_1 + y_2}{2} \right).$$

EXAMPLE 5

Consider the triangle whose vertices are $A(2, -2)$, $B(8, 2)$, and $C(4, 6)$. If D is the midpoint of $\overline{AC}$ and E is the midpoint of $\overline{BC}$, show that the length of $\overline{DE}$ is one-half of the length $\overline{AB}$.

Solution

In Figure 2.16 we plotted the points and produced the figure to help with the analysis of the problem. Using the midpoint formula, we can find the coordinates of points D and E.

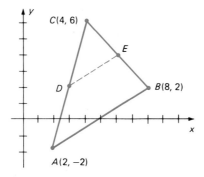

Point D: $\left(\dfrac{4 + 2}{2}, \dfrac{6 + (-2)}{2}\right) = (3, 2)$

Point E: $\left(\dfrac{4 + 8}{2}, \dfrac{6 + 2}{2}\right) = (6, 4)$

FIGURE 2.16

Now using the distance formula, we can find the lengths of $\overline{DE}$ and $\overline{AB}$.

$$DE = \sqrt{(6 - 3)^2 + (4 - 2)^2} = \sqrt{9 + 4} = \sqrt{13}$$

$$AB = \sqrt{(8 - 2)^2 + (2 - (-2))^2} = \sqrt{36 + 16} = \sqrt{52} = 2\sqrt{13}$$

Therefore, $DE = \frac{1}{2}(AB)$.

Slope

It is often helpful to be able to refer to the *steepness* or *slant* of a particular line. The concept of slope is used as a measure of the slant of a line. The slope of a line is the ratio of the vertical change of distance compared to the horizontal change of distance as we move from one point on a line to another point on the line. The following definition can be given.

DEFINITION 2.1

If points P_1 and P_2 with coordinates (x_1, y_1) and (x_2, y_2), respectively, are any two different points on a line, then the slope of the line (denoted by m) is

$$m = \frac{y_2 - y_1}{x_2 - x_1}, \qquad x_2 \neq x_1. \qquad \text{See Figure 2.17}$$

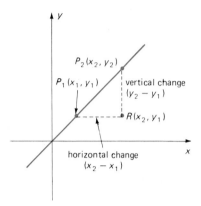

FIGURE 2.17

Since $\dfrac{y_2 - y_1}{x_2 - x_1} = \dfrac{y_1 - y_2}{x_1 - x_2}$, how we designate P_1 and P_2 is not important. Let's use Definition 2.1 to find the slopes of some lines.

EXAMPLE 6

Find the slope of the line determined by each of the following pairs of points and graph each line.

a. $(-1, 1)$ and $(3, 2)$ **b.** $(4, -2)$ and $(-1, 5)$

c. $(2, -3)$ and $(-3, -3)$

Solution

a. Let $(-1, 1)$ be P_1 and $(3, 2)$ be P_2 (Figure 2.18).

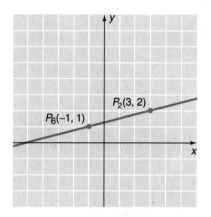

$$m = \frac{y_2 - y_1}{x_2 - x_1} = \frac{2 - 1}{3 - (-1)} = \frac{1}{4}$$

FIGURE 2.18

b. Let $(4, -2)$ be P_1 and $(-1, 5)$ be P_2 (Figure 2.19).

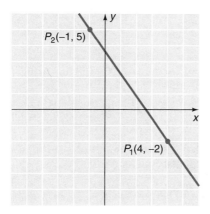

$$m = \frac{5 - (-2)}{-1 - 4} = \frac{7}{-5} = -\frac{7}{5}$$

FIGURE 2.19

c. Let $(2, -3)$ be P_1 and $(-3, -3)$ be P_2 (Figure 2.20).

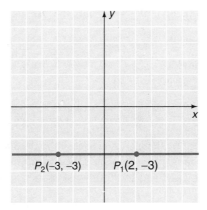

$$m = \frac{-3 - (-3)}{-3 - 2} = \frac{0}{-5} = 0$$

FIGURE 2.20

The three parts of Example 6 illustrate the three basic possibilities for slope; that is, the slope of a line can be positive, negative, or zero. A line that has a positive slope rises as we move from left to right as in Figure 2.18. A line that has a negative slope falls as we move from left to right as in Figure 2.19. A horizontal line, as in Figure 2.20 has a slope of zero. Finally, we need to realize that **the concept of slope is undefined for vertical lines.** This is due to the fact that for any vertical line the horizontal change is zero as we move from one point on the line to another point on the line. Thus, the ratio $(y_2 - y_1)/(x_2 - x_1)$ will have a denominator of zero and be undefined. So in Definition 2.1, the restriction $x_2 \neq x_1$ is made.

Don't forget that the slope of a line is a **ratio**—the ratio of vertical change compared to horizontal change. For example, a slope of $\frac{2}{3}$ means that for every 2 units of vertical change there must be a corresponding 3 units of horizontal change. Thus starting at some point on a line that has a slope of $\frac{2}{3}$, we can locate other points on the line as follows.

$$\frac{2}{3} = \frac{4}{6} \qquad \longrightarrow \text{By moving 4 units } up \text{ and 6 units to the } right;$$

$$\frac{2}{3} = \frac{8}{12} \qquad \longrightarrow \text{By moving 8 units } up \text{ and 12 units to the } right;$$

$$\frac{2}{3} = \frac{-2}{-3} \qquad \longrightarrow \text{By moving 2 units } down \text{ and 3 units to the } left.$$

Likewise, if a line has a slope of $-\frac{3}{4}$, then by starting at some point on the line we could locate other points on the line as follows.

$$-\frac{3}{4} = \frac{-3}{4} \qquad \longrightarrow \text{By moving 3 units } down \text{ and 4 units to the } right;$$

$$-\frac{3}{4} = \frac{3}{-4} \qquad \longrightarrow \text{By moving 3 units } up \text{ and 4 units to the } left;$$

$$-\frac{3}{4} = \frac{-9}{12} \qquad \longrightarrow \text{By moving 9 units } down \text{ and 12 units to the } right;$$

$$-\frac{3}{4} = \frac{15}{-20} \qquad \longrightarrow \text{By moving 15 units } up \text{ and 20 units to the } left.$$

Parallel and Perpendicular Lines

Since the concept of slope is used to indicate the slant of a line, it seems reasonable to expect a tie-up between slope and the concepts of parallelism and perpendicularity. Such is the case, and the following property summarizes this link.

PROPERTY 2.1

If two lines have slopes of m_1 and m_2, then

1. The two lines are parallel if and only if $m_1 = m_2$;
2. The two lines are perpendicular if and only if $(m_1)(m_2) = -1$.

EXAMPLE 7

Verify that the quadrilateral whose vertices are $(0, 7)$, $(-2, -1)$, $(2, -2)$, and $(4, 6)$ is a rectangle.

Solution

Let's plot the points and draw the quadrilateral as in Figure 2.21. Now we can find the slope of each of the sides.

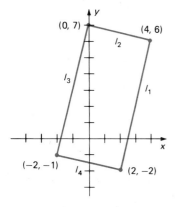

$$m_1 = \frac{6 - (-2)}{4 - 2} = \frac{8}{2} = 4 \qquad m_2 = \frac{7 - 6}{0 - 4} = \frac{1}{-4} = -\frac{1}{4}$$

$$m_3 = \frac{7 - (-1)}{0 - (-2)} = \frac{8}{2} = 4 \qquad m_4 = \frac{-1 - (-2)}{-2 - 2} = \frac{1}{-4} = -\frac{1}{4}$$

Since $m_1 = m_3$ and $m_2 = m_4$, the opposite sides of the quadrilateral are parallel and it is a parallelogram. Furthermore, since $(m_1)(m_2) = -1$, we know that $l_1 \perp l_2$ and the figure is a rectangle.

FIGURE   2.21

PROBLEM SET 2.1

For Problems 1–8, find the indicated distances on a number line.

1. From -4 to 6

2. From 5 to -14

3. From -6 to -11

4. From -7 to 10

5. Between -2 and 4

6. Between -4 and -12

7. Between 5 and -10

8. Between -2 and 13

For Problems 9–14, find the coordinate of each indicated point on a number line.

9. Two-thirds of the distance from 1 to 10

10. Three-fourths of the distance from -2 to 14

11. One-third of the distance from -3 to 7

12. Two-fifths of the distance from -5 to 6

13. Three-fifths of the distance from -1 to -11

14. Five-sixths of the distance from 3 to -7

For Problems 15–20, find the coordinates of each indicated point in the *xy*-plane.

15. One-third of the distance from $(2, 3)$ to $(5, 9)$

16. Two-thirds of the distance from $(1, 4)$ to $(7, 13)$

17. Two-fifths of the distance from $(-2, 1)$ to $(8, 11)$

18. Three-fifths of the distance from $(2, -3)$ to $(-3, 8)$

19. Five-eighths of the distance from $(-1, -2)$ to $(4, -10)$

20. Seven-eighths of the distance from $(-2, 3)$ to $(-1, -9)$

For Problems 21–28, find the length of $\overline{AB}$, the midpoint of $\overline{AB}$, and the slope of $\overline{AB}$.

21. $A(2, 1)$, $B(10, 7)$

22. $A(-2, -1)$, $B(7, 11)$

23. $A(1, -1)$, $B(3, -4)$

24. $A(-5, 2)$, $B(-1, 6)$

25. $A(6, -4)$, $B(9, -7)$

26. $A(-3, 3)$, $B(0, -3)$

27. $A\left(\frac{1}{2}, \frac{1}{3}\right)$, $B\left(-\frac{1}{3}, \frac{3}{2}\right)$

28. $A\left(-\frac{3}{4}, 2\right)$, $B\left(-1, -\frac{5}{4}\right)$

Solve each of the following problems.

29. Find the coordinates of the point that is one-fourth of the distance from $(2, 4)$ to $(10, 13)$ by (a) using the midpoint formula, and (b) using the same approach as used for Problems 15–20.

30. If one endpoint of a line segment is $(-6, 4)$ and the midpoint of the segment is $(-2, 7)$, find the other endpoint.

31. Find x if the line through $(x, 4)$ and $(2, -5)$ has a slope of $-\frac{9}{4}$.

32. Find y if the line through $(5, 2)$ and $(-3, y)$ has a slope of $-\frac{7}{8}$.

33. Suppose that a line contains the point $(2, -1)$ and has a slope of $-\frac{3}{5}$. Find the coordinates of three other points on the line.

34. Suppose that a line contains the point $(-5, -3)$ and has a slope of $\frac{2}{3}$. Find the coordinates of three other points on the line.

35. Find the perimeter of the triangle whose vertices are $(-6, -4)$, $(0, 8)$, and $(6, 5)$.

36. Find x such that the line segment determined by $(x, -2)$ and $(-2, -14)$ is 13 units long.

37. Suppose that $(-2, 5)$, $(6, 3)$ and $(-4, -1)$ are three vertices of a parallelogram. How many possibilities are there for the fourth vertex? Find the coordinates of each of those points. [*Hint:* The diagonals of a parallelogram bisect each other.]

38. Verify that the points $(-2, 7)$, $(2, 1)$, and $(4, -2)$ lie on a straight line by (a) using the concept of distance, and (b) using the concept of slope.

39. Verify that the points $(-3, 8)$, $(7, 4)$, and $(5, -1)$ are vertices of a right triangle.

40. Verify that the points $(0, 3)$, $(2, -3)$, and $(-4, -5)$ are vertices of an isosceles triangle.

41. Verify that the points $(-4, 9)$, $(8, 4)$, $(3, -8)$, and $(-9, -3)$ are vertices of a square.

42. Verify that the points $(4, -5)$, $(6, 7)$, and $(-8, -3)$ lie on a circle having its center at $(-1, 2)$.

43. Consider the triangle whose vertices are $(4, -6)$, $(2, 8)$, and $(-4, 2)$. Verify that the medians of this triangle inter-

sect at a point that is two-thirds of the distance from a vertex to the midpoint of the opposite side. (A median of a triangle is the line segment determined by a vertex and the midpoint of the opposite side. Every triangle has three medians.)

44. Verify that the points $(6, 6)$, $(2, -2)$, $(-8, -5)$, and $(-4, 3)$ are vertices of a parallelogram.

45. The concept of slope is used for highway construction. The grade of a highway, expressed as a percent, means the number of feet that the highway changes in elevation for each 100 feet of horizontal change.

   a. A certain highway has a 2% grade. How many feet does it rise in a horizontal distance of 1 mile? (1 mile = 5280 feet)

   b. The grade of a highway up a hill is 30%. How much change in horizontal distance is there if the vertical height of the hill is 75 feet?

46. Slope is often expressed as the ratio *rise-to-run* in construction of steps.

   a. If the ratio rise-to-run is to be $\frac{3}{5}$ for some steps and the rise is 19 centimeters, find the measure of the run to the nearest centimeter.

   b. If the ratio rise-to-run is to be $\frac{2}{3}$ for some steps and the run is 28 centimeters, find the rise to the nearest centimeter.

47. Suppose that a county ordinance requires a $2\frac{1}{4}\%$ fall for a sewage pipe from the house to the main pipe at the street. How much vertical drop must there be for a horizontal distance of 45 feet? Express your answer to the nearest tenth of a foot.

THOUGHTS into WORDS

48. Consider the line segment determined by the two endpoints $A(2, 1)$ and $B(5, 10)$. Describe how you would find the coordinates of the point that is two-thirds of the distance from A to B. Then describe how you would find

the point that is two-thirds of the distance from B to A.

49. How would you describe coordinate geometry to a group of elementary algebra students?

FURTHER INVESTIGATIONS

50. Prove each part of Property 2.1.

51. The tools of coordinate geometry can be used to prove various geometric properties. For example, consider the following method of proving that the diagonals of a rec-

tangle are equal in length: First, we draw a rectangle and coordinatize it using a convenient position for the origin (Figure 2.22). Now we can use the distance formula to find the lengths of the diagonals $\overline{AC}$ and $\overline{BD}$.

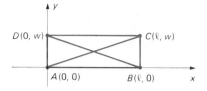

F I G U R E   2 . 2 2

$$AC = \sqrt{(l-0)^2 + (w-0)^2} = \sqrt{l^2 + w^2}$$
$$BD = \sqrt{(0-l)^2 + (w-0)^2} = \sqrt{l^2 + w^2}$$

Thus, $AC = BD$, and we have proven that the diagonals are equal in length.

    Use a coordinate geometry approach to prove each of the following properties.

a. The diagonals of an isosceles trapezoid are equal in length.

b. The line segment joining the midpoints of two sides of a triangle is equal in length to one-half of the third side.

c. The midpoint of the hypotenuse of a right triangle is equally distant from all three vertices.

d. The diagonals of a parallelogram bisect each other.

e. The line segments joining the midpoints of the opposite sides of a quadrilateral bisect each other.

f. The medians of a triangle intersect at a point that is two-thirds of the distance from a vertex to the midpoint of the opposite side. (See Problem 43.)

g. The diagonals of a square are perpendicular.

h. The line segment joining the midpoints of two sides of a triangle is parallel to the third side.

i. The line segments joining the midpoints, in succession, of the sides of a quadrilateral form a parallelogram.

j. The line segments joining the midpoints, in succession, of the sides of a rectangle form a rhombus.

2.2   STRAIGHT LINES

As we stated earlier, there are basically two types of problems in coordinate geometry: (1) Given an algebraic equation, find its geometric graph; (2) Given a set of conditions pertaining to a geometric figure, find its algebraic equation. In this section we shall consider some problems of both types that deal specifically with straight lines.

    Probably the most valuable graphing technique is the ability to recognize the kind of graph that a certain type of equation implies. For example, from previous mathematics courses you probably remember that any equation of the form $Ax + By = C$, where A, B, and C are constants (A and B not both zero) and x and y are variables, is a **linear equation and its graph is a straight line**. Two comments about this description of a linear equation should be made. First, the choice of x and y as variables is arbitrary; any two letters could be used to represent the variables. For example, an equation such as $3r + 2s = 9$ is also a linear equation in two variables. In order to avoid constantly changing the labeling of the coordinate axes when graphing equations, we will use the same two variables, x and y, in all equations. Second, the statement ''any equation of the form $Ax + By = C$'' technically means any equation of the form $Ax + By = C$ or equivalent to that form. For example, the equation $y = 2x - 1$ is equivalent to $-2x + y = -1$; therefore it is linear and produces a straight line graph. Before graphing some linear equations, let's define in general the **intercepts** of a graph.

The x-coordinates of the points that a graph has in common with the x-axis are called the **x-intercepts** of the graph. (To compute the x-intercepts, let $y = 0$ and solve for x. Thus, the points that exhibit the x-intercepts are of the form $(x, 0)$.)

The y-coordinates of the points that a graph has in common with the y-axis are called the **y-intercepts** of the graph. (To compute the y-intercepts, let $x = 0$ and solve for y. The points that exhibit the y-intercepts are of the form $(0, y)$.)

Knowing that any equation of the form $Ax + By = C$ produces a straight line graph, and knowing that two points determine a straight line, we can graph linear equations easily. We can find two points and draw the line determined by those two points. Usually the two points involving the intercepts are easy to find and generally it's a good idea to plot a third point to serve as a check.

EXAMPLE 1

Graph $3x - 2y = 6$.

Solution

First, let's find the intercepts. If $x = 0$, then

$$3(0) - 2y = 6$$
$$-2y = 6$$
$$y = -3.$$

Therefore, the point $(0, -3)$ is on the line. If $y = 0$, then

$$3x - 2(0) = 6$$
$$3x = 6$$
$$x = 2.$$

Thus, the point $(2, 0)$ is also on the line. Now let's find a check point. If $x = -2$, then

$$3(-2) - 2y = 6$$
$$-6 - 2y = 6$$
$$-2y = 12$$
$$y = -6.$$

So the point $(-2, -6)$ is also on the line. In Figure 2.23 the three points are plotted and the graph of $3x - 2y = 6$ is drawn.

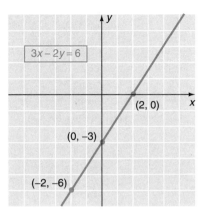

E X A M P L E   2

Graph $y = -2x$.

Solution

If $x = 0$, then $y = -2(0) = 0$; so the origin $(0, 0)$ is on the line. Since both intercepts are determined by the point $(0, 0)$ another point is necessary to determine the line. Then a third point should be found as a check point. The graph of $y = -2x$ is shown in Figure 2.24.

x	y
0	0
1	−2
−1	2

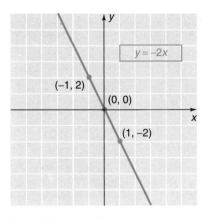

F I G U R E   2 . 24

Example 2 illustrates the general concept that for the form $Ax + By = C$, if $C = 0$, then the line contains the origin. Stated another way, the graph of any equation of the form $y = kx$ where k is any real number, is a straight line that contains the origin.

EXAMPLE 3

Graph $x = 2$.

Solution

Since we are considering linear equations *in two variables,* the equation $x = 2$ is equivalent to $x + 0(y) = 2$. Any value of y can be used, but the x-value must always be 2. Therefore, some of the solutions are $(2, 0)$, $(2, 1)$, $(2, 2)$, $(2, -1)$, and $(2, -2)$. The graph of $x = 2$ is the vertical line shown in Figure 2.25.

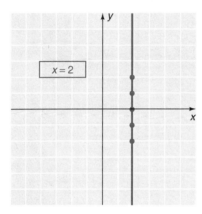

FIGURE 2.25

In general, the graph of any equation of the form $Ax + By = C$, where $A = 0$ or $B = 0$ (not both) is a line parallel to one of the axes. More specifically, any equation of the form $x = a$, where a is any real number, is a line parallel to the y-axis that has an x-intercept of a. Any equation of the form $y = b$, where b is a real number, is a line parallel to the x-axis that has a y-intercept of b.

Graphing Utilities

The term **graphing utility** is used in current literature to refer to either a graphics calculator or a computer with a graphics software package. These devices have a large range of capabilities that allow the user to not only obtain a quick sketch of a graph, but also to study various characteristics of it. For example, one can precisely approximate x-intercepts, y-intercepts, and turning points of a graph. We will introduce some of these features of graphing utilities as needed throughout the text. Since there are so many different types of graphing utilities available, we will use mostly generic terminology and let you consult your user's manual for specific key punching instructions. We also suggest that you study the graphing utility examples in this text even if you do not have access to a graphics calculator or a computer. The examples were chosen to reinforce the concepts being discussed.

EXAMPLE 4

Use a graphing utility to obtain a graph of the line $2.1x + 5.3y = 7.9$.

Solution

First, we need to solve the equation for y in terms of x.

$$2.1x + 5.3y = 7.9$$

$$5.3y = 7.9 - 2.1x$$

$$y = \frac{7.9 - 2.1x}{5.3}$$

Now we can enter the expression $\dfrac{7.9 - 2.1x}{5.3}$ for Y_1 and obtain the graph as shown in Figure 2.26.

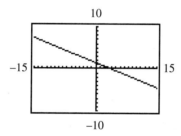

F I G U R E   2 . 26

As indicated in Figure 2.26, the **viewing rectangle** of a graphing utility is a portion of the *xy*-plane shown on the display of the utility. In this display the boundaries were set so that $-15 \le x \le 15$ and $-10 \le y \le 10$. These boundaries were set automatically; however, the fact that boundaries can be assigned as necessary is an important feature of graphing utilities.

Determining the Equation of a Line

Now let's consider some techniques for determining the equation of a line when given certain facts about the line. First, we shall illustrate a general approach that will also be useful later when working with geometric figures other than straight lines.

EXAMPLE 5

Find the equation of the line that has a slope of $\frac{2}{5}$ and contains the point $(3, 1)$.

Solution

First, let's draw the line and record the given information (Figure 2.27). Then choose a point (x, y) that represents any point on the line other than the given point $(3, 1)$. The slope determined by $(3, 1)$ and (x, y) is to be $\frac{2}{5}$. Thus,

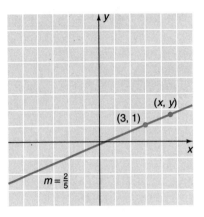

$$\frac{y-1}{x-3} = \frac{2}{5}$$

$$2(x-3) = 5(y-1)$$

$$2x - 6 = 5y - 5$$

$$2x - 5y = 1.$$

FIGURE 2.27

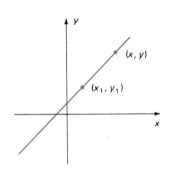

FIGURE 2.28

The basic approach we used in Example 5 can also be used to develop a general point-slope form of equations-of-lines; then this form can be used to determine equations of specific lines. Consider a line that has a slope of m and contains the point (x_1, y_1) as in Figure 2.28. Then choose (x, y) to represent any other point on the line and the slope of the line is

$$m = \frac{y - y_1}{x - x_1}, \qquad x \neq x_1$$

from which we obtain the **point-slope form**

$$y - y_1 = m(x - x_1).$$

EXAMPLE 6

Find the equation of the line that has a slope of $\frac{3}{5}$ and contains the point $(2, 4)$.

Solution

We can substitute $(2, 4)$ for (x_1, y_1) and $\frac{3}{5}$ for m in the point-slope form.

$$y - y_1 = m(x - x_1)$$

$$y - 4 = \tfrac{3}{5}(x - 2)$$

$$5(y - 4) = 3(x - 2)$$

$$5y - 20 = 3x - 6$$

$$-14 = 3x - 5y$$

From the point-slope form of the equation of a line we can develop an even more useful form called the slope-intercept form. Consider a line that has a slope of m and a y-intercept of b. Substitute $(0, b)$ for (x_1, y_1) in the point-slope form to produce

$$y - y_1 = m(x - x_1)$$
$$y - b = m(x - 0)$$
$$y - b = mx$$
$$y = mx + b.$$

We call the equation

$$y = mx + b$$

the **slope-intercept form** of the equation of a straight line. We use it for two primary purposes, as the next two examples illustrate.

EXAMPLE 7

Find the equation of the line that has a slope of $-\frac{3}{7}$ and a y-intercept of -8.

Solution

We can substitute $-\frac{3}{7}$ for m and -8 for b in the slope-intercept form.

$$y = mx + b$$
$$y = -\frac{3}{7}x - 8$$
$$7y = -3x - 56$$
$$3x + 7y = -56$$

EXAMPLE 8

Find the slope and y-intercept of the line having an equation of $2x - 3y = 7$.

Solution

We can solve the equation for y in terms of x and then compare this result to the general slope-intercept form.

$$2x - 3y = 7$$
$$-3y = -2x + 7$$
$$y = \frac{2}{3}x - \frac{7}{3}$$
$$y = \frac{2}{3}x - \frac{7}{3} \qquad y = mx + b$$

The slope of the line is $\frac{2}{3}$ and the y-intercept is $-\frac{7}{3}$.

In general, if the equation of a nonvertical line is written in slope-intercept form, the coefficient of x is the slope of the line and the constant term is the y-intercept.

EXAMPLE 9

Find the equation of the line that is parallel to $2x - y = 4$ and contains the point $(-1, 2)$.

Solution

First, let's draw a figure to help in our analysis of the problem (Figure 2.29). Since the line through $(-1, 2)$ is to be parallel to the given line, it must have the same slope. So let's find the slope by changing $2x - y = 4$ to slope-intercept form.

$$2x - y = 4$$
$$-y = -2x + 4$$
$$y = 2x - 4$$

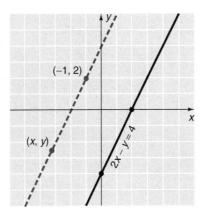

FIGURE 2.29

The slope of both lines is 2. Now, using the point-slope form we obtain

$$y - y_1 = m(x - x_1)$$
$$y - 2 = 2(x - (-1))$$
$$y - 2 = 2(x + 1)$$
$$y - 2 = 2x + 2$$
$$-4 = 2x - y.$$

Property 2.1 in the previous section stated that two lines are parallel if and only if their slopes are equal and two lines are perpendicular if and only if the product of their slopes is a negative one. The following property states these same two relationships in terms of the coefficients and constant terms of the linear equations that represent the lines.

> ### PROPERTY 2.2
>
> Consider the lines represented by the linear equations $Ax + By = C$ and $A'x + B'y = C'$.
>
> **1.** The lines are parallel if and only if
>
> $$\frac{A}{A'} = \frac{B}{B'} \neq \frac{C}{C'}.$$
>
> **2.** The lines are perpendicular if and only if
>
> $$AA' = -BB'.$$

Property 2.2 can be verified by changing both $Ax + By = C$ and $A'x + B'y = C'$ to slope-intercept form, and then by using the previous slope relationships that involve parallel and perpendicular lines. We will have you carry out the details in the next set of problems.

   Using Property 2.2, we can very easily recognize parallel and perpendicular lines. For example, $3x + 2y = 9$ and $6x + 4y = 19$ represent parallel lines because $\frac{3}{6} = \frac{2}{4} \neq \frac{9}{19}$. Likewise, we know that $5x - 2y = 7$ and $2x + 5y = 14$ represent perpendicular lines because $5(2) = -(-2)(5)$. In other words, the product of the coefficients of the x-terms equals the opposite of the product of the coefficients of the y-terms.

   Property 2.2 also provides a very easy way of writing the equations of lines that are parallel and perpendicular to a given line and contain a given point. The final example of this section illustrates this approach.

EXAMPLE 10

Find the equation of the line that is perpendicular to the line $3x + 4y = 12$ and contains the point $(-1, -3)$.

Solution

Using part 2 of Property 2.2, we know that $4x - 3y = k$, where k is a constant, represents a family of lines perpendicular to $3x + 4y = 12$ because we have satisfied the condition $AA' = -BB'$. Therefore, to find the specific line of the family that contains $(-1, -3)$, we substitute -1 for x and -3 for y.

$$4x - 3y = k$$
$$4(-1) - 3(-3) = k$$
$$5 = k$$

Thus, the required line is $4x - 3y = 5$.

PROBLEM SET 2.2

For Problems 1–16, graph each of the linear equations.

1. $x - 2y = 4$

2. $2x + y = -4$

3. $3x + 2y = 6$

4. $2x - 3y = 6$

5. $4x - 5y = 20$

6. $5x + 4y = 20$

7. $x - y = 3$

8. $-x + y = 4$

9. $y = 3x - 1$

10. $y = -2x + 3$

11. $y = -x$

12. $y = 4x$

13. $x = 0$

14. $y = -1$

15. $y = \frac{2}{3}x$

16. $y = -\frac{1}{2}x$

For Problems 17–38, write the equation of each line that satisfies the stated conditions. Express final equations in the form $Ax + By = C$, where B and C are integers and A is a nonnegative integer.

17. Contains the point $(2, 4)$ and $m = \frac{1}{3}$

18. Contains the point $(-1, 4)$ and $m = \frac{3}{5}$

19. Contains the point $(4, -3)$ and $m = -\frac{2}{3}$

20. Contains the point $(-3, 7)$ and $m = -\frac{1}{5}$

21. Contains the points $(2, 3)$ and $(9, 8)$

22. Contains the points $(1, -4)$ and $(4, 4)$

23. Contains the points $(-1, 7)$ and $(5, 2)$

24. Contains the points $(-3, 1)$ and $(6, -2)$

25. Contains the points $(4, -3)$ and $(-7, -3)$

26. Contains the points $(0, 0)$ and $(-2, 5)$

27. $m = -\frac{3}{7}$ and $b = 2$ **28.** $m = -3$ and $b = -4$

29. $m = 4$ and $b = \frac{3}{2}$ **30.** $m = \frac{2}{3}$ and $b = \frac{3}{5}$

31. x-intercept of 4 and y-intercept of -5

32. Contains the point $(3, -1)$ and is parallel to x-axis

33. Contains the point $(-4, 3)$ and is parallel to y-axis

34. Contains the point $(1, 2)$ and is parallel to $3x - y = 5$

35. Contains the point $(4, -3)$ and is parallel to $5x + 2y = 1$

36. Contains the origin and is parallel to $5x - 2y = 10$

37. Contains the point $(-2, 6)$ and is perpendicular to $x - 4y = 7$

38. Contains the point $(-3, -5)$ and is perpendicular to $3x + 7y = 4$

For each pair of lines in Problems 39–46, determine whether they are parallel, perpendicular, or intersecting lines that are not perpendicular.

39. $y = \frac{5}{6}x + 2$
$y = \frac{5}{6}x - 4$

40. $y = 5x - 1$
$y = -\frac{1}{5}x + \frac{2}{3}$

41. $5x - 7y = 14$
$7x + 5y = 12$

42. $2x - y = 4$
$4x - 2y = 17$

43. $4x + 9y = 13$
$-4x + y = 11$

44. $y = 5x$
$y = -5x$

45. $x + y = 0$
$x - y = 0$

46. $2x - y = 14$
$3x - y = 17$

For Problems 47–50, find the slope and the y-intercept of each line.

47. $x - 2y = 7$ **48.** $2x + y = 9$

49. $y + 3x = 0$ **50.** $-5x + 6y = 13$

51. The midpoints of the sides of a triangle are $(-3, 4)$, $(1, -4)$, and $(7, 2)$. Find the equations of the sides of the triangle.

52. The vertices of a triangle are $(2, 6)$, $(5, 1)$, and $(1, -4)$. Find the equations of the three altitudes of the triangle. (An altitude of a triangle is the line segment from a vertex perpendicular to the opposite side.)

53. The vertices of a triangle are $(1, -6)$, $(3, 1)$, and $(-2, 2)$. Find the equations of the three medians of the triangle. (A median of a triangle is the line segment from a vertex to the midpoint of the opposite side.)

54. Find the area of the triangle whose vertices are $(-5, -1)$, $(6, 2)$, and $(10, -4)$.

55. Find the distance between the point $(4, 3)$ and the line $2x + y = 9$. (The distance between a point and a line is measured on a line perpendicular to the given line.)

56. The lines $2x - 3y = 6$ and $2x + y = 8$ determine two sides of a parallelogram and the point $(-3, 4)$ is one vertex. Find the other three vertices of the parallelogram.

57. The slope-intercept form of a line can also be used for graphing purposes. Suppose that we want to graph $y = \frac{2}{3}x + 1$. Since the y-intercept is 1, the point $(0, 1)$ is on the line. Furthermore, since the slope is $\frac{2}{3}$, another point can

be found by moving 2 units *up* and 3 units to the *right*. Thus, the point $(3, 3)$ is also on the line. The two points $(0, 1)$ and $(3, 3)$ determine the line.

Use the slope-intercept form to help graph each of the following lines.

a. $y = \frac{3}{4}x + 2$ **b.** $y = \frac{1}{2}x - 4$

c. $y = -\frac{4}{5}x + 1$ **d.** $y = -\frac{2}{3}x - 6$

e. $y = -2x + \frac{5}{4}$ **f.** $y = x - \frac{3}{2}$

FURTHER INVESTIGATIONS

58. Verify Property 2.2.

59. Graph $|2x + y| = 4$.

60. The form $y - y_1 = \left[\dfrac{(y_2 - y_1)}{(x_2 - x_1)} \right] (x - x_1)$, where $x_1 \neq x_2$, is called the two-point form of the equation of a straight line. (1) Using points (x_1, y_1) and (x_2, y_2) develop the two-point form. (2) Use the two-point form to determine the equation of each of the following lines that contains the indicated pair of points. Express the final equations in the form $Ax + By = C$, where B and C are integers and A is a nonnegative integer.

a. $(4, 3)$ and $(5, 6)$ **b.** $(-3, 5)$ and $(2, -1)$

c. $(0, 0)$ and $(-7, 2)$ **d.** $(-3, -4)$ and $(5, -1)$

61. The form $x/a + y/b = 1$ is called the intercept form of the equation of a straight line. (1) Using a to represent the

x-intercept and b the y-intercept, develop the intercept form. (2) Use the intercept form to write the equation of each of the following lines. Express the final equations in the form $Ax + By = C$, where B and C are integers and A is a nonnegative integer.

a. $a = 2, b = 5$ **b.** $a = -3, b = 3$

c. $a = 6, b = -4$ **d.** $a = -1, b = -2$

62. To graph $|x| + |y| = 4$ we can use the definition of absolute value and consider the portion of the graph in each of the four quadrants. For example, in the first quadrant where $x \geq 0$ and $y \geq 0$, the equation $|x| + |y| = 4$ becomes $x + y = 4$ because $|x| = x$ and $|y| = y$. Graph each of the following equations.

a. $|x| + |y| = 4$ **b.** $|2x| + |y| = 2$

c. $|y| = |x|$ **d.** $|x| - |y| = 3$

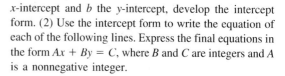 **GRAPHICS CALCULATOR ACTIVITIES**

This is the first of many appearances of a group of problems called *Graphics Calculator Activities*. These problems are specifically designed for those of you who have access to a graphics calculator or a computer with an appropriate software graphing package. Within the framework of these problems you will be given the opportunity to reinforce concepts that have been discussed in the text, lay groundwork for concepts to be introduced later in the text, predict shapes and locations of graphs based on previous graphing experiences, solve problems that are unreasonable or perhaps impossible to solve without a graphing utility, and in general become familiar with the capabilities and limitations of your graphing utility.

For Problems 63–71, (a) use either Property 2.1 or 2.2 to determine whether the equations represent parallel lines, perpendicular lines, or lines that intersect but are not perpendicular, and (b) use your graphing utility to graph each pair of lines on the same set of axes. Set your boundaries so that the distance between tic marks is the same on both axes.

63. $y = \frac{4}{5}x - 3$ and $y = \frac{5}{4}x + 2$

64. $y = -\frac{3}{10}x - 1$ and $y = -\frac{3}{10}x + 4$

65. $y = -10x + 2$ and $y = .1x + 3$

66. $5.2x + 3.3y = 9.4$ and $5.2x + 3.3y = 12.6$

67. $1.3x - 4.7y = 3.4$ and $1.3x - 4.7y = 11.6$

68. $2.7x + 3.9y = 1.4$ and $2.7x - 3.9y = 8.2$

69. $5x - 7y = 17$ and $7x + 5y = 19$

70. $9x + 2y = 14$ and $2x + 9y = 17$

71. $2.1x + 3.4y = 11.7$ and $3.4x - 2.1y = 17.3$

72. Back in Chapter 1 we reviewed various techniques for solving equations. Now we can introduce another technique for solving equations: the use of a graphing utility. For example, to solve the equation $4(2x - 1) = 3(3x + 2)$ we can graph the equation $y = 4(2x - 1) - 3(3x + 2)$ and determine the x-intercepts. (Remember that $y = 0$ at the x-intercepts; therefore, the x-intercepts of the graph of $y = 4(2x - 1) - 3(3x + 2)$ are the solutions for the equation $4(2x - 1) = 3(3x + 2)$.) This graph should be a straight line that appears to intersect the x-axis at -10. By substituting -10 back into the original equation we can verify that it is indeed the solution. (Some graphing utilities have a *root* feature that will make this substitution process very easy to handle.) If the solution set consists of some nonintegral solutions, then we can use the trace and/or zoom and/or root features of the graphing utility to approximate the answers.

Return to Problem Set 1.5 and solve the equations in Problems 7, 9, 11, 17, 19, 23, 27, 29, and 31 using your graphing utility.

73. Return to Problem Set 1.7 and solve the equations in Problems 1, 3, 9, 15, 27, and 29 using your graphing utility. Also use your graphing utility to graphically demonstrate that the equations in Problems 11, 17, and 19 have no real number solutions.

74. A graphing utility can also be used to solve an inequality such as $x^2 - 2x - 15 > 0$. We can graph the equation $y = x^2 - 2x - 15$ and then determine where the graph is above the x-axis. In other words, we can determine the values of x for which $y > 0$.

Return to Problem Set 1.8 and use your graphing utility to help determine the solution sets for Problems 15, 17, 19, 21, 23, 29, 35, 37, 39, 41, 43, 57, 59, 67, and 69.

2.3   SYSTEMS OF LINEAR EQUATIONS AND PROBLEM SOLVING

In Section 2.2 we stated that any equation of the form $Ax + By = C$, where A, B, and C are real numbers (A and B not both zero) is a linear equation in the two variables x and y, and its graph is a straight line. Two linear equations in two variables considered together form a **system of linear equations** as illustrated by the following.

$$\begin{pmatrix} x + y = 6 \\ x - y = 2 \end{pmatrix} \qquad \begin{pmatrix} 3x + 2y = 1 \\ 5x - 2y = 23 \end{pmatrix} \qquad \begin{pmatrix} 4x - 5y = 21 \\ -3x + y = -7 \end{pmatrix}$$

To **solve a system** such as any of the three above means to find all of the ordered pairs that satisfy both equations in the system. For example, if we graph the two equations $x + y = 6$ and $x - y = 2$ on the same set of axes as in Figure 2.30, then the ordered pair associated with the point of intersection of the two lines is the **solution of the system**. Thus, we say that $\{(4, 2)\}$ is the solution set of the system

$$\begin{pmatrix} x + y = 6 \\ x - y = 2 \end{pmatrix}.$$

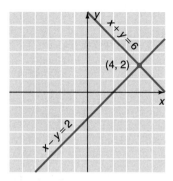

F I G U R E   2 . 30

To check, we substitute 4 for x and 2 for y in the two equations.

$x + y$ becomes $4 + 2 = 6$, a true statement,   and

$x - y$ becomes $4 - 2 = 2$, a true statement.

Because the graph of a linear equation in two variables is a straight line, there are three possible situations that can occur when solving a system of two linear equations in two variables. These situations are illustrated in Figure 2.31.

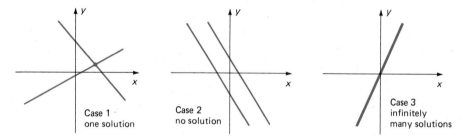

F I G U R E   2 . 31

CASE 1   The graphs of the two equations are two lines intersecting in *one* point. There is one solution and the system is called a **consistent system**.

CASE 2   The graphs of the two equations are parallel lines. There is **no solution** and the system is called an **inconsistent system**.

CASE 3   The graphs of the two equations are the same line and there are **infinitely many solutions** of the system. Any pair of real numbers that satisfies one of the equations will also satisfy the other equation and we say that the equations are **dependent**.

Thus, as we solve a system of two linear equations in two variables we know what to expect. The system will have *no* solutions, *one* ordered pair as a solution, or *infinitely many* ordered pairs as solutions.

Substitution Method

It should be evident that solving specific systems of equations by graphing requires accurate graphs. In fact, unless the solutions are integers it is quite difficult to obtain exact solutions from a graph. Therefore, let's consider some other techniques for solving systems of equations.

The **substitution method**, which works especially well with systems of two equations in two unknowns, can be described as follows.

1. Solve one of the equations for one variable in terms of the other. (If possible, make this choice to avoid fractions.)

2. Substitute the expression obtained in Step 1 in the other equation producing an equation in one variable.

3. Solve the equation obtained in Step 2.

4. Use the solution obtained in Step 3 along with the expression obtained in Step 1 to determine the solution of the system.

EXAMPLE 1

Solve the system

$$\begin{pmatrix} x - 3y = -25 \\ 4x + 5y = 19 \end{pmatrix}.$$

Solution

Solving the first equation for x in terms of y produces

$$x = 3y - 25.$$

Substituting $3y - 25$ for x in the second equation and solving for y we obtain

$$4x + 5y = 19$$
$$4(3y - 25) + 5y = 19$$
$$12y - 100 + 5y = 19$$
$$17y = 119$$
$$y = 7.$$

Now substituting 7 for y in the equation $x = 3y - 25$ we obtain

$$x = 3(7) - 25 = -4.$$

The solution set of the given system is $\{(-4, 7)\}$. (Perhaps you should check this solution in both of the original equations.) ▬▬▬

EXAMPLE 2

Solve the system

$$\begin{pmatrix} 6x - 4y = 18 \\ y = \dfrac{3}{2}x - \dfrac{9}{2} \end{pmatrix}.$$

Solution

The second equation is given in appropriate form to begin the substitution process. Substituting $\frac{3}{2}x - \frac{9}{2}$ for y in the first equation yields

$$6x - 4y = 18$$

$$6x - 4\left(\frac{3}{2}x - \frac{9}{2}\right) = 18$$

$$6x - 6x + 18 = 18$$

$$18 = 18.$$

Obtaining the true numerical statement $18 = 18$ indicates that the system has infinitely many solutions. Any ordered pair that satisfies one of the equations will also satisfy the other equation. Thus, in the second equation of the original system, if we let $x = k$, then $y = \frac{3}{2}k - \frac{9}{2}$. So the solution set can be expressed as $\{(k, \frac{3}{2}k - \frac{9}{2})\}$, where k is any real number. If some specific solutions are needed, they can be generated by the ordered pair $(k, \frac{3}{2}k - \frac{9}{2})$. For example, if we let $k = 1$, then $\frac{3}{2}k - \frac{9}{2}$ becomes $\frac{3}{2}(1) - \frac{9}{2} = -\frac{6}{2} = -3$. Thus, the ordered pair $(1, -3)$ is a member of the solution set of the given system. ■

Take another look at the original system of equations in Example 2. Suppose that we change the first equation to slope-intercept form.

$$6x - 4y = 18$$

$$-4y = -6x + 18$$

$$y = \frac{3}{2}x - \frac{9}{2}$$

Now it is evident that both equations represent the same line and therefore we could proceed to represent the infinitely many solutions for the system.

Elimination-by-Addition Method

Now let's consider the **elimination-by-addition** method for solving a system of equations. This is a very important method since it is the basis for developing other techniques for solving systems containing many equations and variables. The method involves the replacement of systems of equations with **simpler equivalent systems** until we obtain a system where the solutions are obvious. **Equivalent systems of equations are systems that have exactly the same solution set.** The following operations or transformations can be applied to a system of equations to produce an equivalent system.

    1. Any two equations of the system can be interchanged.

    2. Both sides of any equation of the system can be multiplied by any nonzero real number.

    3. Any equation of the system can be replaced by adding a nonzero multiple of another equation to that equation.

EXAMPLE 3

Solve the system

$$\begin{pmatrix} 3x + 5y = -9 \\ 2x - 3y = 13 \end{pmatrix}.$$

$$(1)$$
$$(2)$$

Solution

The given system can be replaced by an equivalent system by multiplying equation (2) by -3.

$$\begin{pmatrix} 3x + 5y = -9 \\ -6x + 9y = -39 \end{pmatrix}$$

$$(3)$$
$$(4)$$

Now let's replace equation (4) with an equation formed by multiplying equation (3) by 2 and adding this result to equation (4).

$$\begin{pmatrix} 3x + 5y = -9 \\ 19y = -57 \end{pmatrix}$$

$$(5)$$
$$(6)$$

From equation (6) we can easily determine that $y = -3$. Then substituting -3 for y in equation (5) produces

$$3x + 5(-3) = -9$$
$$3x - 15 = -9$$
$$3x = 6$$
$$x = 2.$$

The solution set for the given system is $\{(2, -3)\}$.   ▬▬▬▬

> **REMARK**   We are using a format for the elimination-by-addition method that highlights the use of equivalent systems. In Section 11.1 this format will lead naturally to an approach using matrices. Thus, it is beneficial to stress the use of equivalent systems at this time.

EXAMPLE 4

Solve the system

$$\begin{pmatrix} x - 4y = 9 \\ x - 4y = 3 \end{pmatrix}.$$

$$(7)$$
$$(8)$$

Solution

We can replace equation (8) with an equation formed by multiplying equation (7) by -1 and adding this result to equation (8).

$$\begin{pmatrix} x - 4y = 9 \\ 0 = -6 \end{pmatrix}$$

$$(9)$$
$$(10)$$

The statement $0 = -6$ is a contradiction and therefore the original system is **inconsistent**; it has no solution. The solution set is $\varnothing$.

In Example 4 if you recognize that the graphs of the two equations are parallel lines, then there is no need to attempt to solve the system. It is an inconsistent system and has no solution.

Finally, let's consider using a graphing utility to solve a system of two linear equations in two variables.

EXAMPLE 5

Solve the system

$$\left(\begin{array}{l} 1.14x + 2.35y = -7.12 \\ 3.26x - 5.05y = 26.72 \end{array}\right).$$

Solution

First, we need to solve each equation for y in terms of x. Thus, the system becomes

$$\left(\begin{array}{l} y = \dfrac{-7.12 - 1.14x}{2.35} \\[4mm] y = \dfrac{3.26x - 26.72}{5.05} \end{array}\right).$$

Now we can enter both of these equations into a graphing utility and obtain Figure 2.32. From this figure it appears that the point of intersection is at approximately

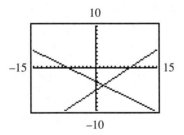

F I G U R E   2 . 32

$x = 2$ and $y = -4$. By direct substitution into the given equations we can verify that the point of intersection is exactly $(2, -4)$.

REMARK   Graphing utilities vary as to how to determine the coordinates of the point of intersection of two lines. To accomplish this some utilities use a *root* feature, which can also express any rational solution in either decimal or common fraction form. You will need to consult your user's manual for specific key punching instructions.

Systems of Three Linear Equations in Three Variables

Consider a linear equation in three variables, x, y, and z, such as $3x - 2y + z = 7$. **Any ordered triple** (x, y, z) that makes the equation a true numerical statement is said to be a solution of the equation. For example, the ordered triple $(2, 1, 3)$ is a solution because $3(2) - 2(1) + 3 = 7$. However, the ordered triple $(5, 2, 4)$ is not a solution because $3(5) - 2(2) + 4 \neq 7$. There are infinitely many solutions in the solution set.

> **REMARK**   The idea of a **linear equation** is generalized to include equations of more than two variables. Thus, an equation such as $5x - 2y + 9z = 8$ is called a linear equation in three variables, the equation $5x - 7y + 2z - 11w = 1$ is called a linear equation in four variables, and so on.

To **solve** a system of three linear equations in three variables, such as

$$\begin{pmatrix} 3x - y + 2z = 13 \\ 4x + 2y + 5z = 30 \\ 5x - 3y - z = 3 \end{pmatrix}$$

means to find all of the ordered triples that satisfy all three equations. In other words, the solution set of the system is the intersection of the solution sets of all three equations in the system.

The graph of a linear equation in three variables is a **plane**, not a line. In fact, graphing equations in three variables requires the use of a three-dimensional coordinate system. Thus using a graphing approach to solve systems of three linear equations in three variables is not at all practical. However, a simple graphic analysis does provide us with some direction as to what we can expect as we begin solving such systems.

In general, because each linear equation in three variables produces a plane, a system of three such equations produces three planes. There are various ways that three planes can be related. For example, they may be mutually parallel, or two of the planes may be parallel and the third one intersect each of the two. (You may want to analyze all of the other possibilities for the three planes!) However, for our purposes at this time we need to realize that from a solution set viewpoint, a system of three linear equations in three variables produces one of the following possibilities.

1. There is **one ordered triple** that satisfies all three equations. The three planes have a common point of intersection as indicated in Figure 2.33.

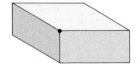

FIGURE 2.33

2. There are **infinitely many ordered triples** in the solution set, all of which are coordinates of points on a line common to the planes. This can happen

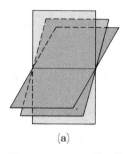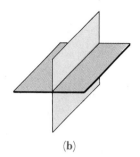

(a)   (b)

FIGURE 2.34

if the three planes have a common line of intersection (Figure 2.34(a)), or if two of the planes coincide and the third plane intersects them (Figure 2.34(b)).

3. There are **infinitely many ordered triples** in the solution set, all of which are coordinates of points on a plane. This can happen if the three planes coincide, as illustrated in Figure 2.35.

FIGURE 2.35

4. The solution set is **empty**; thus, we write ∅. This can happen in various ways, as illustrated in Figure 2.36. Notice that in each situation there are no points common to all three planes.

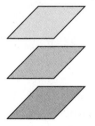   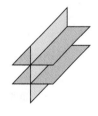   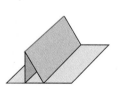

(a) Three parallel planes

(b) Two planes coincide and the third one is parallel to the coinciding planes.

(c) Two planes are parallel and the third intersects them in parallel lines.

(d) No two planes are parallel, but two of them intersect in a line that is parallel to the third plane.

FIGURE 2.36

Now that we know what possibilities exist, let's consider finding the solution set for some systems. Our approach will be the elimination-by-addition method whereby systems are replaced with equivalent systems until a system is obtained where we can easily determine the solution set. The details of this approach should become apparent as we work a few examples.

EXAMPLE 6

Solve the system

$$
\begin{aligned}
4x - 3y - 2z &= 5 \quad &(1)\\
5y + z &= -11 \quad &(2)\\
3z &= 12 \quad &(3)
\end{aligned}
$$

Solution

The given form of this system makes it easy to solve. From equation (3) we obtain $z = 4$. Then substituting 4 for z in equation (2) produces

$$5y + 4 = -11$$

$$5y = -15$$

$$y = -3.$$

Finally, substituting 4 for z and -3 for y in equation (1) yields

$$4x - 3(-3) - 2(4) = 5$$

$$4x + 1 = 5$$

$$4x = 4$$

$$x = 1.$$

Thus, the solution set of the given system is $\{(1, -3, 4)\}$.

EXAMPLE 7

Solve the system

$$
\begin{aligned}
x - 2y + 3z &= 22 \quad &(4)\\
2x - 3y - z &= 5 \quad &(5)\\
3x + y - 5z &= -32 \quad &(6)
\end{aligned}
$$

Solution

Equation (5) can be replaced with the equation formed by multiplying equation (4) by -2 and adding this result to equation (5). Equation (6) can be replaced with the equation formed by multiplying equation (4) by -3 and adding this result to equation (6). The following equivalent system is produced in which equations (8) and (9) contain only the variables y and z.

$$
\begin{aligned}
x - 2y + 3z &= 22 \quad &(7)\\
y - 7z &= -39 \quad &(8)\\
7y - 14z &= -98 \quad &(9)
\end{aligned}
$$

Equation (9) can be replaced with the equation formed by multiplying equation (8) by -7 and adding this result to equation (9). This produces the equivalent system

$$
\begin{aligned}
x - 2y + 3z &= 22 \quad &(10)\\
y - 7z &= -39 \quad &(11)\\
35z &= 175 \quad &(12)
\end{aligned}
$$

From equation (12) we obtain $z = 5$. Then substituting 5 for z in equation (11) we obtain

$$y - 7(5) = -39$$
$$y = -4.$$

Finally, substituting -4 for y and 5 for z in equation (10) produces

$$x - 2(-4) + 3(5) = 22$$
$$x + 23 = 22$$
$$x = -1.$$

The solution set for the original system is $\{(-1, -4, 5)\}$.

EXAMPLE 8

Solve the system

$$\begin{pmatrix} 2x + 3y + z = 14 \\ 3x - 4y - 2z = -30 \\ 5x + 7y + 3z = 32 \end{pmatrix}.$$

(13)
(14)
(15)

Solution

Equation (14) can be replaced with the equation formed by multiplying equation (13) by 2 and adding this result to equation (14). Equation (15) can be replaced with the equation formed by multiplying equation (13) by -3 and adding this result to equation (15). The following equivalent system is produced where equations (17) and (18) contain only the two variables x and y.

$$\begin{pmatrix} 2x + 3y + z = 14 \\ 7x + 2y \quad\quad = -2 \\ -x - 2y \quad\quad = -10 \end{pmatrix}$$

(16)
(17)
(18)

Now equation (18) can be replaced with the equation formed by adding equation (17) to equation (18).

$$\begin{pmatrix} 2x + 3y + z = 14 \\ 7x + 2y \quad\quad = -2 \\ 6x \quad\quad\quad = -12 \end{pmatrix}$$

(19)
(20)
(21)

From equation (21) we obtain $x = -2$. Then substituting -2 for x in equation (20) we obtain

$$7(-2) + 2y = -2$$
$$2y = 12$$
$$y = 6.$$

Finally, substituting 6 for y and -2 for x in equation (19) produces

$$2(-2) + 3(6) + z = 14$$

$$14 + z = 14$$

$$z = 0.$$

The solution set of the original system is $\{(-2, 6, 0)\}$.

REMARK   Your graphing utility may have a special feature that will handle the solving of systems of linear equations involving several equations and unknowns. You may want to investigate that feature at this time or wait until we do more work with systems in Chapter 11.

Using Systems to Solve Problems

Many problems can be conveniently set up and solved using systems of linear equations. Problems involving two or three unknowns often translate naturally into systems of equations involving two or three linear equations.

PROBLEM 1

Investments   Lucinda invested $950, part of it at 11% interest and the remainder at 12%. Her total yearly income from the two investments was $111.50. How much did she invest at each rate?

Solution

Let x represent the amount invested at 11% and y the amount invested at 12%. The problem translates into the following system.

$$\begin{array}{ll}\text{The two investments total \$950} \longrightarrow \\ \text{The yearly interest from the two} \longrightarrow \\ \text{investments totals \$111.50}\end{array} \left(\begin{array}{c} x + y = 950 \\ .11x + .12y = 111.50 \end{array}\right)$$

Multiplying the second equation by 100 produces the equivalent system

$$\left(\begin{array}{c} x + y = 950 \\ 11x + 12y = 11150 \end{array}\right).$$

Since neither equation is solved for one variable in terms of the other, let's use the elimination-by-addition method to solve the system. The second equation can be replaced by an equation formed by multiplying the first equation by -11 and adding this result to the second equation.

$$\left(\begin{array}{c} x + y = 950 \\ y = 700 \end{array}\right)$$

Now substituting 700 for y in the equation $x + y = 950$ yields

$$x + 700 = 950$$

$$x = 250.$$

Therefore, Lucinda must have invested $250 at 11% and $700 at 12%.

PROBLEM 2

Producing golf shirts   A small company that manufactures sporting goods produces three different styles of golf shirts. Each style of shirt requires the services of three departments as indicated by the following table.

	STYLE A	STYLE B	STYLE C
Cutting department	.1 hr	.1 hr	.3 hr
Sewing department	.3 hr	.2 hr	.4 hr
Packaging department	.1 hr	.2 hr	.1 hr

The cutting, sewing, and packaging departments have available a maximum of 340, 580, and 255 work-hours per week, respectively. How many of each style of golf shirt should be produced each week so that the company is operating at full capacity?

Solution

Let a represent the number of shirts of style A produced per week, b the number of style B per week, and c the number of style C per week. Then the problem translates into the following system of equations.

$$\begin{cases} .1a + .1b + .3c = 340 \\ .3a + .2b + .4c = 580 \\ .1a + .2b + .1c = 255 \end{cases} \begin{array}{l} \longleftarrow \text{ Cutting department} \\ \longleftarrow \text{ Sewing department} \\ \longleftarrow \text{ Packaging department} \end{array}$$

Solving this system (we will leave the details for you to carry out) produces $a = 500$, $b = 650$, and $c = 750$. Thus, the company should produce 500 golf shirts of style A, 650 of style B, and 750 of style C per week.

PROBLEM SET 2.3

For Problems 1–14, solve each system by either the substitution method or the elimination-by-addition method, whichever seems more appropriate to you.

1. $\begin{pmatrix} 5x - y = -22 \\ 2x + 3y = -2 \end{pmatrix}$

2. $\begin{pmatrix} 4x + 5y = -41 \\ 3x - 2y = 21 \end{pmatrix}$

3. $\begin{pmatrix} x = 3y - 10 \\ x = -2y + 15 \end{pmatrix}$

4. $\begin{pmatrix} y = 4x - 24 \\ 7x + y = 42 \end{pmatrix}$

5. $\begin{pmatrix} \frac{1}{2}x - \frac{2}{3}y = 22 \\ \frac{1}{2}x + \frac{1}{4}y = 0 \end{pmatrix}$

6. $\begin{pmatrix} \frac{2}{5}x - \frac{1}{3}y = -9 \\ \frac{3}{4}x + \frac{1}{3}y = -14 \end{pmatrix}$

7. $\begin{pmatrix} x + y = 1000 \\ .12x + .14y = 136 \end{pmatrix}$

8. $\begin{pmatrix} x + y = 10 \\ .3x + .7y = 4 \end{pmatrix}$

9. $\begin{pmatrix} y = 5x - 9 \\ 5x - y = 9 \end{pmatrix}$

10. $\begin{pmatrix} 3x - 5y = 9 \\ 6x - 10y = -1 \end{pmatrix}$

11. $\begin{pmatrix} \dfrac{x}{2} - \dfrac{2y}{5} = \dfrac{-23}{60} \\ \dfrac{2x}{3} + \dfrac{y}{4} = \dfrac{-1}{4} \end{pmatrix}$

12. $\begin{pmatrix} \dfrac{2x}{3} - \dfrac{y}{2} = \dfrac{3}{5} \\ \dfrac{x}{4} + \dfrac{y}{2} = \dfrac{7}{80} \end{pmatrix}$

13. $\begin{pmatrix} \dfrac{4x}{5} - \dfrac{3y}{2} = \dfrac{1}{5} \\ -2x + y = -1 \end{pmatrix}$

14. $\begin{pmatrix} \dfrac{3x}{2} - \dfrac{2y}{7} = -1 \\ 4x + y = 2 \end{pmatrix}$

For Problems 15–28, solve each of the systems

15. $\begin{pmatrix} x - 2y + 3z = 7 \\ 2x + y + 5z = 17 \\ 3x - 4y - 2z = 1 \end{pmatrix}$

16. $\begin{pmatrix} x - 2y + z = -4 \\ 2x + 4y - 3z = -1 \\ -3x - 6y + 7z = 4 \end{pmatrix}$

17. $\begin{pmatrix} 2x - y + z = 0 \\ 3x - 2y + 4z = 11 \\ 5x + y - 6z = -32 \end{pmatrix}$

18. $\begin{pmatrix} 2x - y + 3z = -14 \\ 4x + 2y - z = 12 \\ 6x - 3y + 4z = -22 \end{pmatrix}$

19. $\begin{pmatrix} 3x + 2y - z = -11 \\ 2x - 3y + 4z = 11 \\ 5x + y - 2z = -17 \end{pmatrix}$

20. $\begin{pmatrix} 9x + 4y - z = 0 \\ 3x - 2y + 4z = 6 \\ 6x - 8y - 3z = 3 \end{pmatrix}$

21. $\begin{pmatrix} 2x + 3y - 4z = -10 \\ 4x - 5y + 3z = 2 \\ 2y + z = 8 \end{pmatrix}$

22. $\begin{pmatrix} x + 2y - 3z = 2 \\ 3x - z = -8 \\ 2x - 3y + 5z = -9 \end{pmatrix}$

23. $\begin{pmatrix} 3x + 2y - 2z = 14 \\ 2x - 5y + 3z = 7 \\ 4x - 3y + 7z = 5 \end{pmatrix}$

24. $\begin{pmatrix} 4x + 3y - 2z = -11 \\ 3x - 7y + 3z = 10 \\ 9x - 8y + 5z = 9 \end{pmatrix}$

25. $\begin{pmatrix} 2x - 3y + 4z = -12 \\ 4x + 2y - 3z = -13 \\ 6x - 5y + 7z = -31 \end{pmatrix}$

26. $\begin{pmatrix} 3x + 5y - 2z = -27 \\ 5x - 2y + 4z = 27 \\ 7x + 3y - 6z = -55 \end{pmatrix}$

27. $\begin{pmatrix} 5x - 3y - 6z = 22 \\ x - y + z = -3 \\ -3x + 7y - 5z = 23 \end{pmatrix}$

28. $\begin{pmatrix} 4x + 3y - 5z = -29 \\ 3x - 7y - z = -19 \\ 2x + 5y + 2z = -10 \end{pmatrix}$

APPLIED PROBLEMS

For Problems 29–44, solve each problem by setting up and solving a system of linear equations in either two or three variables.

29. *Renting motel rooms* A motel rents double rooms at $32 per day and single rooms at $26 per day. If 23 rooms were rented one day for a total of $688, how many rooms of each kind were rented?

30. *Renting apartments* An apartment complex rents one-bedroom apartments for $325 per month and two-bedroom apartments for $375 per month. One month the number of one-bedroom apartments rented was twice the number of two-bedroom apartments. If the total income for that month was $12,300, how many apartments of each kind were rented?

31. *Ticket sales* The income from a student production was $10,000. The price of a student ticket was $3 and nonstudent tickets were sold at $5 each. Three thousand tickets were sold. How many tickets of each kind were sold?

32. *Buying stamps* Eric bought 50 stamps for $13.30. Some of them were 29-cent stamps and the rest were 23-cent stamps. How many of each kind did he buy?

33. *Investing money* Melinda invested three times as much money at 11% yearly interest as she did at 9%. Her total yearly interest from the two investments was $210. How much did she invest at each rate?

34. *Investing money* Sam invested $1950, part of it at 10% and the rest at 12% yearly interest. The income on the

12% investment was $6 less than twice the income from the 10% investment. How much did he invest at each rate?

35. *Buying sporting goods*   Bill bought 4 tennis balls and 3 golf balls for a total of $10.25. Bret went into the same store and bought 2 tennis balls and 5 golf balls for $11.25. What was the price for each tennis ball and each golf ball?

36. *Buying snacks*   Six cans of pop and 2 bags of potato chips cost $5.12. At the same prices, 8 cans of pop and 5 bags of potato chips cost $9.86. Find the price per can of pop and the price per bag of potato chips.

37. *Coin collection*   A box contains $7.15 in nickels, dimes, and quarters. There are 42 coins in all and the sum of the number of nickels and dimes is two less than the number of quarters. How many coins of each kind are there?

38. *Coin collection*   A handful of 65 coins consists of pennies, nickels, and dimes. The number of nickels is four less than twice the number of pennies and there are 13 more dimes than nickels. How many coins of each kind are there?

39. *Angles of a triangle*   The measure of the largest angle of a triangle is twice the smallest angle. The sum of the smallest and the largest angle is twice the other angle. Find the measure of each angle.

40. *Sides of a triangle*   The perimeter of a triangle is 45 centimeters. The longest side is 4 centimeters less than twice the shortest side. The sum of the lengths of the shortest and longest sides is 7 centimeters less than three times the length of the remaining side. Find the lengths of all three sides of the triangle.

41. *Investing money*   Part of $3000 is invested at 12%, another part at 13%, and the remainder at 14% yearly interest. The total yearly income from the three investments is $400. The sum of the amounts invested at 12% and 13%

equals the amount invested at 14%. How much is invested at each rate?

42. *Investing money*   Different amounts of money were invested at 10%, 11%, and 12% yearly interest. The amount invested at 11% was $300 more than what was invested at 10% and the total income from all three investments was $324. If a total of $2900 was invested, find the amount invested at each rate.

43. *Building birdhouses*   A small company makes three different types of birdhouses. Each type requires the services of three different departments according to the following table.

	Type A	Type B	Type C
Cutting department	.1 hr	.2 hr	.1 hr
Finishing department	.4 hr	.4 hr	.3 hr
Assembling department	.2 hr	.1 hr	.3 hr

The cutting, finishing, and assembling departments have available a maximum of 35, 95, and 62.5 work-hours per week, respectively. How many birdhouses of each type should be made per week so that the company is operating at full capacity?

44. *Dieting*   A certain diet consists of dishes *A*, *B*, and *C*. Each unit of *A* has 1 gram of fat, 2 grams of carbohydrate, and 4 grams of protein. Each unit of *B* has 2 grams of fat, 1 gram of carbohydrate, and 3 grams of protein. Each unit of *C* has 2 grams of fat, 4 grams of carbohydrate, and 3 grams of protein. The diet provides for 15 grams of fat, 24 grams of carbohydrate, and 30 grams of protein. How many units of each type of dish should be used?

THOUGHTS into WORDS

45. Explain how you would solve the system

$$\begin{pmatrix} 3x - 4y = 6 \\ 5x + \ y = -5 \end{pmatrix}$$

using the substitution method.

46. Explain how you would solve the system

$$\begin{pmatrix} 2x + 6y = 9 \\ 5x - 4y = 12 \end{pmatrix}$$

using the elimination-by-addition method.

47. Why does the solution set for the system

$$\begin{pmatrix} x = 2y + 4 \\ 3x - 6y = 12 \end{pmatrix}$$

contain infinitely many ordered pairs as solutions? Find at least five of these ordered pairs.

48. Describe how you would solve the system

$$\begin{pmatrix} x \quad\quad - 3z = 4 \\ 3x - 2y + 7z = -1 \\ 2x \quad\;\; + \;\, z = 9 \end{pmatrix}.$$

FURTHER INVESTIGATIONS

49. Consider the linear system

$$\begin{pmatrix} a_1x + b_1y = c_1 \\ a_2x + b_2y = c_2 \end{pmatrix}.$$

a. Prove that this system has one and only one solution if and only if

$$\frac{a_1}{a_2} \neq \frac{b_1}{b_2}.$$

b. Prove that this system has no solutions if and only if

$$\frac{a_1}{a_2} = \frac{b_1}{b_2} \neq \frac{c_1}{c_2}.$$

c. Prove that this system has infinitely many solutions if and only if

$$\frac{a_1}{a_2} = \frac{b_1}{b_2} = \frac{c_1}{c_2}.$$

50. Use the results from Problem 49 to determine whether each of the following systems is consistent, inconsistent, or dependent.

a. $\begin{pmatrix} 5x + \; y = 9 \\ x - 5y = 4 \end{pmatrix}$ **b.** $\begin{pmatrix} 3x - 2y = 14 \\ 2x + 3y = \; 9 \end{pmatrix}$

c. $\begin{pmatrix} x - 7y = 4 \\ x - 7y = 9 \end{pmatrix}$ **d.** $\begin{pmatrix} 3x - \; 5y = 10 \\ 6x - 10y = \; 1 \end{pmatrix}$

e. $\begin{pmatrix} 3x + 6y = 2 \\ \frac{3}{5}x + \frac{6}{5}y = \frac{2}{5} \end{pmatrix}$ **f.** $\begin{pmatrix} \frac{2}{3}x - \frac{3}{4}y = 2 \\ \frac{1}{2}x + \frac{2}{5}y = 9 \end{pmatrix}$

g. $\begin{pmatrix} 7x + 9y = 14 \\ 8x - 3y = 12 \end{pmatrix}$ **h.** $\begin{pmatrix} 4x - \; 5y = 3 \\ 12x - 15y = 9 \end{pmatrix}$

A system such as

$$\begin{pmatrix} \dfrac{2}{x} + \dfrac{3}{y} = \dfrac{19}{15} \\[2ex] -\dfrac{2}{x} + \dfrac{1}{y} = -\dfrac{7}{15} \end{pmatrix}$$

is not a linear system, but can be solved using the elimination-by-addition method as follows: Multiply the first equation by 1 and add this result to the second equation, which will produce the equivalent system

$$\begin{pmatrix} \dfrac{2}{x} + \dfrac{3}{y} = \dfrac{19}{15} \\[2ex] \dfrac{4}{y} = \dfrac{12}{15} \end{pmatrix}.$$

Now solving $4/y = \frac{12}{15}$ will produce $y = 5$. Substitute 5 for y in the first equation and solve for x, which will produce

$$\frac{2}{x} + \frac{3}{5} = \frac{19}{15}$$

$$\frac{2}{x} = \frac{10}{15}$$

$$10x = 30$$

$$x = 3.$$

The solution set of the original system is $\{(3, 5)\}$. Solve each of the following systems.

51. $\begin{pmatrix} \dfrac{1}{x} + \dfrac{2}{y} = \dfrac{7}{12} \\[2ex] \dfrac{3}{x} - \dfrac{2}{y} = \dfrac{5}{12} \end{pmatrix}$ **52.** $\begin{pmatrix} \dfrac{3}{x} + \dfrac{2}{y} = 2 \\[2ex] \dfrac{2}{x} - \dfrac{3}{y} = \dfrac{1}{4} \end{pmatrix}$

53. $\left(\begin{array}{l} \dfrac{3}{x} - \dfrac{2}{y} = \dfrac{13}{6} \\ \dfrac{2}{x} + \dfrac{3}{y} = 0 \end{array} \right)$

54. $\left(\begin{array}{l} \dfrac{4}{x} + \dfrac{1}{y} = 11 \\ \dfrac{3}{x} - \dfrac{5}{y} = -9 \end{array} \right)$

55. $\left(\begin{array}{l} \dfrac{5}{x} - \dfrac{2}{y} = 23 \\ \dfrac{4}{x} + \dfrac{3}{y} = \dfrac{23}{2} \end{array} \right)$

56. $\left(\begin{array}{l} \dfrac{2}{x} - \dfrac{7}{y} = \dfrac{9}{10} \\ \dfrac{5}{x} + \dfrac{4}{y} = -\dfrac{41}{20} \end{array} \right)$

 GRAPHICS CALCULATOR ACTIVITIES

For Problems 57–66, use your graphics calculator to help solve the system. If the solution contains a nonintegral rational number, approximate the number to the nearest tenth.

57. $\left(\begin{array}{l} 1.6x - 2.3y = -16.3 \\ 2.2x + 5.1y = 18.9 \end{array} \right)$

58. $\left(\begin{array}{l} 2.14x + 4.21y = -33.75 \\ 3.27x - 2.91y = 13.83 \end{array} \right)$

59. $\left(\begin{array}{l} .43x - 4.19y = -49.42 \\ 2.73x + 1.78y = 26.82 \end{array} \right)$

60. $\left(\begin{array}{l} 1.2x + 2.4y = 12.12 \\ 3.1x - 4.9y = -17.53 \end{array} \right)$

61. $\left(\begin{array}{l} 7.3x - 8.4y = -28.98 \\ 9.2x + 1.3y = 47.87 \end{array} \right)$

62. $\left(\begin{array}{l} .2x + 5.3y = 30.53 \\ 4.1x + 7.8y = 30.85 \end{array} \right)$

63. $\left(\begin{array}{l} 7x - 9y = -24.2 \\ 12x + 5y = 19.8 \end{array} \right)$

64. $\left(\begin{array}{l} 8x + 7y = -28.1 \\ 6x - 11y = -48.7 \end{array} \right)$

65. $\left(\begin{array}{l} 1.4x + 2.3y = 98.8 \\ 3.7x - 5.9y = -122.2 \end{array} \right)$

66. $\left(\begin{array}{l} 2.14x - 3.27y = 51.24 \\ 5.76x + 7.49y = 170.5 \end{array} \right)$

67. Use a graphics calculator to check your answers for Problem 50.

2.4 CIRCLES

The distance formula, $d = \sqrt{(x_2 - x_1)^2 + (y_2 - y_1)^2}$, developed in Section 2.1 and applied to the definition of a circle, produces what is known as the **standard form of the equation of a circle**. We start with a precise definition of a circle.

> ### DEFINITION 2.2
>
> A **circle** is the set of all points in a plane equidistant from a given fixed point called the **center**. A line segment determined by the center and any point on the circle is called a **radius**.

Now let's consider a circle having a radius of length r and a center at (h, k) on a coordinate system, as shown in Figure 2.37. For any point P on the circle with coordinates (x, y), the length of a radius denoted by r can be expressed as

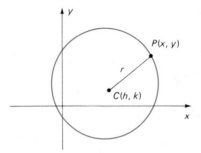

$r = \sqrt{(x - h)^2 + (y - k)^2}$. Thus, squaring both sides of this equation, we obtain the **standard form** of the equation of a circle.

$$(x - h)^2 + (y - k)^2 = r^2$$

The standard form of the equation of a circle can be used to solve the two basic kinds of problems, namely (1) given the coordinates of the center and the length of a radius of a circle, find its equation, and (2) given the equation of a circle, determine its graph. Let's illustrate each of these types of problems.

EXAMPLE 1

Find the equation of a circle having its center at $(-3, 5)$ and a radius of length 4 units.

Solution

Substituting -3 for h, 5 for k, and 4 for r in the standard form and simplifying, we obtain

$$(x - h)^2 + (y - k)^2 = r^2$$
$$(x - (-3))^2 + (y - 5)^2 = 4^2$$
$$(x + 3)^2 + (y - 5)^2 = 4^2$$
$$x^2 + 6x + 9 + y^2 - 10y + 25 = 16$$
$$x^2 + y^2 + 6x - 10y + 18 = 0.$$

Notice in Example 1 that we simplified the equation to the form $x^2 + y^2 + Dx + Ey + F = 0$, where $D, E,$ and F are constants. This is another commonly used form when working with circles.

EXAMPLE 2

Graph $x^2 + y^2 - 6x + 4y + 9 = 0$.

Solution

We can change the given equation into the standard form of a circle by completing the square on x and on y as follows.

$$x^2 + y^2 - 6x + 4y + 9 = 0$$

$$(x^2 - 6x \quad\;\;) + (y^2 + 4y \quad\;\;) = -9$$

$$(x^2 - 6x + 9) + (y^2 + 4y + 4) = -9 + 9 + 4$$

Add 9 to   Add 4 to   Add 9 and 4 to
complete   complete   compensate for
the square   the square   the 4 and 9 added
on x on y on left side

$$(x - 3)^2 + (y + 2)^2 = 2^2$$

$$(x - 3)^2 + (y - (-2))^2 = 2^2$$

$$\qquad h \qquad\qquad k \qquad\qquad r$$

The center is at $(3, -2)$ and the length of a radius is 2 units. Thus, the circle can be drawn as in Figure 2.38.

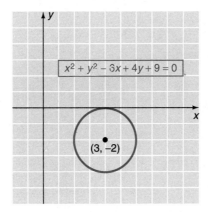

$x^2 + y^2 - 6x + 4y + 9 = 0$

$(3, -2)$

FIGURE   2.38

Now suppose that we substitute 0 for h and 0 for k in the standard form of the equation of a circle.

$$(x - h)^2 + (y - k)^2 = r^2$$

$$(x - 0)^2 + (y - 0)^2 = r^2$$

$$x^2 + y^2 = r^2$$

The form $x^2 + y^2 = r^2$ is called the standard form of the equation of a circle that has its center at the origin. Therefore, by inspection we can recognize that $x^2 + y^2 = 9$ is a circle with its center at the origin with a radius of length 3 units. Likewise, the equation $5x^2 + 5y^2 = 10$ is equivalent to $x^2 + y^2 = 2$ and therefore its graph is a circle with its center at the origin and a radius of length $\sqrt{2}$ units. Furthermore, we can easily determine that the equation of the circle with its center at the origin and a radius of 8 units is $x^2 + y^2 = 64$.

If we expand the standard form $(x - h)^2 + (y - k)^2 = r^2$, we get

$$x^2 + y^2 - 2hx - 2ky + h^2 + k^2 - r^2 = 0.$$

By comparing this to the form

$$x^2 + y^2 + Dx + Ey + F = 0$$

we obtain the relationships

$$D = -2h, \qquad E = -2k, \qquad \text{and} \qquad F = h^2 + k^2 - r^2.$$

These relationships provide us with another convenient way of identifying the center of a circle and the length of a radius; they also determine the equation of a circle by its center and the length of a radius. Consider the following examples.

EXAMPLE 3

Find the center and the length of a radius of the circle

$$x^2 + y^2 - 6x + 12y - 2 = 0.$$

Solution

Using $h = \dfrac{D}{-2}$ and $k = \dfrac{E}{-2}$, we obtain

$$h = \tfrac{-6}{-2} = 3 \qquad \text{and} \qquad k = \tfrac{12}{-2} = -6.$$

So the center is at $(3, -6)$. Now from the relationship $F = h^2 + k^2 - r^2$, we can determine r.

$$r = \sqrt{h^2 + k^2 - F}$$
$$= \sqrt{(3)^2 + (-6)^2 - (-2)} = \sqrt{47}$$

Thus, the length of a radius is $\sqrt{47}$ units. ▬▬▬

EXAMPLE 4

Find the equation of a circle that has its center at $(-5, -9)$ and a radius of length $2\sqrt{3}$ units.

Solution

Using $D = -2h$, $E = -2k$, and $F = h^2 + k^2 - r^2$, we obtain

$$D = -2(-5) = 10, \qquad E = -2(-9) = 18$$

and

$$F = (-5)^2 + (-9)^2 - (2\sqrt{3})^2 = 94.$$

Therefore, substituting into $x^2 + y^2 + Dx + Ey + F = 0$, we obtain

$$x^2 + y^2 + 10x + 18y + 94 = 0.$$ ▬▬▬

From the equations

$$(x - h)^2 + (y - k)^2 = r^2 \qquad \text{and} \qquad x^2 + y^2 + Dx + Ey + F = 0,$$

it should be evident that to determine the equation of a specific circle we need the values of h, k, and r, or D, E, and F. To determine these values from a given set of conditions often requires the use of some of the following concepts from elementary geometry.

1. A tangent to a circle is a line that has one and only one point in common with the circle. This common point is called a point of tangency.

2. A radius drawn to the point of tangency is perpendicular to the tangent line.

3. Three noncollinear points in a plane determine a circle.

4. The perpendicular bisector of a chord contains the center of a circle.

Now let's consider two problems that use some of these concepts. We will show an analysis of these problems but leave the details for you to complete.

PROBLEM 1

Find the equation of the circle that has its center at $(2, 1)$ and is tangent to the line $x - 3y = 9$.

Analysis

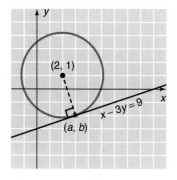

FIGURE 2.39

Let's sketch a figure to help with the analysis of the problem (Figure 2.39). The point of tangency (a, b) is on the line $x - 3y = 9$; so we have $a - 3b = 9$. Also, the line determined by $(2, 1)$ and (a, b) is perpendicular to the line $x - 3y = 9$; so their slopes are negative reciprocals of each other. This relationship produces another equation with the variables a and b. (This equation should be $3a + b = 7$.) Solving the system

$$\begin{pmatrix} a - 3b = 9 \\ 3a + b = 7 \end{pmatrix}$$

will produce the values for (a, b) and this point, along with the center of the circle, determines the length of a radius. Then the center along with the length of a radius determines the equation of the circle. (The equation is $x^2 + y^2 - 4x - 2y - 5 = 0$.)

PROBLEM 2

Find the equation of the circle that passes through the three points $(2, -4)$, $(-6, 4)$, and $(-2, -8)$.

Analysis

Three chords of the circle are determined by the three given points. (The points are noncollinear.) The center of the circle can be found at the intersection of any two of the perpendicular bisectors of the chords. Then the center and one of the given points can be used to find the length of a radius. Using the center and the length of a radius, the equation of the circle can be determined. (The equation is $x^2 + y^2 + 8x + 4y - 20 = 0$.)

OR

Since three noncollinear points in a plane determine a circle, we could substitute the coordinates of the three given points into the general equation $x^2 + y^2 + Dx + Ey + F = 0$. This will produce a system of three linear equations in the three unknowns D, E, and F. (Perhaps you should do this and check your answer from the first analysis.)

> **REMARK**   In this section we used the definition of a circle to develop a standard form for the equation of a circle. Then the standard form was used to solve a variety of problems that pertain to circles. This same basic approach will be used in Chapter 9 to study parabolas, ellipses, and hyperbolas.

When using a graphing utility to graph circles, we need to solve the given equation for y in terms of x and then graph these two equations. Furthermore, it may be necessary to change the boundaries of the viewing rectangle so that a complete graph is shown. Let's consider an example.

EXAMPLE 5

Use a graphing utility to graph $x^2 - 40x + y^2 + 351 = 0$.

Solution

First, we need to solve for y in terms of x.

$$x^2 - 40x + y^2 + 351 = 0$$

$$y^2 = -x^2 + 40x - 351$$

$$y = \pm\sqrt{-x^2 + 40x - 351}$$

Now we can make the following assignments.

$$Y_1 = \sqrt{-x^2 + 40x - 351}$$

$$Y_2 = -Y_1$$

(Note that we assigned Y_2 in terms of Y_1. By doing this we avoid repetitive key strokes and hopefully reduce the chance for errors. You may need to consult your user's manual for instructions on how to key stroke $-Y_1$.) Figure 2.40 shows the graph.

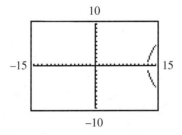

FIGURE 2.40

Since we know from the original equation that this graph is a circle, we need to make some adjustments on the boundaries of the viewing rectangle in order to get a complete graph. This can be done by completing the square on the original equation to change its form to $(x - 20)^2 + y^2 = 49$, or by using the relationships $h = \dfrac{D}{-2}$, $k = \dfrac{E}{-2}$, and $r = \sqrt{h^2 + k^2 - F}$, or simply by a trial-and-error process. By changing the boundaries on x so that $-15 \leq x \leq 30$, we obtain Figure 2.41.

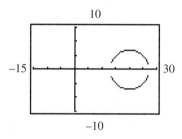

FIGURE 2.41

PROBLEM SET 2.4

For Problems 1–14, write the equation of each of the circles that satisfies the stated conditions. In some cases there may be more than one circle that satisfies the conditions. Express the final equations in the form $x^2 + y^2 + Dx + Ey + F = 0$.

1. Center at $(2, 3)$ and $r = 5$

2. Center at $(-3, 4)$ and $r = 2$

3. Center at $(-1, -5)$ and $r = 3$

4. Center at $(4, -2)$ and $r = 1$

5. Center at $(3, 0)$ and $r = 3$

6. Center at $(0, -4)$ and $r = 6$

7. Center at the origin and $r = 7$

8. Center at the origin and $r = 1$

9. Tangent to the x-axis, a radius of length 4, and abscissa of center is -3

10. Tangent to the y-axis, a radius of length 5, and ordinate of center is 3

11. Tangent to both axes, a radius of 6, and the center in the third quadrant

12. x-intercept of 6, y-intercept of -4, and passes through the origin

13. Tangent to the y-axis, x-intercepts of 2 and 6

14. Tangent to the x-axis, y-intercepts of 1 and 5

For Problems 15–24, find the center and the length of a radius of each of the circles.

15. $x^2 + y^2 - 6x - 10y + 30 = 0$

16. $x^2 + y^2 + 8x - 12y + 43 = 0$

17. $x^2 + y^2 + 10x + 14y + 73 = 0$

18. $x^2 + y^2 + 6y - 7 = 0$

19. $x^2 + y^2 - 10x = 0$

20. $x^2 + y^2 - 4x + 2y = 0$

21. $x^2 + y^2 = 8$

22. $4x^2 + 4y^2 = 1$

23. $4x^2 + 4y^2 - 4x - 8y - 11 = 0$

24. $36x^2 + 36y^2 + 48x - 36y - 11 = 0$

25. Find the equation of the line that is tangent to the circle $x^2 + y^2 - 2x + 3y - 12 = 0$ at the point $(4, 1)$.

26. Find the equation of the line that is tangent to the circle $x^2 + y^2 + 4x - 6y - 4 = 0$ at the point $(-1, -1)$.

27. Find the equation of the circle that passes through the origin and has its center at $(-3, -4)$.

28. Find the equation of the circle for which the line segment determined by $(-4, 9)$ and $(10, -3)$ is a diameter.

29. Find the equations of the circles that have their centers on the line $2x + 3y = 10$ and are tangent to both axes.

30. Find the equation of the circle that has its center at $(-2, -3)$ and is tangent to the line $x + y = -3$.

31. The point $(-1, 4)$ is the midpoint of a chord of a circle whose equation is $x^2 + y^2 + 8x + 4y - 30 = 0$. Find the equation of the chord.

32. Find the equation of the circle that is tangent to the line $3x - 4y = -26$ at the point $(-2, 5)$ and passes through the point $(5, -2)$.

33. Find the equation of the circle that passes through the three points $(1, 2)$, $(-3, -8)$, and $(-9, 6)$.

34. Find the equation of the circle that passes through the three points $(3, 0)$, $(6, -9)$ and $(10, -1)$.

FURTHER INVESTIGATIONS

35. Use a coordinate geometry approach to prove that an angle inscribed in a semicircle is a right angle. (See Figure 2.42.)

36. Use a coordinate geometry approach to prove that a line segment from the center of a circle bisecting a chord is perpendicular to the chord. [*Hint:* Let the ends of the chord be $(r, 0)$ and (a, b).]

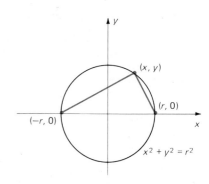

FIGURE   2.42

GRAPHICS CALCULATOR ACTIVITIES

37. For each circle in Problems 15–24, you were asked to find the center of the circle and the length of a radius. Now use your graphics calculator and graph each of those circles. Be sure that your graph is consistent with the information you obtained earlier.

38. For each of the following, graph the two circles on the same set of axes and determine the coordinates of the points of intersection. Express the coordinates to the nearest tenth. If the circles do not intersect, so indicate.

a. $x^2 + 4x + y^2 = 0$ and $x^2 - 2x + y^2 - 3 = 0$

b. $x^2 + y^2 - 12y + 27 = 0$ and $x^2 + y^2 - 6y + 5 = 0$

c. $x^2 - 4x + y^2 - 5 = 0$ and $x^2 - 14x + y^2 + 45.4 = 0$

d. $x^2 - 6x + y^2 - 2y + 1 = 0$ and $x^2 - 6x + y^2 + 4y + 4 = 0$

e. $x^2 - 4x + y^2 - 6y - 3 = 0$ and $x^2 - 8x + y^2 + 2y - 8 = 0$

| **2.5** | **MORE GRAPHING TECHNIQUES** |

It is important to recognize that a certain type of equation produces a particular kind of graph. From our work in the two previous sections, you should be able to identify the equations of straight lines and circles. Throughout this text we will continue to expand your repertoire of *basic curves to be recognized by their equations*. However, we also need to develop some general graphing techniques that can be used for *new* curves, that is, those that we do not recognize from the equation. Let's begin with the following suggestions and then add to the list as we study different curves.

1. Find the intercepts. (To compute the x-intercepts, let $y = 0$ and solve for x. To compute the y-intercepts, let $x = 0$ and solve for y.)

2. Solve the equation for y in terms of x or for x in terms of y if it is not already in such a form.

3. Set up a table of ordered pairs that satisfy the equation.

4. Plot the points associated with the ordered pairs and connect them with a smooth curve.

EXAMPLE 1

Graph $y = \dfrac{4}{x^2 + 1}$.

Solution

First, let's find the intercepts. If $x = 0$, then

$$y = \frac{4}{0 + 1} = 4.$$

This determines the point $(0, 4)$. If $y = 0$, then

$$0 = \frac{4}{x^2 + 1}$$

$$0 = 4.$$

Therefore, y cannot equal zero and the curve has no x-intercept; that is, there are no points of the curve on the x-axis. Second, since the given equation expresses y in terms of x, the form is convenient for setting up a table of ordered pairs. Plotting these points and connecting them with a smooth curve produces Figure 2.43.

x	y
0	4
1	2
2	$\frac{4}{5}$
3	$\frac{2}{5}$
-1	2
-2	$\frac{4}{5}$
-3	$\frac{2}{5}$

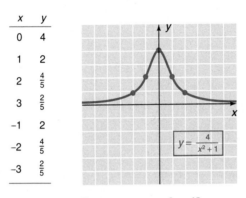

FIGURE 2.43

The curve in Figure 2.43 is said to be **symmetric with respect to the y-axis**. Stated another way, each half of the curve is a mirror image of the other half through the y-axis. Notice in the table of values that for each ordered pair (x, y) the ordered pair $(-x, y)$ is also a solution. Thus, a general test for y-axis symmetry can be stated as follows.

> y-axis symmetry: The graph of an equation is symmetric with respect to the y-axis if replacing x with $-x$ results in an equivalent equation.

For example, the equation $y = x^2 - 4$ exhibits y-axis symmetry because replacing x with $-x$ produces $y = (-x)^2 - 4 = x^2 - 4$. Likewise, the equations $y = x^2 + 6$, $y = x^4$, and $y = x^4 + 2x^2$ exhibit y-axis symmetry.

EXAMPLE 2

Graph $x - 1 = y^2$.

Solution

If $x = 0$, then

$$0 - 1 = y^2$$
$$-1 = y^2.$$

The equation $y^2 = -1$ has no real number solutions. Therefore, this graph has no points on the y-axis. If $y = 0$, then

$$x - 1 = 0$$
$$x = 1.$$

So the point $(1, 0)$ is determined. Solving the original equation for x produces $x = y^2 + 1$, from which the table of values is easily determined. Plotting these points and connecting them with a smooth curve produces Figure 2.44.

x	y	
1	0	intercept
2	1	
2	−1	other
5	2	points
5	−2	

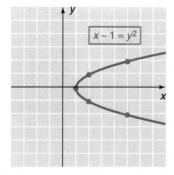

F I G U R E   2 . 44

The curve in Figure 2.44 is said to be **symmetric with respect to the x-axis.** That is to say, each half of the curve is a mirror image of the other half through the x-axis. Notice in the table of values that for each ordered pair (x, y) the ordered pair $(x, -y)$ is also a solution. The following general test for x-axis symmetry can be stated.

> x-axis symmetry: The graph of an equation is symmetric with respect to the x-axis if replacing y with $-y$ results in an equivalent equation.

Thus, the equation $x - 1 = y^2$ exhibits x-axis symmetry because replacing y with $-y$ produces $x - 1 = (-y)^2 = y^2$. Likewise, the equations $x = y^2$, $x = y^4 + 2$, and $x^3 = y^2$ exhibit x-axis symmetry.

EXAMPLE 3

Graph $y = x^3$.

Solution

If $x = 0$, then

$$y = 0^3 = 0.$$

Thus, the origin $(0, 0)$ is on the graph. The table of values is easily determined from the equation. Plotting these points and connecting them with a smooth curve produces Figure 2.45.

x	y	
0	0	intercept
1	1	
2	8	other
−1	−1	points
−2	−8	

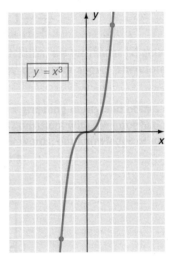

$y = x^3$

FIGURE 2.45

The curve in Figure 2.45 is said to be **symmetric with respect to the origin**. Each half of the curve is a mirror image of the other half through the origin. In the table of values we see that for each ordered pair (x, y) the ordered pair $(-x, -y)$ is also a solution. The following general test for origin symmetry can be stated.

Origin symmetry: The graph of an equation is symmetric with respect to the origin if replacing x with $-x$ and y with $-y$ results in an equivalent equation.

The equation $y = x^3$ exhibits origin symmetry because replacing x with $-x$ and y with $-y$ produces $-y = -x^3$, which is equivalent to $y = x^3$. (Multiplying both sides of $-y = -x^3$ by -1 produces $y = x^3$.) Likewise, the equations $xy = 4$, $x^2 + y^2 = 10$, and $4x^2 - y^2 = 12$ exhibit origin symmetry.

REMARK   From the symmetry tests we should observe that if a curve has both *x*-axis and *y*-axis symmetry, then it must have origin symmetry. However, it is possible for a curve to have origin symmetry and not be symmetrical to either axis. Figure 2.45 is an example of such a curve.

Another graphing consideration is that of **restricting a variable** to insure real number solutions. The following example illustrates this point.

E X A M P L E 4

Graph $y = \sqrt{x}$.

Solution

The radicand must be nonnegative, so $x \geq 0$. If $x = 0$, then $y = 0$ and the origin is a point of the graph. Now, keeping the restriction in mind, the following table of values can be determined. Plotting these points and connecting them with a smooth curve produces Figure 2.46.

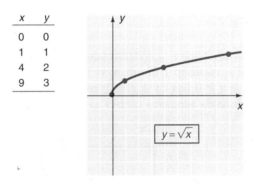

x	y
0	0
1	1
4	2
9	3

$y = \sqrt{x}$

F I G U R E   2 . 46

Now let's restate and add the concepts of symmetry and restrictions to the list of graphing suggestions. The order of the suggestions also indicates the order in which we usually attack a graphing problem if it is a "new" graph, that is, one that we do not recognize from its equation.

1. Determine the type of symmetry that the equation exhibits.
2. Find the intercepts.
3. Solve the equation for *y* in terms of *x* or for *x* in terms of *y* if it is not already in such a form.
4. Determine the necessary restrictions so as to insure real number solutions.
5. Set up a table of ordered pairs that satisfy the equation. The type of symmetry and the restrictions will affect your choice of values in the table.
6. Plot the points associated with the ordered pairs and connect them with a smooth curve. Then, if appropriate, reflect this curve according to the symmetry possessed by the graph.

Now let's consider an example that will help you pull all of these ideas together and will demonstrate the power of having these techniques at your fingertips.

EXAMPLE 5

Graph $x^2 - y^2 = 4$.

Solution

Symmetry: The graph is symmetric with respect to both axes and the origin because replacing x with $-x$ and y with $-y$ produces $(-x)^2 - (-y)^2 = 4$, which is equivalent to $x^2 - y^2 = 4$.

Intercepts: If $x = 0$, then $0^2 - y^2 = 4$
$$-y^2 = 4$$
$$y^2 = -4.$$

Therefore, the graph contains no points on the y-axis.

If $y = 0$, then $x^2 - 0^2 = 4$
$$x^2 = 4$$
$$x = \pm 2.$$

Therefore, the points $(2, 0)$ and $(-2, 0)$ are on the graph.

Restrictions: Solving the given equation for y produces
$$x^2 - y^2 = 4$$
$$-y^2 = 4 - x^2$$
$$y^2 = x^2 - 4$$
$$y = \pm\sqrt{x^2 - 4}.$$

Therefore, $x^2 - 4 \geq 0$, which is equivalent to $x \geq 2$ or $x \leq -2$.

Table of values: Plotting these points and connecting them with a smooth curve produces Figure 2.47(a). Because of symmetry with respect to both axes and the origin, the portion of the curve in Figure 2.47(a) can be reflected across both axes and through the origin to produce the complete curve in Figure 2.47(b).

x	y
2	0
3	$\sqrt{5} \approx 2.2$
4	$2\sqrt{3} \approx 3.5$
5	$\sqrt{21} \approx 4.6$
6	$4\sqrt{2} \approx 5.7$

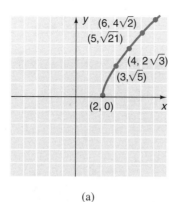

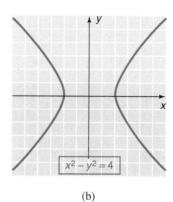

(a)   (b)

F I G U R E   2 . 4 7

The curve in Figure 2.47(b) is called a **hyperbola**. We will discuss hyperbolas in much more detail in Chapter 9, but for now it is sufficient for you to be able to graph them using the techniques of this section.

Even when using a graphing utility, it is often helpful to determine symmetry, intercepts, and restrictions before graphing the equation. This can serve as a partial check against using the utility incorrectly.

E X A M P L E   6

Use a graphing utility to obtain the graph of $y = \sqrt{x^2 - 49}$.

Solution

Symmetry: The graph is symmetric with respect to the y-axis because replacing x with $-x$ produces the same equation.

Intercepts: If $x = 0$, then $y = \sqrt{-49}$; so the graph has no points on the y-axis. If $y = 0$, then $x = \pm7$; so the points $(7, 0)$ and $(-7, 0)$ are on the graph.

Restrictions: Since $x^2 - 49$ has to be nonnegative, we know that $x \le -7$ or $x \ge 7$.

Now let's enter the expression $\sqrt{x^2 - 49}$ for Y_1 and obtain the graph in Figure 2.48. Note that the graph does exhibit the symmetry, intercepts, and restrictions that were determined earlier.

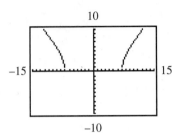

FIGURE 2.48

PROBLEM SET 2.5

For Problems 1–6, determine the points that are symmetric to the given point with respect to the (a) x-axis, (b) y-axis, and (c) origin.

1. $(4, 3)$ **2.** $(-2, 5)$ **3.** $(-6, -1)$

4. $(3, -7)$ **5.** $(0, 4)$ **6.** $(-5, 0)$

For Problems 7–20, determine the type of symmetry (x-axis, y-axis, origin) exhibited by each of the given equations. Do not sketch the graph.

7. $y = x^2 - 6$ **8.** $x = y^2 + 1$

9. $x^3 = y^2$ **10.** $x^2 y^2 = 4$

11. $x^2 + 2y^2 = 6$ **12.** $3x^2 - y^2 + 4x = 6$

13. $x^2 - 2x + y^2 - 3y - 4 = 0$

14. $xy = 4$ **15.** $y = x$

16. $2x - 3y = 15$ **17.** $y = x^3 + 2$

18. $y = x^4 + x^2$ **19.** $5x^2 - y^2 + 2y - 1 = 0$

20. $x^2 + y^2 - 2y - 4 = 0$

For Problems 21–46, use symmetry, intercepts, restrictions, and point plotting to help graph each of the following.

21. $x = y^2$ **22.** $x = -y^2$

23. $x = -y^2 - 1$ **24.** $x = y^2 - 2$

25. $xy = 4$ **26.** $xy = -2$

27. $y = -x^3$ **28.** $y = x^3 + 2$

29. $y^2 = x^3$ **30.** $y^3 = x^2$

31. $y^2 - x^2 = 4$ **32.** $x^2 - 2y^2 = 8$

33. $x = (y - 1)^2$ **34.** $x = -(y + 1)^2$

35. $y = -\sqrt{x}$ **36.** $y = \sqrt{x + 1}$

37. $y = 2\sqrt{x} + 1$ **38.** $y = -\sqrt{x} - 2$

39. $x^2 y = 4$ **40.** $xy^2 = 4$

41. $x^2 y^2 = 2$ **42.** $x^2 y = -1$

43. $x^2 + 2y^2 = 8$ **44.** $2x^2 + y^2 = 4$

45. $y = \dfrac{4}{x^2 + 1}$ **46.** $y = \dfrac{-2}{x^2 + 1}$

THOUGHTS into WORDS

47. What role does the concept of symmetry play when graphing equations?

48. Explain how you would go about graphing $x^2 y^2 = 16$ without using a graphing utility.

GRAPHICS CALCULATOR ACTIVITIES

49. Graph $y = \dfrac{4}{x^2}$, $y = \dfrac{4}{(x-2)^2}$, $y = \dfrac{4}{(x-4)^2}$, and $y = \dfrac{4}{(x+2)^2}$ on the same set of axes. Now predict the graph for $y = \dfrac{4}{(x-6)^2}$. Check your prediction by graphing $y = \dfrac{4}{(x-6)^2}$.

50. Graph $y = \sqrt{x}$, $y = \sqrt{x+1}$, $y = \sqrt{x-2}$, and $y = \sqrt{x-4}$ on the same set of axes. Now predict the graph for $y = \sqrt{x+3}$. Check your predictions by graphing $y = \sqrt{x+3}$.

51. Graph $y = \sqrt{x}$, $y = 2\sqrt{x}$, $y = 4\sqrt{x}$, and $y = 7\sqrt{x}$ on the same set of axes. How does the constant in front of the radical seem to affect the graph?

52. Graph $y = \dfrac{8}{x^2}$ and $y = -\dfrac{8}{x^2}$ on the same set of axes. How does the negative sign seem to affect the graph?

53. Graph $y = \sqrt{x}$ and $y = -\sqrt{x}$ on the same set of axes. How does the negative sign seem to affect the graph?

54. Graph $y = \sqrt{x}$, $y = \sqrt{x}+2$, $y = \sqrt{x}+4$, and $y = \sqrt{x}-3$ on the same set of axes. How does the constant term seem to affect the graphs?

55. Graph $y = \sqrt{x}$, $y = \sqrt{x+3}$, $y = \sqrt{x-1}$, and $y = \sqrt{x-5}$ on the same set of axes. How are the graphs related? Predict the location of $y = \sqrt{x+5}$. Check your prediction.

56. To graph $x = y^2$ we need to first solve for y in terms of x. This produces $y = \pm\sqrt{x}$. Now we can let $Y_1 = \sqrt{x}$ and $Y_2 = -\sqrt{x}$ and graph the two equations on the same set of axes. Then graph $x = y^2 + 4$ on this same set of axes. How are the graphs related? Predict the location of the graph of $x = y^2 - 4$. Check your prediction.

57. To graph $x = y^2 + 2y$, we need to first solve for y in terms of x. Let's complete the square to do this.

$$y^2 + 2y = x$$
$$y^2 + 2y + 1 = x + 1$$
$$(y+1)^2 = (\sqrt{x+1})^2$$
$$y + 1 = \sqrt{x+1} \quad \text{or} \quad y + 1 = -\sqrt{x+1}$$
$$y = -1 + \sqrt{x+1} \quad \text{or} \quad y = -1 - \sqrt{x+1}$$

So let's make the assignments $Y_1 = -1 + \sqrt{x+1}$ and $Y_2 = -1 - \sqrt{x+1}$ and graph them on the same set of axes to produce the graph of $x = y^2 + 2y$. Then graph $x = y^2 + 2y - 4$ on this same set of axes. Now predict the location of the graph of $x = y^2 + 2y + 4$. Check your prediction.

CHAPTER 2 SUMMARY

The following tools of analytic geometry were presented in the first section of this chapter.

Distance formula: $\qquad d = \sqrt{(x_2 - x_1)^2 + (y_2 - y_1)^2}$

Points of division of a line segment: $\qquad x = x_1 + \dfrac{a}{b}(x_2 - x_1)$

$$y = y_1 + \dfrac{a}{b}(y_2 - y_1)$$

Midpoint of a line segment: $\qquad \left(\dfrac{x_1 + x_2}{2}, \dfrac{y_1 + y_2}{2} \right)$

Slope formula: $$m = \frac{y_2 - y_1}{x_2 - x_1}$$

Sections 2.2, 2.4, and 2.5 were centered around the two basic kinds of problems in analytic geometry:

1. Given an algebraic equation, determine its geometric graph;

2. Given a set of conditions pertaining to a geometric figure, determine its algebraic equation.

Graphing

The following graphing techniques were discussed in this chapter.

1. Recognize the type of graph that a certain kind of equation produces.
   a. $Ax + By = C$ produces a straight line.
   b. $x^2 + y^2 + Dx + Ey + F = 0$ produces a circle. The center and the length of a radius can be found by completing the square and comparing it to the standard form of the equation of a circle $(x - h)^2 + (y - k)^2 = r^2$, or by using the relationships $D = -2h$, $E = -2k$, and $F = h^2 + k^2 - r^2$.

2. Determine the symmetry that a graph possesses.
   a. The graph of an equation is symmetric with respect to the y-axis if replacing x with $-x$ results in an equivalent equation.
   b. The graph of an equation is symmetric with respect to the x-axis if replacing y with $-y$ results in an equivalent equation.
   c. The graph of an equation is symmetric with respect to the origin if replacing x with $-x$ and y with $-y$ results in an equivalent equation.

3. Find the intercepts. The x-intercept is found by letting $y = 0$ and solving for x. The y-intercept is found by letting $x = 0$ and solving for y.

4. Determine the necessary restrictions to insure real number solutions.

5. Set up a table of ordered pairs that satisfy the equation. The type of symmetry and the restrictions will affect your choice of values in the table. Furthermore, it may be convenient to change the form of the original equation by solving for y in terms of x or for x in terms of y.

6. Plot the points associated with the ordered pairs in the table and connect them with a smooth curve. Then, if appropriate, reflect the curve according to the symmetry possessed by the graph.

Determining Equations When Given Certain Conditions

You should review Example 5 of Section 2.2 to feel comfortable with the general approach of choosing a point (x, y) and using it to determine the equation that satisfies a given set of conditions.

We also developed some special forms that can be used to determine equations.

Point-slope form of a straight line: $y - y_1 = m(x - x_1)$

Slope-intercept form of a straight line: $y = mx + b$

Standard form of a circle: $(x - h)^2 + (y - k)^2 = r^2$

Remember that parallel lines have equal slopes, and perpendicular lines have slopes that are negative reciprocals of each other.

In Section 2.3, we reviewed two basic methods of solving systems of linear equations.

Substitution Method

With the aid of an example, the substitution method can be described as follows. Solve the system

$$\begin{pmatrix} x - 2y = & 22 \\ 3x + 4y = & -24 \end{pmatrix}.$$

STEP 1   Solve the first equation for x in terms of y.

$$x - 2y = 22$$

$$x = 2y + 22$$

STEP 2   Substitute $2y + 22$ for x in the second equation.

$$3(2y + 22) + 4y = -24$$

STEP 3   Solve the equation obtained in Step 2.

$$6y + 66 + 4y = -24$$

$$10y + 66 = -24$$

$$10y = -90$$

$$y = -9$$

STEP 4   Substitute -9 for y in the equation of Step 1.

$$x = 2(-9) + 22 = 4$$

The solution set is $\{(4, -9)\}$.

Elimination-by-Addition Method

This method involves the replacement of systems of equations with simpler equivalent systems until a system is obtained where the solution is easily determined. The following operations produce equivalent systems.

1. Any two equations of a system can be interchanged.

2. Both sides of any equation of the system can be multiplied by any nonzero real number.

3. Any equation of the system can be replaced by adding a nonzero multiple of another equation to that equation.

For example, through a sequence of operations, you can transform the system

$$\begin{pmatrix} 5x + 3y = -28 \\ \frac{1}{2}x - y = -8 \end{pmatrix}$$

to the equivalent system

$$\begin{pmatrix} x - 2y = -16 \\ 13y = 52 \end{pmatrix}$$

where you can easily determine the solution set $\{(-8, 4)\}$.

CHAPTER 2   REVIEW   PROBLEM   SET

1. On a number line, find the coordinate of the point located three-fifths of the distance from -4 to 11.

2. On a number line, find the coordinate of the point located four-ninths of the distance from 3 to -15.

3. On the xy-plane, find the coordinates of the point located five-sixths of the distance from $(-1, -3)$ to $(11, 1)$.

4. If one endpoint of a line segment is at $(8, 14)$ and the midpoint of the segment is $(3, 10)$, find the coordinates of the other endpoint.

5. Verify that the points $(2, 2)$, $(6, 4)$, and $(5, 6)$ are vertices of a right triangle.

6. Verify that the points $(-3, 1)$, $(1, 3)$, and $(9, 7)$ lie in a straight line.

7. Find the length of the line segment determined by the points $(-2, -4)$ and $(4, 6)$. Also find the coordinates of the midpoint of the line segment.

8. Find the slope of the line determined by the points $(-6, 3)$ and $(4, -6)$.

9. Find the slope of the line determined by the equation $-2x + 7y = 14$.

For Problems 10–15, write the equation of the line that satisfies the stated conditions. Express final equations in the form $Ax + By = C$.

10. Contains the point $(7, 2)$ and has a slope of $-\frac{3}{4}$.

11. Contains the points $(-3, -2)$ and $(1, 6)$.

12. $b = -6$ and $m = -\frac{5}{6}$

13. y-intercept of 7 and x-intercept of -5

14. Contains the point $(2, -4)$ and is parallel to the line $4x + 3y = 17$

15. Contains the point $(-5, 4)$ and is perpendicular to the line $2x - y = 7$

For Problems 16–20, write the equation of each of the circles satisfying the stated conditions. Express final equations in the form $x^2 + y^2 + Dx + Ey + F = 0$.

16. Center at $(5, -6)$ and $r = 1$

17. The endpoints of a diameter are $(-2, 4)$ and $(6, 2)$.

18. Center at $(-5, 12)$ and passes through the origin

19. Tangent to both axes, $r = 4$, and center in the third quadrant

20. Passes through the points $(1, 7)$, $(8, 6)$, and $(7, -1)$

For Problems 21–26, identify the symmetry (x-axis, y-axis, origin) that each equation exhibits. Do not graph the equations.

21. $x = y^2 + 4$

22. $y = x^2 + 6x - 1$

23. $5x^2 - y^2 = 4$

24. $x^2 + y^2 - 2y - 4 = 0$

25. $y = -x$

26. $y = \dfrac{6}{x^2 + 4}$

For Problems 27–40, graph each of the equations.

27. $x^2 + y^2 - 6x + 4y - 3 = 0$

28. $x^2 + 4y^2 = 16$

29. $x^2 - 4y^2 = 16$

30. $-2x + 3y = 6$

31. $-3x - 4y = 12$

32. $x^2 y^2 = 4$

33. $-xy^2 = 4$

34. $4y^2 - 3x^2 = 8$

35. $y = -\sqrt{x - 1} + 2$

36. $y = \dfrac{8}{x^2 + 4}$

37. $x^2 y + 4y = -8$

38. $x^2 + y^2 + 10y = 0$

39. $y = 2x^3$

40. $y = -x^3 + 1$

For Problems 41 and 42, solve each system using the *substitution method*.

41. $\begin{pmatrix} 3x - y = 16 \\ 5x + 7y = -34 \end{pmatrix}$

42. $\begin{pmatrix} 6x + 5y = -21 \\ x - 4y = 11 \end{pmatrix}$

For Problems 43–46, solve each system using the *elimination-by-addition method*.

43. $\begin{pmatrix} 4x - 3y = 34 \\ 3x + 2y = 0 \end{pmatrix}$

44. $\begin{pmatrix} \frac{1}{2}x - \frac{2}{3}y = 1 \\ \frac{3}{4}x + \frac{1}{6}y = -1 \end{pmatrix}$

45. $\begin{pmatrix} 2x - y + 3z = -19 \\ 3x + 2y - 4z = 21 \\ 5x - 4y - z = -8 \end{pmatrix}$

46. $\begin{pmatrix} 3x + 2y - 4z = 4 \\ 5x + 3y - z = 2 \\ 4x - 2y + 3z = 11 \end{pmatrix}$

For Problems 47–50, solve each problem by setting up and solving a system of linear equations.

47. The sum of the digits of a two-digit number is 9. If the digits are reversed, the newly-formed number is 45 less than the original number. Find the original number.

48. Sara invested $2500, part of it at 10% and the rest at 12% yearly interest. The income on the 12% investment was $102 more than the income on the 10% investment. How much money did she invest at each rate?

49. A box contains $17.70 in nickels, dimes, and quarters. The number of dimes is eight less than twice the number of nickels. The number of quarters is two more than the sum of the number of nickels and dimes. How many coins of each kind are there in the box?

50. The measure of the largest angle of a triangle is 10° more than four times the smallest angle. The sum of the smallest and largest angle is three times the measure of the other angle. Find the measure of each angle of the triangle.

FUNCTIONS

One of the fundamental concepts of mathematics is that of a function. We use functions to unify different areas of mathematics and to apply mathematics to many real world problems. Functions also provide a means of studying quantities that vary with one another—that is, when a change in one quantity produces a corresponding change in another.

In this chapter we will (1) introduce the basic ideas of the function concept, (2) use the idea of a function to unify some concepts from Chapter 2, and (3) discuss some applications that use functions.

The function $f(x) = (500 - 25x)(30 + 3x)$ can be used to determine at what price sets of golf clubs should be sold to maximize the gross income.

3

3.1   CONCEPT OF A FUNCTION

The notion of correspondence is central to the concept of a function. Consider the following correspondences.

1. To each person in a class, there corresponds an assigned seat.

2. To each day of a year, there corresponds an assigned integer that represents the average temperature for that day in a certain geographical location.

3. To each book in a library, there corresponds a whole number that represents the number of pages in the book.

Such correspondences are represented visually in Figure 3.1. To each member in set *A* there corresponds *one and only one* member in set *B*. For example, from our first correspondence, set *A* would consist of the students in a class and set *B* would be the assigned seats. In the second example, set *A* would consist of the days of a year and set *B* would be a set of integers. Furthermore, the same integer might be assigned to different days of the year. (Different days might have the same average temperature.) The key idea is that *one and only one* integer is assigned to *each* day of the year. Likewise in the third example, more than one book may have the same number of pages, but to each book there is assigned one and only one number of pages.

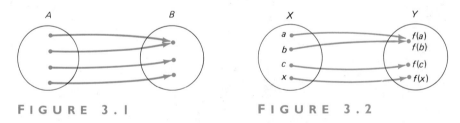

FIGURE   3.1   FIGURE   3.2

Mathematically, the general concept of a function can be defined as follows.

DEFINITION 3.1

A **function** *f* is a correspondence between two sets *X* and *Y* that assigns to each element *x* of set *X* one and only one element *y* of set *Y*. The element *y* being assigned is called the **image** of *x*; the set *X* is called the **domain** of the function; and the set of all images is called the **range** of the function.

In Definition 3.1, the image *y* is usually denoted by $f(x)$. Thus the symbol $f(x)$ (read, *f of x* or, *the value of f at x*) represents the element in the range associated with the element *x* from the domain. Figure 3.2 visually represents this matching. Again, we emphasize that each member of the domain has precisely one image in the range;

however, different members in the domain, such as a and b in Figure 3.2, may have the same image.

In Definition 3.1 we named the function f. It is common to name functions by means of a single letter and the letters f, g, and h are often used. We would suggest more meaningful choices when functions are used to portray real world situations. For example, if a problem involves a profit function, then naming the function p, or even P, would seem natural. Be careful not to confuse f and $f(x)$. Remember that f is used to name a function, whereas $f(x)$ is an element of the range, namely, the element assigned to x by f.

The assignments made by a function are often expressed as ordered pairs. For example, refer back to Figure 3.2: The assignments could be expressed as $(a, f(a))$, $(b, f(b))$, $(c, f(c))$, and $(x, f(x))$, where the first components are from the domain and the second components are from the range. Thus, a function can also be thought of as **a set of ordered pairs for which no two of the ordered pairs have the same first component.**

> **REMARK**   Some texts introduce the concept of a **relation** first and then define functions as special kinds of relations. Thus, a relation is defined as *a set of ordered pairs* and a function is defined as *a relation in which no two ordered pairs have the same first element.*

The ordered pairs that represent a function can be generated by various means, such as a graph or a chart. However, one of the most common ways of generating ordered pairs is by the use of equations. For example, the equation $f(x) = 2x + 3$ indicates that to each value of x in the domain, we assign $2x + 3$ from the range. Therefore,

$f(1) = 2(1) + 3 = 5$ produces the ordered pair $(1, 5)$

$f(4) = 2(4) + 3 = 11$ produces the ordered pair $(4, 11)$

$f(-2) = 2(-2) + 3 = -1$ produces the ordered pair $(-2, -1)$, and so on.

It may be helpful for you to mentally picture the concept of a function as a "function machine" as illustrated in Figure 3.3. Each time that a value of x is put into the machine, the equation $f(x) = 2x + 3$ is used to generate one and only one value for $f(x)$ to be ejected from the machine.

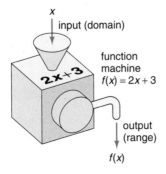

FIGURE 3.3

Using the ordered pair interpretation of a function, we can define the **graph of a function** f **to be the set of all points in a plane of the form** $(x, f(x))$**, where** x **is from the domain of** f. In other words, the graph of f is the same as the graph of the equation $y = f(x)$. Furthermore, since $f(x)$ or y takes on only one value for each value of x, we can easily tell whether or not a given graph represents a function. For example, in Figure 3.4(a) for any choice of x, there is only one value for y. Geometrically, this means that no vertical line intersects the curve in more than one point. On the other hand, Figure 3.4(b) does not represent the graph of a function because certain values of x (all positive values) would produce more than one value for y. In other words, some vertical lines would intersect the curve in more than one point as illustrated in 3.4(b). A **vertical line test** for functions can be stated as follows.

Vertical line test: If each vertical line intersects a graph in no more than one point, then the graph represents a function.

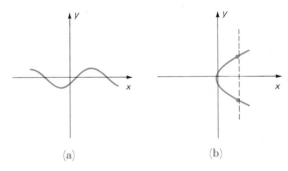

(a)   (b)

FIGURE   3.4

Let's consider some examples to help pull together some of the ideas about functions.

EXAMPLE 1

If $f(x) = x^2 - x + 4$ and $g(x) = x^3 - x^2$, find $f(3)$, $f(-2)$, $g(4)$, and $g(-3)$.

Solution

$$f(3) = 3^2 - 3 + 4 = 10 \qquad f(-2) = (-2)^2 - (-2) + 4 = 10$$
$$g(4) = 4^3 - 4^2 = 48 \qquad g(-3) = (-3)^3 - (-3)^2 = -36$$

In Example 1, notice that we were working with two different functions in the same problem, which is why we used two different names, f and g.

Piecewise-defined Functions

Sometimes the rule of assignment for a function may consist of more than one part. We often refer to such functions as **piecewise-defined** functions. Let's consider an example of such a function.

EXAMPLE 2

If $f(x) = \begin{cases} 2x + 1 & \text{for } x \geq 0 \\ 3x - 1 & \text{for } x < 0 \end{cases}$, find $f(2), f(4), f(-1)$, and $f(-3)$.

Solution

For $x \geq 0$, we use the assignment $f(x) = 2x + 1$.

$$f(2) = 2(2) + 1 = 5$$

$$f(4) = 2(4) + 1 = 9$$

For $x < 0$, we use the assignment $f(x) = 3x - 1$.

$$f(-1) = 3(-1) - 1 = -4$$

$$f(-3) = 3(-3) - 1 = -10$$

Difference Quotient

The quotient

$$\frac{f(a + h) - f(a)}{h}$$

is often called a **difference quotient** and it is used extensively with functions when studying the limit concept in calculus. Examples 3 and 4 illustrate finding the difference quotient for two specific functions.

EXAMPLE 3

If $f(x) = x^2 + 6$, find $f(a), f(a + h)$, and $\dfrac{f(a + h) - f(a)}{h}$.

Solution

$$f(a) = a^2 + 6$$

$$f(a + h) = (a + h)^2 + 6 = a^2 + 2ah + h^2 + 6$$

$$\frac{f(a + h) - f(a)}{h} = \frac{(a^2 + 2ah + h^2 + 6) - (a^2 + 6)}{h}$$

$$= \frac{a^2 + 2ah + h^2 + 6 - a^2 - 6}{h}$$

$$= \frac{2ah + h^2}{h}$$

$$= \frac{h(2a + h)}{h} = 2a + h$$

EXAMPLE 4   For each of the following, find $\dfrac{f(a + h) - f(a)}{h}$:

a. $f(x) = 2x^2 + 3x - 4$ **b.** $f(x) = \dfrac{1}{x}$

Solutions

a. $f(a) = 2a^2 + 3a - 4$

$$f(a + h) = 2(a + h)^2 + 3(a + h) - 4$$
$$= 2(a^2 + 2ha + h^2) + 3a + 3h - 4$$
$$= 2a^2 + 4ha + 2h^2 + 3a + 3h - 4$$

Therefore,

$$f(a + h) - f(a) = (2a^2 + 4ha + 2h^2 + 3a + 3h - 4) - (2a^2 + 3a - 4)$$
$$= 2a^2 + 4ha + 2h^2 + 3a + 3h - 4 - 2a^2 - 3a + 4$$
$$= 4ha + 2h^2 + 3h$$

and

$$\frac{f(a + h) - f(a)}{h} = \frac{4ha + 2h^2 + 3h}{h}$$
$$= \frac{\cancel{h}(4a + 2h + 3)}{\cancel{h}}$$
$$= 4a + 2h + 3.$$

b. $f(a) = \dfrac{1}{a}$

$$f(a + h) = \frac{1}{a + h}$$

Therefore,

$$f(a + h) - f(a) = \frac{1}{a + h} - \frac{1}{a}$$
$$= \frac{a - (a + h)}{a(a + h)}$$
$$= \frac{a - a - h}{a(a + h)}$$
$$= \frac{-h}{a(a + h)} \quad \text{or} \quad -\frac{h}{a(a + h)}$$

and

$$\frac{f(a + h) - f(a)}{h} = -\frac{\dfrac{h}{a(a + h)}}{h}$$

$$= -\frac{h}{a(a + h)} \cdot \frac{1}{h}$$

$$= -\frac{1}{a(a + h)}.$$

Domain and Range

Sometimes the domain of a function is specifically indicated or determined by a real world application. If this is not the case, then we will assume the domain to be those real numbers that will produce real-number functional values.

EXAMPLE 5

Find the domain and range of the function $f(x) = \sqrt{x - 1}$.

Solution

The radicand must be nonnegative; therefore,

$$x - 1 \geq 0$$

$$x \geq 1$$

and the domain (D) is

$$D = \{x \mid x \geq 1\}.$$

The symbol, $\sqrt{}$, indicates the nonnegative square root; thus the range (R) is

$$R = \{f(x) \mid f(x) \geq 0\}.$$

As we will see later, the range of a function is often easier to determine after having graphed the function. However, our equation and inequality solving processes are frequently sufficient to determine the domain of a function. Let's consider some examples.

EXAMPLE 6

Determine the domain for each of the following functions.

a. $f(x) = \dfrac{3}{2x - 5}$

b. $g(x) = \dfrac{1}{x^2 - 9}$

c. $f(x) = \sqrt{x^2 + 4x - 12}$

Solutions

a. We can replace x with any real number except $\frac{5}{2}$, because $\frac{5}{2}$ makes the denominator zero. Thus, the domain is

$$D = \left\{x \mid x \neq \frac{5}{2}\right\}.$$

b. We need to eliminate any values of x that will make the denominator zero. Therefore, let's solve the equation $x^2 - 9 = 0$.

$$x^2 - 9 = 0$$

$$x^2 = 9$$

$$x = \pm 3$$

The domain is the set

$$D = \{x \mid x \neq 3 \text{ and } x \neq -3\}.$$

c. The radicand, $x^2 + 4x - 12$, must be nonnegative. Therefore, let's use a number line approach, as we did in Chapter 1, to solve the inequality $x^2 + 4x - 12 \geq 0$ (Figure 3.5).

$$x^2 + 4x - 12 \geq 0$$

$$(x + 6)(x - 2) \geq 0$$

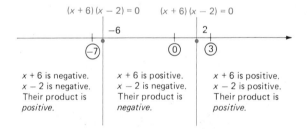

F I G U R E   3 . 5

The product $(x + 6)(x - 2)$ is nonnegative if $x \leq -6$ or $x \geq 2$. Using interval notation, the domain can be expressed as $(-\infty, -6] \cup [2, \infty)$.

Functions and function notation provide the basis for describing many real world relationships. The next example illustrates this point.

E X A M P L E   7

Suppose a factory determines that the overhead for producing a quantity of a certain item is $500 and the cost for each item is $25. Express the total expenses as a function of the number of items produced and compute the expenses for producing 12, 25, 50, 75, and 100 items.

Solution

Let n represent the number of items produced. Then $25n + 500$ represents the total expenses. Using E to represent the expense function, we have

$$E(n) = 25n + 500, \quad \text{where } n \text{ is a whole number.}$$

Therefore, we obtain

$$E(12) = 25(12) + 500 = 800,$$

$$E(25) = 25(25) + 500 = 1125,$$

$$E(50) = 25(50) + 500 = 1750,$$

$$E(75) = 25(75) + 500 = 2375, \quad \text{and}$$

$$E(100) = 25(100) + 500 = 3000.$$

So the total expenses for producing 12, 25, 50, 75, and 100 items are $800, $1125, $1750, $2375, and $3000, respectively. ▬▬▬▬

As stated before, an equation such as $f(x) = 5x - 7$, which is used to determine a function, can also be written as $y = 5x - 7$. In either form, x is referred to as the **independent variable** and y (or $f(x)$) as the **dependent variable**. Many formulas in mathematics and other related areas also determine functions. For example, the area formula for a circular region, $A = \pi r^2$, assigns to each positive real value for r a unique value for A. This formula determines a function f, where $f(r) = \pi r^2$. The variable r is the independent variable and A (or $f(r)$) is the dependent variable.

Even and Odd Functions

Many functions that we will study throughout this text can be classified as even or odd functions. A function f with the property that $f(-x) = f(x)$ for every x in the domain of f is called an **even function**. A function f with the property that $f(-x) = -f(x)$ for every x in the domain of f is called an **odd function**.

EXAMPLE 8

For each of the following, classify the function as even, odd, or neither even nor odd.

a. $f(x) = 2x^3 - 4x$ **b.** $f(x) = x^4 - 7x^2$ **c.** $f(x) = x^2 + 2x - 3$

Solutions

a. The function $f(x) = 2x^3 - 4x$ is an odd function because $f(-x) = 2(-x)^3 - 4(-x) = -2x^3 + 4x$, which equals $-f(x)$.

b. The function $f(x) = x^4 - 7x^2$ is an even function because $f(-x) = (-x)^4 - 7(-x)^2 = x^4 - 7x^2$, which equals $f(x)$.

c. The function $f(x) = x^2 + 2x - 3$ is neither even nor odd because $f(-x) = (-x)^2 + 2(-x) - 3 = x^2 - 2x - 3$, which does not equal $f(x)$ nor $-f(x)$.

▬▬▬▬

PROBLEM SET 3.1

1. If $f(x) = -2x + 5$, find $f(3)$, $f(5)$, and $f(-2)$.

2. If $f(x) = x^2 - 3x - 4$, find $f(2)$, $f(4)$, and $f(-3)$.

3. If $g(x) = -2x^2 + x - 5$, find $g(3)$, $g(-1)$, and $g(-4)$.

4. If $g(x) = -x^2 - 4x + 6$, find $g(0)$, $g(5)$, and $g(-5)$.

5. If $h(x) = \frac{2}{3}x - \frac{3}{4}$, find $h(3)$, $h(4)$, and $h\left(-\frac{1}{2}\right)$.

6. If $h(x) = -\frac{1}{2}x + \frac{2}{3}$, find $h(-2)$, $h(6)$, and $h\left(-\frac{2}{3}\right)$.

7. If $f(x) = \sqrt{2x - 1}$, find $f(5)$, $f\left(\frac{1}{2}\right)$, and $f(23)$.

8. If $f(x) = \sqrt{3x + 2}$, find $f\left(\frac{14}{3}\right)$, $f(10)$, and $f\left(-\frac{1}{3}\right)$.

9. If $f(x) = \begin{cases} 3x + 2 & \text{for } x \geq 0 \\ 5x - 1 & \text{for } x < 0 \end{cases}$, find $f(2)$, $f(6)$, $f(-1)$, and $f(-4)$.

10. If $f(x) = \begin{cases} 2x & \text{for } x \geq 0 \\ -2x & \text{for } x < 0 \end{cases}$, find $f(3)$, $f(5)$, $f(-3)$, and $f(-5)$.

11. If $f(x) = \begin{cases} 2 & \text{for } x < 0 \\ x^2 + 1 & \text{for } 0 \leq x \leq 4, \\ -1 & \text{for } x > 4 \end{cases}$, find $f(3)$, $f(6)$, $f(0)$, and $f(-3)$.

12. If $f(x) = \begin{cases} 1 & \text{for } x > 0 \\ 0 & \text{for } -1 < x \leq 0, \\ -1 & \text{for } x \leq -1 \end{cases}$, find $f(2)$, $f(0)$, $f\left(-\frac{1}{2}\right)$, and $f(-4)$.

For Problems 13–28, find $[f(a + h) - f(a)]/h$ for each of the given functions.

13. $f(x) = -6x + 1$

14. $f(x) = 12x - 9$

15. $f(x) = 2x^2 + 4$

16. $f(x) = 3x^2 - 7$

17. $f(x) = 3x^2 - x + 4$

18. $f(x) = 4x^2 + 2x - 7$

19. $f(x) = -x^2 - 4x + 6$

20. $f(x) = -2x^2 + 3x + 10$

21. $f(x) = x^3$

22. $f(x) = 2x^3 + 4$

23. $f(x) = x^3 - x^2 + 2x - 1$

24. $f(x) = -x^3 + 2x^2$

25. $f(x) = \dfrac{1}{x + 1}$

26. $f(x) = \dfrac{2}{x - 1}$

27. $f(x) = \dfrac{x}{x + 1}$

28. $f(x) = \dfrac{1}{x^2}$

For Problems 29–36, determine whether or not the indicated graph represents a function of x (Figures 3.6–3.13).

29.

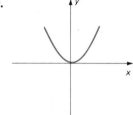

FIGURE 3.6

30.

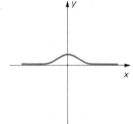

FIGURE 3.7

31.

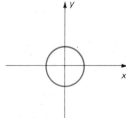

FIGURE 3.8

32.

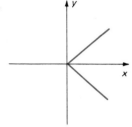

FIGURE 3.9

33.

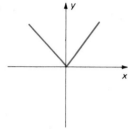

FIGURE 3.10

34.

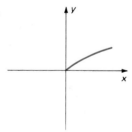

FIGURE 3.11

35.

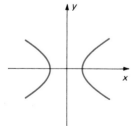

FIGURE 3.12

36.

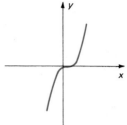

FIGURE 3.13

For Problems 37–44, determine the domain and the range of the given function.

37. $f(x) = \sqrt{x}$ **38.** $f(x) = \sqrt{3x - 4}$

39. $f(x) = x^2 + 1$ **40.** $f(x) = x^2 - 2$

41. $f(x) = x^3$ **42.** $f(x) = |x|$

43. $f(x) = x^4$ **44.** $f(x) = -\sqrt{x}$

For Problems 45–54, determine the domain of the given function.

45. $f(x) = \dfrac{3}{x - 4}$ **46.** $f(x) = \dfrac{-4}{x + 2}$

47. $f(x) = \dfrac{2x}{(x - 2)(x + 3)}$

48. $f(x) = \dfrac{5}{(2x - 1)(x + 4)}$

49. $f(x) = \sqrt{5x + 1}$ **50.** $f(x) = \dfrac{1}{x^2 - 4}$

51. $g(x) = \dfrac{3}{x^2 + 5x + 6}$ **52.** $f(x) = \dfrac{4x}{x^2 - x - 12}$

53. $g(x) = \dfrac{5}{x^2 + 4x}$ **54.** $g(x) = \dfrac{x}{6x^2 + 13x - 5}$

For Problems 55–62, express the domain of the given function using interval notation.

55. $f(x) = \sqrt{x^2 - 1}$ **56.** $f(x) = \sqrt{x^2 - 16}$

57. $f(x) = \sqrt{x^2 + 4}$ **58.** $f(x) = \sqrt{x^2 + 1} - 4$

59. $f(x) = \sqrt{x^2 - 2x - 24}$

60. $f(x) = \sqrt{x^2 - 3x - 40}$

61. $f(x) = \sqrt{12x^2 + x - 6}$

62. $f(x) = -\sqrt{8x^2 + 6x - 35}$

For Problems 63–72, determine whether f is even, odd, or neither even nor odd.

63. $f(x) = x^2$

64. $f(x) = x^3$

65. $f(x) = x^2 + 1$

66. $f(x) = 3x - 1$

67. $f(x) = x^2 + x$

68. $f(x) = x^3 + 1$

69. $f(x) = x^5$

70. $f(x) = x^4 + x^2 + 1$

71. $f(x) = -x^3$

72. $f(x) = x^5 + x^3 + x$

73. Suppose that the profit for selling n items is given by $P(n) = -n^2 + 500n - 61500$. Evaluate $P(200)$, $P(230)$, $P(250)$, and $P(260)$.

74. The equation $A(r) = \pi r^2$ expresses the area of a circular region as a function of the length of a radius (r). Use 3.14 as an approximation for π and compute $A(2)$, $A(3)$, $A(12)$, and $A(17)$.

75. In a physics experiment, it is found that the equation $V(t) = 1667t - 6940t^2$ expresses the velocity of an object as a function of time (t). Compute $V(.1)$, $V(.15)$, and $V(.2)$.

76. The height of a projectile fired vertically into the air (neglecting air resistance) at an initial velocity of 64 feet per second is a function of the time (t) and is given by the equation $h(t) = 64t - 16t^2$. Compute $h(1)$, $h(2)$, $h(3)$, and $h(4)$.

77. A car rental agency charges $50 per day plus $.32 a mile. Therefore, the daily charge for renting a car is a function of the number of miles traveled (m) and can be expressed as $C(m) = 50 + .32\, m$. Compute $C(75)$, $C(150)$, $C(225)$, and $C(650)$.

78. The equation $I(r) = 500r$ expresses the amount of simple interest earned by an investment of $500 for one year as a function of the rate of interest (r). Compute $I(.11)$, $I(.12)$, $I(.135)$, and $I(.15)$.

79. Suppose that the height of a semi-elliptical archway is given by the function $h(x) = \sqrt{64 - 4x^2}$, where x is the distance from the center line of the arch. Compute $h(0)$, $h(2)$, and $h(4)$.

80. The equation $A(r) = 2\pi r^2 + 16\pi r$ expresses the total surface area of a right circular cylinder of height 8 centimeters as a function of the length of a radius (r). Use 3.14 as an approximation for π and compute $A(2)$, $A(4)$, and $A(8)$.

THOUGHTS into WORDS

81. How would you explain the concept of a function to an elementary algebra student?

82. Explain the concept of a piecewise-defined function.

83. Suppose that Julian walks at a constant rate of 3 miles per hour. Explain what it means to say that the distance Julian walks is a *function* of the time that he walks.

84. What does it mean to say that ''sometimes the domain of a function is determined by the real world situation represented by the function.'' Give an example.

3.2   LINEAR AND QUADRATIC FUNCTIONS

As we use the function concept, it is helpful to classify certain types of functions and become familiar with their equations, characteristics, and graphs. Let's begin this section with a discussion of two special types of functions: *linear and quadratic functions*. These functions are merely an outgrowth of our earlier study of linear and quadratic equations.

Linear Functions

Any function that can be written in the form

$$f(x) = ax + b,$$

where a and b are real numbers, is called a **linear function**. The following are examples of linear functions.

$$f(x) = -2x + 4, \qquad f(x) = 7x - 9, \qquad f(x) = \tfrac{2}{3}x + \tfrac{5}{6}$$

The equation $f(x) = ax + b$ can be written as $y = ax + b$. From our work with the slope-intercept form in Chapter 2, we know that $y = ax + b$ is the equation of a straight line that has a slope of a and a y-intercept of b. This information can be used to graph linear functions, as illustrated by the following example.

EXAMPLE 1

Graph $f(x) = -2x + 4$.

Solution

Since the y-intercept is 4, the point $(0, 4)$ is on the line. Furthermore, because the slope is -2, we can move 2 units down and 1 unit to the right of $(0, 4)$ to determine the point $(1, 2)$. The line determined by $(0, 4)$, and $(1, 2)$ is drawn in Figure 3.14.

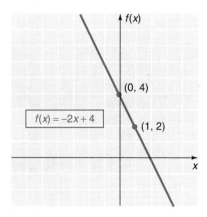

FIGURE 3.14

Note that in Figure 3.14 we labeled the vertical axis $f(x)$. It could also be labeled y since $y = f(x)$. We will use the $f(x)$ labeling for most of our work with graphing functions.

Recall from Chapter 2 that we often graphed linear equations by finding the two intercepts. This same approach can be used with linear functions, as shown in the next example.

EXAMPLE 2

Graph $f(x) = 3x - 6$.

Solution.

First, we see that $f(0) = -6$; thus, the point $(0, -6)$ is on the graph. Secondly, by setting $3x - 6$ equal to zero and solving for x we obtain

$$3x - 6 = 0$$
$$3x = 6$$
$$x = 2.$$

Therefore, $f(2) = 3(2) - 6 = 0$ and the point $(2, 0)$ is on the graph. The line determined by $(0, -6)$ and $(2, 0)$ is drawn in Figure 3.15.

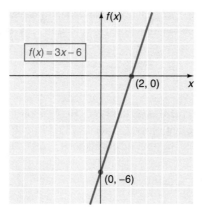

FIGURE 3.15

As you graph functions by using function notation it is often helpful to think of the ordinate of every point on the graph as the value of the function at a specific value of x. Geometrically, this functional value is the directed distance of the point from the x-axis. We illustrated this idea in Figure 3.16 for the function $f(x) = x$ and in Figure 3.17 for the function $f(x) = 2$. The linear function $f(x) = x$ is often called

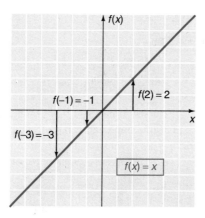

FIGURE 3.16

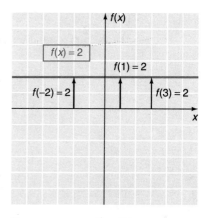

FIGURE 3.17

the identity function. Any linear function of the form $f(x) = ax + b$, where $a = 0$, is called a constant function and its graph is a horizontal line.

Quadratic Functions

Any function that can be written in the form

$$f(x) = ax^2 + bx + c,$$

where a, b, and c are real numbers and $a \neq 0$, is called a quadratic function. Furthermore, the graph of any quadratic function is a parabola. As we work with parabolas, we will use the vocabulary in Figure 3.18.

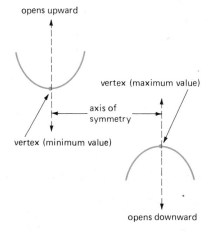

FIGURE 3.18

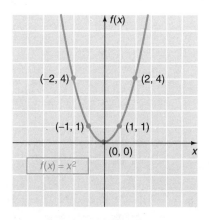

FIGURE 3.19

To graph parabolas you must be able to find the vertex, determine whether the parabola opens upward or downward, and locate two points on opposite sides of the axis of symmetry. It is also very helpful to compare the parabolas that various types of equations produce, such as $f(x) = x^2 + k$, $f(x) = ax^2$, $f(x) = (x - h)^2$, and $f(x) = a(x - h)^2 + k$. We are especially interested in how they compare to the basic parabola, the equation $f(x) = x^2$ produces. The graph of $f(x) = x^2$ is shown in Figure 3.19. Notice that the graph of $f(x) = x^2$ is symmetric with respect to the y- or $f(x)$-axis. Remember that y-axis symmetry is exhibited by an equation if replacing x with $-x$ produces an equivalent equation. Therefore, since $f(-x) = (-x)^2 = x^2$, the equation $f(x) = x^2$ exhibits y-axis symmetry.

Now let's consider an equation of the form $f(x) = x^2 + k$, where k is a constant. (Keep in mind that all such equations exhibit y-axis symmetry).

EXAMPLE 3

Graph $f(x) = x^2 - 2$.

Solution

Observe that functional values for $f(x) = x^2 - 2$ are 2 less than corresponding functional values for $f(x) = x^2$. For example, $f(1) = -1$ for $f(x) = x^2 - 2$, but $f(1) = 1$

for $f(x) = x^2$. Thus, the graph of $f(x) = x^2 - 2$ is the same as the graph of $f(x) = x^2$ except *moved down 2 units* (Figure 3.20).

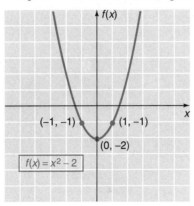

FIGURE   3.20

In general, the graph of a quadratic function of the form $f(x) = x^2 + k$ is the same as the graph of $f(x) = x^2$ except moved up or down $|k|$ units, depending on whether k is positive or negative. We say that the graph of $f(x) = x^2 + k$ is a **vertical translation** of the graph of $f(x) = x^2$.

Now let's consider some quadratic functions of the form $f(x) = ax^2$, where a is a nonzero constant. (The graphs of these equations also have y-axis symmetry.)

Graph $f(x) = 2x^2$.

EXAMPLE 4

Solution

Let's set up a table to make some comparisons of functional values. Notice in the table that the functional values for $f(x) = 2x^2$ are *twice* the corresponding functional values for $f(x) = x^2$. Thus, the parabola associated with $f(x) = 2x^2$ has the same vertex (the origin) as the graph of $f(x) = x^2$, but it is *narrower,* as shown in Figure 3.21.

x	$f(x) = x^2$	$f(x) = 2x^2$
0	0	0
1	1	2
2	4	8
−1	1	2
−2	4	8

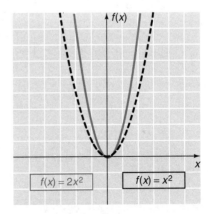

FIGURE   3.21

E X A M P L E   5

Graph $f(x) = \frac{1}{2}x^2$.

Solution

As we see from the table, the functional values for $f(x) = \frac{1}{2}x^2$ are *one-half* of the corresponding functional values for $f(x) = x^2$. Therefore, the parabola associated with $f(x) = \frac{1}{2}x^2$ is *wider* than the basic parabola, as shown in Figure 3.22.

x	$f(x) = x^2$	$f(x) = \frac{1}{2}x^2$
0	0	0
1	1	$\frac{1}{2}$
2	4	2
−1	1	$\frac{1}{2}$
−2	4	2

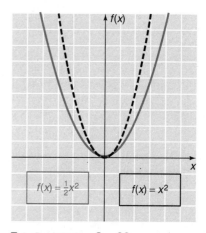

F I G U R E   3 . 22

E X A M P L E   6

Graph $f(x) = -x^2$.

Solution

It should be evident that the functional values for $f(x) = -x^2$ are the *opposites* of the corresponding functional values for $f(x) = x^2$. Therefore, the graph of $f(x) = -x^2$ is a reflection across the x-axis of the basic parabola (Figure 3.23.)

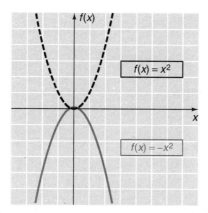

F I G U R E   3 . 23

In general, the graph of a quadratic function of the form $f(x) = ax^2$ has its vertex at the origin and opens upward if a is positive and downward if a is negative. The parabola is "narrower" than the basic parabola if $|a| > 1$ and "wider" if $|a| < 1$.

Let's continue our investigation of quadratic functions by considering those of the form $f(x) = (x - h)^2$, where h is a nonzero constant.

EXAMPLE 7

Graph $f(x) = (x - 3)^2$.

Solution

A fairly extensive table of values illustrates a pattern. Notice that $f(x) = (x - 3)^2$ and $f(x) = x^2$ take on the same functional values, *but* for different values of x. More specifically, if $f(x) = x^2$ achieves a certain functional value at a specific value of x, then $f(x) = (x - 3)^2$ achieves that same functional value at x *plus three*. In other words, the graph of $f(x) = (x - 3)^2$ is the graph of $f(x) = x^2$ *moved three units to the right*. (Figure 3.24).

x	$f(x) = x^2$	$f(x) = (x-3)^2$
−1	1	16
0	0	9
1	1	4
2	4	1
3	9	0
4	16	1
5	25	4
6	36	9
7	49	16

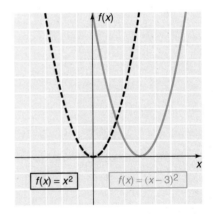

FIGURE 3.24

In general, the graph of a quadratic function of the form $f(x) = (x - h)^2$ is the same as the graph of $f(x) = x^2$ except moved to the right h units if h is positive or moved to the left $|h|$ units if h is negative. We say that the graph of $f(x) = (x - h)^2$ is a horizontal translation of the graph of $f(x) = x^2$.

The following diagram summarizes our work thus far for graphing quadratic functions.

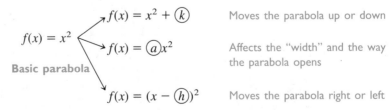

$f(x) = x^2 + \text{\textcircled{k}}$ Moves the parabola up or down

$f(x) = x^2$

Basic parabola

$f(x) = \text{\textcircled{a}}x^2$ Affects the "width" and the way the parabola opens

$f(x) = (x - \text{\textcircled{h}})^2$ Moves the parabola right or left

Now let's consider two examples that combine these ideas.

EXAMPLE 8

Graph $f(x) = 3(x - 2)^2 + 1$.

Solution

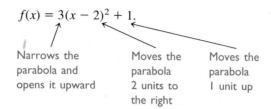

$f(x) = 3(x - 2)^2 + 1.$

Narrows the parabola and opens it upward

Moves the parabola 2 units to the right

Moves the parabola 1 unit up

The vertex is at $(2, 1)$ and the line $x = 2$ is the axis of symmetry. If $x = 1$, then $f(1) = 3(1 - 2)^2 + 1 = 4$. Thus, the point $(1, 4)$ is on the graph and so is its reflection $(3, 4)$, across the line of symmetry. The parabola is drawn in Figure 3.25.

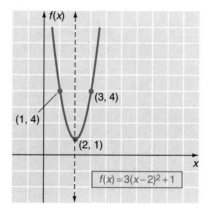

$f(x) = 3(x - 2)^2 + 1$

FIGURE 3.25

EXAMPLE 9

Graph $f(x) = -\frac{1}{2}(x + 1)^2 - 3$.

Solution

$f(x) = -\frac{1}{2}[x - (-1)]^2 - 3.$

Widens the parabola and opens it downward

Moves the parabola 1 unit to the left

Moves the parabola 3 units down

The vertex is at $(-1, -3)$ and the line $x = -1$ is the axis of symmetry. If $x = 0$, then $f(0) = -\frac{1}{2}(0 + 1)^2 - 3 = -\frac{7}{2}$. So the point $\left(0, -\frac{7}{2}\right)$ is on the graph and so is its reflection, $\left(-2, -\frac{7}{2}\right)$, across the line of symmetry. The parabola is drawn in Figure 3.26.

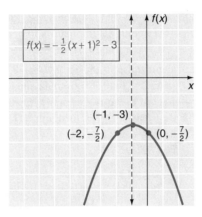

$$f(x) = -\frac{1}{2}(x+1)^2 - 3$$

$(-1, -3)$

$(-2, -\frac{7}{2})$ $(0, -\frac{7}{2})$

FIGURE   3 . 26

Quadratic Functions of the Form
$f(x) = ax^2 + bx + c$

We are now ready to graph quadratic functions of the form $f(x) = ax^2 + bx + c$. The general approach is one of changing from the form $f(x) = ax^2 + bx + c$ to the form $f(x) = a(x - h)^2 + k$ and then proceeding as we did in Examples 8 and 9. The process of *completing the square* serves as the basis for making the change in form. Let's consider two examples to illustrate the details.

EXAMPLE 10

Graph $f(x) = x^2 - 4x + 3$.

Solution

$f(x) = x^2 - 4x + 3$

$= (x^2 - 4x \quad) + 3$ ⟵ Add 4, which is the square of one-half of the coefficient of x.

$= (x^2 - 4x + 4) + 3 - 4$ ⟵ Subtract 4 to compensate for the 4 that was added.

$= (x - 2)^2 - 1.$

The graph of $f(x) = (x - 2)^2 - 1$ is the basic parabola moved 2 units to the right and 1 unit down (Figure 3.27).

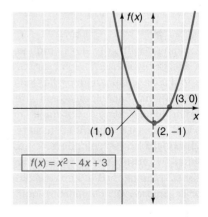

$(3, 0)$

$(1, 0)$ $(2, -1)$

$f(x) = x^2 - 4x + 3$

FIGURE   3 . 27

EXAMPLE 11

Graph $f(x) = -2x^2 - 4x + 1$.

Solution

$f(x) = -2x^2 - 4x + 1$

$\quad = -2(x^2 + 2x \quad) + 1$ Factor -2 from the first two terms.

$\quad = -2(x^2 + 2x + 1) + 1 + 2$ Add 1 inside the parentheses to complete the square.

$\quad = -2(x + 1)^2 + 3.$

Add 2 to compensate for the 1 inside the parentheses times the factor -2.

The graph of $f(x) = -2(x + 1)^2 + 3$ is drawn in Figure 3.28.

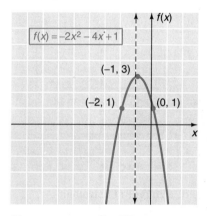

F I G U R E   3 . 28

Piecewise-defined Functions

Some functions are defined by using different rules of assignment for different parts of the domain. Such functions are commonly called **piecewise-defined** functions. Let's graph a piecewise-defined function involving both a linear and a quadratic rule of assignment.

EXAMPLE 12

Graph $f(x) = \begin{cases} 2x & \text{for } x \geq 0 \\ x^2 + 1 & \text{for } x < 0 \end{cases}$.

Solution

If $x \geq 0$, then $f(x) = 2x$. Thus, for nonnegative values of x we graph the linear function $f(x) = 2x$. If $x < 0$, then $f(x) = x^2 + 1$. Thus, for negative values of x we graph the quadratic function $f(x) = x^2 + 1$. The complete graph is shown in Figure 3.29.

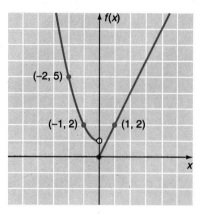

FIGURE 3.29

Recall that we define the concept of absolute value in two parts.

$$|x| = x \quad \text{if } x \geq 0$$
$$|x| = -x \quad \text{if } x < 0$$

Therefore, we can express the basic absolute value function as a piecewise-defined function as follows.

$$f(x) = |x| = \begin{cases} x & \text{if } x \geq 0 \\ -x & \text{if } x < 0 \end{cases}$$

The graph of $f(x) = |x|$ is shown in Figure 3.30.

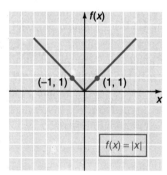

FIGURE 3.30

Another piecewise-defined function is the **greatest integer function**, which we define by the equation $f(x) = [\![x]\!]$ for all real values of x, where $[\![x]\!]$ means the greatest integer less than or equal to x. For example, $[\![2.6]\!] = 2$, $[\![\sqrt{2}]\!] = 1$, $[\![4]\!] = 4$, and $[\![-1.7]\!] = -2$. Thus, the greatest integer function takes on different integral values for different intervals of the domain. The following table contains the intervals for $-3 \le x < 3$ and Figure 3.31 depicts the graph of $f(x) = [\![x]\!]$ for $-3 \le x < 3$. Keep in mind that the complete graph of $f(x) = [\![x]\!]$ continues indefinitely with

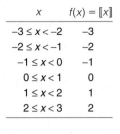

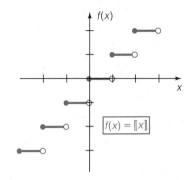

FIGURE 3.31

steps to the right and left. In fact, we sometimes refer to the greatest integer function as a **step function**.

Using a Graphing Utility

What we know about parabolas and the process of completing the square can be helpful when using a graphing utility to graph a quadratic function. Consider the following example.

EXAMPLE 13

Use a graphing utility to obtain the graph of the quadratic function $f(x) = -x^2 + 37x - 311$.

Solution

First, we know that the parabola opens downward ($a < 0$) and its width is the same as that of the basic parabola $f(x) = x^2$. Now suppose that we enter the equation, activate the graphing feature of our graphing utility, and use a viewing rectangle such that $-10 \le x \le 10$ and $-10 \le y \le 10$. Our result is an empty display. In other words, the parabola must be located outside of this viewing rectangle. So let's start the process of completing the square to determine an approximate location of the vertex of the parabola.

$$f(x) = -x^2 + 37x - 311$$

$$= -(x^2 - 37x \quad\quad) - 311$$

$$= -\left(x^2 - 37x + \left(\frac{37}{2}\right)^2\right) - 311 + \left(\frac{37}{2}\right)^2$$

$$= -(x^2 - 37x + (18.5)^2) - 311 + 342.25$$

Thus, the vertex is *near* $x = 18$ and $y = 31$. Therefore set the boundaries of the viewing rectangle so that $-2 \le x \le 25$ and $-10 \le y \le 35$ to obtain the graph shown in Figure 3.32.

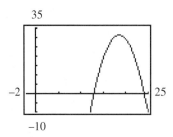

FIGURE 3.32

REMARK   The graph in Figure 3.32 is sufficient for most purposes since it shows the vertex and the x-intercepts of the parabola. Certainly other boundaries could be used that also would give this information.

PROBLEM SET 3.2

For Problems 1–10, graph each of the linear functions.

1. $f(x) = 2x - 4$ **2.** $f(x) = 3x + 6$

3. $f(x) = -x + 1$ **4.** $f(x) = -2x - 4$

5. $f(x) = -2x$ **6.** $f(x) = 3x$

7. $f(x) = \frac{1}{2}x - \frac{3}{4}$ **8.** $f(x) = -\frac{2}{3}x + \frac{1}{2}$

9. $f(x) = -1$ **10.** $f(x) = -3$

For Problems 11–36, graph each of the quadratic functions.

11. $f(x) = x^2 + 1$ **12.** $f(x) = x^2 - 2$

13. $f(x) = 3x^2$ **14.** $f(x) = -\frac{1}{2}x^2$

15. $f(x) = -x^2 + 2$ **16.** $f(x) = -3x^2 - 1$

17. $f(x) = (x + 2)^2$ **18.** $f(x) = (x - 1)^2$

19. $f(x) = -2(x + 1)^2$ **20.** $f(x) = 3(x - 2)^2$

21. $f(x) = (x - 1)^2 + 2$ **22.** $f(x) = -(x + 2)^2 + 3$

23. $f(x) = \frac{1}{2}(x - 2)^2 - 3$ **24.** $f(x) = 2(x - 3)^2 - 1$

25. $f(x) = x^2 + 2x + 4$ **26.** $f(x) = x^2 - 4x + 2$

27. $f(x) = x^2 - 3x + 1$ **28.** $f(x) = x^2 + 5x + 5$

29. $f(x) = 2x^2 + 12x + 17$ **30.** $f(x) = 3x^2 - 6x$

31. $f(x) = -x^2 - 2x + 1$

32. $f(x) = -2x^2 + 12x - 16$

33. $f(x) = 2x^2 - 2x + 3$ **34.** $f(x) = 2x^2 + 3x - 1$

35. $f(x) = -2x^2 - 5x + 1$ **36.** $f(x) = -3x^2 + x - 2$

For Problems 37–52, graph each of the piecewise-defined functions.

37. $f(x) = \begin{cases} x & \text{for } x \ge 0 \\ 3x & \text{for } x < 0 \end{cases}$

38. $f(x) = \begin{cases} -x & \text{for } x \ge 0 \\ -4x & \text{for } x < 0 \end{cases}$

39. $f(x) = \begin{cases} 2x + 1 & \text{for } x \ge 0 \\ x^2 & \text{for } x < 0 \end{cases}$

40. $f(x) = \begin{cases} -x^2 & \text{for } x \geq 0 \\ 2x^2 & \text{for } x < 0 \end{cases}$

41. $f(x) = \begin{cases} 2 & \text{if } x \geq 0 \\ -1 & \text{if } x < 0 \end{cases}$

42. $f(x) = \begin{cases} 2 & \text{if } x > 2 \\ 1 & \text{if } 0 < x \leq 2 \\ -1 & \text{if } x \leq 0 \end{cases}$

43. $f(x) = \begin{cases} 1 & \text{if } 0 \leq x < 1 \\ 2 & \text{if } 1 \leq x < 2 \\ 3 & \text{if } 2 \leq x < 3 \\ 4 & \text{if } 3 \leq x < 4 \end{cases}$

44. $f(x) = \begin{cases} 2x + 3 & \text{if } x < 0 \\ x^2 & \text{if } 0 \leq x < 2 \\ 1 & \text{if } x \geq 2 \end{cases}$

45. $f(x) = x + |x|$

46. $f(x) = \dfrac{|x|}{x}$

47. $f(x) = |x| - x$

48. $f(x) = x - |x|$

49. $f(x) = [\![-x]\!]$ for $-3 < x \leq 3$

50. $f(x) = [\![2x]\!]$ for $-2 \leq x < 2$

51. $f(x) = 2[\![x]\!]$ for $-3 \leq x < 3$

52. $f(x) = x + [\![x]\!]$ for $-3 \leq x < 3$

THOUGHTS into WORDS

53. Explain the procedure that you would use when graphing the function $f(x) = -\frac{1}{2}x + 3$.

54. Explain the procedure that you would use when graphing the function $f(x) = -2x^2 - 8x - 4$.

 GRAPHICS CALCULATOR ACTIVITIES

55. This problem is designed to reinforce some graphing ideas presented in this section. For each part, first predict the shapes and locations of the parabolas, then use your graphics calculator to graph them on the same set of axes.

a. $f(x) = x^2$, $f(x) = x^2 - 4$, $f(x) = x^2 + 1$, $f(x) = x^2 + 5$

b. $f(x) = x^2$, $f(x) = (x - 5)^2$, $f(x) = (x + 5)^2$, $f(x) = (x - 3)^2$

c. $f(x) = x^2$, $f(x) = 5x^2$, $f(x) = \frac{1}{3}x^2$, $f(x) = -2x^2$

d. $f(x) = x^2$, $f(x) = (x - 7)^2 - 3$, $f(x) = -(x + 8)^2 + 4$, $f(x) = -3x^2 - 4$

e. $f(x) = x^2 - 4x - 2$, $f(x) = -x^2 + 4x + 2$, $f(x) = -x^2 - 16x - 58$, $f(x) = x^2 + 16x + 58$

56. a. Graph $f(x) = x^2 - 14x + 51$ and $f(x) = $

$x^2 + 14x + 51$ on the same set of axes. What relationship seems to exist between the two graphs?

b. Graph $f(x) = x^2 + 12x + 34$ and $f(x) = x^2 - 12x + 34$ on the same set of axes. What relationship seems to exist between the two graphs?

c. Graph $f(x) = -x^2 + 8x - 20$ and $f(x) = -x^2 - 8x - 20$ on the same set of axes. What relationship seems to exist between the two graphs?

d. Make a statement that generalizes your findings in parts (a) through (c).

57. Use your graphics calculator to graph the piecewise-defined functions in Problems 37–44. You may need to consult your calculator manual for instructions for graphing these functions. (This problem is designed to help you become more familiar with the capabilities and limitations of your graphics calculator.)

58. Use your graphics calculator to check your graphs for Problems 45–48.

59. For each of the following pairs of functions, predict how their graphs will compare and then use your graphics calculator to check your prediction.

   a. $f(x) = |2x|$ and $f(x) = 2|x|$

   b. $f(x) = |x^2|$ and $f(x) = |x|^2$

   c. $f(x) = |x + 2|$ and $f(x) = |x - 2|$

   d. $f(x) = |-x|$ and $f(x) = -|x|$

   e. $f(x) = \dfrac{|x|}{x}$ and $f(x) = \dfrac{x}{|x|}$

60. If your graphing utility is designed to handle the greatest integer function, check your graphs for Problems 49–52.

3.3   QUADRATIC FUNCTIONS AND PROBLEM SOLVING

In the previous section we used the process of completing the square to change a specific quadratic function such as $f(x) = x^2 - 4x + 3$ to the $f(x) = (x - 2)^2 - 1$ form. From the form $f(x) = (x - 2)^2 - 1$, the vertex $(2, -1)$ and the axis of symmetry $x = 2$ of the parabola are easy to identify. In general, if we complete the square on

$$f(x) = ax^2 + bx + c,$$

we obtain

$$f(x) = a\left(x^2 + \frac{b}{a}x \quad\right) + c$$

$$= a\left(x^2 + \frac{b}{a}x + \frac{b^2}{4a^2}\right) + c - \frac{b^2}{4a}$$

$$= a\left(x + \frac{b}{2a}\right)^2 + \frac{4ac - b^2}{4a}.$$

Therefore, the parabola associated with $f(x) = ax^2 + bx + c$ has its vertex at $(-b/2a, (4ac - b^2)/4a)$; the equation of its axis of symmetry is $x = -b/(2a)$. These facts are illustrated in Figure 3.33. The information in Figure 3.33 gives us

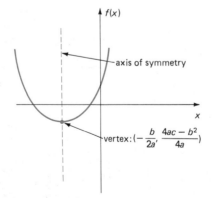

FIGURE 3.33

another way of graphing quadratic functions of the form $f(x) = ax^2 + bx + c$, as indicated by the following steps.

1. Determine whether the parabola opens upward (if $a > 0$) or downward (if $a < 0$).
2. Find $-b/(2a)$, which is the x-coordinate of the vertex.
3. Find $f(-b/(2a))$, which is the y-coordinate of the vertex. (You could also find the y-coordinate by evaluating $(4ac - b^2)/4a$.)
4. Locate another point on the parabola and also locate its image across the axis of symmetry, $x = -b/(2a)$.

The three points found in Steps 2, 3, and 4 should determine the general shape of the parabola. Let's illustrate this procedure with two examples.

EXAMPLE 1

Graph $f(x) = 3x^2 - 6x + 5$.

Solution

STEP 1 Because $a > 0$, the parabola opens upward.

STEP 2 $-\dfrac{b}{2a} = -\dfrac{-6}{6} = 1$

STEP 3 $f(-b/(2a)) = f(1) = 3 - 6 + 5 = 2$
Thus, the vertex is at $(1, 2)$.

STEP 4 Letting $x = 2$, we obtain $f(2) = 12 - 12 + 5 = 5$. Thus, $(2, 5)$ is on the graph and so is its reflection $(0, 5)$ across the line of symmetry $x = 1$.

The three points $(1, 2)$, $(2, 5)$, and $(0, 5)$ are used to graph the parabola in Figure 3.34.

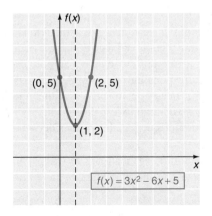

FIGURE 3.34

EXAMPLE 2

Graph $f(x) = -x^2 - 4x - 7$.

Solution

STEP 1 Since $a < 0$, the parabola opens downward.

STEP 2 $-\dfrac{b}{2a} = -\dfrac{-4}{-2} = -2$

STEP 3 $f\left(-\dfrac{b}{2a}\right) = f(-2) = -(-2)^2 - 4(-2) - 7 = -3$

Thus, the vertex is at $(-2, -3)$.

STEP 4 Letting $x = 0$, we obtain $f(0) = -7$. Thus, $(0, -7)$ is on the graph and so is its reflection $(-4, -7)$ across the line of symmetry $x = -2$.

We use the three points $(-2, -3)$, $(0, -7)$, and $(-4, -7)$ to draw the parabola in Figure 3.35.

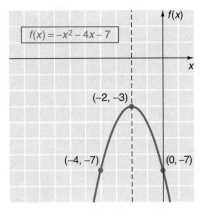

F I G U R E   3 . 3 5

Maximum and Minimum Values

Quadratic functions have numerous applications. We will feature some of those applications in this section and then add some additional ones in Chapter 9. In most applications of quadratic functions, we are interested in the x-intercepts and/or the vertex of the corresponding parabola. As you have seen, the vertex of a parabola associated with a quadratic function is either the lowest or highest point on the parabola. Thus, we commonly use the vocabulary of **minimum value** or **maximum value** of a quadratic function. Let's consider some examples.

EXAMPLE 3

For each of the following quadratic functions, find the x-intercepts of the corresponding parabola and the maximum or minimum value of the function.

a. $f(x) = -x^2 + 11x - 18$ **b.** $f(x) = x^2 - 8x - 3$

c. $f(x) = 2x^2 - 12x + 23$

Solutions

a. To find the x-intercepts, let $y = 0$ and solve the resulting equation.

$$-x^2 + 11x - 18 = 0$$
$$x^2 - 11x + 18 = 0$$
$$(x - 2)(x - 9) = 0$$
$$x - 2 = 0 \quad \text{or} \quad x - 9 = 0$$
$$x = 2 \quad \text{or} \quad x = 9$$

Therefore, the x-intercepts are 2 and 9. To find the vertex, let's determine the point $\left(-\dfrac{b}{2a}, f\left(-\dfrac{b}{2a}\right)\right)$.

$$f(x) = -x^2 + 11x - 18$$

$$-\frac{b}{2a} = -\frac{11}{2(-1)} = -\frac{11}{-2} = \frac{11}{2}$$

$$f\left(\frac{11}{2}\right) = -\left(\frac{11}{2}\right)^2 + 11\left(\frac{11}{2}\right) - 18$$

$$= -\frac{121}{4} + \frac{121}{2} - 18$$

$$= \frac{-121 + 242 - 72}{4}$$

$$= \frac{49}{4}$$

Since $a < 0$, the parabola opens downward and a maximum value of $\frac{49}{4}$ occurs at $x = \frac{11}{2}$.

b. To find the x-intercepts, let $y = 0$ and solve the resulting equation.

$$x^2 - 8x - 3 = 0$$

$$x = \frac{-(-8) \pm \sqrt{(-8)^2 - 4(1)(-3)}}{2(1)}$$

$$= \frac{8 \pm \sqrt{76}}{2}$$

$$= \frac{8 \pm 2\sqrt{19}}{2}$$

$$= 4 \pm \sqrt{19}$$

Therefore, the x-intercepts are $4 + \sqrt{19}$ and $4 - \sqrt{19}$. This time, to find the vertex let's complete the square on x.

$$f(x) = x^2 - 8x - 3$$
$$= x^2 - 8x + 16 - 3 - 16$$
$$= (x - 4)^2 - 19$$

Since $a > 0$, the parabola opens upward and a minimum value of -19 occurs at $x = 4$.

c. To find the x-intercepts, let $y = 0$ and solve the resulting equation.

$$2x^2 - 12x + 23 = 0$$

$$x = \frac{-(-12) \pm \sqrt{(-12)^2 - 4(2)(23)}}{2(2)}$$

$$= \frac{12 \pm \sqrt{-40}}{4}$$

Since these solutions are nonreal complex numbers, there are no x-intercepts. To find the vertex, let's determine the point $\left(-\dfrac{b}{2a}, \ f\left(-\dfrac{b}{2a} \right) \right)$.

$$f(x) = 2x^2 - 12x + 23$$

$$-\frac{b}{2a} = -\frac{-12}{2(2)} = 3$$

$$f(3) = 2(3)^2 - 12(3) + 23$$
$$= 18 - 36 + 23$$
$$= 5$$

Since $a > 0$, the parabola opens upward and a minimum value of 5 occurs at $x = 3$.   ▬

REMARK Note that in parts (a) and (c) we used the general point $\left(-\dfrac{b}{2a}, f\left(-\dfrac{b}{2a} \right) \right)$ to find the vertices. However, in part (b) we completed the square and used that form to determine the vertex. Which approach you use is an individual preference. We chose to complete the square in part (b) because the algebra involved was quite easy.

Back to Problem Solving

Now let's solve some problems with our new knowledge of quadratic functions.

EXAMPLE 4

Fencing in some land   A farmer has 120 rods of fencing and wants to enclose a rectangular plot of land that requires fencing on only three sides, since it is bound by a river on one side. Find the length and width of the plot that will maximize the area.

Solution

Let x represent the width; then $120 - 2x$ represents the length, as indicated in Figure 3.36. The function $A(x) = x(120 - 2x)$ represents the area of the plot in terms of the width x. Since

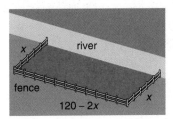

F I G U R E   3 . 36

$$A(x) = x(120 - 2x)$$
$$= 120x - 2x^2$$
$$= -2x^2 + 120x,$$

we have a quadratic function with $a = -2$, $b = 120$, and $c = 0$. Therefore, the x-value where the maximum value of the function is obtained is

$$-\frac{b}{2a} = -\frac{120}{2(-2)}$$
$$= 30.$$

If $x = 30$, then $120 - 2x = 120 - 2(30) = 60$. Thus, the farmer should make the plot 30 rods wide and 60 rods long to maximize the area at $(30)(60) = 1800$ square rods.

EXAMPLE 5

Selling golf clubs   A golf pro-shop operator finds that she can sell 30 sets of golf clubs at $500 per set in a year. Furthermore, she predicts that for each $25 decrease in price, three extra sets of golf clubs can be sold. At what price should she sell the clubs to maximize gross income?

Solution

Sometimes when analyzing such a problem it helps to start by setting up a table as follows.

	NUMBER OF SETS	PRICE PER SET	INCOME
	30	$500	$15,000
	33	$475	$15,675
	36	$450	$16,200

3 additional sets can be sold for a $25 decrease in price.

Let x represent the number of $25 decreases in price. Then the income can be expressed as a function of x as follows.

$$f(x) = (30 + 3x)(500 - 25x)$$

Number of sets   Price per set

Simplifying this, we obtain

$$f(x) = 15,000 - 750x + 1500x - 75x^2$$
$$= -75x^2 + 750x + 15,000.$$

Completing the square we obtain

$$f(x) = -75x^2 + 750x + 15,000$$
$$= -75(x^2 - 10x \quad) + 15,000$$
$$= -75(x^2 - 10x + 25) + 15,000 + 1875$$
$$= -75(x - 5)^2 + 16,875.$$

From this form we know that the vertex of the parabola is at (5,16875). So 5 decreases of $25, that is, a $125 reduction in price, will give a maximum income of $16,875. The golf clubs should be sold at $375 per set. ■

We determined that the vertex of a parabola associated with $f(x) = ax^2 + bx + c$ is located at $\left(-\dfrac{b}{2a}, f\left(-\dfrac{b}{2a}\right)\right)$, and the x-intercepts of the graph can be found by solving the quadratic equation $ax^2 + bx + c = 0$. Therefore, a graphing utility does not provide us with much extra "fire-power" when working with quadratic functions. However, as functions become more complex, a graphing utility becomes more helpful. So let's build our confidence in the use of a graphing utility at this time when we have a way of checking our results.

E·X·A·M·P·L·E 6

Use a graphing utility to graph $f(x) = x^2 - 8x - 3$. Then find the minimum value of the function and the x-intercepts of its graph. (This is the parabola from part (b) of Example 3.)

Solution

A graph of the parabola is shown in Figure 3.37.

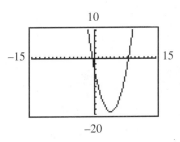

F I G U R E   3 . 37

Using the trace feature we can determine that the vertex of the parabola is at approximately $(4, -19)$. By direct substitution we can verify that the vertex is at *exactly* $(4, -19)$. Thus, the minimum value of the function is -19. From Figure 3.37 one x-intercept appears to be between 0 and -1 and the other between 8 and 9. Let's zoom in on the x-intercept between 8 and 9 as shown in Figure 3.38.

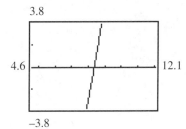

F I G U R E   3 . 38

Now we can use the trace feature to determine that this x-intercept is at approximately 8.4. (This agrees with the answer of $4 + \sqrt{19}$ we obtained earlier in Example 3.) In a similar fashion we can determine that the other intercept is at approximately $-.4$.

PROBLEM SET 3.3

For Problems 1–20, graph each of the quadratic functions.

1. $f(x) = x^2 - 8x + 15$

2. $f(x) = x^2 + 6x + 11$

3. $f(x) = 2x^2 + 20x + 52$

4. $f(x) = 3x^2 - 6x - 1$

5. $f(x) = -x^2 + 4x - 7$

6. $f(x) = -x^2 - 6x - 5$

7. $f(x) = -3x^2 + 6x - 5$

8. $f(x) = -2x^2 - 4x + 2$

9. $f(x) = x^2 + 3x - 1$

10. $f(x) = x^2 + 5x + 2$

11. $f(x) = -2x^2 + 5x + 1$

12. $f(x) = -3x^2 + 2x - 1$

13. $f(x) = -x^2 + 3$

14. $f(x) = (x + 1)^2 + 1$

15. $f(x) = x^2 + x - 1$

16. $f(x) = -x^2 + 3x - 4$

17. $f(x) = -2x^2 + 4x + 1$

18. $f(x) = 4x^2 - 8x + 5$

19. $f(x) = -\left(x + \frac{5}{2}\right)^2 + \frac{3}{2}$

20. $f(x) = x^2 - 4x$

For each of the following quadratic functions, find the x-intercepts of the corresponding parabola and the maximum or minimum value of the function (Problems 21–32).

21. $f(x) = x^2 - 8x + 15$

22. $f(x) = x^2 - 16x + 63$

23. $f(x) = 2x^2 - 28x + 96$

24. $f(x) = 3x^2 - 60x + 297$

25. $f(x) = -x^2 + 10x - 24$

26. $f(x) = -2x^2 + 36x - 160$

27. $f(x) = x^2 - 14x + 44$

28. $f(x) = x^2 - 18x + 68$

29. $f(x) = -x^2 + 9x - 21$

30. $f(x) = 2x^2 + 3x + 3$

31. $f(x) = -4x^2 + 4x + 4$

32. $f(x) = -2x^2 + 3x + 7$

APPLIED PROBLEMS

33. *Profit function*   Suppose that the equation $p(x) = -2x^2 + 280x - 1000$, where x represents the number of items sold, describes the profit function for a certain business. How many items should be sold to maximize the profit?

34. *Cost function*   Suppose that the cost function for a particular item is given by the equation $C(x) = 2x^2 - 320x + 12{,}920$, where x represents the number of items. How many items should be produced to minimize the cost?

35. *Firing a projectile*   The height of a projectile fired vertically into the air (neglecting air resistance) at an initial velocity of 96 feet per second is a function of the time and is given by the equation $f(x) = 96x - 16x^2$, where x represents the time. Find the highest point reached by the projectile.

36. *Number relationships*   Find two numbers whose sum is

30, such that the sum of the square of one number plus ten times the other number is a minimum.

37. *Maximizing a product*   Find two numbers whose sum is 50 and whose product is a maximum.

38. *Minimizing a product*   Find two numbers whose difference is 40 and whose product is a minimum.

39. *Maximizing area*   Two hundred and forty meters of fencing is available to enclose a rectangular playground. What should be the dimensions of the playground to maximize the area?

40. *Maximizing motel revenue*   A motel advertises that they will provide dinner, a dance, and drinks for $50 per couple for a New Year's Eve party. They must have a guarantee of 30 couples. Furthermore, they will agree that for each couple in excess of 30, they will reduce the price per couple for all attending by $.50. How many couples will it take to maximize the motel's revenue?

41. *Cable company subscribers* A Cable TV company has 1000 subscribers who each pay $15 per month. Based on a survey, they feel that for each decrease of $.25 on the monthly rate, they could obtain 20 additional subscribers. At what rate will maximum revenue be obtained and how many subscribers will it take at that rate?

42. *Maximizing profit* A manufacturer finds that for the first 500 units of his product that are produced and sold, the profit is $50 per unit. The profit in each of the units beyond 500 is decreased by $.10 times the number of additional units sold. What level of output will maximize profit?

GRAPHICS CALCULATOR ACTIVITIES

43. Graph each of the following parabolas; keep in mind that you may need to change the dimensions of the viewing rectangle to obtain a graph that will show the x-intercepts (if there are any) and the vertex.

a. $f(x) = x^2 - 2x + 12$

b. $f(x) = -x^2 - 4x - 16$

c. $f(x) = x^2 + 12x + 44$

d. $f(x) = x^2 - 30x + 229$

e. $f(x) = 2x^2 - 48x + 299$

f. $f(x) = -2x^2 + 8x - 19$

g. $f(x) = 3x^2 + 12x - 3$

h. $f(x) = -3x^2 + 24x - 28$

44. For each of the following parabolas, use a graphics calculator to graph the parabola, and use the trace feature to help estimate the x-intercepts and the vertex. Then use the approach of Example 3 to find the x-intercepts and the vertex.

a. $f(x) = x^2 - 6x + 3$

b. $f(x) = x^2 - 18x + 66$

c. $f(x) = -x^2 + 8x - 3$

d. $f(x) = -x^2 + 24x - 129$

e. $f(x) = 14x^2 - 7x + 1$

f. $f(x) = -\frac{1}{2}x^2 + 5x - \frac{17}{2}$

3.4 TRANSFORMATIONS OF SOME BASIC CURVES

From our work in Section 3.2, we know that the graph of $f(x) = (x - 5)^2$ is the basic parabola, $f(x) = x^2$, translated five units to the right. Likewise, we know that the graph of $f(x) = -x^2 - 2$ is the basic parabola reflected across the x-axis and translated downward two units. Translations and reflections apply not only to parabolas but to curves in general. Therefore, if we know the shapes of a few basic curves, then numerous transformations of these curves can be easily sketched using the concepts of translation and reflection. Now let's give a general definition for each kind of transformation and use the basic curves $f(x) = x^3$ (Figure 2.45), $f(x) = \sqrt{x}$ (Figure 2.46), and $f(x) = |x|$ (Figure 3.30) to illustrate the definitions.

Translations

The graph of $f(x) = x^2 + 3$ is the graph of $f(x) = x^2$ shifted upward three units. Likewise, the graph of $f(x) = x^2 - 2$ is the graph of $f(x) = x^2$ shifted downward two units. We can describe the general concept of a vertical translation as follows.

Vertical Translation

The graph of $y = f(x) + k$ is the graph of $y = f(x)$ shifted k units upward if $k > 0$ or shifted $|k|$ units downward if $k < 0$.

In Figure 3.39 the graph of $f(x) = |x| + 2$ is obtained by shifting the graph of $f(x) = |x|$ upward two units and the graph of $f(x) = |x| - 3$ is obtained by shifting the graph of $f(x) = |x|$ downward three units. (Remember that $f(x) = |x| - 3$ can be written as $f(x) = |x| + (-3)$.)

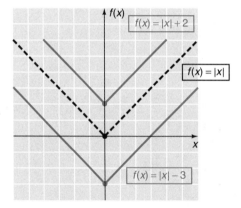

FIGURE 3.39

We also graphed horizontal translations of the basic parabola in Section 3.2. For example, the graph of $f(x) = (x - 4)^2$ is the graph of $f(x) = x^2$ shifted four units to the right and the graph of $f(x) = (x + 5)^2$ is the graph of $f(x) = x^2$ shifted five units to the left. We can describe the general concept of a horizontal translation as follows.

Horizontal Translation

The graph of $y = f(x - h)$ is the graph of $y = f(x)$ shifted h units to the right if $h > 0$ or shifted $|h|$ units to the left if $h < 0$.

In Figure 3.40 the graph of $f(x) = (x - 3)^3$ is obtained by shifting the graph of $f(x) = x^3$ three units to the right. Likewise, the graph of $f(x) = (x + 2)^3$ is obtained by shifting the graph of $f(x) = x^3$ two units to the left.

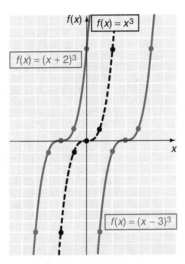

F I G U R E   3 . 40

Reflections

From our work in Section 3.2 we know that the graph of $f(x) = -x^2$ is the graph of $f(x) = x^2$ reflected through the x-axis. We can describe the general concept of an x-axis reflection as follows.

x-axis Reflection

The graph of $y = -f(x)$ is the graph of $y = f(x)$ reflected through the x-axis.

In Figure 3.41 the graph of $f(x) = -\sqrt{x}$ is obtained by reflecting the graph of $f(x) = \sqrt{x}$ through the x-axis. We sometimes refer to these reflections as **mirror images**. Thus, in Figure 3.41 if we think of the x-axis as a mirror, the graphs of $f(x) = \sqrt{x}$ and $f(x) = -\sqrt{x}$ are mirror images of each other.

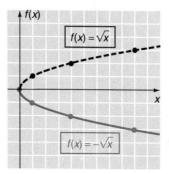

In Section 3.2 we did not consider a y-axis reflection of the basic parabola $f(x) = x^2$ because it is symmetric with respect to the y-axis. In other words, a y-axis reflection of $f(x) = x^2$ produces the same figure. However, at this time let's describe the general concept of a y-axis reflection.

y-axis Reflection

The graph of $y = f(-x)$ is the graph of $y = f(x)$ reflected through the y-axis.

Now suppose that we want to do a y-axis reflection of $f(x) = \sqrt{x}$. Since $f(x) = \sqrt{x}$ is defined for $x \geq 0$, the y-axis reflection $f(x) = \sqrt{-x}$ is defined for $-x \geq 0$, which is equivalent to $x \leq 0$. Figure 3.42 shows the y-axis reflection of $f(x) = \sqrt{x}$.

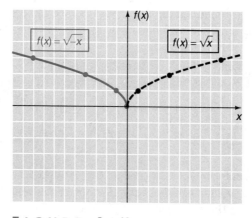

FIGURE   3 . 42

Vertical Stretching and Shrinking

Translations and reflections are called **rigid transformations** because the basic shape of the curve being transformed is not changed. In other words, only the positions of the graphs are changed. Now we want to consider some transformations that distort the shape of the original figure somewhat.

In Section 3.2 we graphed the equation $y = 2x^2$ by doubling the y-coordinates of the ordered pairs that satisfy the equation $y = x^2$. We obtained a parabola with its vertex at the origin, symmetric to the y-axis, but *narrower* than the basic parabola. Likewise, we graphed the equation $y = \frac{1}{2}x^2$ by halving the y-coordinates of the ordered pairs that satisfy $y = x^2$. In this case, we obtained a parabola with its vertex at the origin, symmetric to the y-axis, but *wider* than the basic parabola.

The concepts of *narrower* and *wider* can be used to describe parabolas but cannot be used to accurately describe some other curves. Instead we use the more general concepts of vertical *stretching* and *shrinking*.

Vertical Stretching and Shrinking

The graph of $y = cf(x)$ is obtained from the graph of $y = f(x)$ by multiplying the y-coordinates of $y = f(x)$ by c. If $c > 1$, the graph is said to be *stretched* by a factor of c, and if $0 < c < 1$, the graph is said to be *shrunk* by a factor of c.

In Figure 3.43, the graph of $f(x) = 2\sqrt{x}$ is obtained by doubling the y-coordinates of points on the graph of $f(x) = \sqrt{x}$. Likewise, in Figure 3.43, the graph of $f(x) = \frac{1}{2}\sqrt{x}$ is obtained by halving the y-coordinates of points on the graph of $f(x) = \sqrt{x}$.

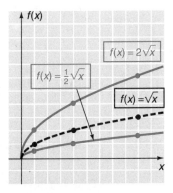

F I G U R E   3 . 4 3

Successive Transformations

Some curves are the result of performing more than one transformation on a basic curve. Let's consider the graph of a function that involves a stretching, a reflection, a horizontal translation, and a vertical translation of the basic absolute value function.

EXAMPLE 1

Graph $f(x) = -2|x - 3| + 1$.

Solution

This is the basic absolute value curve stretched by a factor of two, reflected through the x-axis, shifted three units to the right, and shifted one unit upward. To sketch the graph, we locate the point $(3, 1)$, and then determine a point on each of the rays. The graph is shown in Figure 3.44.

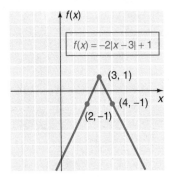

FIGURE   3.44

REMARK   Note in Example 1 that we did not sketch the original basic curve $f(x) = |x|$ nor any of the intermediate transformations. However, it is helpful to mentally picture each transformation. This locates the point $(3, 1)$ and establishes the fact that the two rays point downward. Then a point on each ray determines the final graph.

Graphing New Functions

Suppose that we are faced with the problem of graphing a new function, such as $f(x) = 4x/(x^4 + 1)$. This is not a basic function that we recognize nor a transformation of a familiar basic function. We can use some of the graphing suggestions offered in Chapter 2, but first let's restate them in terms of function vocabulary and notation.

1. Determine the domain of the function.
2. Find the y-intercept (we are labeling the y-axis with $f(x)$) by evaluating $f(0)$. Find the x-intercept(s) by finding the value(s) of x such that $f(x) = 0$.

3. Determine the type of symmetry that the equation possesses. If $f(-x) = f(x)$, then the function exhibits y-axis symmetry. If $f(-x) = -f(x)$, then the function exhibits origin symmetry. (Note that the definition of a function rules out the possibility that the graph of a function has x-axis symmetry.)

4. Set up a table of ordered pairs that satisfy the equation. The type of symmetry and the domain will affect your choice of values of x in the table.

5. Plot the points associated with the ordered pairs and connect them with a smooth curve. Then, if appropriate, reflect this part of the curve according to the symmetry possessed by the graph.

Now let's tackle graphing the function $f(x) = \dfrac{4x}{x^4 + 1}$. The domain is the set of real numbers. Since $f(0) = 0$, the origin is on the graph. The graph has origin symmetry because

$$f(-x) = \frac{4(-x)}{(-x)^4 + 1}$$

$$= \frac{-4x}{x^4 + 1} = -f(x).$$

Therefore, we can concentrate our table of values on the positive values of x. In Figure 3.45(a) we plotted the points determined by the table. From these values we feel confident about the shape of the curve to the right of $x = 1$; however, we are not sure about the graph between $x = 0$ and $x = 1$. So let's determine some additional points in that region such as $(.2, .80)$, $(.4, 1.56)$, $(.6, 2.12)$, $(.8, 2.27)$, and $(.9, 2.17)$. Thus, the curve must reach a high point at approximately $(.8, 2.27)$. Now we can draw the part of the curve that is in the first quadrant and then reflect this part through the origin to obtain the complete graph as shown in Figure 3.45(b).

x	$f(x)$
0	0
1	2
2	$\frac{8}{17}$
3	$\frac{6}{41}$
4	$\frac{16}{257}$

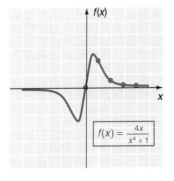

(a)   (b)

F I G U R E   3 . 45

Now let's use a graphing utility to investigate the function $f(x) = \dfrac{4x}{x^4 + 1}$ in more detail. First, let's use a viewing rectangle such that $-7.5 \le x \le 7.5$ and $-5 \le y \le 5$ (Figure 3.46) to get a picture of the function.

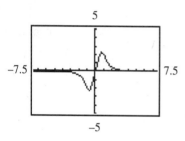

F I G U R E   3 . 46

Figure 3.46 confirms our graph in Figure 3.45 where we did not use a graphing utility. Next, we can take a better look at the high point of the curve in the first quadrant by changing the viewing rectangle so that $0 \le x \le 2$ and $0 \le y \le 3$ (Figure 3.47). By using the trace feature we can determine that the high point of the curve is reached at approximately $(.76, 2.28)$. This approximation is quite close to what we had earlier when plotting points.

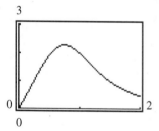

F I G U R E   3 . 47

Finally, let's use the graphing utility to obtain graphs that are transformations of $f(x) = 4x/(x^4 + 1)$. For example, the graph of $f(x) = -4x/(x^4 + 1)$ should be an x-axis reflection, the graph of $f(x) = 4x/(x^4 + 1) + 2$ should be an upward translation of two units, and the graph of $f(x) = 8x/(x^4 + 1)$ should be a stretching by a factor of 2. To validate these claims let's make the following assignments for our graphing utility.

$$Y_1 = \frac{4x}{x^4 + 1}$$

$$Y_2 = -Y_1$$

$$Y_3 = Y_1 + 2$$

$$Y_4 = 2Y_1$$

By activating Y_1 and Y_2 we obtain Figure 3.48. By activating Y_1 and Y_3 we obtain Figure 3.49. By activating Y_1 and Y_4 we obtain Figure 3.50.

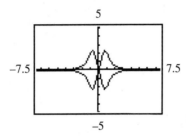

FIGURE 3.48

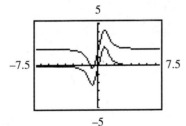

FIGURE 3.49

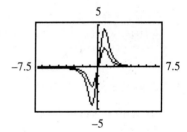

FIGURE 3.50

PROBLEM SET 3.4

For Problems 1–24, graph each of the functions. Each graph represents a transformation or a sequence of transformations of one of the basic curves $f(x) = |x|$, $f(x) = \sqrt{x}$, or $f(x) = x^3$.

1. $f(x) = -|x|$

2. $f(x) = |x - 2|$

3. $f(x) = |x + 4|$

4. $f(x) = 2|x|$

5. $f(x) = |x - 1| + 2$

6. $f(x) = -|x + 2|$

7. $f(x) = 2|x + 2| + 4$

8. $f(x) = -2|x + 1| - 1$

9. $f(x) = -\sqrt{x}$

10. $f(x) = \sqrt{x-3}$

11. $f(x) = \sqrt{x} + 2$

12. $f(x) = 2\sqrt{x-1} + 1$

13. $f(x) = -\sqrt{x} - 3$

14. $f(x) = -\sqrt{x-3}$

15. $f(x) = 2\sqrt{x+2} + 3$

16. $f(x) = \sqrt{-3-x}$

17. $f(x) = -x^3$

18. $f(x) = -2x^3$

19. $f(x) = x^3 - 2$

20. $f(x) = (x+2)^3 - 2$

21. $f(x) = -2(x+1)^3 + 3$

22. $f(x) = -(x-2)^3 - 4$

23. $f(x) = (x-3)^3 - 1$

24. $f(x) = 2x^3 + 1$

25. Graph $f(x) = x^4$. Then graph $f(x) = -x^4$, $f(x) = (x-4)^4$, $f(x) = x^4 - 3$, and $f(x) = (x+3)^4 - 2$.

26. Suppose that the graph of $y = f(x)$ with a domain of $-2 \le x \le 2$ is as follows (Figure 3.51).

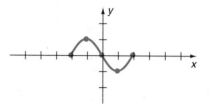

F I G U R E   3 . 51

Sketch the graph of each of the following transformations of $y = f(x)$.

a. $y = f(x) + 3$ **b.** $y = f(x - 2)$

c. $y = -f(x)$ **d.** $y = f(x + 3) - 4$

THOUGHTS into WORDS

27. Are the graphs of the two functions $f(x) = \sqrt{x-2}$ and $g(x) = \sqrt{2-x}$ y-axis reflections of each other? Explain your answer.

28. Are the graphs of $f(x) = 2\sqrt{x}$ and $g(x) = \sqrt{2x}$ identical? Explain your answer.

29. Are the graphs of $f(x) = \sqrt{x+4}$ and $g(x) = \sqrt{-x+4}$ y-axis reflections of each other? Explain your answer.

 GRAPHICS CALCULATOR ACTIVITIES

30. Use your graphics calculator to check your graphs for Problems 1–25.

31. Graph $f(x) = \sqrt{x^2 + 8}$, $f(x) = \sqrt{x^2 + 4}$, and $f(x) = \sqrt{x^2 + 1}$ on the same set of axes. Look at these graphs and predict the graph of $f(x) = \sqrt{x^2 - 4}$. Now graph it with the calculator to test your prediction.

32. For each of the following, (a) predict the general shape and location of the graph, and (b) use your calculator to graph the function to check your prediction.

a. $f(x) = \sqrt{x^2}$

b. $f(x) = \sqrt{x^3}$

c. $f(x) = |x^2|$

d. $f(x) = |x^3|$

33. Graph $f(x) = x^4 + x^3$. Now predict the graph for each of the following and check each prediction with your graphics calculator.

a. $f(x) = x^4 + x^3 - 4$

b. $f(x) = (x-3)^4 + (x-3)^3$

c. $f(x) = -x^4 - x^3$

d. $f(x) = x^4 - x^3$

34. Graph $f(x) = \sqrt[3]{x}$. Now predict the graph for each of the following and check each prediction with your graphics calculator.

a. $f(x) = 5 + \sqrt[3]{x}$ **b.** $f(x) = \sqrt[3]{x+4}$

c. $f(x) = -\sqrt[3]{x}$ **d.** $f(x) = \sqrt[3]{x-3} - 5$

e. $f(x) = \sqrt[3]{-x}$

35. Graph $f(x) = x^5$. Now predict the graph for each of the following and check each prediction with your graphics calculator.

    a. $f(x) = x^5 + 3$

    b. $f(x) = (x + 3)^5$

    c. $f(x) = -x^5$

    d. $f(x) = -2(x - 4)^5 + 2$

36. Graph $f(x) = x^2 - 6x + 13$. Now predict the graph for each of the following and check each prediction with your graphics calculator.

    a. $f(x) = x^2 + 6x + 13$

    b. $f(x) = -x^2 + 6x - 13$

    c. $f(x) = x^2 - 6x$

    d. $f(x) = (x + 3)^2 - 6(x + 3) + 9$

3.5   OPERATIONS ON FUNCTIONS

In subsequent mathematics courses it is common to encounter functions that are defined in terms of sums, differences, products, and quotients of simpler functions. For example, if $h(x) = x^2 + \sqrt{x - 1}$, then we may consider the function h as the sum of f and g where $f(x) = x^2$ and $g(x) = \sqrt{x - 1}$. **In general, if f and g are functions and D is the intersection of their domains**, then the following definitions can be made:

Sum: $(f + g)(x) = f(x) + g(x)$

Difference: $(f - g)(x) = f(x) - g(x)$

Product: $(f \cdot g)(x) = f(x) \cdot g(x)$

Quotient: $\left(\dfrac{f}{g}\right)(x) = \dfrac{f(x)}{g(x)}, \qquad g(x) \neq 0$

EXAMPLE 1

If $f(x) = 3x - 1$ and $g(x) = x^2 - x - 2$, find

    a. $(f + g)(x)$,   **b.** $(f - g)(x)$,

    c. $(f \cdot g)(x)$ **d.** $(f/g)(x)$.

Determine the domain of each.

Solution

    a. $(f + g)(x) = f(x) + g(x) = (3x - 1) + (x^2 - x - 2)$
$$= x^2 + 2x - 3$$

b. $(f - g)(x) = f(x) - g(x) = (3x - 1) - (x^2 - x - 2)$
$$= 3x - 1 - x^2 + x + 2$$
$$= -x^2 + 4x + 1$$

c. $(f \cdot g)(x) = f(x) \cdot g(x) = (3x - 1)(x^2 - x - 2)$
$$= 3x^3 - 3x^2 - 6x - x^2 + x + 2$$
$$= 3x^3 - 4x^2 - 5x + 2$$

d. $\left(\dfrac{f}{g}\right)(x) = \dfrac{f(x)}{g(x)} = \dfrac{3x - 1}{x^2 - x - 2}$

The domain of both f and g is the set of all real numbers. Therefore, the domain of $f + g$, $f - g$, and $f \cdot g$ is the set of all real numbers. For f/g, the denominator $x^2 - x - 2$ cannot equal zero. Solving $x^2 - x - 2 = 0$ produces

$$(x - 2)(x + 1) = 0$$

$$x - 2 = 0 \quad \text{or} \quad x + 1 = 0$$

$$x = 2 \quad \text{or} \quad x = -1.$$

Thus, the domain for f/g is the set of all real numbers except 2 and -1.

Composition of Functions

Besides adding, subtracting, multiplying, and dividing functions there is another important operation called **composition**. The composition of two functions can be defined as follows.

DEFINITION 3.2

The **composition** of functions f and g is defined by

$$(f \circ g)(x) = f(g(x)),$$

for all x in the domain of g such that $g(x)$ is in the domain of f.

The left side, $(f \circ g)(x)$, of the equation in Definition 3.2 can be read, *the composition of f and g* and the right side can be read, *f of g of x*. It may also be helpful for you to mentally picture Definition 3.2 as two function machines hooked together to produce another function (called the **composite function**) as illustrated in Figure 3.52. Notice that what comes out of the g function is substituted into the f function. Thus, composition is sometimes called the **substitution of functions**.

Figure 3.52 also illustrates the fact that $f \circ g$ is defined **for all x in the domain of g such that $g(x)$ is in the domain of f**. In other words, what comes out of g must be capable of being fed into f. Let's consider some examples.

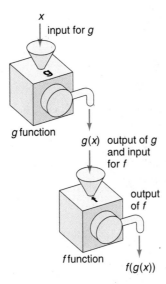

input for g

g function

$g(x)$ output of g
and input
for f

output
of f

f function

$f(g(x))$

F I G U R E   3 . 52

E X A M P L E   2

If $f(x) = x^2$ and $g(x) = 3x - 4$, find $(f \circ g)(x)$ and determine its domain.

Solution

Apply Definition 3.2 to obtain

$$
\begin{aligned}
(f \circ g)(x) &= f(g(x)) \\
&= f(3x - 4) \\
&= (3x - 4)^2 \\
&= 9x^2 - 24x + 16.
\end{aligned}
$$

Because g and f are both defined for all real numbers, so is $f \circ g$.

Definition 3.2, with f and g interchanged, defines the composition of g and f as $(g \circ f)(x) = g(f(x))$.

E X A M P L E   3

If $f(x) = x^2$ and $g(x) = 3x - 4$, find $(g \circ f)(x)$ and determine its domain.

Solution

$$
\begin{aligned}
(g \circ f)(x) &= g(f(x)) \\
&= g(x^2) \\
&= 3x^2 - 4
\end{aligned}
$$

Because f and g are defined for all real numbers, so is $g \circ f$.

The results of Examples 2 and 3 demonstrate an important idea, namely, that the composition of functions is **not a commutative operation**. In other words, $f \circ g \neq g \circ f$ for all functions f and g. However, as you will see in the next section, there is a special class of functions for which $f \circ g = g \circ f$.

EXAMPLE 4

If $f(x) = -x + 2$ and $g(x) = 2x^2 - x + 1$, find $(g \circ f)(x)$ and determine its domain.

Solution

$$
\begin{aligned}
(g \circ f)(x) &= g(f(x)) \\
&= g(-x + 2) \\
&= 2(-x + 2)^2 - (-x + 2) + 1 \\
&= 2(x^2 - 4x + 4) + x - 2 + 1 \\
&= 2x^2 - 8x + 8 + x - 1 \\
&= 2x^2 - 7x + 7
\end{aligned}
$$

Because f and g are defined for all real numbers, so is $g \circ f$.

EXAMPLE 5

If $f(x) = \sqrt{x}$ and $g(x) = 2x - 1$, find $(f \circ g)(x)$ and determine its domain.

Solution

$$
\begin{aligned}
(f \circ g)(x) &= f(g(x)) \\
&= f(2x - 1) \\
&= \sqrt{2x - 1}
\end{aligned}
$$

The domain and range of g is the set of all real numbers, but the domain of f is the nonnegative real numbers. Therefore $g(x)$, which is $2x - 1$, must be nonnegative. So,

$$2x - 1 \geq 0$$

$$2x \geq 1$$

$$x \geq \frac{1}{2}$$

and the domain of $f \circ g$ is $D = \{x \mid x \geq \frac{1}{2}\}$.

EXAMPLE 6

If $f(x) = 2/(x - 1)$ and $g(x) = 1/x$, find $(f \circ g)(x)$ and determine its domain.

Solution

$$
(f \circ g)(x) = f(g(x))
$$

$$
= f\left(\frac{1}{x}\right) = \frac{2}{\dfrac{1}{x} - 1}
$$

$$
= \frac{2}{\dfrac{1 - x}{x}} = \frac{2x}{1 - x}
$$

The domain of g is all real numbers except 0, and the domain of f is all real numbers except 1. Since $g(x)$, which is $1/x$, cannot equal 1,

$$\frac{1}{x} \neq 1$$

$$x \neq 1.$$

Therefore, the domain of $f \circ g$ is $D = \{x \,|\, x \neq 0 \text{ and } x \neq 1\}$.

EXAMPLE 7

If $f(x) = 4/(x + 1)$ and $g(x) = 3/(x - 2)$, find $(g \circ f)(x)$ and determine its domain.

Solution

$$(g \circ f)(x) = g(f(x))$$

$$= g\left(\frac{4}{x + 1}\right)$$

$$= \frac{3}{\dfrac{4}{x + 1} - 2}$$

$$= \frac{3}{\dfrac{4 - 2(x + 1)}{x + 1}}$$

$$= \frac{3}{\dfrac{4 - 2x - 2}{x + 1}}$$

$$= \frac{3(x + 1)}{2 - 2x}$$

The domain of f is all real numbers except -1 and the domain of g is all real numbers except 2. Since $f(x)$, which is $4/(x + 1)$, cannot equal 2

$$\frac{4}{x + 1} \neq 2$$

$$x \neq 1.$$

Therefore, the domain of $g \circ f$ is $D = \{x \,|\, x \neq -1 \text{ and } x \neq 1\}$.

Sometimes in calculus it is necessary to identify two functions that can be used to make up a given composite function. In other words, we have to reverse the process used in the previous examples. Let's consider two examples of this type.

EXAMPLE 8

Express the function $h(x) = \sqrt{5x + 6}$ as the composition of two functions f and g such that $f(g(x)) = h(x)$.

Solution

Think in terms of $f(g(x))$ and let $g(x) = 5x + 6$ and $f(x) = \sqrt{x}$. Then we have

$$f(g(x)) = f(5x + 6)$$
$$= \sqrt{5x + 6}$$
$$= h(x).$$

EXAMPLE 9

Express the function $h(x) = 1/(2x + 1)^3$ as the composition of two functions f and g such that $f(g(x)) = h(x)$.

Solution

Let $g(x) = 2x + 1$ and $f(x) = 1/x^3$. Then we have

$$f(g(x)) = f(2x + 1)$$

$$= \frac{1}{(2x + 1)^3}$$

$$= h(x).$$

Graphical Approach to Composition

A graphing utility can be used to find the graph of a composite function without actually forming the function algebraically. Let's see how this works.

EXAMPLE 10

If $f(x) = x^3$ and $g(x) = x - 4$, use a graphing utility to obtain the graph of $y = (f \circ g)(x)$ and of $y = (g \circ f)(x)$.

Solution

To find the graph of $y = (f \circ g)(x)$ we can make the following assignments.

$$Y_1 = x - 4$$

$$Y_2 = (Y_1)^3$$

Now by activating only Y_2, the graph of $y = (f \circ g)(x)$ will appear as in Figure 3.53. To find the graph of $y = (g \circ f)(x)$ we can make the following assignments.

$$Y_1 = x^3$$

$$Y_2 = Y_1 - 4$$

Again by activating only Y_2, the graph of $y = (g \circ f)(x)$ will appear as in Figure 3.54.

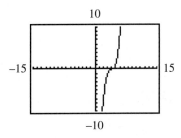

F I G U R E   3 . 53

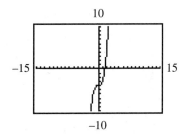

F I G U R E   3 . 54

Take another look at Figure 3.53 and Figure 3.54. Note that in Figure 3.53 the graph of $y = (f \circ g)(x)$ is the basic cubic curve $f(x) = x^3$ shifted 4 units to the right. Likewise, in Figure 3.54 the graph of $y = (g \circ f)(x)$ is the basic cubic curve shifted 4 units downward. These are examples of using composite functions to represent various geometric transformations (a more general concept).

P R O B L E M   S E T   3 . 5

For Problems 1–8, find $f + g, f - g, f \cdot g$, and f/g.

1. $f(x) = 3x - 4, \quad g(x) = 5x + 2$

2. $f(x) = -6x - 1, \quad g(x) = -8x + 7$

3. $f(x) = x^2 - 6x + 4, \quad g(x) = -x - 1$

4. $f(x) = 2x^2 - 3x + 5, \quad g(x) = x^2 - 4$

5. $f(x) = x^2 - x - 1, \quad g(x) = x^2 + 4x - 5$

6. $f(x) = x^2 - 2x - 24, \quad g(x) = x^2 - x - 30$

7. $f(x) = \sqrt{x - 1}, \quad g(x) = \sqrt{x}$

8. $f(x) = \sqrt{x + 2}, \quad g(x) = \sqrt{3x - 1}$

For Problems 9–22, find $(f \circ g)(x)$ and $(g \circ f)(x)$. Also specify the domain for each.

9. $f(x) = 2x, \quad g(x) = 3x - 1$

10. $f(x) = 4x + 1$, $g(x) = 3x$

11. $f(x) = 5x - 3$, $g(x) = 2x + 1$

12. $f(x) = 3 - 2x$, $g(x) = -4x$

13. $f(x) = 3x + 4$, $g(x) = x^2 + 1$

14. $f(x) = 3$, $g(x) = -3x^2 - 1$

15. $f(x) = 3x - 4$, $g(x) = x^2 + 3x - 4$

16. $f(x) = 2x^2 - x - 1$, $g(x) = x + 4$

17. $f(x) = \dfrac{1}{x}$, $g(x) = 2x + 7$

18. $f(x) = \dfrac{1}{x^2}$, $g(x) = x$

19. $f(x) = \sqrt{x - 2}$, $g(x) = 3x - 1$

20. $f(x) = \dfrac{1}{x}$, $g(x) = \dfrac{1}{x^2}$

21. $f(x) = \dfrac{1}{x - 1}$, $g(x) = \dfrac{2}{x}$

22. $f(x) = \dfrac{4}{x + 2}$, $g(x) = \dfrac{3}{2x}$

23. If $f(x) = 3x - 2$ and $g(x) = x^2 + 1$, find $(f \circ g)(-1)$ and $(g \circ f)(3)$.

24. If $f(x) = x^2 - 2$ and $g(x) = x + 4$, find $(f \circ g)(2)$ and $(g \circ f)(-4)$.

25. If $f(x) = 2x - 3$ and $g(x) = x^2 - 3x - 4$, find $(f \circ g)(-2)$ and $(g \circ f)(1)$.

26. If $f(x) = \dfrac{1}{x}$ and $g(x) = 2x + 1$, find $(f \circ g)(1)$ and $(g \circ f)(2)$.

27. If $f(x) = \sqrt{x}$ and $g(x) = 3x - 1$, find $(f \circ g)(4)$ and $(g \circ f)(4)$.

28. If $f(x) = x + 5$ and $g(x) = |x|$, find $(f \circ g)(-4)$ and $(g \circ f)(-4)$.

For Problems 29–34, show that $(f \circ g)(x) = x$ and $(g \circ f)(x) = x$.

29. $f(x) = 2x$, $g(x) = \frac{1}{2}x$

30. $f(x) = \frac{3}{4}x$, $g(x) = \frac{4}{3}x$

31. $f(x) = x - 2$, $g(x) = x + 2$

32. $f(x) = 2x + 1$, $g(x) = \dfrac{x - 1}{2}$

33. $f(x) = 3x + 4$, $g(x) = \dfrac{x - 4}{3}$

34. $f(x) = 4x - 3$, $g(x) = \dfrac{x + 3}{4}$

For Problems 35–40, find two functions f and g such that $f(g(x)) = h(x)$. (You may find more than one correct answer for each of these exercises.)

35. $h(x) = \sqrt[3]{3x - 1}$

36. $h(x) = \sqrt{5 - x}$

37. $h(x) = \dfrac{-2}{5x - 1}$

38. $h(x) = \dfrac{3}{(4x + 1)^2}$

39. $h(x) = (3x - 1)^{2/3}$

40. $h(x) = (2x + 5)^{3/2}$

THOUGHTS into WORDS

41. Discuss whether or not addition, subtraction, multiplication, and division of functions are commutative operations.

42. Explain why the composition of two functions is not a commutative operation.

43. Suppose that we take the composition of two linear functions. Is the newly formed composite function a linear function? Explain your answer.

FURTHER INVESTIGATIONS

44. If $f(x) = 3x - 4$ and $g(x) = ax + b$, find conditions on a and b that will guarantee that $f \circ g = g \circ f$.

45. If $f(x) = x^2$ and $g(x) = \sqrt{x}$, and both have a domain of the set of nonnegative real numbers, then show that $(f \circ g)(x) = x$ and $(g \circ f)(x) = x$.

46. If $f(x) = 3x^2 - 2x - 1$ and $g(x) = x$, find $f \circ g$ and $g \circ f$. (Recall that we have previously named $f(x) = x$ the identity function.)

47. In Section 3.1 we defined an *even function* to be a function such that $f(-x) = f(x)$ and an *odd function* to be one such that $f(-x) = -f(x)$. Verify that (a) the sum of two even functions is an even function, and (b) the sum of two odd functions is an odd function.

 GRAPHICS CALCULATOR ACTIVITIES

48. For each of the following, (a) predict the general shape and location of the graph, and (b) use your calculator to graph the function to check your prediction. (Your knowledge of the graphs of the basic functions that are being added or subtracted should be helpful when making your predictions.)

a. $f(x) = x^4 + x^2$ **b.** $f(x) = x^3 + x^2$

c. $f(x) = x^4 - x^2$ **d.** $f(x) = x^2 - x^4$

e. $f(x) = x^2 - x^3$ **f.** $f(x) = x^3 - x^2$

g. $f(x) = |x| + \sqrt{x}$ **h.** $f(x) = |x| - \sqrt{x}$

49. For each of the following, find the graph of $y = (f \circ g)(x)$ and of $y = (g \circ f)(x)$.

a. $f(x) = x^2$ and $g(x) = x + 5$

b. $f(x) = x^3$ and $g(x) = x + 3$

c. $f(x) = x - 6$ and $g(x) = -x^3$

d. $f(x) = x^2 - 4$ and $g(x) = \sqrt{x}$

e. $f(x) = \sqrt{x}$ and $g(x) = x^2 + 4$

f. $f(x) = \sqrt[3]{x}$ and $g(x) = x^3 - 5$

3.6 INVERSE FUNCTIONS

Recall that the vertical line test stated that, *if each vertical line intersects a graph in no more than one point, then the graph represents a function.* There is also a useful distinction between two basic types of functions. Consider the graphs of the two functions $f(x) = 2x - 1$ and $f(x) = x^2$ in Figure 3.55. In part (a), any *horizontal line* will intersect the graph in more than one point. Therefore, every value of $f(x)$ has one value of x associated with it. Any function that has the additional property of having only one value of x associated with each value of $f(x)$ is called a **one-to-one function**. The function $f(x) = x^2$ is not a one-to-one function because the horizontal line in Figure 3.55(b) intersects the parabola in two points.

Stated another way, a function f is said to be one-to-one if $x_1 \neq x_2$ implies that $f(x_1) \neq f(x_2)$. In other words, different values for x always result in different values for $f(x)$. Thus, without a graph we can show that $f(x) = 2x - 1$ is a one-to-one function as follows: If $x_1 \neq x_2$, then $2x_1 \neq 2x_2$ and therefore $2x_1 - 1 \neq 2x_2 - 1$. Furthermore, we can show that $f(x) = x^2$ is not a one-to-one function because

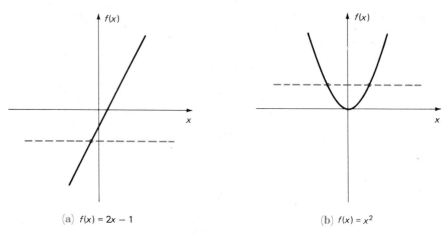

(a) $f(x) = 2x - 1$ (b) $f(x) = x^2$

F I G U R E   3 . 5 5

$f(2) = 4$ and $f(-2) = 4$; that is, different values for x produce the same value for $f(x)$.

Now let's consider a one-to-one function f that assigns to each x in its domain D, the value $f(x)$ in its range R (Figure 3.56(a)). We can define a new function g that will assign $f(x)$ in R back to x in D as indicated in Figure 3.56(b). The functions f and g are called **inverse functions** of one another. The following definition precisely states this concept.

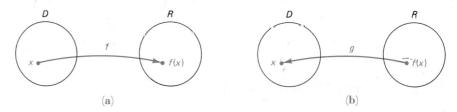

(a)   (b)

F I G U R E   3 . 5 6

D E F I N I T I O N   3 . 3

Let f be a one-to-one function with a domain of X and a range of Y. A function g with a domain of Y and a range of X is called the **inverse function** of f if

$$(f \circ g)(x) = x \quad \text{for every } x \text{ in } Y$$

and

$$(g \circ f)(x) = x \quad \text{for every } x \text{ in } X.$$

In Definition 3.3, note that for f and g to be inverses of each other, the domain of f must equal the range of g and the range of f must equal the domain of g. Furthermore, g must reverse the correspondences given by f, and f must reverse the correspondences given by g. In other words, inverse functions *undo* each other. Let's use Definition 3.3 to verify that two specific functions are inverses of each other.

E X A M P L E   1

Verify that $f(x) = 4x - 5$ and $g(x) = (x + 5)/4$ are inverse functions.

Solution

Because the set of real numbers is the domain and range of both functions, we know that the domain of f equals the range of g, and the range of f equals the domain of g. Furthermore, we can show that

$$(f \circ g)(x) = f(g(x))$$

$$= f\left(\frac{x + 5}{4}\right)$$

$$= 4\left(\frac{x + 5}{4}\right) - 5 = x$$

and

$$(g \circ f)(x) = g(f(x))$$

$$= g(4x - 5)$$

$$= \frac{4x - 5 + 5}{4} = x.$$

Therefore, f and g are inverses of each other. ▬▬▬

E X A M P L E   2

Verify that $f(x) = x^2 + 1$ for $x \geq 0$ and $g(x) = \sqrt{x - 1}$ for $x \geq 1$ are inverse functions.

Solution

First, notice that the domain of f equals the range of g, namely, the set of nonnegative real numbers. Also, the range of f equals the domain of g, namely, the set of real numbers greater than or equal to one. Furthermore, we can show that

$$(f \circ g)(x) = f(g(x))$$

$$= f(\sqrt{x - 1})$$

$$= (\sqrt{x - 1})^2 + 1$$

$$= x - 1 + 1 = x$$

and

$$(g \circ f)(x) = g(f(x))$$
$$= g(x^2 + 1)$$
$$= \sqrt{x^2 + 1 - 1} = \sqrt{x^2} = x. \qquad \sqrt{x^2} = x \text{ because } x \geq 1.$$

Therefore, f and g are inverses of each other.

The inverse of a function f is commonly denoted by f^{-1} (read, f *inverse* or *the inverse of f*). Do not confuse the -1 in f^{-1} with a negative exponent. The symbol f^{-1} *does not* mean $1/f^1$, but refers to the inverse function of function f.

Remember that a function can also be thought of as a set of ordered pairs for which no two of the ordered pairs have the same first element. A one-to-one function further requires that no two of the ordered pairs have the same second element. Then, if the components of each ordered pair of a given one-to-one function are interchanged, the resulting function and the given function are inverses of each other. Thus, if

$$f = \{(1, 4), (2, 7), (5, 9)\}$$

then

$$f^{-1} = \{(4, 1), (7, 2), (9, 5)\}.$$

Graphically, two functions that are inverses of each other are *mirror images* with reference to the line $y = x$. This is due to the fact that ordered pairs (a, b) and (b, a) are mirror images with respect to the line $y = x$, as illustrated in Figure 3.57.

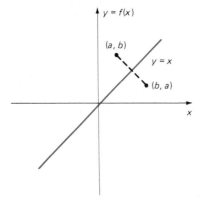

F I G U R E   3 . 57

(We will have you verify this in the next set of exercises.) Therefore, if the graph of a function f is known, as in Figure 3.58(a), then the graph of f^{-1} can be determined by reflecting f across the line $y = x$ (Figure 3.58(b)).

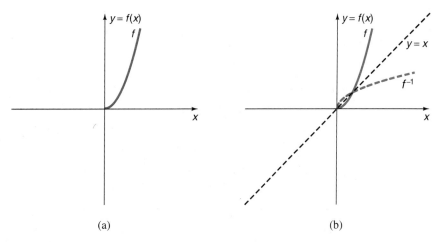

(a)   (b)

F I G U R E   3 . 58

Finding Inverse Functions

The idea of inverse functions *undoing each other* provides the basis for an informal approach to finding the inverse of a function. Consider the function

$$f(x) = 2x + 1.$$

To each x this function assigns *twice x plus 1*. To undo this function, we can *subtract 1 and divide by 2*. So the inverse should be

$$f^{-1}(x) = \frac{x - 1}{2}.$$

Now let's verify that f and f^{-1} are inverses of each other.

$$(f \circ f^{-1})(x) = f(f^{-1}(x))$$

$$= f\left(\frac{x - 1}{2}\right)$$

$$= 2\left(\frac{x - 1}{2}\right) + 1 = x - 1 + 1 = x$$

and

$$(f^{-1} \circ f)(x) = f^{-1}(f(x))$$

$$= f^{-1}(2x + 1)$$

$$= \frac{2x + 1 - 1}{2}$$

$$= \frac{2x}{2} = x$$

Thus, the inverse of $f(x) = 2x + 1$ is $f^{-1}(x) = (x - 1)/2$. This informal approach may not work very well with more complex functions, but it does emphasize how inverse functions are related to each other. A more formal and systematic technique for finding the inverse of a function is the following.

1. Replace the symbol $f(x)$ by its equivalent y.
2. Interchange x and y.
3. Solve the equation for y in terms of x.
4. Replace y by the symbol $f^{-1}(x)$.

The following examples illustrate this technique.

EXAMPLE 3

Find the inverse of $f(x) = \frac{2}{3}x + \frac{3}{5}$.

Solution

Replace $f(x)$ by y and the equation becomes

$$y = \frac{2}{3}x + \frac{3}{5}.$$

Interchange x and y, which produces

$$x = \frac{2}{3}y + \frac{3}{5}.$$

Now, solve for y and you obtain

$$x = \frac{2}{3}y + \frac{3}{5}$$

$$15(x) = 15\left(\frac{2}{3}y + \frac{3}{5}\right)$$

$$15x = 10y + 9$$

$$15x - 9 = 10y$$

$$\frac{15x - 9}{10} = y$$

Finally, replace y by $f^{-1}(x)$ and the inverse function can be expressed as

$$f^{-1}(x) = \frac{15x - 9}{10}.$$

The domain of f is equal to the range of f^{-1} (both are the set of real numbers), and the range of f equals the domain of f^{-1} (both are the set of real numbers). Furthermore, we could show that $(f \circ f^{-1})(x) = x$ and $(f^{-1} \circ f)(x) = x$. We will leave this for you to complete.

Does $f(x) = x^2 - 2$ have an inverse? Sometimes a graph of the function helps answer such a question. In Figure 3.59(a) it should be evident that f is not a one-to-one function and therefore it cannot have an inverse. However, it should also be apparent from the graph that if we restrict the domain of f to be the nonnegative real numbers, then it is a one-to-one function and it should have an inverse (Figure 3.59(b)). The next example illustrates finding this inverse.

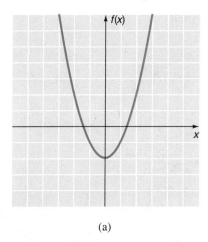   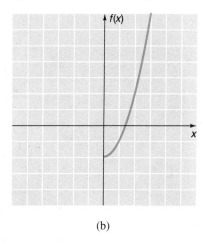

(a)   (b)

F I G U R E   3 . 59

E X A M P L E   4

Find the inverse of $f(x) = x^2 - 2$, where $x \geq 0$.

Solution

Replace $f(x)$ by y and the equation becomes

$$y = x^2 - 2, \qquad x \geq 0.$$

Interchange x and y, which produces

$$x = y^2 - 2, \qquad y \geq 0.$$

Now let's solve for y; keep in mind that y is to be nonnegative.

$$x = y^2 - 2$$
$$x + 2 = y^2$$
$$\sqrt{x + 2} = y, \quad \text{where } x \geq -2$$

Finally, replace y by $f^{-1}(x)$, and the inverse function can be expressed as

$$f^{-1}(x) = \sqrt{x + 2}, \quad \text{where } x \geq -2.$$

The domain of f equals the range of f^{-1} (both are the nonnegative real numbers), and the range of f equals the domain of f^{-1} (both are the real numbers greater than or equal to -2). It can be shown that $(f \circ f^{-1})(x) = x$ and $(f^{-1} \circ f)(x) = x$. We will, again, leave this for you to complete.

Increasing and Decreasing Functions

Some general ideas can be formulated that were specifically illustrated in Example 4. In Figure 3.60, the function f is said to be *increasing* on the intervals $(-\infty, x_1]$ and $[x_2, \infty)$, and f is said to be *decreasing* on the interval $[x_1, x_2]$. More specifically, increasing and decreasing functions are defined as follows.

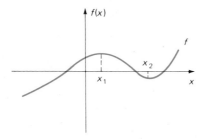

F I G U R E   3 . 60

DEFINITION 3.4

Let f be a function, with the interval I a subset of the domain of f. Let x_1 and x_2 be in I. Then

1. f is *increasing on I* if $f(x_1) < f(x_2)$ whenever $x_1 < x_2$,

2. f is *decreasing on I* if $f(x_1) > f(x_2)$ whenever $x_1 < x_2$, and

3. f is *constant on I* if $f(x_1) = f(x_2)$ for every x_1 and x_2.

Apply Definition 3.4 and you will see that the quadratic function $f(x) = x^2$ shown in Figure 3.61 is decreasing on $(-\infty, 0]$ and increasing on $[0, \infty)$. Likewise, the linear function $f(x) = 2x$ in Figure 3.62 is increasing throughout its domain of real numbers, so we say it is increasing on $(-\infty, \infty)$. The function $f(x) = -2x$ in Figure 3.63 is decreasing on $(-\infty, \infty)$. For our purposes in this text, we will rely on plotting points to determine where functions are increasing and decreasing. More formal techniques for determining where functions increase and decrease are developed in calculus.

A function that is always increasing (or always decreasing) over its entire domain is one-to-one and so has an inverse. Furthermore, as illustrated by Example 4, even if a function is not one-to-one over its entire domain, it may be so over some subset of the domain. It then has an inverse over this restricted domain. We will use this idea in Chapter 6 to construct inverses of the basic trigonometric functions.

As functions become more complex, a graphing utility can be used to help with problems of the type we've been discussing in this section. For example,

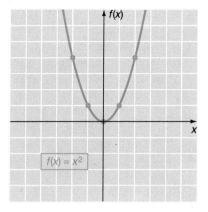

FIGURE   3.61

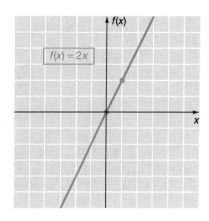

FIGURE   3.62

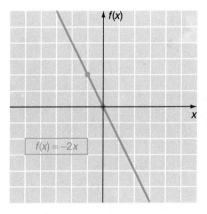

FIGURE   3.63

suppose that we want to know if the function $f(x) = (3x + 1)/(x - 4)$ is a one-to-one function and has an inverse. Using a graphing utility, we can quickly get a sketch of the graph as shown in Figure 3.64. Then by applying the horizontal line test to the graph we feel fairly certain that the function is one-to-one. (Later we will develop some concepts that will allow us to be absolutely certain of this conclusion.)

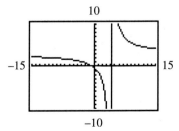

FIGURE   3.64

A graphing utility can also be used to help determine intervals on which a function is increasing or decreasing. For example, to determine such intervals for the function $f(x) = \sqrt{x^2 + 4}$, let's use a graphing utility to get a sketch of the curve as shown in Figure 3.65. From this graph we see that the function is decreasing on the interval $(-\infty, 0]$ and increasing on the interval $[0, \infty)$.

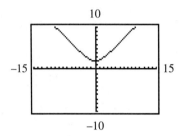

FIGURE 3.65

PROBLEM SET 3.6

For Problems 1–6, determine whether or not the graph represents a one-to-one function (Figures 3.66–3.71).

1.

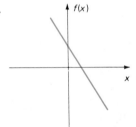

FIGURE 3.66

2.

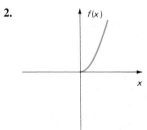

FIGURE 3.67

3.

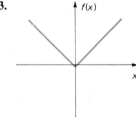

FIGURE 3.68

4.

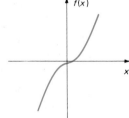

FIGURE 3.69

5.

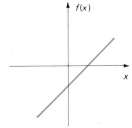

FIGURE 3.70

6.

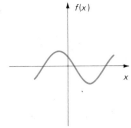

FIGURE 3.71

For Problems 7–14, determine whether the function f is one-to-one.

7. $f(x) = 5x + 4$ **8.** $f(x) = -3x + 4$

9. $f(x) = x^3$ **10.** $f(x) = x^5 + 1$

11. $f(x) = |x| + 1$ **12.** $f(x) = -|x| - 2$

13. $f(x) = -x^4$ **14.** $f(x) = x^4 + 1$

For each of the functions in Problems 15–18 (a) list the domain and range, (b) form the inverse function f^{-1}, and (c) list the domain and range of f^{-1}.

15. $f = \{(1, 5), (2, 9), (5, 21)\}$

16. $f = \{(1, 1), (4, 2), (9, 3), (16, 4)\}$

17. $f = \{(0, 0), (2, 8), (-1, -1), (-2, -8)\}$

18. $f = \{(-1, 1), (-2, 4), (-3, 9), (-4, 16)\}$

For each of the Problems 19–26, verify that the two given functions are inverses of each other.

19. $f(x) = 5x - 9$ and $g(x) = \dfrac{x + 9}{5}$

20. $f(x) = -3x + 4$ and $g(x) = \dfrac{4 - x}{3}$

21. $f(x) = -\dfrac{1}{2}x + \dfrac{5}{6}$ and $g(x) = -2x + \dfrac{5}{3}$

22. $f(x) = x^3 + 1$ and $g(x) = \sqrt[3]{x - 1}$

23. $f(x) = \dfrac{1}{x - 1}$ for $x > 1$, and $g(x) = \dfrac{x + 1}{x}$ for $x > 0$

24. $f(x) = x^2 + 2$ for $x \geq 0$, and $g(x) = \sqrt{x - 2}$ for $x \geq 2$

25. $f(x) = \sqrt{2x - 4}$ for $x \geq 2$, and $g(x) = \dfrac{x^2 + 4}{2}$ for $x \geq 0$

26. $f(x) = x^2 - 4$ for $x \geq 0$, and $g(x) = \sqrt{x + 4}$ for $x \geq -4$

For Problems 27–36, determine if f and g are inverse functions.

27. $f(x) = 3x$ and $g(x) = -\dfrac{1}{3}x$

28. $f(x) = \dfrac{3}{4}x - 2$ and $g(x) = \dfrac{4}{3}x + \dfrac{8}{3}$

29. $f(x) = x^3$ and $g(x) = \sqrt[3]{x}$

30. $f(x) = \dfrac{1}{x + 1}$ and $g(x) = \dfrac{1 - x}{x}$

31. $f(x) = x$ and $g(x) = \dfrac{1}{x}$

32. $f(x) = \dfrac{3}{5}x + \dfrac{1}{3}$ and $g(x) = \dfrac{5}{3}x - 3$

33. $f(x) = x^2 - 3$ for $x \geq 0$, and $g(x) = \sqrt{x + 3}$ for $x \geq -3$

34. $f(x) = |x - 1|$ for $x \geq 1$, and $g(x) = |x + 1|$ for $x \geq 0$

35. $f(x) = \sqrt{x + 1}$ and $g(x) = x^2 - 1$ for $x \geq 0$

36. $f(x) = \sqrt{2x - 2}$ and $g(x) = \dfrac{1}{2}x^2 + 1$

For Problems 37–48, (a) find f^{-1}, and (b) verify that $(f \circ f^{-1})(x) = x$ and $(f^{-1} \circ f)(x) = x$.

37. $f(x) = x - 4$ **38.** $f(x) = 2x - 1$

39. $f(x) = -3x - 4$ **40.** $f(x) = -5x + 6$

41. $f(x) = \dfrac{3}{4}x - \dfrac{5}{6}$ **42.** $f(x) = \dfrac{2}{3}x - \dfrac{1}{4}$

43. $f(x) = -\dfrac{2}{3}x$ **44.** $f(x) = \dfrac{4}{3}x$

45. $f(x) = \sqrt{x}$ **46.** $f(x) = \dfrac{1}{x}$

47. $f(x) = x^2 + 4$ for $x \geq 0$

48. $f(x) = x^2 + 1$ for $x \leq 0$

For Problems 49–56 (a) find f^{-1}, and (b) graph f and f^{-1} on the same set of axes.

49. $f(x) = 3x$ **50.** $f(x) = -x$

51. $f(x) = 2x + 1$ **52.** $f(x) = -3x - 3$

53. $f(x) = \dfrac{2}{x - 1}$ for $x > 1$

54. $f(x) = \dfrac{-1}{x - 2}$ for $x > 2$

55. $f(x) = x^2 - 4$ for $x \geq 0$

56. $f(x) = \sqrt{x - 3}$ for $x \geq 3$

For Problems 57–64 indicate the intervals on which the given function is increasing and the intervals on which it is decreasing.

57. $f(x) = x^2 + 1$ **58.** $f(x) = x^3$

59. $f(x) = -3x + 1$ **60.** $f(x) = (x - 3)^2 + 1$

61. $f(x) = -(x + 2)^2 - 1$ **62.** $f(x) = x^2 - 2x + 6$

63. $f(x) = -2x^2 - 16x - 35$

64. $f(x) = x^2 + 3x - 1$

THOUGHTS into WORDS

65. Are the functions $f(x) = x^4$ and $g(x) = \sqrt[4]{x}$ inverses of each other? Explain your answer.

66. Are the functions $f(x) = x^4 + 1$ for $x \geq 0$ and $g(x) = \sqrt[4]{x - 1}$ for $x \geq 1$ inverses of each other? Explain your answer.

67. What does it mean to say that 2 and -2 are additive inverses of each other? What does it mean to say that 2 and $\frac{1}{2}$ are multiplicative inverses of each other? What does it mean to say that the functions $f(x) = x - 2$ and $g(x) = x + 2$ are inverses of each other? Do you think that the concept of "inverse" is being used in a consistent manner? Explain your answer.

FURTHER INVESTIGATIONS

68. Explain why every nonconstant linear function has an inverse.

69. The function notation and the operation of composition can be used to find inverses as follows: To find the inverse of $f(x) = 5x + 3$, we know $f(f^{-1}(x))$ must produce x. Therefore,

$$f(f^{-1}(x)) = 5(f^{-1}(x)) + 3 = x$$

$$5(f^{-1}(x)) = x - 3$$

$$f^{-1}(x) = \frac{x - 3}{5}.$$

Use this approach to find the inverse of each of the following functions.

a. $f(x) = 3x - 9$ **b.** $f(x) = -2x + 6$

c. $f(x) = -x + 1$ **d.** $f(x) = 2x$

e. $f(x) = -5x$ **f.** $f(x) = x^2 + 6$ for $x \geq 0$

70. If $f(x) = 2x + 3$ and $g(x) = 3x - 5$, find
(a) $(f \circ g)^{-1}(x)$, (b) $(f^{-1} \circ g^{-1})(x)$, and
(c) $(g^{-1} \circ f^{-1})(x)$.

GRAPHICS CALCULATOR ACTIVITIES

71. For Problems 37–44, graph the given function, the inverse function that you found, and $f(x) = x$ on the same set of axes. In each case the given function and its inverse should produce graphs that are reflections of each other through the line $f(x) = x$.

72. There is another way that we can use the graphics calculator to help show that two functions are inverses of each other. Suppose that we want to show that $f(x) = x^2 - 2$ for $x \geq 0$ and $g(x) = \sqrt{x + 2}$ for $x \geq -2$ are inverses of each other. Let's make the following assignments for our graphics calculator.

$$f: \qquad Y_1 = x^2 - 2$$

$$g: \qquad Y_2 = \sqrt{x + 2}$$

$$f \circ g: \qquad Y_3 = (Y_2)^2 - 2$$

$$g \circ f: \qquad Y_4 = \sqrt{Y_1 + 2}$$

Now we can proceed as follows:

a. Graph $Y_1 = x^2 - 2$ and note that for $x \geq 0$, the range is greater than or equal to -2.

b. Graph $Y_2 = \sqrt{x + 2}$ and note that for $x \geq -2$, the range is greater than or equal to 0.

$\left(\text{Thus, the domain of } f \text{ equals the range of } g \atop \text{and the range of } f \text{ equals the domain of } g. \right)$

c. Graph $Y_3 = (Y_2)^2 - 2$ for $x \geq -2$ and observe the line $y = x$ for $x \geq -2$.

d. Graph $Y_4 = \sqrt{Y_1 + 2}$ for $x \geq 0$ and observe the line $y = x$ for $x \geq 0$.

$\left(\text{Thus, } (f \circ g)(x) = x \text{ and } (g \circ f)(x) = x \text{ and the} \atop \text{two functions are inverses of each other.} \right)$

Use this approach to check your answer for Problems 45–48.

73. Use the technique demonstrated in Problem 72 to show that $f(x) = x/\sqrt{x^2 + 1}$ and $g(x) = x/\sqrt{1 - x^2}$ for $-1 < x < 1$ are inverses of each other.

CHAPTER 3 SUMMARY

The function concept serves as a thread to tie Chapter 3 together.

Function Concept

DEFINITION 3.1

A function f is a correspondence between two sets X and Y that assigns to each element x of set X one and only one element y of set Y. The element y that is assigned is called the **image** of x. The set X is called the **domain** of the function and the set of all images is called the **range of the function**.

The following facts about functions are important to remember.

1. A function can also be thought of as a set of ordered pairs for which no two of the ordered pairs have the same first component.

2. If each vertical line intersects a graph in no more than one point, then the graph represents a function.

3. If no member of the range is assigned to more than one member of the domain, then the function is a one-to-one function.

4. If each horizontal line intersects the graph of a function in no more than one point, then the graph represents a one-to-one function.

Graphing Functions

Any function that can be written in the form

$$f(x) = ax + b,$$

where a and b are real numbers, is a linear function. The graph of a linear function is a straight line. Any function that can be written in the form

$$f(x) = ax^2 + bx + c,$$

where a, b, and c are real numbers and $a \neq 0$, is a quadratic function. The graph of any quadratic function is a parabola that can be drawn using either one of the following methods.

1. Express the function in the form $f(x) = a(x - h)^2 + k$ and use the values of a, h, and k to determine the parabola.

2. Express the function in the form $f(x) = ax^2 + bx + c$ and use the fact that the vertex is at $(-b/(2a), f(-b/(2a)))$ and the axis of symmetry is $x = -b/(2a)$.

Another important graphing technique is the ability to recognize equations of transformations of basic curves. We worked with the following transformations in this chapter.

Vertical Translation

The graph of $y = f(x) + k$ is the graph of $y = f(x)$ shifted k units upward if $k > 0$ or shifted $|k|$ units downward if $k < 0$.

Horizontal Translation

The graph of $y = f(x - h)$ is the graph of $y = f(x)$ shifted h units to the right if $h > 0$ or shifted $|h|$ units to the left if $h < 0$.

x-axis Reflection

The graph of $y = -f(x)$ is the graph of $y = f(x)$ reflected through the x-axis.

y-axis Reflection

The graph of $y = f(-x)$ is the graph of $y = f(x)$ reflected through the y-axis.

Vertical Stretching and Shrinking

The graph of $y = cf(x)$ is obtained from the graph of $y = f(x)$ by multiplying the y-coordinates of $y = f(x)$ by c. If $c > 1$, the graph is said to be *stretched* by a factor of c, and if $0 < c < 1$, the graph is said to be *shrunk* by a factor of c.

The following suggestions are made for graphing functions that are not familiar to you.

1. Determine the domain of the function.
2. Find the intercepts.
3. Determine the type of symmetry that the equation exhibits.
4. Set up a table of values that will satisfy the equation. The type of symmetry and the domain will affect your choice of values for x in the table.
5. Plot the points associated with the ordered pairs and connect them with a smooth curve. Then, if appropriate, reflect this part of the curve according to the symmetry possessed by the graph.

Operations on Functions

Sum of two functions: $(f + g)(x) = f(x) + g(x)$

Difference of two functions: $(f - g)(x) = f(x) - g(x)$

Product of two functions: $(f \cdot g)(x) = f(x) \cdot g(x)$

Quotient of two functions: $\left(\dfrac{f}{g}\right)(x) = \dfrac{f(x)}{g(x)}, \qquad g(x) \neq 0$

DEFINITION 3.2

The composition of functions f and g is defined by

$$(f \circ g)(x) = f(g(x)),$$

for all x in the domain of g such that $g(x)$ is in the domain of f.

Remember that the composition of functions is *not a commutative operation*.

Inverse Functions

DEFINITION 3.3

Let f be a one-to-one function with a domain of X and a range of Y. A function g, with a domain of Y and a range of X, is called the inverse function of f if

$$(f \circ g)(x) = x \quad \text{for every } x \text{ in } Y$$

and

$$(g \circ f)(x) = x \quad \text{for every } x \text{ in } X.$$

Keep in mind the following facts about inverse functions.

1. The inverse of a function f is denoted by f^{-1}.
2. Graphically, two functions that are inverses of each other are *mirror images with reference to the line $y = x$*.
3. A systematic technique for finding the inverse of a function can be described as follows:
   a. Replace the symbol $f(x)$ by its equivalent y.
   b. Interchange x and y.
   c. Solve the equation for y in terms of x.
   d. Replace y by the symbol $f^{-1}(x)$.

Don't forget that the domain of f must equal the range of f^{-1}, and the domain of f^{-1} must equal the range of f.

Applications of Functions

Quadratic functions produce parabolas that have either a *minimum* or *maximum value*. Therefore, real world minimum or maximum value problems that can be described by a quadratic function can be solved using the techniques we studied in this chapter.

CHAPTER 3 REVIEW PROBLEM SET

1. a. If $f(x) = 3x^2 - 2x - 1$, find $f(2)$, $f(-1)$, and $f(-3)$.

b. If $f(x) = \begin{cases} 2x + 6 & \text{for } x \geq 0 \\ 3x - 4 & \text{for } x < 0 \end{cases}$, find $f(4)$, $f(0)$, and $f(-2)$.

2. For each of the following functions, find
$$\frac{f(a + h) - f(a)}{h}.$$

a. $f(x) = -5x + 4$

b. $f(x) = 2x^2 - x + 4$

c. $f(x) = -3x^2 + 2x - 5$

3. Determine the domain and range of the function $f(x) = x^2 + 5$.

4. Determine the domain of the function
$$f(x) = \frac{2}{2x^2 + 7x - 4}.$$

5. Express the domain of $f(x) = \sqrt{x^2 - 7x + 10}$ using interval notation.

For Problems 6–15, graph each of the functions.

6. $f(x) = -2x + 2$ **7.** $f(x) = 2x^2 - 1$

8. $f(x) = -\sqrt{x - 2} + 1$ **9.** $f(x) = x^2 - 8x + 17$

10. $f(x) = -x^3 + 2$ **11.** $f(x) = 2|x - 1| + 3$

12. $f(x) = -2x^2 - 12x - 19$ **13.** $f(x) = -\frac{1}{3}x + 1$

14. $f(x) = -\frac{2}{x^2}$ **15.** $f(x) = 2|x| - x$

16. If $f(x) = 2x + 3$ and $g(x) = x^2 - 4x - 3$, find $f + g$, $f - g$, $f \cdot g$, and $\frac{f}{g}$.

For Problems 17–20, find $(f \circ g)(x)$ and $(g \circ f)(x)$. Also specify the domain for each.

17. $f(x) = 3x - 9$ and $g(x) = -2x + 7$

18. $f(x) = x^2 - 5$ and $g(x) = 5x - 4$

19. $f(x) = \sqrt{x - 5}$ and $g(x) = x + 2$

20. $f(x) = \frac{1}{x - 3}$ and $g(x) = \frac{1}{x + 2}$

21. If $f(x) = |x|$ and $g(x) = x^2 - x - 1$, find $(f \circ g)(1)$ and $(g \circ f)(-3)$.

22. Verify that $f(x) = x^2 + 8$ for $x \geq 0$ and $g(x) = \sqrt{x - 8}$ for $x \geq 8$ are inverse functions.

For Problems 23–26, determine if f and g are inverse functions.

23. $f(x) = 7x - 1$ and $g(x) = \dfrac{x + 1}{7}$

24. $f(x) = -\dfrac{2}{3}x$ and $g(x) = \dfrac{3}{2}x$

25. $f(x) = x^2 - 6$ for $x \geq 0$ and $g(x) = \sqrt{x + 6}$

26. $f(x) = 2 - x^2$ for $x \geq 0$ and $g(x) = \sqrt{2 - x}$

For Problems 27–30, (a) find f^{-1}, and (b) verify that $(f \circ f^{-1})(x) = x$ and $(f^{-1} \circ f)(x) = x$.

27. $f(x) = 4x + 5$ **28.** $f(x) = -3x - 7$

29. $f(x) = \dfrac{5}{6}x - \dfrac{1}{3}$ **30.** $f(x) = -2 - x^2$ for $x \geq 0$

31. A group of students is arranging a chartered flight to Europe. The charge per person is $496 if 100 students go on the flight. If more than 100 students go, the charge per student is reduced by an amount equal to $4 times the number of students above 100. How many students should the airline try to get in order to maximize their revenue?

32. For each of the following functions, determine whether it is even, odd, or neither even nor odd.

a. $f(x) = 2x^3 + 3$ **b.** $f(x) = x^3 + x$

c. $f(x) = 4x^2 + 1$

33. Find the minimum value of the function $f(x) = 3x^2 - 12x + 26$.

34. Find the maximum value of the function $f(x) = -2x^2 - 4x + 3$.

35. If $h(x) = \sqrt{5x - 2}$, find f and g such that $f(g(x)) = h(x)$.

For Problems 36 and 37, find the intervals on which the function is increasing and the intervals on which it is decreasing.

36. $f(x) = -2x^2 + 16x - 35$ **37.** $f(x) = 2\sqrt{x - 3}$

EXPONENTIAL AND LOGARITHMIC FUNCTIONS

E arthquakes in San Francisco in 1989 and in Iran in 1990 were reported to have Richter numbers of 6.9 and 7.7, respectively. Using the definition of a Richter number, which is given in terms of the concept of a logarithm, we can estimate that the earthquake in Iran was approximately 6 times as intense as the one in San Francisco.

In this chapter we will (1) review the basic relationships between roots and exponents, (2) review the basic relationships between exponents and logarithms, (3) study a variety of exponential and logarithmic functions, and (4) use the concepts of exponents and logarithms to expand our problem solving skills. Your calculator will be a valuable tool throughout this chapter.

4

Did you know that if you would invest $500 today at 8% interest compounded annually, in 40 years that $500 would grow to $10,862.26? Compound interest is one of the many applications of exponential growth.

4.1 RADICALS

We did a little work with radicals in Chapter 1, but now it is time to unify some ideas pertaining to roots and exponents. To **square a number** means to use the number as a factor twice. For example, $4^2 = 4 \cdot 4 = 16$, and $(-4)^2 = (-4)(-4) = 16$. A **square root of a number** is one of its two equal factors. Thus, 4 and -4 are square roots of 16. Likewise, $2i$ and $-2i$ are square roots of -4 because $(2i)^2 = 4i^2 = 4(-1) = -4$, and $(-2i)^2 = 4i^2 = 4(-1) = -4$. In general, a is a square root of b if $a^2 = b$. The following generalizations are a direct consequence of the previous statement.

1. Every positive real number has two real number square roots; one is positive and the other is negative; they are opposites of each other.

2. Every negative real number has two complex but nonreal square roots; they are opposites of each other.

3. The square root of 0 is 0.

The symbol, $\sqrt{}$, called a **radical sign**, is used to designate the nonnegative square root, which is called the **principal square root**. The number under the radical sign is called the **radicand** and the entire expression, such as $\sqrt{16}$, we refer to as a **radical**. Thus, we can write $\sqrt{25} = 5$, $-\sqrt{25} = -5$, $\sqrt{-9} = i\sqrt{9} = 3i$, and $-\sqrt{-9} = -i\sqrt{9} = -3i$.

To **cube a number** means to use the number as a factor three times. For example, $2^3 = 2 \cdot 2 \cdot 2 = 8$, and $(-2)^3 = (-2)(-2)(-2) = -8$. A **cube root of a number** is one of its three equal factors. Thus, 2 is a cube root of 8 and -2 is a cube root of -8. Two other cube roots of 8 can be found by solving the equation $x^3 = 8$ as follows.

$$x^3 = 8$$

$$x^3 - 8 = 0$$

$$(x - 2)(x^2 + 2x + 4) = 0 \qquad \text{Factor the difference of two cubes}$$

$$x - 2 = 0 \qquad \text{or} \qquad x^2 + 2x + 4 = 0$$

$$x = 2 \qquad \text{or} \qquad x = \frac{-2 \pm \sqrt{4 - 16}}{2} = \frac{-2 \pm \sqrt{-12}}{2}$$

$$= \frac{-2 \pm 2i\sqrt{3}}{2} = -1 \pm i\sqrt{3}$$

So the three cube roots of 8 are 2, $-1 + i\sqrt{3}$, and $-1 - i\sqrt{3}$. In general, a is a cube root of b if $a^3 = b$. We can make the following generalizations.

1. Every positive real number has one positive real number cube root and two nonreal complex cube roots.

2. Every negative real number has one negative real number cube root and two nonreal complex cube roots.

3. The cube root of 0 is 0.

The symbol $\sqrt[3]{}$ is used to designate the real number cube root. Thus we can write $\sqrt[3]{8} = 2$, $\sqrt[3]{-8} = -2$, $\sqrt[3]{\frac{1}{27}} = \frac{1}{3}$, and $\sqrt[3]{-\frac{1}{27}} = -\frac{1}{3}$.

The concept of root can be extended to fourth roots, fifth roots, sixth roots, and in general, nth roots. In Chapter 7 we will develop a technique for finding all of the roots of a given number, but for now let's direct our attention to only the real roots of real numbers. The following generalizations pertaining to real nth roots can be made.

If n is an *even positive* integer, then the following statements are true.

1. Every positive real number has exactly two real nth roots, one positive and one negative. For example, the real fourth roots of 16 are 2 and -2.

2. Negative real numbers do not have nth roots. For example, there are no real fourth roots of -16.

If n is an *odd positive integer greater than one,* then the following statements are true.

1. Every real number has exactly one real nth root.

2. The real nth root of a positive number is positive. For example, the real fifth root of 32 is 2.

3. The real nth root of a negative number is negative. For example, the real fifth root of -32 is -2.

The **real roots** of real numbers are defined by the statement

$$\sqrt[n]{b} = a \quad \text{if and only if} \quad a^n = b$$

provided that both a and b are nonnegative and n is a positive integer greater than one, or that both a and b are negative and n is an odd positive integer greater than one. The symbol $\sqrt[n]{b}$ designates the nonnegative root if n is even and designates the unique real root if n is odd. Thus, we can write $\sqrt[4]{81} = 3$, $\sqrt[3]{-27} = -3$, and $\sqrt[5]{32} = 2$.

To complete our terminology, the n in the radical $\sqrt[n]{b}$ is called the **index** of the radical. If $n = 2$, we commonly write $\sqrt{b}$ instead of $\sqrt[2]{b}$. In this chapter as we use symbols such as $\sqrt[n]{b}$, $\sqrt[m]{y}$, and $\sqrt[r]{x}$ we will assume the previous agreements relative to the existence of real roots (without listing the various restrictions, unless a special restriction is needed.)

If n is a positive integer greater than one and $\sqrt[n]{b}$ exists, then

$$(\sqrt[n]{b})^n = b.$$

For example, $(\sqrt{4})^2 = 4$, $(\sqrt[3]{-8})^3 = -8$, and $(\sqrt[4]{81})^4 = 81$. Furthermore, if $b \geq 0$ and n is a positive integer greater than one, or if $b < 0$ and n is an odd positive integer greater than one, then

$$\sqrt[n]{b^n} = b.$$

For example, $\sqrt{4^2} = 4$, $\sqrt[3]{(-2)^3} = -2$, and $\sqrt[5]{6^5} = 6$. However, we must be careful because $\sqrt{(-2)^2} \neq -2$ and $\sqrt[4]{(-3)^4} \neq -3$.

Manipulating with Radicals

For many purposes it is convenient to express radicals in **simplest radical form** which means that the following conditions are satisfied.

1. No fraction appears within a radical sign. ($\sqrt{3/4}$ violates this condition.)
2. No radical appears in the denominator. ($\sqrt{2}/\sqrt{3}$ violates this condition.)
3. No radicand contains a perfect power of the index. ($\sqrt{7^2 \cdot 5}$ violates this condition.)

Before we discuss the process of simplifying radicals, there is one point pertaining to radicals that contain variables that we need to call to your attention. Let's look at some examples to clarify the idea. Consider the radical $\sqrt{x^2}$ as follows.

Let $x = 3$; then $\sqrt{x^2} = \sqrt{3^2} = \sqrt{9} = 3$.
Let $x = -3$; then $\sqrt{x^2} = \sqrt{(-3)^2} = \sqrt{9} = 3$.

Thus, if $x \geq 0$, then $\sqrt{x^2} = x$, but if $x < 0$, then $\sqrt{x^2} = -x$. Using the concept of absolute value, we can state that *for all real numbers*, $\sqrt{x^2} = |x|$.

Now consider the radical $\sqrt{x^3}$. Since x^3 is negative when x is negative, we need to restrict x to the nonnegative reals when working with $\sqrt{x^3}$. Thus, we can write "if $x \geq 0$, then $\sqrt{x^3} = \sqrt{x^2}\sqrt{x} = x\sqrt{x}$," and no absolute value sign is needed.

Finally, let's consider the radical $\sqrt[3]{x^3}$.

Let $x = 2$; then $\sqrt[3]{x^3} = \sqrt[3]{2^3} = \sqrt[3]{8} = 2$.
Let $x = -2$; then $\sqrt[3]{x^3} = \sqrt[3]{(-2)^3} = \sqrt[3]{-8} = -2$.

Thus, it is correct to write "$\sqrt[3]{x^3} = x$ for all real numbers" and again no absolute value sign is needed.

The previous discussion indicates that technically we need to analyze every radical expression involving variables in the radicands individually to impose the necessary restrictions on the variables. However, to avoid restrictions on a problem-by-problem basis we shall merely **assume that all variables represent positive real numbers**.

Two properties form the basis for simplifying radicals as well as for performing other basic operations with radicals. We shall state each property and illustrate some of its uses.

PROPERTY 4.1

$$\sqrt[n]{bc} = \sqrt[n]{b}\sqrt[n]{c} \qquad \sqrt[n]{b} \text{ and } \sqrt[n]{c} \text{ are real numbers}$$

Property 4.1 states that **the nth root of a product is equal to the product of the nth roots**. It can be used to remove perfect powers of the index from the radicand, as illustrated by the following examples.

E X A M P L E 1

Express each of the following in simplest radical form.

a. $\sqrt{52}$ **b.** $\sqrt[3]{24}$

c. $\sqrt{72x^3y^7}$ **d.** $\sqrt[3]{40x^4y^8}$

Solution

a. $\sqrt{52} = \sqrt{4 \cdot 13} = \sqrt{4}\sqrt{13} = 2\sqrt{13}$

b. $\sqrt[3]{24} = \sqrt[3]{8 \cdot 3} = \sqrt[3]{8}\sqrt[3]{3} = 2\sqrt[3]{3}$

c. $\sqrt{72x^3y^7} = \sqrt{36x^2y^6}\sqrt{2xy} = 6xy^3\sqrt{2xy}$

d. $\sqrt[3]{40x^4y^8} = \sqrt[3]{8x^3y^6}\sqrt[3]{5xy^2} = 2xy^2\sqrt[3]{5xy^2}$

Sometimes it may be easier to determine perfect powers of the index by expressing the radicand in exponential form.

$$\sqrt{80} = \sqrt{2^4 \cdot 5} = \sqrt{2^4}\sqrt{5} = 2^2\sqrt{5} = 4\sqrt{5}$$

$$\sqrt[3]{108} = \sqrt[3]{2^2 \cdot 3^3} = \sqrt[3]{3^3}\sqrt[3]{2^2} = 3\sqrt[3]{4}$$

The distributive property can be used to combine radicals that have the same index and the same radicand. Consider the following examples.

E X A M P L E 2

Simplify each of the following.

a. $3\sqrt{2} + 5\sqrt{2} - \sqrt{2}$ **b.** $7\sqrt[3]{5} - 13\sqrt[3]{5} + 2\sqrt[3]{5}$

Solution

a. $3\sqrt{2} + 5\sqrt{2} - \sqrt{2} = (3 + 5 - 1)\sqrt{2} = 7\sqrt{2}$

b. $7\sqrt[3]{5} - 13\sqrt[3]{5} + 2\sqrt[3]{5} = (7 - 13 + 2)\sqrt[3]{5} = -4\sqrt[3]{5}$

Sometimes it is necessary to simplify the radicals first and then combine by applying the distributive property.

E X A M P L E 3

Simplify $3\sqrt{8} + 2\sqrt{18} - 4\sqrt{2}$.

Solution

$$3\sqrt{8} + 2\sqrt{18} - 4\sqrt{2} = 3\sqrt{4}\sqrt{2} + 2\sqrt{9}\sqrt{2} - 4\sqrt{2}$$

$$= 6\sqrt{2} + 6\sqrt{2} - 4\sqrt{2}$$

$$= (6 + 6 - 4)\sqrt{2} = 8\sqrt{2}$$

Property 4.1 (when viewed as $\sqrt[n]{b}\sqrt[n]{c} = \sqrt[n]{bc}$) along with the commutative and associative properties of the real numbers provides the basis for multiplying radicals that have the same index. Consider the following examples.

EXAMPLE 4

Multiply and express the product in simplest radical form.

a. $(7\sqrt{6})(3\sqrt{8})$ **b.** $(2\sqrt[3]{6})(5\sqrt[3]{4})$

Solution

a. $(7\sqrt{6})(3\sqrt{8}) = 7 \cdot 3 \cdot \sqrt{6} \cdot \sqrt{8} = 21\sqrt{48} = 21\sqrt{16}\sqrt{3}$

$$= 21 \cdot 4 \cdot \sqrt{3}$$

$$= 84\sqrt{3}$$

b. $(2\sqrt[3]{6})(5\sqrt[3]{4}) = 2 \cdot 5 \cdot \sqrt[3]{6} \cdot \sqrt[3]{4} = 10\sqrt[3]{24} = 10\sqrt[3]{8}\sqrt[3]{3}$

$$= 10 \cdot 2 \cdot \sqrt[3]{3}$$

$$= 20\sqrt[3]{3}$$

The next examples illustrate how to use the distributive property and Property 4.1 to handle special products involving radicals.

EXAMPLE 5

Multiply and express the product in simplest radical form.

a. $(2\sqrt{2} - \sqrt{7})(3\sqrt{2} + 5\sqrt{7})$ **b.** $(\sqrt{5} + \sqrt{2})(\sqrt{5} - \sqrt{2})$

Solution

a. $(2\sqrt{2} - \sqrt{7})(3\sqrt{2} + 5\sqrt{7}) = (2\sqrt{2}(3\sqrt{2} + 5\sqrt{7}) - \sqrt{7}(3\sqrt{2} + 5\sqrt{7})$

$$= (2\sqrt{2})(3\sqrt{2}) + (2\sqrt{2})(5\sqrt{7}) - (\sqrt{7})(3\sqrt{2}) - (\sqrt{7})(5\sqrt{7})$$

$$= 6(2) + 10\sqrt{14} - 3\sqrt{14} - 5(7)$$

$$= -23 + 7\sqrt{14}$$

b. $(\sqrt{5} + \sqrt{2})(\sqrt{5} - \sqrt{2}) = \sqrt{5}(\sqrt{5} - \sqrt{2}) + \sqrt{2}(\sqrt{5} - \sqrt{2})$

$$= (\sqrt{5})(\sqrt{5}) - (\sqrt{5})(\sqrt{2}) + (\sqrt{2})(\sqrt{5}) - (\sqrt{2})(\sqrt{2})$$

$$= 5 - \sqrt{10} + \sqrt{10} - 2$$

$$= 3$$

Pay special attention to part (b) of Example 5. It fits the product pattern $(a + b)(a - b) = a^2 - b^2$. We will use that idea again in a moment. The second property that is used to simplify radicals can be stated as follows.

PROPERTY 4.2

$$\sqrt[n]{\frac{b}{c}} = \frac{\sqrt[n]{b}}{\sqrt[n]{c}} \qquad \sqrt[n]{b} \text{ and } \sqrt[n]{c} \text{ are real numbers and } c \neq 0.$$

Property 4.2 states that the *n*th root of a quotient is equal to the quotient of the *n*th roots. To evaluate radicals where the numerator and denominator of the fractional radicand are perfect *n*th powers, we may use Property 4.2, or rely on the definition of *n*th roots.

$$\sqrt{\frac{4}{25}} = \frac{\sqrt{4}}{\sqrt{25}} = \frac{2}{5} \quad \text{or} \quad \sqrt{\frac{4}{25}} = \frac{2}{5} \text{ because } \frac{2}{5} \cdot \frac{2}{5} = \frac{4}{25}.$$

$$\sqrt[3]{\frac{27}{8}} = \frac{\sqrt[3]{27}}{\sqrt[3]{8}} = \frac{3}{2} \quad \text{or} \quad \sqrt[3]{\frac{27}{8}} = \frac{3}{2} \text{ because } \frac{3}{2} \cdot \frac{3}{2} \cdot \frac{3}{2} = \frac{27}{8}.$$

Radicals in which only the denominators of the radicands are perfect *n*th powers can be simplified as follows.

EXAMPLE 6

Express each of the following in simplest radical form.

a. $\sqrt{\dfrac{28}{9}}$ **b.** $\sqrt[3]{\dfrac{24}{27}}$

Solution

a. $\sqrt{\dfrac{28}{9}} = \dfrac{\sqrt{28}}{\sqrt{9}} = \dfrac{\sqrt{4}\sqrt{7}}{3} = \dfrac{2\sqrt{7}}{3}$

b. $\sqrt[3]{\dfrac{24}{27}} = \dfrac{\sqrt[3]{24}}{\sqrt[3]{27}} = \dfrac{\sqrt[3]{8}\sqrt[3]{3}}{3} = \dfrac{2\sqrt[3]{3}}{3}$

Now let's consider an example in which neither the numerator nor the denominator is a perfect *n*th power.

EXAMPLE 7

Simplify. $\sqrt{\dfrac{2}{3}}$.

Solution

$$\sqrt{\frac{2}{3}} = \frac{\sqrt{2}}{\sqrt{3}} = \frac{\sqrt{2}}{\sqrt{3}} \cdot \frac{\sqrt{3}}{\sqrt{3}} = \frac{\sqrt{6}}{3}$$

Form of 1

We refer to the process used to simplify the radical in the previous example as **rationalizing the denominator**. There are additional ways to rationalize the denominator, as illustrated by the next example.

EXAMPLE 8

Simplify $\dfrac{\sqrt{5}}{\sqrt{8}}$.

Solution A

$$\frac{\sqrt{5}}{\sqrt{8}} = \frac{\sqrt{5}}{\sqrt{8}} \cdot \frac{\sqrt{8}}{\sqrt{8}} = \frac{\sqrt{40}}{8} = \frac{\sqrt{4}\sqrt{10}}{8} = \frac{2\sqrt{10}}{8} = \frac{\sqrt{10}}{4}$$

Solution B

$$\frac{\sqrt{5}}{\sqrt{8}} = \frac{\sqrt{5}}{\sqrt{8}} \cdot \frac{\sqrt{2}}{\sqrt{2}} = \frac{\sqrt{10}}{\sqrt{16}} = \frac{\sqrt{10}}{4}$$

Solution C

$$\frac{\sqrt{5}}{\sqrt{8}} = \frac{\sqrt{5}}{\sqrt{4}\sqrt{2}} = \frac{\sqrt{5}}{2\sqrt{2}} = \frac{\sqrt{5}}{2\sqrt{2}} \cdot \frac{\sqrt{2}}{\sqrt{2}} = \frac{\sqrt{10}}{4}$$

The three approaches to Example 8 again illustrate the need to think first and then push the pencil. You may find one approach easier than another. Notice the approach used in the next two examples.

EXAMPLE 9

Simplify each of the following.

a. $\dfrac{\sqrt{5}}{\sqrt{12a^3}}$ **b.** $\dfrac{3}{\sqrt[3]{4x}}$

Solution

a. $\dfrac{\sqrt{5}}{\sqrt{12a^3}} = \dfrac{\sqrt{5}}{\sqrt{12a^3}} \cdot \dfrac{\sqrt{3a}}{\sqrt{3a}} = \dfrac{\sqrt{15a}}{\sqrt{36a^4}} = \dfrac{\sqrt{15a}}{6a^2}$

b. $\dfrac{3}{\sqrt[3]{4x}} = \dfrac{3}{\sqrt[3]{4x}} \cdot \dfrac{\sqrt[3]{2x^2}}{\sqrt[3]{2x^2}} = \dfrac{3\sqrt[3]{2x^2}}{\sqrt[3]{8x^3}} = \dfrac{3\sqrt[3]{2x^2}}{2x}$

Remember that a moment ago we found that $(\sqrt{5} + \sqrt{2})(\sqrt{5} - \sqrt{2}) = 3$. This fact can be used to rationalize the denominator in the next example.

EXAMPLE 10

Simplify $4/(\sqrt{5} + \sqrt{2})$ by rationalizing the denominator.

Solution

$$\frac{4}{\sqrt{5} + \sqrt{2}} = \left(\frac{4}{\sqrt{5} + \sqrt{2}}\right)\left(\frac{\sqrt{5} - \sqrt{2}}{\sqrt{5} - \sqrt{2}}\right)$$

$$= \frac{4(\sqrt{5} - \sqrt{2})}{(\sqrt{5} + \sqrt{2})(\sqrt{5} - \sqrt{2})}$$

$$= \frac{4(\sqrt{5} - \sqrt{2})}{3}$$

The process of rationalizing the denominator does agree with the previously listed conditions. However, for certain problems in calculus it is necessary to **rationalize the numerator**. Again the fact that $(\sqrt{a} + \sqrt{b})(\sqrt{a} - \sqrt{b}) = a - b$ can be used.

EXAMPLE 11

Change the form of $(\sqrt{x + h} - \sqrt{x})/h$ by rationalizing the numerator.

Solution

$$\frac{\sqrt{x + h} - \sqrt{x}}{h} = \left(\frac{\sqrt{x + h} - \sqrt{x}}{h}\right)\left(\frac{\sqrt{x + h} + \sqrt{x}}{\sqrt{x + h} + \sqrt{x}}\right)$$

$$= \frac{(x + h) - x}{h(\sqrt{x + h} + \sqrt{x})}$$

$$= \frac{h}{h(\sqrt{x + h} + \sqrt{x})}$$

$$= \frac{1}{\sqrt{x + h} + \sqrt{x}}$$

Radical Equations

An equation such as $\sqrt{2x - 4} = x - 2$, which contains a radical with the variable in the radicand is often referred to as a radical equation. To solve radical equations we need the following additional property of equality.

PROPERTY 4.3

Let a and b be real numbers and n a positive integer.

If $a = b$, then $a^n = b^n$.

Property 4.3 states that we can **raise both sides of an equation to a positive integral power.** However, when applying Property 4.3 we must be very careful. Raising both sides of an equation to a positive integral power sometimes produces results that do not satisfy the original equation. Consider the following example.

EXAMPLE 12

Solve $\sqrt{x} + 6 = x$.

Solution

$$\sqrt{x} + 6 = x$$

$$\sqrt{x} = x - 6$$

$$(\sqrt{x})^2 = (x - 6)^2 \qquad \text{Square both sides}$$

$$x = x^2 - 12x + 36$$

$$0 = x^2 - 13x + 36$$

$$0 = (x - 4)(x - 9)$$

$$x - 4 = 0 \qquad \text{or} \qquad x - 9 = 0$$

$$x = 4 \qquad \text{or} \qquad x = 9$$

 Check

$$\sqrt{x} = x - 6 \qquad \sqrt{x} = x - 6$$

$$\sqrt{4} \overset{?}{=} 4 - 6 \qquad \sqrt{9} \overset{?}{=} 9 - 6$$

$$2 \neq -2 \qquad 3 = 3$$

The only solution is 9; the solution set is {9}.

In general, raising both sides of an equation to a positive integral power produces an equation that has all of the solutions of the original equation, *but* it may also have some extra solutions that will not satisfy the original equation. Such extra solutions are called **extraneous solutions.** Therefore when using Property 4.3, you *must check* each potential solution in the original equation.

EXAMPLE 13

Solve $\sqrt[3]{2x + 3} = -3$.

Solution

$$\sqrt[3]{2x + 3} = -3$$

$$(\sqrt[3]{2x + 3})^3 = (-3)^3 \qquad \text{Cube both sides}$$

$$2x + 3 = -27$$

$$2x = -30$$

$$x = -15$$

Check

$$\sqrt[3]{2x + 3} = -3$$
$$\sqrt[3]{2(-15) + 3} \stackrel{?}{=} -3$$
$$\sqrt[3]{-27} \stackrel{?}{=} -3$$
$$-3 = -3$$

The solution set is $\{-15\}$.

EXAMPLE 14

Solve $\sqrt{x + 4} = \sqrt{x - 1} + 1$.

Solution

$$\sqrt{x + 4} = \sqrt{x - 1} + 1$$
$$(\sqrt{x + 4})^2 = (\sqrt{x - 1} + 1)^2 \qquad \text{Square both sides}$$
$$x + 4 = x - 1 + 2\sqrt{x - 1} + 1 \qquad \text{Don't forget middle term when squaring binomial on right side}$$
$$4 = 2\sqrt{x - 1}$$
$$2 = \sqrt{x - 1}$$
$$2^2 = (\sqrt{x - 1})^2 \qquad \text{Square both sides}$$
$$4 = x - 1$$
$$5 = x$$

 Check

$$\sqrt{x + 4} = \sqrt{x - 1} + 1$$
$$\sqrt{5 + 4} \stackrel{?}{=} \sqrt{5 - 1} + 1$$
$$\sqrt{9} \stackrel{?}{=} \sqrt{4} + 1$$
$$3 = 3$$

The solution set is $\{5\}$.

PROBLEM SET 4.1

Evaluate each of the following.

1. $\sqrt{\dfrac{36}{49}}$

2. $-\sqrt{49}$

3. $\sqrt[3]{125}$

4. $\sqrt[3]{-\dfrac{27}{8}}$

5. $\sqrt[4]{256}$

6. $-\sqrt[4]{16}$

7. $\sqrt{.09}$

8. $\sqrt{.01}$

9. $\sqrt[3]{.008}$

10. $\sqrt[5]{\dfrac{32}{243}}$

Express each of the following in simplest radical form. All variables represent positive real numbers.

11. $\sqrt{72}$

12. $6\sqrt{28}$

13. $-3\sqrt{44}$

14. $-5\sqrt{68}$

15. $\frac{3}{4}\sqrt{20}$

16. $\frac{3}{8}\sqrt{72}$

17. $\sqrt{12x^2}$

18. $\sqrt{45xy^2}$

19. $\sqrt{64x^4y^7}$

20. $3\sqrt{32a^3}$

21. $\frac{3}{7}\sqrt{45xy^6}$

22. $\sqrt[3]{32}$

23. $\sqrt[3]{128}$

24. $\sqrt[3]{54x^3}$

25. $\sqrt[3]{16x^4}$

26. $\sqrt[3]{81x^5y^6}$

27. $\sqrt[4]{48x^5}$

28. $\sqrt[4]{162x^6y^7}$

29. $\sqrt{\dfrac{12}{25}}$

30. $\sqrt{\dfrac{75}{81}}$

31. $\sqrt{\dfrac{7}{8}}$

32. $\sqrt{\dfrac{35}{7}}$

33. $\dfrac{4\sqrt{3}}{\sqrt{5}}$

34. $\dfrac{\sqrt{27}}{\sqrt{18}}$

35. $\dfrac{6\sqrt{3}}{7\sqrt{6}}$

36. $\sqrt{\dfrac{3x}{2y}}$

37. $\dfrac{\sqrt{5}}{\sqrt{12x^4}}$

38. $\dfrac{\sqrt{5y}}{\sqrt{18x^3}}$

39. $\dfrac{\sqrt{12a^2b}}{\sqrt{5a^3b^3}}$

40. $\dfrac{5}{\sqrt[3]{3}}$

41. $\dfrac{\sqrt[3]{27}}{\sqrt[3]{4}}$

42. $\sqrt[3]{\dfrac{5}{2x}}$

43. $\dfrac{\sqrt[3]{2y}}{\sqrt[3]{3x}}$

44. $\dfrac{\sqrt[3]{12xy}}{\sqrt[3]{3x^2y^5}}$

Use the distributive property to help simplify each of the following. For example,

$$3\sqrt{8} + 5\sqrt{2} = 3\sqrt{4}\sqrt{2} + 5\sqrt{2}$$
$$= 6\sqrt{2} + 5\sqrt{2}$$
$$= (6 + 5)\sqrt{2} = 11\sqrt{2}.$$

45. $5\sqrt{12} + 2\sqrt{3}$

46. $4\sqrt{50} - 9\sqrt{32}$

47. $2\sqrt{28} - 3\sqrt{63} + 8\sqrt{7}$

48. $4\sqrt[3]{2} + 2\sqrt[3]{16} - \sqrt[3]{54}$

49. $\frac{5}{6}\sqrt{48} - \frac{3}{4}\sqrt{12}$

50. $\frac{2}{5}\sqrt{40} + \frac{1}{6}\sqrt{90}$

51. $\dfrac{2\sqrt{8}}{3} - \dfrac{3\sqrt{18}}{5} - \dfrac{\sqrt{50}}{2}$

52. $\dfrac{3\sqrt[3]{54}}{2} + \dfrac{5\sqrt[3]{16}}{3}$

Multiply and express the results in simplest radical form. All variables represent nonnegative real numbers.

53. $(4\sqrt{3})(6\sqrt{8})$

54. $(5\sqrt{8})(3\sqrt{7})$

55. $2\sqrt{3}(5\sqrt{2} + 4\sqrt{10})$

56. $3\sqrt{6}(2\sqrt{8} - 3\sqrt{12})$

57. $3\sqrt{x}(\sqrt{6xy} - \sqrt{8y})$

58. $\sqrt{6y}(\sqrt{8x} + \sqrt{10y^2})$

59. $(\sqrt{3} + 2)(\sqrt{3} + 5)$

60. $(\sqrt{2} - 3)(\sqrt{2} + 4)$

61. $(4\sqrt{2} + \sqrt{3})(3\sqrt{2} + 2\sqrt{3})$

62. $(2\sqrt{6} + 3\sqrt{5})(3\sqrt{6} + 4\sqrt{5})$

For each of the following, *rationalize the denominator* and simplify. All variables represent positive real numbers.

63. $\dfrac{3}{\sqrt{5} + 2}$

64. $\dfrac{7}{\sqrt{10} - 3}$

65. $\dfrac{\sqrt{2}}{2\sqrt{5} + 3\sqrt{7}}$

66. $\dfrac{5}{5\sqrt{2} - 3\sqrt{5}}$

67. $\dfrac{\sqrt{x}}{\sqrt{x} + \sqrt{y}}$

68. $\dfrac{2\sqrt{x}}{\sqrt{x} - \sqrt{y}}$

69. $\dfrac{2\sqrt{x} + \sqrt{y}}{3\sqrt{x} - 2\sqrt{y}}$

70. $\dfrac{3\sqrt{x} - 2\sqrt{y}}{2\sqrt{x} + 5\sqrt{y}}$

For each of the following, *rationalize the numerator* and simplify. All variables represent positive real numbers.

71. $\dfrac{\sqrt{x-1+h}-\sqrt{x-1}}{h}$

72. $\dfrac{\sqrt{x+2+h}-\sqrt{x+2}}{h}$

73. $\dfrac{\sqrt{2(x+h)-1}-\sqrt{2x-1}}{h}$

74. $\dfrac{\sqrt{3(x+h)+1}-\sqrt{3x+1}}{h}$

Solve each of the following equations.

75. $\sqrt{3x-2}=4$

76. $\sqrt{2x-3}=1$

77. $\sqrt{3x-8}-\sqrt{x-2}=0$

78. $\sqrt{2x-1}-\sqrt{x+2}=0$

79. $\sqrt{4x-3}+2=0$

80. $\sqrt{5x-1}+4=0$

81. $\sqrt[3]{2x+3}+3=0$

82. $\sqrt[3]{n^2-1}+1=0$

83. $\sqrt{3x-2}=3x-2$

84. $5x-4=\sqrt{5x-4}$

85. $\sqrt{2t-1}+2=t$

86. $p=\sqrt{-4p+17}+3$

87. $\sqrt{7n+23}-\sqrt{3n+7}=2$

88. $\sqrt{5t+31}-\sqrt{t+3}=4$

89. $\sqrt{3x+1}+\sqrt{2x+4}=3$

90. $\sqrt{2x-1}-\sqrt{x+3}=1$

91. $\sqrt{x-2}-\sqrt{2x-11}=\sqrt{x-5}$

92. $\sqrt{-2x-7}+\sqrt{x+9}=\sqrt{8-x}$

93. $\sqrt{1+2\sqrt{x}}=\sqrt{x+1}$

94. $\sqrt{7+3\sqrt{x}}=\sqrt{x+1}$

THOUGHTS into WORDS

95. Is the equation $\sqrt{x^2y}=x\sqrt{y}$ true for all real number values for x and y?

96. Is the equation $\sqrt{x^2y^2}=xy$ true for all real number values for x and y?

97. Give a step-by-step description of how you would change $\sqrt{252}$ to simplest radical form.

FURTHER INVESTIGATIONS

98. Find the three cube roots of -8 by solving $x^3=-8$.

99. Find the three cube roots of 27 by solving $x^3=27$.

100. Find the four fourth roots of 16 by solving $x^4=16$.

101. Verify that $x=a$ and $x^2=a^2$ are not equivalent equations.

102. For each of the following, (1) give a whole number estimate for each expression, and (2) use your calculator to find a rational approximation, to the nearest hundredth, for each expression.

a. $\sqrt{590}$ **b.** $\sqrt{2576}$

c. $\sqrt[3]{813}$ **d.** $\sqrt[4]{20400}$

e. $5\sqrt{17}+9\sqrt{17}-2\sqrt{17}-\sqrt{17}+12\sqrt{17}$

f. $3\sqrt{10}+5\sqrt{24}-3\sqrt{48}$

g. $5\sqrt{2}+7\sqrt{3}-\sqrt{2}-2\sqrt{3}+9\sqrt{2}+14\sqrt{3}$

h. $3\sqrt{8}+7\sqrt{18}+12\sqrt{32}-4\sqrt{128}$

i. $3\sqrt[3]{26}+12\sqrt[3]{26}-2\sqrt[3]{26}+9\sqrt[3]{26}$

j. $\sqrt{156}+\sqrt{691}+\sqrt{3249}$

k. $6\sqrt[3]{9}+4\sqrt[3]{28}+3\sqrt[3]{127}$

l. $\dfrac{\sqrt{40}+\sqrt{75}}{\sqrt{5}}$ **m.** $\dfrac{3\sqrt{2}+5\sqrt{12}}{\sqrt{8}}$

4.2   ROOTS AND RATIONAL EXPONENTS

Let's use the properties of integral exponents to motivate definitions for the use of all rational numbers as exponents. These definitions will tie together the concepts of exponent and root. Consider the following comparisons.

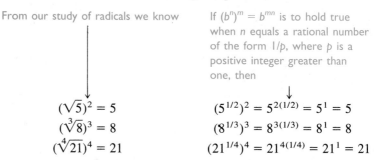

From our study of radicals we know

$$(\sqrt{5})^2 = 5$$
$$(\sqrt[3]{8})^3 = 8$$
$$(\sqrt[4]{21})^4 = 21$$

If $(b^n)^m = b^{mn}$ is to hold true when n equals a rational number of the form $1/p$, where p is a positive integer greater than one, then

$$(5^{1/2})^2 = 5^{2(1/2)} = 5^1 = 5$$
$$(8^{1/3})^3 = 8^{3(1/3)} = 8^1 = 8$$
$$(21^{1/4})^4 = 21^{4(1/4)} = 21^1 = 21$$

Such examples motivate the following definition.

DEFINITION 4.1

If b is a real number, n a positive integer greater than one, and $\sqrt[n]{b}$ exists, then

$$b^{1/n} = \sqrt[n]{b}.$$

Definition 4.1 states that $b^{1/n}$ means the nth root of b. We shall assume that b and n are chosen so that $\sqrt[n]{b}$ exists in the real number system. For example, $(-25)^{1/2}$ is not meaningful at this time because $\sqrt{-25}$ is not a real number. The following examples illustrate the use of Definition 4.1.

$$25^{1/2} = \sqrt{25} = 5 \qquad 16^{1/4} = \sqrt[4]{16} = 2$$
$$8^{1/3} = \sqrt[3]{8} = 2 \qquad (-27)^{1/3} = \sqrt[3]{-27} = -3$$

Now the following definition provides the basis for the use of *all* rational numbers as exponents.

DEFINITION 4.2

If m/n is a rational number, where n is a positive integer greater than one, m is any integer, and b is a real number such that $\sqrt[n]{b}$ exists, then

$$b^{m/n} = \sqrt[n]{b^m} = (\sqrt[n]{b})^m.$$

In Definition 4.2, whether we use the form $\sqrt[n]{b^m}$ or $(\sqrt[n]{b})^m$ for computational purposes depends somewhat on the magnitude of the problem. Let's use both forms on two problems to illustrate this point.

$$8^{2/3} = \sqrt[3]{8^2} = \sqrt[3]{64} = 4 \quad \text{or} \quad 8^{2/3} = (\sqrt[3]{8})^2 = (2)^2 = 4$$
$$27^{2/3} = \sqrt[3]{27^2} = \sqrt[3]{729} = 9 \quad \text{or} \quad 27^{2/3} = (\sqrt[3]{27})^2 = (3)^2 = 9$$

To compute $8^{2/3}$, either form seems to work about as well as the other. However, to compute $27^{2/3}$, it should be obvious that the form $(\sqrt[3]{27})^2$ is much easier to handle. The following examples further illustrate Definition 4.2.

$$25^{3/2} = (\sqrt{25})^3 = 5^3 = 125$$

$$(32)^{-2/5} = \frac{1}{(32)^{2/5}} = \frac{1}{(\sqrt[5]{32})^2} = \frac{1}{2^2} = \frac{1}{4}$$

$$(-64)^{2/3} = (\sqrt[3]{-64})^2 = (-4)^2 = 16$$

$$-8^{4/3} = -(\sqrt[3]{8})^4 = -(2)^4 = -16$$

All of the results pertaining to integral exponents that we listed in Property 1.1 (on page 10) also hold for all rational exponents. Let's consider some examples to illustrate each of those results.

$$x^{1/2} \cdot x^{2/3} = x^{1/2+2/3}$$
$$= x^{3/6+4/6} \qquad b^n \cdot b^m = b^{n+m}$$
$$= x^{7/6}$$

$$(a^{2/3})^{3/2} = a^{(3/2)(2/3)} \qquad (b^n)^m = b^{mn}$$
$$= a^1 = a$$

$$(16y^{2/3})^{1/2} = (16)^{1/2}(y^{2/3})^{1/2} \qquad (ab)^n = a^n b^n$$
$$= 4y^{1/3}$$

$$\frac{y^{3/4}}{y^{1/2}} = y^{3/4-1/2} \qquad \frac{b^n}{b^m} = b^{n-m}$$
$$= y^{3/4-2/4}$$
$$= y^{1/4}$$

$$\left(\frac{x^{1/2}}{y^{1/3}}\right)^6 = \frac{(x^{1/2})^6}{(y^{1/3})^6} \qquad \left(\frac{a}{b}\right)^n = \frac{a^n}{b^n}$$
$$= \frac{x^3}{y^2}$$

The link between exponents and roots provides a basis for multiplying and dividing some radicals even if they have a different index. The general procedure is one of changing from radical to exponential form, applying the properties of exponents, and then changing back to radical form. Let's consider three examples to illustrate this process.

$$\sqrt{2}\sqrt[3]{2} = 2^{1/2} \cdot 2^{1/3} = 2^{1/2+1/3} = 2^{5/6} = \sqrt[6]{2^5} = \sqrt[6]{32}$$

$$\sqrt{xy}\sqrt[5]{x^2y} = (xy)^{1/2}(x^2y)^{1/5} = x^{1/2}y^{1/2}x^{2/5}y^{1/5}$$

$$= x^{1/2+2/5}y^{1/2+1/5}$$

$$= x^{9/10}y^{7/10}$$

$$= (x^9y^7)^{1/10}$$

$$= \sqrt[10]{x^9y^7}$$

$$\frac{\sqrt{5}}{\sqrt[3]{5}} = \frac{5^{1/2}}{5^{1/3}} = 5^{1/2-1/3} = 5^{1/6} = \sqrt[6]{5}$$

Earlier we agreed that a radical such as $\sqrt[3]{x^4}$ is not in simplest form because the radicand contains a perfect power of the index. Thus, we simplified $\sqrt[3]{x^4}$ by expressing it as $\sqrt[3]{x^3}\sqrt[3]{x}$, which in turn can be written as $x\sqrt[3]{x}$. Such simplification can also be done while in exponential form as follows.

$$\sqrt[3]{x^4} = x^{4/3} = x^{3/3} \cdot x^{1/3} = x \cdot x^{1/3} = x\sqrt[3]{x}$$

Note the use of this type of simplification in the following problems.

EXAMPLE 1

Perform the indicated operations and express the answers in simplest radical form.

a. $\sqrt[3]{x^2}\sqrt[4]{x^3}$ **b.** $\sqrt{2}\sqrt[3]{4}$ **c.** $\dfrac{\sqrt{27}}{\sqrt[3]{3}}$

Solutions

a. $\sqrt[3]{x^2}\sqrt[4]{x^3} = x^{2/3}x^{3/4} = x^{2/3+3/4} = x^{17/12}$

$$= x^{12/12}x^{5/12} = x\sqrt[12]{x^5}$$

b. $\sqrt{2}\sqrt[3]{4} = 2^{1/2}4^{1/3} = 2^{1/2}(2^2)^{1/3} = 2^{1/2}2^{2/3}$

$$= 2^{1/2+2/3} = 2^{7/6}$$

$$= 2^{6/6}2^{1/6} = 2\sqrt[6]{2}$$

c. $\dfrac{\sqrt{27}}{\sqrt[3]{3}} = \dfrac{27^{1/2}}{3^{1/3}} = \dfrac{(3^3)^{1/2}}{3^{1/3}} = \dfrac{3^{3/2}}{3^{1/3}} = 3^{3/2-1/3} = 3^{7/6}$

$$= 3^{6/6}3^{1/6} = 3\sqrt[6]{3}$$

Note that the process of rationalizing the denominator can sometimes be handled while in exponential form. Consider the following examples, which illustrate this procedure.

EXAMPLE 2

Rationalize the denominator and express the answer in simplest radical form.

a. $\dfrac{2}{\sqrt[3]{x}}$ **b.** $\dfrac{\sqrt[3]{y}}{\sqrt{y}}$

Solutions

a. $\dfrac{2}{\sqrt[3]{x}} = \dfrac{2}{x^{1/3}} = \dfrac{2}{x^{1/3}} \cdot \dfrac{x^{2/3}}{x^{2/3}} = \dfrac{2x^{2/3}}{x} = \dfrac{2\sqrt[3]{x^2}}{x}$

b. $\dfrac{\sqrt[3]{x}}{\sqrt{y}} = \dfrac{x^{1/3}}{y^{1/2}} = \dfrac{x^{1/3}}{y^{1/2}} \cdot \dfrac{y^{1/2}}{y^{1/2}} = \dfrac{x^{1/3}y^{1/2}}{y} = \dfrac{x^{2/6}y^{3/6}}{y} = \dfrac{\sqrt[6]{x^2 y^3}}{y}$

Note in part (b) that if we had changed back to radical form at the step $(x^{1/3}y^{1/2})/y$, we would have obtained the product of two radicals $(\sqrt[3]{x}\sqrt{y})$ in the numerator. Instead, we used the exponential form to find this product and expressed the final result with a single radical in the numerator.

Finally, let's consider an example involving the root-of-a-root situation.

EXAMPLE 3

Simplify $\sqrt[3]{\sqrt{2}}$.

Solution

$$\sqrt[3]{\sqrt{2}} = (2^{1/2})^{1/3} = 2^{1/6} = \sqrt[6]{2}$$

Exponential Equations

An equation such as $2^x = 32$ is often called an **exponential equation** because the variable is in the exponent. Another property of equality that can be used to solve certain types of exponential equations can be stated as follows.

PROPERTY 4.4

If $b > 0$, $b \neq 1$, and m and n are rational numbers, then $b^n = b^m$ if and only if $n = m$.

The following examples illustrate the use of Property 4.4.

EXAMPLE 4

Solve $2^x = 32$.

Solution

$2^x = 32$

$2^x = 2^5$ $32 = 2^5$

$x = 5$ Apply Property 4.4

The solution set is $\{5\}$.

EXAMPLE 5

Solve $2^{3x} = \frac{1}{64}$.

Solution

$$2^{3x} = \frac{1}{64}$$

$$2^{3x} = \frac{1}{2^6}$$

$$2^{3x} = 2^{-6}$$

$$3x = -6 \qquad \text{Apply Property 4.4}$$

$$x = -2$$

The solution set is $\{-2\}$.

EXAMPLE 6

Solve $9^{2x-1} = 27^{x+2}$.

Solution

$$9^{2x-1} = 27^{x+2}$$

$$(3^2)^{2x-1} = (3^3)^{x+2}$$

$$3^{4x-2} = 3^{3x+6}$$

$$4x - 2 = 3x + 6$$

$$x = 8$$

The solution set is $\{8\}$.

EXAMPLE 7

Solve $(8^{2x})(4^{2x-1}) = 16$.

Solution

$$(8^{2x})(4^{2x-1}) = 16$$

$$(2^3)^{2x}(2^2)^{2x-1} = 2^4$$

$$(2^{6x})(2^{4x-2}) = 2^4$$

$$2^{6x+4x-2} = 2^4$$

$$2^{10x-2} = 2^4$$

$$10x - 2 = 4$$

$$10x = 6$$

$$x = \frac{6}{10}$$

$$x = \frac{3}{5}$$

The solution set is $\left\{\frac{3}{5}\right\}$.

PROBLEM SET 4.2

Evaluate each of the following.

1. $49^{1/2}$ **2.** $64^{1/3}$

3. $32^{3/5}$ **4.** $(-8)^{1/3}$

5. $-8^{2/3}$ **6.** $64^{-1/2}$

7. $\left(\frac{1}{4}\right)^{-1/2}$ **8.** $\left(-\frac{27}{8}\right)^{-1/3}$

9. $16^{3/2}$ **10.** $(.008)^{1/3}$

11. $(.01)^{3/2}$ **12.** $\left(\frac{1}{27}\right)^{-2/3}$

13. $64^{-5/6}$ **14.** $-16^{5/4}$

15. $\left(\frac{1}{8}\right)^{-1/3}$ **16.** $\left(-\frac{1}{8}\right)^{-2/3}$

Perform the indicated operations and simplify. Express final answers using positive exponents only.

17. $(3x^{1/4})(5x^{1/3})$ **18.** $(2x^{2/5})(6x^{1/4})$

19. $(y^{2/3})(y^{-1/4})$ **20.** $(3x^{1/3})(x^{-1/2})$

21. $(4x^{1/4}y^{1/2})^3$ **22.** $(5x^{1/2}y)^2$

23. $\dfrac{24x^{3/5}}{6x^{1/3}}$ **24.** $\dfrac{18x^{1/2}}{9x^{1/3}}$

25. $\dfrac{56a^{1/6}}{8a^{1/4}}$ **26.** $\dfrac{48b^{1/3}}{12b^{3/4}}$

27. $\left(\dfrac{2x^{1/3}}{3y^{1/4}}\right)^4$ **28.** $\left(\dfrac{6x^{2/5}}{7y^{2/3}}\right)^2$

29. $\left(\dfrac{x^2}{y^3}\right)^{-1/2}$ **30.** $\left(\dfrac{a^3}{b^{-2}}\right)^{-1/3}$

31. $\left(\dfrac{4a^2x}{2a^{1/2}x^{1/3}}\right)^3$ **32.** $\left(\dfrac{3ax^{-1}}{a^{1/2}x^{-2}}\right)^2$

Perform the indicated operations and express answers in simplest radical form.

33. $\sqrt{2}\sqrt[4]{2}$ **34.** $\sqrt[3]{3}\sqrt{3}$

35. $\sqrt[3]{x}\sqrt[4]{x}$ **36.** $\sqrt[3]{x^2}\sqrt[5]{x^3}$

37. $\sqrt{xy}\sqrt[4]{x^3y^5}$ **38.** $\sqrt[3]{x^2y^4}\sqrt[4]{x^3y}$

39. $\sqrt[3]{a^2b^2}\sqrt[4]{a^3b}$ **40.** $\sqrt{ab}\sqrt[3]{a^4b^5}$

41. $\sqrt[3]{4}\sqrt{8}$ **42.** $\sqrt[3]{9}\sqrt{27}$

43. $\dfrac{\sqrt{2}}{\sqrt[3]{2}}$ **44.** $\dfrac{\sqrt{9}}{\sqrt[3]{3}}$

45. $\dfrac{\sqrt[3]{8}}{\sqrt[4]{4}}$ **46.** $\dfrac{\sqrt[3]{16}}{\sqrt[6]{4}}$

47. $\dfrac{\sqrt[4]{x^9}}{\sqrt[3]{x^2}}$ **48.** $\dfrac{\sqrt[5]{x^7}}{\sqrt[3]{x}}$

Rationalize the denominators and express final answers in simplest radical form.

49. $\dfrac{5}{\sqrt[3]{x}}$ **50.** $\dfrac{3}{\sqrt[3]{x^2}}$

51. $\dfrac{\sqrt{x}}{\sqrt[3]{y}}$ **52.** $\dfrac{\sqrt[4]{x}}{\sqrt{y}}$

53. $\dfrac{\sqrt[4]{x^3}}{\sqrt[5]{y^3}}$ **54.** $\dfrac{2\sqrt{x}}{3\sqrt[3]{y}}$

55. $\dfrac{5\sqrt[3]{y^2}}{4\sqrt[4]{x}}$ **56.** $\dfrac{\sqrt{xy}}{\sqrt[3]{a^2b}}$

Simplify each of the following and express the final result as one radical. For example,

$$\sqrt{\sqrt{3}} = (3^{1/2})^{1/2} = 3^{1/4} = \sqrt[4]{3}.$$

57. $\sqrt{\sqrt[3]{2}}$ **58.** $\sqrt[3]{\sqrt[4]{3}}$

59. $\sqrt[3]{\sqrt{x^3}}$ **60.** $\sqrt{\sqrt[3]{x^4}}$

61. $\sqrt[3]{\sqrt[3]{x^2}}$ **62.** $\sqrt[4]{\sqrt{x^3}}$

63. $\sqrt[4]{\sqrt{x^5}}$ **64.** $\sqrt[3]{\sqrt{x^4}}$

Solve each of the following equations.

65. $3^x = 27$ **66.** $2^x = 64$

67. $\left(\frac{1}{2}\right)^x = \frac{1}{8}$ **68.** $\left(\frac{1}{2}\right)^n = 4$

69. $3^{-x} = \frac{1}{81}$ **70.** $3^{x+1} = 9$

71. $5^{2n-1} = 125$ **72.** $2^{3-n} = 8$

73. $\left(\frac{2}{3}\right)^t = \frac{9}{4}$ **74.** $\left(\frac{3}{4}\right)^n = \frac{64}{27}$

75. $4^{3x-1} = 256$ **76.** $16^x = 64$

77. $4^n = 8$ **78.** $27^{4x} = 9^{x+1}$

79. $32^x = 16^{1-x}$ **80.** $\left(\frac{1}{8}\right)^{-2t} = 2^{t+3}$ **83.** $(3^x)(3^{5x}) = 81$ **84.** $(4^x)(16^{3x-1}) = 8$

81. $(2^{2x-1})(2^{x+2}) = 32$ **82.** $(27)(3^x) = 9^x$

FURTHER INVESTIGATIONS

85. Use your calculator to evaluate each of the following.

    a. $\sqrt[3]{1728}$ **b.** $\sqrt[3]{5832}$

    c. $\sqrt[4]{2401}$ **d.** $\sqrt[4]{65536}$

    e. $\sqrt[5]{161051}$ **f.** $\sqrt[5]{6436343}$

86. In Definition 1.7 we stated that $b^{m/n} = \sqrt[n]{b^m} = (\sqrt[n]{b})^m$. Use your calculator to verify each of the following.

    a. $\sqrt[3]{27^2} = (\sqrt[3]{27})^2$ **b.** $\sqrt[3]{8^5} = (\sqrt[3]{8})^5$

    c. $\sqrt[4]{16^3} = (\sqrt[4]{16})^3$ **d.** $\sqrt[3]{16^2} = (\sqrt[3]{16})^2$

    e. $\sqrt[5]{9^4} = (\sqrt[5]{9})^4$ **f.** $\sqrt[3]{12^4} = (\sqrt[3]{12})^4$

87. Use your calculator to evaluate each of the following.

    a. $16^{5/2}$ **b.** $25^{7/2}$

    c. $16^{9/4}$ **d.** $27^{5/3}$

    e. $343^{2/3}$ **f.** $512^{4/3}$

88. Use your calculator to estimate each of the following to the nearest thousandth.

    a. $7^{4/3}$ **b.** $10^{4/5}$

    c. $12^{2/5}$ **d.** $19^{2/5}$

    e. $7^{3/4}$ **f.** $10^{5/4}$

Sometimes we meet the following type of simplification problem in calculus.

$$\frac{(x-1)^{1/2} - x(x-1)^{-(1/2)}}{[(x-1)^{1/2}]^2}$$

$$= \left(\frac{(x-1)^{1/2} - x(x-1)^{-(1/2)}}{(x-1)^{2/2}}\right) \cdot \left(\frac{(x-1)^{1/2}}{(x-1)^{1/2}}\right)$$

$$= \frac{x - 1 - x(x-1)^0}{(x-1)^{3/2}}$$

$$= \frac{x - 1 - x}{(x-1)^{3/2}} \qquad (x-1)^0 = 1$$

$$= \frac{-1}{(x-1)^{3/2}} \quad \text{or} \quad -\frac{1}{(x-1)^{3/2}}$$

Another approach is to begin by factoring the numerator.

$$\frac{(x-1)^{1/2} - x(x-1)^{-(1/2)}}{[(x-1)^{1/2}]^2} = \frac{(x-1)^{-(1/2)}(x-1-x)}{x-1}$$

$$= \frac{(x-1)^{-(1/2)}(-1)}{x-1}$$

$$= -\frac{1}{(x-1)^{3/2}}$$

For Problems 89–94, simplify each expression.

89. $\dfrac{2(x+1)^{1/2} - x(x+1)^{-(1/2)}}{[(x+1)^{1/2}]^2}$

90. $\dfrac{2(2x-1)^{1/2} - 2x(2x-1)^{-(1/2)}}{[(2x-1)^{1/2}]^2}$

91. $\dfrac{2x(4x+1)^{1/2} - 2x^2(4x+1)^{-(1/2)}}{[(4x+1)^{1/2}]^2}$

92. $\dfrac{(x^2+2x)^{1/2} - x(x+1)(x^2+2x)^{-(1/2)}}{[(x^2+2x)^{1/2}]^2}$

93. $\dfrac{(3x)^{1/3} - x(3x)^{-(2/3)}}{[(3x)^{1/3}]^2}$

94. $\dfrac{3(2x)^{1/3} - 2x(2x)^{-(2/3)}}{[(2x)^{1/3}]^2}$

4.3   EXPONENTIAL FUNCTIONS AND APPLICATIONS

To formally extend the concept of an exponent to include the use of irrational numbers requires some ideas from calculus, which is therefore beyond the scope of this text. However, we can give you a brief glimpse at the general idea involved. Consider the number $2^{\sqrt{3}}$. By using the nonterminating and nonrepeating decimal representation $1.73205\ldots$ for $\sqrt{3}$, we can form the sequence of numbers 2^{1}, $2^{1.7}$, $2^{1.73}$, $2^{1.732}$, $2^{1.7320}$, $2^{1.73205}$ .... It should seem reasonable that each successive power gets closer to $2^{\sqrt{3}}$. This is precisely what happens if b^n, where n is irrational, is properly defined by using the concept of a limit. Furthermore, this will insure that an expression such as 2^x will yield exactly one value for each value of x. So from now on we can use any real number as an exponent and the basic properties stated in Chapter 1 along with Property 4.4 ($b^n = b^m$ if and only if $n = m$) can be extended to include all real numbers as exponents.

If b is any positive number, then the expression b^x designates exactly one real number for every real value of x. Therefore, the equation $f(x) = b^x$ defines a function whose domain is the set of real numbers. Furthermore, if we place the additional restriction $b \neq 1$, then any equation of the form $f(x) = b^x$ describes a one-to-one function and is called an **exponential function**. This leads to the following definition.

DEFINITION 4.3

If $b > 0$ and $b \neq 1$, then the function f defined by

$$f(x) = b^x,$$

where x is any real number, is called the **exponential function with base b.**

REMARK   The function $f(x) = 1^x$ is a constant function and therefore it is not a one-to-one function. Remember from Chapter 3 that one-to-one functions have inverses; this becomes a key issue in a later section.

Now let's consider graphing some exponential functions.

EXAMPLE 1

Graph the function $f(x) = 2^x$.

Solution

Let's set up a table of values; keep in mind that the domain is the set of real numbers and the equation $f(x) = 2^x$ exhibits no symmetry. Plot these points and connect them with a smooth curve to produce Figure 4.1.

x	2^x
-2	$\frac{1}{4}$
-1	$\frac{1}{2}$
0	1
1	2
2	4
3	8

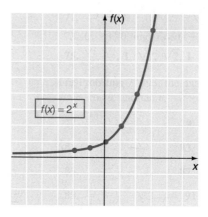

FIGURE   4.1

In the table for Example 1, we chose integral values for x to keep the computation simple. However, with the use of a calculator we could easily acquire functional values by using nonintegral exponents. Consider the following additional values for $f(x) = 2^x$.

$$f(.5) \approx 1.41, \qquad f(1.7) \approx 3.25,$$
$$f(-.5) \approx .71, \qquad f(-2.6) \approx .16$$

Use your calculator to check these results. Also notice that the points generated by these values do fit the graph in Figure 4.1.

EXAMPLE 2

Graph $f(x) = \left(\frac{1}{2}\right)^x$.

Solution

Again, let's set up a table of values, plot the points, and connect them with a smooth curve. The graph is shown in Figure 4.2.

x	$\left(\frac{1}{2}\right)^x$
-2	4
-1	2
0	1
1	$\frac{1}{2}$
2	$\frac{1}{4}$
3	$\frac{1}{8}$

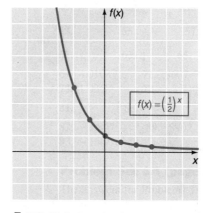

FIGURE   4.2

REMARK Since $\left(\frac{1}{2}\right)^x = \frac{1}{2^x} = 2^{-x}$, the graphs of $f(x) = 2^x$ and $f(x) = \left(\frac{1}{2}\right)^x$ are reflections of each other across the y-axis. Therefore, Figure 4.2 could have been acquired by reflecting Figure 4.1 across the y-axis.

The graphs in Figures 4.1 and 4.2 illustrate a general behavior pattern of exponential functions. That is to say, if $b > 1$, then the exponential functions of the form $f(x) = b^x$ are **increasing functions.** If $0 < b < 1$, then the functions $f(x) = b^x$ are **decreasing functions.** Generally speaking, the graphs are of the types shown in Figure 4.3. Notice that $b^0 = 1$ for any $b > 0$; thus, all graphs of $f(x) = b^x$ contain the point $(0, 1)$.

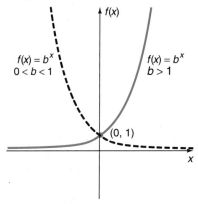

F I G U R E   4 . 3

As you graph exponential functions, don't forget to use your previous graphing experiences. For example, consider the following transformations of the graph of $f(x) = 2^x$.

1. The graph of $f(x) = 2^x + 3$ is the graph of $f(x) = 2^x$ translated three units upward.

2. The graph of $f(x) = 2^{x-4}$ is the graph of $f(x) = 2^x$ translated four units to the right.

3. The graph of $f(x) = -2^x$ is the graph of $f(x) = 2^x$ reflected across the x-axis.

4. The graph of $f(x) = 2^{x+2} - 4$ is the graph of $f(x) = 2^x$ translated two units to the left and four units downward.

Furthermore, if you are faced with an exponential function that is not one of the basic ones of the form $f(x) = b^x$ nor a transformation of such a function, then use the other graphing suggestions offered in Chapter 3. Consider one such example.

E X A M P L E 3

Graph $f(x) = 2^{-x^2}$.

Solution

Since $f(-x) = 2^{-(-x)^2} = 2^{-x^2} = f(x)$, we know that this curve is symmetrical with respect to the y-axis. Therefore, let's set up a table of values with nonnegative values for x. Plot these points, connect them with a smooth curve, and reflect this portion of the curve across the y-axis to produce the graph in Figure 4.4.

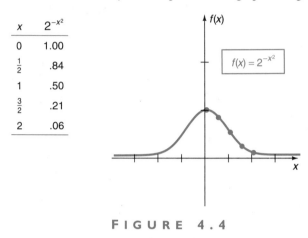

x	2^{-x^2}
0	1.00
$\frac{1}{2}$	.84
1	.50
$\frac{3}{2}$	.21
2	.06

$f(x) = 2^{-x^2}$

F I G U R E   4 . 4

Applications of Exponential Functions

Many real world situations that exhibit growth or decay can be represented by equations that describe exponential functions. For example, suppose that an economist predicts an annual inflation rate of 5% per year for the next 10 years. This means that an item that presently costs $8 will cost $8(105\%) = 8(1.05) = \$8.40$ in a year from now. The same item will cost $[8(105\%)](105\%) = 8(1.05)^2 = \$8.82$ in 2 years. In general, the equation

$$P = P_0(1.05)^t$$

yields the predicted price P of an item in t years if the present cost is P_0 and the annual inflation rate is 5%. By using this equation, we can look at some future prices based on the prediction of a 5% inflation rate.

1. A $3.27 container of hot cocoa mix will cost $\$3.27(1.05)^3 = \$3.79$ in 3 years;

2. A $4.07 jar of coffee will cost $\$4.07(1.05)^5 = \$5.19$ in 5 years;

3. A $9500 car will cost $\$9500(1.05)^7 = \$13{,}367$ (nearest dollar) in 7 years.

Compound Interest

Compound interest provides another illustration of exponential growth. Suppose that $500 (called the **principal**) is invested at an interest rate of 8% **compounded annually**. The interest earned the first year is $500(.08) = \$40$ and this amount is added to the original $500 to form a new principal of $540 for the second year. The interest earned during the second year is $540(.08) = \$43.20$ and this amount is added to $540 to form a new principal of $583.20 for the third year. Each year a new principal is formed by reinvesting the interest earned during that year.

In general, suppose that a sum of money P (called the principal) is invested at an interest rate of r percent compounded annually. The interest earned the first year is Pr and the new principal for the second year is $P + Pr$ or $P(1 + r)$. Note that the new principal for the second year can be found by multiplying the original principal P by $(1 + r)$. In a like fashion, the new principal for the third year can be found by multiplying the previous principal $P(1 + r)$ by $1 + r$, thus obtaining $P(1 + r)^2$. If this process is continued, then after t years the total amount of money accumulated, A, is given by

$$A = P(1 + r)^t.$$

Consider the following examples of investments made at a certain rate of interest compounded annually.

1. $750 invested for 5 years at 9% compounded annually produces

$$A = \$750(1.09)^5 = \$1153.97.$$

2. $1000 invested for 10 years at 11% compounded annually produces

$$A = \$1000(1.11)^{10} = \$2839.42.$$

3. $5000 invested for 20 years at 12% compounded annually produces

$$A = \$5000(1.12)^{20} = \$48,231.47.$$

The compound interest formula can be used to determine what rate of interest is needed to accumulate a certain amount of money based on a given initial investment. The next example illustrates this idea.

EXAMPLE 4

What rate of interest is needed for an investment of $1000 to yield $4000 in 10 years if the interest is compounded annually?

Solution

Let's substitute $1000 for P, $4000 for A, and 10 years for t in the compound interest formula, and solve for r.

$$A = P(1 + r)^t$$

$$4000 = 1000(1 + r)^{10}$$

$$4 = (1 + r)^{10}$$

$$4^{.1} = [(1 + r)^{10}]^{.1} \qquad \text{Raise both sides to the .1}$$

$$\qquad\qquad\qquad\qquad \text{power.}$$

$$1.148698355 \approx 1 + r$$

$$.148698355 \approx r$$

$$r = 14.9\% \quad \text{to the nearest tenth of a percent.}$$

Therefore, a rate of interest of approximately 14.9% is needed. (Perhaps you should check this answer.)

If money invested at a certain rate of interest is to be compounded more than once a year, then the basic formula $A = P(1 + r)^t$, can be adjusted according to the number of compounding periods in a year. For example, when **compounding semi-annually**, the formula becomes $A = P\left(1 + \frac{r}{2}\right)^{2t}$ and when **compounding quarterly**, the formula becomes $A = P\left(1 + \frac{r}{4}\right)^{4t}$. In general, if n represents the number of compounding periods in a year, the formula becomes

$$A = P\left(1 + \frac{r}{n}\right)^{nt}.$$

The following examples illustrate the use of the formula.

1. $750 invested for 5 years at 9% compounded semiannually produces
$$A = \$750\left(1 + \tfrac{.09}{2}\right)^{2(5)} = \$750(1.045)^{10} = \$1164.73.$$

2. $1000 invested for 10 years at 11% compounded quarterly produces
$$A = \$1000\left(1 + \tfrac{.11}{4}\right)^{4(10)} = \$1000(1.0275)^{40} = \$2959.87.$$

3. $5000 invested for 20 years at 12% compounded monthly produces
$$A = \$5000\left(1 + \tfrac{.12}{12}\right)^{12(20)} = \$5000(1.01)^{240} = \$54,462.77.$$

You may find it interesting to compare these results with those obtained earlier for compounding annually.

Exponential Decay

Suppose that a car depreciates 15% per year for the first 5 years. Therefore, a car that costs $9500 will be worth $9500 × (100% − 15%) = $9500(85%) = $9500(0.85) = $8075 in 1 year. In 2 years the value of the car will have depreciated to $9500(0.85)^2 = \$6864$ (to the nearest dollar). The equation

$$V = V_0(0.85)^t$$

yields the value V of a car in t years if the initial cost is V_0 and it depreciates 15% per year. Therefore, we can estimate some car values to the nearest dollar.

1. A $6900 car will be worth $\$6900(0.85)^3 = \$4237$ in 3 years.
2. A $10,900 car will be worth $\$10,900(0.85)^4 = \$5690$ in 4 years.
3. A $13,000 car will be worth $\$13,000(0.85)^5 = \$5768$ in 5 years.

Another example of exponential decay is associated with radioactive substances. The rate of decay is exponential and is based on the half-life of a substance.

The half-life of a radioactive substance is the amount of time that it takes for one-half of an initial amount of the substance to disappear as the result of decay. For example, suppose that we have 200 grams of a certain substance that has a half-life of 5 days. After 5 days, $200\left(\frac{1}{2}\right) = 100$ grams remain. After 10 days, $200\left(\frac{1}{2}\right)^2 = 50$ grams remain. After 15 days, $200\left(\frac{1}{2}\right)^3 = 25$ grams remain. In general, after t days, $200\left(\frac{1}{2}\right)^{t/5}$ grams remain.

The previous discussion leads to the following half-life formula. Suppose there is an initial amount, Q_0, of a radioactive substance with a half-life of h. The amount of substance remaining, Q, after a time period of t, is given by the formula

$$Q = Q_0\left(\frac{1}{2}\right)^{t/h}.$$

The units of measure for t and h must be the same.

EXAMPLE 5

Half-life   Barium-140 has a half-life of 13 days. If there are 500 milligrams of barium initially, how many milligrams remain after 26 days? After 100 days?

Solution

Using $Q_0 = 500$ and $h = 13$, the half-life formula becomes

$$Q = 500\left(\frac{1}{2}\right)^{t/13}$$

If $t = 26$, then

$$Q = 500\left(\frac{1}{2}\right)^{26/13}$$

$$= 500\left(\frac{1}{2}\right)^2$$

$$= 500\left(\frac{1}{4}\right)$$

$$= 125.$$

So, 125 milligrams remain after 26 days. If $t = 100$, then

$$Q = 500\left(\frac{1}{2}\right)^{100/13}$$

$$= 500(.5)^{100/13}$$

$$= 2.4 \text{ to the nearest tenth of a milligram.}$$

So, approximately 2.4 milligrams remain after 100 days.

Number e

An interesting situation occurs if we consider the compound interest formula for $P = \$1$, $r = 100\%$, and $t = 1$ year. The formula becomes $A = 1\left(1 + \dfrac{1}{n}\right)^n$. The following table shows some values, rounded to eight decimal places, of $\left(1 + \dfrac{1}{n}\right)^n$ for different values of n.

n	$\left(1 + \dfrac{1}{n}\right)^n$
1	2.00000000
10	2.59374246
100	2.70481383
1000	2.71692393
10,000	2.71814593
100,000	2.71826824
1,000,000	2.71828047
10,000,000	2.71828169
100,000,000	2.71828181
1,000,000,000	2.71828183

The table suggests that as n increases, the value of $\left(1 + \dfrac{1}{n}\right)^n$ gets closer and closer to some fixed number; the fixed number is called e. To five decimal places, $e = 2.71828$.

x	$f(x) = e^x$
0	1.0
1	2.7
2	7.4
−1	.4
−2	.1

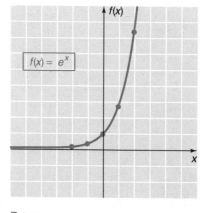

$f(x) = e^x$

FIGURE 4.5

The function defined by the equation $f(x) = e^x$ is the **natural exponential function**. It has a great many real world applications, some of which we will look at in a moment. First, however, let's get a picture of the natural exponential function. Since $2 < e < 3$, the graph of $f(x) = e^x$ must fall between the graphs of $f(x) = 2^x$ and $f(x) = 3^x$. To be more specific, let's use our calculator to determine a table of values. Use the $\boxed{e^x}$ key, and round the results to the nearest tenth to obtain the following table. Plot the points determined by the table and connect them with a smooth curve to produce Figure 4.5.

Back to Compound Interest

Let's return to the concept of compound interest. If the number of compounding periods in a year is increased indefinitely, we arrive at the concept of **compounding continuously**. Mathematically, we apply the limit concept to the expression $P(1 + r/n)^{nt}$. We will not show the details here, but the following result is obtained. The formula

$$A = Pe^{rt}$$

yields the accumulated rate (A) of a sum of money (P) that has been invested for t years at a rate of r percent compounded continuously. The following examples illustrate the use of this formula.

1. $750 invested for 5 years at 9% compounded continuously produces

$$A = 750e^{(.09)(5)} = 750e^{.45} = \$1176.23.$$

2. $1000 invested for 10 years at 11% compounded continuously produces

$$A = 1000e^{(.11)(10)} = 1000e^{1.1} = \$3004.17.$$

3. $5000 invested for 20 years at 12% compounded continuously produces

$$A = 5000e^{(.12)(20)} = 5000e^{2.4} = \$55,115.88.$$

Again you may find it interesting to compare these results with those you obtained earlier using a different number of compounding periods.

Is it better to invest at 6% compounded quarterly or at 5.75% compounded continuously? To answer such a question, we can use the concept of **effective yield** (sometimes called *effective annual rate of interest*). The effect yield of an investment is the simple interest rate that would yield the same amount in one year. Thus, for the ''6% compounded quarterly'' investment, we can calculate the effective yield as follows.

$$P(1 + r) = P\left(1 + \frac{.06}{4}\right)^4$$

$$1 + r = \left(1 + \frac{.06}{4}\right)^4 \qquad \text{Multiply both sides by } \frac{1}{P}.$$

$$1 + r = (1.015)^4$$

$$r = (1.015)^4 - 1$$

$$r \approx 0.613635506$$

$$r = 6.14\% \quad \text{to the nearest hundredth of a percent}$$

Likewise, for the "5.75% compounded continuously" investment we can calculate the effective yield as follows.

$$P(1 + r) = Pe^{.0575}$$

$$1 + r = e^{.0575}$$

$$r = e^{.0575} - 1$$

$$r \approx .0591852707$$

$$r = 5.92\% \quad \text{to the nearest hundredth of a percent}$$

Therefore, comparing the two effective yields, we see that it is better to invest at 6% compounded quarterly than to invest at 5.75% compounded continuously.

Law of Exponential Growth

The ideas behind compounded continuously carry over to other growth situations. The law of exponential growth

$$Q(t) = Q_0 e^{kt}$$

is used as a mathematical model for numerous growth-and-decay applications. In this equation, $Q(t)$ represents the quantity of a given substance at any time t, Q_0 is the initial amount of the substance (when $t = 0$), and k is a constant that depends on the particular application. If $k < 0$, then $Q(t)$ decreases as t increases, and we refer to the model as the **law of decay**. Let's consider some growth-and-decay applications.

EXAMPLE 6

Bacteria growth　Suppose that in a certain culture, the equation $Q(t) = 15000e^{.3t}$ expresses the number of bacteria present as a function of the time t, where t is expressed in hours. Find (a) the initial number of bacteria, and (b) the number of bacteria after 3 hours.

Solution

a. The initial number of bacteria is produced when $t = 0$.

$$Q(0) = 15000e^{.3(0)}$$

$$= 15000e^0$$

$$= 15000 \qquad e^0 = 1$$

b. $Q(3) = 15000e^{.3(3)}$

$\qquad = 15000e^{.9}$

$\qquad = 36894$ to the nearest whole number

Therefore, there should be approximately 36,894 bacteria present after 3 hours.

E X A M P L E   7

Bacteria growth   Suppose the number of bacteria present in a certain culture after t minutes is given by the equation $Q(t) = Q_0 e^{.05t}$, where Q_0 represents the initial number of bacteria. If 5000 bacteria are present after 20 minutes, how many bacteria were present initially?

Solution

If 5000 bacteria are present after 20 minutes, then $Q(20) = 5000$.

$\qquad 5000 = Q_0 e^{.05(20)}$

$\qquad 5000 = Q_0 e^{1}$

$\qquad \dfrac{5000}{e} = Q_0$

$\qquad 1839 = Q_0$ to the nearest whole number

Therefore, there were approximately 1839 bacteria present initially.

E X A M P L E   8

Radioactive decay   The number of grams of a certain radioactive substance present after t seconds is given by the equation $Q(t) = 200e^{-.3t}$. How many grams remain after 7 seconds?

Solution

Use $Q(t) = 200e^{-0.3t}$ to obtain

$\qquad Q(7) = 200e^{(-0.3)(7)}$

$\qquad\quad\ = 200e^{-2.1}$

$\qquad\quad\ = 24.5$ to the nearest tenth.

Thus, approximately 24.5 grams remain after 7 seconds.

As you might expect, a graphing utility is extremely helpful when solving problems involving exponential functions. Let's consider two examples.

E X A M P L E   9

Compounding continuously   Suppose that $1000 was invested at 6.5% interest compounded continuously. How long would it take for the money to double itself?

Solution

Substituting $1000 for P and .065 for r in the formula $A = Pe^{rt}$ produces $A = 1000e^{.065t}$. If we let $y = A$ and $x = t$, we can graph the equation $y = 1000e^{.065x}$. By letting $x = 20$, we obtain $y = 1000e^{.065(20)} = 1000e^{1.3} \approx 3670$. Therefore, let's set the boundaries of the viewing rectangle so that $0 \le x \le 20$ and $0 \le y \le 3700$ with a y-scale of 1000. Then we obtain the graph in Figure 4.6. Now we want to find the value of x so that $y = 2000$. (The money is to double itself.) Using the zoom and trace features of the graphing utility we can determine that an x-value of approximately 10.7 will produce a y-value of 2000. Thus, it will take approximately 10.7 years for the $1000 investment to double itself.

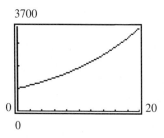

FIGURE 4.6

EXAMPLE 10   *Normal distribution curve*   Graph the function $y = \dfrac{1}{\sqrt{2\pi}} e^{-x^2/2}$ and find its maximum value.

Solution

If $x = 0$, then $y = \dfrac{1}{\sqrt{2\pi}} e^0 = \dfrac{1}{\sqrt{2\pi}} \approx .4$. Let's set the boundaries of the viewing rectangle so that $-5 \le x \le 5$ and $0 \le y \le 1$ with a y-scale of .1. With these boundaries the graph of the function is shown in Figure 4.7.

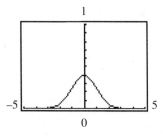

FIGURE 4.7

From the graph we see that the maximum value of the function occurs at $x = 0$, which we have already determined to be approximately .4.

REMARK The curve in Figure 4.7 is called the **normal distribution curve**. Some instructors assign grades based on the "normal curve." You may want to ask your instructor to explain what it means to assign grades based on the normal distribution curve.

PROBLEM SET 4.3

Graph each of the following exponential functions.

1. $f(x) = 3^x$

2. $f(x) = \left(\frac{1}{3}\right)^x$

3. $f(x) = \left(\frac{1}{4}\right)^x$

4. $f(x) = 4^x$

5. $f(x) = \left(\frac{2}{3}\right)^x$

6. $f(x) = \left(\frac{3}{2}\right)^x$

7. $f(x) = 2^x + 1$

8. $f(x) = 2^x - 3$

9. $f(x) = 2^{x-1}$

10. $f(x) = 2^{x+2}$

11. $f(x) = -3^x$

12. $f(x) = -2^x$

13. $f(x) = 2^{-x+1}$

14. $f(x) = 2^{-x-2}$

15. $f(x) = 2^x + 2^{-x}$

16. $f(x) = 2^{x^2}$

17. $f(x) = 3^{1-x^2}$

18. $f(x) = 2^{|x|}$

19. $f(x) = 2^{-|x|}$

20. $f(x) = 2^x - 2^{-x}$

21. $f(x) = e^x + 1$

22. $f(x) = e^x - 2$

23. $f(x) = 2e^x$

24. $f(x) = -e^x$

25. $f(x) = e^{2x}$

26. $f(x) = e^{-x}$

27. Assuming that the rate of inflation is 3.5% per year, the equation $P = P_0(1.035)^t$ yields the predicted price P of an item in t years that presently costs P_0. Find the predicted price of each of the following items for the indicated years ahead.

  a. $.55 can of soup in 3 years

  b. $3.43 container of cocoa mix in 5 years

  c. $1.76 jar of coffee-creamer in 4 years

  d. $.44 can of beans and bacon in 10 years

  e. $9000 car in 5 years (nearest dollar)

  f. $50,000 house in 8 years (nearest dollar)

  g. $500 TV set in 7 years (nearest dollar)

28. Suppose that it is estimated that the value of a car depreciates 20% per year for the first 5 years. The equation

$A = P_0(.8)^t$ yields the value (A) of a car after t years if the original price is P_0. Find the value (to the nearest dollar) of each of the following priced cars after the indicated time.

  a. $9000 car after 4 years

  b. $15,000 car after 2 years

  c. $22,500 car after 5 years

  d. $31,595 car after 3 years

For Problems 29–38, use the formula $A = P\left(1 + \dfrac{r}{n}\right)^{nt}$ to find the total amount of money accumulated at the end of the indicated time period for each of the following investments.

29. $250 for 5 years at 9% compounded annually

30. $350 for 7 years at 11% compounded annually

31. $300 for 6 years at 8% compounded semiannually

32. $450 for 10 years at 10% compounded semiannually

33. $600 for 12 years at 12% compounded quarterly

34. $750 for 15 years at 9% compounded quarterly

35. $1000 for 5 years at 12% compounded monthly

36. $1250 for 8 years at 9% compounded monthly

37. $600 for 10 years at $8\frac{1}{2}\%$ compounded annually

38. $1500 for 15 years at $9\frac{1}{4}\%$ compounded semiannually

For Problems 39–47 use the formula $A = Pe^{rt}$ to find the total amount of money accumulated at the end of the indicated time period by compounding continuously.

39. $400 for 5 years at 7%

40. $500 for 7 years at 6%

41. $750 for 8 years at 8%

42. $1000 for 10 years at 9%

43. $2000 for 15 years at 10%

44. $5000 for 20 years at 11%

45. $7500 for 10 years at 8.5%

46. $10,000 for 25 years at 9.25%

47. $15,000 for 10 years at 7.75%

APPLIED PROBLEMS

48. *Finding rate of interest*   What rate of interest, to the nearest tenth of a percent, compounded annually, is needed for an investment of $200 to grow to $350 in 5 years?

49. *Finding rate of interest*   What rate of interest, to the nearest tenth of a percent, compounded quarterly, is needed for an investment of $1500 to grow to $2700 in 10 years?

50. *Effective yield*   Find the effective yield, to the nearest tenth of a percent, of an investment at 7.5% compounded monthly.

51. *Effective yield*   Find the effective yield, to the nearest hundredth of a percent, of an investment at 7.75% compounded continuously.

52. *Comparing investments*   What investment yields the greater return: 7% compounded monthly or 6.85% compounded continuously?

53. *Comparing investments*   What investment yields the greatest return: 8.25% compounded quarterly or 8.3% compounded semiannually?

54. *Half-life*   Suppose that a certain radioactive substance has a half-life of 20 years. If there are presently 2500 milligrams of the substance, how much, to the nearest milligram, will remain after 40 years? After 50 years?

55. *Half-life*   Strontium-90 has a half-life of 29 years. If there are 400 grams of strontium initially, how much, to the nearest gram, will remain after 87 years? After 100 years?

56. *Half-life*   The half-life of radium is approximately 1600 years. If the present amount of radium in a certain location is 500 grams, how much will remain after 800 years? Express your answer to the nearest gram.

57. *Bacteria growth*   Suppose that in a certain culture, the equation $Q(t) = 1000e^{.4t}$ expresses the number of bacte-

ria present as a function of the time t, where t is expressed in hours. How many bacteria are present at the end of 2 hours? 3 hours? 5 hours?

58. *Bacteria growth*   The number of bacteria present at a given time under certain conditions is given by the equation $Q(t) = 5000e^{.05t}$, where t is expressed in minutes. How many bacteria are present at the end of 10 minutes? 30 minutes? 1 hour?

59. *Bacteria growth*   The number of bacteria present in a certain culture after t hours is given by the equation $Q(t) = Q_0e^{.3t}$, where Q_0 represents the initial number of bacteria. If 6640 bacteria are present after 4 hours, how many bacteria were present initially?

60. *Radioactive decay*   The number of grams Q of a certain radioactive substance present after t seconds is given by the equation $Q(t) = 1500e^{-.4t}$. How many grams remain after 5 seconds? After 10 seconds? After 20 seconds?

61. *Atmospheric pressure*   The atmospheric pressure, measured in pounds per square inch, is a function of the altitude above sea level. The equation $P(a) = 14.7e^{-.21a}$, where a is the altitude measured in miles, can be used to approximate atmospheric pressure. Find the atmospheric pressure at each of the following locations.

   a. Mount McKinley in Alaska—altitude of 3.85 miles

   b. Denver, Colorado—the "mile-high" city

   c. Asheville, North Carolina—altitude of 1985 feet

   d. Phoenix, Arizona—altitude of 1090 feet

62. *Population growth*   Suppose that the present population of a city is 75,000. Using the equation $P(t) = 75000e^{.01t}$ to estimate future growth, estimate the population

   a. 10 years from now,

   b. 15 years from now, and

   c. 25 years from now.

63. Why is the base of an exponential function restricted to positive numbers not including one?

64. How would you go about graphing the function $f(x) = -\left(\frac{1}{3}\right)^x$?

65. Explain how you would solve the equation $(4^{x-1})(8^{2x+3}) = 128$.

FURTHER INVESTIGATIONS

66. Complete the following chart that illustrates what happens to $1000 invested at various rates of interest for different lengths of time but always compounded continuously. Round your answers to the nearest dollar.

$1000 COMPOUNDED CONTINUOUSLY

	8%	10%	12%	14%
5 years				
10 years				
15 years				
20 years				
25 years				

67. Complete the following chart that illustrates what happens to $1000 invested at 12% for different lengths of time and different numbers of compounding periods. Round all of your answers to the nearest dollar.

$1000 AT 12%

	1 year	5 years	10 years	20 years
Compounded annually				
Compounded semiannually				
Compounded quarterly				
Compounded monthly				
Compounded continuously				

68. Complete the following chart that illustrates what happens to $1000 in 10 years based on different rates of interest and different numbers of compounding periods. Round your answers to the nearest dollar.

$1000 FOR 10 YEARS

	8%	10%	12%	14%
Compounded annually				
Compounded semiannually				
Compounded quarterly				
Compounded monthly				
Compounded continuously				

For Problems 69–74, graph each of the functions. These functions are called hyperbolic functions and have a special significance in calculus.

69. $f(x) = \dfrac{e^x - e^{-x}}{2}$

70. $f(x) = \dfrac{e^x + e^{-x}}{2}$

71. $f(x) = \dfrac{e^x - e^{-x}}{e^x + e^{-x}}$

72. $f(x) = \dfrac{2}{e^x - e^{-x}}$

73. $f(x) = \dfrac{2}{e^x + e^{-x}}$

74. $f(x) = \dfrac{e^x + e^{-x}}{e^x - e^{-x}}$

GRAPHICS CALCULATOR ACTIVITIES

75. Use your graphics calculator to check your graphs for Problems 69–74.

76. How should the graphs of $f(x) = 2^x$, $f(x) = e^x$, and $f(x) = 3^x$ compare? Graph them on the same set of axes to check your answer.

77. Graph $f(x) = e^x$. Where should the graphs of $f(x) = e^{x-2}$, $f(x) = e^{x+4}$, and $f(x) = e^{x-6}$ be located? Graph all three functions on the same set of axes with $f(x) = e^x$.

78. Graph $f(x) = e^x$ again. Now predict the graphs for $f(x) = -e^x$, $f(x) = e^{-x}$, and $f(x) = -e^{-x}$. Graph these three functions on the same set of axes with the graph of $f(x) = e^x$.

79. How do you think the graphs of $f(x) = e^x$, $f(x) = e^{2x}$, and $f(x) = 2e^x$ will compare? Graph them on the same set of axes to see if you were right.

80. Use a graphing approach to argue that it is better to invest money at 6% compounded quarterly than it is at 5.75% compounded continuously.

81. Use a graphing approach to determine how long it will take for $500 to be worth $1500 if it is invested at 7.5% interest compounded semiannually. Be sure to check your answer.

82. Use a graphing approach to determine how long it will take for $5000 to triple itself if it is invested at 6.75% interest compounded quarterly. Be sure to check your answer.

83. Graph $f(x) = 4^x$. Where should the graphs of $f(x) = 4^{x-2}$, $f(x) = 4^{x-4}$, and $f(x) = 4^{x+3}$ be located? Graph all three functions on the same set of axes with $f(x) = 4^x$.

84. Graph $f(x) = \left(\frac{1}{4}\right)^x$. Where should the graphs of $f(x) = \left(\frac{1}{4}\right)^x - 2$, $f(x) = \left(\frac{1}{4}\right)^x + 3$, and $f(x) = \left(\frac{1}{4}\right)^x - 4$ be located? Graph all three functions on the same set of axes with $f(x) = \left(\frac{1}{4}\right)^x$.

85. Graph $f(x) = \left(\frac{3}{4}\right)^x$. Now predict the graphs for $f(x) = -\left(\frac{3}{4}\right)^x$, $f(x) = \left(\frac{3}{4}\right)^{-x}$, and $f(x) = -\left(\frac{3}{4}\right)^{-x}$. Graph all three functions on the same set of axes with $f(x) = \left(\frac{3}{4}\right)^x$.

86. Graph $f(x) = (-2)^x$. Explain your result.

87. What is the solution for $3^x = 5$? Do you agree that it is between 1 and 2 since $3^1 = 3$ and $3^2 = 9$? Now graph $f(x) = 3^x - 5$ and use the zoom and trace features of your graphics calculator to find an approximation, to the nearest hundredth, for the x-intercept. You should get an answer of 1.46, to the nearest hundredth. Do you see that this is an approximation for the solution of $3^x = 5$? Try it; raise 3 to the 1.46 power.

Find an approximate solution, to the nearest hundredth, for each of the following equations by graphing the appropriate function and finding the x-intercept. Be sure to check your answers.

a. $2^x = 19$ **b.** $3^x = 50$

c. $4^x = 47$ **d.** $5^x = 120$

e. $2^x = 1500$ **f.** $3^{x-1} = 34$

4.4   LOGARITHMS

In Sections 4.2 and 4.3, we gave meaning to exponential expressions of the form b^n, where b is any positive real number and n is any real number; we used exponential expressions of the form b^n to define exponential functions; and we used exponential functions to help solve problems. In the next three sections we will follow the same basic pattern with respect to a new concept, that of a **logarithm**. Let's begin with the following definition.

DEFINITION   4.4

If r is any positive real number, then the unique exponent t such that $b^t = r$ is called the **logarithm of r with base b** and is denoted by $\log_b r$.

According to Definition 4.4, the logarithm of 16 base 2 is the exponent t such that $2^t = 16$; thus, we can write $\log_2 16 = 4$. Likewise, we can write $\log_{10} 1000 = 3$ because $10^3 = 1000$. In general, Definition 4.4 can be remembered in terms of the statement

$$\log_b r = t \quad \text{is equivalent to} \quad b^t = r.$$

Therefore, we can easily switch back and forth between exponential and logarithmic forms of equations, as the next examples illustrate.

$$\log_2 8 = 3 \qquad \text{is equivalent to } 2^3 = 8$$

$$\log_{10} 100 = 2 \qquad \text{is equivalent to } 10^2 = 100$$

$$\log_3 81 = 4 \qquad \text{is equivalent to } 3^4 = 81$$

$$\log_{10} .001 = -3 \qquad \text{is equivalent to } 10^{-3} = .001$$

$$2^7 = 128 \qquad \text{is equivalent to } \log_2 128 = 7$$

$$5^3 = 125 \qquad \text{is equivalent to } \log_5 125 = 3$$

$$\left(\tfrac{1}{2}\right)^4 = \tfrac{1}{16} \qquad \text{is equivalent to } \log_{1/2}\left(\tfrac{1}{16}\right) = 4$$

$$10^{-2} = .01 \qquad \text{is equivalent to } \log_{10} .01 = -2$$

Some logarithms can be determined by changing to exponential form and using the properties of exponents, as the next three examples illustrate.

EXAMPLE 1

Evaluate $\log_2 64$.

Solution

Let $x = \log_2 64$. Then by changing to exponential form we obtain $2^x = 64$, which can be solved as follows.

$$2^x = 64$$

$$2^x = 2^6$$

$$x = 6$$

Therefore, $\log_2 64 = 6$.

EXAMPLE 2

Evaluate $\log_{10}.0001$.

Solution

Let $\log_{10}.0001 = x$. Then by changing to exponential form we have $10^x = .0001$, which can be solved as follows.

$$10^x = .0001$$

$$10^x = 10^{-4} \qquad .0001 = \frac{1}{10000} = \frac{1}{10^4} = 10^{-4}$$

$$x = -4$$

Thus, we have $\log_{10}.0001 = -4$.

EXAMPLE 3

Evaluate $\log_9(\sqrt[5]{27}/3)$.

Solution

Let $\log_9(\sqrt[5]{27}/3) = x$. Then by changing to exponential form we have $9^x = (\sqrt[5]{27}/3)$, which can be solved as follows.

$$9^x = \frac{(27)^{1/5}}{3}$$

$$(3^2)^x = \frac{(3^3)^{1/5}}{3}$$

$$3^{2x} = \frac{3^{3/5}}{3}$$

$$3^{2x} = 3^{-2/5}$$

$$2x = -\frac{2}{5}$$

$$x = -\frac{1}{5}$$

Therefore, we have $\log_9(\sqrt[5]{27}/3) = -1/5$.

Some equations involving logarithms can also be solved by changing to exponential form and using our knowledge of exponents.

EXAMPLE 4

Solve $\log_8 x = \frac{2}{3}$.

Solution

Changing $\log_8 x = \frac{2}{3}$ to exponential form, we obtain

$$8^{2/3} = x.$$

Therefore,

$$x = (\sqrt[3]{8})^2$$

$$= 2^2$$

$$= 4.$$

The solution set is $\{4\}$.

EXAMPLE 5

Solve $\log_b\left(\frac{27}{64}\right) = 3$.

Solution

Changing $\log_b\left(\frac{27}{64}\right) = 3$ to exponential form, we obtain

$$b^3 = \frac{27}{64}.$$

Therefore,

$$b = \sqrt[3]{\frac{27}{64}}$$

$$= \frac{3}{4}.$$

The solution set is $\left\{\frac{3}{4}\right\}$.

Properties of Logarithms

There are some properties of logarithms that are a direct consequence of Definition 4.4 and the properties of exponents. For example, by writing the exponential equations $b^1 = b$ and $b^0 = 1$ in logarithmic form, the following property is obtained.

PROPERTY 4.5

For $b > 0$ and $b \neq 1$,

$$\log_b b = 1 \qquad \text{and} \qquad \log_b 1 = 0.$$

Therefore, according to Property 4.5 we can write

$$\log_{10} 10 = 1, \qquad \log_4 4 = 1,$$

$$\log_{10} 1 = 0, \qquad \text{and} \qquad \log_5 1 = 0.$$

Also from Definition 4.4 we know that $\log_b r$ is the exponent t such that $b^t = r$. Therefore, raising b to the $\log_b r$ power must produce r. This fact is stated in Property 4.6.

PROPERTY 4.6

For $b > 0$, $b \neq 1$, and $r > 0$,

$$b^{\log_b r} = r.$$

Therefore, according to Property 4.6, we can write

$$10^{\log_{10} 72} = 72, \qquad 3^{\log_3 85} = 85,$$
and $\qquad e^{\log_e 7} = 7.$

Because a logarithm is by definition an exponent, it would seem reasonable to predict that there are some properties of logarithms that correspond to the basic exponential properties. This prediction is accurate; these properties provide a basis for computational work with logarithms. Let's state the first of these properties and show how it can be verified by our knowledge of exponents.

PROPERTY 4.7

For positive numbers b, r, and s, where $b \neq 1$,

$$\log_b rs = \log_b r + \log_b s.$$

To verify Property 4.7, we can proceed as follows. Let $m = \log_b r$ and $n = \log_b s$. Change each of these equations to exponential form:

$$m = \log_b r \quad \text{becomes} \quad r = b^m;$$

$$n = \log_b s \quad \text{becomes} \quad s = b^n.$$

Thus, the product rs becomes

$$rs = b^m \cdot b^n = b^{m+n}.$$

Now, by changing $rs = b^{m+n}$ back to logarithmic form, we obtain

$$\log_b rs = m + n.$$

Replacing m with $\log_b r$ and n with $\log_b s$ yields

$$\log_b rs = \log_b r + \log_b s.$$

The following two examples illustrate a use of Property 4.7.

EXAMPLE 6

If $\log_2 5 = 2.3219$ and $\log_2 3 = 1.5850$, evaluate $\log_2 15$.

Solution

Because $15 = 5 \cdot 3$, we can apply Property 4.7 as follows.

$$\begin{aligned} \log_2 15 &= \log_2(5 \cdot 3) \\ &= \log_2 5 + \log_2 3 \\ &= 2.3219 + 1.5850 \\ &= 3.9069 \end{aligned}$$

E X A M P L E   7

If $\log_{10} 178 = 2.2504$ and $\log_{10} 89 = 1.9494$, evaluate $\log_{10}(178 \cdot 89)$.

Solution

$$\begin{aligned} \log_{10}(178 \cdot 89) &= \log_{10} 178 + \log_{10} 89 \\ &= 2.2504 + 1.9494 \\ &= 4.1998 \end{aligned}$$

Since $b^m/b^n = b^{m-n}$, we would expect a corresponding property pertaining to logarithms. Property 4.8 is that property. It can be verified by using an approach similar to the one used to verify Property 4.7. This verification is left for you to do as an exercise in the next problem set.

P R O P E R T Y   4 . 8

For positive numbers b, r, and s, where $b \neq 1$,

$$\log_b\left(\frac{r}{s}\right) = \log_b r - \log_b s.$$

Property 4.8 can be used to change a division problem into an equivalent subtraction problem as the next two examples illustrate.

E X A M P L E   8

If $\log_5 36 = 2.2266$ and $\log_5 4 = .8614$, evaluate $\log_5 9$.

Solution

Since $9 = \frac{36}{4}$, we can use Property 4.8 as follows.

$$\begin{aligned} \log_5 9 &= \log_5\left(\frac{36}{4}\right) \\ &= \log_5 36 - \log_5 4 \\ &= 2.2266 - .8614 \\ &= 1.3652 \end{aligned}$$

EXAMPLE 9

Evaluate $\log_{10}\left(\frac{379}{86}\right)$ given that $\log_{10}379 = 2.5786$ and $\log_{10}86 = 1.9345$.

Solution

$$\log_{10}\left(\frac{379}{86}\right) = \log_{10}379 - \log_{10}86$$

$$= 2.5786 - 1.9345$$

$$= .6441$$

Another property of exponents states that $(b^n)^m = b^{mn}$. The corresponding property of logarithms is stated in Property 4.9. Again we will leave the verification of this property as an exercise for you to do in the next set of problems.

PROPERTY 4.9

If r is a positive real number, b is a positive real number other than 1, and p is any real number, then

$$\log_b r^p = p(\log_b r).$$

The next two examples illustrate a use of Property 4.9.

EXAMPLE 10

Evaluate $\log_2 22^{1/3}$ given that $\log_2 22 = 4.4594$.

Solution

$$\log_2 22^{1/3} = \frac{1}{3}\log_2 22 \qquad \text{Property 4.9}$$

$$= \frac{1}{3}(4.4594)$$

$$= 1.4865$$

EXAMPLE 11

Evaluate $\log_{10}(8540)^{3/5}$ given that $\log_{10}8540 = 3.9315$.

Solution

$$\log_{10}(8540)^{3/5} = \frac{3}{5}\log_{10}8540$$

$$= \frac{3}{5}(3.9315)$$

$$= 2.3589$$

The properties of logarithms can be used to change the forms of various logarithmic expressions, as the next two examples illustrate.

EXAMPLE 12

Evaluate $\log_b \sqrt{\dfrac{xy}{z}}$ in terms of the logarithms of x, y, and z.

Solution

$$\log_b \sqrt{\frac{xy}{z}} = \log_b \left(\frac{xy}{z}\right)^{1/2}$$

$$= \frac{1}{2} \log_b \left(\frac{xy}{z}\right)$$

$$= \frac{1}{2} (\log_b xy - \log_b z)$$

$$= \frac{1}{2} (\log_b x + \log_b y - \log_b z).$$

━━━━

EXAMPLE 13

Express $2 \log_b x + 3 \log_b y - 4 \log_b z$ as one logarithm.

Solution

$$2 \log_b x + 3 \log_b y - 4 \log_b z = \log_b x^2 + \log_b y^3 + \log_b z^4$$

$$= \log_b x^2 y^3 - \log_b z^4$$

$$= \log_b \left(\frac{x^2 y^3}{z^4}\right).$$

━━━━

The properties of logarithms along with the link between logarithmic form and exponential form provide the basis for solving certain types of equations involving logarithms. Keep in mind that logarithms are defined for only positive numbers.

EXAMPLE 14

Solve $\log_{10} x + \log_{10}(x + 9) = 1$.

Solution

$$\log_{10} x + \log_{10}(x + 9) = 1$$

$$\log_{10}[x(x + 9)] = 1 \qquad \text{Property 4.7}$$

$$10^1 = x(x + 9) \qquad \text{Change to exponential form}$$

$$10 = x^2 + 9x$$

$$0 = x^2 + 9x - 10$$

$$0 = (x + 10)(x - 1)$$

$$x + 10 = 0 \qquad \text{or} \qquad x - 1 = 0$$

$$x = -10 \qquad \text{or} \qquad x = 1$$

Since the left-hand number of the original equation is meaningful only if $x > 0$ and $x + 9 > 0$, the solution -10 must be discarded. Thus, the solution set is $\{1\}$.

━━━━

EXAMPLE 15

Solve $\log_5(x + 4) - \log_5 x = 2$.

Solution

$$\log_5(x + 4) - \log_5 x = 2$$

$$\log_5\left(\frac{x + 4}{x}\right) = 2$$

$$5^2 = \frac{x + 4}{x} \qquad \text{Change to exponential form}$$

$$25 = \frac{x + 4}{x}$$

$$25x = x + 4$$

$$24x = 4$$

$$x = \frac{4}{24} = \frac{1}{6}$$

The solution set is $\left\{\frac{1}{6}\right\}$.

PROBLEM SET 4.4

Write each of the following in logarithmic form. For example, $2^4 = 16$ becomes $\log_2 16 = 4$.

1. $3^2 = 9$ **2.** $2^5 = 32$

3. $5^3 = 125$ **4.** $10^1 = 10$

5. $2^{-4} = \frac{1}{16}$ **6.** $\left(\frac{2}{3}\right)^{-3} = \frac{27}{8}$

7. $10^{-2} = .01$ **8.** $10^5 = 100,000$

Write each of the following in exponential form. For example, $\log_2 8 = 3$ becomes $2^3 = 8$.

9. $\log_2 64 = 6$ **10.** $\log_3 27 = 3$

11. $\log_{10} 1 = -1$ **12.** $\log_5\left(\frac{1}{25}\right) = -2$

13. $\log_2\left(\frac{1}{16}\right) = -4$ **14.** $\log_{10} .00001 = -5$

Evaluate each of the following.

15. $\log_6 36$ **16.** $\log_3 243$

17. $\log_5\left(\frac{1}{5}\right)$ **18.** $\log_4\left(\frac{1}{64}\right)$

19. $\log_{10} 10$ **20.** $\log_{10} 1$

21. $\log_3 \sqrt{3}$ **22.** $\log_5 \sqrt[3]{25}$

23. $\log_3\left(\frac{\sqrt{27}}{3}\right)$ **24.** $\log_{1/2}\left(\frac{\sqrt[4]{8}}{2}\right)$

25. $\log_{1/4}\left(\frac{\sqrt[4]{32}}{2}\right)$ **26.** $\log_2\left(\frac{\sqrt[3]{16}}{4}\right)$

27. $10^{\log_{10} 7}$ **28.** $5^{\log_5 13}$

29. $\log_2(\log_5 5)$ **30.** $\log_6(\log_2 64)$

Solve each of the following equations.

31. $\log_5 x = 2$ **32.** $\log_{10} x = 3$

33. $\log_8 t = \frac{5}{3}$ **34.** $\log_4 m = \frac{3}{2}$

35. $\log_b 3 = \frac{1}{2}$ **36.** $\log_b 2 = \frac{1}{2}$

37. $\log_{10} x = 0$ **38.** $\log_{10} x = 1$

Given that $\log_2 5 = 2.3219$ and $\log_2 7 = 2.8074$, evaluate each of the following by using Properties 4.7–4.9.

39. $\log_2 35$ **40.** $\log_2\left(\frac{7}{5}\right)$

41. $\log_2 125$ **42.** $\log_2 49$

43. $\log_2 \sqrt{7}$ **44.** $\log_2 \sqrt[3]{5}$

45. $\log_2 175$ **46.** $\log_2 56$

47. $\log_2 80$

Given that $\log_8 5 = .7740$ and $\log_8 11 = 1.1531$, evaluate each of the following using Properties 4.7–4.9.

48. $\log_8 55$ **49.** $\log_8\left(\frac{5}{11}\right)$

50. $\log_8 25$ **51.** $\log_8 \sqrt{11}$

52. $\log_8 (5)^{2/3}$ **53.** $\log_8 88$

54. $\log_8 320$ **55.** $\log_8\left(\frac{25}{11}\right)$

56. $\log_8\left(\frac{121}{25}\right)$

Express each of the following as the sum or difference of simpler logarithmic quantities. (Assume that all variables represent positive real numbers.) For example,

$$\log_b\left(\frac{x^3}{y^2}\right) = \log_b x^3 - \log_b y^2$$

$$= 3\log_b x - 2\log_b y.$$

57. $\log_b xyz$ **58.** $\log_b\left(\frac{x^2}{y}\right)$

59. $\log_b x^2 y^3$ **60.** $\log_b x^{2/3} y^{3/4}$

61. $\log_b \sqrt{xy}$ **62.** $\log_b \sqrt[3]{x^2 z}$

63. $\log_b \sqrt{\dfrac{x}{y}}$ **64.** $\log_b (x)\left(\sqrt{\dfrac{x}{y}}\right)$

Express each of the following as a single logarithm. (Assume all variables represent positive real numbers.) For example,

$$3\log_b x + 5\log_b y = \log_b x^3 y^5.$$

65. $\log_b x + \log_b y - \log_b z$

66. $2\log_b x - 4\log_b y$

67. $(\log_b x - \log_b y) - \log_b z$

68. $\log_b x - (\log_b y - \log_b z)$

69. $\log_b x + \frac{1}{2}\log_b y$

70. $2\log_b x + 4\log_b y - 3\log_b z$

71. $2\log_b x + \frac{1}{2}\log_b (x - 1) - 4\log_b (2x + 5)$

72. $\frac{1}{2}\log_b x - 3\log_b x + 4\log_b y$

Solve each of the following equations.

73. $\log_3 x + \log_3 4 = 2$

74. $\log_7 5 + \log_7 x = 1$

75. $\log_{10} x + \log_{10}(x - 21) = 2$

76. $\log_{10} x + \log_{10}(x - 3) = 1$

77. $\log_2 x + \log_2(x - 3) = 2$

78. $\log_3 x + \log_3(x - 2) = 1$

79. $\log_{10}(2x - 1) - \log_{10}(x - 2) = 1$

80. $\log_{10}(9x - 2) = 1 + \log_{10}(x - 4)$

81. $\log_5(3x - 2) = 1 + \log_5(x - 4)$

82. $\log_6 x + \log_6(x + 5) = 2$

83. $\log_8(x + 7) + \log_8 x = 1$

84. $\log_6(x + 1) + \log_6(x - 4) = 2$

85. Verify Property 4.8.

86. Verify Property 4.9.

THOUGHTS into WORDS

87. How would you explain the concept of a logarithm to someone who has never studied algebra?

88. Explain, without using Property 4.6, why $4^{\log_4 9}$ equals 9.

89. In the next section we are going to show that the logarithmic function $f(x) = \log_2 x$ is the inverse of the exponential function $f(x) = 2^x$. From that information how could you sketch a graph of $f(x) = \log_2 x$?

4.5   LOGARITHMIC FUNCTIONS

The concept of a logarithm can now be used to define a logarithmic function as follows.

> ### DEFINITION 4.5
>
> If $b > 0$ and $b \neq 1$, then the function defined by
>
> $$f(x) = \log_b x,$$
>
> where x is any positive real number, is called the **logarithmic function with base b**.

We obtain the graph of a specific logarithmic function in various ways. For example, the equation $y = \log_2 x$ can be changed to the exponential equation $2^y = x$ and a table of values can be determined. You will graph some logarithmic functions using this approach in the next set of exercises.

The graph of a logarithmic function can also be obtained by setting up a table of values directly from the logarithmic equation. Let's illustrate this approach.

EXAMPLE 1

Graph $f(x) = \log_2 x$.

Solution

Let's choose some values for x where the corresponding values for $\log_2 x$ are easily determined. (Remember: Logarithms are only defined for the positive real numbers.)

x	$f(x)$	
$\frac{1}{8}$	-3	$\log_2 \frac{1}{8} = -3$ because $2^{-3} = \frac{1}{2^3} = \frac{1}{8}$
$\frac{1}{4}$	-2	
$\frac{1}{2}$	-1	
1	0	$\log_2 1 = 0$ because $2^0 = 1$
2	1	
4	2	
8	3	

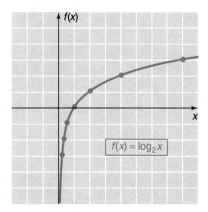

FIGURE 4.8

Plotting these points and connecting them with a smooth curve produces Figure 4.8.

Now suppose that we consider two functions f and g as follows:

$f(x) = b^x$ Domain: All real numbers

                     Range: Positive real numbers

$g(x) = \log_b x$ Domain: Positive real numbers

                     Range: All real numbers

Furthermore, suppose that we consider the composition of f and g, and the composition of g and f.

$$(f \circ g)(x) = f(g(x)) = f(\log_b x) = b^{\log_b x} = x$$
$$(g \circ f)(x) = g(f(x)) = g(b^x) = \log_b b^x = x \log_b b = x(1) = x$$

Therefore, because the domain of f is the range of g, the range of f is the domain of g, $f(g(x)) = x$, and $g(f(x)) = x$, the two functions f and g *are inverses of each other.*

Remember also from Chapter 3 that the graphs of a function and its inverse are reflections of each other through the line $y = x$. Thus, the graph of a logarithmic function can also be determined by reflecting the graph of its inverse exponential function through the line $y = x$. This idea is illustrated in Figure 4.9, where the graph of $y = 2^x$ was reflected across the line $y = x$ to produce the graph of $y = \log_2 x$.

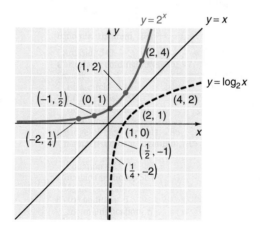

FIGURE 4.9

The *general behavior* patterns of exponential functions were illustrated by two graphs in Figure 4.3. We can now reflect each of these graphs through the line

$y = x$ and observe the **general behavior patterns** of logarithmic functions as shown in Figure 4.10.

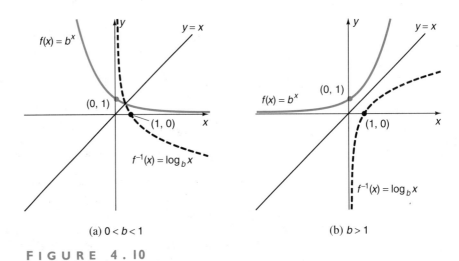

$$(a)\ 0 < b < 1 \qquad\qquad (b)\ b > 1$$

FIGURE 4.10

Finally, when graphing logarithmic functions, don't forget about transformations of the basic curves.

1. The graph of $f(x) = 3 + \log_2 x$ is the graph of $f(x) = \log_2 x$ *moved up three units.* (Since $\log_2 x + 3$ is apt to be confused with $\log_2(x + 3)$, we commonly write $3 + \log_2 x$.)

2. The graph of $f(x) = \log_2(x - 4)$ is the graph of $f(x) = \log_2 x$ *moved four units to the right.*

3. The graph of $f(x) = -\log_2 x$ is the graph of $f(x) = \log_2 x$ *reflected across the x-axis.*

Natural Logarithmic Function

In Section 4.3 we defined the natural exponential function by means of the equation $f(x) = e^x$. The logarithmic function with base e, described by the equation $f(x) = \log_e x$, or more commonly, $f(x) = \ln x$, is called the **natural logarithmic function**. The natural exponential and natural logarithmic functions are inverse functions of one another. Thus, one way of obtaining a graph of $f(x) = \ln x$ is to reflect the graph of $f(x) = e^x$ across the line $y = x$.

Natural logarithms can be found with an appropriately equipped calculator or with a table of natural logarithms. (Appendix A contains a table of natural logarithms and some instructions on how to use the table.) Using a calculator with a natural logarithm function (ordinarily a key labeled $\boxed{\ln x}$), we obtained the following results rounded to the nearest ten-thousandth.

$$\ln 3 = 1.0986 \qquad \ln 5 = 1.6094$$
$$\ln 7 = 1.9460 \qquad \ln 10 = 2.3026$$
$$\ln .5 = -.6931 \qquad \ln .1 = -2.3026$$

Keep in mind the significance of a statement such as $\ln 3 = 1.0986$. By changing to exponential form we are claiming that e raised to the 1.0986 power is approximately 3. Using a calculator we obtain $e^{1.0986} = 2.999963134$. Let's do a few more problems where we are to find x when given $\ln x$. Be sure that you agree with these results that were rounded to five significant digits.

If $\ln x = 2.4156$, then $x = e^{2.4156} = 11.196$.

If $\ln x = .9847$, then $x = e^{.9847} = 2.6770$.

If $\ln x = 4.1482$, then $x = e^{4.1482} = 63.320$.

If $\ln x = -1.7654$, then $x = e^{-1.7654} = .17112$.

For the purpose of sketching a graph of $f(x) = \ln x$, let's round the previously determined natural logarithms to the nearest tenth and then plot the points determined by the ordered pairs $(.1, -2.3)$, $(.5, -.7)$, $(3, 1.1)$, $(5, 1.6)$, $(7, 1.9)$, and $(10, 2.3)$. (We also included the point $(1, 0)$, which is determined by the fact that $\ln 1 = 0$ because $e^0 = 1$.) Connecting these points with a smooth curve produces the graph of the natural logarithmic function in Figure 4.11.

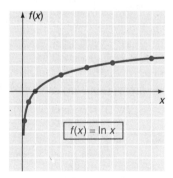

F I G U R E   4 . 11

Common Logarithmic Function

The properties of logarithms we discussed in Section 4.4 are true for any valid base. However, since the Hindu-Arabic numeration system that we use is a base 10 system, logarithms to base 10 have historically been used for computational purposes.

Base 10 logarithms are called common logarithms and are frequently denoted by $\log x$ instead of $\log_{10}x$.

Originally, common logarithms were developed to aid in complicated numerical calculations that involve products, quotients, and powers of real numbers. Today they are seldom used for that purpose because the calculator and computer can much more effectively handle the messy computational problems. However, common logarithms do still occur in applications, so they deserve our attention.

> REMARK   In Appendix B we have included a short discussion relative to the computational aspects of common logarithms. You may find it interesting to at least browse through this material. It probably will enhance your appreciation of the calculator.

As we know from earlier work, the definition of a logarithm allows us to evaluate $\log_{10}x$ for values of x that are integral powers of 10. Consider the following examples.

$$\log_{10}1000 = 3 \qquad \text{because } 10^3 = 1000.$$
$$\log_{10}100 = 2 \qquad \text{because } 10^2 = 100.$$
$$\log_{10}10 = 1 \qquad \text{because } 10^1 = 10.$$
$$\log_{10}1 = 0 \qquad \text{because } 10^0 = 1.$$
$$\log_{10}.1 = -1 \qquad \text{because } 10^{-1} = \frac{1}{10} = .1.$$
$$\log_{10}.01 = -2 \qquad \text{because } 10^{-2} = \frac{1}{10^2} = .01.$$
$$\log_{10}.001 = -3 \qquad \text{because } 10^{-3} = \frac{1}{10^3} = .001.$$

To find the common logarithm of a positive number that is not an integral power of 10, we can use an appropriately equipped calculator or a table such as the one in Appendix B. Using a calculator, we obtained the following results rounded to four decimal places.

$$\log 1.75 = .2430,$$

$$\log 23.8 = 1.3766, \qquad \text{Be sure that you can use a}$$
$$\text{calculator and obtain these results.}$$

$$\log 134 = 2.1271,$$

$$\log .192 = -.7167,$$

$$\log .0246 = -1.6091$$

Again, keep in mind the significance of a statement such as $\log 1.75 = .2430$. This means that 10 raised to the .2430 power should produce approximately 1.75. Using a calculator we obtain $10^{.2430} = 1.749846689$. Let's do a few more problems where we are to find x when given log x. Be sure that you agree with these results that were rounded to five significant digits.

If $\log x = .7629$, then $x = 10^{.7629} = 5.7930$.

If $\log x = 1.4825$, then $x = 10^{1.4825} = 30.374$.

If $\log x = 4.0214$, then $x = 10^{4.0214} = 10505$.

If $\log x = -1.5162$, then $x = 10^{-1.5162} = .030465$.

If $\log x = -3.8921$, then $x = 10^{-3.8921} = .00012820$.

The **common logarithmic function** is defined by the equation $f(x) = \log x$. Its graph can be easily determined by plotting some points as we did in Figure 4.12. Remember that $f(x) = \log x$ and $g(x) = 10^x$ are inverses of each other. Therefore, we could also get the graph of $f(x) = \log x$ by reflecting the graph of $g(x) = 10^x$ across the line $y = x$.

x	$f(x) = \log x$
.1	−1
1	0
4	.6
8	.9
10	1

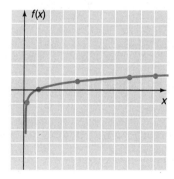

F I G U R E   4 . 12

Transformations of Logarithmic Curves

Having established the graphs of $f(x) = \ln x$ and $f(x) = \log x$, we can now graph various transformations of these basic graphs. Let's use a graphing utility to save time plotting points. For example, in Figure 4.13 we graphed $f(x) = \ln x$, $f(x) = -\ln x$, and $f(x) = \ln(x - 5)$. As we should expect, the graph of $f(x) = -\ln x$ is an x-axis reflection of the graph of $f(x) = \ln x$. Likewise, the graph of $f(x) = \ln(x - 5)$ is the graph of $f(x) = \ln x$ shifted five units to the right.

In Figure 4.14 we used a graphing utility to produce the graphs of $f(x) = \log x$, $f(x) = 2 + \log(x + 4)$, and $f(x) = 4 - \log x$. Again as we should expect, the graph of $f(x) = 2 + \log(x + 4)$ is the graph of $f(x) = \log x$ shifted four units to the left and two units upward. Likewise, the graph of $f(x) = 4 - \log x$ is the graph of $f(x) = \log x$ reflected across the x-axis and shifted upward four units.

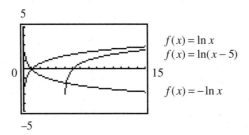

FIGURE 4.13

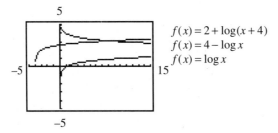

FIGURE 4.14

Notice in Figure 4.14 that the graphs of $f(x) = 2 + \log(x + 4)$ and $f(x) = 4 - \log x$ intersect in the viewing rectangle. By using the trace and zoom features of the graphing utility we can determine that x is approximately 8.2 at this point of intersection. In a moment, we will confirm that value by using an algebraic approach.

Logarithmic Equations

In Example 14 of Section 4.4, we solved the logarithmic equation $\log_{10} x + \log_{10}(x + 9) = 1$ by simplifying the left side of the equation to $\log_{10}[x(x + 9)]$, and then changing the equation to exponential form to complete the solution. At this time, with the aid of another property of equality, we can solve such a logarithmic equation another way, and also expand our equation solving capabilities. First, let's state the additional property of equality we need.

> ### PROPERTY 4.10
>
> If $x > 0$, $y > 0$, $b > 0$, and $b \neq 1$, then
>
> $$x = y \quad \text{if and only if} \quad \log_b x = \log_b y.$$

Property 4.10 is stated in terms of any valid base b; however, for most applications, either common logarithms or natural logarithms are used. Let's consider some examples.

E X A M P L E   2

Solve $\log x + \log(x - 15) = 2$.

Solution

Since $\log 100 = 2$, the given equation becomes

$$\log x + \log(x - 15) = \log 100.$$

Now simplifying the left side and applying Property 4.10 we can proceed as follows.

$$\log(x)(x - 15) = \log 100$$
$$x(x - 15) = 100$$
$$x^2 - 15x - 100 = 0$$
$$(x - 20)(x + 5) = 0$$
$$x - 20 = 0 \qquad \text{or} \qquad x + 5 = 0$$
$$x = 20 \qquad \text{or} \qquad x = -5$$

The domain of a logarithmic function must contain only positive numbers, so x and $x - 15$ must be positive in this problem. Therefore, the solution of -5 is discarded and the solution set is $\{20\}$. ▬

E X A M P L E   3

Solve $\ln(x + 2) = \ln(x - 4) + \ln 3$.

Solution

$$\ln(x + 2) = \ln(x - 4) + \ln 3$$
$$\ln(x + 2) = \ln[3(x - 4)]$$
$$x + 2 = 3(x - 4)$$
$$x + 2 = 3x - 12$$
$$14 = 2x$$
$$7 = x$$

The solution set is $\{7\}$. ▬

E X A M P L E   4

Solve the equation $2 + \log(x + 4) = 4 - \log x$.

Solution

$$2 + \log(x + 4) = 4 - \log x$$

$$\log x + \log(x + 4) = 2$$

$$\log x(x + 4) = \log 100$$

$$x^2 + 4x = 100$$

$$x^2 + 4x - 100 = 0$$

Now let's use the quadratic formula.

$$x = \frac{-4 \pm \sqrt{16 + 400}}{2}$$

$$x = \frac{-4 \pm \sqrt{416}}{2}$$

Since x and $x + 4$ must be positive numbers, the potential solution of $\dfrac{-4 - \sqrt{416}}{2}$

is discarded. Thus, the only solution is

$$x = \frac{-4 + \sqrt{416}}{2} = 8.2 \quad \text{to the nearest tenth.}$$

The solution set is $\{8.2\}$.

Note that Example 4 uses an algebraic approach to find the x-value of the point of intersection of the two curves $f(x) = 2 + \log(x + 4)$ and $f(x) = 4 - \log x$ shown in Figure 4.14. Our answer of 8.2 agrees with what we found when we used the graphics calculator.

P R O B L E M   S E T   4 . 5

For Problems 1–12, use your calculator to find each **natural logarithm**. Express your results to the nearest ten-thousandth.

1. ln 2   **2.** ln 9

3. ln 21.4   **4.** ln 87.6

5. ln 412   **6.** ln 384.2

7. ln .32   **8.** ln .417

9. ln .0715   **10.** ln .006285

11. ln .0008   **12.** ln 52173

For Problems 13–22, use your calculator to find each **common logarithm**. Express your results to the nearest ten-thousandth.

13. log 9.45   **14.** log 1.07

15. log 34.62   **16.** log 578.1

17. log 4721.4   **18.** log 52698

19. log .612   **20.** log .08134

21. $\log .0047$ **22.** $\log .000076$

For Problems 23–36, use your calculator to find x. Express your results to the nearest thousandth.

23. $\ln x = 1.5690$ **24.** $\ln x = 2.0176$

25. $\ln x = 3.2187$ **26.** $\ln x = 5.6148$

27. $\ln x = -.7618$ **28.** $\ln x = -1.3482$

29. $\ln x = -3.4166$ **30.** $\ln x = -5.1612$

31. $\log x = 1.2194$ **32.** $\log x = 2.9164$

33. $\log x = 3.5114$ **34.** $\log x = 4.6108$

35. $\log x = -1.1416$ **36.** $\log x = -2.1479$

For Problems 37–60, graph each of the functions.

37. $f(x) = \log_3 x$ **38.** $f(x) = \log_4 x$

39. $f(x) = \log_5 x$ **40.** $f(x) = \log_6 x$

41. $f(x) = \log_{1/2} x$ **42.** $f(x) = \log_{1/3} x$

43. $f(x) = \ln(x - 2)$ **44.** $f(x) = \ln(x + 1)$

45. $f(x) = 2 + \ln x$ **46.** $f(x) = -1 + \ln x$

47. $f(x) = -\ln x$ **48.** $f(x) = \ln|x|$

49. $f(x) = \ln x^3$ **50.** $f(x) = \ln x^2$

51. $f(x) = \ln\left(\dfrac{1}{x}\right)$ **52.** $f(x) = \dfrac{1}{\ln x}$

53. $f(x) = \log x$ **54.** $f(x) = \log(2x)$

55. $f(x) = \log\sqrt{x}$ **56.** $f(x) = -\log x$

57. $f(x) = \log_3(x - 1)$ **58.** $f(x) = \log_2(x - 3)$

59. $f(x) = 2 + \log_2 x$ **60.** $f(x) = -1 + \log_3 x$

61. Graph $f(x) = \log_{1/2} x$ by reflecting $f(x) = \left(\frac{1}{2}\right)^x$ across the line $y = x$.

62. Graph $f(x) = \log_{1/3} x$ by reflecting the graph of $f(x) = \left(\frac{1}{3}\right)^x$ across the line $y = x$.

For Problems 63–74 solve each of the logarithmic equations; express irrational solutions in lowest radical form.

63. $\log x + \log(x + 3) = 1$

64. $\log x + \log(x + 21) = 2$

65. $\log(2x - 1) - \log(x - 3) = 1$

66. $\log(3x - 1) = 1 + \log(5x - 2)$

67. $\log(x - 2) = 1 - \log(x + 3)$

68. $\ln(x + 1) = \ln 3 - \ln(2x - 1)$

69. $\ln(x + 1) - \ln(x + 2) = \ln\dfrac{1}{x}$

70. $\ln(x + 2) - \ln(2x + 1) = \ln x$

71. $\ln(3t - 4) - \ln(t + 1) = \ln 2$

72. $\ln(2t + 5) = \ln 3 + \ln(t - 1)$

73. $\log(x^2) = (\log x)^2$

74. $\log\sqrt{x} = \sqrt{\log x}$

FURTHER INVESTIGATIONS

75. a. Graph the function $f(x) = \log_2 x^2$.
   b. Graph the function $f(x) = 2\log_2 x$.

   c. Explain why the graphs for parts (a) and (b) are different because by Property 4.9 $\log_2 x^2 = 2\log_2 x$.

GRAPHICS CALCULATOR ACTIVITIES

76. Graph $f(x) = x$, $f(x) = e^x$, and $f(x) = \ln x$ on the same set of axes.

77. Graph $f(x) = x$, $f(x) = 10^x$, and $f(x) = \log x$ on the same set of axes.

78. Graph $f(x) = \ln x$. How should the graphs of $f(x) = 2\ln x$, $f(x) = 4\ln x$, and $f(x) = 6\ln x$ compare to this

basic curve? Graph the three functions on the same set of axes with the graph of $f(x) = \ln x$.

79. Graph $f(x) = \log x$. Now predict the graphs for $f(x) = 3 + \log x$, $f(x) = -2 + \log x$, and $f(x) = -4 + \log x$. Graph them on the same set of axes with the graph of $f(x) = \log x$.

80. For each of the following, (a) predict the general shape and location of the graph, and (b) use your graphics calculator to graph the function to check your prediction.

a. $f(x) = \log x + \ln x$ **b.** $f(x) = \log x - \ln x$

c. $f(x) = \ln x - \log x$ **d.** $f(x) = \ln x^2$

4.6   LOGARITHMS AND PROBLEM SOLVING

In Section 4.1 we solved exponential equations such as $3^x = 81$ by expressing both sides of the equation as a power of 3 and then applying the property, *if $b^n = b^m$, then $n = m$.* However, if we try this same approach with an equation such as $3^x = 5$, we face the difficulty of expressing 5 as a power of 3. We can solve this type of problem by using the properties of logarithms and Property 4.10 (*$x = y$ if and only if $\log_b x = \log_b y$*).

EXAMPLE 1

Solve $3^x = 5$, and express the solution to the nearest hundredth.

Solution

Since $3^1 = 3$ and $3^2 = 9$, we know that our answer must be between 1 and 2. We can use either common or natural logarithms to solve such an equation. Let's use common logarithms for this one.

$$3^x = 5$$

$$\log 3^x = \log 5 \qquad \text{Property 4.10}$$

$$x \log 3 = \log 5 \qquad \log r^p = p \log r$$

$$x = \frac{\log 5}{\log 3}$$

$$x = 1.46 \quad \text{nearest hundredth}$$

 Check   Since $3^{1.46} \approx 4.972754647$, we say that, to the nearest hundredth, the solution set for $3^x = 5$ is $\{1.46\}$.   ■

A word of caution!   The expression $\dfrac{\log 5}{\log 3}$ means that we must *divide*, not subtract, the logarithms. That is $\dfrac{\log 5}{\log 3}$ *does not* mean $\log \left(\frac{5}{3}\right)$. Remember that $\log \left(\frac{5}{3}\right) = \log 5 - \log 3$.

EXAMPLE 2

Solve $e^{x+1} = 5$ to the nearest hundredth.

Solution

Since base e is used in the exponential expression, let's use natural logarithms to help solve this equation.

$$e^{x+1} = 5$$

$$\ln e^{x+1} = \ln 5 \qquad \text{Property 4.10}$$

$$(x + 1)\ln e = \ln 5 \qquad \ln r^p = p \ln r$$

$$(x + 1)(1) = \ln 5 \qquad \ln e = 1$$

$$x = \ln 5 - 1$$

$$x = .61 \quad \text{nearest hundredth}$$

The solution set is {.61}. Check it!

EXAMPLE 3

Solve $2^{3x-2} = 3^{2x+1}$, to the nearest hundredth.

Solution

$$2^{3x-2} = 3^{2x+1}$$

$$\ln 2^{3x-2} = \ln 3^{2x+1}$$

$$(3x - 2) \ln 2 = (2x + 1) \ln 3$$

$$3x \ln 2 - 2 \ln 2 = 2x \ln 3 + \ln 3$$

$$3x \ln 2 - 2x \ln 3 = \ln 3 + 2 \ln 2$$

$$x(3 \ln 2 - 2 \ln 3) = \ln 3 + 2 \ln 2$$

$$x = \frac{\ln 3 + 2 \ln 2}{3 \ln 2 - 2 \ln 3}$$

$$x = -21.10 \quad \text{to the nearest hundredth}$$

The solution set is {−21.10}. Check it!

Applications

in Section 4.3 we used the compound interest formula

$$A = P\left(1 + \frac{r}{n}\right)^{nt}$$

to determine the amount of money (A) accumulated at the end of t years if P dollars is invested at r rate of interest compounded n times per year. Now let's use this formula to solve other types of problems that deal with compound interest.

EXAMPLE 4

Double your money   How long will it take to double $500 if it is invested at 12% compounded quarterly?

Solution

To "double $500" means that the $500 will grow into $1000. Thus,

$$1000 = 500\left(1 + \tfrac{.12}{4}\right)^{4t}$$
$$= 500(1 + .03)^{4t}$$
$$= 500(1.03)^{4t}.$$

Multiplying both sides of $1000 = 500(1.03)^{4t}$ by $\frac{1}{500}$ yields

$$2 = (1.03)^{4t}.$$

Therefore,

$$\ln 2 = \ln(1.03)^{4t} \qquad \text{Property 4.10}$$
$$= 4t \log 1.03. \qquad \ln r^p = p \ln r$$

Solving for t, we obtain

$$\ln 2 = 4t \ln 1.03$$

$$\frac{\ln 2}{\ln 1.03} = 4t$$

$$\frac{\ln 2}{4 \ln 1.03} = t \qquad \text{Multiply both sides by } \frac{1}{4}$$

$$t = 5.9. \quad \text{to the nearest tenth}$$

Therefore, we are claiming that \$500 invested at 12% interest compounded quarterly will double itself in approximately 5.9 years. (Perhaps you should check this answer!)

EXAMPLE 5

Bacteria growth Suppose the number of bacteria present in a certain culture after t minutes is given by the equation $Q(t) = Q_0 e^{.04t}$, where Q_0 represents the initial number of bacteria. How long would it take for the bacteria count to grow from 500 to 2000?

Solution

$$2000 = 500 e^{.04t}$$
$$4 = e^{.04t}$$
$$\ln 4 = \ln e^{.04t}$$
$$\ln 4 = .04t \ln e$$
$$\ln 4 = .04t$$
$$\frac{\ln 4}{.04} = t$$

$$t = 34.7 \quad \text{to the nearest tenth.}$$

It should take approximately 34.7 minutes.

Richter numbers

Seismologists use the Richter scale to measure and report the magnitude of earthquakes. The equation

$$R = \log \frac{I}{I_0}$$ R is called a Richter number.

compares the intensity I of an earthquake to a minimal or reference intensity I_0. The reference intensity is the smallest earth movement that can be recorded on a seismograph. Suppose that the intensity of an earthquake was determined to be 50,000 times the reference intensity. In this case, $I = 50,000 \, I_0$ and the Richter number would be calculated as follows.

$$R = \log \frac{50,000 \, I_0}{I_0}$$

$$R = \log 50,000$$

$$R \approx 4.698970004$$

Thus, a Richter number of 4.7 would be reported. Let's consider two more examples that involve Richter numbers.

E X A M P L E   6

Intensity of an earthquake   An earthquake in San Francisco in 1989 was reported to have a Richter number of 6.9. How did its intensity compare to the reference intensity?

Solution

$$6.9 = \log \frac{I}{I_0}$$

$$10^{6.9} = \frac{I}{I_0}$$

$$I = (10^{6.9})(I_0)$$

$$I \approx 7,943,282 \, I_0$$

So its intensity was a little less than 8 million times the reference intensity.

E X A M P L E   7

Comparing intensities   Early in the morning on January 17, 1994 the Los Angeles area had an earthquake that measured 6.6 on the Richter scale. Compare the intensity level of that earthquake to the one in Example 6.

Solution

From Example 6 we have $I = (10^{6.9})(I_0)$ for the earthquake in San Francisco. Then using a Richter number of 6.6 we obtain $I = (10^{6.6})(I_0)$ for the earthquake in Los Angeles. Therefore, by comparison

$$\frac{(10^{6.9})(I_0)}{(10^{6.6})(I_0)} = 10^{6.9-6.6} = 10^{0.3} \approx 1.99.$$

Thus, the earthquake in San Francisco was about twice as intense as the one in Los Angeles.

Logarithms with Base Other Than *10* or *e*

The basic approach of applying Property 4.10 and using either common or natural logarithms can also be used to evaluate a logarithm to some base other than 10 or e. The next example illustrates this idea.

EXAMPLE 8

Evaluate $\log_3 41$.

Solution

Let $x = \log_3 41$. Changing to exponential form we obtain

$$3^x = 41.$$

Now we can apply Property 4.10 and proceed as follows.

$$\log 3^x = \log 41$$

$$x \log 3 = \log 41$$

$$x = \frac{\log 41}{\log 3} = 3.3802, \quad \text{to the nearest ten-thousandth}$$

Therefore, we claim that 3 raised to the 3.3802 power is approximately 41. Check it!

Using the method of Example 8 to evaluate $\log_a r$ produces the following formula (often referred to as the *change-of-base* formula for logarithms).

PROPERTY 4.11

If a, b, and r are positive numbers with $a \neq 1$ and $b \neq 1$, then

$$\log_a r = \frac{\log_b r}{\log_b a}.$$

Property 4.11 provides us with a convenient way of expressing logarithms with bases other than 10 or e in terms of common or natural logarithms. For example, $\log_3 41$ is of the form $\log_a r$ with $r = 41$ and $a = 3$. Therefore, in terms of common logarithms (base 10), we have

$$\log_3 41 = \frac{\log_{10} 41}{\log_{10} 3}.$$

Using the abbreviated notation for base 10 logarithms we have

$$\log_3 41 = \frac{\log 41}{\log 3}.$$

Thus, the following format could be used to evaluate $\log_3 41$.

$$\log_3 41 = \frac{\log 41}{\log 3}$$

$$= 3.3802 \quad \text{rounded to four decimal places}$$

In a similar fashion, we can use natural logarithms to evaluate expressions such as $\log_3 41$.

$$\log_3 41 = \frac{\ln 41}{\ln 3}$$

$$= 3.3802 \quad \text{rounded to four decimal places}$$

Property 4.11 also provides us with another way of solving equations such as $3^x = 5$.

$$3^x = 5$$

$$x = \log_3 5 \qquad \text{Changed to logarithmic form}$$

$$x = \frac{\log 5}{\log 3} \qquad \text{Applied Property 4.11}$$

$$x = 1.46 \quad \text{to the nearest hundredth}$$

Finally, by using Property 4.11, we can obtain a relationship between common and natural logarithms by letting $a = 10$ and $b = e$. Then

$$\log_a r = \frac{\log_b r}{\log_b a}$$

becomes

$$\log_{10} r = \frac{\log_e r}{\log_e 10}$$

$$\log_e r = (\log_e 10)(\log_{10} r)$$

$$\log_e r \approx (2.3026)(\log_{10} r).$$

Thus, we can write $\ln r \approx 2.3026 \log r$ and verbally state that the natural logarithm of any positive number is approximately equal to 2.3026 times the common logarithm of the number.

Now we can use a graphing utility to graph logarithmic functions such as $f(x) = \log_2 x$. Using the change-of-base formula this function can be expressed as

$$f(x) = \frac{\log x}{\log 2} \quad \text{or} \quad f(x) = \frac{\ln x}{\ln 2}.$$

The graph of $f(x) = \log_2 x$ is shown in Figure 4.15.

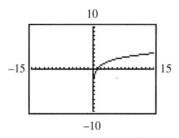

FIGURE 4.15

Finally, let's use a graphical approach to solve an equation that would be cumbersome to solve using an algebraic approach.

EXAMPLE 9   Solve the equation $\dfrac{5^x - 5^{-x}}{2} = 3$.

Solution

First, we need to recognize that the solutions for the equation $(5^x - 5^{-x})/2 = 3$ are the x-intercepts of the graph of the equation $y = (5^x - 5^{-x})/2 - 3$. So let's use a graphing utility to obtain the graph of this equation as shown in Figure 4.16. Use the zoom and trace features to determine that the graph crosses the x-axis at approximately 1.13. Thus, the solution set of the original equation is $\{1.13\}$.

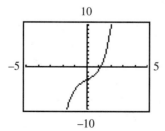

FIGURE 4.16

PROBLEM SET 4.6

Solve each of the following exponential equations and express approximate solutions to the nearest hundredth.

1. $2^x = 9$ **2.** $3^x = 20$ **3.** $5^t = 23$

4. $4^t = 12$ **5.** $2^{x+1} = 7$ **6.** $3^{x-2} = 11$

7. $7^{2t-1} = 35$ **8.** $5^{3t+1} = 9$ **9.** $e^x = 4.1$

10. $e^x = 30$ **11.** $e^{x-1} = 8.2$ **12.** $e^{x-2} = 13.1$

13. $2e^x = 12.4$ **14.** $3e^x - 1 = 17$

15. $3^{x-1} = 2^{x+3}$ **16.** $5^{2x+1} = 7^{x+3}$

17. $5^{x-1} = 2^{2x+1}$ **18.** $3^{2x+1} = 2^{3x+2}$

Approximate each of the following logarithms to the nearest ten-thousandth. (Example 8 and/or Property 4.11 should be of some help.)

19. $\log_3 14$ **20.** $\log_4 94$ **21.** $\log_5 2.1$

22. $\log_6 .345$ **23.** $\log_7 176$ **24.** $\log_8 296$

25. $\log_9 14.32$ **26.** $\log_7 .024$

APPLIED PROBLEMS

Solve each of the following problems.

27. *Double your money* How long will it take $1000 to double itself if it is invested at 9% interest compounded semiannually?

28. *Compounding quarterly* How long will it take $750 to be worth $1000 if it is invested at 12% interest compounded quarterly?

29. *Triple your money* How long will it take $500 to triple itself if it is invested at 9% interest compounded continuously?

30. *Double your money* How long will it take $2000 to double itself if it is invested at 13% interest compounded continuously?

31. *Rate of interest* What rate of interest, to the nearest tenth of a percent, compounded annually is needed so that an investment of $200 will grow to $350 in 5 years?

32. *Rate of interest* What rate of interest, to the nearest tenth of a percent, compounded continuously is needed so that an investment of $500 will grow to $900 in 10 years?

33. *Machinery depreciation* A piece of machinery valued at $30,000 depreciates at a rate of 10% annually. How long will it take until it has a value of $15,000?

34. *Bacteria growth* For a certain strain of bacteria, the number present after t hours is given by the equation $Q(t) = Q_0 e^{.34t}$, where Q_0 represents the initial number of

bacteria. How long will it take 400 bacteria to increase to 4000 bacteria?

35. *Radioactive decay* The number of grams of a certain radioactive substance present after t hours is given by the equation $Q(t) = Q_0 e^{-.45t}$, where Q_0 represents the initial number of grams. How long would it take for 2500 grams to be reduced to 1250 grams?

36. *Atmospheric pressure* The equation $P(a) = 14.7e^{-.21a}$, where a is the altitude above sea level measured in miles, yields the atmospheric pressure in pounds per square inch. If the atmospheric pressure at Cheyenne, Wyoming is approximately 11.53 pounds per square inch, find its altitude above sea level. Express your answer to the nearest hundred feet.

37. *Population growth* Suppose that the equation $P(t) = P_0 e^{.02t}$, where P_0 represents an initial population and t is the time in years, is used to predict population growth. How long would it take a city of 50,000 to double its population?

38. *Bacteria growth* In a certain culture, the equation $Q(t) = Q_0 e^{.4t}$, where Q_0 is an initial number of bacteria and t is the time measured in hours, yields the number of bacteria as a function of the time. How long will it take 500 bacteria to increase to 2000?

39. *Richter number* An earthquake in Los Angeles in 1971 had an intensity of approximately five million times the reference intensity. What was the Richter number associated with that earthquake?

40. *Intensity of an earthquake*   An earthquake in San Francisco in 1906 was reported to have a Richter number of 8.3. How did its intensity compare to the reference intensity?

41. *Comparing intensities*   Calculate how many times more intense an earthquake with a Richter number of 7.3 is than an earthquake with a Richter number of 6.4.

42. *Comparing intensities*   Calculate how many times more intense an earthquake with a Richter number of 8.9 is than an earthquake with a Richter number of 6.2.

43. Use the approach of Example 8 to develop Property 4.11.

44. Let $r = b$ in Property 4.11 and verify that $\log_a b = \dfrac{1}{\log_b a}$.

THOUGHTS into WORDS

45. Explain the concept of a Richter number.

46. Explain how you would solve the equation $7^x = 134$.

47. Explain how you would evaluate $\log_4 79$.

48. How do logarithms with a base of 9 compare to logarithms with a base of 3?

FURTHER INVESTIGATIONS

49. To solve the equation $(5^x - 5^{-x})/2 = 3$ let's begin as follows.

$$(5^x - 5^{-x})/2 = 3$$

$$5^x - 5^{-x} = 6$$

$$5^x(5^x - 5^{-x}) = 6(5^x) \qquad \text{Multiply both sides by } 5^x.$$

$$5^{2x} - 1 = 6(5^x)$$

$$5^{2x} - 6(5^x) - 1 = 0$$

This final equation is of quadratic form. Finish the solution and check your answer against the answer in Example 9.

50. Solve the equation $y = \dfrac{10^x + 10^{-x}}{2}$ for x in terms of y.

51. Solve the equation $y = \dfrac{e^x - e^{-x}}{2}$ for x in terms of y.

GRAPHICS CALCULATOR ACTIVITIES

52. Check your answers for Problems 15–18 by graphing the appropriate function and finding the x-intercept.

53. Graph $f(x) = \log_2 x$. Then predict the graphs for $f(x) = \log_3 x$, $f(x) = \log_4 x$, and $\log_8 x$. Now graph these three functions on the same set of axes with the graph of $f(x) = \log_2 x$.

54. Graph $f(x) = x$, $f(x) = 2^x$, and $f(x) = \log_2 x$ on the same set of axes.

55. Graph $f(x) = x$, $f(x) = \left(\frac{1}{2}\right)^x$, and $f(x) = \log_{1/2} x$ on the same set of axes.

56. Use both a graphical and an algebraic approach to solve the equation $(2^x - 2^{-x})/3 = 4$.

CHAPTER 4 SUMMARY

This chapter can be summarized by four main topics, namely, (1) roots, (2) exponents and exponential functions, (3) logarithms and logarithmic functions, and (4) applications of exponential and logarithmic functions.

Roots

The real roots of real numbers are defined by the statement

$$\sqrt[n]{b} = a \quad \text{if and only if } a^n = b$$

provided that both a and b are nonnegative and n is a positive integer greater than one, or that both a and b are negative and n is an odd positive integer greater than one.

The following properties provide the basis for manipulating with radicals.

1. $\sqrt[n]{bc} = \sqrt[n]{b}\sqrt[n]{c}$
2. $\sqrt[n]{\dfrac{b}{c}} = \dfrac{\sqrt[n]{b}}{\sqrt[n]{c}}$

The following property provides the basis for solving radical equations.

3. If $a = b$, then $a^n = b^n$, where a and b are real numbers and n is a positive integer.

Exponents and Exponential Functions

Definitions 4.1 and 4.2 link the concepts of root and exponent.

The following properties provide the basis for manipulating with exponents. If a and b are positive numbers, and m and n are real numbers, then

1. $b^n \cdot b^m = b^{n+m}$ Product of two powers
2. $(b^n)^m = b^{mn}$ Power of a power
3. $(ab)^n = a^n b^n$ Power of a product
4. $\left(\dfrac{a}{b}\right)^n = \dfrac{a^n}{b^n}$ Power of a quotient
5. $\dfrac{b^n}{b^m} = b^{n-m}$ Quotient of two powers

A function defined by an equation of the form

$$f(x) = b^x, \qquad b > 0 \text{ and } b \neq 1$$

is called an exponential function. Figure 4.3 in the text illustrates the general behavior of the graphs of exponential functions of the form $f(x) = b^x$.

Logarithms and Logarithmic Functions

If r is any positive real number, then the unique exponent t such that $b^t = r$ is called the logarithm of r with base b and is denoted by $\log_b r$.

The following properties of logarithms are used frequently.

1. $\log_b b = 1$
2. $\log_b 1 = 0$
3. $b^{\log_b r} = r$
4. $\log_b rs = \log_b r + \log_b s$
5. $\log_b \left(\dfrac{r}{s} \right) = \log_b r - \log_b s$
6. $\log_b (r^p) = p \log_b r$

Natural logarithms are logarithms that have a base of e, where e is an irrational number whose decimal approximation to eight digits is 2.7182818. Natural logarithms are denoted by $\log_e x$ or $\ln x$.

Logarithms with a base of 10 are called common logarithms. The expression $\log_{10} x$ is commonly written as $\log x$.

A function defined by an equation of the form

$$f(x) = \log_b x, \qquad h > 0 \text{ and } b \neq 1$$

is called a logarithmic function.

The graph of a logarithmic function, such as $y = \log_2 x$, can be determined by changing the equation to exponential form ($2^y = x$) and plotting points, or by reflecting the graph of $y = 2^x$ across the line $y = x$. This last approach is based on the fact that exponential and logarithmic functions are inverses of each other. Figure 4.10 in the text illustrates the general behavior of the graphs of logarithmic functions of the form $f(x) = \log_b x$.

Applications

The following properties of equality are used frequently when solving exponential and logarithmic equations.

1. If $b > 0$, $b \neq 1$, and m and n are real numbers, then
$$b^n = b^m \quad \text{if and only if } n = m.$$
2. If $x > 0$, $y > 0$, $b > 0$, and $b \neq 1$, then
$$x = y \quad \text{if and only if } \log_b x = \log_b y.$$

A general formula for any principal (P) being compounded n times per year for any number (t) of years at a rate (r) is

$$A = P\left(1 + \frac{r}{n}\right)^{nt}$$

where A represents the total amount of money accumulated at the end of t years.

The formula

$$A = Pe^{rt}$$

yields the accumulated value, A, of a sum of money P that has been invested for t years at a rate of r percent compounded continuously.

The formula

$$Q = Q_0\left(\frac{1}{2}\right)^{t/h}$$

is referred to as the *half-life* formula.

The equation

$$Q(t) = Q_0 e^{kt}$$

is used as a mathematical model for exponential growth and decay problems.

The formula

$$R = \log\frac{I}{I_0}$$

yields the Richter number associated with an earthquake.

The formula

$$\log_a r = \frac{\log_b r}{\log_b a}$$

is often called the change-of-base formula.

CHAPTER 4 REVIEW PROBLEM SET

Evaluate each of the following

1. $8^{5/3}$

2. $-25^{3/2}$

3. $(-27)^{4/3}$

4. $\log_6 216$

5. $\log_7\left(\frac{1}{49}\right)$

6. $\log_2 \sqrt[3]{2}$

7. $\log_2\left(\frac{\sqrt[4]{32}}{2}\right)$

8. $\log_{10}.00001$

9. $\ln e$

10. $7^{\log_7 12}$

Express each of the following in simplest radical form. All variables represent positive real numbers.

11. $5\sqrt{48}$

12. $3\sqrt{24x^3}$

13. $\sqrt[3]{32x^4y^5}$

14. $\dfrac{3\sqrt{8}}{2\sqrt{6}}$

15. $\sqrt{\dfrac{5x}{2y^2}}$

16. $\dfrac{3}{\sqrt{2}+5}$

17. $\dfrac{4\sqrt{2}}{3\sqrt{2}+\sqrt{3}}$

18. $\dfrac{3\sqrt{x}}{\sqrt{x}-2\sqrt{y}}$

Perform the indicated operations and express answers in simplest radical form.

19. $\sqrt{5}\sqrt[3]{5}$

20. $\sqrt[3]{x^2}\sqrt[4]{x}$

21. $\sqrt{x^3}\sqrt[3]{x^4}$

22. $\sqrt{xy}\sqrt[5]{x^3y^2}$

23. $\dfrac{\sqrt{5}}{\sqrt[3]{5}}$

24. $\dfrac{\sqrt[3]{x^2}}{\sqrt[4]{x^3}}$

Perform the indicated operations and simplify. Express final answers using positive exponents only.

25. $(3x^{-2}y^{-1})(4x^4y^2)$

26. $(5x^{2/3})(-6x^{1/2})$

27. $(-8a^{-1/2})(-6a^{1/3})$

28. $(3x^{-2/3}y^{1/5})^3$

29. $\dfrac{64x^{-2}y^3}{16x^3y^{-2}}$

30. $\dfrac{56x^{-1/3}y^{2/5}}{7x^{1/4}y^{-3/5}}$

31. $\left(\dfrac{-8x^2y^{-1}}{2x^{-1}y^2}\right)^2$

32. $\left(\dfrac{36a^{-1}b^4}{-12a^2b^5}\right)^{-1}$

Solve each of the following equations. Express approximate solutions to the nearest hundredth.

33. $\log_{10}2 + \log_{10}x = 1$

34. $\log_3 x = -2$

35. $4^x = 128$

36. $3^t = 42$

37. $\log_2 x = 3$

38. $\left(\dfrac{1}{27}\right)^{3x} = 3^{2x-1}$

39. $2e^x = 14$

40. $2^{2x+1} = 3^{x+1}$

41. $\ln(x+4) - \ln(x+2) = \ln x$

42. $\log x + \log(x-15) = 2$

43. $\log(\log x) = 2$

44. $\log(7x-4) - \log(x-1) = 1$

45. $\ln(2t-1) = \ln 4 + \ln(t-3)$

46. $64^{2t+1} = 8^{-t+2}$

47. $\sqrt{5+2x} = 1 + \sqrt{2x}$

48. $\sqrt{3+2n} + \sqrt{2-2n} = 3$

49. $\sqrt{3-t} - \sqrt{3+t} = \sqrt{t}$

For Problems 50–53, if $\log 3 = .4771$ and $\log 7 = .8451$, evaluate each of the following.

50. $\log\left(\dfrac{7}{3}\right)$ **51.** $\log 21$ **52.** $\log 27$ **53.** $\log(7)^{2/3}$

54. Express each of the following as the sum or difference of simpler logarithmic quantities. Assume that all variables represent positive real numbers.

a. $\log_b\left(\dfrac{x}{y^2}\right)$ **b.** $\log_b\sqrt[4]{xy^2}$ **c.** $\log_b\left(\dfrac{\sqrt{x}}{y^3}\right)$

55. Express each of the following as a single logarithm. Assume that all variables represent positive real numbers.

a. $3\log_b x + 2\log_b y$ **b.** $\frac{1}{2}\log_b y - 4\log_b x$

c. $\frac{1}{2}(\log_b x + \log_b y) - 2\log_b z$

For Problems 56–59, approximate each of the logarithms to the nearest ten-thousandth.

56. $\log_2 3$ **57.** $\log_3 2$

58. $\log_4 191$ **59.** $\log_7 .23$

For Problems 60–69, graph each of the functions.

60. $f(x) = \left(\dfrac{3}{4}\right)^x$ **61.** $f(x) = 2^{x+2}$

62. $f(x) = e^{x-1}$ **63.** $f(x) = -1 + \log x$

64. $f(x) = 3^x - 3^{-x}$ **65.** $f(x) = e^{-(x^2/2)}$

66. $f(x) = \log_2(x-3)$ **67.** $f(x) = 3\log_3 x$

68. $f(x) = 2\ln x$ **69.** $f(x) = -\ln(x-1)$

For Problems 70–72, use the compound interest formula $A = P\left(1 + \dfrac{r}{n}\right)^{nt}$ to find the total amount of money accumulated at the end of the indicated time period for each of the investments.

70. $750 for 10 years at 11% compounded quarterly

71. $1250 for 15 years at 9% compounded monthly

72. $2500 for 20 years at 9.5% compounded semiannually

APPLIED PROBLEMS

Solve each of the following problems.

73. *Doubling your money*   How long will it take $100 to double itself if it is invested at 14% interest compounded annually?

74. *Compounding quarterly*   How long will it take $1000 to be worth $3500 if it is invested at 10.5% interest compounded quarterly?

75. *Rate of interest*   What rate of interest (nearest tenth of a percent) compounded continuously is needed so that an investment of $500 will grow to $1000 in 8 years?

76. *Population growth*   Suppose that the present population of a city is 50,000 and suppose that the equation $P(t) = P_0e^{.02t}$, where P_0 represents an initial population and t the time in years, can be used to estimate future growth. Esti-

mate the population of that city in 10 years, 15 years, and 20 years.

77. *Bacteria growth*   The number of bacteria present in a certain culture after t hours is given by the equation $Q = Q_0e^{.29t}$, where Q_0 represents the initial number of bacteria. How long will it take for 500 bacteria to increase to 2000 bacteria?

78. *Half-life*   Suppose that a certain radioactive substance has a half-life of 40 days. If there are presently 750 grams of the substance, how much, to the nearest gram, will remain after 100 days?

79. *Richter number*   An earthquake occurred in Mexico City in 1985 that had an intensity level about 125,000,000 times the reference intensity. Find the Richter number associated with that earthquake.

POLYNOMIAL AND RATIONAL FUNCTIONS

E arlier in this text we solved linear and quadratic equations and we graphed linear and quadratic functions. In this chapter we will expand our equation solving processes and graphing techniques to include more general polynomial equations and functions. Then our knowledge of polynomial functions will enable us to work with rational functions. The function concept will again serve as a unifying thread throughout the chapter. To facilitate our study in this chapter we will first review the concept of dividing polynomials and we will introduce a special division technique called synthetic division.

An open box is formed by cutting out square corners from a 14-inch by 20-inch piece of cardboard and folding up the flaps. The volume function $V(x) = x(14 - 2x)(20 - 2x)$ can be used to determine the size of the squares to maximize the volume of the box.

5.1   SYNTHETIC DIVISION AND THE FACTOR THEOREM

The format used to divide a polynomial by a binomial resembles the long division format in arithmetic. Consider the following example.

$$
\begin{array}{r}
x^2 - 2x\ + 4 \\
3x + 1\overline{\smash{\big)}\,3x^3 - 5x^2 + 10x + 1} \\
\underline{3x^3 + \ x^2} \\
-6x^2 + 10x + 1 \\
\underline{-6x^2 - \ 2x} \\
12x + 1 \\
\underline{12x + 4} \\
-3
\end{array}
$$

Therefore, $3x^3 - 5x^2 + 10x + 1 = (3x + 1)(x^2 - 2x + 4) + (-3)$, which is of the familiar form

Dividend = (Divisor)(Quotient) + Remainder.

This result is commonly called the **division algorithm for polynomials**, which can be stated in general terms as follows.

PROPERTY 5.1 *Division Algorithm for Polynomials*

If $f(x)$ and $g(x)$ are polynomials and $g(x) \neq 0$, then there exist unique polynomials $q(x)$ and $r(x)$ such that

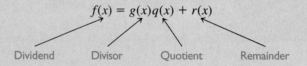

$$f(x) = g(x)q(x) + r(x)$$

Dividend   Divisor   Quotient   Remainder

where $r(x) = 0$ or the degree of $r(x)$ is less than the degree of $g(x)$.

If the divisor is of the form $x - c$, where c is a constant, then the typical long division algorithm can be simplified into a process called **synthetic division**. First, let's consider another division problem and use the regular algorithm. Then, in a step-by-step fashion, we will list some shortcuts that can be made that will lead us into the synthetic division procedure. Consider the division problem $(2x^4 + x^3 - 17x^2 + 13x + 2) \div (x - 2)$.

$$
\begin{array}{r}
2x^3 + 5x^2 - 7x - 1 \\
x - 2\overline{)\,2x^4 + x^3 - 17x^2 + 13x + 2} \\
\underline{2x^4 - 4x^3} \\
5x^3 - 17x^2 \\
\underline{5x^3 - 10x^2} \\
-7x^2 + 13x \\
\underline{-7x^2 + 14x} \\
-x + 2 \\
\underline{-x + 2}
\end{array}
$$

Because the dividend is written in descending powers of x, the quotient is produced in descending powers of x. In other words, the numerical coefficients are the key issues. So let's rewrite the above problem in terms of its coefficients.

$$
\begin{array}{r}
2\quad 5\quad -7\quad -1 \\
1 - 2\overline{)\,2\quad\; 1\quad -17\quad 13\quad\;\; 2} \\
② \;\;-4 \\
5\;\;(-17) \\
⑤\;\; -10 \\
-7\;\;(13) \\
(-7)\;\; 14 \\
-1\;\;\;② \\
(-1)\;\; 2
\end{array}
$$

Now observe that the numbers circled are simply repetitions of the numbers directly above them in the format. Thus, the circled numbers could be omitted and the format would be as follows. (Disregard the arrows for the moment.)

$$
\begin{array}{r}
2\quad 5\quad -7\quad -1 \\
1 - 2\overline{)\,2\quad 1\quad -17\quad 13\quad 2} \\
-4 \\
5 \\
-10 \\
-7 \\
14 \\
-1 \\
2
\end{array}
$$

Next, by moving some numbers up as indicated by the arrows and omitting the writing of 1 as the coefficient of x in the divisor, the following more compact form is obtained.

$$
\begin{array}{r}
2\quad\; 5\quad -7\quad -1 \\
-2\overline{)\,2\quad\; 1\quad -17\quad 13\quad 2} \\
\underline{-4\quad -10\quad 14\quad 2} \\
5\quad -7\quad -1
\end{array}
$$

(1)

(2)

(3)

(4)

Notice that line (4) reveals all of the coefficients of the quotient, (line (1)), except for the first coefficient of 2. Thus, we can omit line (1) and begin line (4) with the first coefficient and then use the following form.

$$-2 \overline{\big)\ 2 \quad 1 \quad -17 \quad 13 \quad 2}$$
$$ -4 \quad -10 \quad 14 \quad 2$$
$$ \overline{2 \quad 5 \quad -7 \quad -1 \quad 0}$$

(5)

(6)

(7)

Line (7) contains the coefficients of the quotient where the 0 indicates the remainder.

Finally, by changing the constant in the divisor to 2 (instead of -2), which will change the signs of the numbers in line (6), we can add the corresponding entries in lines (5) and (6) rather than subtract. Thus, the final synthetic division form for this problem is as follows.

$$2 \overline{\big)\ 2 \quad 1 \quad -17 \quad 13 \quad 2}$$
$$ 4 \quad 10 \quad -14 \quad -2$$
$$ \overline{2 \quad 5 \quad -7 \quad -1 \quad 0}$$

Equivalent to

$$2x^3 + 5x^2 - 7x - 1 \ R = 0$$
$$x - 2 \overline{\big)\ 2x^4 + x^3 - 17x^2 + 13x + 2}$$

Now we will consider another problem and indicate a step-by-step procedure for setting up and carrying out the synthetic division process. Suppose that we want to do the following division problem.

$$x + 4 \overline{\big)\ 2x^3 + 5x^2 - 13x - 2}$$

STEP 1 Write the coefficients of the dividend as follows.

$$\overline{\big)\ 2 \quad 5 \quad -13 \quad -2}$$

STEP 2 In the divisor, since $x + 4 = x - (-4)$, use -4 instead of 4.

$$-4 \overline{\big)\ 2 \quad 5 \quad -13 \quad -2}$$

STEP 3 Bring down the first coefficient of the dividend.

$$-4 \overline{\big)\ 2 \quad 5 \quad -13 \quad -2}$$
$$ \overline{2}$$

STEP 4 Multiply that first coefficient times the divisor, which yields $2(-4) = -8$. This result is to be added to the second coefficient of the dividend.

$$-4 \overline{\big)\ 2 \quad 5 \quad -13 \quad -2}$$
$$ -8$$
$$ \overline{2 \quad -3}$$

STEP 5 Multiply $(-3)(-4)$, which yields 12; this result is to be added to the third coefficient of the dividend.

$$-4 \overline{\big)\ 2 \quad 5 \quad -13 \quad -2}$$
$$ -8 \quad 12$$
$$ \overline{2 \quad -3 \quad -1}$$

STEP 6   Multiply $(-1)(-4)$, which yields 4; this result is to be added to the last term of the dividend.

$$\begin{array}{r|rrrr}
-4 & 2 & 5 & -13 & -2 \\
 & & -8 & 12 & 4 \\
\hline
 & 2 & -3 & -1 & 2
\end{array}$$

The last row indicates a quotient of $2x^2 - 3x - 1$ and a remainder of 2 when we divide $2x^3 + 5x^2 - 13x - 2$ by $x + 4$.

EXAMPLE 1

Find the quotient and the remainder for $(3x^4 + 5x^3 - 29x^2 - 45x + 14) \div (x - 3)$.

Solution

$$\begin{array}{r|rrrrr}
3 & 3 & 5 & -29 & -45 & 14 \\
 & & 9 & 42 & 39 & -18 \\
\hline
 & 3 & 14 & 13 & -6 & -4
\end{array}$$

Thus, the quotient is $3x^3 + 14x^2 + 13x - 6$ and the remainder is -4. ▬▬

EXAMPLE 2

Find the quotient and remainder for $(x^3 + 8x^2 + 13x - 6) \div (x + 3)$.

Solution

$$\begin{array}{r|rrrr}
-3 & 1 & 8 & 13 & -6 \\
 & & -3 & -15 & 6 \\
\hline
 & 1 & 5 & -2 & 0
\end{array}$$

Thus, the quotient is $x^2 + 5x - 2$ and the remainder is 0. ▬▬

EXAMPLE 3

Find the quotient and remainder for $(4x^4 - 2x^3 + 6x - 1) \div (x - 1)$.

Solution

$$\begin{array}{r|rrrrr}
1 & 4 & -2 & 0 & 6 & -1 \\
 & & 4 & 2 & 2 & 8 \\
\hline
 & 4 & 2 & 2 & 8 & 7
\end{array}$$

Notice that a zero has been inserted as coefficient of missing x^2 term

Thus, the quotient is $4x^3 + 2x^2 + 2x + 8$ and the remainder is 7. ▬▬

EXAMPLE 4

Find the quotient and remainder for $(x^4 + 16) \div (x + 2)$.

Solution

$$\begin{array}{r|rrrrr}
-2 & 1 & 0 & 0 & 0 & 16 \\
 & & -2 & 4 & -8 & 16 \\
\hline
 & 1 & -2 & 4 & -8 & 32
\end{array}$$

Notice that zeros have been inserted as coefficients of the missing terms in the dividend.

Thus, the quotient is $x^3 - 2x^2 + 4x - 8$ and the remainder is 32. ▬▬

Remainder Theorem

Let's consider the division algorithm (Property 5.1) when the dividend, $f(x)$, is divided by a linear polynomial of the form $x - c$. Then the division algorithm

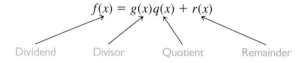

$$f(x) = g(x)q(x) + r(x)$$

Dividend   Divisor   Quotient   Remainder

becomes

$$f(x) = (x - c)q(x) + r(x).$$

Because the degree of the remainder, $r(x)$, must be less than the degree of the divisor, $x - c$, the remainder is a constant. Therefore, letting R represent the remainder, we have

$$f(x) = (x - c)q(x) + R.$$

If the functional value at c is found, we obtain

$$f(c) = (c - c)q(c) + R$$

$$= 0 \cdot q(c) + R$$

$$= R.$$

In other words, if a polynomial is divided by a linear polynomial of the form $x - c$, the remainder is given by the value of the polynomial at c. Let's state this more formally as the remainder theorem.

PROPERTY 5.2   *Remainder Theorem*

If the polynomial $f(x)$ is divided by $x - c$, then the remainder is equal to $f(c)$.

EXAMPLE 5

If $f(x) = x^3 + 2x^2 - 5x - 1$, find $f(2)$ by (a) using synthetic division and the remainder theorem, and (b) evaluating $f(2)$ directly.

Solutions

$$
\begin{array}{r|rrrr}
2 & 1 & 2 & -5 & -1 \\
  &   & 2 & 8 & 6 \\
\hline
  & 1 & 4 & 3 & \boxed{5} \quad \longleftarrow \; R = f(2)
\end{array}
$$

b. $f(2) = 2^3 + 2(2)^2 - 5(2) - 1 = 8 + 8 - 10 - 1 = 5$

EXAMPLE 6

If $f(x) = x^4 + 7x^3 + 8x^2 + 11x + 5$, find $f(-6)$ by (a) using synthetic division and the remainder theorem, and (b) evaluating $f(-6)$ directly.

Solutions

$$
\begin{array}{r|rrrrr}
-6 & 1 & 7 & 8 & 11 & 5 \\
   &   & -6 & -6 & -12 & 6 \\
\hline
   & 1 & 1 & 2 & -1 & \boxed{11}
\end{array}
\quad \longleftarrow \ R = f(-6)
$$

b. $f(-6) = (-6)^4 + 7(-6)^3 + 8(-6)^2 + 11(-6) + 5$

$\qquad = 1296 - 1512 + 288 - 66 + 5 = 11$

In Example 6, notice that finding $f(-6)$ using synthetic division and the remainder theorem involves much easier computation than evaluating $f(-6)$ directly. This is not always the case, but often the computation in synthetic division is easier than evaluating $f(c)$ directly.

EXAMPLE 7

Find the remainder when $x^3 + 3x^2 - 13x - 15$ is divided by $x + 1$.

Solution

Letting $f(x) = x^3 + 3x^2 - 13x - 15$ and writing $x + 1$ as $x - (-1)$, we can apply the remainder theorem.

$$f(-1) = (-1)^3 + 3(-1)^2 - 13(-1) - 15 = 0$$

Thus, the remainder is 0.

Example 7 illustrates an important special case of the remainder theorem—the situation in which the remainder is *zero*. Thus, we can say that $x + 1$ is a factor of $x^3 + 3x^2 - 13x - 15$.

Factor Theorem

We can formulate a general factor theorem by considering the equation

$$f(x) = (x - c)q(x) = R.$$

If $x - c$ is a factor of $f(x)$, then the remainder R, which is also $f(c)$, must be zero. Conversely, if $R = f(c) = 0$, then $f(x) = (x - c)q(x)$; in other words, $x - c$ is a factor of $f(x)$. The factor theorem can be stated as follows.

PROPERTY 5.3   *Factor Theorem*

A polynomial $f(x)$ has a factor of $x - c$ if and only if $f(c) = 0$.

EXAMPLE 8

Is $x - 1$ a factor of $x^3 + 5x^2 + 2x - 8$?

Solution

Let $f(x) = x^3 + 5x^2 + 2x - 8$ and compute $f(1)$ to obtain

$$f(1) = 1^3 + 5(1)^2 + 2(1) - 8 = 0.$$

Therefore, by the factor theorem, $x - 1$ is a factor of $f(x)$.

EXAMPLE 9

Is $x + 3$ a factor of $2x^3 + 5x^2 - 6x - 7$?

Solution

Use synthetic division to obtain the following.

$$
\begin{array}{r|rrrr}
-3 & 2 & 5 & -6 & -7 \\
   &   & -6 & 3 & 9 \\
\hline
   & 2 & -1 & -3 & ②
\end{array}
\quad \longleftarrow \; R = f(-3)
$$

Since $f(-3) \neq 0$, we know that $x + 3$ is not a factor of the given polynomial.

In Examples 8 and 9 we were only concerned with determining whether a linear polynomial of the form $x - c$ was a factor of another polynomial. For such problems, it is reasonable to compute $f(c)$ either directly or by synthetic division, whichever way seems easier for a particular problem. However, if more information is required, such as the complete factorization of the given polynomial, then the use of synthetic division becomes appropriate, as the next two examples illustrate.

EXAMPLE 10

Show that $x - 1$ is a factor of $x^3 - 2x^2 - 11x + 12$ and find the other linear factors of the polynomial.

Solution

Let's use synthetic division to divide $x^3 - 2x^2 - 11x + 12$ by $x - 1$.

$$
\begin{array}{r|rrrr}
1 & 1 & -2 & -11 & 12 \\
  &   & 1 & -1 & -12 \\
\hline
  & 1 & -1 & -12 & 0
\end{array}
$$

The last line indicates a quotient of $x^2 - x - 12$ and a remainder of 0. The remainder of 0 means that $x - 1$ is a factor. Furthermore, we can write

$$x^3 - 2x^2 - 11x + 12 = (x - 1)(x^2 - x - 12).$$

The quadratic polynomial $x^2 - x - 12$ can be factored as $(x - 4)(x + 3)$ by using our conventional factoring techniques. Thus, we obtain

$$x^3 - 2x^2 - 11x + 12 = (x - 1)(x - 4)(x + 3).$$

EXAMPLE 11

Show that $x + 4$ is a factor of $f(x) = x^3 - 5x^2 - 22x + 56$ and complete the factorization of $f(x)$.

Solution

Using synthetic division to divide $x^3 - 5x^2 - 22x + 56$ by $x + 4$, we obtain

$$
\begin{array}{r|rrrr}
-4 & 1 & -5 & -22 & 56 \\
   &   & -4 & 36 & -56 \\
\hline
   & 1 & -9 & 14 & 0
\end{array}
$$

The last line indicates a quotient of $x^2 - 9x + 14$ and a remainder of 0. The remainder of 0 means that $x + 4$ is a factor. Furthermore, we can write

$$x^3 - 5x^2 - 22x + 56 = (x + 4)(x^2 - 9x + 14)$$

and then complete the factoring to obtain

$$f(x) = x^3 - 5x^2 - 22x + 56 = (x + 4)(x - 7)(x - 2).$$ ▬▬▬

The factor theorem also plays a significant role in determining some general factorization ideas, as the last example of this section illustrates.

EXAMPLE 12

Verify that $x + 1$ is a factor of $x^n + 1$ for all odd positive integral values of n.

Solution

Let $f(x) = x^n + 1$ and compute $f(-1)$ to obtain

$$f(-1) = (-1)^n + 1$$
$$= -1 + 1 \qquad \text{Any odd power of } -1 \text{ is } -1$$
$$= 0.$$

Since $f(-1) = 0$, we know that $x + 1$ is a factor of $f(x)$. ▬▬▬

PROBLEM SET 5.1

Use the conventional long division format to find the quotient and remainder for each of the following division problems.

1. $(3x^3 + 7x^2 - 10x - 4) \div (3x + 1)$

2. $(4x^3 - 17x^2 + 7x + 10) \div (4x - 5)$

3. $(3x^3 + 2x^2 - 5x - 1) \div (x^2 + 2x)$

4. $(4x^3 - 5x^2 + 2x - 6) \div (x^2 - 3x)$

5. $(3x^2 - 2xy - 8y^2) \div (x - 2y)$

6. $(4a^2 - 8ab + 4b^2) \div (a - b)$

7. $(2x^3 - 2x - 1) \div (2x - 2)$

8. $(3x^3 + 6x^2 - 1) \div (3x + 3)$

Use synthetic division to determine the quotient and remainder for each of the following.

9. $(3x^2 + x - 4) \div (x - 1)$

10. $(2x^2 - 5x - 3) \div (x - 3)$

11. $(x^3 - 2x^2 - x + 2) \div (x - 2)$

12. $(x^3 - 5x^2 + 2x + 8) \div (x + 1)$

13. $(3x^4 - x^3 + 2x^2 - 7x - 1) \div (x + 1)$

14. $(2x^3 - 5x^2 \quad 4x + 6) \div (x - 2)$

15. $(x^3 - 7x - 6) \div (x + 2)$

16. $(2x^4 + 3x^2 + 3) \div (x + 2)$

17. $(x^3 + 6x^2 + 11x + 6) \div (x + 3)$

18. $(x^3 - 4x^2 - 11x + 30) \div (x - 5)$

19. $(x^5 - 1) \div (x - 1)$

20. $(x^5 - 1) \div (x + 1)$

21. $(x^5 + 1) \div (x - 1)$

22. $(x^5 + 1) \div (x + 1)$

23. $(2x^3 + 3x^2 - 2x + 3) \div \left(x + \frac{1}{2}\right)$

24. $(9x^3 - 6x^2 + 3x - 4) \div \left(x - \frac{1}{3}\right)$

25. $(4x^4 - 5x^2 + 1) \div \left(x - \frac{1}{2}\right)$

26. $(3x^4 - 2x^3 + 5x^2 - x - 1) \div \left(x + \frac{1}{3}\right)$

For each of the following, find $f(c)$ by either using synthetic division and the remainder theorem, or by evaluating $f(c)$ directly.

27. $f(x) = x^3 + x^2 - 2x - 4$ and $c = -1$

28. $f(x) = 2x^4 + x^2 + 6$ and $c = 1$

29. $f(x) = x^4 - 2x^3 - 3x^2 + 5x - 1$ and $c = -2$

30. $f(x) = 2x^4 + x^3 - 4x^2 - x + 1$ and $c = 2$

31. $f(t) = 6t^3 - 35t^2 + 8t - 10$ and $c = 6$

32. $f(n) = 3n^4 - 2n^3 + 4n - 1$ and $c = 3$

33. $f(x) = 5x^6 - x^3 - 1$ and $c = -1$

34. $f(x) = 2x^3 - 3x^2 - 5x + 4$ and $c = 4$

35. $f(x) = x^4 - 8x^3 - 9x^2 - 15x + 2$ and $c = 7$

36. $f(t) = 5t^3 - 8t^2 + 9t - 4$ and $c = -5$

37. $f(n) = -2n^4 + 2n^2 - n - 5$ and $c = -2$

38. $f(x) = 4x^7 + 3$ and $c = 3$

39. $f(x) = 2x^3 - 5x^2 + 4x - 3$ and $c = \frac{1}{2}$

40. $f(x) = 3x^3 + 4x^2 - 5x - 7$ and $c = -\frac{1}{3}$

For Problems 41–50, use the factor theorem to help answer some questions about factors.

41. Is $x - 2$ a factor of $3x^2 - 4x - 4$?

42. Is $x + 3$ a factor of $6x^2 + 13x - 15$?

43. Is $x + 2$ a factor of $x^3 + x^2 - 7x - 10$?

44. Is $x - 3$ a factor of $2x^3 - 3x^2 - 10x + 3$?

45. Is $x - 1$ a factor of $3x^3 + 5x^2 - x - 2$?

46. Is $x + 4$ a factor of $x^3 - 4x^2 + 2x - 8$?

47. Is $x - 2$ a factor of $x^3 - 8$?

48. Is $x + 2$ a factor of $x^3 + 8$?

49. Is $x - 3$ a factor of $x^4 - 81$?

50. Is $x + 3$ a factor of $x^4 - 81$?

For Problems 51–56, use synthetic division to show that $g(x)$ is a factor of $f(x)$ and complete the factorization of $f(x)$.

51. $g(x) = x + 2, f(x) = x^3 + 7x^2 + 4x - 12$

52. $g(x) = x - 1, f(x) = 3x^3 + 19x^2 - 38x + 16$

53. $g(x) = x - 3, f(x) = 6x^3 - 17x^2 - 5x + 6$

54. $g(x) = x + 2, f(x) = 12x^3 + 29x^2 + 8x - 4$

55. $g(x) = x + 1, f(x) = x^3 - 2x^2 - 7x - 4$

56. $g(x) = x - 5, f(x) = 2x^3 + x^2 - 61x + 30$

For Problems 57–60, find the value(s) of k that makes the second polynomial a factor of the first.

57. $x^3 - kx^2 + 5x + k; x - 2$

58. $k^2x^4 - 3kx^2 - 4; x - 1$

59. $x^3 + 4x^2 - 11x + k; x + 2$

60. $kx^3 + 19x^2 + x - 6$; $x + 3$

61. Show that $x + 2$ is a factor of $x^{12} - 4096$.

62. Argue that $f(x) = 2x^4 + x^2 + 3$ has no factor of the form $x - c$, where c is a real number.

63. Verify that $x - 1$ is a factor of $x^n - 1$ for all positive integral values of n.

64. Verify that $x + 1$ is a factor of $x^n - 1$ for all even positive integral values of n.

65. a. Verify that $x - y$ is a factor of $x^n - y^n$ for all positive integral values of n.

   b. Verify that $x + y$ is a factor of $x^n - y^n$ for all even positive integral values of n.

   c. Verify that $x + y$ is a factor of $x^n + y^n$ for all odd positive integral values of n.

THOUGHTS into WORDS

66. How would you describe synthetic division to someone who just completed an elementary algebra course?

67. Why is synthetic division restricted to situations where the divisor is of the form $x - c$?

FURTHER INVESTIGATIONS

The remainder and factor theorems are true for any complex value of c. Therefore, for Problems 68–70, find $f(c)$ by (a) using synthetic division and the remainder theorem, and (b) evaluating $f(c)$ directly.

68. $f(x) = x^3 - 5x^2 + 2x + 1$ and $c = i$

69. $f(x) = x^2 + 4x - 2$ and $c = 1 + i$

70. $f(x) = x^3 + 2x^2 + x - 2$ and $c = 2 - 3i$

71. Show that $x - 2i$ is a factor of $f(x) = x^4 + 6x^2 + 8$.

72. Show that $x + 3i$ is a factor of $f(x) = x^4 + 14x^2 + 45$.

73. Consider changing the form of the polynomial $f(x) = x^3 + 4x^2 - 3x + 2$ as follows.

$$f(x) = x^3 + 4x^2 - 3x + 2$$
$$= x(x^2 + 4x - 3) + 2$$
$$= x[x(x + 4) - 3] + 2$$

The final form $f(x) = x[x(x - 4) - 3] + 2$ is called the **nested form** of the polynomial, which is particularly well suited for evaluating functional values of f either by hand or with a calculator.

For each of the following, find the indicated functional values using the nested form of the given polynomial.

a. $f(4)$, $f(-5)$, and $f(7)$, for $f(x) = x^3 + 5x^2 - 2x + 1$

b. $f(3)$, $f(6)$, and $f(-7)$ for $f(x) = 2x^3 - 4x^2 - 3x + 2$

c. $f(4)$, $f(5)$, and $f(-3)$ for $f(x) = -2x^3 + 5x^2 - 6x - 7$

d. $f(5)$, $f(6)$, and $f(-3)$ for $f(x) = x^4 + 3x^3 - 2x^2 + 5x - 1$

5.2 POLYNOMIAL EQUATIONS

In Chapter 1 we solved a large variety of **linear equations** of the form $ax + b = 0$ and **quadratic equations** of the form $ax^2 + bx + c = 0$. Linear and quadratic equations are special cases of a general class of equations we refer to as **polynomial equations** The equation

$$a_n x^n + a_{n-1} x^{n-1} + \cdots + a_1 x + a_0 = 0,$$

where the coefficients $a_0, a_1, \ldots, a_n$ are real numbers and n is a positive integer, is called a **polynomial equation of degree** n. The following are examples of polynomial equations.

$$\sqrt{2}x - 6 = 0 \qquad \text{Degree 1}$$

$$\frac{3}{4}x^2 - \frac{2}{3}x + 5 = 0 \qquad \text{Degree 2}$$

$$4x^3 - 3x^2 - 7x - 9 = 0 \qquad \text{Degree 3}$$

$$5x^4 - x + 6 = 0 \qquad \text{Degree 4}$$

REMARK The most general polynomial equation would allow complex numbers to be coefficients. However, for our purposes in this text we will restrict the coefficients to be real numbers. We refer to this restriction as **polynomial equations over the reals.**

In general, solving polynomial equations of a degree greater than two can be very difficult and often requires mathematics beyond the scope of this text. However, you should be familiar with some general properties for solving polynomial equations. Furthermore, certain types of polynomial equations can be solved using the techniques available to us at this time. Let's begin by listing some polynomial equations and their corresponding solution sets we previously encountered in this text.

EQUATION	SOLUTION SET
$3x + 4 = 7$	$\{1\}$
$x^2 + x - 6 = 0$	$\{-3, 2\}$
$2x^3 - 3x^2 - 2x + 3 = 0$	$\{-1, 1, \frac{3}{2}\}$
$x^4 - 16 = 0$	$\{-2, 2, -2i, 2i\}$

Notice that in each of the above examples the number of solutions corresponds to the degree of the equation. The 1st degree equation has 1 solution, the 2nd degree equation has 2 solutions, the 3rd degree equation has 3 solutions, and the 4th degree equation has 4 solutions. Now consider the equation

$$(x - 4)^2(x + 5)^3 = 0.$$

It can be written as

$$(x - 4)(x - 4)(x + 5)(x + 5)(x + 5) = 0,$$

which implies that

$$x - 4 = 0 \quad \text{or} \quad x - 4 = 0 \quad \text{or} \quad x + 5 = 0 \quad \text{or}$$

$$x + 5 = 0 \quad \text{or} \quad x + 5 = 0,$$

and, therefore,

$$x = 4 \quad \text{or} \quad x = 4 \quad \text{or} \quad x = -5 \quad \text{or}$$

$$x = -5 \quad \text{or} \quad x = -5$$

We state that the solution set of the original equation is $\{-5, 4\}$, but we also say that the equation has a solution of 4 with a **multiplicity of two**, and a solution of -5 with a **multiplicity of three**. Furthermore, notice that the sum of the multiplicities is 5, which agrees with the degree of the equation. The following general property can be stated.

PROPERTY 5.4

A polynomial equation of degree n has n solutions, where any solution of multiplicity p is counted p times.

REMARK The topics of this section are from an area of mathematics commonly called *the theory of equations*. In a more formal development of this material, Property 5.4 is deduced from the fundamental theorem of algebra and the factor theorem of the previous section. The fundamental theorem of algebra essentially states that every polynomial equation with complex coefficients has at least one complex solution.

Finding Rational Solutions

As we previously stated, solving polynomial equations of degree greater than two can be very difficult. However, **rational solutions of polynomial equations with integral coefficients** can be found using techniques of this chapter. The following property restricts the potential rational solutions of such an equation.

PROPERTY 5.5 *Rational Root Theorem*

Consider the polynomial equation

$$a_n x^n + a_{n-1} x^{n-1} + \cdots + a_1 x + a_0 = 0,$$

where the coefficients $a_0, a_1, \ldots, a_n$ are **integers**. If the rational number c/d, reduced to lowest terms, is a solution of the equation, then c is a factor of the constant term a_0, and d is a factor of the leading coefficient a_n.

A proof of the rational root theorem is based on some simple factoring ideas, as indicated by the following outline of such a proof.

Outline of Proof

If c/d is to be a solution, then

$$a_n\left(\frac{c}{d}\right)^n + a_{n-1}\left(\frac{c}{d}\right)^{n-1} + \cdots + a_1\left(\frac{c}{d}\right) + a_0 = 0.$$

Multiplying both sides of this equation by d^n and adding $-a_0d^n$ to both sides yields

$$a_nc^n + a_{n-1}c^{n-1}d + \cdots + a_1cd^{n-1} = -a_0d^n.$$

Because c is a factor of the left side of this equation, c must also be a factor of $-a_0d^n$. Furthermore, because c/d is in reduced form, c and d have no common factors other than -1 or 1. Thus, c is a factor of a_0. In the same way, from the equation

$$a_{n-1}c^{n-1}d + \cdots + a_1cd^{n-1} + a_0d^n = -a_nc^n$$

we can conclude that d is a factor of the left side and, therefore, d is also a factor of a_n.   ▬▬▬

The rational root theorem, synthetic division, the factor theorem, and some previous knowledge that pertains to solving linear and quadratic equations merge to form a basis for finding rational solutions. Let's consider some examples.

EXAMPLE 1

Find all rational solutions of $3x^3 + 8x^2 - 15x + 4 = 0$.

Solution

If c/d is a rational solution, then c must be a factor of 4 and d a factor of 3. Therefore, the possible values for c and d are as follows:

$$\text{For } c: \quad \pm 1, \quad \pm 2, \quad \pm 4$$
$$\text{For } d: \quad \pm 1, \quad \pm 3,$$

Thus, the possible values for c/d are

$$\pm 1, \quad \pm\tfrac{1}{3}, \quad \pm 2, \quad \pm\tfrac{2}{3}, \quad \pm 4, \quad \pm\tfrac{4}{3}.$$

By using synthetic division we obtain

$$
\begin{array}{r|rrrr}
1 & 3 & 8 & -15 & 4 \\
  &   & 3 & 11 & -4 \\
\hline
  & 3 & 11 & -4 & 0
\end{array}
$$

which shows that $x - 1$ is a factor of the given polynomial; therefore, 1 is a rational solution of the equation. Furthermore, the synthetic division result also indicates that we can factor the given polynomial as follows.

$$3x^3 + 8x^2 - 15x + 4 = 0$$

$$(x - 1)(3x^2 + 11x - 4) = 0$$

The quadratic factor can be factored further by using our previous techniques and we can proceed as follows.

$$(x - 1)(3x^2 + 11x - 4) = 0$$

$$(x - 1)(3x - 1)(x + 4) = 0$$

$$x - 1 = 0 \quad \text{or} \quad 3x - 1 = 0 \quad \text{or} \quad x + 4 = 0$$

$$x = 1 \quad \text{or} \quad x = \tfrac{1}{3} \quad \text{or} \quad x = -4$$

Thus, the entire solution set consists of rational numbers, which can be listed as $\{-4, \tfrac{1}{3}, 1\}$.

In Example 1, we were fortunate that a rational solution was the result of our first use of synthetic division. Frequently, this does not happen and we need to conduct a little organized search, as the next example illustrates.

EXAMPLE 2

Find all rational solutions of $3x^3 + 7x^2 - 22x - 8 = 0$.

Solution

If c/d is a rational solution, then c must be a factor of -8 and d a factor of 3. Therefore, the possible values for c and d are as follows.

For c: $\quad \pm 1, \quad \pm 2, \quad \pm 4, \quad \pm 8$

For d: $\quad \pm 1, \quad \pm 3,$

Thus, the possible values for c/d are

$$\pm 1, \quad \pm\tfrac{1}{3}, \quad \pm 2, \quad \pm\tfrac{2}{3}, \quad \pm 4, \quad \pm\tfrac{4}{3}, \quad \pm 8, \quad \pm\tfrac{8}{3}.$$

Let's begin our search for rational solutions by trying the integers first.

$$
\begin{array}{r|rrrr}
1 & 3 & 7 & -22 & -8 \\
  &   & 3 & 10 & -12 \\
\hline
  & 3 & 10 & -12 & \boxed{-20}
\end{array}
$$

← This indicates that $x - 1$ is not a factor; thus 1 is not a solution

$$
\begin{array}{r|rrrr}
-1 & 3 & 7 & -22 & -8 \\
   &   & -3 & -4 & 26 \\
\hline
   & 3 & 4 & -26 & \boxed{18}
\end{array}
$$

← This indicates that -1 is not a solution

$$
\begin{array}{r|rrr}
2 & 3 & 7 & -22 & -8 \\
  &   & 6 & 26 & 8 \\
\hline
  & 3 & 13 & 4 & 0
\end{array}
$$

Now we know that $x - 2$ is a factor and we can proceed as follows.

$$3x^3 + 7x^2 - 22x - 8 = 0$$

$$(x - 2)(3x^2 + 13x + 4) = 0$$

$$(x - 2)(3x + 1)(x + 4) = 0$$

$$x - 2 = 0 \quad \text{or} \quad 3x + 1 = 0 \quad \text{or} \quad x + 4 = 0$$

$$x = 2 \quad \text{or} \quad 3x = -1 \quad \text{or} \quad x = -4$$

$$x = 2 \quad \text{or} \quad x = -\tfrac{1}{3} \quad \text{or} \quad x = -4$$

The solution set is $\{-4, -\tfrac{1}{3}, 2\}$.

In Examples 1 and 2, we were solving third degree equations. Therefore, after finding one linear factor by synthetic division we were able to factor the remaining quadratic factor in the usual way. However, if the given equation is of degree four or more, we may need to find more than one linear factor by synthetic division, as the next example illustrates.

EXAMPLE 3

Solve $x^4 - 6x^3 + 22x^2 - 30x + 13 = 0$.

Solution

The possible values for c/d are as follows.

$$\pm 1, \quad \pm 13$$

By synthetic division we find that

$$
\begin{array}{r|rrrr}
1 & 1 & -6 & 22 & -30 & 13 \\
  &   & 1 & -5 & 17 & -13 \\
\hline
  & 1 & -5 & 17 & -13 & 0
\end{array}
$$

which indicates that $x - 1$ is a factor of the given polynomial. The bottom line of the synthetic division indicates that the given polynomial can be factored as follows.

$$x^4 - 6x^3 + 22x^2 - 30x + 13 = 0$$

$$(x - 1)(x^3 - 5x^2 + 17x - 13) = 0$$

Therefore,

$$x - 1 = 0 \quad \text{or} \quad x^3 - 5x^2 + 17x - 13 = 0.$$

Now we can use the same approach to look for rational solutions of $x^3 - 5x^2 + 17x - 13 = 0$. The possible values of c/d are as follows.

$$\pm 1, \qquad \pm 13$$

By synthetic division we find that

$$
\begin{array}{r|rrrr}
1 & 1 & -5 & 17 & -13 \\
  &   & 1 & -4 & 13 \\
\hline
  & 1 & -4 & 13 & 0
\end{array}
$$

which indicates that $x - 1$ is a factor of $x^3 - 5x^2 + 17x - 13$ and that the other factor is $x^2 - 4x + 13$. Now we can solve the original equation as follows.

$$x^4 - 6x^3 + 22x^2 - 30x + 13 = 0$$

$$(x - 1)(x^3 - 5x^2 + 17x - 13) = 0$$

$$(x - 1)(x - 1)(x^2 - 4x + 13) = 0$$

$$x - 1 = 0 \qquad \text{or} \qquad x - 1 = 0 \qquad \text{or} \qquad x^2 - 4x + 13 = 0$$

$$x = 1 \qquad \text{or} \qquad x = 1 \qquad \text{or} \qquad x^2 - 4x + 13 = 0$$

Using the quadratic formula on $x^2 - 4x + 13 = 0$ produces

$$x = \frac{4 \pm \sqrt{16 - 52}}{2} = \frac{4 \pm \sqrt{-36}}{2} = \frac{4 \pm 6i}{2} = 2 \pm 3i.$$

Thus, the original equation has a rational solution of 1 with a multiplicity of two, and two complex solutions, $2 + 3i$ and $2 - 3i$. The solution set would be listed as $\{1, 2 \pm 3i\}$. ▬▬▬

Example 3 illustrates two general properties. First, notice that the coefficient of x^4 is 1, and this fact forced the possible rational solutions to be integers. **In general, the possible rational solutions of $x^n + a_{n-1}x^{n-1} + \cdots + a_1 x + a_0 = 0$ are the integral factors of a_0.** Secondly, notice that the complex solutions of Example 3 are conjugates of each other. Note the following general property.

PROPERTY 5.6

Nonreal complex solutions of polynomial equations with real co-efficients, if they exist, must occur in conjugate pairs.

REMARK The justification of Property 5.6 is based on some properties of conjugates that were presented in Problem 85 of Problem Set 1.5. We will not show the details of such a proof at this time.

Each of the Properties 5.4, 5.5, and 5.6 yields some information about the solutions of a polynomial equation. Before we state a final property of this section, which will give us some additional information, we need to illustrate two ideas. In a polynomial that is arranged in descending powers of x, if two successive terms differ in sign, then we say there is a **variation in sign**. We disregard terms with zero coefficients when counting sign variations. For example, the polynomial

$$3x^3 - 2x^2 + 4x + 7$$

has *two* sign variations, whereas the polynomial

$$x^5 - 4x^3 + x - 5$$

has *three* variations.

Another idea that we need to understand is the fact that the solutions of

$$a_n(-x)^n + a_{n-1}(-x)^{n-1} + \cdots + a_1(-x) + a_0 = 0$$

are the opposites of the solutions of

$$a_n x^n + a_{n-1}x^{n-1} + \cdots + a_1 x + a_0 = 0.$$

In other words, if a new equation is formed by replacing x with $-x$ in a given equation, then the solutions of the newly formed equation are the opposites of the solutions of the given equation. For example, the solution set of $x^2 + 7x + 12 = 0$ is $\{-4, -3\}$ and the solution set of $(-x)^2 + 7(-x) + 12 = 0$ (which simplifies to $x^2 - 7x + 12 = 0$) is $\{3, 4\}$.

Now we can state a property that can help you determine the nature of the solutions of a polynomial equation without actually solving the equation.

PROPERTY 5.7   *Descartes' Rule of Signs*

Let $a_n x^n + a_{n-1}x^{n-1} + \cdots + a_1 x + a_0 = 0$ be a polynomial equation with real coefficients.

1. The number of **positive real** solutions of the given equation is either equal to the number of variations in sign of the polynomial, or else it is less than the number of variations by a positive even integer.

2. The number of **negative real** solutions of the given equation is either equal to the number of variations in sign of the polynomial $a_n(-x)^n + a_{n-1}(-x)^{n-1} + \cdots + a_1(-x) + a_0$, or else it is less than the number of variations by a positive even integer.

Property 5.7, along with Properties 5.4 and 5.6, allows us to acquire some information about the solutions of a polynomial equation without actually solving the equation. Let's consider some equations and indicate how much we know about their solutions without solving them.

$$x^3 + 3x^2 + 5x + 4 = 0$$

1. No variations of sign in $x^3 + 3x^2 + 5x + 4$ means that there are **no positive solutions**

2. Replacing x with $-x$ in the given polynomial produces $(-x)^3 + 3(-x)^2 + 5(-x) + 4$, which simplifies to $-x^3 + 3x^2 - 5x + 4$ and contains 3 variations of sign; there are **3 or 1 negative solutions**

Conclusion: The given equation has (a) 3 negative real solutions or (b) 1 negative real solution and 2 nonreal complex solutions.

$$2x^4 + 3x^2 - x - 1 = 0$$

1. There is 1 variation of sign in the given polynomial; thus, the equation has **1 positive solution**

2. Replacing x with $-x$ produces $2(-x)^4 + 3(-x)^2 - (-x) - 1$, which simplifies to $2x^4 + 3x^2 + x - 1$ and contains 1 variation of sign. Thus, the given equation has **1 negative solution**

Conclusion: The given equation has 1 positive, 1 negative, and 2 nonreal complex solutions.

$$3x^4 + 2x^2 + 5 = 0$$

1. No variations of sign in the given polynomial means that there are **no positive solutions**

2. Replacing x with $-x$ produces $3(-x)^4 + 2(-x)^2 + 5$, which simplifies to $3x^4 + 2x^2 + 5$ and contains no variations of sign. Thus, there are **no negative solutions**

Conclusion: The given equation contains 4 nonreal complex solutions. We also know that these solutions will appear in conjugate pairs.

$$2x^5 - 4x^3 + 2x - 5 = 0$$

1. Three variations of sign in the given polynomial implies that the **number of positive solutions is 3 or 1**

2. Replacing x with $-x$ produces $2(-x)^5 - 4(-x)^3 + 2(-x) - 5$, which simplifies to $-2x^5 + 4x^3 - 2x - 5$ and contains 2 variations of sign; thus, the **number of negative solutions is 2 or 0**

Conclusion: The given equation has (a) 3 positive and 2 negative solutions, or (b) 3 positive and 2 nonreal complex solutions, or (c) 1 positive, 2 negative, and 2 nonreal complex solutions, or (d) 1 positive and 4 nonreal complex solutions.

It should be evident from the previous discussions that sometimes we can truly pinpoint the nature of the solutions of a polynomial equation. However, for some equations (such as the last example) the best that we can do with the properties discussed in this section is to restrict the possibilities of the solutions to a few.

E X A M P L E   4

Find a polynomial equation with integral coefficients that has the given numbers as solutions and the indicated degree.

a. $1, \frac{1}{2}, -2$; degree 3

b. 2 of multiplicity 4; degree 4

c. $1 + i, -3i$; degree 4

Solution

a. If $1, \frac{1}{2}$, and -2 are solutions, then $(x - 1)$, $\left(x - \frac{1}{2}\right)$, and $(x + 2)$ are factors of the polynomial. Thus, the following third-degree polynomial equation can be formed.

$$(x - 1)\left(x - \frac{1}{2}\right)(x + 2) = 0$$
$$(x - 1)(2x - 1)(x + 2) = 0$$
$$2x^3 + x^2 - 5x + 2 = 0$$

b. If 2 is to be a solution with multiplicity 4, then the equation $(x - 2)^4 = 0$ can be formed. Using the binomial expansion pattern we can express the equation as follows.

$$(x - 2)^4 = 0$$

$$x^4 - 8x^3 + 24x^2 - 32x + 16 = 0$$

c. By Property 5.6 if $1 + i$ is a solution, then so is $1 - i$. Likewise, since $-3i$ is a solution, so is $3i$. Therefore, we can form the following equation

$$[x - (1 + i)][x - (1 - i)](x + 3i)(x - 3i) = 0$$

$$[(x - 1) - i][(x - 1) + i](x^2 + 9) = 0$$

$$[(x - 1)^2 - i^2](x^2 + 9) = 0$$

$$(x^2 - 2x + 1 + 1)(x^2 + 9) = 0$$

$$(x^2 - 2x + 2)(x^2 + 9) = 0$$

$$x^4 - 2x^3 + 11x^2 - 18x + 18 = 0$$ ▬▬▬

A graphing utility can be very helpful when solving polynomial equations, especially if they are of degree greater than two. Even the search for possible rational solutions can be simplified by looking at a graph. To find the rational solutions of $3x^3 + 8x^2 - 15x + 4 = 0$ (Example 1) we could begin by graphing the equation $y = 3x^3 + 8x^2 - 15x + 4$. This graph is shown in Figure 5.1. From the graph it looks as if 1 and -4 are two of the x-intercepts and therefore solutions of the original equation. We can verify this by checking them in the equation.

$$3(1)^3 + 8(1)^2 - 15(1) + 4 = 3 + 8 - 15 + 4 = 0$$

$$3(-4)^3 + 8(-4)^2 - 15(-4) + 4 = -192 + 128 + 60 + 4 = 0$$

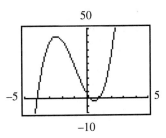

FIGURE 5.1

Thus, $x - 1$ and $x + 4$ are factors of $3x^3 + 8x^2 - 15x + 4$ and the remaining factor could be found by division. The solution set could then be determined as we did in Example 1.

Now let's use a graphing utility to *approximate* the real number solutions of a polynomial equation.

EXAMPLE 5

Find the real number solutions of the equation $x^4 - 2x^3 - 5 = 0$.

Solution

Let's use a graphing utility to get a sketch of the graph of $y = x^4 - 2x^3 - 5$ (Figure 5.2). From this graph we see that one x-intercept is between -1 and -2 and another

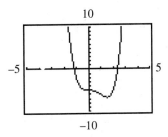

FIGURE 5.2

between 2 and 3. We can use the zoom and trace features to approximate these values at -1.2 and 2.4, to the nearest tenth. Thus, the real solutions for the equation $x^4 - 2x^3 - 5 = 0$ are approximately -1.2 and 2.4. (The other two solutions must be conjugate complex numbers.)

PROBLEM SET 5.2

Use the rational root theorem and the factor theorem to help solve each of the following equations. Be sure that your number of solutions for each equation agrees with Property 5.4, taking into account multiplicity of solutions.

1. $x^3 + x^2 - 4x - 4 = 0$

2. $x^3 - 2x^2 - 11x + 12 = 0$

3. $6x^3 + x^2 - 10x + 3 = 0$

4. $8x^3 - 2x^2 - 41x - 10 = 0$

5. $3x^3 + 13x^2 - 52x + 28 = 0$

6. $15x^3 + 14x^2 - 3x - 2 = 0$

7. $x^3 - 2x^2 - 7x - 4 = 0$

8. $x^3 - x^2 - 8x + 12 = 0$

9. $x^4 - 4x^3 - 7x^2 + 34x - 24 = 0$

10. $x^4 + 4x^3 - x^2 - 16x - 12 = 0$

11. $x^3 - 10x - 12 = 0$

12. $x^3 - 4x^2 + 8 = 0$

13. $3x^4 - x^3 - 8x^2 + 2x + 4 = 0$

14. $2x^4 + 3x^3 - 11x^2 - 9x + 15 = 0$

15. $6x^4 - 13x^3 - 19x^2 + 12x = 0$

16. $x^3 - x^2 + x - 1 = 0$

17. $x^4 - 3x^3 + 2x^2 + 2x - 4 = 0$

18. $x^4 + x^3 - 3x^2 - 17x - 30 = 0$

19. $2x^5 - 5x^4 + x^3 + x^2 - x + 6 = 0$

20. $4x^4 + 12x^3 + x^2 - 12x + 4 = 0$

Verify that the following equations have no rational solutions.

21. $x^4 - x^3 - 8x^2 - 3x + 1 = 0$

22. $x^4 + 3x - 2 = 0$

23. $2x^4 - 3x^3 + 6x^2 - 24x + 5 = 0$

24. $3x^4 - 4x^3 - 10x^2 + 3x - 4 = 0$

25. $x^5 - 2x^4 + 3x^3 + 4x^2 + 7x - 1 = 0$

26. $x^5 + 2x^4 - 2x^3 + 5x^2 - 2x - 3 = 0$

27. The rational root theorem pertains to polynomial equations with integral coefficients. However, if the coefficients are nonintegral rational numbers, we can first apply the multiplication property of equality to produce an equivalent equation with integral coefficients. Solve each of the following equations.

a. $\dfrac{1}{10}x^3 + \dfrac{1}{2}x^2 + \dfrac{1}{5}x - \dfrac{4}{5} = 0$

b. $\dfrac{1}{10}x^3 + \dfrac{1}{5}x^2 - \dfrac{1}{2}x - \dfrac{3}{5} = 0$

c. $x^3 + \dfrac{9}{2}x^2 - x - 12 = 0$

d. $x^3 - \dfrac{5}{6}x^2 - \dfrac{22}{3}x + \dfrac{5}{2} = 0$

For Problems 28–37, use Descartes' rule of signs (Property 5.7) to help list the possibilities for the solutions for each of the equations. *Do not solve the equations.*

28. $6x^2 + 7x - 20 = 0$

29. $8x^2 - 14x + 3 = 0$

30. $2x^3 + x - 3 = 0$

31. $4x^3 + 3x + 7 = 0$

32. $3x^3 - 2x^2 + 6x + 5 = 0$

33. $4x^3 + 5x^2 - 6x - 2 = 0$

34. $x^5 - 3x^4 + 5x^3 - x^2 + 2x - 1 = 0$

35. $2x^5 + 3x^3 - x + 1 = 0$ **36.** $x^5 + 32 = 0$

37. $2x^6 + 3x^4 - 2x^2 - 1 = 0$

For Problems 38–47, find a polynomial equation with integral coefficients that has the given numbers as solutions and the indicated degree.

38. 2, 4, −3;   degree 3

39. 1, −1, 2, −4;   degree 4

40. $-2, \frac{1}{2}, \frac{2}{3}$; degree 3

41. $3, -\frac{2}{3}, \frac{3}{4}$; degree 3

42. 1 of multiplicity 5; degree 5

43. -3 of multiplicity 4; degree 4

44. $3, 2 + 3i$; degree 3

45. $-2, 1 - 4i$; degree 3

46. $1 - i, 2i$; degree 4

47. $-2 + 3i, -i$; degree 4

THOUGHTS into WORDS

48. Explain the concept of *multiplicity of roots* of an equation.

49. How would you defend the statement that the equation $2x^4 + 3x^3 + x^2 + 5 = 0$ has no positive solutions? Does it have any negative solutions? Defend your answer.

FURTHER INVESTIGATIONS

50. Use the rational root theorem to argue that $\sqrt{2}$ is not a rational number. [*Hint:* The solutions of $x^2 - 2 = 0$ are $\pm\sqrt{2}$.]

51. Use the rational root theorem to argue that $\sqrt{12}$ is not a rational number.

52. Defend the statement, *every polynomial equation of odd degree with real coefficients has at least one real number solution.*

53. The following synthetic division shows that 2 is a solution of $x^4 + x^3 + x^2 - 9x - 10 = 0$.

$$
\begin{array}{r|rrrrr}
2 & 1 & 1 & 1 & -9 & -10 \\
  &   & 2 & 6 & 14 & 10 \\
\hline
  & 1 & 3 & 7 & 5 & 0 \leftarrow
\end{array}
$$

Notice that the new quotient row (indicated by the arrow) consists entirely of nonnegative numbers. This indicates that searching for solutions greater than 2 would be a waste of time since larger divisors would continue to increase each of the numbers (except the one on the far left) in the new quotient row. (Try 3 as a divisor!) Thus, we say that 2 is an **upper bound** for the real number solutions of the given equation.

Now consider the following synthetic division that shows that -1 is also a solution of $x^4 + x^3 + x^2 - 9x - 10 = 0$.

$$
\begin{array}{r|rrrrr}
-1 & 1 & 1 & 1 & -9 & -10 \\
   &   & -1 & 0 & -1 & 10 \\
\hline
   & 1 & 0 & 1 & -10 & 0 \leftarrow
\end{array}
$$

The new quotient row (indicated by the arrow) shows that there is no need to look for solutions less than -1

because any divisor less than -1 would increase, in absolute value, the size of each number (except the one on the far left) in the new quotient row. (Try -2 as a divisor!) Thus, we say that -1 is a **lower bound** for the real number solutions of the given equation.

The following general property can be stated: If

$$a_n x^n + a_{n-1} x^{n-1} + \cdots + a_1 x + a_0 = 0$$

is a polynomial equation with real coefficients and $a_n > 0$, and if the polynomial is divided synthetically by $x - c$, then,

1. If $c > 0$ and all numbers in the new quotient row of the synthetic division are nonnegative, then c is an upper bound of the solutions of the given equation.

2. If $c < 0$ and the numbers in the new quotient row alternate in sign (with 0 considered either positive or negative as needed) then c is a lower bound of the solutions of the given equation.

Find the smallest positive integer and the largest negative integer that are upper and lower bounds, respectively, for the real number solutions of each of the following equations. Keep in mind that the integers that serve as bounds do not necessarily have to be solutions of the equation.

a. $x^3 - 3x^2 + 25x - 75 = 0$

b. $x^3 + x^2 - 4x - 4 = 0$

c. $x^4 + 4x^3 - 7x^2 - 22x + 24 = 0$

d. $3x^3 + 7x^2 - 22x - 8 = 0$

e. $x^4 - 2x^3 - 9x^2 + 2x + 8 = 0$

GRAPHICS CALCULATOR ACTIVITIES

54. Suppose that we want to solve the equation $x^3 + 2x^2 - 14x - 40 = 0$. Let's graph the function $f(x) = x^3 + 2x^2 - 14x - 40$. Since the graph has only one x-intercept, the equation must have one real number solution and two nonreal complex solutions. The graph also indicates that the real solution is approximately 4. We can determine that 4 is a solution and then we can proceed to solve the equation using the ideas of this section.

Solve each of the following equations using a graphics calculator whenever it seems to be helpful. Express all irrational solutions in lowest radical form.

a. $x^3 + 2x^2 - 14x - 40 = 0$

b. $x^3 + x^2 - 7x + 65 = 0$

c. $x^4 - 6x^3 - 6x^2 + 32x + 24 = 0$

d. $x^4 + 3x^3 - 39x^2 + 11x + 24 = 0$

e. $x^3 - 14x^2 + 26x - 24 = 0$

f. $x^4 + 2x^3 - 3x^2 - 4x + 4 = 0$

55. Use a graphics calculator to help determine the nature of the solutions for each of the following equations. You may also need to use the property stated in Problem 53.

a. $2x^3 - 3x^2 - 3x + 2 = 0$

b. $3x^3 + 7x^2 + 8x + 2 = 0$

c. $2x^4 + 3x^2 + 1 = 0$

d. $4x^5 - 8x^4 - 5x^3 + 10^2 + x - 2 = 0$

e. $x^4 - x^3 + 2x^2 - x - 1 = 0$

f. $x^5 - x^4 + x^3 - x^2 + x - 3 = 0$

g. $x^4 - 14x^3 + 23x^2 + 14x - 24 = 0$

h. $x^3 + 13x^2 - 28x + 30 = 0$

56. Find approximations, to the nearest hundredth, of the real number solutions of each of the following equations.

a. $x^2 - 4x + 1 = 0$

b. $3x^3 - 2x^2 + 12x - 8 = 0$

c. $x^4 - 8x^3 + 14x^2 - 8x + 13 = 0$

d. $x^4 + 6x^3 - 10x^2 - 22x + 161 = 0$

e. $7x^5 - 5x^4 + 35x^3 - 25x^2 + 28x - 20 = 0$

5.3   GRAPHING POLYNOMIAL FUNCTIONS

Analogous to the linear equation–quadratic equation–polynomial equation vocabulary, we have terms that classify functions. In Chapter 3 we defined a linear function in terms of the equation

$$f(x) = ax + b$$

and a **quadratic function** in terms of the equation

$$f(x) = ax^2 + bx + c.$$

Both of these are specific cases of a general class of functions called **polynomial functions**. Any function of the form

$$f(x) = a_n x^n + a_{n-1} x^{n-1} + \cdots + a_1 x + a_0,$$

is called a **polynomial function of degree** n, where a_n is a nonzero real number, and $a_{n-1}, \ldots, a_1 a_0$ are real numbers, and n is a nonnegative integer. The following are examples of polynomial functions.

$$f(x) = 5x^3 - 2x^2 + x - 4 \qquad\qquad \text{Degree 3}$$

$$f(x) = -2x^4 - 5x^3 + 3x^2 + 4x - 1 \qquad \text{Degree 4}$$

$$f(x) = 3x^5 + 2x^2 - 3 \qquad\qquad \text{Degree 5}$$

REMARK   Our previous work with polynomial equations is sometimes presented as *finding zeros of polynomial functions*. The **solutions**, or **roots**, of a polynomial equation are also called the **zeros** of the polynomial function. For example, -2 and 2 are solutions of $x^2 - 4 = 0$ and they are zeros of $f(x) = x^2 - 4$; that is, $f(-2) = 0$ and $f(2) = 0$.

For a complete discussion of graphing polynomial functions, we would need some tools from calculus. However, the graphing techniques that we have discussed in this text will allow us to graph certain kinds of polynomial functions. For example, polynomial functions of the form

$$f(x) = ax^n$$

are quite easy to graph. We know from our previous work that if $n = 1$, then functions such as $f(x) = 2x$, $f(x) = -3x$, and $f(x) = \frac{1}{2}x$ are lines through the origin that have slopes of 2, -3, and $\frac{1}{2}$, respectively. Furthermore, if $n = 2$ we know that the graphs of functions of the form $f(x) = ax^2$ are parabolas symmetrical with respect to the y-axis that have their vertices at the origin.

We have also previously graphed the special case of $f(x) = ax^n$ where $a = 1$ and $n = 3$, namely, the function $f(x) = x^3$. This graph is shown in Figure 5.3. The

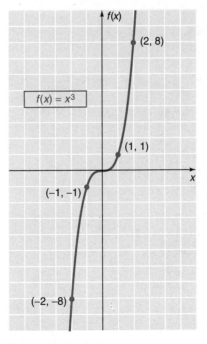

F I G U R E   5 . 3

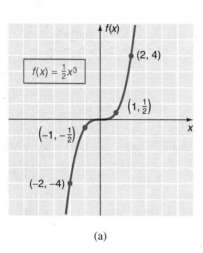

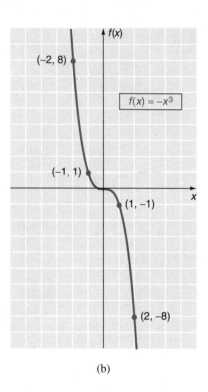

(a)   (b)

FIGURE 5.4

graphs of functions of the form $f(x) = ax^3$ for which $a \neq 1$ are slight variations of $f(x) = x^3$ and can be easily determined by plotting a few points. We have indicated the graphs of $f(x) = \frac{1}{2}x^3$ and $f(x) = -x^3$ in Figure 5.4.

There are two general patterns that emerge from studying functions of the form $f(x) = x^n$. If n is odd and greater than three, then graphs are produced that closely resemble Figure 5.3. For example, the graph of $f(x) = x^5$ is shown in Figure 5.5. Notice that it *flattens out* a little more around the origin than does the graph of

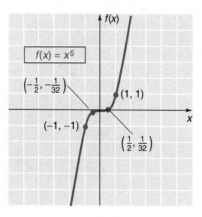

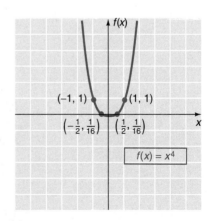

FIGURE 5.5   **FIGURE 5.6**

$f(x) = x^3$, and it increases and decreases more rapidly because of the larger exponent. If n is even and greater than two, then the graphs of $f(x) = x^n$ are not parabolas, but they do resemble the basic parabola except steeper and flatter at the bottom. Figure 5.6 shows the graph of $f(x) = x^4$.

Graphs of functions of the form $f(x) = ax^n$, where n is an integer greater than two and $a \neq 1$ are variations of those shown in Figures 5.3 and 5.6. If n is odd, then the curve is symmetrical about the origin and if n is even, the graph is symmetrical about the y-axis.

Transformations of these basic curves are easy to sketch. For example, in Figure 5.7 we translated the graph of $f(x) = x^3$ upward 2 units to produce the graph of $f(x) = x^3 + 2$. In Figure 5.8 we obtained the graph of $f(x) = (x - 1)^5$ by translating the graph of $f(x) = x^5$ one unit to the right. In Figure 5.9 we sketched the graph of $f(x) = -x^4$ as the x-axis reflection of $f(x) = x^4$.

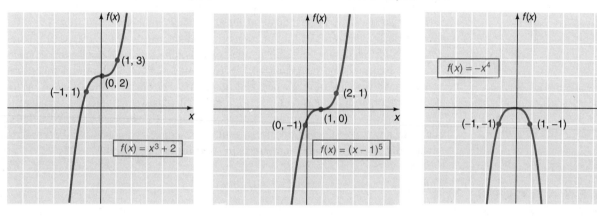

FIGURE 5.7   **FIGURE 5.8**   **FIGURE 5.9**

Graphing Polynomial Functions in Factored Form

As we mentioned earlier, a complete discussion of graphing polynomial functions of degree greater than two requires some tools from calculus. In fact, as the degree increases, the graphs often become more complicated. We do know that polynomial functions produce smooth continuous curves with a number of turning points, as illustrated in Figures 5.10 and 5.11.

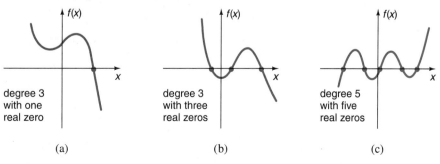

degree 3 with one real zero

degree 3 with three real zeros

degree 5 with five real zeros

(a)   (b)   (c)

FIGURE 5.10

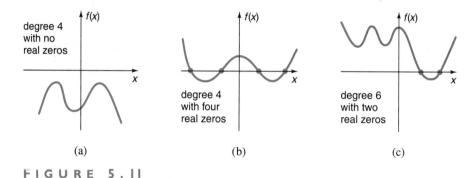

FIGURE 5.11

Some typical graphs of polynomial functions of odd degree are shown in Figure 5.10. As suggested by the graphs, every polynomial function of odd degree has at least one real zero, that is, at least one real number c such that $f(c) = 0$. Geometrically, the zeros of the function are the x-intercepts of the graph. In Figure 5.11 we illustrated some possible graphs of polynomial functions of even degree.

As indicated by the graphs in Figures 5.10 and 5.11, polynomial functions usually have **turning points** where the function either changes from increasing to decreasing or from decreasing to increasing. In calculus we are able to verify that a **polynomial function of degree n has at most $n - 1$ turning points.** Now let's illustrate how this information along with some other techniques can be used to graph polynomial functions that are expressed in factored form.

EXAMPLE 1

Graph $f(x) = (x + 2)(x - 1)(x - 3)$.

Solution

First, let's find the x-intercepts (zeros of the function) by setting each factor equal to zero and solving for x.

$$x + 2 = 0 \quad \text{or} \quad x - 1 = 0 \quad \text{or} \quad x - 3 = 0$$
$$x = -2 \quad \text{or} \quad x = 1 \quad \text{or} \quad x = 3$$

Thus, the points $(-2, 0)$, $(1, 0)$, and $(3, 0)$ are on the graph. Secondly, the points associated with the x-intercepts divide the x-axis into four intervals (Figure 5.12). In each of these intervals, $f(x)$ is either always positive or always negative. That is to say, the graph is either above or below the x-axis, which can be determined by selecting a *test value* for x in each of the intervals. Any additional points improve the accuracy of the graph. The following table summarizes the results.

FIGURE 5.12

INTERVAL	TEST VALUE	SIGN OF $f(x)$	LOCATION OF GRAPH
$x < -2$	$f(-3) = -24$	Negative	Below x-axis
$-2 < x < 1$	$f(0) = 6$	Positive	Above x-axis
$1 < x < 3$	$f(2) = -4$	Negative	Below x-axis
$x > 3$	$f(4) = 18$	Positive	Above x-axis

Additional values: $f(-1) = 8$

We use the x-intercepts and the information in the table to sketch the graph in Figure 5.13. (The points $(-3, -24)$ and $(4, 18)$ are not shown, but they indicate a rapid decrease and increase of the curve in those regions.)

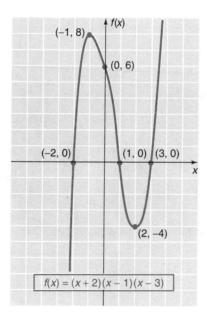

$$f(x) = (x + 2)(x - 1)(x - 3)$$

F I G U R E   5 . 13

REMARK   In Figure 5.13 we indicated that the graph turns at $(2, -4)$ and $(-1, 8)$. Keep in mind that these are approximations because we are using integers. Again, we need the tools of calculus to find the exact turning points; however, a graphing utility could be used to find very good approximations. Using a graphics calculator we found the turning points to be at approximately $(2.12, -4.06)$ and $(-0.79, 8.21)$.

EXAMPLE 2

Graph $f(x) = -x^4 + 3x^3 - 2x^2$.

Solution

The polynomial can be factored as follows.

$$f(x) = -x^4 + 3x^3 - 2x^2$$
$$= -x^2(x^2 - 3x + 2) = -x^2(x - 1)(x - 2)$$

Now we can find the x-intercepts.

$$-x^2 = 0 \quad \text{or} \quad x - 1 = 0 \quad \text{or} \quad x - 2 = 0$$
$$x = 0 \quad \text{or} \quad x = 1 \quad \text{or} \quad x = 2$$

The points $(0, 0)$, $(1, 0)$, and $(2, 0)$ are on the graph and divide the x-axis into four intervals as shown in Figure 5.14. The following table determines some points and summarizes the sign behavior of $f(x)$.

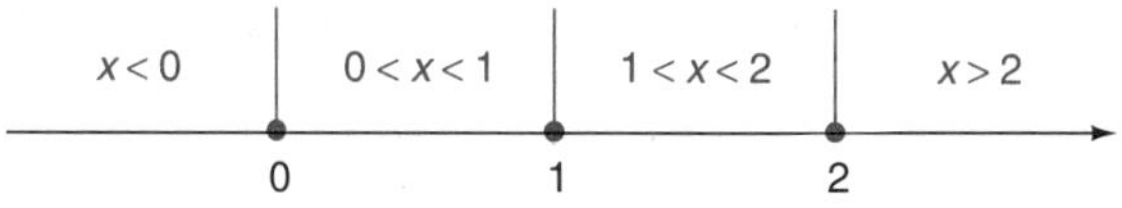

| $x < 0$ | $0 < x < 1$ | $1 < x < 2$ | $x > 2$ |

0   1   2

FIGURE 5.14

INTERVAL	TEST VALUE	SIGN OF $f(x)$	LOCATION OF GRAPH
$x < 0$	$f(-1) = -6$	Negative	Below x-axis
$0 < x < 1$	$f(\frac{1}{2}) = -\frac{3}{16}$	Negative	Below x-axis
$1 < x < 2$	$f(\frac{3}{2}) = \frac{9}{16}$	Positive	Above x-axis
$x > 2$	$f(3) = -18$	Negative	Below x-axis

We use the table and the x-intercepts to sketch the graph in Figure 5.15.

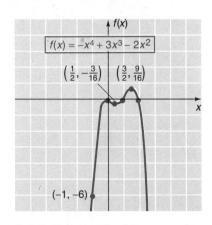

$f(x) = -x^4 + 3x^3 - 2x^2$

$\left(\frac{1}{2}, -\frac{3}{16}\right)$ $\left(\frac{3}{2}, \frac{9}{16}\right)$

$(-1, -6)$

FIGURE 5.15

EXAMPLE 3

Graph $f(x) = x^3 + 3x^2 - 4$.

Solution

Use the rational root theorem, synthetic division, and the factor theorem to factor the given polynomial as follows.

$$f(x) = x^3 + 3x^2 - 4$$

$$= (x - 1)(x^2 + 4x + 4) = (x - 1)(x + 2)^2$$

Now we can find the x-intercepts.

$$x - 1 = 0 \quad \text{or} \quad (x + 2)^2 = 0$$

$$x = 1 \quad \text{or} \quad x = -2$$

The points $(-2, 0)$ and $(1, 0)$ are on the graph and divide the x-axis into three intervals as in Figure 5.16. The following table determines some points and summarizes the sign behavior of $f(x)$.

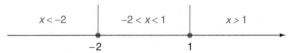

FIGURE 5.16

INTERVAL	TEST VALUE	SIGN OF $f(x)$	LOCATION OF GRAPH
$x < -2$	$f(-3) = -4$	Negative	Below x-axis
$-2 < x < 1$	$f(0) = -4$	Negative	Below x-axis
$x > 1$	$f(2) = 16$	Positive	Above x-axis
Additional values:	$f(-1) = -2$	$f(-4) = -20$	

As a result of the table and the x-intercepts, we can sketch the graph as in Figure 5.17.

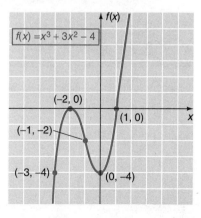

FIGURE 5.17

Finally, let's use a graphical approach to solve a problem that involves a polynomial function.

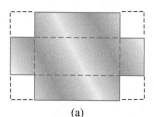

EXAMPLE 4

Suppose that we have a rectangular piece of cardboard that measures 20 inches by 14 inches. From each corner a square piece is cut out and then the flaps are turned up to form an open box (see Figure 5.18). Determine the length of a side of the square pieces to be cut out so that the volume of the box is as large as possible.

Solution

Let x represent the length of a side of the squares to be cut from each corner. Then $20 - 2x$ represents the length of the open box and $14 - 2x$ represents the width. The volume of a rectangular box is given by the formula $V = lwh$. So the volume of this box can be represented by the function $V(x) = x(20 - 2x)(14 - 2x)$. Figure 5.19 shows the graph of this function. For this problem we are only interested in the part of the graph between $x = 0$ and $x = 7$ because the length of a side of the squares has to be less than 7 inches for a box to be formed. Figure 5.20 gives us a view of that part of the graph. Now we can use the zoom and trace features to

(a)

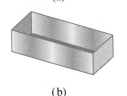

(b)

FIGURE 5.18

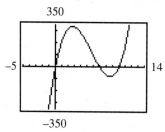

FIGURE 5.19

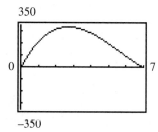

FIGURE 5.20

determine that when x equals approximately 2.7 the value of $f(x)$ is a maximum of approximately 339.0. Thus, square pieces of length approximately 2.7 inches on a side should be cut from each corner of the rectangular piece of cardboard. The open box formed will have a volume of approximately 339.0 cubic inches. ▬▬▬

PROBLEM SET 5.3

Graph each of the following polynomial functions.

1. $f(x) = x^3 - 3$

2. $f(x) = (x + 1)^3$

3. $f(x) = (x - 2)^3 + 1$

4. $f(x) = -(x - 3)^3$

5. $f(x) = x^4 - 2$

6. $f(x) = (x + 3)^4$

7. $f(x) = (x + 1)^4 + 3$

8. $f(x) = -x^5$

9. $f(x) = (x - 1)^5 + 2$

10. $f(x) = -(x - 2)^4$

11. $f(x) = (x - 1)(x + 1)(x - 3)$

12. $f(x) = (x - 2)(x + 1)(x + 3)$

13. $f(x) = (x + 4)(x + 1)(1 - x)$

14. $f(x) = x(x + 2)(2 - x)$

15. $f(x) = -x(x + 3)(x - 2)$

16. $f(x) = -x^2(x - 1)(x + 1)$

17. $f(x) = (x + 3)(x + 1)(x - 1)(x - 2)$

18. $f(x) = (2x - 1)(x - 2)(x - 3)$

19. $f(x) = (x - 1)^2(x + 2)$

20. $f(x) = (x + 2)^3(x - 4)$

21. $f(x) = (x + 1)^2(x - 1)^2$

22. $f(x) = x(x - 2)^2(x + 1)$

Graph each of the following polynomial functions by first factoring the given polynomial. You may need to use some factoring techniques from Chapter 1 as well as the rational root theorem and the factor theorem.

23. $f(x) = x^3 + x^2 - 2x$

24. $f(x) = -x^3 - x^2 + 6x$

25. $f(x) = -x^4 - 3x^3 - 2x^2$

26. $f(x) = x^4 - 6x^3 + 8x^2$

27. $f(x) = x^3 - x^2 - 4x + 4$

28. $f(x) = x^3 + 2x^2 - x - 2$

29. $f(x) = x^3 - 13x + 12$

30. $f(x) = x^3 - x^2 - 9x + 9$

31. $f(x) = x^3 - 2x^2 - 11x + 12$

32. $f(x) = 2x^3 - 3x^2 - 3x + 2$

33. $f(x) = -x^3 + 6x^2 - 11x + 6$

34. $f(x) = x^4 - 5x^2 + 4$

For each of the following, (a) find the y-intercepts, (b) find the x-intercepts, and (c) find the intervals of x for which $f(x) > 0$ and for which $f(x) < 0$. **Do not** sketch the graph.

35. $f(x) = (x - 5)(x + 4)(x - 3)$

36. $f(x) = (x + 3)(x - 6)(8 - x)$

37. $f(x) = (x - 4)^2(x + 3)^3$

38. $f(x) = (x + 3)^4(x - 1)^3$

39. $f(x) = (x + 2)^2(x - 1)^3(x - 2)$

40. $f(x) = x(x - 6)^2(x + 4)$

41. $f(x) = (x + 2)^5(x - 4)^2$

THOUGHTS into WORDS

42. Explain how you would go about graphing

$$f(x) = -(x - 1)(x + 2)^3.$$

43. Suppose that someone indicated that the graph of $f(x) = (x + 1)^2(x - 2)^2$ is shown in Figure 5.21. How do you know that this graph is incorrect?

44. Explain why a polynomial function of odd degree must have at least one real zero.

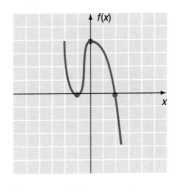

FIGURE 5.21

FURTHER INVESTIGATIONS

45. A polynomial function with real coefficients is continuous everywhere; that is, its graph has no holes or breaks. This fact is the basis for the following property: If $f(x)$ is a polynomial with real coefficients, and if $f(a)$ and $f(b)$ are of opposite sign, then there is at least one real zero between a and b. This property, along with our previous knowledge of polynomial functions, provides the basis for locating and approximating irrational solutions of a polynomial equation.

Consider the equation $x^3 + 2x - 4 = 0$. Applying Descartes' rule of signs, we can determine that this equation has 1 positive real solution and 2 nonreal complex solutions. (You may want to confirm this!) The rational root theorem indicates that the only possible positive rational solutions are 1, 2, and 4. Using a little more compact format for synthetic division, we obtain the following results when testing for 1 and 2 as possible solutions.

	1	0	2	-4
1	1	1	3	-1
2	1	2	6	8

Since $f(1) = -1$ and $f(2) = 8$, there must be an irrational solution between 1 and 2. Furthermore, since -1 is closer to 0 than 8, our guess is that the solution is closer to 1 than to 2. Let's start looking at 1.0, 1.1, 1.2, etc. until we can fit the solution between two numbers.

	1	0	2	-4
1.0	1	1	3	-1
1.1	1	1.1	3.21	-.469
1.2	1	1.2	3.44	.128

A calculator is very helpful at this time.

Since $f(1.1) = -.469$ and $f(1.2) = .128$, the irrational solution must be between 1.1 and 1.2. Furthermore, since .128 is closer to 0 than $-.469$, our guess is that the solu-

tion is closer to 1.2 than to 1.1. Let's start looking at 1.15, 1.16, etc.

	1	0	2	-4
1.15	1	1.15	3.3225	-.179
1.16	1	1.16	3.3456	-.119
1.17	1	1.17	3.3689	-.058
1.18	1	1.18	3.3924	.003

Since $f(1.17) = -.058$ and $f(1.18) = .003$, the irrational solution must be between 1.17 and 1.18. Therefore, we can use 1.2 as a rational approximation to the nearest tenth.

For each of the following equations, (a) verify that the equation has exactly one irrational solution, and (b) find an approximation, to the nearest tenth, of that solution.

a. $x^3 + x - 6 = 0$

b. $x^3 + 6x + 4 = 0$

c. $x^3 + 27x + 18 = 0$

d. $x^3 - x^2 - x - 1 = 0$

e. $x^3 + 24x - 32 = 0$

f. $x^3 + 5x^2 + 3 = 0$

 GRAPHICS CALCULATOR ACTIVITIES

46. Graph $f(x) = x^3$. Now predict the graphs for $f(x) = x^3 + 2$, $f(x) = -x^3 + 2$, and $f(x) = -x^3 - 2$. Graph these three functions on the same set of axes with the graph of $f(x) = x^3$.

47. Draw a rough sketch of the graphs of the functions $f(x) = x^3 - x^2$, $f(x) = -x^3 + x^2$, and $f(x) = -x^3 - x^2$. Now graph these three functions to check your sketches.

48. Graph $f(x) = x^4 + x^3 + x^2$. What should the graphs of $f(x) = x^4 - x^3 + x^2$ and $f(x) = -x^4 - x^3 - x^2$ look like? Graph them to see if you were right.

49. How should the graphs of $f(x) = x^3$, $f(x) = x^5$, and $f(x) = x^7$ compare? Graph these three functions on the same set of axes.

50. How should the graphs of $f(x) = x^2$, $f(x) = x^4$, and $f(x) = x^6$ compare? Graph these three functions on the same set of axes.

51. For each of the following functions, find the x-intercepts and find the intervals of x where $f(x) > 0$ and those where $f(x) < 0$.

a. $f(x) = x^3 - 3x^2 - 6x + 8$

b. $f(x) = x^3 - 8x^2 - x + 8$

c. $f(x) = x^3 - 7x^2 + 16x - 12$

d. $f(x) = x^3 - 19x^2 + 90x - 72$

e. $f(x) = x^4 + 3x^3 - 3x^2 - 11x - 6$

f. $f(x) = x^4 + 12x^2 - 64$

52. Find the coordinates of the turning points of each of the following graphs. Express x- and y-values to the nearest integer.

a. $f(x) = 2x^3 - 3x^2 - 12x + 40$

b. $f(x) = 2x^3 - 33x^2 + 60x + 1050$

c. $f(x) = -2x^3 - 9x^2 + 24x + 100$

d. $f(x) = x^4 - 4x^3 - 2x^2 + 12x + 3$

e. $f(x) = x^3 - 30x^2 + 288x - 900$

f. $f(x) = x^5 - 2x^4 - 3x^3 - 2x^2 + x - 1$

53. For each of the following functions, find the x-intercepts and find the turning points. Express your answers to the nearest tenth.

a. $f(x) = x^3 + 2x^2 - 3x + 4$

b. $f(x) = 42x^3 - x^2 - 246x - 35$

c. $f(x) = x^4 - 4x^2 - 4$

54. A rectangular piece of cardboard is 13 inches long and 9 inches wide. From each corner a square piece is cut out and then the flaps are turned up to form an open box. Determine the length of a side of the square pieces so that the volume of the box is as large as possible.

55. A company determines that its weekly profit from manufacturing and selling x units of a certain item is given by $P(x) = -x^3 + 3x^2 + 2880x - 500$. What weekly production rate will maximize the profit?

56. A slice of thickness 1 inch is cut off from one side of a cube. If the volume of the remaining figure is 48 cubic inches, find the length of an edge of the original cube.

5.4 GRAPHING RATIONAL FUNCTIONS

A function of the form

$$f(x) = \frac{p(x)}{q(x)}, \qquad q(x) \neq 0,$$

where $p(x)$ and $q(x)$ are polynomial functions, is called a **rational function**. The following are examples of rational functions.

$$f(x) = \frac{2}{x-1}, \qquad f(x) = \frac{x}{x-2}, \qquad f(x) = \frac{x^2}{x^2 - x - 6}, \qquad f(x) = \frac{x^3 - 8}{x + 4}$$

In each example the domain of the rational function is the set of all real numbers except for those that make the denominator zero. For example, the domain of $f(x) = 2/(x - 1)$ is the set of all real numbers except 1. As we will soon see, these exclusions from the domain are important numbers from a graphing standpoint. They represent breaks in an otherwise continuous curve.

Let's set the stage for graphing rational functions by considering in detail the function $f(x) = 1/x$. First, note that at $x = 0$, the function is undefined. Second, let's consider a rather extensive table of values to show some number trends and to build a basis for defining the concept of an asymptote.

REMARK We have introduced some symbolism that is not absolutely necessary for our work in this text. However, symbolism of this type is commonly used in calculus and therefore it is to your advantage to become familiar with it now.

x	$f(x) = \dfrac{1}{x}$	
1	1	
2	.5	These values indicate that $f(x)$ is approaching zero from above as x increases without bound. Symbolically, we write $f(x) \to 0^+$ as $x \to \infty$.
10	.1	
100	.01	
1000	.001	
.5	2	
1	10	These values indicate that $f(x)$ is increasing without bound as x approaches zero from the right. Symbolically, we write $f(x) \to \infty$ as $x \to 0^+$.
.01	100	
.001	1000	
.0001	10,000	
−.5	−2	
−.1	−10	These values indicate that $f(x)$ is decreasing without bound as x approaches zero from the left. Symbolically, we write $f(x) \to -\infty$ as $x \to 0^-$.
−.01	−100	
−.001	−1000	
−.0001	−10,000	
−1	−1	
−2	−.5	These values indicate that $f(x)$ is approaching zero from below as x decreases without bound. Symbolically, we write $f(x) \to 0^-$ as $x \to -\infty$.
−10	−.1	
−100	−.01	
−1000	−.001	

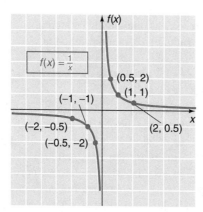

F I G U R E   5 . 2 2

We used a few points from this table and the patterns we discussed to sketch $f(x) = 1/x$ as shown in Figure 5.22. Notice that the graph approaches, but does not touch, either axis. We say that the y-axis (or $f(x)$-axis) is a **vertical asymptote** and the x-axis is a **horizontal asymptote**. In general, the following definitions can be given.

REMARK We should recognize that the equation $f(x) = 1/x$ exhibits origin symmetry because $f(-x) = -f(x)$. Thus, the graph in Figure 5.22 could have been drawn by first determining the part of the curve in the first quadrant and then reflecting that part through the origin.

Vertical Asymptote

A line $x = a$ is a vertical asymptote for the graph of a function f if

1. $f(x)$ either increases or decreases without bound as x approaches the number a from the right as in Figure 5.23.

2. $f(x)$ either increases or decreases without bound as x approaches the number a from the left as in Figure 5.24.

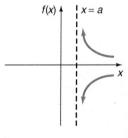

FIGURE 5.23

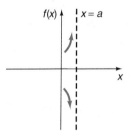

FIGURE 5.24

Horizontal Asymptote

A line $y = b$ (or $f(x) = b$) is a horizontal asymptote for the graph of a function f if

1. $f(x)$ approaches the number b from above or below as x decreases without bound as in Figure 5.25.

2. $f(x)$ approaches the number b from above or below as x increases without bound as in Figure 5.26.

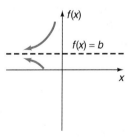

FIGURE 5.25

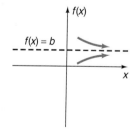

FIGURE 5.26

To graph rational functions of the type we're considering in this section we would offer the following suggestions.

1. Check for y-axis and origin symmetry.

2. Find any vertical asymptote by setting the denominator equal to zero and solving for x.

3. Find any horizontal asymptote by studying the behavior of $f(x)$ as x increases or decreases without bound.

4. Study the behavior of the graph when it is close to the asymptotes.

5. Plot as many points as necessary to determine the shape of the graph. (The x- and y-intercepts, if they exist, may be easy to find.) The number of points needed may be affected by whether or not the graph has any kind of symmetry.

Keep these suggestions in mind as you study the following examples.

EXAMPLE 1

Graph $f(x) = \dfrac{-2}{x - 1}$.

Solution

Since $x = 1$ makes the denominator zero, the line $x = 1$ is a vertical asymptote, which we indicated with a dashed line in Figure 5.27. Now let's look for a horizontal asymptote by checking some large and small values of x.

x	$f(x)$	
10	$-\frac{2}{9}$	
100	$-\frac{2}{99}$	this portion of the table shows that $f(x) \rightarrow 0^+$ as $x \rightarrow -\infty$
1000	$-\frac{2}{999}$	
-10	$\frac{2}{11}$	
-100	$\frac{2}{101}$	this portion of the table shows that $f(x) \rightarrow 0^-$ as $x \rightarrow \infty$
-1000	$\frac{2}{1001}$	

Therefore, the x-axis is a horizontal asymptote. Finally, let's check the behavior of the graph near the vertical asymptote.

x	$f(x)$	
2	-2	
1.5	-4	
1.1	-20	$f(x) \rightarrow -\infty$ as $x \rightarrow 1^+$
1.01	-200	
1.001	-2000	
0	2	
.5	4	
.9	20	$f(x) \rightarrow \infty$ as $x \rightarrow 1^-$
.99	200	
.999	2000	

The graph of $f(x) = -2/(x - 1)$ is shown in Figure 5.27.

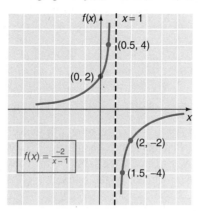

F I G U R E 5 . 2 7

EXAMPLE 2

Graph $f(x) = \dfrac{x}{x + 2}$.

Solution

Since $x = -2$ makes the denominator zero, the line $x = -2$ is a vertical asymptote. To study the denominator of $f(x)$ as x gets very large or very small, let's change the form of the rational expression by dividing the numerator and denominator by x.

$$f(x) = \frac{x}{x + 2}$$

$$= \frac{\dfrac{x}{x}}{\dfrac{x + 2}{x}} = \frac{1}{\dfrac{x}{x} + \dfrac{2}{x}} = \frac{1}{1 + \dfrac{2}{x}}$$

Now we can see that (1) $f(x) \to 1^-$ as $x \to \infty$ and (2) $f(x) \to 1^+$ as $x \to -\infty$. Thus, the line $f(x) = 1$ is a horizontal asymptote. Draw the asymptotes (dashed lines) and plot a few points to complete the graph in Figure 5.28.

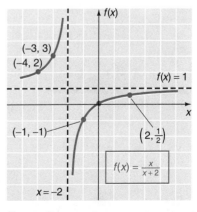

F I G U R E 5 . 2 8

In the next two examples, pay special attention to the role of symmetry. It will allow us to direct our efforts on quadrants I and IV and then to reflect that portion of the curve across the vertical axis to complete the graph.

EXAMPLE 3

Graph $f(x) = \dfrac{2x^2}{x^2 + 4}$.

Solution

First, notice that $f(-x) = f(x)$; therefore, this graph is symmetrical with respect to the vertical axis. Secondly, the denominator $x^2 + 4$ cannot equal zero for any real number values of x. Thus, there is no vertical asymptote. Thirdly, dividing both numerator and denominator of the rational expression by x^2 produces

$$f(x) = \frac{2x^2}{x^2 + 4}$$

$$= \frac{\dfrac{2x^2}{x^2}}{\dfrac{x^2 + 4}{x^2}} = \frac{2}{\dfrac{x^2}{x^2} + \dfrac{4}{x^2}} = \frac{2}{1 + \dfrac{4}{x^2}}.$$

Now we can see that $f(x) \to 2^-$ as $x \to \infty$. Therefore, the line $f(x) = 2$ is a horizontal asymptote. So we can plot a few points using positive values for x, sketch this part of the curve, and then reflect across the $f(x)$-axis to obtain the complete graph as shown in Figure 5.29.

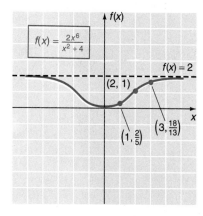

$$f(x) = \frac{2x^6}{x^2 + 4}$$

$f(x) = 2$

$(2, 1)$

$\left(1, \frac{2}{5}\right)$ $\left(3, \frac{18}{13}\right)$

FIGURE 5.29

EXAMPLE 4

Graph $f(x) = \dfrac{3}{x^2 - 4}$.

Solution

First, notice that $f(-x) = f(x)$; therefore, this graph is symmetrical about the $f(x)$-axis. Secondly, by setting the denominator equal to zero and solving for x, we obtain

$$x^2 - 4 = 0$$

$$x^2 = 4$$

$$x = \pm 2.$$

The lines $x = 2$ and $x = -2$ are vertical asymptotes. Next, we can see that $f(x) \to 0^+$ as $x \to \infty$, $f(x) \to \infty$ as $x \to 2^+$, and $f(x) \to -\infty$ as $x \to 2^-$. Finally, we can plot a few points using positive values for x (not 2), sketch this part of the curve, and then reflect it across the $f(x)$-axis to obtain the complete graph as shown in Figure 5.30.

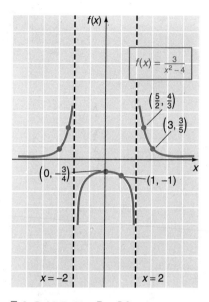

F I G U R E   5 . 30

Now suppose that we use a graphing utility to obtain a graph of the function $f(x) = 4x^2/(x^4 - 16)$. Before we enter this function into a graphing utility, let's analyze what we know about the graph.

1. Since $f(0) = 0$, the origin is a point on the graph.

2. Since $f(-x) = f(x)$, the graph is symmetric with respect to the y-axis.

3. By setting the denominator equal to zero and solving for x, we can determine the vertical asymptotes.

$$x^4 - 16 = 0$$
$$(x^2 + 4)(x^2 - 4) = 0$$
$$x^2 + 4 = 0 \qquad \text{or} \qquad x^2 - 4 = 0$$
$$x^2 = -4 \qquad \text{or} \qquad x^2 = 4$$
$$x = \pm 2i \qquad \text{or} \qquad x = \pm 2$$

Remember that we are working with ordered pairs of real numbers. Thus, the lines $x = -2$ and $x = 2$ are vertical asymptotes.

4. Dividing both the numerator and denominator of the rational expression by x^4 produces

$$\frac{4x^2}{x^4 - 16} = \frac{\dfrac{4x^2}{x^4}}{\dfrac{x^4 - 16}{x^4}}$$

$$= \frac{\dfrac{4}{x^2}}{1 - \dfrac{16}{x^4}}.$$

From the last expression, we see that as $|x|$ gets larger and larger, the value of $f(x)$ approaches zero from above. Therefore, the x-axis is a horizontal asymptote,

Let's enter the function in a graphing utility and obtain a graph as shown in Figure 5.31. Note that the graph is consistent with the information we gathered before using the graphing utility. In other words, our knowledge of graphing techniques enhances our use of a graphing utility.

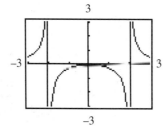

FIGURE 5.31

REMARK   In Figure 5.31 the origin is a point of the graph on the horizontal asymptote. More will be said about such situations in the next section.

Back in Problem Set 1.5 you were asked to solve the following problem: How much pure alcohol should be added to 6 liters of a 40% alcohol solution to raise it to a 60% alcohol solution? The answer of 3 liters can be found by solving the following equation, where x represents the amount of pure alcohol to be added.

Pure alcohol to start with	+	Pure alcohol added	=	Pure alcohol in final solution
↓		↓		↓
$.40(6)$	$+$	x	$=$	$.60(6 + x)$

Now let's consider this problem in a more general setting so that we can answer the various questions that surface regarding the given information. Again using x to represent the amount of pure alcohol to be added, the rational expression $\dfrac{2.4 + x}{6 + x}$ represents the concentration of pure alcohol in the final solution. Let's graph the rational function $f(x) = \dfrac{2.4 + x}{6 + x}$ as shown in Figure 5.32.

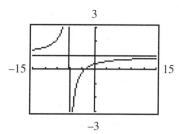

F I G U R E 5 . 32

For this particular situation, x is nonnegative, so we are only interested in the part of the graph that is in the first quadrant. Changing the boundaries of the viewing rectangle so that $0 \le x \le 15$ and $0 \le y \le 2$, we obtain Figure 5.33. Now we are ready to answer various questions about this situation.

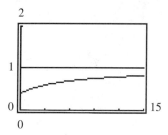

F I G U R E 5 . 33

1. How much pure alcohol needs to be added to raise the 40% solution to a 60% solution? (*Answer:* Using the trace feature of the graphing utility we find that $y = .6$ when $x = 3$. Therefore, 3 liters of pure alcohol needs to be added.)

2. How much pure alcohol needs to be added to raise the 40% solution to a 70% solution? (*Answer:* Using the trace feature we find that $y = .7$ when $x = 6$. Therefore, 6 liters of pure alcohol need to be added.)

3. What percent of alcohol do we have if we add 9 liters of pure alcohol to the 6 liters of a 40% solution? (*Answer:* Using the trace feature we find that $y = .76$ when $x = 9$. Therefore, adding 9 liters of pure alcohol will give us a 76% alcohol solution.)

PROBLEM SET 5.4

Graph each of the following rational functions.

1. $f(x) = \dfrac{-1}{x}$

2. $f(x) = \dfrac{1}{x^2}$

3. $f(x) = \dfrac{3}{x + 1}$

4. $f(x) = \dfrac{-1}{x - 3}$

5. $f(x) = \dfrac{2}{(x - 1)^2}$

6. $f(x) = \dfrac{-3}{(x + 2)^2}$

7. $f(x) = \dfrac{x}{x - 3}$

8. $f(x) = \dfrac{2x}{x - 1}$

9. $f(x) = \dfrac{-3x}{x + 2}$

10. $f(x) = \dfrac{-x}{x + 1}$

11. $f(x) = \dfrac{1}{x^2 - 1}$

12. $f(x) = \dfrac{-2}{x^2 - 4}$

13. $f(x) = \dfrac{-2}{(x + 1)(x - 2)}$

14. $f(x) = \dfrac{3}{(x + 2)(x - 4)}$

15. $f(x) = \dfrac{2}{x^2 + x - 2}$

16. $f(x) = \dfrac{-1}{x^2 + x - 6}$

17. $f(x) = \dfrac{x + 2}{x}$

18. $f(x) = \dfrac{2x - 1}{x}$

19. $f(x) = \dfrac{4}{x^2 + 2}$

20. $f(x) = \dfrac{4x^2}{x^2 + 1}$

21. $f(x) = \dfrac{2x^4}{x^4 + 1}$

22. $f(x) = \dfrac{x^2 - 4}{x^2}$

23. The rational function $f(x) = [(x - 2)(x + 3)]/(x - 2)$ has a domain of all real numbers except 2 and can be simplified to $f(x) = x + 3$. Thus, its graph is a straight line with a hole at $(2, 5)$. Graph each of the following functions.

a. $f(x) = \dfrac{(x + 4)(x - 1)}{x + 4}$

b. $f(x) = \dfrac{x^2 - 5x + 6}{x - 2}$

c. $f(x) = \dfrac{x - 1}{x^2 - 1}$

d. $f(x) = \dfrac{x + 2}{x^2 + 6x + 8}$

GRAPHICS CALCULATOR ACTIVITIES

24. Use a graphics calculator to check your graphs for Problem 23. What feature of the graph does not show up on the calculator?

25. Each of the following graphs is a transformation of $f(x) = 1/x$. First, predict the general shape and location of the graph and then check your prediction with a graphics calculator.

a. $f(x) = \dfrac{1}{x} - 2$

b. $f(x) = \dfrac{1}{x + 3}$

c. $f(x) = -\dfrac{1}{x}$

d. $f(x) = \dfrac{1}{x - 2} + 3$

e. $f(x) = \dfrac{2x + 1}{x}$

26. Graph $f(x) = \dfrac{1}{x^2}$. How should the graphs of $f(x) = \dfrac{1}{(x - 4)^2}, f(x) = \dfrac{1 + 3x^2}{x^2}$, and $f(x) = -\dfrac{1}{x^2}$ compare to the graph of $f(x) = \dfrac{1}{x^2}$? Graph the three functions on the same set of axes with the graph of $f(x) = \dfrac{1}{x^2}$.

27. Graph $f(x) = \dfrac{1}{x^3}$. How should the graphs of $f(x) = \dfrac{2x^3 + 1}{x^3}, f(x) = \dfrac{1}{(x + 2)^3}$, and $f(x) = -\dfrac{1}{x^3}$ compare to the graph of $f(x) = \dfrac{1}{x^3}$? Graph the three functions on the same set of axes with the graph of $f(x) = \dfrac{1}{x^3}$.

28. Use a graphics calculator to check your graphs for Problems 19–22.

29. Graph each of the following functions. Be sure that you get a complete graph for each one. Sketch each graph on a sheet of paper and keep them handy as you study the next section.

a. $f(x) = \dfrac{x^2}{x^2 - x - 2}$ **b.** $f(x) = \dfrac{x}{x^2 - 4}$

c. $f(x) = \dfrac{3x}{x^2 + 1}$ **d.** $f(x) = \dfrac{x^2 - 1}{x - 2}$

30. Suppose that x ounces of pure acid were added to 14 ounces of a 15% acid solution.

a. Set up the rational expression that represents the concentration of pure acid in the final solution.

b. Graph the rational function that displays the level of concentration.

c. How many ounces of pure acid need to be added to the 14 ounces of a 15% solution to raise it to a 40.5% solution? Check your answer.

d. How many ounces of pure acid need to be added to the 14 ounces of a 15% solution to raise it to a 50% solution? Check your answer.

e. What percent of acid do we obtain if we add 12 ounces of pure acid to the 14 ounces of a 15% solution? Check your answer.

31. Solve the following problem both algebraically and graphically: One solution contains 50% alcohol and another solution contains 80% alcohol. How many liters of each solution should be mixed to produce 10.5 liters of a 70% alcohol solution? Check your answer.

5.5 MORE ON GRAPHING RATIONAL FUNCTIONS

The rational functions that we studied in the previous section behaved rather well. In fact, once we established the vertical and horizontal asymptotes, a little bit of point plotting usually determined the graph easily—this is not always the case with rational functions. In this section we want to investigate some rational functions that behave a little differently.

Since vertical asymptotes occur at values of x for which the denominator is zero, there can be no points of a graph on a vertical asymptote. However, recall that horizontal asymptotes are created by the behavior of $f(x)$ as x increases or decreases without bound. This does not restrict the possibility that for some values of x, there will be points of the graph on the horizontal asymptote. Let's consider some examples.

EXAMPLE 1

Graph

$$f(x) = \frac{x^2}{x^2 - x - 2}.$$

Solution

First, let's identify the vertical asymptotes by setting the denominator equal to zero and solving for x.

$$x^2 - x - 2 = 0$$

$$(x - 2)(x + 1) = 0$$

$$x - 2 = 0 \quad \text{or} \quad x + 1 = 0$$

$$x = 2 \quad \text{or} \quad x = -1$$

Thus, the lines $x = 2$ and $x = -1$ are vertical asymptotes. Secondly, we can divide both numerator and denominator of the rational expression by x^2.

$$f(x) = \frac{x^2}{x^2 - x - 2} = \frac{\dfrac{x^2}{x^2}}{\dfrac{x^2 - x - 2}{x^2}} = \frac{1}{1 - \dfrac{1}{x} - \dfrac{2}{x^2}}$$

Now we can see that $f(x) \to 1^+$ as $x \to \infty$. Thus, the line $f(x) = 1$ is a horizontal asymptote. To determine if any points of the graph are on the horizontal asymptote, we can see if the equation

$$\frac{x^2}{x^2 - x - 2} = 1$$

has any solutions.

$$\frac{x^2}{x^2 - x - 2} = 1$$

$$x^2 = x^2 - x - 2$$

$$0 = -x - 2$$

$$x = -2$$

Therefore, the point $(-2, 1)$ is on the graph. Now by drawing the asymptotes, plotting a few points including $(-2, 1)$, and studying the behavior of the function close to the asymptotes, we can sketch the curve in Figure 5.34. Notice that the left branch of the curve crosses the horizontal asymptote, $f(x) = 1$, at the point $(-2, 1)$ and then approaches it from below as x decreases without bound.

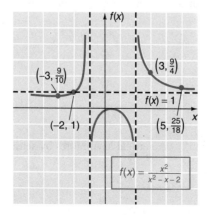

FIGURE 5.34

EXAMPLE 2   Graph $f(x) = \dfrac{x}{x^2 - 4}$.

Solution

First, notice that $f(-x) = -f(x)$; therefore, this graph has origin symmetry. Second, let's identify the vertical asymptotes.

$$x^2 - 4 = 0$$

$$x^2 = 4$$

$$x = \pm 2$$

Thus, the lines $x = -2$ and $x = 2$ are vertical asymptotes. Next, by dividing the numerator and denominator of the rational expression by x^2 we obtain

$$f(x) = \frac{x}{x^2 - 4} = \frac{\dfrac{x}{x^2}}{\dfrac{x^2 - 4}{x^2}}$$

$$= \frac{\dfrac{1}{x}}{1 - \dfrac{4}{x^2}}.$$

From this form we see that $f(x) \to 0^+$ as $x \to \infty$. Therefore, the x-axis is a horizontal asymptote. Since $f(0) = 0$, we know that the origin is a point of the graph. Finally, by concentrating our point plotting on positive values for x, we can sketch the portion of the curve to the right of the vertical axis and then use the fact that the graph is symmetric with respect to the origin to complete the graph in Figure 5.35.

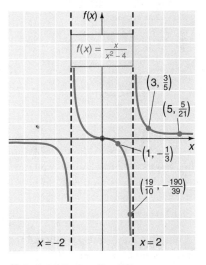

FIGURE 5.35

EXAMPLE 3

Graph $f(x) = \dfrac{3x}{x^2 + 1}$.

Solution

First, observe that $f(-x) = -f(x)$; therefore, this graph is also symmetrical with respect to the origin. Second, since $x^2 + 1$ is a positive number for all real number values of x, there are no vertical asymptotes for this graph. Third, by dividing the numerator and denominator of the rational expression by x^2 we obtain

$$f(x) = \frac{3x}{x^2 + 1} = \frac{\dfrac{3x}{x^2}}{\dfrac{x^2 + 1}{x^2}} = \frac{\dfrac{3}{x}}{1 + \dfrac{1}{x^2}}.$$

We can see that $f(x) \to 0^+$ as $x \to \infty$. Thus, the x-axis is a horizontal asymptote. Since $f(0) = 0$, the origin is a point of the graph. Finally, by concentrating our point plotting on positive values for x, we can sketch the portion of the curve to the right of the vertical axis and then use origin symmetry to complete the graph in Figure 5.36.

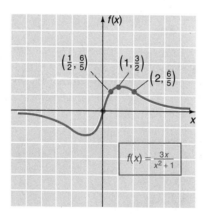

FIGURE 5.36

REMARK   Yes, Figure 5.36 should look familiar. We graphed a function like this back in Chapter 3 before any formal introduction to asymptotes had been presented. At that time it required plotting of many more points.

Oblique Asymptotes

Thus far, we have restricted our study of rational functions to those where the degree of the numerator is less than or equal to the degree of the denominator. Now let's consider a function where the degree of the numerator is one greater than the degree of the denominator.

E X A M P L E 4

Graph

$$f(x) = \frac{x^2 - 1}{x - 2}.$$

Solution

First, let's observe that $x = 2$ is a vertical asymptote. Secondly, since the degree of the numerator is greater than the degree of the denominator, we can change the form of the rational expression by division. Using synthetic division we obtain

$$\begin{array}{r} 2\underline{\smash{\big|}\,1 \quad\; 0 \quad -1} \\ 2 \quad\;\; 4. \\ \hline 1 \quad\; 2 \quad\;\; 3 \end{array}$$

Therefore, the original function can be written as

$$f(x) = \frac{x^2 - 1}{x - 2} = x + 2 + \frac{3}{x - 2}.$$

Now for very large values of $|x|$ the fraction $3/(x - 2)$ is close to zero. Therefore, the graph of $f(x) = x + 2 + 3/(x - 2)$ will get closer and closer to the line $f(x) = x + 2$. We call the line an **oblique asymptote** and we indicate it with a dashed line in Figure 5.37. Finally, since this is a new situation for us, it may be necessary to plot a large number of points on both sides of the vertical asymptote. So let's make an extensive table of values.

x	$f(x) = \dfrac{x^2 - 1}{x - 2}$
2.1	34.1
2.5	10.5
3	8
4	7.5
5	8
6	8.75
10	12.375

These values indicate the behavior of $f(x)$ to the right of the vertical asymptote $x = 2$.

x	$f(x)$
1.9	-26.1
1.5	-2.5
1	0
0	.5
-1	0
-3	-1.6
-5	-3.4
-10	-8.25

These values indicate the behavior of $f(x)$ to the left of the vertical asymptote $x = 2$.

The graph of this function is shown in Figure 5.37.

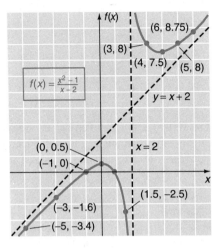

If the degree of the numerator of a rational function is *exactly one more* than the degree of its denominator, then the graph of the function has an oblique asymptote. (If the graph is a line, which is the case with $f(x) = \dfrac{(x-2)(x+1)}{x-2}$, then we consider it to be its own asymptote.) As in Example 4, we find the equation of the oblique asymptote by changing the form of the function using long division. Let's consider another example.

EXAMPLE 5

Graph $f(x) = \dfrac{x^2 - x - 2}{x - 1}$.

Solution

From the given form of the function, we see that $x = 1$ is a vertical asymptote. Then, by factoring the numerator, we can change the form to

$$f(x) = \frac{(x-2)(x+1)}{(x-1)},$$

which indicates x-intercepts of 2 and -1. Then, by long division, we can change the original form of the function to

$$f(x) = x - \frac{2}{x-1},$$

which indicates an oblique asymptote $f(x) = x$. Finally, by plotting a few additional points, we can determine the graph as shown in Figure 5.38.

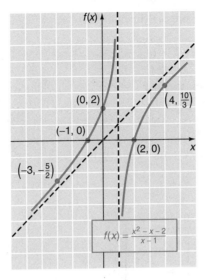

$$f(x) = \frac{x^2 - x - 2}{x - 1}$$

FIGURE 5.38

Finally, let's combine our knowledge of rational functions with the use of a graphing utility to obtain the graph of a fairly complex rational function.

EXAMPLE 6

Graph the rational function $f(x) = \dfrac{x^3 - 2x^2 - x - 1}{x^2 - 36}$.

Solution

Before we enter this function into a graphing utility, let's analyze what we know about the graph.

1. Since $f(0) = \frac{1}{36}$, the point $\left(0, \frac{1}{36}\right)$ is on the graph.

2. Since $f(-x) \neq f(x)$ and $f(-x) \neq -f(x)$, there is no symmetry with respect to the origin nor the y-axis.

3. The denominator is zero at $x = \pm 6$. Thus, the lines $x = 6$ and $x = -6$ are vertical asymptotes.

4. Let's change the form of the rational expression by division.

$$
\begin{array}{r}
x - 2 \\
x^2 - 36 \overline{\smash{\big)}\, x^3 - 2x^2 - x - 1} \\
\underline{x^3 - 36x } \\
-2x^2 + 35x - 1 \\
\underline{-2x^2 + 72} \\
35x - 73
\end{array}
$$

Thus, the original function can be rewritten as

$$f(x) = x - 2 + \frac{35x - 73}{x^2 - 36}.$$

Therefore, the line $y = x - 2$ is an oblique asymptote. Now let

$$Y_1 = x - 2 \quad \text{and} \quad Y_2 = \frac{x^3 - 2x^2 - x - 1}{x^2 - 36}$$

and use a viewing rectangle so that $-15 \le x \le 15$ and $-30 \le y \le 30$ (Figure 5.39).

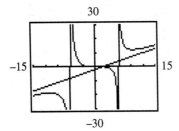

FIGURE 5.39

Note that the graph in Figure 5.39 is consistent with the information that we listed prior to using the graphing utility. Furthermore, notice that the curve does intersect the oblique asymptote. We can use the zoom and trace features of the graphing utility to find that point of intersection or we can do it algebraically as follows: Since $y = \dfrac{x^3 - 2x^2 - x - 1}{x^2 - 36}$ and $y = x - 2$, we can equate the two expressions for y and solve the resulting equation for x.

$$\frac{x^3 - 2x^2 - x - 1}{x^2 - 36} = x - 2$$

$$x^3 - 2x^2 - x - 1 = (x - 2)(x^2 - 36)$$

$$x^3 - 2x^2 - x - 1 = x^3 - 2x^2 - 36x + 72$$

$$35x = 73$$

$$x = \frac{73}{35}$$

If $x = \frac{73}{35}$, then $y = x - 2 = \frac{73}{35} - 2 = \frac{3}{35}$. The point of intersection of the curve and the oblique asymptote is $\left(\frac{73}{35}, \frac{3}{35}\right)$.

PROBLEM SET 5.5

Graph each of the following rational functions. Be sure to check for symmetry and identify the asymptotes.

1. $f(x) = \dfrac{x^2}{x^2 + x - 2}$

2. $f(x) = \dfrac{x^2}{x^2 + 2x - 3}$

3. $f(x) = \dfrac{2x^2}{x^2 - 2x - 8}$

4. $f(x) = \dfrac{-x^2}{x^2 + 3x - 4}$

5. $f(x) = \dfrac{-x}{x^2 - 1}$

6. $f(x) = \dfrac{2x}{x^2 - 9}$

7. $f(x) = \dfrac{x}{x^2 + x - 6}$

8. $f(x) = \dfrac{-x}{x^2 - 2x - 8}$

9. $f(x) = \dfrac{x^2}{x^2 - 4x + 3}$

10. $f(x) = \dfrac{1}{x^3 + x^2 - 6x}$

11. $f(x) = \dfrac{x}{x^2 + 2}$

12. $f(x) = \dfrac{6x}{x^2 + 1}$

13. $f(x) = \dfrac{-4x}{x^2 + 1}$

14. $f(x) = \dfrac{-5x}{x^2 + 2}$

15. $f(x) = \dfrac{x^2 + 2}{x - 1}$

16. $f(x) = \dfrac{x^2 - 3}{x + 1}$

17. $f(x) = \dfrac{x^2 - x - 6}{x + 1}$

18. $f(x) = \dfrac{x^2 + 4}{x + 2}$

19. $f(x) = \dfrac{x^2 + 1}{1 - x}$

20. $f(x) = \dfrac{x^3 + 8}{x^2}$

THOUGHTS into WORDS

21. Explain the concept of an asymptote.

22. Explain why it is possible that the graph of a function might intersect a horizontal asymptote but will not intersect a vertical asymptote.

23. How would you go about graphing $f(x) = \dfrac{x^2 - x - 12}{x - 4}$?

24. How would you go about graphing $f(x) = \dfrac{x^2 - x - 12}{x - 2}$?

 GRAPHICS CALCULATOR ACTIVITIES

25. Use your graphics calculator to graph each of the following rational functions. Be sure first to check for symmetry and identify the horizontal and vertical asymptotes.

a. $f(x) = \dfrac{4x^2}{x^2 + x - 2}$

b. $f(x) = \dfrac{-2x}{x^2 - 5x - 6}$

c. $f(x) = \dfrac{x^2}{x^2 - 9}$

d. $f(x) = \dfrac{x^2 - 4}{x^2 - 9}$

e. $f(x) = \dfrac{x^2 - 9}{x^2 - 4}$

f. $f(x) = \dfrac{x^2 + 2x + 1}{x^2 - 5x + 6}$

26. For each of the following, first determine and graph any oblique asymptote. Then on the same set of axes graph the function.

a. $f(x) = \dfrac{x^2 - 1}{x - 2}$

b. $f(x) = \dfrac{x^2 + 1}{x + 2}$

c. $f(x) = \dfrac{2x^2 + x + 1}{x + 1}$

d. $f(x) = \dfrac{x^2 + 4}{x - 3}$

e. $f(x) = \dfrac{3x^2 - x - 2}{x - 2}$

f. $f(x) = \dfrac{4x^2 + x + 1}{x + 1}$

g. $f(x) = \dfrac{x^3 + x^2 - x - 1}{x^2 + 2x + 3}$

h. $f(x) = \dfrac{x^3 + 2x^2 + x - 3}{x^2 - 4}$

5.6   PARTIAL FRACTIONS

The addition of rational expressions can be demonstrated as follows.

$$\frac{3}{x-2} + \frac{2}{x+3} = \frac{3(x+3) + 2(x-2)}{(x-2)(x+3)}$$

$$= \frac{3x + 9 + 2x - 4}{(x-2)(x+3)}$$

$$= \frac{5x + 5}{(x-2)(x+3)}$$

Now suppose that we want to reverse the process. That is, suppose we were given the rational expression

$$\frac{5x + 5}{(x-2)(x+3)}$$

and we wanted to express it as the sum of two simpler rational expressions, called **partial fractions**. This process, called **partial fraction decomposition**, has several applications in calculus and differential equations. The following property provides the basis for partial fraction decomposition.

PROPERTY 5.8

Let $f(x)$ and $g(x)$ be polynomials with real coefficients such that the degree of $f(x)$ is less than the degree of $g(x)$. The indicated quotient $f(x)/g(x)$ can be decomposed into partial fractions as follows.

1. If $g(x)$ has a linear factor of the form $ax + b$, then the partial fraction decomposition contains a term of the form

$$\frac{A}{ax + b}, \quad \text{where } A \text{ is a constant.}$$

2. If $g(x)$ has a linear factor of the form $ax + b$ raised to the kth power, then the partial fraction decomposition contains terms of the form

$$\frac{A_1}{ax + b} + \frac{A_2}{(ax+b)^2} + \cdots + \frac{A_k}{(ax+b)^k},$$

where $A_1, A_2, \ldots, A_k$ are constants.

3. If $g(x)$ has a quadratic factor of the form $ax^2 + bx + c$, where $b^2 - 4ac < 0$, then the partial fraction decomposition contains a term of the form

$$\frac{Ax + B}{ax^2 + bx + c}, \quad \text{where } A \text{ and } B \text{ are constants.}$$

4. If $g(x)$ has a quadratic factor of the form $ax^2 + bx + c$, where $b^2 - 4ac < 0$, raised to the kth power, then the partial fraction decomposition contains terms of the form

$$\frac{A_1 x + B_1}{ax^2 + bx + c} + \frac{A_2 x + B_2}{(ax^2 + bx + c)^2}$$

$$+ \cdots + \frac{A_k x + B_k x}{(ax^2 + bx + c)^k},$$

where $A_1, A_2, \ldots, A_k, B_1, \ldots, B_k$ are constants.

Notice that Property 5.8 applies to **proper fractions**, that is, fractions where the degree of the numerator is less than the degree of the denominator. If the numerator is not of lower degree, we can divide and then apply Property 5.8 to the remainder, which will be a proper fraction. For example,

$$\frac{x^3 - 3x^2 - 3x - 5}{x^2 - 4} = x - 3 + \frac{x - 17}{x^2 - 4}$$

and the proper fraction $(x - 17)/(x^2 - 4)$ can be decomposed into partial fractions by applying Property 5.8. Now let's consider some examples to illustrate the four parts of Property 5.8.

EXAMPLE 1

Find the partial fraction decomposition of

$$\frac{11x + 2}{2x^2 + x - 1}.$$

Solution

The denominator can be expressed as $(x + 1)(2x - 1)$. Therefore, according to part 1 of Property 5.8, each of the linear factors produces a partial fraction of the form *constant-over-linear factor*. In other words, we can write

$$\frac{11x + 2}{(x + 1)(2x - 1)} = \frac{A}{x + 1} + \frac{B}{2x - 1} \tag{1}$$

for some constants A and B. To find A and B, let's multiply both sides of equation (1) by the least common denominator $(x + 1)(2x - 1)$ to produce

$$11x + 2 = A(2x - 1) + B(x + 1). \tag{2}$$

Equation (2) is an identity; **it is true for all values of** x. Therefore, let's choose some convenient values for x that will determine the values for A and B. If we let $x = -1$, then equation (2) becomes

$$11(-1) + 2 = A(2(-1) - 1) + B(-1 + 1)$$

$$-9 = -3A$$

$$3 = A.$$

If we let $x = \frac{1}{2}$, then equation (2) becomes

$$11\left(\tfrac{1}{2}\right) + 2 = A\left(2\left(\tfrac{1}{2}\right) - 1\right) + B\left(\tfrac{1}{2} + 1\right)$$

$$\tfrac{15}{2} = \tfrac{3}{2}B$$

$$5 = B.$$

Therefore, the given rational expression can be written as

$$\frac{11x + 2}{2x^2 + x - 1} = \frac{3}{x + 1} + \frac{5}{2x - 1}.$$

In Example 1 after Property 5.8 was applied, the key idea was the statement that *equation (2) is true for all values of* x. We could have chosen any two values for x and been able to determine the values for A and B. For example, letting $x = 1$ and then $x = 2$ produces the equations $13 = A + 2B$ and $24 = 3A + 3B$. Solving this system of two equations in two unknowns produces $A = 3$ and $B = 5$. In Example 1, our choice of letting $x = -1$ and then $x = \frac{1}{2}$ simply eliminated the need for solving a system of equations to find A and B.

E X A M P L E 2

Find the partial fraction decomposition of

$$\frac{-2x^2 + 7x + 2}{x(x - 1)^2}.$$

Solution

According to part 1 of Property 5.8, there is a partial fraction of the form A/x that corresponds to the factor of x. Next, apply part 2 of Property 5.8, and the squared factor $(x - 1)^2$ yields a sum of partial fractions of the form $B/(x - 1) + C/(x - 1)^2$. Therefore, the complete partial fraction decomposition is of the form

$$\frac{-2x^2 + 7x + 2}{x(x - 1)^2} = \frac{A}{x} + \frac{B}{x - 1} + \frac{C}{(x - 1)^2}. \tag{1}$$

Multiply both sides of equation (1) by $x(x - 1)^2$ to produce

$$-2x^2 + 7x + 2 = A(x - 1)^2 + Bx(x - 1) + Cx, \tag{2}$$

which is true for all values of x. If we let $x = 1$, then equation (2) becomes

$$-2(1)^2 + 7(1) + 2 = A(1 - 1)^2 + B(1)(1 - 1) + C(1)$$

$$7 = C.$$

If we let $x = 0$, then equation (2) becomes

$$-2(0)^2 + 7(0) + 2 = A(0 - 1)^2 + B(0)(0 - 1) + C(0)$$

$$2 = A.$$

If we let $x = 2$, then equation (2) becomes

$$-2(2)^2 + 7(2) + 2 = A(2 - 1)^2 + B(2)(2 - 1) + C(2)$$

$$8 = A + 2B + 2C.$$

Since we already know that $A = 2$ and $C = 7$, we can determine B.

$$8 = 2 + 2B + 14$$

$$-8 = 2B$$

$$-4 = B$$

Therefore, the original given rational expression can be written as

$$\frac{-2x^2 + 7x + 2}{x(x - 1)^2} = \frac{2}{x} - \frac{4}{x - 1} + \frac{7}{(x - 1)^2}.$$

E X A M P L E 3

Find the partial fraction decomposition of

$$\frac{4x^2 + 6x - 10}{(x + 3)(x^2 + x + 2)}.$$

Solution

According to part 1 of Property 5.8 there is a partial fraction of the form $A/(x + 3)$ that corresponds to the factor of $x + 3$. According to part 3 of Property 5.8 there is also a partial fraction of the form $(Bx + C)/(x^2 + x + 2)$. Thus, the complete partial fraction decomposition is of the form

$$\frac{4x^2 + 6x - 10}{(x + 3)(x^2 + x + 2)} = \frac{A}{x + 3} + \frac{Bx + C}{x^2 + x + 2}. \tag{1}$$

Multiply both sides of equation (1) by $(x + 3)(x^2 + x + 2)$ to produce

$$4x^2 + 6x - 10 = A(x^2 + x + 2) + (Bx + C)(x + 3), \tag{2}$$

which is true for all values of x. If we let $x = -3$, then equation (2) becomes

$$4(-3)^2 + 6(-3) - 10 = A[(-3)^2 + (-3) + 2] + [B(-3) + C][(-3) + 3]$$

$$8 = 8A$$

$$1 = A.$$

If we let $x = 0$, then equation (2) becomes

$$4(0)^2 + 6(0) - 10 = A(0^2 + 0 + 2) + [B(0) + C][0 + 3]$$

$$-10 = 2A + 3C.$$

Since $A = 1$, we obtain

$$-10 = 2 + 3C$$

$$-12 = 3C$$

$$-4 = C.$$

If we let $x = 1$, then equation (2) becomes

$$4(1)^2 + 6(1) - 10 = A(1^2 + 1 + 2) + [B(1) + C][1 + 3]$$

$$0 = 4A + 4B + 4C.$$

Since $A = 1$ and $C = -4$, we obtain

$$0 = 4 + 4B - 16$$

$$12 = 4B$$

$$3 = B.$$

Therefore, the original given rational expression can be written as

$$\frac{4x^2 + 6x - 10}{(x + 3)(x^2 + x + 2)} = \frac{1}{x + 3} + \frac{3x - 4}{x^2 + x + 2}.$$

EXAMPLE 4

Find the partial fraction decomposition of

$$\frac{x^3 + x^2 + x + 3}{(x^2 + 1)^2}.$$

Solution

According to part 4 of Property 5.8 the partial fraction decomposition of this fraction is of the form

$$\frac{x^3 + x^2 + x + 3}{(x^2 + 1)^2} = \frac{Ax + B}{x^2 + 1} + \frac{Cx + D}{(x^2 + 1)^2}. \qquad (1)$$

Multiplying both sides of equation (1) by $(x^2 + 1)^2$ produces

$$x^3 + x^2 + x + 3 = (Ax + B)(x^2 + 1) + Cx + D, \qquad (2)$$

which is true for all values of x. Since equation (2) is an identity, we know that the coefficients of similar terms on both sides of the equation must be equal. Therefore, let's collect similar terms on the right side of equation (2).

$$x^3 + x^2 + x + 3 = Ax^3 + Ax + Bx^2 + B + Cx + D$$
$$= Ax^3 + Bx^2 + (A + C)x + B + D$$

Now we can equate coefficients from both sides to produce

$$1 = A, \quad 1 = B, \quad 1 = A + C, \quad \text{and} \quad 3 = B + D.$$

From these equations we can determine that $A = 1$, $B = 1$, $C = 0$, and $D = 2$. Therefore, the original given rational expression can be written as

$$\frac{x^3 + x^2 + x + 3}{(x^2 + 1)^2} = \frac{x + 1}{x^2 + 1} + \frac{2}{(x^2 + 1)^2}.$$

PROBLEM SET 5.6

Find the partial fraction decomposition for each of the following.

1. $\dfrac{11x - 10}{(x - 2)(x + 1)}$

2. $\dfrac{11x - 2}{(x + 3)(x - 4)}$

3. $\dfrac{-2x - 8}{x^2 - 1}$

4. $\dfrac{-2x + 32}{x^2 - 4}$

5. $\dfrac{20x - 3}{6x^2 + 7x - 3}$

6. $\dfrac{-2x - 8}{10x^2 - x - 2}$

7. $\dfrac{x^2 - 18x + 5}{(x - 1)(x + 2)(x - 3)}$

8. $\dfrac{-9x^2 + 7x - 4}{x^3 - 3x^2 - 4x}$

9. $\dfrac{-6x^2 + 7x + 1}{x(2x - 1)(4x + 1)}$

10. $\dfrac{15x^2 + 20x + 30}{(x + 3)(3x + 2)(2x + 3)}$

11. $\dfrac{2x + 1}{(x - 2)^2}$

12. $\dfrac{-3x + 1}{(x + 1)^2}$

13. $\dfrac{-6x^2 + 19x + 21}{x^2(x + 3)}$

14. $\dfrac{10x^2 - 73x + 144}{x(x - 4)^2}$

15. $\dfrac{-2x^2 - 3x + 10}{(x^2 + 1)(x - 4)}$

16. $\dfrac{8x^2 + 15x + 12}{(x^2 + 4)(3x - 4)}$

17. $\dfrac{3x^2 + 10x + 9}{(x + 2)^3}$

18. $\dfrac{2x^3 + 8x^2 + 2x + 4}{(x + 1)^2(x^2 + 3)}$

19. $\dfrac{5x^2 + 3x + 6}{x(x^2 - x + 3)}$

20. $\dfrac{x^3 + x^2 + 2}{(x^2 + 2)^2}$

21. $\dfrac{2x^3 + x + 3}{(x^2 + 1)^2}$

22. $\dfrac{4x^2 + 3x + 14}{x^3 - 8}$

THOUGHTS into WORDS

23. How would you explain the concept of partial fraction decomposition to an elementary algebra student without going into the details of the various techniques?

CHAPTER 5 SUMMARY

Two themes unify this chapter, namely

    1. solving polynomial equations, and

    2. graphing polynomial and rational functions.

Solving Polynomial Equations

The following concepts and properties provide the basis for solving polynomial equations.

    1. Synthetic division.

    2. The factor theorem: A polynomial $f(x)$ has a factor $x - c$ if and only if $f(c) = 0$.

    3. Property 5.4: A polynomial equation of degree n has n solutions, where any solution of multiplicity p is counted p times.

    4. Rational root theorem: Consider the polynomial equation

$$a_n x^n + a_{n-1} x^{n-1} + \cdots + a_1 x + a_0 = 0$$

    where the coefficients are integers. If the rational number $\dfrac{c}{d}$, reduced to lowest terms, is a solution of the equation, then c is a factor of the constant term a_0 and d is a factor of the leading coefficient a_n.

    5. Property 5.6: Nonreal complex solutions of polynomial equations with real coefficients, if they exist, must occur in conjugate pairs.

    6. Descartes' rule of signs: Let

$$a_n x^n + a_{n-1} x^{n-1} + \cdots + a_1 x + a_0 = 0$$

    be a polynomial equation with real coefficients.

    a. The number of positive real solutions is either equal to the number of sign variations or else is less than the number of sign variations by a positive even integer.

    b. The number of negative real solutions is either equal to the number of sign variations in

$$a_n(-x)^n + a_{n-1}(-x)^{n-1} + \cdots + a_1(-x) + a_0,$$

    or else it is less than the number of sign variations by a positive even integer.

Graphing Polynomial and Rational Functions

Graphs of polynomial functions of the form $f(x) = ax^n$, where n is an integer greater than two and $a \neq 1$, are variations of the graphs shown in Figures 5.3 and 5.6. If n is odd, the curve is symmetrical about the origin, and if n is even, the graph is symmetrical about the vertical axis.

Graphs of polynomial functions of the form $f(x) = ax^n$ can be translated horizontally and vertically, and reflected across the x-axis. For example,

1. The graph of $f(x) = 2(x - 4)^3$ is the graph of $f(x) = 2x^3$ moved four units to the right.
2. The graph of $f(x) = 3x^4 + 4$ is the graph of $f(x) = 3x^4$ moved up four units.
3. The graph of $f(x) = -x^5$ is the graph of $f(x) = x^5$ reflected across the x-axis.

To graph a polynomial function that is expressed in factored form the following steps are helpful.

1. Find the x-intercepts, which are also called the zeros of the polynomial.
2. Use a test value in each of the intervals determined by the x-intercepts to find out whether the function is positive or negative over that interval.
3. Plot any additional points that are needed to determine the graph.

To graph a rational function, the following steps are useful.

1. Check for vertical-axis and origin symmetry.
2. Find any vertical asymptotes by setting the denominator equal to zero and solving it for x.
3. Find any horizontal asymptotes by studying the behavior of $f(x)$ as x gets very large or very small. This may require changing the form of the original rational expression.
4. If the degree of the numerator is one larger than the degree of the denominator, determine the equation of the oblique asymptote.
5. Study the behavior of the graph when it is close to the asymptotic lines.
6. Plot as many points as necessary to determine the graph. This may be affected by whether the graph has any symmetries.

Be sure that you understand the process of partial fraction decomposition based on Property 5.8, which we discussed in Section 5.6.

CHAPTER 5 REVIEW PROBLEM SET

For Problems 1 and 2, find the quotient and remainder of the division problems.

1. $(6x^3 + 11x^2 - 27x + 32) \div (2x + 7)$

2. $(2a^3 - 3a^2 + 13a - 1) \div (a^2 - a + 6)$

For Problems 3–6, use synthetic division to determine the quotient and remainder.

3. $(3x^3 - 4x^2 + 6x - 2) \div (x - 1)$

4. $(5x^3 + 7x^2 - 9x + 10) \div (x + 2)$

5. $(-2x^4 + x^3 - 2x^2 - x - 1) \div (x + 4)$

6. $(-3x^4 - 5x^2 + 9) \div (x - 3)$

For Problems 7–10, find $f(c)$ by either using synthetic division and the remainder theorem or by evaluating $f(c)$ directly.

7. $f(x) = 4x^5 - 3x^3 + x^2 - 1$ and $c = 1$

8. $f(x) = 4x^3 - 7x^2 + 6x - 8$ and $c = -3$

9. $f(x) = -x^4 + 9x^2 - x - 2$ and $c = -2$

10. $f(x) = x^4 - 9x^3 + 9x^2 - 10x + 16$ and $c = 8$

For Problems 11–14, use the factor theorem to help answer some questions about factors.

11. Is $x + 2$ a factor of $2x^3 + x^2 - 7x - 2$?

12. Is $x - 3$ a factor of $x^4 + 5x^3 - 7x^2 - x + 3$?

13. Is $x - 4$ a factor of $x^5 - 1024$?

14. Is $x + 1$ a factor of $x^5 + 1$?

For Problems 15–18, use the rational root theorem and the factor theorem to help solve each of the equations.

15. $x^3 - 3x^2 - 13x + 15 = 0$

16. $8x^3 + 26x^2 - 17x - 35 = 0$

17. $x^4 - 5x^3 + 34x^2 - 82x + 52 = 0$

18. $x^3 - 4x^2 - 10x + 4 = 0$

For Problems 19 and 20, use Descartes' rule of signs (Property 5.7) to help list the possibilities for the nature of the solutions. *Do not solve* the equations.

19. $4x^4 - 3x^3 + 2x^2 + x + 4 = 0$

20. $x^5 + 3x^3 + x + 7 = 0$

For Problems 21–23, determine a polynomial equation with integral coefficients that has the given numbers as solutions and the indicated degree.

21. $3, -\frac{1}{2}, -2$;   degree 3

22. 2 of multiplicity 3, -1;   degree 4

23. $-4, 1 + 6i$;   degree 3

For Problems 24–27, graph each of the polynomial functions.

24. $f(x) = -(x - 2)^3 + 3$

25. $f(x) = (x + 3)(x - 1)(3 - x)$

26. $f(x) = x^4 - 4x^2$

27. $f(x) = x^3 - 4x^2 + x + 6$

For Problems 28–31, graph each of the rational functions. Be sure to identify the asymptotes.

28. $f(x) = \dfrac{2x}{x - 3}$

29. $f(x) = \dfrac{-3}{x^2 + 1}$

30. $f(x) = \dfrac{-x^2}{x^2 - x - 6}$

31. $f(x) = \dfrac{x^2 + 3}{x + 1}$

For Problems 32 and 33 find the partial fraction decomposition.

32. $\dfrac{5x^2 - 4}{x^2(x + 2)}$

33. $\dfrac{x^2 - x - 21}{(x^2 + 4)(2x - 1)}$

For Problems 1–10, evaluate each numerical expression.

1. $\left(\dfrac{3}{4}\right)^{-3}$

2. $\sqrt[3]{-\dfrac{8}{27}}$

3. -5^{-2}

4. $8^{4/3}$

5. $9^{-(3/2)}$

6. $\log_4 64$

7. $\log_{10} .0001$

8. $\log_2\left(\dfrac{1}{32}\right)$

9. $(-64)^{2/3}$

10. $\ln e^3$

For Problems 11–33, solve each problem.

11. Express the domain of the function $f(x) = \sqrt{2x^2 + 11x - 6}$ using interval notation.

12. If $f(x) = 3x - 1$ and $g(x) = x^2 - x + 3$, find $(f \circ g)(-2)$ and $(g \circ f)(3)$.

13. If $f(x) = -\dfrac{2}{x}$ and $g(x) = \dfrac{1}{x-4}$, find $(f \circ g)(x)$ and $(g \circ f)(x)$. Also indicate the domain of each composite function.

14. If $f(x) = -2x + 7$, find the inverse of f.

15. If $f(x) = x^2 + 7x - 2$, find $\dfrac{f(a+h) - f(a)}{h}$.

16. If $f(x) = 2x^4 - 17x^3 - 10x^2 + 11x + 15$, find $f(9)$.

17. Find the quotient for $(3x^5 - 25x^3 - 7x^2 + x + 6) \div (x - 3)$.

18. Is $x + 2$ a factor of $2x^4 + 3x^3 + x^2 + x + 2x - 16$?

19. Evaluate $\log_2 50$ to the nearest hundredth.

20. Find the center and the length of a radius of the circle $x^2 + y^2 + 6x - 4y + 4 = 0$.

21. Write the equation of the line that contains the points $(-4, 2)$ and $(5, -1)$.

22. Write the equation of the perpendicular bisector of the line segment determined by $(-2, -4)$ and $(6, 2)$.

23. Find the solution set of the system of linear equations
$$\begin{pmatrix} 7x - y = -23 \\ 3x + 4y = 30 \end{pmatrix}.$$

24. Find the solution set of the system of linear equations
$$\begin{pmatrix} x - 4y + z = 17 \\ 2x + y - 2z = 2 \\ 3x - 2y + 5z = 9 \end{pmatrix}.$$

25. If y varies directly as x, and if $y = 3$ when $x = 4$, find y when $x = 16$.

26. If y varies inversely as the square root of x, and if $y = \frac{2}{5}$ when $x = 25$, find y when $x = 49$.

27. Find the total amount of money accumulated at the end of 8 years if $450 is invested at 7% compounded quarterly.

28. How long will it take $500 to double itself if it is invested at 8% interest compounded continuously?

29. Sandy has a collection of 57 coins worth $10. They consist of nickels, dimes, and quarters, and the number of quarters is 2 more than three times the number of nickels. How many coins of each kind does she have?

30. A retailer bought a dress for $75 and wants to sell it at a profit of 40% of the selling price. What price should she ask for the dress?

31. A container has 8 quarts of a 30% alcohol solution. How much pure alcohol should be added to raise it to a 40% solution?

32. Claire rode her bicycle out into the country at a speed of 15 miles per hour and returned along the same route at 10 miles per hour. If the entire trip took $7\frac{1}{2}$ hours, how far out did she ride?

33. Adam can do a job in 2 hours less time than it takes Carl to do the same job. Working together they can do the job in 2 hours and 24 minutes. How long would it take Adam to do the job by himself?

For Problems 34–45, solve each equation.

34. $(2x - 5)(6x + 1) = (3x + 2)(4x - 7)$

35. $(2x + 1)(x - 2) = (3x - 2)(x + 4)$

36. $4x^3 + 20x^2 - 56x = 0$

37. $6x^3 + 17x^2 + x - 10 = 0$

38. $|4x - 3| = 7$

39. $\dfrac{2x - 1}{3} - \dfrac{3x + 2}{4} = -\dfrac{5}{6}$

40. $3^{x-2} = 27^x$

41. $\ln(t + 2) = \ln t + \ln 4$

42. $\log 5 + \log(x - 1) = 1$

43. $x^4 + 3x^2 - 54 = 0$

44. $(2x - 1)(x + 3) = 49$

45. $x^4 - 2x^3 + 2x^2 - 7x + 6 = 0$

For Problems 46–53, solve each inequality and express the solution set using interval notation.

46. $3(x - 1) - 5(x + 2) > 3(x + 4)$

47. $\dfrac{x - 1}{2} + \dfrac{2x + 1}{5} \geq \dfrac{x - 2}{3}$

48. $x^2 - 3x < 18$

49. $(x - 1)(x + 3)(2 - x) \leq 0$

50. $|2x - 1| > 6$

51. $|3x + 2| \leq 8$

52. $\dfrac{4x - 3}{x - 2} \geq 0$

53. $\dfrac{x + 3}{x - 4} < 3$

For Problems 54–64, graph each function.

54. $f(x) = -2x + 4$

55. $f(x) = 2x^2 - 3$

56. $f(x) = 2^x - 3$

57. $f(x) = \log_2(x - 1)$

58. $f(x) = \dfrac{2x}{x + 1}$

59. $f(x) = -|x - 2| + 1$

60. $f(x) = 2\sqrt{x} + 1$

61. $f(x) = 3x^2 + 12x + 9$

62. $f(x) = -(x - 3)^3 + 1$

63. $f(x) = (x + 1)(x - 2)(x - 4)$

64. $f(x) = x^4 - x^2$

TRIGONOMETRIC FUNCTIONS

T he word trigonometry was derived from two Greek words that mean *measurement of triangles.* Historically, trigonometry began with the study of the various relationships that exist between the angles and sides of triangles. This aspect of trigonometry has many applications in surveying, navigation, carpentry, and the various branches of engineering.

Originally, the trigonometric functions were restricted to domains of angles. However, a more modern viewpoint allows for the domains to be the set of real numbers independent of any angle association. This viewpoint resulted in a larger variety of applications for the trigonometric functions in such areas as light, sound, and electrical wave theories.

Our approach to trigonometry in this text will follow the historical route. That is to say, we will first introduce the trigonometric functions in terms of angles and then define them with real number domains. Let's begin by reviewing some basic geometric concepts that we will use in our study of trigonometry.

6

The sine function is sometimes used to describe the predator-prey relationship in a balanced ecological system.

6.1 GEOMETRIC BASIS FOR TRIGONOMETRY

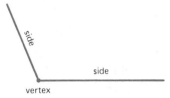

FIGURE 6.1

In geometry, we usually define a **plane angle** as the set of points that consists of two rays with a common endpoint. The common endpoint is called the **vertex** of the angle, and the rays are called the **sides** of the angle (Figure 6.1). In trigonometry it is more convenient to think of an angle in terms of rotating a ray about its endpoint. In Figure 6.2 let's begin with a ray r_1 and rotate it, in a plane, about its endpoint O to a position indicated by the ray r_2. We call r_1 the **initial side**, r_2 the **terminal side**, and O the **vertex** of the angle. If the rotation is in a counterclockwise direction as indicated by an arrow, then the angle is a **positive angle**. If the rotation is in a clockwise direction, then we have a **negative angle**. There is no restriction as to the amount of rotation (Figure 6.3). As we indicated in parts (a) and (c) of Figure 6.3, different angles can have the same initial and terminal sides (the amount of rotation is different). Any two such angles are called **coterminal**.

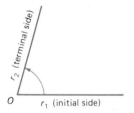

FIGURE 6.2

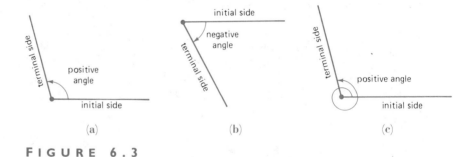

(a)　　　　　　(b)　　　　　　(c)

FIGURE 6.3

The size of an angle (amount of rotation from initial side to terminal side) can be described using **degree measure**. The angle formed by rotating a complete counterclockwise revolution has a measure of 360 degrees, written 360°. Thus, one degree (1°) is $\frac{1}{360}$ of a complete revolution. The following terminology is commonly used: A **right angle** has a measure of 90° and a **straight angle** has a measure of 180°. An **acute angle** has a measure between 0° and 90°, and an **obtuse angle** has a measure between 90° and 180°. Two acute angles are **complementary** if their sum is 90°, and two positive angles are **supplementary** if their sum is 180°.

The degree system for angle measurement is quite similar to the hour-minute-second relationship of our time system. Each degree is divided into 60 parts, called **minutes**, and each minute is divided into 60 parts, called **seconds**. Thus, when we speak of an angle that has a measure of 73 degrees, 12 minutes, and 36 seconds, we write 73°12′36″.

When using a calculator, fractional parts of a degree are written in decimal form. For example, an angle may have a measure of 73.21°. Some calculators are equipped with a special key sequence that will switch back and forth between the degree-minute-second form and the decimal form. Without a calculator you can proceed as follows.

From degree-minute-second form to decimal form:

$$73°12'36'' = 73° + \left(\tfrac{12}{60}\right)° + \left(\tfrac{36}{3600}\right)°$$

if $1° = 60'$ and $1' = 60''$, then $1° = 3600''$

$$= 73° + \left(\tfrac{1}{5}\right)° + \left(\tfrac{1}{100}\right)°$$

$$= 73° + (.2°) + (.01)°$$

$$= 73.21°$$

From decimal form to degree-minute-second form:

$$73.21° = 73° + .21(60')$$

$$= 73° + 12.6'$$

$$= 73° + 12' + .6(60'')$$

$$= 73° + 12' + 36''$$

$$= 73°12'36''$$

Radian Measure

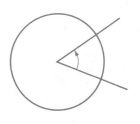

FIGURE 6.4

The radian is another basic unit of angle measure that is used extensively in subsequent mathematics courses and in various mathematical applications in the physical sciences. One **radian** is the measure of the central angle of a circle (a central angle has its vertex at the center of the circle) where the sides of the angle intercept an arc equal in length to the radius of the circle (Figure 6.4).

The circumference of a circle is given by $C = 2\pi r$, and each arc of length r determines an angle of one radian; therefore, there are $2\pi r/r = 2\pi$ radians in one complete revolution. Thus,

$$2\pi \text{ radians} = 360°$$

or, equivalently,

$$\pi \text{ radians} = 180°.$$

So we have the following two basic relationships between degree and radian measure.

$$1 \text{ radian} = \frac{180}{\pi} \text{ degrees}$$

and

$$1 \text{ degree} = \frac{\pi}{180} \text{ radians}$$

REMARK   Evaluating $180/\pi$, we can determine that 1 radian is approximately 57.3 degrees. This relationship need not be memorized, but it may strengthen your perception of the size of one radian.

Sometimes it is necessary to switch back and forth between degree and radian measure. This creates no great difficulty, as illustrated by the following examples.

EXAMPLE 1

Change 150° to radians.

Solution

Since 1 degree = $\pi/180$ radians,

$$150 \text{ degrees} = 150\left(\frac{\pi}{180}\right) \text{ radians}$$

$$= \frac{5\pi}{6} \text{radians}.$$

EXAMPLE 2

Change $3\pi/4$ radians to degrees.

Solution

Since 1 radian = $180/\pi$ degrees,

$$\frac{3\pi}{4} \text{ radians} = \frac{3\pi}{4}\left(\frac{180}{\pi}\right) \text{ degrees}$$

$$= 135 \text{ degrees}.$$

Some calculators have a $\boxed{d \leftrightarrow r}$ key that can be used for direct conversion between degrees and radians. If not, you will need to use $\pi/180$ to convert degrees to radians and $180/\pi$ to convert radians to degrees. Therefore,

$$5 \text{ radians} = 5\left(\frac{180}{\pi}\right) = 286.5 \text{ degrees} \qquad \text{To the nearest tenth of a degree}$$

and

$$127.4 \text{ degrees} = 127.4\left(\frac{\pi}{180}\right) = 2.2 \text{ radians} \qquad \text{To the nearest tenth of a radian}$$

Arc Length

Consider, as in Figure 6.5, a circle of radius r and a central angle θ measured in radians that intercept an arc of length s. The arc length s compares to the total circumference of $2\pi r$ as θ radians compare to a complete revolution of 2π radians, so we have the proportion

$$\frac{s}{2\pi r} = \frac{\theta}{2\pi}.$$

Solving for s produces

$$(s)(2\pi) = (2\pi r)(\theta)$$

FIGURE 6.5

$$s = r\theta.$$

EXAMPLE 3

Find the length of the arc intercepted by a central angle of $\pi/6$ radians if a radius of the circle is 11 inches long.

Solution

Using $s = r\theta$, we obtain

$$s = r\theta$$

$$= 11\left(\frac{\pi}{6}\right)$$

$$= 5.8 \text{ inches} \quad \text{to the nearest tenth of an inch.}$$

EXAMPLE 4

How high will the weight in Figure 6.6 be lifted if the drum is rotated through an angle of $70°$?

Solution

First, we need to change $70°$ to radians.

$$70° = 70\left(\frac{\pi}{180}\right) = \frac{7\pi}{18} \text{ radians.}$$

Therefore, point A will move

$$s = r\theta = 6\left(\frac{7\pi}{18}\right) = 7.3 \text{ inches} \quad \text{to the nearest tenth of an inch.}$$

Thus, the weight will be lifted approximately 7.3 inches.

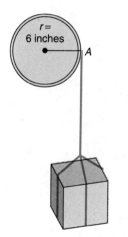

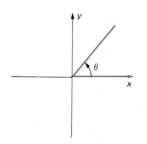

FIGURE 6.6

Trigonometric Functions

If a rectangular coordinate system is introduced, then the **standard position** of an angle is obtained by taking the vertex at the origin and letting the initial side coincide with the positive side of the x-axis. The angles in Figure 6.7 are each in standard position. Each angle is named by a Greek letter positioned next to the curved arrow. Thus, we can refer to angles θ(theta), ϕ(phi), α(alpha), and β(beta). Angle θ is called a **first-quadrant angle** because its terminal side lies in the first

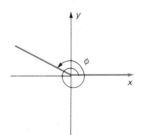 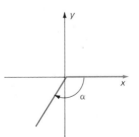 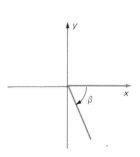

FIGURE 6.7

quadrant. Angles ϕ, α, and β are second-quadrant, third-quadrant, and fourth-quadrant angles, respectively. Also note that θ and ϕ are positive angles, whereas α and β are negative angles. If the terminal side of an angle in standard position coincides with a coordinate axis, then the angle is called a quadrantal angle.

Now the six basic trigonometric functions can be defined as follows.

DEFINITION 6.1

Let θ be an angle in standard position and let $P(x, y)$ be any point (except the origin) on the terminal side of θ (Figure 6.8). The six trigonometric functions are defined as follows.

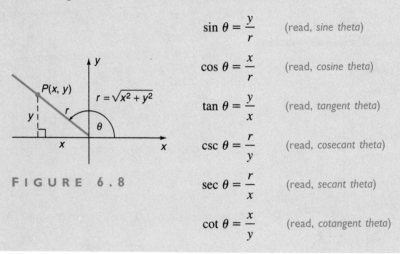

FIGURE 6.8

$$\sin \theta = \frac{y}{r} \qquad \text{(read, \textit{sine theta})}$$

$$\cos \theta = \frac{x}{r} \qquad \text{(read, \textit{cosine theta})}$$

$$\tan \theta = \frac{y}{x} \qquad \text{(read, \textit{tangent theta})}$$

$$\csc \theta = \frac{r}{y} \qquad \text{(read, \textit{cosecant theta})}$$

$$\sec \theta = \frac{r}{x} \qquad \text{(read, \textit{secant theta})}$$

$$\cot \theta = \frac{x}{y} \qquad \text{(read, \textit{cotangent theta})}$$

In Definition 6.1, r is the distance between the origin and point P; it is always a positive number and it is determined by $r = \sqrt{x^2 + y^2}$. Recall that a function assigns to each member of a set (called the domain) a unique member of another set (called the range). The domain of each of the six trigonometric functions is a set of angles, and Definition 6.1 assigns to each angle (with a few exceptions) a real number determined by the ratios, y/r, x/r, y/x, r/y, r/x, and x/y. (The fact that a *unique* number is assigned to each angle will be demonstrated a bit later.) Because division by zero is not permitted, $\tan \theta$ and $\sec \theta$ cannot be defined for $x = 0$, and $\csc \theta$ and $\cot \theta$ cannot be defined for $y = 0$. Furthermore, notice that $\csc \theta$, $\sec \theta$, and $\cot \theta$ are the reciprocals of $\sin \theta$, $\cos \theta$, and $\tan \theta$, respectively. That is to say,

$$\csc \theta = \frac{1}{\sin \theta}, \qquad \sin \theta \neq 0$$

$$\sec \theta = \frac{1}{\cos \theta}, \qquad \cos \theta \neq 0$$

$$\cot \theta = \frac{1}{\tan \theta}, \qquad \tan \theta \neq 0.$$

Another very useful relationship that follows directly from Definition 6.1 is $\sin^2\theta + \cos^2\theta = 1$ for any angle θ.

The notation $\sin^2\theta$ (usually read, *sine squared of theta*) means $(\sin \theta)^2$; therefore, $\sin^2\theta = (\sin \theta)(\sin \theta)$. This relationship can be verified as follows.

$$\sin^2\theta + \cos^2\theta = \left(\frac{y}{r}\right)^2 + \left(\frac{x}{r}\right)^2$$

$$= \frac{y^2}{r^2} + \frac{x^2}{r^2} = \frac{y^2 + x^2}{r^2} = \frac{r^2}{r^2} = 1$$

The reciprocal relationships and the property $\sin^2\theta + \cos^2\theta = 1$ are called trigonometric identities. More identities will be discussed in Section 6.7

EXAMPLE 5

Find the values of the six trigonometric functions of an angle θ if θ is in standard position and the point $(-3, 4)$ is on the terminal side of θ.

Solution

Figure 6.9 shows θ and the point $(-3, 4)$ on the terminal side of θ. Using $r = \sqrt{x^2 + y^2}$, we obtain

$$r = \sqrt{(-3)^2 + 4^2}$$

$$= \sqrt{9 + 16}$$

$$= \sqrt{25}$$

$$= 5.$$

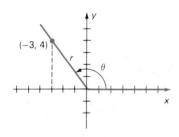

FIGURE   6.9

Now using $x = -3$, $y = 4$, and $r = 5$, the values of the six trigonometric functions of θ can be determined.

$$\sin \theta = \frac{y}{r} = \frac{4}{5} \qquad\qquad \cos \theta = \frac{x}{r} = \frac{-3}{5} = -\frac{3}{5}$$

$$\tan \theta = \frac{y}{x} = \frac{4}{-3} = -\frac{4}{3} \qquad\qquad \csc \theta = \frac{r}{y} = \frac{5}{4}$$

$$\sec \theta = \frac{r}{x} = \frac{5}{-3} = -\frac{5}{3} \qquad\qquad \cot \theta = \frac{x}{y} = \frac{-3}{4} = -\frac{3}{4}$$

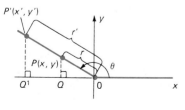

FIGURE   6.10

It is important to realize that *any point* (other than the origin) on the terminal side of an angle in standard position can be used to determine the trigonometric functions of the angle. This fact is based on a property of similar triangles illustrated in Figure 6.10. Triangles OQP and $OQ'P'$ are similar triangles, and corresponding sides of similar triangles are proportional. That is to say, the ratios of corresponding sides are equal. For example $y/r = y'/r'$, and therefore either of the ratios can be used to determine $\sin \theta$. Similar arguments hold for the remaining five trigonometric functions.

E X A M P L E   6

Find $\sin \theta$ and $\cos \theta$ if the terminal side of θ lies on the line $y = 2x$ in the third quadrant.

Solution

First, let's sketch the line $y = 2x$ (Figure 6.11). The point $(-2, -4)$ is a point on the terminal side of θ, which can be used to sketch the line. Therefore,

$$r = \sqrt{(-2)^2 + (-4)^2} = \sqrt{4 + 16} = \sqrt{20} = 2\sqrt{5}.$$

Now the values for $\sin \theta$ and $\cos \theta$ can be determined.

$$\sin \theta = \frac{y}{r} = \frac{-4}{2\sqrt{5}} = -\frac{2}{\sqrt{5}} = -\frac{2\sqrt{5}}{5}$$

$$\cos \theta = \frac{x}{r} = \frac{-2}{2\sqrt{5}} = -\frac{1}{\sqrt{5}} = -\frac{\sqrt{5}}{5}$$

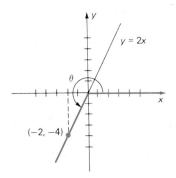

FIGURE   6 . II

E X A M P L E   7

Find $\sin \theta$, $\cos \theta$, and $\tan \theta$ for $\theta = 30°$.

Solution

Let's choose a point P on the terminal side of θ so that $r = 1$ (Figure 6.12). Because $\theta = 30°$, the right triangle indicated is a $30° - 60°$ right triangle. Therefore, $y = \frac{1}{2}$ because it is the side opposite the $30°$ angle. Then, by using the Pythagorean theorem we can determine that $x = \frac{\sqrt{3}}{2}$. Therefore, using $r = 1$, $x = \frac{\sqrt{3}}{2}$, and $y = \frac{1}{2}$, we obtain

$$\sin 30° = \frac{y}{r} = \frac{\frac{1}{2}}{1} = \frac{1}{2},$$

$$\cos 30° = \frac{x}{r} = \frac{\frac{\sqrt{3}}{2}}{1} = \frac{\sqrt{3}}{2},$$

and

$$\tan 30° = \frac{y}{x} = \frac{\frac{1}{2}}{\frac{\sqrt{3}}{2}} = \frac{1}{\sqrt{3}} = \frac{\sqrt{3}}{3}.$$

FIGURE   6 . 12

Before considering another example, let's agree on some symbolism. It is customary to omit writing the word "radian" when using radian measure. For example, an angle θ of radian measure π is usually written as $\theta = \pi$ instead of $\theta = \pi$ radians. However, if the measure is stated in degrees, then be sure to use the degree symbol. In other words, an angle θ of measure 70 degrees is written as $\theta = 70°$ and not $\theta = 70$.

EXAMPLE 8

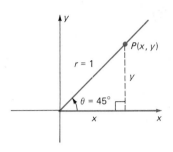

FIGURE   6.13

Find $\sin \theta$, $\cos \theta$, and $\tan \theta$ for $\theta = \pi/4$.

Solution

Remember that $\pi/4$ radians equals $45°$. Therefore, in Figure 6.13 we sketched a $45°$ angle and chose a point P on the terminal side so that $r = 1$. Since $\theta = 45°$, the indicated right triangle is an isosceles right triangle with $x = y$. Using the Pythagorean theorem we can determine that $x = y = \frac{\sqrt{2}}{2}$. (The values of x and y are both positive since P is in the first quadrant.) Thus, the coordinates of point P are $\left(\frac{\sqrt{2}}{2}, \frac{\sqrt{2}}{2} \right)$ and we can determine the trigonometric functional values of $\pi/4$.

$$\sin \frac{\pi}{4} = \frac{y}{r} = \frac{\frac{\sqrt{2}}{2}}{1} = \frac{\sqrt{2}}{2}$$

$$\cos \frac{\pi}{4} = \frac{x}{r} = \frac{\frac{\sqrt{2}}{2}}{1} = \frac{\sqrt{2}}{2}$$

$$\tan \frac{\pi}{4} = \frac{y}{x} = \frac{\frac{\sqrt{2}}{2}}{\frac{\sqrt{2}}{2}} = 1$$

In Examples 7 and 8, notice the convenience of choosing $r = 1$. In general, for any angle θ by choosing $r = 1$ we obtain

$$\sin \theta = \frac{y}{r} = \frac{y}{1} = y \qquad \text{and} \qquad \cos \theta = \frac{x}{r} = \frac{x}{1} = x.$$

In other words, if P is a point one unit from the origin on the terminal side of θ, then the coordinates of point P are $(\cos \theta, \sin \theta)$ as indicated in Figure 6.14. Furthermore, the tangent function can be expressed as $\tan \theta = y/x = \sin \theta/\cos \theta$, for $\cos \theta \neq 0$.

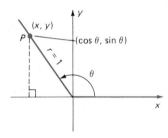

FIGURE   6.14

EXAMPLE 9

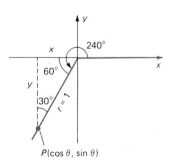

FIGURE   6.15

Find $\sin \theta$, $\cos \theta$, and $\tan \theta$ for $\theta = 240°$.

Solution

In Figure 6.15 we sketched a $240°$ angle and indicated a point P on the terminal side so that $r = 1$. The indicated right triangle is a $30° - 60°$ right triangle with the $30°$ angle at P. Therefore, $x = -\frac{1}{2}$ and $y = -\frac{\sqrt{3}}{2}$ (x and y are both negative because P is in the third quadrant) and the coordinates of P are $\left(-\frac{1}{2}, -\frac{\sqrt{3}}{2} \right)$. Thus, we obtain

$$\sin 240° = y = -\frac{\sqrt{3}}{2},$$
$$\cos 240° = x = -\frac{1}{2},$$

and

$$\tan 240° = \frac{\sin 240°}{\cos 240°} = \frac{-\frac{\sqrt{3}}{2}}{-\frac{1}{2}} = \sqrt{3}.$$

Find $\sin \theta$, $\cos \theta$, and $\tan \theta$ for $\theta = -240°$.

EXAMPLE 10

Solution

In Figure 6.16 we sketched an angle of $-240°$ and indicated a point P on the terminal side so that $r = 1$. The indicated right triangle is a $30° - 60°$ right triangle with the $30°$ angle at P. Therefore, $x = -\frac{1}{2}$ and $y = \frac{\sqrt{3}}{2}$ and we can express the functional values as follows.

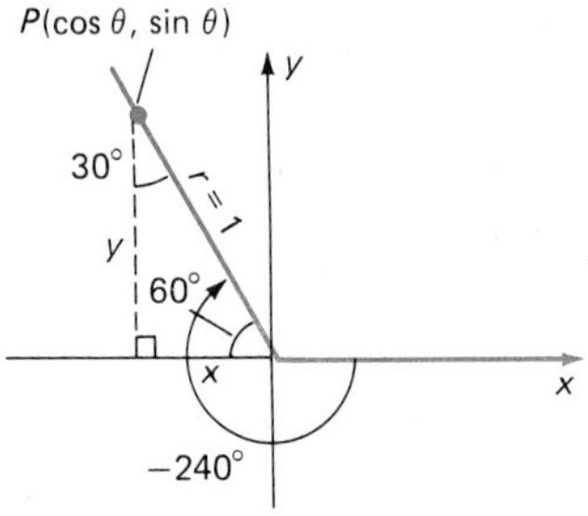

$$\sin(-240°) = y = \frac{\sqrt{3}}{2}$$

$$\cos(-240°) = x = -\frac{1}{2}$$

$$\tan(-240°) = \frac{\sin(-240°)}{\cos(-240°)}$$

$$= \frac{\frac{\sqrt{3}}{2}}{-\frac{1}{2}} = -\sqrt{3}$$

FIGURE 6.16

Compare your results for Examples 9 and 10. Note that $\sin 240° = -\frac{\sqrt{3}}{2}$ and $\sin(-240°) = \frac{\sqrt{3}}{2}$. In other words, $\sin(-240°) = -\sin 240°$. Likewise, observe that $\cos(-240°) = \cos 240°$, and $\tan(-240°) = -\tan 240°$. We will discuss more general relationships of this type in the next section.

If θ is a quadrantal angle (terminal side lies on an axis), it is quite easy to determine the values of the trigonometric functions. The next example illustrates this point.

EXAMPLE 11

Find the values of the six trigonometric functions of θ if $\theta = \pi/2$.

Solution

First, remember that $\pi/2 = 90°$. Then, as indicated in Figure 6.17, let's choose a point P on the terminal side of a $90°$ angle so that $r = 1$. The coordinates of P are $(0, 1)$. Therefore,

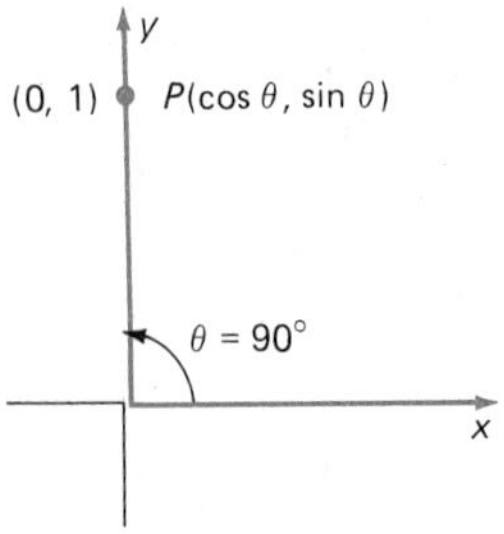

$$\sin \frac{\pi}{2} = y = 1,$$

$$\cos \frac{\pi}{2} = x = 0,$$

$$\tan \frac{\pi}{2} = \frac{\sin \frac{\pi}{2}}{\cos \frac{\pi}{2}} = \frac{1}{0} \qquad \text{Undefined}$$

FIGURE 6.17

$$\csc \frac{\pi}{2} = \frac{1}{\sin \dfrac{\pi}{2}} = \frac{1}{1} = 1,$$

$$\sec \frac{\pi}{2} = \frac{1}{\cos \dfrac{\pi}{2}} = \frac{1}{0} \qquad \text{Undefined}$$

and

$$\cot \frac{\pi}{2} = \frac{x}{y} = \frac{0}{1} = 0.$$

(The reciprocal relationship $\cot \theta = 1/\tan \theta$ cannot be used here because $\tan \pi/2$ is undefined.)

PROBLEM SET 6.1

In Problems 1–12, if the measurement is given in degree-minute-second form, change it to decimal form to the nearest one-hundredth of a degree. If the measurement is given in decimal form, change it to degree-minute-second form.

1. $14°30'$ **2.** $62°15'$ **3.** $22.3°$

4. $114.6°$ **5.** $8°45'18''$ **6.** $34°50'30''$

7. $45.32°$ **8.** $132.15°$ **9.** $150°10'$

10. $94°45'$ **11.** $9.13°$ **12.** $73.47°$

In Problems 13–24, change each angle to radians. Do not use a calculator.

13. $10°$ **14.** $15°$ **15.** $80°$

16. $120°$ **17.** $150°$ **18.** $210°$

19. $225°$ **20.** $300°$ **21.** $-30°$

22. $-330°$ **23.** $-570°$ **24.** $480°$

In Problems 25–36, each angle is expressed in radians. Change each angle to degrees without using a calculator.

25. $\dfrac{\pi}{9}$ **26.** $\dfrac{5\pi}{18}$

27. $\dfrac{13\pi}{18}$ **28.** $\dfrac{7\pi}{12}$

29. $\dfrac{4\pi}{3}$ **30.** $\dfrac{7\pi}{4}$

31. $\dfrac{13\pi}{6}$ **32.** $\dfrac{17\pi}{6}$

33. $-\dfrac{\pi}{4}$ **34.** $-\dfrac{5\pi}{9}$

35. $-\dfrac{7\pi}{6}$ **36.** $-\dfrac{7\pi}{3}$

In Problems 37–42, each angle is expressed in radians. Use your calculator and change each angle to the nearest tenth of a degree.

37. 2 **38.** 3

39. 7 **40.** 4.1

41. -4 **42.** -6.2

In Problems 43–48, use your calculator to help change each angle to the nearest tenth of a radian.

43. $27°$ **44.** $212°$

45. $14.5°$ **46.** $141.8°$

47. $-251.6°$ **48.** $-373.4°$

49. Find, to the nearest tenth of an inch, the length of the arc intercepted by a central angle of $(2\pi)/3$ radians if a radius of the circle is 22 inches long.

50. Find, to the nearest tenth of a meter, the length of the arc intercepted by a central angle of $130°$ if a radius of the circle is 8 meters long.

51. Find, to the nearest tenth of a centimeter, the length of a radius of a circle if a central angle of $80°$ intercepts an arc of 25 centimeters.

52. Find, to the nearest tenth of a foot, the length of a radius of a circle if a central angle of $(3\pi)/5$ radians intercepts an arc of 12 feet.

53. Find, to the nearest tenth of a degree, the measure of a central angle that intercepts an arc of 7.1 centimeters if a radius of the circle is 3.2 centimeters long.

54. Refer to Figure 6.18. How much will the weight be lifted if the drum is rotated through an angle of $150°$? Express the result to the nearest tenth of an inch.

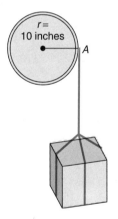

F I G U R E   6 . 18

55. Refer to Figure 6.18 in Problem 54. Through what angle, to the nearest tenth of a degree, must the drum be rotated to raise the weight 6 feet?

56. Two pulleys are connected with a belt as indicated in Figure 6.19. If the smaller pulley makes a complete revolution, through what size angle does the larger pulley turn? Express your result to the nearest tenth of a degree.

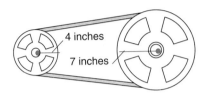

F I G U R E   6 . 19

57. Refer to Figure 6.19 in Problem 56. Through what angle does the smaller pulley turn while the larger pulley makes a complete revolution?

58. Figure 6.20 depicts the back-wheel-drive chain apparatus of a bicycle. How far will the bicycle move forward for each complete revolution of the drive sprocket? Express your result to the nearest inch.

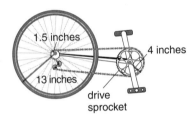

F I G U R E   6 . 20

59. Refer to Figure 6.20 in Problem 58. How much rotation of the drive sprocket is needed to move the bicycle forward 50 feet? Express your result to the nearest tenth of a revolution.

For Problems 60–67, point P is on the terminal side of θ and θ is a positive angle less than $360°$ in standard position. Draw θ, and determine the values of the six trigonometric functions of θ.

60. $P(3, -4)$ **61.** $P(-3, -4)$

62. $P(-5, 12)$ **63.** $P(12, 5)$

64. $P(1, -1)$ **65.** $P(-1, -1)$

66. $P(-2, -3)$ **67.** $P(3, -2)$

For Problems 68–75, point P is on the terminal side of θ and $0° > \theta > -360°$ in standard position. Draw θ, and determine the values of the six trigonometric functions of θ.

68. $P(2, 4)$ **69.** $P(1, -3)$

70. $P(3, -1)$ **71.** $P(-2, 2)$

72. $P(0, 2)$ **73.** $P(-1, 0)$

74. $P(0, -1)$ **75.** $P(4, 4)$

For Problems 76–93, determine $\sin \theta$, $\cos \theta$, and $\tan \theta$.

76. $\theta = 60°$ **77.** $\theta = 150°$

78. $\theta = \dfrac{3}{4}\pi$ **79.** $\theta = \dfrac{7\pi}{6}$

80. $\theta = 300°$ **81.** $\theta = 330°$

82. $\theta = -\dfrac{\pi}{4}$ **83.** $\theta = -\dfrac{\pi}{3}$

84. $\theta = -30°$ **85.** $\theta = -210°$

86. $\theta = 225°$ **87.** $\theta = 315°$

88. $\theta = 390°$ **89.** $\theta = 480°$

90. $\theta = 585°$ **91.** $\theta = 660°$

92. $\theta = \dfrac{23\pi}{6}$ **93.** $\theta = \dfrac{11\pi}{4}$

94. Complete the following table.

θ	θ In Radians	Sin θ	Cos θ	Tan θ	Csc θ	Sec θ	Cot θ
0°							
30°							
45°							
60°							
90°							
180°							
270°							

95. Find $\sin \theta$ if the terminal side of θ lies on the line $y = x$ in the third quadrant.

96. Find $\cos \theta$ if the terminal side of θ lies on the line $y = -x$ in the second quadrant.

97. Find $\tan \theta$ if the terminal side of θ lies on the line $y = -2x$ in the fourth quadrant.

98. Find $\sin \theta$ if the terminal side of θ lies on the line $y = 3x$ in the first quadrant.

99. If $\sin \theta = -\frac{4}{5}$ and the terminal side of θ is in the fourth quadrant, find $\cos \theta$ and $\tan \theta$.

100. If $\cos \theta = -\frac{4}{5}$ and the terminal side of θ is in the third quadrant, find $\sin \theta$ and $\cot \theta$.

101. If $\tan \theta = -\frac{5}{12}$ and the terminal side of θ is in the second quadrant, find $\sin \theta$ and $\cos \theta$.

102. If $\tan \theta = \frac{7}{24}$ and the terminal side of θ is in the first quadrant, find $\sin \theta$ and $\sec \theta$.

103. In which quadrant(s) must the terminal side of θ lie if $\sin \theta$ and $\tan \theta$ are to have the same sign?

104. In which quadrant(s) must the terminal side of θ lie if $\sin \theta$ is negative and $\cos \theta$ is positive?

105. In which quadrant(s) must the terminal side of θ lie if $\sin \theta$, $\cos \theta$, and $\tan \theta$ are all to have the same sign?

106. In which quadrant(s) must the terminal side of θ lie if $\sin \theta$ and $\cos \theta$ have opposite signs?

For Problems 107–112, determine θ if θ is a positive angle less than 360° that satisfies the stated conditions.

107. $\tan \theta = 1$ and $\sin \theta$ is negative

108. $\cos \theta = \frac{1}{2}$ and $\tan \theta$ is positive

109. $\sin \theta = \frac{\sqrt{3}}{2}$ and $\cos \theta$ is negative

110. $\cos \theta = -\frac{\sqrt{3}}{2}$ and $\sin \theta$ is negative

111. $\cos \theta = -\frac{1}{2}$ and $\tan \theta$ is positive

112. $\sin \theta = -1$ and $\cos \theta = 0$

THOUGHTS into WORDS

113. How would you explain the difference between degree measure and radian measure to an elementary geometry student?

114. How could you find the circumference of a bicycle tire without finding the length of a radius?

115. Explain why $\tan 210° = \tan(-150°)$.

116. Explain why $\sin 30° = \sin 390°$.

FURTHER INVESTIGATIONS

117. The *angular speed* of a circular wheel that is rotating at a constant rate is the angle generated in one unit of time by a radius. For example, suppose that a wheel is rotating at a rate of 600 revolutions per minute. Since each revolution generates an angle of 2π radians, the angular speed of the wheel is $600(2\pi) = 1200\pi$ radians per minute.

    If P is a point on the wheel, the *linear speed* of P is the distance that P travels in one unit of time. For example, suppose that the wheel that is rotating at 600 revolutions per minute has a radius of length 2 feet. The distance that a point P on the wheel travels in a minute is given by $s = r\theta = 2(1200\pi) = 2400\pi$ feet. Thus, the linear speed is 2400π feet per minute. To the nearest foot, this is approximately 7540 feet per minute.

a. A wheel with a radius of 3 inches is rotating at 1500 revolutions per minute. Find the angular speed of the wheel and the linear speed of a point on the wheel.

b. A wheel with a diameter of 5 feet is rotating at 850 revolutions per minute. Find the angular speed of the wheel and the linear speed of a point on the wheel.

c. A truck is moving at the rate of 55 miles per hour, and the diameter of each of its wheels is 2.5 feet. Find the number of revolutions per minute that the wheels are rotating and find the angular speed of the wheels.

6.2   TRIGONOMETRIC FUNCTIONS OF ANY ANGLE

Let's begin by summarizing some ideas from the previous section and its problem set. It is easy to determine the signs (positive or negative) of the trigonometric functions in each of the quadrants. For example, using Definition 6.1 with $r = 1$, we know that $\sin \theta = y$, and therefore $\sin \theta$ is positive in quadrants I and II and negative in quadrants III and IV. Furthermore, because $\csc \theta$ is the reciprocal of $\sin \theta$, its signs will agree with $\sin \theta$. The following chart summarizes the signs of all six trigonometric functions in the four quadrants.

QUADRANT CONTAINING θ	POSITIVE FUNCTIONS	NEGATIVE FUNCTIONS
I	All	None
II	sin, csc	cos, sec, tan, cot
III	tan, cot	sin, csc, cos, sec
IV	cos, sec	sin, csc, tan, cot

Table 6.1 summarizes the trigonometric functional values of some special angles that we have worked with thus far. It will be *very helpful* for you to have these values at your fingertips.

TABLE 6.1

θ	θ IN RADIANS	SIN θ	COS θ	TAN θ
$0°$	0	0	1	0
$30°$	$\dfrac{\pi}{6}$	$\dfrac{1}{2}$	$\dfrac{\sqrt{3}}{2}$	$\dfrac{\sqrt{3}}{3}$
$45°$	$\dfrac{\pi}{4}$	$\dfrac{\sqrt{2}}{2}$	$\dfrac{\sqrt{2}}{2}$	1
$60°$	$\dfrac{\pi}{3}$	$\dfrac{\sqrt{3}}{2}$	$\dfrac{1}{2}$	$\sqrt{3}$
$90°$	$\dfrac{\pi}{2}$	1	0	Undefined
$180°$	π	0	-1	0
$270°$	$\dfrac{3\pi}{2}$	-1	0	Undefined

Coterminal Angles

Recall that coterminal angles have the same initial and terminal sides. Therefore, angles in standard position that have the same terminal side are coterminal. Coterminal angles differ from each other by a multiple of $360°$ or of 2π radians. For example, angles of $120°$ and $480°$ are coterminal, as are angles of π and 5π. The angles that are coterminal with any angle θ can be represented by $\theta + 360°n$ or $\theta + 2\pi n$ where n is any integer. Furthermore, it follows from the definitions of the trigonometric functions that **corresponding functions of coterminal angles are equal.** Therefore, when using some values from Table 6.1, you can make the following statements.

$$\sin 390° = \sin 30° = \tfrac{1}{2} \quad \text{because } 390° \text{ and } 30° \text{ are coterminal.}$$

$$\tan 780° = \tan 60° = \sqrt{3} \quad \text{because } 780° \text{ and } 60° \text{ are coterminal.}$$

$$\cos \frac{9\pi}{4} = \cos \frac{\pi}{4} = \frac{\sqrt{2}}{2} \quad \text{because } \frac{9\pi}{4} \text{ and } \frac{\pi}{4} \text{ are coterminal.}$$

$$\sin(-300°) = \sin 60° = \tfrac{\sqrt{3}}{2} \quad \text{because } -300° \text{ and } 60° \text{ are coterminal.}$$

Reference Angle

The concept of a **reference angle** can be defined as follows.

DEFINITION 6.2

Let θ be any angle in standard position with its terminal side in one of the four quadrants. The **reference angle** associated with θ (we will call it θ') is the **acute angle** formed by the terminal side of θ and the x-axis.

In Figure 6.21 we indicated the reference angle θ' for the four different situations in which the terminal side of θ lies in quadrants I, II, III, or IV.

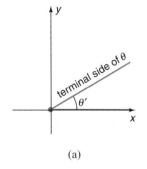

(a)

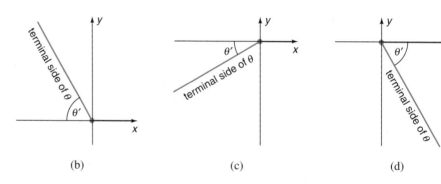

(b)   (c)   (d)

FIGURE 6.21

From our work in the previous section the following fact becomes evident: **The trigonometric functions of any angle θ are equal to those of the reference angle associated with θ, except possibly for the sign. You can determine the sign by considering the quadrant in which the terminal side of θ lies.** Let's consider an example.

EXAMPLE 1

Find $\cos \theta$ if $\theta = 225°$.

Solution

In Figure 6.22, we sketched $\theta = 225°$ and indicated its reference angle $\theta' = 45°$. Since the terminal side of θ lies in the third quadrant, $\cos \theta$ is negative. Therefore,

$$\cos 225° = -\cos 45° = -\frac{\sqrt{2}}{2}.$$

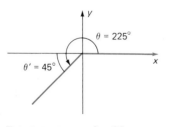

FIGURE 6.22

If you use the information from Table 6.1 and your knowledge of coterminal angles, reference angles, signs of the trigonometric functions in each of the quadrants, and the reciprocal relationships, you can determine the six trigonometric functions of many special angles.

E X A M P L E   2

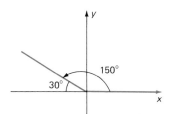

F I G U R E   6 . 2 3

Find the six trigonometric functions of θ for $\theta = 510°$.

Solution

An angle of $510°$ is coterminal with an angle of $510° - 360° = 150°$. The reference angle associated with a $150°$ angle is a $30°$ angle (Figure 6.23). Because θ is a second-quadrant angle, $\sin \theta$ is positive, $\cos \theta$ is negative, and $\tan \theta$ is negative. Therefore, we obtain

$$\sin 510° = \sin 30° = \tfrac{1}{2}$$

$$\cos 510° = -\cos 30° = -\tfrac{\sqrt{3}}{2}$$

$$\tan 510° = -\tan 30° = -\tfrac{\sqrt{3}}{3}.$$

Use the reciprocal relationships to obtain

$$\csc 510° = \frac{1}{\sin 510°} = \frac{1}{\tfrac{1}{2}} = 2,$$

$$\sec 510° = \frac{1}{\cos 510°} = \frac{1}{-\tfrac{\sqrt{3}}{2}} = -\frac{2\sqrt{3}}{3},$$

$$\cot 510° = \frac{1}{\tan 510°} = \frac{1}{-\tfrac{\sqrt{3}}{3}} = -\sqrt{3}.$$

E X A M P L E   3

F I G U R E   6 . 2 4

Find $\sin \theta$ for $\theta = (15\pi)/4$.

Solution

An angle of $(15\pi)/4$ radians is coterminal with an angle of $(15\pi)/4 - 2\pi = (7\pi)/4$. The reference angle associated with an angle of $(7\pi)/4$ radians is an angle of $\pi/4$ radians (Figure 6.24). Because θ is a fourth-quadrant angle, $\sin \theta$ is negative. Therefore,

$$\sin \frac{15\pi}{4} = -\sin \frac{\pi}{4} = -\frac{\sqrt{2}}{2}.$$

REMARK   For a problem such as Example 3, you may find it easier to begin by switching from radians to degrees. That's acceptable, but it is advantageous in later sections to feel comfortable working with radian measure.

E X A M P L E   4

Find $\cos \theta$ for $\theta = -480°$.

Solution

An angle of $-480°$ is coterminal with an angle of $-480° + 720° = 240°$. The reference angle associated with an angle of $240°$ is a $60°$ angle. (Try to mentally picture it without drawing a figure.) Because θ is a third-quadrant angle, $\cos \theta$ is negative. Therefore,

$$\cos(-480°) = -\cos 60° = -\tfrac{1}{2}.$$

Trigonometric Functions of Any Angle

Until now, we have been finding **exact values** for the trigonometric functions of some **special angles**. Now suppose we need a value for $\sin 23°$. An approximate value could be found by drawing, in standard position, a $23°$ angle with a protractor (Figure 6.25). The ordinate of point P, measured in terms of the unit used for r, is an approximate value for $\sin 23°$. Obviously this approach would yield a very crude approximation, but it does emphasize one of the interpretations of the trigonometric functions. For our purposes at this time, better approximations can be found more efficiently by using a calculator or a table of trigonometric values. If you are going to use a table, then turn to Appendix C in the back of the book. You will find a table of trigonometric values and a brief discussion regarding the use of the table.

The following examples illustrate the use of a calculator to find trigonometric functional values.

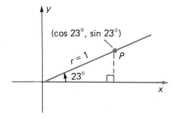

FIGURE   6.25

EXAMPLE 5

Use a calculator to find the value of (a) $\sin 23°$, (b) $\cos 212°$, (c) $\tan(-114.2°)$, and (d) $\tan 90°$.

Solution

First, be sure that your calculator is set for degree measure. Your calculator manual will indicate that procedure. Many calculators are automatically set for degree measure when turned on.

a. To find $\sin 23°$, enter the number 23 and press the $\boxed{\text{SIN}}$ key. The display, to seven decimal places, should read .3907311. Therefore, to the nearest ten-thousandth, $\sin 23° = .3907$.

b. To find $\cos 212°$, enter the number 212 and press the $\boxed{\text{COS}}$ key. The display, to seven decimal places, should read $-.8480481$. Therefore, to the nearest ten-thousandth, $\cos 212° = -.8480$.

c. To evaluate $\tan(-114.2°)$, enter the number 114.2, press the $\boxed{+/-}$ key, and then press the $\boxed{\text{TAN}}$ key. The display, to seven decimal places, will read 2.2251009. Therefore, to the nearest ten-thousandth, $\tan(-114.2°) = 2.2251$.

d. To attempt to evaluate $\tan 90°$, enter the number 90 and press the $\boxed{\text{TAN}}$ key. The display will either blink 9s or give an "error" message. Either way, it is telling us that $\tan 90°$ is undefined.

You can evaluate the trigonometric functions $\csc \theta$, $\sec \theta$, and $\cot \theta$ by using the reciprocal relationships, as the next example illustrates.

Use a calculator to find csc θ, sec θ, and cot θ for $\theta = 57°$.

E X A M P L E 6

Solution

Because csc $57° = 1/\sin 57°$, we can enter 57, press the $\boxed{\text{SIN}}$ key, and then press the $\boxed{1/x}$ key. This will yield, to the nearest ten-thousandth, csc $57° = 1.1924$. In a like manner, because sec $57° = 1/\cos 57°$, we can enter 57, press the $\boxed{\text{COS}}$ key, and then press the $\boxed{1/x}$ key. To the nearest ten-thousandth, we will obtain sec $57° = 1.8361$.

Similarly, because cot $57° = 1/\tan 57°$, we can enter 57, press the $\boxed{\text{TAN}}$ key, and then press the $\boxed{1/x}$ key. To the nearest ten-thousandth, we will obtain cot $57° = .6494$.

REMARK　We have demonstrated key sequences that work on some calculators. There are other sequences that are used on some calculators. For example, with some calculators, to find sin 23° you first push the SIN key and then enter the number 23. Likewise, some calculators have a $\boxed{x^{-1}}$ key rather than a $\boxed{1/x}$ key. As always, you need to know how your calculator works.

From Examples 5 and 6 it is evident that using a calculator to evaluate the six trigonometric functions of any angle is very easy. However, we do suggest that you organize your use of the calculator to minimize the chances of making a human error, such as pressing the wrong key. Along this line, we have two specific suggestions to offer at this time. Suppose we want to evaluate $\sin(-23°)$. First, before pressing any keys on your calculator, mentally picture the terminal side of a $-23°$ angle in the fourth quadrant. Therefore, $\sin(-23°)$ must be a negative number. Secondly, after entering -23, check your display to be sure you entered the correct number. Now by pressing the $\boxed{\text{SIN}}$ key, you should be sure of the result $\sin(-23°) = -.3907$, to the nearest ten-thousandth. We will use the calculator and radian measure in the next section.

In Example 6 we used the reciprocal relationships to help determine some trigonometric values. The relationship $\sin^2\theta + \cos^2\theta = 1$ can also be used at times for that purpose. For example, suppose that θ is a second-quadrant angle and $\sin \theta = \frac{1}{2}$. We can determine the value for $\cos \theta$ from $\sin^2\theta + \cos^2\theta = 1$.

$$\left(\frac{1}{2}\right)^2 + \cos^2\theta = 1$$
$$\frac{1}{4} + \cos^2\theta = 1$$
$$\cos^2\theta = \frac{3}{4}$$
$$\cos \theta = -\frac{\sqrt{3}}{2} \qquad \text{\small cos } \theta \text{ \small is negative since } \theta \text{ \small is a second-quadrant angle}$$

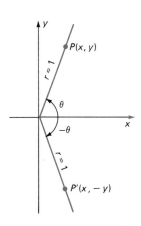

F I G U R E　6 . 2 6

We suggest some additional relationships in Figure 6.26. Points P and P' are located one unit from the origin on the terminal sides of θ and $-\theta$, respectively. The points P and P' are x-axis reflections of each other. Therefore, the coordinates of P' are $(x, -y)$. Then the following relationships can be observed.

$$\sin(-\theta) = -y = -\sin\theta$$

$$\cos(-\theta) = x = \cos\theta$$

$$\tan(-\theta) = \frac{-y}{x} = -\frac{y}{x} = -\tan\theta$$

These properties allow us to make statements such as the following.

$$\sin(-30°) = -\sin 30° = -\frac{1}{2} \qquad \cos(-30°) = \cos 30° = \frac{\sqrt{3}}{2}$$

$$\tan(-30°) = -\tan 30° = -\frac{\sqrt{3}}{3} \qquad \sin\left(-\frac{\pi}{3}\right) = -\sin\frac{\pi}{3} = -\frac{\sqrt{3}}{2}$$

$$\cos\left(-\frac{\pi}{3}\right) = \cos\frac{\pi}{3} = \frac{1}{2} \qquad \tan\left(-\frac{\pi}{3}\right) = -\tan\frac{\pi}{3} = -\sqrt{3}$$

PROBLEM SET 6.2

For Problems 1–8, find the quadrant that contains the terminal side of θ if the given conditions are true.

1. $\sin\theta > 0$ and $\cos\theta > 0$

2. $\sin\theta < 0$ and $\cos\theta < 0$

3. $\sin\theta < 0$ and $\cos\theta > 0$

4. $\tan\theta < 0$ and $\cos\theta > 0$

5. $\sin\theta < 0$ and $\cot\theta > 0$

6. $\sec\theta < 0$ and $\tan\theta < 0$

7. $\csc\theta > 0$ and $\cot\theta < 0$

8. $\cos\theta > 0$ and $\cot\theta < 0$

For Problems 9–16, find α such that $0° < \alpha < 360°$ and α is coterminal with θ.

9. $\theta = 510°$ **10.** $\theta = 570°$

11. $\theta = 960°$ **12.** $\theta = 750°$

13. $\theta = -60°$ **14.** $\theta = -210°$

15. $\theta = -480°$ **16.** $\theta = -660°$

For Problems 17–22, find α such that $0 < \alpha < 2\pi$ and α is coterminal with θ.

17. $\theta = \dfrac{7\pi}{2}$ **18.** $\theta = \dfrac{11\pi}{4}$

19. $\theta = \dfrac{31\pi}{6}$ **20.** $\theta = \dfrac{17\pi}{3}$

21. $\theta = -\dfrac{5\pi}{4}$ **22.** $\theta = -\dfrac{2\pi}{3}$

For Problems 23–34, find the reference angle θ' for each of the given values of θ.

23. $\theta = 265°$ **24.** $\theta = 285.3°$

25. $\theta = 431.8°$ **26.** $\theta = 510°$

27. $\theta = -73°$ **28.** $\theta = -190°$

29. $\theta = \dfrac{5\pi}{4}$ **30.** $\theta = \dfrac{11\pi}{6}$

31. $\theta = \dfrac{8\pi}{3}$ **32.** $\theta = \dfrac{13\pi}{4}$

33. $\theta = -\dfrac{4\pi}{3}$ **34.** $\theta = -\dfrac{5\pi}{6}$

For Problems 35–66, find exact values. Do not use a calculator or a table.

35. $\sin 120°$ **36.** $\cos 150°$

37. $\cos 210°$ **38.** $\sin 210°$

39. $\tan 300°$ **40.** $\tan 315°$

41. $\csc 135°$ **42.** $\sec 240°$

43. $\sec 420°$ **44.** $\csc 480°$

45. $\sin(-150°)$ **46.** $\cos(-210°)$

47. $\cos(-300°)$ **48.** $\sin(-390°)$

49. $\cot(-930°)$ **50.** $\cot(-480°)$

51. $\sin 630°$ **52.** $\cos 540°$

53. $\cos 315°$ **54.** $\sin(-315°)$

55. $\sin \dfrac{2\pi}{3}$ **56.** $\cos \dfrac{3\pi}{4}$

57. $\tan \dfrac{4\pi}{3}$ **58.** $\cot \dfrac{5\pi}{3}$

59. $\cos \dfrac{11\pi}{4}$ **60.** $\sin \dfrac{13\pi}{4}$

61. $\cot \dfrac{13\pi}{3}$ **62.** $\tan \dfrac{31\pi}{6}$

63. $\sin\left(-\dfrac{7\pi}{6}\right)$ **64.** $\cos\left(-\dfrac{5\pi}{3}\right)$

65. $\tan\left(-\dfrac{3\pi}{2}\right)$ **66.** $\tan(-3\pi)$

For Problems 67–80, use your calculator (or the table in Appendix C) to find approximate values. Express the values to the nearest ten-thousandth.

67. $\sin 75°$ **68.** $\cos 80°$

69. $\tan 256°$ **70.** $\tan 171.4°$

71. $\sin 59.4°$ **72.** $\cos 117.6°$

73. $\cos(-156°)$ **74.** $\sin(-43.7°)$

75. $\sec 15.1°$ **76.** $\csc 114.9°$

77. $\csc(-14.7°)$ **78.** $\cot 214.3°$

79. $\cot 328°$ **80.** $\sec 412.3°$

For Problems 81–88, use as necessary the reciprocal relationships, $\sin^2\theta + \cos^2\theta = 1$, $\sin(-\theta) = -\sin \theta$, $\cos(-\theta) = \cos \theta$, and $\tan(-\theta) = -\tan \theta$ to find the required values.

81. If $\sin \theta = \dfrac{\sqrt{3}}{2}$ and θ is a second-quadrant angle, find $\cos \theta$.

82. If $\cos \theta = -\dfrac{1}{2}$ and θ is a third-quadrant angle, find $\sin \theta$.

83. If $\cos \theta = -\dfrac{\sqrt{3}}{2}$, find $\sec \theta$.

84. If $\sin \theta = -\dfrac{1}{2}$, find $\csc \theta$.

85. If $\sin \theta = .1080$, find $\sin(-\theta)$.

86. If $\cos \theta = .2062$, find $\cos(-\theta)$.

87. If $\tan \theta = 1.897$, find $\tan(-\theta)$.

88. If $\sin \theta = \dfrac{3}{4}$ and θ is a second-quadrant angle, find $\tan \theta$.

For Problems 89–94, use your calculator to find approximate values to the nearest ten-thousandth.

89. $\sin 117°6'$ **90.** $\cos 234°12'$

91. $\tan(-114°48')$ **92.** $\sec 221°36'$

93. $\csc 317°54'$ **94.** $\cot 373°24'$

For Problems 95–100, verify each of the statements using a calculator.

95. $\sin 25° = \cos 65°$ **96.** $\cos 72° = \sin 18°$

97. $\sec 10° = \csc 80°$ **98.** $\csc 14.3° = \sec 75.7°$

99. $\tan 47° = \cot 43°$ **100.** $\cot 25.7° = \tan 64.3°$

THOUGHTS into WORDS

101. Give a step-by-step description of how you would determine $\sin 855°$ without using a calculator or a table of trigonometric values.

102. Give a step-by-step description of how you would determine $\cos 17\pi/3$ without using a calculator or a table of trigonometric values.

103. Explain why $\sin(-\theta) = -\sin \theta$.

6.3 CIRCULAR FUNCTIONS: SINE AND COSINE CURVES

Consider the circle $x^2 + y^2 = 1$ that has a radius of length one unit and its center at the origin (Figure 6.27). This is commonly referred to as the **unit circle**. The terminal side of any angle in standard position intersects the unit circle at a point $P(x, y)$ such that $r = 1$. (Note that this is equivalent to choosing a point on the terminal side such that $r = 1$ as we did in Section 6.1.) Again, you should observe that $\sin \theta = y$ and $\cos \theta = x$; so the coordinates of point P are $(\cos \theta, \sin \theta)$. In other words, you can think of the trigonometric functions $\sin \theta$ and $\cos \theta$ as the **ordinate** and **abscissa** values, respectively, of the point of intersection of the terminal side of θ and the unit circle.

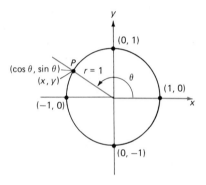

FIGURE 6.27

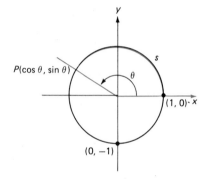

FIGURE 6.28

The formula for arc length $s = r\theta$, developed in Section 6.1, takes on special significance when applied to the unit circle. In Figure 6.28 we consider a central angle θ in standard position that intercepts an arc s on the unit circle. Since $r = 1$, the formula $s = r\theta$ becomes $s = \theta$. That is to say, numerically the length of the arc from $(1, 0)$ to P equals the measure of angle θ in radians. For example, if

$$\theta = \frac{7\pi}{6}, \quad \text{then } s = \frac{7\pi}{6} \text{ units (Figure 6.29(a))};$$

$$\theta = \frac{7\pi}{3}, \quad \text{then } s = \frac{7\pi}{3} \text{ units (Figure 6.29(b))};$$

$$\theta = -\frac{3\pi}{4}, \quad \text{then } s = -\frac{3\pi}{4} \text{ units (Figure 6.29(c))}.$$

In general, to each real number that represents the radian measure of a central angle θ in standard position, we can associate a real number s that represents the length of the arc intercepted by the angle on the unit circle. If θ is positive, then we measure the arc from $(1, 0)$ in a counterclockwise direction to P, where P is the point of intersection of the terminal side of θ and the unit circle. If θ is negative, we measure

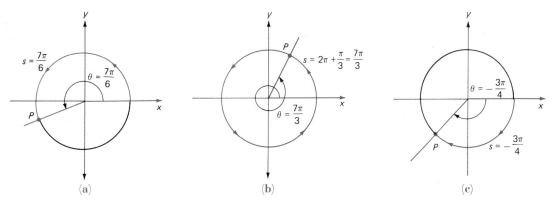

FIGURE 6.29

the arc from $(1, 0)$ in a clockwise direction to P. If $\theta = 0$, then $s = 0$. We refer to the point $P(x, y)$ as **the point on the unit circle that corresponds to** s.

An important consequence of the previous discussion is that we can now use a domain of real numbers independent of any reference to angles to consider the trigonometric functions. In such a setting, we often refer to the trigonometric functions as the **circular functions. If s is a real number and $P(x, y)$ is the point on the unit circle that corresponds to** s, **then**

$$\sin s = y \qquad\qquad \csc s = \frac{1}{y} \quad \text{if } y \neq 0$$

$$\cos s = x \qquad\qquad \sec s = \frac{1}{x} \quad \text{if } x \neq 0$$

$$\tan s = \frac{y}{x} \quad \text{if } x \neq 0 \qquad \cot s = \frac{x}{y} \quad \text{if } y \neq 0.$$

EXAMPLE I

Determine the circular functions $\sin s$, $\cos s$, and $\tan s$ for

a. $s = \pi$ **b.** $s = \dfrac{\pi}{4}$ **c.** $s = -\dfrac{3\pi}{2}.$

Solution

a. Since the circumference of the unit circle is 2π, the point that corresponds to $s = \pi$ is $(-1, 0)$ as indicated in Figure 6.30. Therefore,

$$\sin \pi = y = 0,$$

$$\cos \pi = x = -1,$$

and

$$\tan \pi = \frac{y}{x} = \frac{0}{-1} = 0.$$

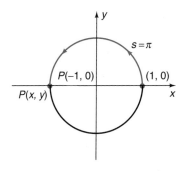

FIGURE 6.30

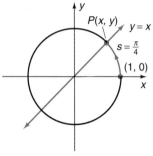

FIGURE   6.31

b. Since $\pi/4 = (1/8)2\pi$, the point $P(x, y)$ must lie on the line $y = x$ that bisects the first quadrant (Figure 6.31). Therefore, substituting x for y in the equation $x^2 + y^2 = 1$, we obtain

$$x^2 + x^2 = 1$$

$$2x^2 = 1$$

$$x^2 = \frac{1}{2}$$

$$x = \sqrt{\frac{1}{2}}$$

$$= \frac{\sqrt{2}}{2}.$$ x and y are positive because P is in the first quadrant

The coordinates of P are $(\sqrt{2}/2, \sqrt{2}/2)$ and the circular functions are determined.

$$\sin \frac{\pi}{4} = y = \frac{\sqrt{2}}{2}$$

$$\cos \frac{\pi}{4} = x = \frac{\sqrt{2}}{2}$$

$$\tan \frac{\pi}{4} = \frac{y}{x} = \frac{\dfrac{\sqrt{2}}{2}}{\dfrac{\sqrt{2}}{2}} = 1$$

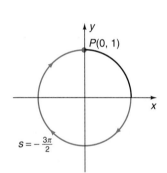

FIGURE   6.32

c. Since $-(3\pi/2) = -(3/4)(2\pi)$, the point $P(x, y)$ that corresponds to $s = -(3\pi/2)$ is $(0, 1)$, as indicated in Figure 6.32. Therefore,

$$\sin\left(-\frac{3\pi}{2}\right) = y = 1$$

$$\cos\left(-\frac{3\pi}{2}\right) = x = 0$$

$$\tan\left(-\frac{3\pi}{2}\right) = \frac{y}{x} = \frac{1}{0}.$$ Undefined   ▬▬▬

In Example 1 we determined the values of some trigonometric (circular) functions without any reference to angles, but don't get the wrong idea. We are not trying to completely eliminate the relationships between angles and trigonometric functions. As a matter of fact, there are many applications of trigonometry that are based on an angle definition of the trigonometric functions. However, there are also numerous applications, especially in the calculus, that use the trigonometric (circular) functions without any reference to angles. So you need to be able to work with these functions in different settings.

Sine Curve

As we graph the trigonometric functions using an xy-coordinate system, equations of the type $f(x) = \sin x$, $f(x) = \cos x$, $f(x) = \tan x$, and so on, will be used. Be careful not to confuse the use of the variable x in these equations with the x we employed earlier in the unit circle approach (where x denoted the x-coordinate of the point P on the unit circle). What is the graph of the function $f(x) = \sin x$? We could begin by making a fairly extensive table of values and then plotting the corresponding points. However, in this case our previous work with the sine function gives us some initial guidance. For example, we know that the sine function behaves as follows.

AS x INCREASES	SINE FUNCTION
From 0 to $\dfrac{\pi}{2}$	Increases from 0 to 1
From $\dfrac{\pi}{2}$ to π	Decreases from 1 to 0
From π to $\dfrac{3\pi}{2}$	Decreases from 0 to -1
From $\dfrac{3\pi}{2}$ to 2π	Increases from -1 to 0

Furthermore, we know from our work with coterminal angles (or the unit circle) that the sine function will repeat itself every 2π radians. More formally, we say that the sine function has a **period** of 2π. (A precise definition of the term *period* is given in a moment.) Now, with these ideas in mind and our knowledge of some specific angles, let's set up a table of values that allows x to vary from 0 to 2π at intervals of $\pi/6$. (For graphing purposes we will use decimal approximations of the radical expressions such as $\sqrt{3}/2$.) Plot the points $(x, f(x))$, determined by the table and connect them with a smooth curve to produce Figure 6.33.

From Figure 6.33 it would be easy to draw as much of the sine curve as we desire; it would repeat itself every 2π units in both directions. Furthermore, in the table for Figure 6.33 we used special angles so that we could determine the functional values without a calculator or a table. Using a calculator, we could easily obtain the following additional functional values: $f(1) = .84, f(2) = .91, f(3) = .14,$ $f(4) = -.76,$ $f(5) = -.96,$ and $f(6) = -.28.$ These values were rounded to the nearest hundredth. Perhaps it would be helpful for you to check these values with your calculator. Be sure that your calculator is set for radian measure. Also note where each of the ordered pairs determined by these functional values would be plotted on the graph in Figure 6.33.

x	$f(x) = \sin x$
0	0
$\pi/6$	$\frac{1}{2}$
$\pi/3$	$\frac{\sqrt{3}}{2} \approx .87$
$\pi/2$	1
$2\pi/3$	$\frac{\sqrt{3}}{2} \approx .87$
$5\pi/6$	$\frac{1}{2}$
π	0
$7\pi/6$	$-\frac{1}{2}$
$4\pi/3$	$-\frac{\sqrt{3}}{2} \approx -.87$
$3\pi/2$	-1
$5\pi/3$	$-\frac{\sqrt{3}}{2} \approx -.87$
$11\pi/6$	$-\frac{1}{2}$
2π	0

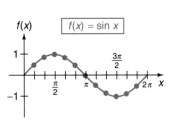

FIGURE 6.33

Cosine Curve

x	$f(x) = \cos x$
0	1
$\pi/6$	$\frac{\sqrt{3}}{2} \approx .87$
$\pi/3$	$\frac{1}{2}$
$\pi/2$	0
$2\pi/3$	$-\frac{1}{2}$
$5\pi/6$	$-\frac{\sqrt{3}}{2} \approx -.87$
π	-1
$7\pi/6$	$-\frac{\sqrt{3}}{2} \approx -.87$
$4\pi/3$	$-\frac{1}{2}$
$3\pi/2$	0
$5\pi/3$	$\frac{1}{2}$
$11\pi/6$	$\frac{\sqrt{3}}{2} \approx .87$
2π	1

As you might expect from the definitions of the sine and cosine functions, their graphs are very similar. The cosine function also has a period of 2π; that is to say, the graph repeats itself every 2π units. In Figure 6.34 we graphed $f(x) = \cos x$, for x between 0 and 2π, by plotting the points determined by the accompanying table.

As with the sine curve, we can sketch as much of the cosine curve as we desire from Figure 6.34 by having it repeat itself every 2π units in both directions. Also note that the cosine curve is identical to the sine curve, but shifted $\pi/2$ units to the left; that is to say,

$$\cos x = \sin\left(x + \frac{\pi}{2}\right).$$

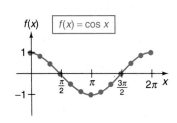

FIGURE 6.34

QUICK REFERENCE CARD

Other Books In THE KAUFMANN SERIES

PWS PUBLISHING COMPANY
A Division of International Thomson
Publishing Inc. I⊤P

FORMULAS FROM TRIGONOMETRY

TRIGONOMETRIC FUNCTIONS

OF REAL NUMBERS

$s = t$
$\theta = t$
$(1, 0)$
(x, y)

$$\sin t = y \qquad \csc t = \frac{1}{y}$$

$$\cos t = x \qquad \sec t = \frac{1}{x}$$

$$\tan t = \frac{y}{x} \qquad \cot t = \frac{x}{y}$$

OF ACUTE ANGLES

hyp, opp, adj, θ

$$\sin \theta = \frac{\text{opp}}{\text{hyp}} \qquad \csc \theta = \frac{\text{hyp}}{\text{opp}}$$

$$\cos \theta = \frac{\text{adj}}{\text{hyp}} \qquad \sec \theta = \frac{\text{hyp}}{\text{adj}}$$

$$\tan \theta = \frac{\text{opp}}{\text{adj}} \qquad \cot \theta = \frac{\text{adj}}{\text{opp}}$$

LAW OF SINES

$$\frac{\sin \alpha}{a} = \frac{\sin \beta}{b} = \frac{\sin \gamma}{c}$$

OBLIQUE TRIANGLE

A, B, C, a, b, c, α, β, γ

LAW OF COSINES

$$a^2 = b^2 + c^2 - 2bc \cos \alpha$$
$$b^2 = a^2 + c^2 - 2ac \cos \beta$$
$$c^2 = a^2 + b^2 - 2ab \cos \gamma$$

$y = \sin t, \ 0 \le t \le 2\pi$

$y = \cos t, \ 0 \le t \le 2\pi$

$y = \tan t$

FUNDAMENTAL IDENTITIES

$$\csc t = \frac{1}{\sin t}$$

$$\sec t = \frac{1}{\cos t}$$

$$\cot t = \frac{1}{\tan t}$$

$$\tan t = \frac{\sin t}{\cos t}$$

$$\cot t = \frac{\cos t}{\sin t}$$

$$\sin^2 t + \cos^2 t = 1$$
$$1 + \tan^2 t = \sec^2 t$$
$$1 + \cot^2 t = \csc^2 t$$

FORMULAS FOR NEGATIVES

$$\sin (-t) = -\sin t$$
$$\cos (-t) = \cos t$$
$$\tan (-t) = -\tan t$$
$$\cot (-t) = -\cot t$$
$$\sec (-t) = \sec t$$
$$\csc (-t) = -\csc t$$

ADDITION FORMULAS

$$\sin (u + v) = \sin u \cos v + \cos u \sin v$$
$$\cos (u + v) = \cos u \cos v - \sin u \sin v$$
$$\tan (u + v) = \frac{\tan u + \tan v}{1 - \tan u \tan v}$$

SUBTRACTION FORMULAS

$$\sin (u - v) = \sin u \cos v - \cos u \sin v$$
$$\cos (u - v) = \cos u \cos v + \sin u \sin v$$
$$\tan (u - v) = \frac{\tan u - \tan v}{1 + \tan u \tan v}$$

HALF-ANGLE FORMULAS

$$\sin \frac{u}{2} = \pm \sqrt{\frac{1 - \cos u}{2}}$$

$$\cos \frac{u}{2} = \pm \sqrt{\frac{1 + \cos u}{2}}$$

$$\tan \frac{u}{2} = \frac{1 - \cos u}{\sin u} = \frac{\sin u}{1 + \cos u}$$

DOUBLE-ANGLE FORMULAS

$$\sin 2u = 2 \sin u \cos u$$
$$\cos 2u = \cos^2 u - \sin^2 u$$
$$= 1 - 2 \sin^2 u$$
$$= 2 \cos^2 u - 1$$

$$\tan 2u = \frac{2 \tan u}{1 - \tan^2 u}$$

FORMULAS FROM GEOMETRY

area A circumference (or perimeter) C
volume V curved surface area S
altitude h radius r

RIGHT TRIANGLE

Pythagorean theorem:
$c^2 = a^2 + b^2$

TRIANGLE

$A = \dfrac{1}{2}bh$ $C = a + b + c$

CIRCLE

$A = \pi r^2$ $C = 2\pi r$

SPHERE

$V = \dfrac{4}{3}\pi r^3$ $S = 4\pi r^2$

RIGHT CIRCULAR CYLINDER

$V = \pi r^2 h$ $S = 2\pi rh$

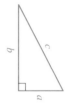

RIGHT CIRCULAR CONE

$V = \dfrac{1}{3}\pi r^2 h$ $S = \pi r\sqrt{r^2 + h^2}$

FORMULAS FROM ALGEBRA

QUADRATIC FORMULA

If $a \neq 0$, the roots of $ax^2 + bx + c = 0$ are

$$x = \frac{-b \pm \sqrt{b^2 - 4ac}}{2a}$$

SPECIAL FACTORING FORMULAS

$x^2 - y^2 = (x + y)(x - y)$

$x^2 + 2xy + y^2 = (x + y)^2$

$x^2 - 2xy + y^2 = (x - y)^2$

$x^3 - y^3 = (x - y)(x^2 + xy + y^2)$

$x^3 + y^3 = (x + y)(x^2 - xy + y^2)$

EXPONENTIALS AND LOGARITHMS

$y = \log_a x$ means $a^y = x$

$\log_a xy = \log_a x + \log_a y$

$\log_a \dfrac{x}{y} = \log_a x - \log_a y$

$\log_a x^r = r \log_a x$

$a^{\log_a x} = x$

$\log_a a^x = x$

$\log_a a = 1$

$\log_a 1 = 0$

$\log x = \log_{10} x$

$\ln x = \log_e x$

$\log_b u = \dfrac{\log_a u}{\log_a b}$

EXPONENTS AND RADICALS

$a^m a^n = a^{m+n}$ $a^{1/n} = \sqrt[n]{a}$

$(a^m)^n = a^{mn}$ $a^{m/n} = \sqrt[n]{a^m}$

$(ab)^n = a^n b^n$ $a^{m/n} = (\sqrt[n]{a})^m$

$\left(\dfrac{a}{b}\right)^n = \dfrac{a^n}{b^n}$ $\sqrt[n]{ab} = \sqrt[n]{a}\,\sqrt[n]{b}$

$\dfrac{a^m}{a^n} = a^{m-n}$ $\sqrt[n]{\dfrac{a}{b}} = \dfrac{\sqrt[n]{a}}{\sqrt[n]{b}}$

$a^{-n} = \dfrac{1}{a^n}$ $\sqrt[m]{\sqrt[n]{a}} = \sqrt[mn]{a}$

POINT-SLOPE FORM OF A LINE

$y - y_1 = m(x - x_1)$
m is the slope

SLOPE-INTERCEPT FORM OF A LINE

$y = mx + b$ m is the slope

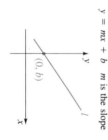

CIRCLE

$(x - h)^2 + (y - k)^2 = r^2$

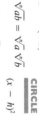 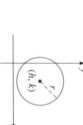

CONIC SECTIONS

PARABOLA

$x^2 = 4py$

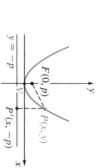

ELLIPSE

$\dfrac{x^2}{a^2} + \dfrac{y^2}{b^2} = 1$ with $a^2 = b^2 + c^2$

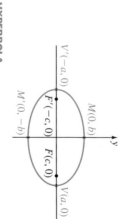

HYPERBOLA

$\dfrac{x^2}{a^2} - \dfrac{y^2}{b^2} = 1$ with $c^2 = a^2 + b^2$

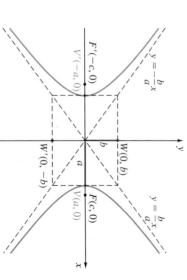

Variations of Sine and Cosine Curves

The concepts of **period**, **amplitude**, and **phase shift** provide a basis for studying variations of the basic sine and cosine curves. First, let's state a precise definition for the concept of a period and then illustrate its effect on certain types of curves.

DEFINITION 6.3

A function f is called **periodic** if a positive real number p exists such that

$$f(x + p) = f(x)$$

for all x in the domain of f. The smallest value for p is called the **period** of the function.

From our work with the sine and cosine functions, it is evident that 2π is the smallest positive number such that $\sin(x + 2\pi) = \sin x$ and $\cos(x + 2\pi) = \cos x$. Thus, as before, we conclude that both the sine and cosine functions are periodic with a period of 2π.

Now suppose we consider the graph of a function that has an equation of the form $f(x) = \sin bx$, where $b > 0$. One cycle of the graph is completed as bx increases from 0 to 2π. When $bx = 0$, $x = 0$ and when $bx = 2\pi$, $x = (2\pi)/b$. A similar line of reasoning holds for $f(x) = \cos bx$ and therefore we can state, **the period of $f(x) = \sin bx$ and also of $f(x) = \cos bx$, where $b > 0$, is $(2\pi)/b$.** If $b < 0$, then we can first apply the appropriate property, $\sin(-x) = -\sin x$ or $\cos(-x) = \cos x$. For example, to graph $f(x) = \sin(-3x)$, we can first change to $f(x) = -\sin 3x$ and then proceed.

EXAMPLE 2

Find the period of $f(x) = \cos 3x$ and sketch the graph for one period beginning at $x = 0$.

Solution

The period of $f(x) = \cos 3x$ is $(2\pi)/3$. Therefore, let's divide the interval from 0 to $(2\pi)/3$ on the x-axis into 4 equal subintervals. Each subinterval will be of length

$$\frac{\dfrac{2\pi}{3} - 0}{4} = \frac{\dfrac{2\pi}{3}}{4}$$

$$= \frac{2\pi}{12} = \frac{\pi}{6}.$$

Then we can plot points determined by the endpoint values of the subintervals and sketch the curve as in Figure 6.35.

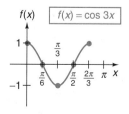

FIGURE   6 . 35

EXAMPLE 3

Find the period of $f(x) = \sin \pi x$ and sketch the graph for one period beginning at $x = 0$.

Solution

The period of $f(x) = \sin \pi x$ is $(2\pi)/\pi = 2$. Again, by dividing the interval from 0 to 2 into 4 equal subintervals, we can plot points determined by the endpoint values of the subintervals and sketch the curve as in Figure 6.36.

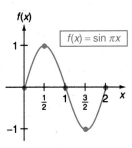

FIGURE 6.36

Amplitude

Consider the graph of $f(x) = 2 \sin x$. It should be evident that for each x-coordinate, the y-coordinate is twice that of the corresponding y-coordinate on the basic sine graph. Likewise, the corresponding y-coordinates of $f(x) = 3 \sin x$ are three times those of the basic sine graph. Thus, in Figure 6.37 we sketched the graphs of $f(x) = 2 \sin x$ and $f(x) = 3 \sin x$ in the interval from 0 to 2π.

The maximum functional value attained by $f(x) = 2 \sin x$ is 2 and by $f(x) = 3 \sin x$ is 3. Each of these maximum functional values is called the amplitude of the graph. In general, we can state that the amplitude of the graph of $f(x) = a \sin x$ or $f(x) = a \cos x$ is $|a|$. For example, the amplitude of $f(x) = \frac{1}{2} \sin x$ is $\left|\frac{1}{2}\right| = \frac{1}{2}$ and the amplitude of $f(x) = -2 \cos x$ is $|-2| = 2$. Together the concepts of period and amplitude help us graph functions of the form $f(x) = a \sin bx$ or $f(x) = a \cos bx$.

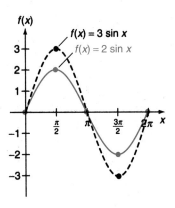

FIGURE 6.37

EXAMPLE 4

Find the period and amplitude of $f(x) = -3 \sin \frac{1}{2}x$, and sketch the curve for one period beginning at $x = 0$.

Solution

The period is $(2\pi)/\frac{1}{2} = 4\pi$ and the amplitude is $|-3| = 3$. The curve $f(x) = -3 \sin \frac{1}{2}x$ is an x-axis reflection of $f(x) = 3 \sin \frac{1}{2}x$. Thus, we obtain Figure 6.38.

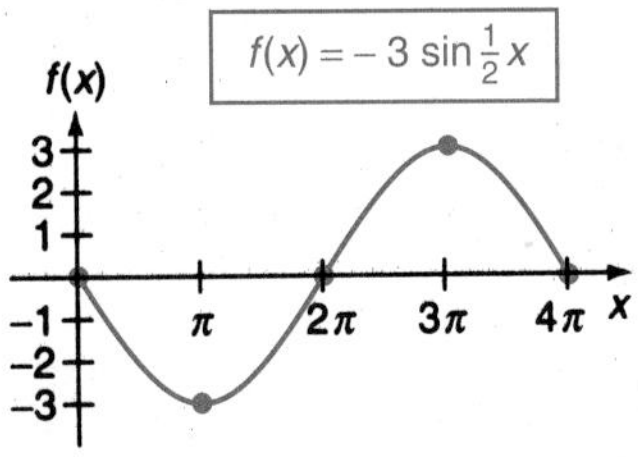

Phase Shift

Recall that the graph $f(x) = (x - 4)^2$ is the graph of $f(x) = x^2$ shifted four units to the right. Likewise, the graph of $f(x) = (x + 2)^2$ is the graph of $f(x) = x^2$ shifted two units to the left. In a similar fashion, the graph of $f(x) = \sin(x - (\pi)/2)$ is the

FIGURE 6.38

graph of $f(x) = \sin x$ shifted $\pi/2$ units to the right and the graph of $f(x) = \cos(x + \pi)$ is the graph of $f(x) = \cos x$ shifted π units to the left. Each of the numbers, $\pi/2$ and π, which represents the amount of shift, is called the **phase shift** of the graph. In general, **the phase shift of $f(x) = \sin(x - c)$ or $f(x) = \cos(x - c)$ is $|c|$. If c is positive, the shift is to the right and if c is negative, the shift is to the left.** Now let's pull together the concepts of period, amplitude, and phase shift in one very useful property.

PROPERTY 6.1

Consider the functions $f(x) = a \sin b(x - c)$ and $f(x) = a \cos b(x - c)$, where $b > 0$.

1. The period of both curves is $2\pi/b$.
2. The amplitude of both curves is $|a|$.
3. The phase shift of both curves is $|c|$. The shift is to the right if c is positive and to the left if c is negative.

EXAMPLE 5

Find the period, amplitude, and phase shift of $f(x) = 2 \sin(x - \pi)$, and sketch the curve.

Solution

By applying Property 6.1 we can determine the following information directly from the equation.

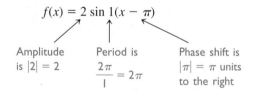

$$f(x) = 2 \sin 1(x - \pi)$$

Amplitude is $|2| = 2$ Period is $\dfrac{2\pi}{1} = 2\pi$ Phase shift is $|\pi| = \pi$ units to the right

Thus, one complete cycle of the sine curve having an amplitude of 2 is contained in the interval from $x = \pi$ to $x = \pi + 2\pi = 3\pi$. The curve repeats itself every 2π units in both directions (Figure 6.39).

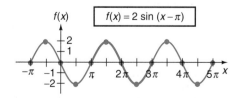

F I G U R E   6 . 3 9

EXAMPLE 6

Find the period, amplitude, and phase shift of $f(x) = \frac{1}{2}\sin(2x + \pi)$ and sketch the curve.

Solution

First, let's change the form of the equation so that Property 6.1 can be applied.

$$f(x) = \frac{1}{2}\sin(2x + \pi)$$

$$= \frac{1}{2}\sin 2\left(x + \frac{\pi}{2}\right)$$

$$= \frac{1}{2}\sin 2\left(x - \left(-\frac{\pi}{2}\right)\right)$$

Now we can obtain some information about the graph as follows.

$$f(x) = \frac{1}{2}\sin 2\left(x - \left(-\frac{\pi}{2}\right)\right).$$

Amplitude   Period is   Phase shift is

is $\left|\frac{1}{2}\right| = \frac{1}{2}$ $\frac{2\pi}{2} = \pi$ $\left|-\frac{\pi}{2}\right| = \frac{\pi}{2}$ units

to the left

Therefore, one complete cycle of the sine curve that has an amplitude of $\frac{1}{2}$ is contained in the interval from $x = -(\pi/2)$ to $x = -(\pi/2) + \pi = (\pi/2)$. The curve repeats itself every π units in both directions (Figure 6.40).

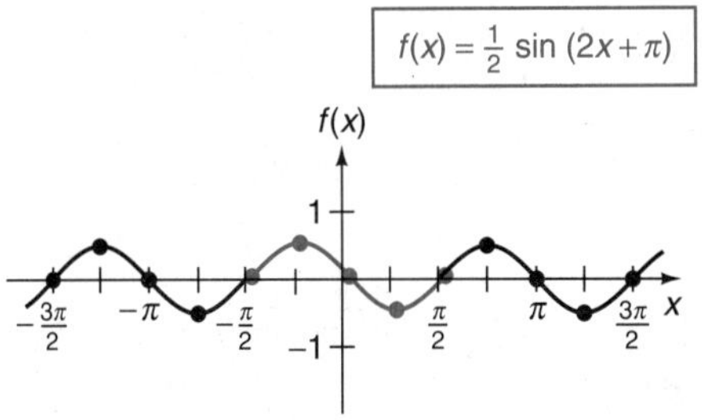

$$f(x) = \tfrac{1}{2}\sin(2x + \pi)$$

FIGURE 6.40

EXAMPLE 7

Find the period, amplitude, and phase shift of $f(x) = 3\cos(2x - (\pi/2))$, and sketch the curve.

Solution

The given equation can be written as

$$f(x) = 3\cos\left(2x - \frac{\pi}{2}\right) = 3\cos 2\left(x - \frac{\pi}{4}\right).$$

From this form we can obtain the following information.

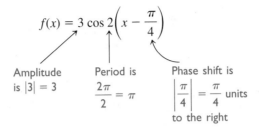

$$f(x) = 3 \cos 2\left(x - \frac{\pi}{4}\right)$$

Amplitude is $|3| = 3$ Period is $\dfrac{2\pi}{2} = \pi$ Phase shift is $\left|\dfrac{\pi}{4}\right| = \dfrac{\pi}{4}$ units to the right

Therefore, one complete cycle of the cosine curve that has an amplitude of 3 is contained in the interval from $x = \pi/4$ to $x = \pi/(4) + \pi = 5\pi/4$. The curve repeats itself every π units in both directions (Figure 6.41).

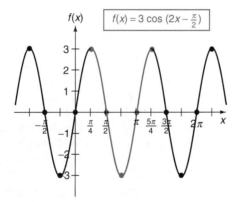

$f(x) = 3 \cos \left(2x - \frac{\pi}{2}\right)$

FIGURE 6.41

Sometimes a mathematical application involves a function that is the sum (or difference) of two or more functions. In such situations a graph of the function is often helpful when solving a problem. For example, suppose that we need the graph of the function $f(x) = \sin x + \cos x$ for $0 \le x \le 2\pi$. Certainly we could set up a table of values and plot some points, but it would take a rather large number of points to determine an accurate graph. Another approach would be to graph the sine curve and cosine curve on the same set of axes and then with a ruler and/or compass graphically add y-coordinates for a number of x-values. Again this approach would require quite a number of points in order to obtain an accurate graph. By far the most efficient way of obtaining the graph is by using a graphing utility as in the following example.

EXAMPLE 8

Use a graphing utility to graph the function $f(x) = \sin x + \cos x$ for $0 \le x \le 2\pi$.

Solution

Let's set a viewing rectangle so that $0 \le x \le 2\pi$ and $-2 \le y \le 2$. Then we can make the following assignments.

$$Y_1 = \sin x, \qquad Y_2 = \cos x, \qquad Y_3 = \sin x + \cos x$$

(Remember that we could also let $Y_3 = Y_1 + Y_2$.) Now the graphing utility can be set to produce all three graphs on the same set of axes as in Figure 6.42(a) or only the final graph of $f(x) = \sin x + \cos x$ as in Figure 6.42(b). Watch your graphing utility produce Figure 6.42(a) to get a dynamic view of the addition of y-coordinates.

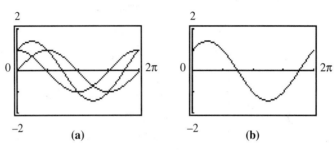

(a)   **(b)**

F I G U R E   6 . 42

Simple Harmonic Motion

Many phenomena in our world behave in a cyclic or rhythmic manner. We can often describe such behavior mathematically using variations of the sine and cosine curves. Such phenomena occur in a large variety of applications ranging from alternating current in electricity to the sound waves generated by a vibrating tuning fork. There is a large class of problems known as simple harmonic motion problems. An example of simple harmonic motion is illustrated in Figure 6.43. Suppose that a weight, W, is attached to a spring. If the weight is pulled down and then released, it will oscillate up and down about the rest or equilibrium point marked O in Figure 6.43. Vibratory motion of this type is called **simple harmonic motion**.

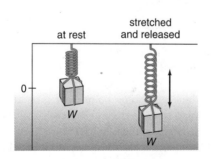

F I G U R E   6 . 43

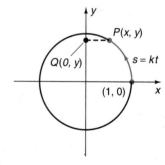

F I G U R E   6 . 44

To obtain a mathematical model of simple harmonic motion, let's use the unit circle in Figure 6.44. Consider a point $P(x, y)$ moving at a constant rate of k radians per unit of time in a counterclockwise direction around the circle. Using $(1, 0)$ as the initial position of P (when $t = 0$), then the arc distance s is given by $s = kt$ after t units of time. So, $y = \sin s = \sin kt$. Now consider point Q, which is the projection of P on the vertical axis. As P moves around the circle, point Q oscillates up and down (simple harmonic motion). At any time t, the distance of point Q from the center of the circle is given by $y = \sin kt$.

PROBLEM SET 6.3

For Problems 1–12, sketch the unit circle and indicate the given arc s along with its initial and terminal points. Then determine the exact values of the six circular functions of s without using a calculator or a table.

1. $s = \dfrac{3\pi}{4}$ **2.** $s = \dfrac{7\pi}{4}$ **3.** $s = \dfrac{3\pi}{2}$

4. $s = 2\pi$ **5.** $s = -\dfrac{\pi}{4}$ **6.** $s = -\pi$

7. $s = \dfrac{4\pi}{3}$ **8.** $s = \dfrac{7\pi}{6}$ **9.** $s = \dfrac{5\pi}{2}$

10. $s = \dfrac{7\pi}{3}$ **11.** $s = -\dfrac{11\pi}{4}$ **12.** $s = -\dfrac{15\pi}{4}$

For Problems 13–38, graph each of the given functions in the indicated interval.

13. $f(x) = \cos 2x, \quad 0 \le x \le 2\pi$

14. $f(x) = \cos \pi x, \quad 0 \le x \le 2$

15. $f(x) = \sin 3x, \quad -\dfrac{2\pi}{3} \le x \le \dfrac{2\pi}{3}$

16. $f(x) = \sin 2x, \quad -2\pi \le x \le 2\pi$

17. $f(x) = 2 \cos x, \quad 0 \le x \le 2\pi$

18. $f(x) = -3 \cos x, \quad 0 \le x \le 2\pi$

19. $f(x) = \dfrac{1}{2} \sin x, \quad -2\pi \le x \le 2\pi$

20. $f(x) = \dfrac{1}{2} \cos x, \quad -2\pi \le x \le 2\pi$

21. $f(x) = 2 \sin \dfrac{1}{2} x, \quad 0 \le x \le 4\pi$

22. $f(x) = 3 \cos \dfrac{1}{2} x, \quad 0 \le x \le 4\pi$

23. $f(x) = \cos\left(x + \dfrac{\pi}{2}\right), \quad -\dfrac{\pi}{2} \le x \le \dfrac{3\pi}{2}$

24. $f(x) = \sin(x - \pi), \quad \pi \le x \le 3\pi$

25. $f(x) = -\sin\left(x - \dfrac{\pi}{2}\right), \quad \dfrac{\pi}{2} \le x \le \dfrac{5\pi}{2}$

26. $f(x) = -\cos(x - \pi), \quad \pi \le x \le 3\pi$

27. $f(x) = \sin(-x), \quad -2\pi \le x \le 2\pi$

28. $f(x) = \cos(-x), \quad -2\pi \le x \le 2\pi$

29. $f(x) = \sin(-2x), \quad 0 \le x \le 2\pi$

30. $f(x) = \sin(-\pi x), \quad 0 \le x \le 4$

31. $f(x) = \cos(-\pi x), \quad 0 \le x \le 4$

32. $f(x) = \cos(-2x), \quad 0 \le x \le 2\pi$

33. $f(x) = 1 + \sin(x - \pi), \quad \pi \le x \le 3\pi$

34. $f(x) = -2 + \sin\left(x - \dfrac{\pi}{2}\right), \quad \dfrac{\pi}{2} \le x \le \dfrac{5\pi}{2}$

35. $f(x) = -1 + \cos(x + \pi), \quad -\pi \le x \le \pi$

36. $f(x) = 1 + \cos\left(x - \dfrac{\pi}{2}\right), \quad \dfrac{\pi}{2} \le x \le \dfrac{5\pi}{2}$

37. $f(x) = 1 - \sin(x - \pi), \quad \pi \le x \le 3\pi$

38. $f(x) = 2 - \cos(x + \pi), \quad -\pi \le x \le \pi$

For Problems 39–60, find the period, amplitude, and phase shift of the given function and draw the graph of the function.

39. $f(x) = 3 \sin\left(x + \dfrac{\pi}{2}\right)$ **40.** $f(x) = \dfrac{1}{2} \sin\left(x - \dfrac{\pi}{2}\right)$

41. $f(x) = 2 \cos(x - \pi)$ **42.** $f(x) = 3 \cos\left(x + \dfrac{\pi}{2}\right)$

43. $f(x) = \dfrac{1}{2} \cos\left(x + \dfrac{\pi}{4}\right)$ **44.** $f(x) = 2 \sin\left(x - \dfrac{\pi}{3}\right)$

45. $f(x) = -2 \sin(x + \pi)$ **46.** $f(x) = -3 \cos(x + \pi)$

47. $f(x) = 2 \sin 2(x - \pi)$ **48.** $f(x) = 3 \cos 2\left(x - \dfrac{\pi}{2}\right)$

49. $f(x) = \dfrac{1}{2} \cos 3(x + \pi)$ **50.** $f(x) = 2 \sin 3(x - \pi)$

51. $f(x) = \sin(2x - \pi)$ **52.** $f(x) = \cos\left(2x + \dfrac{\pi}{2}\right)$

53. $f(x) = 2\cos(3x - \pi)$ **54.** $f(x) = 4\sin(2x + \pi)$

55. $f(x) = \dfrac{1}{2}\sin(3x - \pi)$

56. $f(x) = 2\sin\left(\dfrac{1}{2}x - \dfrac{\pi}{2}\right)$

57. $f(x) = 2\cos\left(\dfrac{1}{2}x + \dfrac{\pi}{2}\right)$

58. $f(x) = -2\sin(2x - \pi)$

59. $f(x) = -3\sin(2x + \pi)$

60. $f(x) = -\dfrac{1}{2}\cos\left(2x - \dfrac{\pi}{2}\right)$

For Problems 61–64, graph each of the given functions in the indicated interval.

61. $f(x) = 1 + 2\sin\left(x - \dfrac{\pi}{2}\right), \quad \dfrac{\pi}{2} \le x \le \dfrac{5\pi}{2}$

62. $f(x) = 2 - 3\cos\left(x + \dfrac{\pi}{2}\right), \quad -\dfrac{\pi}{2} \le x \le \dfrac{3\pi}{2}$

63. $f(x) = -1 + 2\cos(2x + \pi), \quad -\dfrac{\pi}{2} \le x \le \dfrac{3\pi}{2}$

64. $f(x) = -2 + 2\sin\left(2x - \dfrac{\pi}{2}\right), \quad \dfrac{\pi}{4} \le x \le \dfrac{9\pi}{4}$

THOUGHTS into WORDS

65. a. Give an *angle interpretation* of the fact that $\sin 45° = \sqrt{2}/2$.
   b. Give an *arc length interpretation* of the fact that $\sin(\pi/4) = \sqrt{2}/2$.

66. Explain in your own words the concepts of period, amplitude, and phase shift.

67. Explain how you would graph the function $f(x) = -1 - \sin x$.

 GRAPHICS CALCULATOR ACTIVITIES

Set your graphics calculator to graph trigonometric functions using radian measure. If necessary, consult your user's manual for specific instructions. Now graph the functions $f(x) = \sin x$ and $f(x) = \cos x$ for $0 \le x \le 2\pi$. Be sure that your graphs agree with Figures 6.33 and 6.34. Then graph the functions in Examples 2, 3, and 4 of this section. Be sure to set the domain and range so that your graphs look like Figures 6.35, 6.36, and 6.38.

The following activities are designed to reinforce and extend some of the concepts of this section.

68. Use your graphics calculator to check your graphs for Problems 27–32 and Problems 61–64.

69. Graph $f(x) = \sin x$, $f(x) = \sin 2x$, and $f(x) = \sin 4x$ on the same set of axes. What effect do the 2 and 4 seem to have on the graphs? Predict the graph of $f(x) = \sin 8x$. Then graph $f(x) = \sin x$ and $f(x) = \sin 8x$ on the same set of axes.

70. Graph $f(x) = \sin x$, $f(x) = 2\sin x$, $f(x) = 3\sin x$, and $f(x) = 4\sin x$ on the same set of axes. What effect do the 2, 3, and 4 seem to have on the graphs? Predict the graph of $f(x) = 5\sin x$. Now graph $f(x) = \sin x$ and $f(x) = 5\sin x$ on the same set of axes.

71. Graph $f(x) = \sin x$ and $f(x) = \sin\left(x - \dfrac{\pi}{2}\right)$ on the same set of axes. Predict the graph of $f(x) = \sin\left(x + \dfrac{\pi}{2}\right)$, and then graph $f(x) = \sin x$ and $f(x) = \sin\left(x + \dfrac{\pi}{2}\right)$ on the same set of axes.

72. Use your graphics calculator to demonstrate the truth of each of the following.
   a. $\sin\left(x + \dfrac{\pi}{2}\right) = \cos x$
   b. $\sin\left(x - \dfrac{\pi}{2}\right) = -\cos x$
   c. $\sin(x + \pi) = -\sin x$
   d. $\sin(x - \pi) = -\sin x$

73. Use your graphics calculator to determine what relationship holds between $\cos\left(x + \dfrac{\pi}{2}\right)$ and $\sin x$.

74. For each of the following, (a) predict the general shape and location of the graph, and (b) use your graphics calculator to graph the function to check your prediction.

a. $f(x) = 2 \sin x + \cos x$

b. $f(x) = \sin 2x + \cos x$

c. $f(x) = \sin x + \cos 2x$

d. $f(x) = \sin x - \cos x$

e. $f(x) = \cos x - \sin x$

f. $f(x) = 2 \cos x + \sin x$

75. Graph $f(x) = |x|$, $f(x) = -|x|$, and $f(x) = x \sin x$ on the same set of axes. The graph of $f(x) = x \sin x$ is called a *damped sine wave* and the x factor is called the *damping factor*. Look at your display and note that the curve for $f(x) = x \sin x$ appears to be clamped between $f(x) = |x|$ and $f(x) = -|x|$. Construct an algebraic argument to verify that $-|x| \le x \sin x \le |x|$.

76. How do you think the graph of $f(x) = x \cos x$ compares to the graph of $f(x) = x \sin x$? Graph $f(x) = |x|$, $f(x) = -|x|$, $f(x) = x \sin x$, and $f(x) = x \cos x$ on the same set of axes to check your prediction.

6.4   GRAPHING THE OTHER BASIC TRIGONOMETRIC FUNCTIONS

Recall that $\tan x = (\sin x)/\cos x$, and therefore it is not defined at those values of x for which $\cos x = 0$ (namely, at $x = \pm\pi/2, \pm 3\pi/2, \pm 5\pi/2$, etc.). Thus, to graph $f(x) = \tan x$, we will first use vertical dashed lines to indicate those values of x where the tangent function is undefined (Figure 6.45). Next, let's consider some functional values in the interval between $x = -\pi/2$ and $x = \pi/2$ as indicated in the table. We plot the points determined by these values in Figure 6.45. Notice that $\tan x$ is getting larger as x increases from $\pi/6$ to $\pi/4$ to $\pi/3$. By choosing more values of x between $\pi/3$ and $\pi/2$, and using a calculator, we obtain the following results.

$$\tan 1.1 = 2.0 \qquad \tan 1.2 = 2.6$$

$$\tan 1.3 = 3.6 \qquad \tan 1.4 = 5.8$$

$$\tan 1.5 = 14.1 \qquad \tan 1.55 = 48.1$$

x	$f(x) = \tan x$
$-\dfrac{\pi}{3}$	$-\sqrt{3} \approx -1.73$
$-\dfrac{\pi}{4}$	-1
$-\dfrac{\pi}{6}$	$-\dfrac{\sqrt{3}}{3} \approx -.58$
0	0
$\dfrac{\pi}{6}$	$\dfrac{\sqrt{3}}{3} \approx .58$
$\dfrac{\pi}{4}$	1
$\dfrac{\pi}{3}$	$\sqrt{3} \approx 1.73$

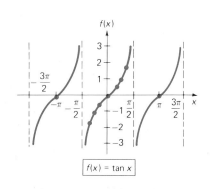

FIGURE   6.45

It should be evident that $\tan x$ increases without bound as x approaches $\pi/2$ from the left. Likewise, we could show that $\tan x$ decreases without bound as x approaches $-\pi/2$ from the right. Using a similar approach, we could show that this pattern repeats itself in the intervals $\pi/2 < x < 3\pi/2$, $-3\pi/2 < x < -\pi/2$, and so on, in both directions at intervals of length π. In other words, the tangent function has period π. Figure 6.45 shows the tangent function through three periods.

We can graph the cotangent function in much the same manner that we graphed the tangent function. First, because $\cot x = (\cos x)/\sin x$, where $\sin x \neq 0$, we know that the cotangent function is not defined at $x = 0$, $\pm\pi$, $\pm2\pi$, etc. These values locate the vertical asymptotes as indicated in Figure 6.46. As the reciprocal of the tangent function, the cotangent function also has a period of π. Finally, by plotting a few points $(\pi/6, \sqrt{3})$, $(\pi/4, 1)$, $(\pi/3, \sqrt{3}/3)$, $(2\pi/3, -\sqrt{3}/3)$, $(3\pi/4, -1)$, and $(5\pi/6, -\sqrt{3})$ in the interval $0 < x < \pi$, we can sketch the cotangent curve as in Figure 6.46.

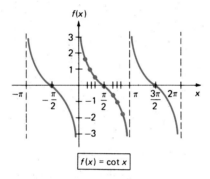

$$f(x) = \cot x$$

FIGURE 6.46

Variations of Tangent and Cotangent Curves

We have seen that both the tangent and cotangent functions have a period of π; that is, they repeat themselves every π units. This also means that their asymptotes are π units apart. Furthermore, because the tangent and cotangent functions increase and decrease without bound, the concept of amplitude has no meaning. However, to see the effect of a number a on the graph of a function of the form $f(x) = a \tan x$ or $f(x) = a \cot x$, the graphs of one period of $f(x) = 3 \tan x$ and $f(x) = \frac{1}{2} \cot x$ are shown in Figure 6.47. Notice how the 3 in $f(x) = 3 \tan x$ sort of *stretches* the tangent curve and the $\frac{1}{2}$ in $f(x) = \frac{1}{2} \cot x$ sort of *compresses* the cotangent curve. We need to keep these facts in mind as we use the general equations $f(x) = a \tan b(x - c)$ and $f(x) = a \cot b(x - c)$, $b > 0$, to study variations of the basic tangent and cotangent curves. The number a affects ordinate values but has no significance in terms of amplitude. In each case, the period is determined by π/b and the phase shift is again $|c|$. Let's consider some examples.

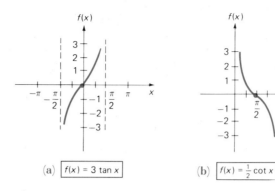

(a) $f(x) = 3 \tan x$ (b) $f(x) = \frac{1}{2} \cot x$

FIGURE 6.47

EXAMPLE I

Find the period and phase shift of $f(x) = 2 \tan(x - \pi/4)$, and sketch the curve.

Solution

From the equation we can determine the period and the phase shift.

$$f(x) = 2 \tan 1\left(x - \frac{\pi}{4}\right)$$

Period is
$\pi/1 = \pi$

Phase shift is
$\pi/4$ units to the right

Let's shift the asymptotes $x = -\pi/2$ and $x = \pi/2$ of $g(x) = \tan x$ to the right $\pi/4$ units. So we have asymptotes at $x = -\pi/4$ and at $x = 3\pi/4$ as shown in Figure 6.48. The curve crosses the x-axis at $x = \pi/4$ since $f(\pi/4) = 0$. The points $(0, -2)$ and $(\pi/2, 2)$ help determine the shape of the curve. Figure 6.48 shows the graph through three periods.

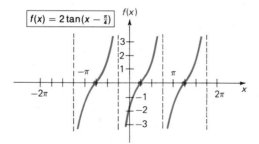

$f(x) = 2 \tan(x - \frac{\pi}{4})$

FIGURE 6.48

Before we consider the next example, let's make an important observation. Remember that two asymptotes of the curve $f(x) = \cot x$ are located at $x = 0$ and at $x = \pi$. Now consider the function $g(x) = \cot 2x$. If $2x = 0$, then $x = 0$ and if $2x =$

π, then $x = \pi/2$. So, two asymptotes of the curve $g(x) = \cot 2x$ are located at $x = 0$ and $x = \pi/2$. Keep this in mind as we consider the next example.

EXAMPLE 2

Find the period and phase shift of $f(x) = \frac{1}{2} \cot(2x + \pi)$, and sketch the curve.

Solution

First, let's change the form of the equation so that it yields some useful information.

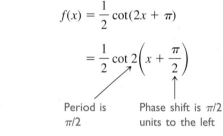

$$f(x) = \frac{1}{2} \cot(2x + \pi)$$

$$= \frac{1}{2} \cot 2\left(x + \frac{\pi}{2}\right)$$

Period is
$\pi/2$

Phase shift is $\pi/2$
units to the left

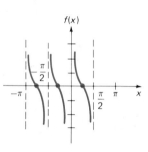

$f(x) = \frac{1}{2}\cot(2x + \pi)$

FIGURE 6.49

Let's shift the asymptotes, $x = 0$ and $x = \pi/2$, *of* $g(x) = \cot 2x$, to the left $\pi/2$ units. So we have asymptotes at $x = -\pi/2$ and at $x = 0$, as shown in Figure 6.49. The curve crosses the x-axis at $x = -\pi/4$ since $f(-\pi/4) = 0$. The points $\left(-\pi/8, -\frac{1}{2}\right)$ and $\left(-3\pi/8, \frac{1}{2}\right)$ help determine the shape of the curve. Figure 6.49 shows the graph through three periods.

Cosecant and Secant Curves

The graphs of $f(x) = \csc x$ and $f(x) = \sec x$ can be sketched easily by using the reciprocal relationships $\csc x = 1/\sin x$ and $\sec x = 1/\cos x$. In Figures 6.50 and 6.51 we have first drawn the sine and cosine curves (dashed curves) and then used

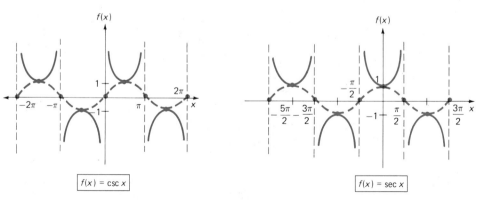

$f(x) = \csc x$

$f(x) = \sec x$

FIGURE 6.50   **FIGURE 6.51**

those curves to help sketch the cosecant and secant curves, respectively. The following general properties should be noted.

1. Because all functional values of $\sin x$ and $\cos x$ are between ± 1, inclusive, we know that all functional values for $\csc x$ and $\sec x$ are greater than or equal to 1, or less than or equal to -1.

2. For graphing $f(x) = \csc x$, vertical asymptotes exist at $x = 0$, $\pm \pi$, $\pm 2\pi$, etc.

3. For graphing $f(x) = \sec x$, vertical asymptotes exist at $x = \pm\frac{\pi}{2}$, $\pm\frac{3\pi}{2}$, $\pm\frac{5\pi}{2}$, etc.

4. Both the cosecant function and the secant function have a period of 2π.

The two equations $f(x) = a \csc b(x - c)$ and $f(x) = a \sec b(x - c)$ are used to express variations of the cosecant and secant curves, respectively. As with tangent and cotangent curves, the concept of amplitude has no meaning with cosecant and secant curves. Thus, the number a simply affects ordinate values, but has no significance relative to amplitude. **For both $f(x) = a \csc b(x - c)$ and $f(x) = a \sec b(x - c)$, where $b > 0$, the period is determined by $2\pi/b$ and the phase shift is again $|c|$.**

In Figure 6.50, notice that three asymptotes of the curve $f(x) = \csc x$ are located at $x = 0$, $x = \pi$, and $x = 2\pi$. Now consider the function $g(x) = \csc 2x$.

If $2x = 0$, then $x = 0$.

If $2x = \pi$, then $x = \frac{\pi}{2}$.

If $2x = 2\pi$, then $x = \pi$.

So, the curve $g(x) = \csc 2x$ has three asymptotes at $x = 0$, $x = \pi/2$, and $x = \pi$.

EXAMPLE 3

Find the period and phase shift of $f(x) = \csc 2(x - \pi/4)$, and sketch the curve.

Solution

From the equation we can determine the period and phase shift.

$$f(x) = \csc 2\left(x - \frac{\pi}{4}\right)$$

Period is   Phase shift is $\pi/4$
$2\pi/2 = \pi$ units to the right.

Let's shift the asymptotes, $x = 0$, $x = \pi/2$, and $x = \pi$ of $g(x) = \csc 2x$, to the right $\pi/4$ units. So, we have asymptotes at $x = \pi/4$, $x = 3\pi/4$, and $x = 5\pi/4$ as indicated in Figure 6.52. The points $(\pi/2, 1)$ and $(\pi, -1)$ determine the turning points. One period of the graph is shown in Figure 6.52.

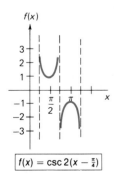

$f(x) = \csc 2(x - \frac{\pi}{4})$

F I G U R E   6 . 52

E X A M P L E   4

Use a graphing utility to graph the function $f(x) = \csc x + \sec x$ for $0 \le x \le 2\pi$.

Solution

Before using a graphing utility, let's go back and take another look at the cosecant and secant curves between $x = 0$ and $x = 2\pi$ in Figures 6.50 and 6.51, respectively. From these graphs we can tell that the graph of the sum of these two functions will have vertical asymptotes at $x = 0$, $x = \pi/2$, $x = \pi$, $x = 3\pi/2$, and $x = 2\pi$. Furthermore, between $x = 0$ and $x = \pi/2$, the graph should be entirely above the *x*-axis, but between $x = \pi/2$ and $x = \pi$, the graph will appear both above and below the *x*-axis. Then between $x = \pi$, and $x = 3\pi/2$, the graph will be below the *x*-axis, but between $x = 3\pi/2$, and $x = 2\pi$, the graph will be both above and below the *x*-axis.

Now let's use a graphing utility to obtain the graph of $f(x) = \csc x + \sec x$. Figure 6.53 below shows this display where we used a viewing rectangle such that $0 \le x \le 2\pi$ and $-5 \le y \le 5$.

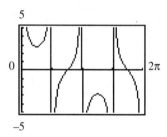

F I G U R E   6 . 5 3

P R O B L E M   S E T   6 . 4

For Problems 1–22, graph each of the functions in the indicated interval.

1. $f(x) = \tan x$, $0 \le x \le \pi$

2. $f(x) = -\tan x$, $-\dfrac{\pi}{2} \le x \le \dfrac{\pi}{2}$

3. $f(x) = -2 \tan x$, $-\dfrac{\pi}{2} \le x \le \dfrac{\pi}{2}$

4. $f(x) = \dfrac{1}{2} \tan x$, $-\dfrac{\pi}{2} \le x \le \dfrac{\pi}{2}$

5. $f(x) = 2 + \tan x$, $-\dfrac{\pi}{2} \le x \le \dfrac{\pi}{2}$

6. $f(x) = -1 + \tan x$, $-\dfrac{\pi}{2} \le x \le \dfrac{\pi}{2}$

7. $f(x) = \tan(-x)$, $-\dfrac{\pi}{2} \le x \le \dfrac{\pi}{2}$

8. $f(x) = \tan 2x$, $-\dfrac{\pi}{4} \le x \le \dfrac{\pi}{4}$

9. $f(x) = 1 + \cot x$, $0 \le x \le 2\pi$

10. $f(x) = -2 + \cot x$, $0 \le x \le 2\pi$

11. $f(x) = \cot(-x)$, $0 \le x \le \pi$

12. $f(x) = -\cot x$, $0 \le x \le \pi$

13. $f(x) = \cot 3x, \quad 0 \le x \le \pi$

14. $f(x) = \cot \pi x, \quad -1 \le x \le 1$

15. $f(x) = \csc 2x, \quad 0 \le x \le \pi$

16. $f(x) = -\csc x, \quad 0 \le x \le 2\pi$

17. $f(x) = 3 \csc \pi x, \quad 0 \le x \le 2$

18. $f(x) = 1 + \csc x, \quad 0 \le x \le 2\pi$

19. $f(x) = -\sec x, \quad -\dfrac{\pi}{2} \le x \le \dfrac{3\pi}{2}$

20. $f(x) = \sec 3x, \quad -\dfrac{\pi}{6} \le x \le \dfrac{\pi}{2}$

21. $f(x) = \sec(-x), \quad -\dfrac{\pi}{2} \le x \le \dfrac{3\pi}{2}$

22. $f(x) = 1 + \sec x, \quad -\dfrac{\pi}{2} \le x \le \dfrac{3\pi}{2}$

For Problems 23–36, find the period and phase shift of the given function, and sketch the graph through two periods.

23. $f(x) = \tan\left(x + \dfrac{\pi}{2}\right)$

24. $f(x) = \tan(x - \pi)$

25. $f(x) = 2 \tan\left(x - \dfrac{\pi}{4}\right)$

26. $f(x) = 3 \tan\left(x + \dfrac{\pi}{4}\right)$

27. $f(x) = \tan(2x + \pi)$

28. $f(x) = \tan(3x - \pi)$

29. $f(x) = -2 \tan\left(x - \dfrac{\pi}{2}\right)$

30. $f(x) = -\tan(x + \pi)$

31. $f(x) = \tan(3x - 2\pi)$

32. $f(x) = \tan(2x + 3\pi)$

33. $f(x) = \dfrac{1}{2} \cot\left(x - \dfrac{\pi}{4}\right)$

34. $f(x) = -\dfrac{1}{2} \cot\left(x + \dfrac{\pi}{2}\right)$

35. $f(x) = \cot \dfrac{1}{2}\left(x + \dfrac{\pi}{2}\right)$

36. $f(x) = \cot(2x - 2\pi)$

For Problems 37–46, find the period and phase shift of the given function, and sketch the graph through one period.

37. $f(x) = \csc\left(x - \dfrac{\pi}{2}\right)$

38. $f(x) = \csc(x + \pi)$

39. $f(x) = -\csc\left(x + \dfrac{\pi}{4}\right)$

40. $f(x) = -\csc\left(x - \dfrac{\pi}{2}\right)$

41. $f(x) = \csc(2x + \pi)$

42. $f(x) = \csc \dfrac{1}{2}\left(x + \dfrac{\pi}{2}\right)$

43. $f(x) = \sec(x + \pi)$

44. $f(x) = 2 \sec\left(x - \dfrac{\pi}{2}\right)$

45. $f(x) = -2 \sec\left(x - \dfrac{\pi}{4}\right)$

46. $f(x) = \sec(3x - 3\pi)$

47. Give a step-by-step description of how you would graph the function $f(x) = 2 \tan(2x - \pi)$.

48. Why does the concept of amplitude have no significance with respect to tangent, cotangent, secant, and cosecant curves?

GRAPHICS CALCULATOR ACTIVITIES

49. Be sure that you agree with each of the graphs in Figures 6.45–6.52.

50. How should the graphs of $f(x) = 2 \tan x$ and $f(x) = 3 \tan x$ compare to the graph of $f(x) = \tan x$? Graph all three functions on the same set of axes to check your prediction.

51. How should the graph of $f(x) = -\tan x$ compare to the graph of $f(x) = \tan x$? Graph both functions on the same set of axes to check your prediction.

52. For each of the following, (a) predict how the graph of the given function will compare to the graph of $f(x) = \csc x$, and (b) graph the given function on a set of axes with the graph of $f(x) = \csc x$ to check your prediction.

    a. $f(x) = -\csc x$

    b. $f(x) = \csc(2x)$

    c. $f(x) = 1 - \csc x$

d. $f(x) = 1 + \csc x$

e. $f(x) = 2 \csc x$

f. $f(x) = 2 + \csc(x - 2)$

53. For each of the following, (a) predict the general shape and location of the graph, and (b) use your graphics calculator to graph the function to check your prediction.

    a. $f(x) = \sin x + \tan x$

    b. $f(x) = \sin x - \tan x$

    c. $f(x) = \tan x - \sin x$

    d. $f(x) = \tan x + \cot x$

    e. $f(x) = \sin x + \csc x$

    f. $f(x) = \cos x + \sec x$

6.5   INVERSE TRIGONOMETRIC FUNCTIONS

Before we introduce the inverse trigonometric functions, let's review some general ideas pertaining to inverse functions.

1. If the components of each ordered pair of a given one-to-one function are interchanged, the resulting function and the given function are called **inverses** of each other. (Remember that only one-to-one functions have inverses.)

2. Symbolically, the inverse of function f is denoted by f^{-1} (read, *f inverse* or *the inverse of f*).

3. If f and g are inverses, then $f(g(x)) = x$ for all x in the domain of g and $g(f(x)) = x$ for all x in the domain of f.

4. Graphically, two functions that are inverses of each other are mirror images with reference to the line $y = x$.

It is evident that the sine function over the domain of all real numbers is not a one-to-one function. For example, suppose that we consider the solutions for $\sin x = \frac{1}{2}$. Certainly, $\pi/6$ is a solution, but there are infinitely many more solutions, such as $5\pi/6$, $13\pi/6$, $17\pi/6$, $-7\pi/6$, $-11\pi/6$, etc. as indicated in Figure 6.54. However, we can form a one-to-one function from the sine function, without eliminating any values from its range, by restricting the domain to the interval

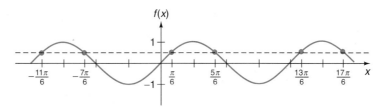

FIGURE 6.54

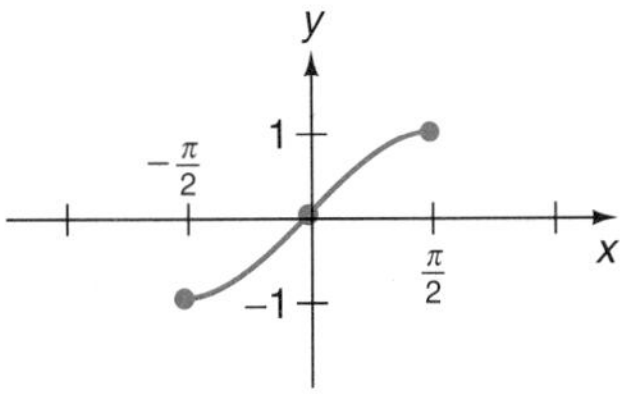

$-\pi/2 \le x \le (\pi)/2$. Therefore, we have a new function defined by the equation $y = \sin x$ that has a domain of $-\pi/2 \le x \le \pi/2$ and a range of $-1 \le y \le 1$ (Figure 6.55).

Now the inverse sine function can be defined as follows.

FIGURE 6.55

DEFINITION 6.4

The **inverse sine function** is defined by

$$y = \sin^{-1}x \quad \text{if and only if} \quad x = \sin y$$

where $-1 \le x \le 1$ and $-\dfrac{\pi}{2} \le y \le \dfrac{\pi}{2}$.

In Definition 6.4 the equation $y = \sin^{-1}x$ can be read, *y is the angle whose sine is x*. Therefore, $y = \sin^{-1}\frac{1}{2}$ means *y is the angle, between $-\pi/2$ and $\pi/2$, inclusive, whose sine is $\frac{1}{2}$*; thus, $y = \pi/6$. (The angle could also be expressed as 30°.)

EXAMPLE 1

Solve $y = \sin^{-1}(-\sqrt{2}/2)$ for y, where $-\pi/2 \le y \le \pi/2$.

Solution

From our previous work with special angles, recall that the angle between $-\pi/2$ and $\pi/2$, inclusive, whose sine equals $-\sqrt{2}/2$ is $-\pi/4$. Therefore, $y = -\pi/4$.

EXAMPLE 2

Use a calculator and solve each of the following for y:

a. $y = \sin^{-1}(.7256), \quad -\dfrac{\pi}{2} \le y \le \dfrac{\pi}{2}$

b. $y = \sin^{-1}(-.3402), \quad -\dfrac{\pi}{2} \le y \le \dfrac{\pi}{2}$

c. $y = \sin^{-1}(.6378), \quad -90° \le y \le 90°$

Solution

For parts (a) and (b), be sure that your calculator is set for radian measure.

a. Enter .7256, press the $\boxed{\text{INV}}$ and $\boxed{\text{SIN}}$ keys in that order, and obtain $y = .812$, to three decimal places.

b. Enter $-.3402$, press the $\boxed{\text{INV}}$ and $\boxed{\text{SIN}}$ keys in that order, and obtain $y = -.347$, to three decimal places.

c. Set your calculator for degree measure. Then enter .6378, press the $\boxed{\text{INV}}$ and $\boxed{\text{SIN}}$ keys in that order, and obtain $y = 39.6°$, to the nearest tenth of a degree.

REMARK   Some calculators have a $\boxed{\text{SIN}^{-1}}$ key that will produce the inverse function directly. Note also that your calculator has been designed to yield values that agree with the range of the inverse sine function. In other words, your calculator will produce inverse sine values between $-\pi/2$ and $\pi/2$, inclusive, or between $-90°$ and $90°$, inclusive.

EXAMPLE 3

Evaluate $\cos\left(\sin^{-1}\left(-\frac{1}{2}\right)\right)$.

Solution

The expression $\cos\left(\sin^{-1}\left(-\frac{1}{2}\right)\right)$ means **the cosine of the angle between $-\pi/2$ and $\pi/2$, inclusive, whose sine is $-\frac{1}{2}$.** From our previous work with special angles we know that the angle between $-\pi/2$ and $\pi/2$, inclusive, whose sine is $-\frac{1}{2}$ is $-\pi/6$. Then we know that $\cos(-\pi/6) = \sqrt{3}/2$. Therefore,

$$\cos\left(\sin^{-1}\left(-\tfrac{1}{2}\right)\right) = \tfrac{\sqrt{3}}{2}.$$

EXAMPLE 4

Graph $y = \sin^{-1}x$.

Solution

A table of values can be easily formed from our previous work with special angles. Plot the points determined by the table and connect them with a smooth curve to produce Figure 6.56.

x	$y = \sin^{-1}x$
-1	$-\pi/2$
$-\sqrt{3}/2$	$-\pi/3$
$-1/2$	$-\pi/6$
0	0
$1/2$	$\pi/6$
$\sqrt{3}/2$	$\pi/3$
1	$\pi/2$

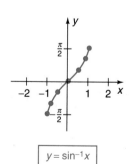

$y = \sin^{-1}x$

FIGURE 6.56

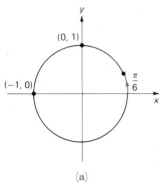

(a)

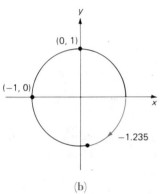

(b)

FIGURE 6.57

Remember that for two functions f and g to be inverses of each other, the following two conditions must be satisfied: (1) $f(g(x)) = x$ for all x in the domain of g, and (2) $g(f(x)) = x$ for all x in the domain of f. Let's show that the two functions

$$f(x) = \sin x \quad \text{for} \quad -\frac{\pi}{2} \le x \le \frac{\pi}{2}$$

and

$$g(x) = \sin^{-1}x \quad \text{for} \quad -1 \le x \le 1$$

satisfy these conditions.

$$f(g(x)) = f(\sin^{-1}x) = \sin(\sin^{-1}x) = x \quad \text{for} \quad -1 \le x \le 1$$

and

$$g(f(x)) = g(\sin x) = \sin^{-1}(\sin x) = x \quad \text{for} \quad -\frac{\pi}{2} \le x \le \frac{\pi}{2}$$

The fact that $f(x) = \sin x$ and $g(x) = \sin^{-1}x$ are inverses could also be used for graphing purposes. That is to say, their graphs are reflections of each other through the line $y = x$. We will have you use this idea to graph $f(x) = \sin^{-1}x$ in the next set of problems.

The inverse sine function is also called the **arcsine function** and the notation **arcsin** x can be used in place of $\sin^{-1}x$. The *arc* vocabulary refers to the fact that $y = \arcsin x$ means $x = \sin y$; that is, y is a real number (that can be geometrically interpreted as arc-length on a unit circle) whose sine is x. Therefore, arcsin $\frac{1}{2}$ can also refer to the arc indicated in Figure 6.57(a) that is $\pi/6$ units long. Likewise, arcsin $(-.9440)$ can refer to the arc indicated in Figure 6.57(b) that is -1.235 units long.

Inverse Cosine Function

The other trigonometric functions can also be used to introduce inverse functions. In each case, a restriction needs to be placed on the original domain to create a one-to-one function that contains the entire range of the original function. Then a corresponding inverse function can be defined.

By restricting the domain of the cosine function to real numbers between 0 and π, inclusive, we can obtain a one-to-one function with a range between -1 and 1, inclusive. Then the following definition creates the inverse cosine function.

DEFINITION 6.5

The **inverse cosine function** or **arccosine function** is defined by

$$y = \cos^{-1}x = \arccos x \quad \text{if and only if} \quad x = \cos y$$

where $-1 \le x \le 1$ and $0 \le y \le \pi$.

EXAMPLE 5

Solve $y = \cos^{-1}(-\sqrt{3}/2)$ for y, where $0 \le y \le \pi$.

Solution

The expression $\cos^{-1}(-\sqrt{3}/2)$ can be interpreted as *the angle whose cosine is* $-\sqrt{3}/2$. From our previous work with special angles, we know that $y = 5\pi/6$.

EXAMPLE 6

Use a calculator and solve each of the following for y:

a. $y = \cos^{-1}(.3214), \quad 0 \le y \le \pi$

b. $y = \arccos(.7914), \quad 0 \le y \le \pi$

c. $y = \cos^{-1}(-.7120), \quad 0° \le y \le 180°$

Solution

For parts (a) and (b), be sure that your calculator is set for radian measure.

a. Enter .3214, press the $\boxed{\text{INV}}$ and $\boxed{\text{COS}}$ keys in that order, and obtain $y = 1.244$, to three decimal places.

b. Enter .7914, press the $\boxed{\text{INV}}$ and $\boxed{\text{COS}}$ keys in that order, and obtain $y = .658$, to three decimal places.

c. Set your calculator for degree measure. Then enter $-.7120$, press the $\boxed{\text{INV}}$ and $\boxed{\text{COS}}$ keys in that order, and obtain $y = 135.4°$, to the nearest tenth of a degree.

EXAMPLE 7

Evaluate $\sin\left(\cos^{-1}\frac{1}{2}\right)$.

Solution

The expression $\sin\left(\cos^{-1}\frac{1}{2}\right)$ means **the sine of the angle between 0 and π, inclusive, whose cosine is $\frac{1}{2}$.** We know that $\pi/3$ is the angle whose cosine is $\frac{1}{2}$ and we know that $\sin(\pi/3) = \sqrt{3}/2$. Therefore, $\sin\left(\cos^{-1}\frac{1}{2}\right) = \sqrt{3}/2$.

EXAMPLE 8

Graph $y = \cos^{-1}x$.

Solution

A table of values can be formed from our previous work with special angles. Then we can plot the points determined by the table and connect them with a smooth curve to produce Figure 6.58.

x	$y = \cos^{-1}x$
1	0
$\sqrt{2}/2$	$\pi/4$
0	$\pi/2$
$-\sqrt{2}/2$	$3\pi/4$
-1	π

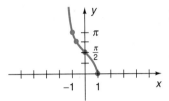

FIGURE 6.58

REMARK   Don't forget that the graph of $y = \cos^{-1}x$ can also be obtained by reflecting the graph of $y = \cos x$ for $0 \le x \le \pi$ through the line $y = x$.

Inverse Tangent Function

By restricting the domain of the tangent function to real numbers between $-\pi/2$ and $\pi/2$, ($-\pi/2$ and $\pi/2$ are not included since the tangent is undefined at those values) we can obtain a one-to-one function. Therefore, the inverse tangent function can be defined.

> ## DEFINITION 6.6
>
> The **inverse tangent function** or **arctangent function** is defined by
>
> $$y = \tan^{-1}x = \arctan x \quad \text{if and only if } x = \tan y$$
>
> where $-\infty < x < \infty$ and $-\pi/2 < y < \pi/2$.

EXAMPLE 9

Solve $y = \tan^{-1}(-\sqrt{3}/3)$ for y, where $-90° < y < 90°$.

Solution

The expression $\tan^{-1}(-\sqrt{3}/3)$ can be interpreted as *the angle between $-90°$ and $90°$, inclusive, whose tangent is $-\sqrt{3}/3$.* Therefore, from our previous work with special angles, we know that $y = -30°$.

EXAMPLE 10

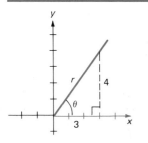

FIGURE 6.59

Find an exact value for $\sin\left(\tan^{-1}\frac{4}{3}\right)$ without using a calculator or a table.

Solution

Let $\theta = \tan^{-1}\frac{4}{3}$; that is, θ is the angle between $-\pi/2$ and $\pi/2$ whose tangent is $\frac{4}{3}$. Therefore, θ is a first-quadrant angle as indicated in Figure 6.59. From the right triangle formed, we obtain

$$r^2 = 3^2 + 4^2 = 9 + 16 = 25$$

$$r = 5.$$

Therefore, $\sin\theta = \frac{4}{5}$ and we have $\sin\left(\tan^{-1}\frac{4}{3}\right) = \frac{4}{5}$.

EXAMPLE 11

Graph $y = \tan^{-1}x$

Solution

Again a table of values can be easily formed from our previous work with special angles. Furthermore, we know that as x becomes infinitely large, the value of $y = \tan^{-1}x$ approaches $\pi/2$. Thus, we have a horizontal asymptote at $y = \pi/2$. Likewise, we have another horizontal asymptote at $y = -\pi/2$. Using these asymptotes and connecting the points determined by the table with a smooth curve produces Figure 6.60.

x	$y = \tan^{-1}x$
$-\sqrt{3}$	$-\pi/3$
$-\sqrt{3}/3$	$-\pi/6$
0	0
$\sqrt{3}/3$	$\pi/6$
$\sqrt{3}$	$\pi/3$

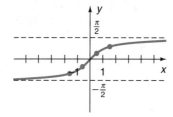

FIGURE 6.60

REMARK Don't forget that the graph of $y = \tan^{-1}x$ can also be obtained by reflecting the graph of $y = \tan x$ for $-\pi/2 < x < \pi/2$ through the line $y = x$.

REMARK By restricting the domains of the cotangent, cosecant, and secant functions, an inverse for each of these functions can be defined. However, since the role of these inverses is very limited prior to calculus, we will not define them in this text.

As a final example of this section, let's use a graphing utility to *watch* some transformations being performed with the basic inverse sine curve.

EXAMPLE 12

Use a graphing utility to graph $f(x) = \sin^{-1}x, f(x) = -\sin^{-1}x, f(x) = -\sin^{-1}(x - 3)$, and $f(x) = -\sin^{-1}(x - 3) + 2$ on the same set of axes.

Solution

Let's make the following assignments.

$$Y_1 = \sin^{-1}x, \ Y_2 = -\sin^{-1}x, \ Y_3 = -\sin^{-1}(x - 3),$$

$$Y_4 = -\sin^{-1}(x - 3) + 2$$

Now activate the graphing feature of the utility to observe the following sequence of graphs.

1. The graph of $f(x) = \sin^{-1}x$ will appear.

2. The graph of $f(x) = -\sin^{-1}x$, which is the x-axis reflection of $f(x) = \sin^{-1}x$, will appear.

3. The graph of $f(x) = -\sin^{-1}(x - 3)$, which is a 3-unit horizontal shift to the right of the graph of $f(x) = -\sin^{-1}x$, will appear.

4. The graph of $f(x) = -\sin^{-1}(x - 3) + 2$, which is a 2-unit vertical shift upward of the graph of $f(x) = -\sin^{-1}(x - 3)$, will appear.

Figure 6.61 shows the graph of all four of the functions on the same set of axes.

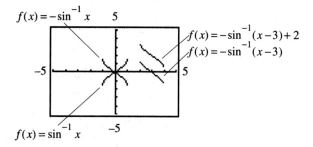

FIGURE 6.61

PROBLEM SET 6.5

For Problems 1–14, solve for y and express y in radian measure. Do not use a calculator or a table.

1. $y = \sin^{-1}\frac{\sqrt{2}}{2}$

2. $y = \sin^{-1}\frac{\sqrt{3}}{2}$

3. $y = \sin^{-1}\left(-\frac{\sqrt{3}}{2}\right)$

4. $y = \sin^{-1}1$

5. $y = \cos^{-1}\frac{1}{2}$

6. $y = \cos^{-1}\left(-\frac{1}{2}\right)$

7. $y = \cos^{-1}\frac{\sqrt{3}}{2}$

8. $y = \cos^{-1} 0$

9. $y = \arctan 1$

10. $y = \arctan(-1)$

11. $y = \arctan \sqrt{3}$

12. $y = \arctan 0$

13. $y = \arcsin(-1)$

14. $y = \arccos(-1)$

For Problems 15–22, solve for y and express y in degree measure. Do not use a calculator or a table.

15. $y = \tan^{-1}\frac{\sqrt{3}}{3}$

16. $y = \tan^{-1}\left(-\frac{\sqrt{3}}{3}\right)$

17. $y = \cos^{-1}\left(-\frac{\sqrt{2}}{2}\right)$

18. $y = \cos^{-1}\left(-\frac{\sqrt{3}}{2}\right)$

19. $y = \sin^{-1} 0$

20. $y = \sin^{-1}\left(-\frac{1}{2}\right)$

21. $y = \sin^{-1}\left(-\frac{\sqrt{2}}{2}\right)$

22. $y = \tan^{-1}(-\sqrt{3})$

For Problems 23–34, use a calculator or the table in the back of the book to solve for y. Express answers in radians to three decimal places.

23. $y = \sin^{-1}(.3578)$

24. $y = \sin^{-1}(.8629)$

25. $y = \arcsin(-.9142)$

26. $y = \arcsin(-.1654)$

27. $y = \arccos(.5894)$

28. $y = \arccos(.0428)$

29. $y = \cos^{-1}(-.4162)$

30. $y = \cos^{-1}(-.8894)$

31. $y = \tan^{-1}(8.6214)$

32. $y = \tan^{-1}(.9145)$

33. $y = \arctan(-.1986)$

34. $y = \arctan(-56.2413)$

For Problems 35–46, use a calculator or the table in the back of the book to solve for y. Express answers to the nearest tenth of a degree.

35. $y = \sin^{-1}(.4310)$

36. $y = \sin^{-1}(.7214)$

37. $y = \sin^{-1}(-.8214)$

38. $y = \sin^{-1}(-.2318)$

39. $y = \cos^{-1}(.2644)$

40. $y = \cos^{-1}(.8419)$

41. $y = \cos^{-1}(-.1620)$

42. $y = \cos^{-1}(-.6217)$

43. $y = \tan^{-1}(14.2187)$

44. $y = \tan^{-1}(.9854)$

45. $y = \tan^{-1}(-8.2176)$

46. $y = \tan^{-1}(-21.1765)$

For Problems 47–70, evaluate each expression without using a calculator or a table.

47. $\sin\left(\cos^{-1}\left(-\frac{1}{2}\right)\right)$

48. $\cos\left(\sin^{-1}\frac{1}{2}\right)$

49. $\cos(\sin^{-1} 1)$

50. $\sin(\cos^{-1}(-1))$

51. $\tan\left(\sin^{-1}\frac{\sqrt{2}}{2}\right)$

52. $\tan\left(\cos^{-1}\left(-\frac{\sqrt{3}}{2}\right)\right)$

53. $\sin\left(\tan^{-1}\sqrt{3}\right)$

54. $\cos\left(\tan^{-1}\left(-\frac{\sqrt{3}}{3}\right)\right)$

55. $\sin\left(\sin^{-1}\frac{\sqrt{2}}{2}\right)$

56. $\cos(\cos^{-1} 0)$

57. $\cos\left(\arcsin\frac{4}{5}\right)$

58. $\cos\left(\arcsin\frac{5}{13}\right)$

59. $\sin\left(\arctan\frac{3}{4}\right)$

60. $\cos\left(\arctan\left(-\frac{4}{3}\right)\right)$

61. $\tan\left(\sin^{-1}\left(-\frac{4}{5}\right)\right)$

62. $\tan\left(\cos^{-1}\left(-\frac{5}{13}\right)\right)$

63. $\cos\left(\sin^{-1}\frac{2}{3}\right)$

64. $\sin\left(\tan^{-1}\left(-\frac{2}{3}\right)\right)$

65. $\tan\left(\cos^{-1}\left(-\frac{1}{3}\right)\right)$

66. $\tan\left(\sin^{-1}\frac{2}{5}\right)$

67. $\sec\left(\sin^{-1}\left(-\frac{3}{4}\right)\right)$

68. $\csc\left(\cos^{-1}\left(-\frac{2}{3}\right)\right)$

69. $\cot\left(\cos^{-1}\left(-\frac{3}{7}\right)\right)$

70. $\sec\left(\sin\left(-\frac{1}{5}\right)\right)$

71. Graph $y = \sin^{-1}x$ by reflecting $y = \sin x$, where $-\dfrac{\pi}{2} \le x \le \dfrac{\pi}{2}$, across the line $y = x$.

72. Graph $y = \cos^{-1}x$ by reflecting the graph of $y = \cos x$, where $0 \le x \le \pi$, through the line $y = x$.

73. Graph $y = \tan^{-1}x$ by reflecting the graph of $y = \tan x$, where $-\pi/2 < x < \pi/2$, through the line $y = x$.

For Problems 74–81, graph each function.

74. $y = 2 \sin^{-1}x$

75. $y = 2 + \cos^{-1}x$

76. $y = \cos^{-1}(x - 1)$

77. $y = \sin^{-1} 2x$

78. $y = \sin(\sin^{-1}x)$

79. $y = \sin(\cos^{-1}x)$

80. $y = -\sin^{-1}x$

81. $y = -2 \cos^{-1}x$

THOUGHTS into WORDS

82. Suppose that you are asked to evaluate $\sin^{-1}\sqrt{2}$. How would you react to this problem?

83. Solve each of the equations $\sin x = .5$ and $x = \sin^{-1}(.5)$ for x. Are your solution sets the same? Explain your answer.

GRAPHICS CALCULATOR ACTIVITIES

84. Use your graphics calculator to check your graphs for Problems 74–81.

85. How should the graphs of $f(x) = 2 \sin^{-1}x$ and $f(x) = 3 \sin^{-1}x$ compare to the graph of $f(x) = \sin^{-1}x$? Graph all three functions on the same set of axes to check your prediction.

86. How should the graphs of $f(x) = 1 + \sin^{-1}x$ and $f(x) = -1 + \sin^{-1}x$ compare to the graph of $f(x) = \sin^{-1}x$? Graph all three functions on the same set of axes to check your prediction.

87. How should the graph of $f(x) = 1 - \cos^{-1}x$ compare to the graph of $f(x) = \cos^{-1}x$? Graph both functions on the same set of axes to check your prediction.

88. How should the graphs of $f(x) = \cos^{-1}(x + 2)$ and $f(x) = \cos^{-1}(x - 2)$ compare to the graph of $f(x) = \cos^{-1}x$? Graph all three functions on the same set of axes to check your prediction.

89. a. Evaluate $\left(\sin^{-1}\frac{\sqrt{2}}{2} + \cos^{-1}\frac{\sqrt{2}}{2}\right)$, $\left(\sin^{-1}\frac{1}{2} + \cos^{-1}\frac{1}{2}\right)$, and $\left(\sin^{-1}\frac{\sqrt{3}}{2} + \cos^{-1}\frac{\sqrt{3}}{2}\right)$.

b. Graph $f(x) = \sin^{-1}x$ and $f(x) = \cos^{-1}x$ on the same set of axes.

c. What do you think the graph of $f(x) = \sin^{-1}x + \cos^{-1}x$ should be?

d. Graph $f(x) = \sin^{-1}x + \cos^{-1}x$.

90. For each of the following, (a) predict the general shape and location of the graph, and (b) graph the function to check your prediction.

a. $f(x) = \cos(\sin^{-1}x)$

b. $f(x) = \sin^{-1}x + \tan^{-1}x$

c. $f(x) = \sin^{-1}x - \tan^{-1}x$

d. $f(x) = \tan^{-1}x - \sin^{-1}x$

e. $f(x) = \sin^{-1}x - \cos^{-1}x$

f. $f(x) = \cos^{-1}x - \sin^{-1}x$

6.6 TRIGONOMETRIC IDENTITIES

In algebra, a statement such as $3x + 4 = 7$ is called an **equation**, or sometimes more specifically, a **conditional equation**. Solving an algebraic equation refers to the process of finding, from a set of potential replacements, those values for the variable that will make a true statement. Likewise, in trigonometry we are confronted with **trigonometric equations** such as $2 \sin \theta = 1$. Solving a trigonometric equation also refers to the process of finding replacements for the variables that will make a true statement.

The algebraic equation $1/x + 2/x = 3/x$ is called an **identity** because it is true for all replacements for x when both sides of the equation are defined. Similarly, in trigonometry a statement such as $\csc \theta = 1/\sin \theta$ is called a **trigonometric identity** because it is true for all values of θ for which both sides of the equation are defined.

Earlier in this chapter we used the reciprocal relationships. They are actually trigonometric identities and they can be verified using the definitions of the trigonometric functions (Definition 6.1). For example,

$$\sin \theta = \frac{y}{r} \quad \text{and} \quad \csc \theta = \frac{r}{y}.$$

Therefore, because

$$\frac{r}{y} = \frac{1}{\dfrac{y}{r}}$$

the identity

$$\csc \theta = \frac{1}{\sin \theta}$$

is established. In a like manner, the identities

$$\sec \theta = \frac{1}{\cos \theta} \qquad \text{and} \qquad \cot \theta = \frac{1}{\tan \theta}$$

can be verified. Remember that an identity such as $\csc \theta = 1/\sin \theta$ is true for all values of θ when both sides of the equation are defined.

Again, using the definitions of the trigonometric functions we can show that

$$\frac{\sin \theta}{\cos \theta} = \frac{\dfrac{y}{r}}{\dfrac{x}{r}} = \left(\frac{y}{r}\right)\left(\frac{r}{x}\right) = \frac{y}{x} = \tan \theta.$$

Therefore, the identity

$$\tan \theta = \frac{\sin \theta}{\cos \theta}$$

is established. Similarly, the identity

$$\cot \theta = \frac{\cos \theta}{\sin \theta}$$

can be verified.

In Section 6.1 we verified the identity

$$\sin^2\theta + \cos^2\theta = 1.$$

From this identity two additional identities can be developed as follows. Dividing both sides of $\sin^2\theta + \cos^2\theta = 1$ by $\cos^2\theta$ and simplifying produces

$$\frac{\sin^2\theta}{\cos^2\theta} + \frac{\cos^2\theta}{\cos^2\theta} = \frac{1}{\cos^2\theta}$$

$$\tan^2\theta + 1 = \sec^2\theta.$$

Likewise, dividing both sides of $\sin^2\theta + \cos^2\theta = 1$ by $\sin^2\theta$ and simplifying yields

$$\frac{\sin^2\theta}{\sin^2\theta} + \frac{\cos^2\theta}{\sin^2\theta} = \frac{1}{\sin^2\theta}$$

$$1 + \cot^2\theta = \csc^2\theta.$$

Let's pause for a moment and list the identities we've discussed thus far.

$$\csc \theta = \frac{1}{\sin \theta}, \qquad \sec \theta = \frac{1}{\cos \theta}, \qquad \cot \theta = \frac{1}{\tan \theta},$$

$$\tan \theta = \frac{\sin \theta}{\cos \theta}, \qquad \cot \theta = \frac{\cos \theta}{\sin \theta},$$

$$\sin^2\theta + \cos^2\theta = 1, \qquad 1 + \tan^2\theta = \sec^2\theta, \qquad 1 + \cot^2\theta = \csc^2\theta.$$

You should know this list; it is sometimes referred to as containing the **basic** or **fundamental identities** of trigonometry.

The basic identities are used for various purposes, such as (1) to determine the remaining functional values from a given value, (2) to simplify trigonometric expressions, (3) to verify additional trigonometric identities, (4) to aid in the derivation of formulas, and (5) to aid in the solving of trigonometric equations. Let's consider examples of some of these uses at this time.

EXAMPLE 1

If $\sin \theta = \frac{3}{5}$ and $\cos \theta < 0$, find the values of the other trigonometric functions.

Solution

Using $\csc \theta = 1/\sin \theta$ produces

$$\csc \theta = \frac{1}{\frac{3}{5}} = \frac{5}{3}.$$

Substituting $\frac{3}{5}$ for $\sin \theta$ in the identity $\sin^2\theta + \cos^2\theta = 1$, and solving for $\cos \theta$, we obtain

$$\sin^2\theta + \cos^2\theta = 1$$

$$\left(\tfrac{3}{5}\right)^2 + \cos^2\theta = 1$$

$$\cos^2\theta = 1 - \tfrac{9}{25}$$

$$\cos^2\theta = \tfrac{16}{25}$$

$$\cos \theta = -\tfrac{4}{5}. \qquad \text{Remember we were given that } \cos \theta < 0$$

Using $\sec \theta = 1/\cos \theta$ produces

$$\sec \theta = \frac{1}{-\frac{4}{5}} = -\frac{5}{4}.$$

Finally, using $\tan \theta = \sin \theta/\cos \theta$ and $\cot \theta = 1/\tan \theta$, we obtain

$$\tan \theta = \frac{\frac{3}{5}}{-\frac{4}{5}} = \left(\frac{3}{5}\right)\left(-\frac{5}{4}\right) = -\frac{3}{4}$$

and

$$\cot \theta = \frac{1}{\tan \theta} = \frac{1}{-\frac{3}{4}} = -\frac{4}{3}.$$

You should recognize that a problem such as Example 1 can be worked in many different ways. For example, after we found that $\csc \theta = \frac{5}{3}$, the identity $1 + \cot^2\theta = \csc^2\theta$ could be used to determine the value of $\cot \theta$. Likewise, after finding that $\sec \theta = -\frac{5}{4}$, we could use $1 + \tan^2\theta = \sec^2\theta$ to determine the value of $\tan \theta$. In fact, don't forget that the entire problem could be solved by applying the definitions of the trigonometric functions as we did in Section 6.1. However, at this time we would prefer to use the basic identities as much as possible.

EXAMPLE 2

Simplify $\sin \theta \cot \theta$.

Solution

Replacing $\cot \theta$ with $(\cos \theta)/\sin \theta$ we can proceed as follows.

$$\sin \theta \cot \theta = \sin \theta \left(\frac{\cos \theta}{\sin \theta} \right)$$

$$= \cos \theta$$

Therefore, $\sin \theta \cot \theta$ simplifies to $\cos \theta$.

EXAMPLE 3

Simplify $\dfrac{\sin \theta}{\csc \theta} + \dfrac{\cos \theta}{\sec \theta}$.

Solution

$$\frac{\sin \theta}{\csc \theta} + \frac{\cos \theta}{\sec \theta} = \frac{\sin \theta}{\dfrac{1}{\sin \theta}} + \frac{\cos \theta}{\dfrac{1}{\cos \theta}}$$

$$= \sin^2\theta + \cos^2\theta = 1$$

Therefore, $\dfrac{\sin \theta}{\csc \theta} + \dfrac{\cos \theta}{\sec \theta} = 1$.

EXAMPLE 4

Simplify $\cos x + \cos x \tan^2x$.

Solution

By factoring and then substituting $\sec^2x$ for $1 + \tan^2x$, we can proceed as follows.

$$\cos x + \cos x \tan^2 x = \cos x(1 + \tan^2 x)$$

$$= \cos x \sec^2 x$$

$$\cos x \left(\frac{1}{\cos^2 x} \right)$$

$$= \frac{1}{\cos x} = \sec x$$

Therefore, $\cos x + \cos x \tan^2 x$ simplifies to $1/\cos x$ or $\sec x$. ▬▬▬

From Examples 2, 3, and 4, we see that the end result of simplifying a trigonometric expression may be a constant as in Example 3 or a simpler trigonometric expression as in Examples 2 and 4. In Example 4, whether we use the final result of $1/\cos x$ or $\sec x$ depends on the context of the problem being simplified.

Verifying Identities

The process of verifying trigonometric identities is much the same as simplifying trigonometric expressions, except that we know the desired result in advance. Consider the following examples and be sure that you can supply reasons for all of the steps.

EXAMPLE 5

Verify the identity $\sec \theta \cot \theta = \csc \theta$.

Solution

Let's simplify the left side.

$$\sec \theta \cot \theta = \left(\frac{1}{\cos \theta} \right) \left(\frac{\cos \theta}{\sin \theta} \right)$$

$$= \frac{1}{\sin \theta} = \csc \theta$$

Therefore, we have verified that $\sec \theta \cot \theta = \csc \theta$. ▬▬▬

EXAMPLE 6

Verify the identity $1/\sec^2 x = (1 + \sin x)(1 - \sin x)$.

Solution

By finding the indicated product on the right side, we can proceed as follows.

$$(1 + \sin x)(1 - \sin x) = 1 - \sin^2 x$$

$$= \cos^2 x = \frac{1}{\sec^2 x}$$

Therefore, we have verified that $1/\sec^2 x = (1 + \sin x)(1 - \sin x)$. ▬▬▬

Notice in Example 5 that we transformed the left side into the right side, but in Example 6 we transformed the right side into the left side. In general, we suggest that you attempt to transform the more complicated side into the other side. In some examples, like Example 7, the choice of either side will require about the same amount of work.

EXAMPLE 7

Verify the identity $\sec x - \cos x = \sin x \tan x$.

Solution A

We can transform the left side into the right side as follows.

$$\sec x - \cos x = \frac{1}{\cos x} - \cos x$$

$$= \frac{1 - \cos^2 x}{\cos x}$$

$$= \frac{\sin^2 x}{\cos x} = \sin x \left(\frac{\sin x}{\cos x} \right) = \sin x \tan x$$

Solution B

We can transform the right side into the left side as follows.

$$\sin x \tan x = \sin x \left(\frac{\sin x}{\cos x} \right)$$

$$= \frac{\sin^2 x}{\cos x}$$

$$= \frac{1 - \cos^2 x}{\cos x} = \frac{1}{\cos x} - \cos x$$

$$= \sec x - \cos x$$

A word of caution is in order before we consider additional identities. Either transforming the left side into the right side or transforming the right side into the left side is an acceptable procedure for verifying an identity. However, *do not* assume the truth of the identity at the beginning and apply properties of equality to both sides.

EXAMPLE 8

Verify the identity

$$\frac{\cos x}{1 + \sin x} + \frac{\cos x}{1 - \sin x} = 2 \sec x.$$

Solution

Adding the two fractions on the left, we can transform the left side into the right side as follows.

$$\frac{\cos x}{1 + \sin x} + \frac{\cos x}{1 - \sin x} = \frac{\cos x(1 - \sin x) + \cos x(1 + \sin x)}{(1 + \sin x)(1 - \sin x)}$$

$$= \frac{\cos x - \cos x \sin x + \cos x + \cos x \sin x}{(1 + \sin x)(1 - \sin x)}$$

$$= \frac{2 \cos x}{(1 + \sin x)(1 - \sin x)}$$

$$= \frac{2 \cos x}{1 - \sin^2 x}$$

$$= \frac{2 \cos x}{\cos^2 x}$$

$$= \frac{2}{\cos x}$$

$$= 2 \sec x$$

EXAMPLE 9

Verify the identity

$$\frac{\cos x + \tan x}{\sin x \cos x} = \csc x + \sec^2 x.$$

Solution

Let's apply the property of fractions $(a + c)/b = a/b + c/b$ to the left side and then proceed as follows.

$$\frac{\cos x + \tan x}{\sin x \cos x} = \frac{\cos x}{\sin x \cos x} + \frac{\tan x}{\sin x \cos x}$$

$$= \frac{1}{\sin x} + \frac{\dfrac{\sin x}{\cos x}}{\sin x \cos x}$$

$$= \frac{1}{\sin x} + \frac{\sin x}{\sin x \cos^2 x}$$

$$= \frac{1}{\sin x} + \frac{1}{\cos^2 x} = \csc x + \sec^2 x$$

EXAMPLE 10

Verify the identity

$$\frac{\cos x}{1 - \sin x} = \frac{1 + \sin x}{\cos x}.$$

Solution

We can apply the property of fractions $a/b = ac/bc$ and multiply both the numerator and denominator of the left side by $1 + \sin x$.

$$\frac{\cos x}{1 - \sin x} = \frac{\cos x}{1 - \sin x} \cdot \frac{1 + \sin x}{1 + \sin x}$$

$$= \frac{\cos x(1 + \sin x)}{1 - \sin^2 x}$$

$$= \frac{\cos x(1 + \sin x)}{\cos^2 x}$$

$$= \frac{1 + \sin x}{\cos x}$$

We cannot outline for you a specific procedure that will guarantee success at verifying identities. However, we do offer the following suggestions.

1. Know the basic identities listed at the beginning of this section. You must have these at your fingertips.

2. Attempt to transform the more complicated side into the other side.

3. Keep in mind that many properties from algebra apply to trigonometric expressions. Similar terms can be combined. Trigonometric expressions can be multiplied and factored. Trigonometric fractions can be simplified, added, subtracted, multiplied, and divided using the same properties that we use with algebraic fractions.

4. Because 1 can be substituted for $\sin^2\theta + \cos^2\theta$, it is often helpful to simplify in terms of the sine and cosine functions.

A graphing utility can be used to provide visual support for a claim that a particular equation is or is not an identity. In Example 4 we verified that the equation $\cos x + \cos x \tan^2 x = \sec x$ is an identity by simplifying $\cos x + \cos x \tan^2 x$ to $\sec x$. Now let's use a graphing utility to give visual support to this claim. By letting $Y_1 = \cos x + \cos x \tan^2 x$, $Y_2 = \sec x$, and graphing both of these equations on the same set of axes we obtain Figure 6.62. Since the graphs appear to be identical, this supports the claim that $\cos x + \cos x \tan^2 x = \sec x$ is an identity.

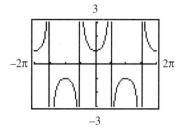

F I G U R E   6 . 6 2

Is $(\sin x - \cos x)^2 = 1 + 2 \sin x \cos x$ an identity? First, let's use a graphing utility to obtain the graphs of $Y_1 = (\sin x - \cos x)^2$ and $Y_2 = 1 + 2 \sin x \cos x$ on the same set of axes as shown in Figure 6.63. Since two different graphs are pro-

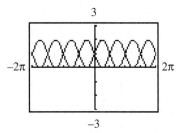

FIGURE 6.63

duced, we know that the equation $(\sin x - \cos x)^2 = 1 + 2 \sin x \cos x$ is not an identity. Furthermore, the points of intersection of the two graphs seem to indicate that the equation is satisfied by the values $n(\pi/2)$, where n is any integer. We will discuss the use of an algebraic approach to solve such equations in the next section.

PROBLEM SET 6.6

1. Use Definition 6.1 and prove that $\sec \theta = 1/\cos \theta$ and $\cot \theta = 1/\tan \theta$.

2. Use Definition 6.1 and prove that $\cos \theta / \sin \theta = \cot \theta$.

For Problems 3–12, use the basic trigonometric identities listed at the beginning of this section to help find the remaining five trigonometric functional values.

3. $\sin \theta = \frac{4}{5}$ and the terminal side of θ lies in the first quadrant.

4. $\cos \theta = -\frac{5}{13}$ and the terminal side of θ lies in the second quadrant.

5. $\tan \theta = \frac{12}{3}$ and the terminal side of θ lies in the third quadrant.

6. $\sin \theta = -\frac{8}{17}$ and the terminal side of θ lies in the fourth quadrant.

7. $\sin \theta = \frac{4}{5}$ and $\cos \theta < 0$

8. $\csc \theta = -\frac{5}{4}$ and $\sec \theta < 0$

9. $\tan \theta = -\frac{1}{2}$ and $\cos \theta > 0$

10. $\sec \theta = 3$ and $\sin \theta < 0$

11. $\csc \theta = \frac{3}{2}$ and $\sec \theta < 0$

12. $\cot \theta = \frac{1}{3}$ and $\csc \theta < 0$

For Problems 13–24, simplify the given trigonometric expression to a single trigonometric function or a constant.

13. $\cos \theta \tan \theta$

14. $\dfrac{\tan \theta}{\sin \theta}$

15. $\cos x \csc x$

16. $\sec x - \sin x \tan x$

17. $(\cos^2 x - 1)(\tan^2 x + 1)$

18. $\sin x + \sin x \cot^2 x$

19. $(\cos^2 x)(1 + \tan^2 x)$

20. $(1 - \sin^2 x)\sec^2 x$

21. $\cos \theta + \tan \theta \sin \theta$

22. $\dfrac{\sec \theta - \cos \theta}{\tan \theta}$

23. $\dfrac{\tan x \sin x}{\sec^2 x - 1}$

24. $\tan x(\sin x + \cot x \cos x)$

For Problems 25–60, verify each of the following identities.

25. $\sin \theta \sec \theta = \tan \theta$

26. $\cos \theta \tan \theta \csc \theta = 1$

27. $\sin \theta + \sin \theta \tan^2 \theta = \tan \theta \sec \theta$

28. $\cos \theta + \cos \theta \cot^2 \theta = \cot \theta \csc \theta$

29. $\dfrac{\sin x + \cos x}{\cos x} = 1 + \tan x$

30. $\dfrac{\sin x + \tan x}{\sin x} = 1 + \sec x$

31. $\dfrac{\tan x + \cos x}{\sin x} = \sec x + \cot x$

32. $\csc x - \sin x = \cos x \cot x$

33. $\csc x \sec x = \tan x + \cot x$

34. $\dfrac{(\tan x)(1 + \cot^2 x)}{1 + \tan^2 x} = \cot x$

35. $\tan x = \dfrac{\cot x(1 + \tan^2 x)}{1 + \cot^2 x}$

36. $\dfrac{\cot x \cos x}{\csc^2 x - 1} = \sin x$

37. $\sin x(\csc x - \sin x) = \cos^2 x$

38. $1 - 2 \sin^2 \theta = 2 \cos^2 \theta - 1$

39. $2 \sec^2 \theta - 1 = 1 + 2 \tan^2 \theta$

40. $\cos^2 \theta - \sin^2 \theta = 1 - 2 \sin^2 \theta$

41. $\cos^2 \theta - \sin^2 \theta = 2 \cos^2 \theta - 1$

42. $\dfrac{1 + \cos x}{\sin x} + \dfrac{\sin x}{1 + \cos x} = 2 \csc x$

43. $\dfrac{1}{1 - \cos x} + \dfrac{1}{1 + \cos x} = 2 \csc^2 x$

44. $(\sec x - \tan x)(\csc x + 1) = \cot x$

45. $(\cos x - \sin x)(\cos x + \sin x) = 1 - 2 \sin^2 x$

46. $\dfrac{1 + \sec x}{\sin x + \tan x} = \csc x$

47. $\cos^2 x = \dfrac{\csc^2 x - \cot^2 x}{\sec^2 x}$

48. $\dfrac{\cos x + \tan x}{\sin x \cos x} = \csc x + \sec^2 x$

49. $\sin^4 x - \cos^4 x = 1 - 2 \cos^2 x$

50. $\tan^4 x - \sec^4 x = 1 - 2 \sec^2 x$

51. $(\sin x - \cos x)^2 = 1 - 2 \sin x \cos x$

52. $1 - \sin x = \dfrac{\cot x - \cos x}{\cot x}$

53. $1 + \tan x = \dfrac{\sec^2 x + 2 \tan x}{1 + \tan x}$

54. $\dfrac{\sin x}{\sin x + \cos x} = \dfrac{\tan x}{1 + \tan x}$

55. $\dfrac{\sin x}{1 + \cos x} = \dfrac{1 - \cos x}{\sin x}$

56. $\dfrac{\tan x}{\sec x - 1} = \dfrac{\sec x + 1}{\tan x}$

57. $\dfrac{\csc x - 1}{\cot x} = \dfrac{\cot x}{\csc x + 1}$

58. $(\tan x - \sec x)^2 = \dfrac{1 - \sin x}{1 + \sin x}$

59. $\dfrac{1}{\tan x + \cot x} = \sin x \cos x$

60. $\dfrac{\sin x + \cos x}{\sin x - \cos x} = \dfrac{\sec x + \csc x}{\sec x - \csc x}$

GRAPHICS CALCULATOR ACTIVITIES

61. To demonstrate graphically that $\sin^2x + \cos^2x = 1$ is an identity, we need to show that $y = \sin^2x + \cos^2x$ and $y = 1$ produce identical graphs. In other words, the graph of $y = \sin^2x + \cos^2x$ should be the horizontal line $y = 1$.

Use your graphics calculator to demonstrate that each of the following is an identity.

a. $\sin^2x + \cos^2x = 1$ **b.** $1 + \tan^2x = \sec^2x$

c. $1 + \cot^2x = \csc^2x$

62. Use your graphics calculator to demonstrate the validity of each of the identities in Examples 4–9 of this section.

63. Another technique for verifying that an equation $p = q$ is an identity is to transform the left side p into another expression s, and to make sure that all steps taken are *reversible*. Therefore, $p = s$ is an identity. Then if the right side of q of the original equation can also be transformed to s using reversible steps, we have $q = s$ is an

identity. Thus, $p = s$ and $s = q$ implies that $p = q$ is an identity.

Use this approach to verify each of the following identities. Then use your graphics calculator to demonstrate the validity of each identity.

a. $\sec \theta + \csc \theta - \cos \theta - \sin \theta = \sin \theta \tan \theta +\\ \cos \theta \cot \theta$

b. $(1 - \tan^2x)^2 = \sec^4x - 4\tan^2x$

c. $(\tan x - \sec x)^2 = \dfrac{1 - \sin x}{1 + \sin x}$

d. $\dfrac{\sin \theta}{1 - \cos \theta} = \csc \theta + \cot \theta$

e. $\dfrac{1}{\csc x - \cot x} = \csc x + \cot x$

6.7 TRIGONOMETRIC EQUATIONS

As stated in the introductory paragraph of the previous section, solving a conditional trigonometric equation such as $2 \sin x = 1$ refers to the process of finding the values of the variable x that will make a true numerical statement. Because the trigonometric functions are periodic, most trigonometric equations have infinitely many solutions. However, once the solutions within one period have been found, the remainder of the solutions are easily determined. For example, $\pi/6$ and $5\pi/6$ are the solutions between 0 and 2π (remember that 2π is the period of the sine function) that satisfy the equation $\sin x = \frac{1}{2}$. Then by adding multiples of 2π to each of these, all of the solutions can be represented by $\pi/6 + 2\pi n$ and $5\pi/6 + 2\pi n$, where n is an integer. The expressions $\pi/6 + 2\pi n$ and $5\pi/6 + 2\pi n$ are referred to as the **general solutions** of the equation. Using degree measure, the general solutions could be represented by $30° + n \cdot 360°$ and $150° + n \cdot 360°$, where n is an integer.

Solving trigonometric equations requires the use of many of the techniques used to solve algebraic equations. These examples will illustrate some of those techniques.

EXAMPLE 1

Solve $2 \cos \theta + 1 = 0$, if $0° \le 0 < 360°$.

Solution

$$2 \cos \theta + 1 = 0$$

$$2 \cos \theta = -1 \qquad \text{Add } -1 \text{ to both sides}$$

$$\cos \theta = -\tfrac{1}{2} \qquad \text{Multiplied both sides by } \tfrac{1}{2}$$

From our work with special angles, we know that $\cos 120° = -\frac{1}{2}$ and $\cos 240° = -\frac{1}{2}$. The solutions are $120°$ and $240°$.

EXAMPLE 2

Solve $\sin x \cos x = 0$, if $0 \leq x < 2\pi$.

Solution

By applying the property, if $ab = 0$, then $a = 0$ or $b = 0$, we can proceed as follows.

$$\sin x \cos x = 0$$

$$\sin x = 0 \quad \text{or} \quad \cos x = 0$$

We know that $\sin 0 = 0$, $\sin \pi = 0$, $\cos \pi/2 = 0$, and $\cos 3\pi/2 = 0$. Therefore, the solutions are 0, $\pi/2$, π, and $3\pi/2$.

In Example 1, because the statement of the problem contained degree measure ($0° \leq \theta < 360°$), we expressed the solutions in degrees. Likewise, in Example 2 the statement $0 \leq x < 2\pi$ implies the use of real numbers or radian measure.

EXAMPLE 3

Find the general solutions for $\sin x \tan x = \sin x$.

Solution

$$\sin x \tan x = \sin x$$

$\sin x \tan x - \sin x = 0$ Added $-\sin x$ to both sides

$\sin x(\tan x - 1) = 0$ Factored left side

$\sin x = 0 \quad \text{or} \quad \tan x - 1 = 0$ Applied if $ab = 0$, then $a = 0$ or $b = 0$

$\sin x = 0 \quad \text{or} \quad \tan x = 1$

Since the sine function has a period of 2π, it is sufficient to find the solutions of $\sin x = 0$ for $0 \leq x < 2\pi$. Those solutions are 0 and π. The general expression $n\pi$, where n is an integer, will generate all of the solutions for $\sin x = 0$. The tangent function has a period of π, so it is sufficient to find the solutions of $\tan x = 1$ for $0 \leq x < \pi$. The only solution is $\pi/4$. The general expression $\pi/4 + n\pi$, where n is an integer, will generate all of the solutions for $\tan x = 1$. Therefore, the solutions for $\sin x \tan x = \sin x$ can be represented by

$$n\pi \text{ and } \frac{\pi}{4} + n\pi, \quad \text{where } n \text{ is an integer.}$$

Note that in Example 3 we *did not* begin by dividing both sides of the original equation by $\sin x$. Doing so would cause us to lose the solutions for $\sin x = 0$. As in algebra, we want to avoid dividing both sides of an equation by a variable, or an expression that contains a variable.

EXAMPLE 4

Solve $2 \sin^2 x + \sin x - 1 = 0$, if $0 \le x < 2\pi$.

Solution

Factoring the left side, we can proceed as follows.

$$2 \sin^2 x + \sin x - 1 = 0$$

$$(2 \sin x - 1)(\sin x + 1) = 0$$

$$2 \sin x - 1 = 0 \quad \text{or} \quad \sin x + 1 = 0$$

$$2 \sin x = 1 \quad \text{or} \quad \sin x = -1$$

$$\sin x = \frac{1}{2} \quad \text{or} \quad \sin x = -1$$

If $\sin x = \frac{1}{2}$, then $x = \pi/6$ or $5\pi/6$. If $\sin x = -1$, then $x = 3\pi/2$. The solutions are $\pi/6$, $5\pi/6$, and $3\pi/2$. ▬

Sometimes it is necessary to make a substitution using one of the basic identities. The next example illustrates this technique.

EXAMPLE 5

Solve $\sec^2 x + \tan^2 x = 3$, if $0 \le x < 2\pi$.

Solution

Using the identity $1 + \tan^2 x = \sec^2 x$, we can substitute $1 + \tan^2 x$ for $\sec^2 x$ in the given equation and proceed as follows.

$$\sec^2 x + \tan^2 x = 3$$

$$(1 + \tan^2 x) + \tan^2 x = 3$$

$$2 \tan^2 x = 2$$

$$\tan^2 x = 1$$

$$\tan x = \pm 1$$

If $\tan x = 1$, then $x = \pi/4$, or $5\pi/4$. If $\tan x = -1$, then $x = 3\pi/4$ or $7\pi/4$. The solutions are $\pi/4$, $3\pi/4$, $5\pi/4$, and $7\pi/4$. ▬

Recall from algebra that squaring both sides of an equation may produce some extraneous solutions. Therefore, we learned that potential solutions **must be checked** if the squaring property is applied.

EXAMPLE 6

Solve $\sin x + \cos x = \sqrt{2}$, if $0 \le x < 2\pi$.

Solution

$$\sin x + \cos x = \sqrt{2}$$

$$\sin x = \sqrt{2} - \cos x$$

$$\sin^2 x = 2 - 2\sqrt{2}\cos x + \cos^2 x \qquad \text{Square both sides}$$

$$1 - \cos^2 x = 2 - 2\sqrt{2}\cos x + \cos^2 x \qquad \text{Substitute } 1 - \cos^2 x \text{ for } \sin^2 x$$

$$0 = 2\cos^2 x - 2\sqrt{2}\cos x + 1$$

Now we can use the quadratic formula to solve for $\cos x$.

$$\cos x = \frac{2\sqrt{2} \pm \sqrt{8 - 8}}{4}$$

$$= \frac{2\sqrt{2}}{4} = \frac{\sqrt{2}}{2}$$

If $\cos x = \sqrt{2}/2$, then $x = \pi/4$ or $7\pi/4$.

Check $\sin x + \cos x = \sqrt{2}$ $\qquad\qquad$ $\sin x + \cos x = \sqrt{2}$

$$\sin\frac{\pi}{4} + \cos\frac{\pi}{4} \overset{?}{=} \sqrt{2} \qquad\qquad \sin\frac{7\pi}{4} + \cos\frac{7\pi}{4} \overset{?}{=} \sqrt{2}$$

$$\frac{\sqrt{2}}{2} + \frac{\sqrt{2}}{2} \overset{?}{=} \sqrt{2} \qquad\qquad -\frac{\sqrt{2}}{2} + \frac{\sqrt{2}}{2} \overset{?}{=} \sqrt{2}$$

$$\frac{2\sqrt{2}}{2} = \sqrt{2} \qquad\qquad\qquad 0 \neq \sqrt{2}$$

The only solution is $\pi/4$.

Thus far in this section we have been able to determine solutions without the use of a calculator or a table. Now let's consider two examples where we can obtain approximate solutions using a calculator or a table.

EXAMPLE 7

Approximate, to the nearest hundredth of a radian, the solutions for

$$5\sin^2 x + 7\sin x - 6 = 0, \qquad 0 \le x < 2\pi.$$

Solution

Factoring the left side of the equation, we can proceed as follows.

$$5\sin^2 x + 7\sin x - 6 = 0$$

$$(\sin x + 2)(5\sin x - 3) = 0$$

$$\sin x + 2 = 0 \qquad \text{or} \qquad 5\sin x - 3 = 0$$

$$\sin x = -2 \qquad \text{or} \qquad 5\sin x = 3$$

$$\sin x = -2 \qquad \text{or} \qquad \sin x = \tfrac{3}{5}$$

The equation $\sin x = -2$ produces no solutions because sine values must be between -1 and 1, inclusive. If $\sin x = \tfrac{3}{5} = .6$, then by using a calculator or the table in Appendix C in the back of the book, we can determine that $x = .64$, to the nearest hundredth of a radian. Because the sine function is also positive in the second quadrant, x can be $\pi - .64 = 3.14 - .64 = 2.50$, to the nearest hundredth of a radian. Therefore, the approximate solutions of the original equation are .64 and 2.50.

EXAMPLE 8

Approximate, to the nearest tenth of a degree, the solutions for

$$\tan^2\theta + 2\tan\theta - 1 = 0, \qquad 0° \le \theta < 360°.$$

Solution

Using the quadratic formula we can determine approximate values for $\tan\theta$.

$$\tan\theta = \frac{-2 \pm \sqrt{4 + 4}}{2} = \frac{-2 \pm \sqrt{8}}{2}$$

$$= \frac{-2 \pm 2.8284}{2} \qquad \text{to the nearest ten-thousandth}$$

$$\tan\theta = \frac{-2 + 2.8284}{2} \qquad \text{or} \qquad \tan\theta = \frac{-2 - 2.8284}{2}$$

$$= .4142 \qquad\qquad\qquad = -2.4142$$

Now using a calculator or the table in Appendix C, we can find the approximate solutions of the original equation. Tan $\theta = .4142$ implies that $\theta = 22.5°$. Since the tangent is also positive in the third quadrant, another approximate solution is $180° + 22.5° = 202.5°$. To solve $\tan\theta = -2.4142$, consider the reference angle θ' such that $\tan\theta' = 2.4142$. Solving this equation for θ', we find that $\theta' = 67.5°$. Since the tangent function is negative in the second and fourth quadrants, we obtain

$$\theta = 180° - 67.5° = 112.5°$$

or

$$\theta = 360° - 67.5° = 292.5°.$$

Therefore, the approximate solutions of the original equation are $22.5°$, $112.5°$, $202.5°$, and $292.5°$.

A graphing utility can be a very useful tool for solving trigonometric equations. Let's demonstrate this by checking our answers for Example 7 using a graphing utility. First, we can graph the equation $y = 5\sin^2 x + 7\sin x - 6$ in the interval $0 \le x < 2\pi$ as shown in Figure 6.64. Then we can use the trace and zoom features to approximate the x-intercepts of the graph. Doing this we will find that, to the nearest hundredth, the x-intercepts are .64 and 2.50. These answers agree with our solutions in Example 7.

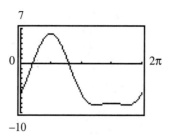

7

0 ⊢——————————— 2π

−10

FIGURE 6.64

If you have access to a graphing utility, we would suggest that you check our answers for Example 8. You can find the solutions in radians and then convert to degrees to see if you agree with the four solutions given.

PROBLEM SET 6.7

Solve each of the following equations for θ, if $0° \leq \theta < 360°$. Do not use a calculator or a table.

1. $2 \sin \theta = \sqrt{3}$

2. $2 \cos \theta + 1 = 0$

3. $2 \cos \theta + 2 = 0$

4. $2 \sin \theta + \sqrt{2} = 0$

5. $3 \tan \theta + 3\sqrt{3} = 0$

6. $\tan^2\theta = 3$

7. $2 \sin \theta = \sin \theta - 1$

8. $3 \cos \theta + 1 = \cos \theta + 3$

Solve each of the following equations for x, if $0 \leq x < 2\pi$. Do not use a calculator or a table.

9. $2 \sin x + \sqrt{3} = 0$

10. $-2 \cos x = \sqrt{2}$

11. $3 \cos x - 2 - \cos x = 0$

12. $\sin^2 x - 1 = 0$

13. $(2 \sin x + 1)(\tan x - 1) = 0$

14. $(\cos x + 1)(\sec x - 1) = 0$

15. $3 \sin x + 5 = 0$

16. $\tan x \sin x = 0$

Solve each of the following equations. If the variable is θ, find all solutions such that $0° \leq \theta < 360°$. If the variable is x,
find all solutions such that $0 \leq x < 2\pi$. Do not use a calculator or a table.

17. $2 \sin^2 x = \sin x$

18. $\sin x \tan^2 x = \sin x$

19. $\tan^2\theta - \tan \theta = 0$

20. $2 \tan \theta \sec \theta - \tan \theta = 0$

21. $2 \cos^3\theta = \cos \theta$

22. $2 \cos x = \cos x \csc x$

23. $2 \cos^2 x + 3 \cos x + 1 = 0$

24. $2 \sin^2 x - \sin x - 1 = 0$

25. $\sec^2\theta - \sec \theta - 2 = 0$

26. $\sin \theta \cos \theta - \cos \theta + \sin \theta - 1 = 0$

27. $2 \sin^2 x - \cos x - 1 = 0$

28. $2 \cos^2 x - \sin x - 1 = 0$

29. $\sin^2 x + \cos x = 1$

30. $2 \cos^2 x + \sin x - 2 = 0$

31. $\sin x = 1 - \cos x$

32. $\tan x + 1 = \sec x$

33. $\tan x = \cot x$

34. $\sin x - \cos x = 1$

Find *all* solutions of each of the following equations. If the variable is θ, express the solutions in degrees and if the variable is x, express the solutions in radians. Do not use a calculator or a table.

35. $2 \cos \theta = \sqrt{3}$

36. $\sin \theta + 1 = 0$

37. $2 \sin x + \sqrt{3} = 0$

38. $2 \cos x - 1 = 0$

39. $\tan x + 1 = 0$

40. $\cot x - 1 = 0$

41. $\sec^2\theta = 4$

42. $\csc^2\theta = 4$

43. $\cot^2 x - \cot x = 0$

44. $\sec^2 x = \sec x$

45. $\csc^2 x - \csc x - 2 = 0$

46. $(\tan x - 1)(\tan x - \sqrt{3}) = 0$

Use your calculator or the table in Appendix C to help find approximate solutions for θ, where $0° \le \theta < 360°$. Express the solutions to the nearest tenth of a degree.

47. $\sin \theta = -.2157$

48. $\sin \theta = .8217$

49. $\cos \theta = -.6427$

50. $\cos \theta = -.2179$

51. $\tan \theta = -3.1426$

52. $\tan \theta = 14.2789$

53. $(3 \sin \theta - 1)(2 \sin \theta + 3) = 0$

54. $(4 \sin \theta - 1)(\sin \theta + 2) = 0$

55. $6 \cos^2\theta - 13 \cos \theta + 6 = 0$

56. $12 \cos^2\theta - 13 \cos \theta + 3 = 0$

57. $\sin^2\theta - 4 \sin \theta + 1 = 0$

58. $\cos^2\theta - 3 \cos \theta + 1 = 0$

Use your calculator or the table in Appendix C to help find approximate solutions for x, where $0 \le x < 2\pi$. Express the solutions to the nearest hundredth of a radian.

59. $\sin x = -.7126$

60. $\sin x = .2314$

61. $\cos x = -.8214$

62. $\cos x = -.1429$

63. $\tan x = -1.2784$

64. $\tan x = 9.1275$

65. $4 \sin^2 x + 11 \sin x - 3 = 0$

66. $12 \cos^2 x + 5 \cos x - 3 = 0$

67. $\sin^2 x - 3 \sin x - 2 = 0$

68. $\sin^2 x - \sin x - 1 = 0$

69. $\cos^2 x + \cos x - 1 = 0$

70. $2 \cos^2 x - 3 \cos x - 1 = 0$

THOUGHTS into WORDS

71. Is $\sin x + \cos x = 1$ a conditional equation or an identity? Defend your answer.

 GRAPHICS CALCULATOR ACTIVITIES

73. Use a graphics calculator and check your solutions for Problems 59–70.

72. Give a step-by-step description of how you would find all solutions for the equation $3 \tan^4 x = 1 + \sec^2 x$.

74. Use your graphics calculator to approximate the solutions for each of the following equations. Express your answers to the nearest tenth.

a. $\cos x = x$ **b.** $\sin x = \frac{1}{2}x$

c. $\cos x = -2x$

75. Use your graphics calculator to determine the number of solutions for the equation $\cos x = -.1x$.

76. Return to Example 6 of this section and use your graphics calculator to show that $\dfrac{7\pi}{4}$ must be an extraneous solution.

6.8   SUM AND DIFFERENCE FORMULAS

We offer the following suggestions before you study these next two sections. First, read each section and look for the big ideas; don't be concerned about the details of proofs and worked-out examples. Then read the section again and pay attention to the details. This material is not difficult, but it is messy because of an abundance of formulas. However, you will soon see that most of the formulas are easily derived from a few key formulas. The following identities were established in Section 6.2 and will be used at times in this section.

$$\sin(-\theta) = -\sin\theta \qquad \cos(-\theta) = \cos\theta \qquad \tan(-\theta) = -\tan\theta$$

Does $\cos(\alpha - \beta) = \cos\alpha - \cos\beta$? The following example gives an immediate response to this question.

EXAMPLE I

Evaluate $\cos(\alpha - \beta)$ and $\cos\alpha - \cos\beta$ for $\alpha = 90°$ and $\beta = 60°$.

Solution

$$\cos(\alpha - \beta) = \cos(90° - 60°) = \cos 30° = \tfrac{\sqrt{3}}{2}$$
$$\cos\alpha - \cos\beta = \cos 90° - \cos 60° = 0 - \tfrac{1}{2} = -\tfrac{1}{2}$$

In general, $\cos(\alpha - \beta) \neq \cos\alpha - \cos\beta$. Additional examples would demonstrate that $\sin(\alpha - \beta) \neq \sin\alpha - \sin\beta$, $\cos 2\alpha \neq 2\cos\alpha$, $\sin\frac{1}{2}\alpha \neq \frac{1}{2}\sin\alpha$, and so on. We need special formulas (identities) for these situations. To develop a formula for $\cos(\alpha - \beta)$, let's consider two angles α and β, the angle that represents $\alpha - \beta$, and the unit circle, as in Figure 6.65. The terminal side of α intersects the unit circle at the point $(\cos\alpha, \sin\alpha)$ and the terminal side of β intersects the unit circle at $(\cos\beta, \sin\beta)$. The distance d between the two points is given by

$$d = \sqrt{(\cos\alpha - \cos\beta)^2 + (\sin\alpha - \sin\beta)^2}.$$

Therefore,

$$d^2 = (\cos\alpha - \cos\beta)^2 + (\sin\alpha - \sin\beta)^2$$
$$= \cos^2\alpha - 2\cos\alpha\cos\beta + \cos^2\beta + \sin^2\alpha - 2\sin\alpha\sin\beta + \sin^2\beta.$$

Since $\cos^2\alpha + \sin^2\alpha = 1$ and $\cos^2\beta + \sin^2\beta = 1$, we obtain

$$d^2 = 2 - 2\cos\alpha\cos\beta - 2\sin\alpha\sin\beta.$$

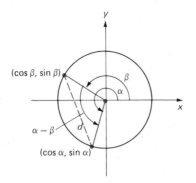

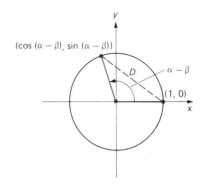

FIGURE 6.65   **FIGURE 6.66**

Now, looking back at Figure 6.65, let's construct angle $(\alpha - \beta)$ in standard position as indicated in Figure 6.66. The terminal side of $(\alpha - \beta)$ intersects the unit circle at the point $(\cos(\alpha - \beta), \sin(\alpha - \beta))$. The distance D between this point and $(1, 0)$ is given by

$$D = \sqrt{[\cos(\alpha - \beta) - 1]^2 + [\sin(\alpha - \beta) - 0]^2}.$$

Therefore,

$$D^2 = [\cos(\alpha - \beta) - 1]^2 + [\sin(\alpha - \beta) - 0]^2$$
$$= \cos^2(\alpha - \beta) - 2\cos(\alpha - \beta) + 1 + \sin^2(\alpha - \beta).$$

Since $\cos^2(\alpha - \beta) + \sin^2(\alpha - \beta) = 1$, we obtain

$$D^2 = 2 - 2\cos(\alpha - \beta).$$

The isosceles triangles formed in Figures 6.65 and 6.66 are congruent; thus, $d = D$ and we can equate the expressions for D^2 and d^2.

$$2 - 2\cos(\alpha - \beta) = 2 - 2\cos\alpha\cos\beta - 2\sin\alpha\sin\beta$$

Subtract 2 from both sides and then divide both sides by -2 to produce the following important identity.

$$\cos(\alpha - \beta) = \cos\alpha\cos\beta + \sin\alpha\sin\beta$$

The previous development assumes that α and β are positive angles with $\alpha > \beta$. However, the identity holds for all angles measured in radians or degrees, and, in fact, is true for all real numbers.

EXAMPLE 2

Find an exact value for $\cos 15°$.

Solution

Let $\alpha = 45°$ and $\beta = 30°$. Therefore,

$$\cos 15° = \cos(45° - 30°) = \cos 45° \cos 30° + \sin 45° \sin 30°$$
$$= \left(\frac{\sqrt{2}}{2}\right)\left(\frac{\sqrt{3}}{2}\right) + \left(\frac{\sqrt{2}}{2}\right)\left(\frac{1}{2}\right) = \frac{\sqrt{6}}{4} + \frac{\sqrt{2}}{4}$$
$$= \frac{\sqrt{6} + \sqrt{2}}{4}.$$

If in the formula for $\cos(\alpha - \beta)$ we replace β with $-\beta$, we obtain

$$\cos(\alpha - (-\beta)) = \cos \alpha \cos(-\beta) + \sin \alpha \sin(-\beta).$$

Using the identities $\cos(-\beta) = \cos \beta$ and $\sin(-\beta) = -\sin \beta$, the following sum formula is produced.

$$\cos(\alpha + \beta) = \cos \alpha \cos \beta - \sin \alpha \sin \beta$$

EXAMPLE 3

For an exact value for $\cos 5\pi/12$.

Solution

Let $\alpha = \pi/4$ and $\beta = \pi/6$. Therefore,

$$\cos \frac{5\pi}{12} = \cos\left(\frac{\pi}{4} + \frac{\pi}{6}\right) = \cos \frac{\pi}{4} \cos \frac{\pi}{6} - \sin \frac{\pi}{4} \sin \frac{\pi}{6}$$
$$= \left(\frac{\sqrt{2}}{2}\right)\left(\frac{\sqrt{3}}{2}\right) - \left(\frac{\sqrt{2}}{2}\right)\left(\frac{1}{2}\right)$$
$$= \frac{\sqrt{6}}{4} - \frac{\sqrt{2}}{4}$$
$$= \frac{\sqrt{6} - \sqrt{2}}{4}.$$

Before we develop formulas for $\sin(\alpha + \beta)$ and $\sin(\alpha - \beta)$, let's consider some identities that involve a 90° angle.

$$\cos(90° - \alpha) = \cos 90° \cos \alpha + \sin 90° \sin \alpha$$
$$= 0 \cdot \cos \alpha + 1 \cdot \sin \alpha = \sin \alpha$$

Therefore,

$$\cos(90° - \alpha) = \sin \alpha.$$

Now, substituting $90° - \alpha$ for α in the previous identity, we obtain

$$\cos(90° - (90° - \alpha)) = \sin(90° - \alpha)$$
$$\cos(90° - 90° + \alpha) = \sin(90° - \alpha)$$
$$\cos \alpha = \sin(90° - \alpha).$$

$$\sin(90° - \alpha) = \cos \alpha$$

An identity involving $\tan(90° - \alpha)$ follows directly from the sine and cosine relationships.

$$\tan(90° - \alpha) = \frac{\sin(90° - \alpha)}{\cos(90° - \alpha)} = \frac{\cos \alpha}{\sin \alpha} = \cot \alpha$$

$$\tan(90° - \alpha) = \cot \alpha$$

Now let's use the identity $\sin \alpha = \cos(90° - \alpha)$ to develop a formula for $\sin(\alpha + \beta)$.

$$\begin{aligned}
\sin(\alpha + \beta) &= \cos[90° - (\alpha + \beta)] \\
&= \cos[(90° - \alpha) - \beta] \\
&= \cos(90° - \alpha)\cos \beta + \sin(90° - \alpha)\sin \beta \\
&= \sin \alpha \cos \beta + \cos \alpha \sin \beta
\end{aligned}$$

$$\sin(\alpha + \beta) = \sin \alpha \cos \beta + \cos \alpha \sin \beta$$

Substituting $-\beta$ for β into the formula for $\sin(\alpha + \beta)$ produces

$$\begin{aligned}
\sin(\alpha + (-\beta)) &= \sin \alpha \cos(-\beta) + \cos \alpha \sin(-\beta) \\
&= \sin \alpha \cos \beta - \cos \alpha \sin \beta.
\end{aligned}$$

$$\sin(\alpha - \beta) = \sin \alpha \cos \beta - \cos \alpha \sin \beta$$

As you might expect, a formula for $\tan(\alpha + \beta)$ follows directly from the sine and cosine relationships.

$$\tan(\alpha + \beta) = \frac{\sin(\alpha + \beta)}{\cos(\alpha + \beta)} = \frac{\sin \alpha \cos \beta + \cos \alpha \sin \beta}{\cos \alpha \cos \beta - \sin \alpha \sin \beta}$$

Dividing both numerator and denominator by $\cos \alpha \cos \beta$ produces

$$\tan(\alpha + \beta) = \frac{\dfrac{\sin \alpha \cos \beta}{\cos \alpha \cos \beta} + \dfrac{\cos \alpha \sin \beta}{\cos \alpha \cos \beta}}{\dfrac{\cos \alpha \cos \beta}{\cos \alpha \cos \beta} - \dfrac{\sin \alpha \sin \beta}{\cos \alpha \cos \beta}} = \frac{\tan \alpha + \tan \beta}{1 - \tan \alpha \tan \beta}.$$

$$tan(\alpha + \beta) = \frac{\tan \alpha + \tan \beta}{1 - \tan \alpha \tan \beta}$$

If in the formula for $\tan(\alpha + \beta)$ we replace β with $-\beta$, the following result will be obtained. (We will leave the details for you as an exercise.)

$$\tan(\alpha - \beta) = \frac{\tan \alpha - \tan \beta}{1 + \tan \alpha \tan \beta}$$

EXAMPLE 4

Find an exact value for $\sin(\pi/12)$.

Solution

Let $\alpha = \pi/3$ and $\beta = \pi/4$. Therefore,

$$\sin \tfrac{\pi}{12} = \sin\left(\tfrac{\pi}{3} - \tfrac{\pi}{4}\right) = \sin \tfrac{\pi}{3} \cos \tfrac{\pi}{4} - \cos \tfrac{\pi}{3} \sin \tfrac{\pi}{4}$$

$$= \left(\tfrac{\sqrt{3}}{2}\right)\left(\tfrac{\sqrt{2}}{2}\right) - \left(\tfrac{1}{2}\right)\left(\tfrac{\sqrt{2}}{2}\right)$$

$$= \tfrac{\sqrt{6}}{4} - \tfrac{\sqrt{2}}{4} = \tfrac{\sqrt{6} - \sqrt{2}}{4}.$$

EXAMPLE 5

Find an exact value for $\tan 195°$.

Solution

Let $\alpha = 135°$ and $\beta = 60°$. Therefore,

$$\tan 195° = \tan(135° + 60°) = \frac{\tan 135° + \tan 60°}{1 - \tan 135° \tan 60°}$$

$$= \frac{-1 + \sqrt{3}}{1 - (-1)(\sqrt{3})}$$

$$= \frac{-1 + \sqrt{3}}{1 + \sqrt{3}}$$

$$= \frac{-1 + \sqrt{3}}{1 + \sqrt{3}} \cdot \frac{1 - \sqrt{3}}{1 - \sqrt{3}}$$

$$= \frac{-1 + 2\sqrt{3} - 3}{1 - 3}$$

$$= \frac{-4 + 2\sqrt{3}}{-2} = 2 - \sqrt{3}.$$

EXAMPLE 6

Given that $\sin\alpha = \frac{3}{5}$ with α in the first quadrant, and $\cos\beta = -\frac{7}{25}$ with β in the second quadrant, find $\cos(\alpha - \beta)$, $\sin(\alpha + \beta)$, and $\tan(\alpha + \beta)$.

Solution

If $\sin\alpha = \frac{3}{5}$ and α is in the first quadrant, then $\cos\alpha = \frac{4}{5}$ and $\tan\alpha = \frac{3}{4}$ (Figure 6.67). Likewise, if $\cos\beta = -\frac{7}{25}$ and β is in the second quadrant, then $\sin\beta = \frac{24}{25}$ and $\tan\beta = -\frac{24}{7}$.

$$\cos(\alpha - \beta) = \cos\alpha\cos\beta + \sin\alpha\sin\beta$$

$$= \left(\tfrac{4}{5}\right)\left(-\tfrac{7}{25}\right) + \left(\tfrac{3}{5}\right)\left(\tfrac{24}{25}\right) = -\tfrac{28}{125} + \tfrac{72}{125} = \tfrac{44}{125}$$

$$\sin(\alpha + \beta) = \sin\alpha\cos\beta + \cos\alpha\sin\beta$$

$$= \left(\tfrac{3}{5}\right)\left(-\tfrac{7}{25}\right) + \left(\tfrac{4}{5}\right)\left(\tfrac{24}{25}\right) = -\tfrac{21}{125} + \tfrac{96}{125} = \tfrac{75}{125} = \tfrac{3}{5}$$

$$\tan(\alpha + \beta) = \frac{\tan\alpha + \tan\beta}{1 - \tan\alpha\tan\beta}$$

$$= \frac{\tfrac{3}{4} + \left(-\tfrac{24}{7}\right)}{1 - \left(\tfrac{3}{4}\right)\left(-\tfrac{24}{7}\right)} = \frac{-\tfrac{75}{28}}{1 + \tfrac{72}{28}} = \frac{-\tfrac{75}{28}}{\tfrac{100}{28}} = -\tfrac{75}{100} = -\tfrac{3}{4}$$

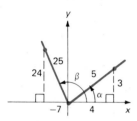

FIGURE 6.67

EXAMPLE 7

Evaluate $\sin\left(\tan^{-1}\tfrac{1}{2} + \cos^{-1}\tfrac{3}{5}\right)$.

Solution

Let $\alpha = \tan^{-1}\tfrac{1}{2}$ and $\beta = \cos^{-1}\tfrac{3}{5}$. From the definitions of the inverse trigonometric functions in Section 6.5, and because $\tan\alpha$ and $\cos\beta$ are positive, we can determine that α and β are acute angles as shown in Figure 6.68. Therefore,

$$\sin(\alpha + \beta) = \sin\alpha\cos\beta + \cos\alpha\sin\beta$$

$$= \left(\frac{\sqrt{5}}{5}\right)\left(\frac{3}{5}\right) + \left(\frac{2\sqrt{5}}{5}\right)\left(\frac{4}{5}\right)$$

$$= \frac{3\sqrt{5}}{25} + \frac{8\sqrt{5}}{25} = \frac{11\sqrt{5}}{25}.$$

Thus,

$$\sin\left(\tan^{-1}\frac{1}{2} + \cos^{-1}\frac{3}{5}\right) = \frac{11\sqrt{5}}{25}.$$

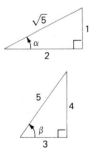

FIGURE 6.68

EXAMPLE 8

Use a graphing utility to demonstrate that $\cos\left(\frac{\pi}{2} - x\right) = \sin x$ is an identity.

Solution

Let $Y_1 = \cos\left(\frac{\pi}{2} - x\right)$ and $Y_2 = \sin x$ and graph both of these curves on the same set of axes (Figure 6.69). Since their graphs appear to be identical, this visually demonstrates that $\cos\left(\frac{\pi}{2} - x\right) = \sin x$.

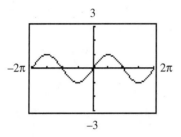

F I G U R E   6 . 69

A graphing utility can also be used to *predict* possible identities. For example, suppose that we graph the function $f(x) = \sin(x + (3\pi/2))$ as shown in Figure 6.70. This curve appears to be the x-axis reflection of the cosine curve; that is, the graph of $f(x) = -\cos x$. So let's graph $f(x) = -\cos x$ on the same set of axes and we do indeed obtain the same graph as in Figure 6.70. Thus, from a graphing viewpoint we

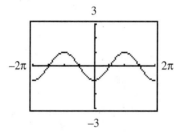

F I G U R E   6 . 70

have demonstrated the identity $\sin(x + (3\pi/2)) = -\cos x$. Using the sum identity we can verify this identity as follows.

$$\sin\left(x + \frac{3\pi}{2}\right) = \sin x \cos \frac{3\pi}{2} + \cos x \sin \frac{3\pi}{2}$$

$$= (\sin x)(0) + (\cos x)(-1)$$

$$= -\cos x$$

If you are following the suggestion offered at the beginning of this section, it is now time to go back and fill in some details. Keep the following continuity pattern in mind. The first formula derived was

$$\cos(\alpha - \beta) = \cos \alpha \cos \beta + \sin \alpha \sin \beta. \tag{1}$$

Then substituting $-\beta$ for β produced

$$cos(\alpha + \beta) = cos\, \alpha\, cos\, \beta - sin\, \alpha\, sin\, \beta. \tag{2}$$

Then applying $cos(\alpha - \beta)$ to $cos(90° - \alpha)$ produced

$$cos(90° - \alpha) = sin\, \alpha. \tag{3}$$

Then substituting $(\alpha + \beta)$ for α in (3) produced

$$sin(\alpha + \beta) = sin\, \alpha\, cos\, \beta + cos\, \alpha\, sin\, \beta. \tag{4}$$

Then substituting $-\beta$ for β produced

$$sin(\alpha - \beta) = sin\, \alpha\, cos\, \beta - cos\, \alpha\, sin\, \beta. \tag{5}$$

Then using the formulas for $sin(\alpha + \beta)$ and $cos(\alpha + \beta)$, we obtained

$$tan(\alpha + \beta) = \frac{tan\, \alpha + tan\, \beta}{1 - tan\, \alpha\, tan\, \beta}. \tag{6}$$

Finally, substituting $-\beta$ for β produced

$$tan(\alpha - \beta) = \frac{tan\, \alpha - tan\, \beta}{1 + tan\, \alpha\, tan\, \beta}. \tag{7}$$

PROBLEM SET 6.8

For Problems 1–14, find the exact values without using a table or a calculator.

1. $sin\, 15°$

2. $tan\, 15°$

3. $tan\, 75°$

4. $sin\, 75°$

5. $sin\, 105°$

6. $cos\, 105°$

7. $cos\, 195°$

8. $sin\, 195°$

9. $tan\, 255°$

10. $cos\, 345°$

11. $cos\, \frac{\pi}{12}$

12. $cos\, \frac{5\pi}{12}$

13. $sin\, \frac{7\pi}{12}$

14. $sin\, \frac{11\pi}{12}$

15. Given that $cos\, \alpha = \frac{3}{5}$ with α in the first quadrant, and $sin\, \beta = \frac{15}{17}$ with β in the second quadrant, find $sin(\alpha - \beta)$ and $tan(\alpha + \beta)$.

16. If α and β are acute angles such that $cos\, \alpha = \frac{4}{5}$ and $tan\, \beta = \frac{8}{15}$, find $cos(\alpha + \beta)$ and $sin(\alpha + \beta)$.

17. If $cos\, \alpha = -\frac{3}{5}$ and $tan\, \beta = \frac{8}{15}$, where α is a second-quadrant angle and β is a third-quadrant angle, find $sin(\alpha + \beta)$ and $cos(\alpha - \beta)$.

18. If $tan\, \alpha = -\frac{4}{3}$ and $sin\, \beta = -\frac{3}{5}$, where α is a second-quadrant angle and β is a fourth-quadrant angle, find $sin(\alpha - \beta)$ and $tan(\alpha + \beta)$.

19. Given that $tan\, \alpha = \frac{8}{15}$ with α in the first quadrant, and $cos\, \beta = \frac{7}{25}$ with β in the fourth quadrant, find $sin(\alpha - \beta)$ and $cos(\alpha - \beta)$.

20. Given that $tan\, \alpha = -\frac{2}{3}$ with α in the second quadrant, and $tan\, \beta = \frac{3}{5}$ with β in the third quadrant, find $tan(\alpha + \beta)$ and $tan(\alpha - \beta)$.

For Problems 21–26, find exact values without using a calculator or a table.

21. $sin\left(tan^{-1}\frac{3}{4} + cos^{-1}\frac{24}{25}\right)$

22. $cos\left(tan^{-1}\frac{7}{24} - sin^{-1}\frac{4}{5}\right)$

23. $\tan\left(\arcsin \frac{15}{17} + \arccos \frac{4}{5}\right)$

24. $\tan\left[\arcsin \frac{3}{5} + \arccos\left(-\frac{3}{5}\right)\right]$

25. $\cos\left(\tan^{-1} \frac{1}{3} + \cos^{-1} \frac{8}{17}\right)$

26. $\sin\left(\tan^{-1} \frac{1}{2} - \cos^{-1} \frac{4}{5}\right)$

Verify each of the identities in Problems 27–38.

27. $\sin(\alpha + 90°) = \cos \alpha$

28. $\cos(\alpha + 90°) = -\sin \alpha$

29. $\sin(\alpha + \pi) = -\sin \alpha$

30. $\cos(\alpha - \pi) = -\cos \alpha$

31. $\tan(\alpha + \pi) = \tan \alpha$

32. $\tan(\alpha - \pi) = \tan \alpha$

33. $\sin(\alpha + 45°) = \frac{\sqrt{2}}{2}(\sin \alpha + \cos \alpha)$

34. $\cos(\alpha - 45°) = \frac{\sqrt{2}}{2}(\cos \alpha + \sin \alpha)$

35. $\tan\left(\alpha + \frac{\pi}{4}\right) = \frac{1 + \tan \alpha}{1 - \tan \alpha}$

36. $\tan\left(\alpha - \frac{\pi}{4}\right) = \frac{\tan \alpha - 1}{\tan \alpha + 1}$

37. $\sin(\alpha + 270°) = -\cos \alpha$

38. $\cos(\alpha - 270°) = -\sin \alpha$

39. Develop the formula for $\tan(\alpha - \beta)$ by replacing β with $-\beta$ in the formula for $\tan(\alpha + \beta)$.

40. Derive the formula $\cot(\alpha + \beta) = \dfrac{\cot \alpha \cot \beta - 1}{\cot \alpha + \cot \beta}$.

41. Derive the formula $\cot(\alpha - \beta) = \dfrac{\cot \alpha \cot \beta + 1}{\cot \beta - \cot \alpha}$.

42. If α and β are complementary angles, verify that $\sin^2\alpha + \sin^2\beta = 1$.

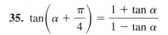

GRAPHICS CALCULATOR ACTIVITIES

43. We want to decide if each of the following represents a conditional equation or an identity. Therefore, let's try some specific examples, make a prediction based on these examples, and then use a graphing utility to confirm our predictions. If the equation is a conditional equation, use your graphing utility to approximate (to the nearest tenth of a radian) solutions such that $0 \leq x < 2\pi$.

a. $\sin 2x = 2 \sin x$

b. $\sin 2x = 2 \sin x \cos x$

c. $\cos 2x = 2 \cos^2 x - 1$

d. $\cos 2x = \cos^2 x - \sin^2 x$

e. $\cos 2x = 2 \cos x$

f. $\cos 2x = 1 - 2 \sin^2 x$

g. $\sin 3x = 3 \sin x \cos x$

h. $\sin 3x = 3 \sin x - 4 \sin^3 x$

6.9   MULTIPLE AND HALF-ANGLE FORMULAS

Again let's emphasize the point that $\sin 2\alpha \neq 2 \sin \alpha$. For example, $\sin 2(30°) = \sin 60° = \frac{\sqrt{3}}{2}$, but $2 \sin 30° = 2\left(\frac{1}{2}\right) = 1$. Thus, **multiple angle formulas** are needed. As you might expect, the multiple angle formulas are nothing more than special cases of the sum formulas developed in the previous section. For example, in the formula for $\sin(\alpha + \beta)$, if we let $\alpha = \beta$ we obtain the following.

$$\sin(\alpha + \beta) = \sin \alpha \cos \beta + \cos \alpha \sin \beta$$

becomes

$$\sin(\alpha + \alpha) = \sin \alpha \cos \alpha + \cos \alpha \sin \alpha, \text{ or, equivalently,}$$

$$\sin 2\alpha = 2 \sin \alpha \cos \alpha.$$

EXAMPLE 1

Find $\sin 2\alpha$ if $\alpha = \frac{4}{5}$ and α is in the first quadrant.

Solution

If $\sin \alpha = \frac{4}{5}$ and α is in the first quadrant, then $\cos \alpha = \frac{3}{5}$. Therefore,

$$\sin 2\alpha = 2 \sin \alpha \cos \alpha = 2\left(\tfrac{4}{5}\right)\left(\tfrac{3}{5}\right) = \tfrac{24}{25}.$$

Substituting α for β in the formula for $\cos(\alpha + \beta)$ produces

$$\cos(\alpha + \beta) = \cos \alpha \cos \beta - \sin \alpha \sin \beta$$

$$\cos(\alpha + \alpha) = \cos \alpha \cos \alpha - \sin \alpha \sin \alpha$$

$$\cos 2\alpha = \cos^2\alpha - \sin^2\alpha.$$

Two other forms for $\cos 2\alpha$ can be obtained by using the basic identity $\sin^2\alpha + \cos^2\alpha = 1$. Substituting $1 - \sin^2\alpha$ for $\cos^2\alpha$ produces

$$\cos^2\alpha - \sin^2\alpha = (1 - \sin^2\alpha) - \sin^2\alpha = 1 - 2 \sin^2\alpha.$$

Similarly, substituting $1 - \cos^2\alpha$ for $\sin^2\alpha$ produces

$$\cos^2\alpha - \sin^2\alpha = \cos^2\alpha - (1 - \cos^2\alpha) = 2 \cos^2\alpha - 1.$$

$$\cos 2\alpha = \cos^2\alpha - \sin^2\alpha$$

or

$$\cos 2\alpha = 1 - 2 \sin^2\alpha$$

or

$$\cos 2\alpha = 2 \cos^2\alpha - 1$$

Substituting α for β in the formula for $\tan(\alpha + \beta)$ produces

$$\tan(\alpha + \beta) = \frac{\tan \alpha + \tan \beta}{1 - \tan \alpha \tan \beta}$$

$$\tan(\alpha + \alpha) = \frac{\tan \alpha + \tan \alpha}{1 - \tan \alpha \tan \alpha}$$

$$\tan 2\alpha = \frac{2 \tan \alpha}{1 - \tan^2\alpha}.$$

EXAMPLE 2

Find $\sin 2\theta$, $\cos 2\theta$, and $\tan 2\theta$ if $\sin \theta = -\frac{5}{13}$ and θ is a fourth-quadrant angle.

Solution

Figure 6.71 depicts the situation. Therefore, $\cos \theta = \frac{12}{13}$ and $\tan \theta = -\frac{5}{12}$. Now we can use the double-angle identities.

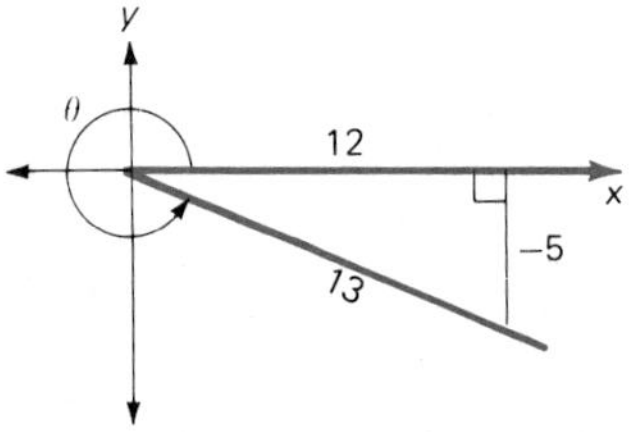

$$\sin 2\theta = 2 \sin \theta \cos \theta = 2\left(-\tfrac{5}{13}\right)\left(\tfrac{12}{13}\right) = -\tfrac{120}{169}$$

$$\cos 2\theta = \cos^2\theta - \sin^2\theta$$

$$= \left(\tfrac{12}{13}\right)^2 - \left(-\tfrac{5}{13}\right)^2 = \tfrac{144}{169} - \tfrac{25}{169} = \tfrac{119}{169}$$

$$\tan 2\theta = \frac{2 \tan \theta}{1 - \tan^2\theta}$$

$$= \frac{2\left(-\tfrac{5}{12}\right)}{1 - \left(-\tfrac{5}{12}\right)^2} = \frac{-\tfrac{10}{12}}{1 - \tfrac{25}{144}} = \frac{-\tfrac{5}{6}}{\tfrac{119}{144}} = \left(-\tfrac{5}{6}\right)\left(\tfrac{144}{119}\right) = -\tfrac{120}{119} \quad \blacksquare$$

FIGURE 6.71

REMARK   In Example 2, after finding the values for $\sin 2\theta$ and $\cos 2\theta$, the identity $\tan 2\theta = (\sin 2\theta)/\cos 2\theta$ could also be used to find the value of $\tan 2\theta$.

The double-angle identities provide a broader base for proving identities and solving trigonometric equations, as the next examples illustrate.

EXAMPLE 3

Verify the identity $\cos 2\alpha = \cos^4\alpha - \sin^4\alpha$.

Solution

The right side can be factored as the difference of two squares.

$$\cos^4\alpha - \sin^4\alpha = (\cos^2\alpha + \sin^2\alpha)(\cos^2\alpha - \sin^2\alpha)$$

We know that $\cos^2\alpha + \sin^2\alpha = 1$ and $\cos^2\alpha - \sin^2\alpha = \cos 2\alpha$. Therefore,

$$\cos^4\alpha - \sin^4\alpha = 1 \cdot \cos 2\alpha = \cos 2\alpha \quad \blacksquare$$

EXAMPLE 4

Solve the equation $\cos 2x - \cos x = 0$, where $0 \le x < 2\pi$.

Solution

We can substitute $2 \cos^2 x - 1$ for $\cos 2x$ and proceed as follows.

$$\cos 2x - \cos x = 0$$

$$(2 \cos^2 x - 1) - \cos x = 0$$

$$2 \cos^2 x - \cos x - 1 = 0$$

$$(2 \cos x + 1)(\cos x - 1) = 0$$

$$2 \cos x + 1 = 0 \qquad \text{or} \qquad \cos x - 1 = 0$$

$$2 \cos x = -1 \qquad \text{or} \qquad \cos x = 1$$

$$\cos x = -\tfrac{1}{2} \qquad \text{or} \qquad \cos x = 1$$

If $\cos x = -\tfrac{1}{2}$, then $x = 2\pi/3$ or $4\pi/3$. If $\cos x = 1$, then $x = 0$. The solutions are 0, $2\pi/3$, and $4\pi/3$.

EXAMPLE 5

Express $\sin 3\theta$ in terms of $\sin \theta$.

Solution

$$\sin 3\theta = \sin(2\theta + \theta)$$

$$= \sin 2\theta \cos\theta + \cos 2\theta \sin \theta$$

$$= (2 \sin \theta \cos \theta)\cos \theta + (1 - 2 \sin^2\theta)\sin \theta$$

$$= 2 \sin \theta \cos^2\theta + \sin \theta - 2 \sin^3\theta$$

$$= 2 \sin \theta(1 - \sin^2\theta) + \sin \theta - 2 \sin^3\theta$$

$$= 2 \sin \theta - 2 \sin^3\theta + \sin \theta - 2 \sin^3\theta$$

$$= -4 \sin^3\theta + 3 \sin \theta$$

Now let's change the form of the identity $\cos 2\alpha = 1 - 2 \sin^2\alpha$ by solving for $\sin^2\alpha$.

$$\cos 2\alpha = 1 - 2 \sin^2\alpha$$

$$2 \sin^2\alpha = 1 - \cos 2\alpha$$

$$\sin^2\alpha = \frac{1 - \cos 2\alpha}{2}$$

In a similar fashion the identity $\cos 2\alpha = 2 \cos^2\alpha - 1$ can be written as $\cos^2\alpha = (1 + \cos 2\alpha)/2$. Then using the fact that $\tan^2\alpha = (\sin^2\alpha)/\cos^2\alpha$ we can express $\tan^2\alpha$ as $\tan^2\alpha = (1 - \cos 2\alpha)/(1 + \cos 2\alpha)$. Thus, the following three identities are formed.

$$\sin^2\alpha = \frac{1 - \cos 2\alpha}{2}, \qquad \cos^2\alpha = \frac{1 + \cos 2\alpha}{2}, \qquad \tan^2\alpha = \frac{1 - \cos 2\alpha}{1 + \cos 2\alpha}.$$

These identities are used in calculus to change the form of some expressions that involve powers of trigonometric functions as you will see in the next example.

EXAMPLE 6

Express $\sin^4\alpha$ as an expression with no powers of the trigonometric functions.

Solution

$$\sin^4\alpha = (\sin^2\alpha)^2$$

$$= \left(\frac{1 - \cos 2\alpha}{2}\right)^2 \qquad \text{Substitute } \frac{1 - \cos 2\alpha}{2} \text{ for } \sin^2\alpha$$

$$= \frac{1 - 2\cos 2\alpha + \cos^2 2\alpha}{4}$$

$$= \tfrac{1}{4} - \tfrac{1}{2}\cos 2\alpha + \tfrac{1}{4}\cos^2 2\alpha$$

$$= \tfrac{1}{4} - \tfrac{1}{2}\cos 2\alpha + \tfrac{1}{4}\left(\frac{1 + \cos 4\alpha}{2}\right) \qquad \begin{array}{l}\text{Substitute } \dfrac{1 + \cos 4\alpha}{2} \\ \text{for } \cos^2 2\alpha\end{array}$$

$$= \tfrac{3}{8} - \tfrac{1}{2}\cos 2\alpha + \tfrac{1}{8}\cos 4\alpha.$$

REMARK   In Example 8 we changed a simple looking expression, $\sin^4\alpha$, to a more complicated expression, $\tfrac{3}{8} - \tfrac{1}{2}\cos 2\alpha + \tfrac{1}{8}\cos 4\alpha$. Sometimes in calculus the multiple angle expressions can be handled more easily than powers of a trigonometric function.

Half-Angle Formulas

By substituting $\alpha/2$ for α in the three identities in the previous box, and then solving for $\sin(\alpha/2)$, $\cos(\alpha/2)$, and $\tan(\alpha/2)$, we obtain the following three half-angle formulas.

$$\sin\frac{\alpha}{2} = \pm\sqrt{\frac{1 - \cos\alpha}{2}}, \qquad \cos\frac{\alpha}{2} = \pm\sqrt{\frac{1 + \cos\alpha}{2}},$$

$$\tan\frac{\alpha}{2} = \pm\sqrt{\frac{1 - \cos\alpha}{1 + \cos\alpha}}$$

In the formulas for $\sin(\alpha/2)$ and $\cos(\alpha/2)$, the choice of the plus or minus sign is determined by the quadrant in which $\alpha/2$ lies. For example, if $\alpha/2$ is in the first or second quadrant, then we would use

$$\sin\frac{\alpha}{2} = \sqrt{\frac{1 - \cos\alpha}{2}}.$$

However, if $\alpha/2$ is a third- or fourth-quadrant angle, then we would use

$$\sin\frac{\alpha}{2} = -\sqrt{\frac{1 - \cos\alpha}{2}}.$$

An alternative form for the $\tan(\alpha/2)$ formula can be obtained by multiplying the radicand by a form of one, namely, $(1 - \cos\alpha)/(1 - \cos\alpha)$.

$$\tan\frac{\alpha}{2} = \pm\sqrt{\frac{1-\cos\alpha}{1+\cos\alpha}\cdot\frac{1-\cos\alpha}{1-\cos\alpha}}$$

$$= \pm\sqrt{\frac{(1-\cos\alpha)^2}{1-\cos^2\alpha}}$$

$$= \pm\sqrt{\frac{(1-\cos\alpha)^2}{\sin^2\alpha}} = \frac{1-\cos\alpha}{\sin\alpha}.$$

We no longer need the $\pm$ sign because $1-\cos\alpha$ is never negative, and $\sin\alpha$ and $\tan(\alpha/2)$ will always agree in sign. For example, if $0 < \alpha < \pi$, then $0 < \alpha/2 < \pi/2$ and therefore both $\sin\alpha$ and $\tan(\alpha/2)$ are positive. If $\pi < \alpha < 2\pi$, then $\pi/2 < \alpha/2 < \pi$ and both $\sin\alpha$ and $\tan(\alpha/2)$ are negative. Furthermore, the form of $(1-\cos\alpha)/\sin\alpha$ can be changed as follows.

$$\frac{1-\cos\alpha}{\sin\alpha}\cdot\frac{1+\cos\alpha}{1+\cos\alpha} = \frac{1-\cos^2\alpha}{\sin\alpha(1+\cos\alpha)}$$

$$= \frac{\sin^2\alpha}{\sin\alpha(1+\cos\alpha)}$$

$$= \frac{\sin\alpha}{1+\cos\alpha}.$$

Therefore, either of the following two identities can be used.

$$\tan\frac{\alpha}{2} = \frac{1-\cos\alpha}{\sin\alpha} \qquad \text{or} \qquad \tan\frac{\alpha}{2} = \frac{\sin\alpha}{1+\cos\alpha}.$$

EXAMPLE 7

If $\cos\alpha = -\frac{4}{5}$ and α is in the third quadrant, find $\sin(\alpha/2)$, $\cos(\alpha/2)$, and $\tan(\alpha/2)$.

Solution

Because α is in the third quadrant, $\alpha/2$ is in the second quadrant; thus, $\sin(\alpha/2)$ is positive and $\cos(\alpha/2)$ is negative.

$$\sin\frac{\alpha}{2} = \sqrt{\frac{1-\cos\alpha}{2}} = \sqrt{\frac{1-\left(-\frac{4}{5}\right)}{2}} = \sqrt{\frac{1+\frac{4}{5}}{2}}$$

$$= \sqrt{\frac{\frac{9}{5}}{2}} = \sqrt{\frac{9}{10}} = \frac{3\sqrt{10}}{10}.$$

$$\cos\frac{\alpha}{2} = -\sqrt{\frac{1+\cos\alpha}{2}} = -\sqrt{\frac{1+\left(-\frac{4}{5}\right)}{2}} = -\sqrt{\frac{\frac{1}{5}}{2}}$$

$$= -\sqrt{\frac{1}{10}} = -\frac{\sqrt{10}}{10}.$$

If $\cos \alpha = -\frac{4}{5}$ and α is in the third quadrant, then $\sin \alpha = -\frac{3}{5}$. Therefore,

$$\tan \frac{\alpha}{2} = \frac{1 - \cos \alpha}{\sin \alpha} = \frac{1 - \left(-\frac{4}{5}\right)}{-\frac{3}{5}} = \frac{\frac{9}{5}}{-\frac{3}{5}} = -3.$$

EXAMPLE 8

Find an exact value for $\tan 67.5°$.

Solution

$$\tan 67.5° = \tan \tfrac{1}{2}(135°)$$

$$= \frac{1 - \cos 135°}{\sin 135°}$$

$$= \frac{1 - \left(-\frac{\sqrt{2}}{2}\right)}{\frac{\sqrt{2}}{2}} = \frac{1 + \frac{\sqrt{2}}{2}}{\frac{\sqrt{2}}{2}} = \frac{\frac{2 + \sqrt{2}}{2}}{\frac{\sqrt{2}}{2}}$$

$$= \frac{2 + \sqrt{2}}{\sqrt{2}} = 1 + \sqrt{2}$$

EXAMPLE 9

Verify the identity $2 \sin^2(x/2)\tan x = \tan x - \sin x$.

Solution

Let's simplify the left side of the equation.

$$2 \sin^2 \frac{x}{2} \tan x = 2\left(\pm \sqrt{\frac{1 - \cos x}{2}}\right)^2 \tan x$$

$$= 2\left(\frac{1 - \cos x}{2}\right)\tan x$$

$$= (1 - \cos x)\tan x$$

$$= \tan x - \tan x \cos x$$

$$= \tan x - \left(\frac{\sin x}{\cos x}\right)\cos x$$

$$= \tan x - \sin x$$

Finally, let's consider three different approaches for solving an equation that involves a half-angle formula.

EXAMPLE 10

Solve $4 \cos^2(x/2) = 1$, where $0 \le x < 2\pi$.

Solution A

First, let's recognize that if $0 \le x < 2\pi$, then $0 \le \dfrac{x}{2} < \pi$. In other words, we want to find the solutions for $x/2$ that are greater than or equal to 0 and less than π.

$$4 \cos^2 \frac{x}{2} = 1$$

$$\cos^2 \frac{x}{2} = \frac{1}{4}$$

$$\cos \frac{x}{2} = \frac{1}{2} \qquad \text{or} \qquad \cos \frac{x}{2} = -\frac{1}{2}$$

If $\cos x/2 = \frac{1}{2}$, then $x/2 = \pi/3$, and therefore $x = 2\pi/3$. If $\cos x/2 = -\frac{1}{2}$, then $x/2 = 2\pi/3$, and therefore, $x = 4\pi/3$. The solutions are $2\pi/3$ and $4\pi/3$.

Solution B

Using the half-angle formula we can substitute $(1 + \cos x)/2$ for $\cos^2(x/2)$.

$$4 \cos^2 \frac{x}{2} = 1$$

$$4 \left(\frac{1 + \cos x}{2} \right) = 1$$

$$2(1 + \cos x) = 1$$

$$1 + \cos x = \frac{1}{2}$$

$$\cos x = -\frac{1}{2}$$

If $\cos x = -\frac{1}{2}$, then $x = 2\pi/3$ or $x = 4\pi/3$. Thus the solutions are $2\pi/3$ and $4\pi/3$.

Solution C

Using a graphing utility with a viewing rectangle such that $0 \le x < 2\pi$ and $-3 \le y \le 3$, we can graph the function $f(x) = 4 \cos^2(x/2) - 1$ and obtain Figure 6.72.

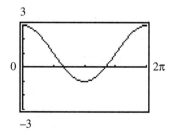

F I G U R E   6 . 72

Now we can use the trace and zoom features to approximate the x-intercepts that are the solutions to the given equation. To the nearest hundredth we find these to be 2.09 and 4.19. These answers agree with the previous answers of $2\pi/3$ and $4\pi/3$.

PROBLEM SET 6.9

For Problems 1–8, find the exact value for $\sin 2\theta$, $\cos 2\theta$, and $\tan 2\theta$. Do not use a calculator or a table.

1. $\cos \theta = \frac{4}{5}$ and θ is a first-quadrant angle

2. $\sin \theta = -\frac{4}{5}$ and θ is a third-quadrant angle

3. $\tan \theta = -\frac{12}{5}$ and θ is a second-quadrant angle

4. $\cot \theta = \frac{12}{5}$ and θ is a first-quadrant angle

5. $\sin \theta = -\frac{7}{25}$ and θ is a fourth-quadrant angle

6. $\cos \theta = \frac{15}{17}$ and θ is a fourth-quadrant angle

7. $\tan \theta = \frac{1}{2}$ and θ is a first-quadrant angle

8. $\tan \theta = -\frac{3}{2}$ and θ is a second-quadrant angle

For Problems 9–20, use the half-angle formulas to find exact values. Do not use a calculator or a table.

9. $\sin 15°$ **10.** $\cos 15°$

11. $\tan 15°$ **12.** $\sin 67.5°$

13. $\tan 157.5°$ **14.** $\tan 22.5°$

15. $\cos \frac{3\pi}{8}$ **16.** $\sin \frac{5\pi}{12}$

17. $\tan \frac{5\pi}{12}$ **18.** $\tan \frac{7\pi}{12}$

19. $\cos \frac{7\pi}{12}$ **20.** $\cos \frac{5\pi}{8}$

For Problems 21–28, find the exact values for $\sin(\theta/2)$, $\cos(\theta/2)$, and $\tan(\theta/2)$. Do not use a calculator or a table.

21. $\sin \theta = \frac{3}{5}$ and $0° < \theta < 90°$

22. $\sin \theta = \frac{4}{5}$ and $90° < \theta < 180°$

23. $\cos \theta = -\frac{3}{5}$ and $180° < \theta < 270°$

24. $\tan \theta = -\frac{5}{12}$ and $270° < \theta < 360°$

25. $\tan \theta = -\frac{12}{5}$ and $90° < \theta < 180°$

26. $\cos \theta = \frac{1}{3}$ and $0° < \theta < 90°$

27. $\sec \theta = \frac{3}{2}$ and $270° < \theta < 360°$

28. $\sec \theta = -\frac{4}{3}$ and $180° < \theta < 270°$

For Problems 29–38, solve each equation for θ, where $0° \leq \theta < 360°$. Do not use a calculator or a table.

29. $\sin 2\theta = \sin \theta$

30. $\cos 2\theta + \cos \theta = 0$

31. $\cos 2\theta + 3 \sin \theta - 2 = 0$

32. $\tan 2\theta = \tan \theta$

33. $2 - \cos^2\theta = 4 \sin^2 \frac{\theta}{2}$

34. $\sin 2\theta \sin \theta + \cos \theta = 0$

35. $\cos \theta = \cos \frac{\theta}{2}$

36. $\sin \frac{\theta}{2} + \cos \theta = 1$

37. $\sin 4\theta = \sin 2\theta$

38. $\cos 4\theta = \cos 2\theta$

For Problems 39–48, solve each equation for x, where $0 \leq x < 2\pi$. Do not use a calculator or a table.

39. $\cos x = \sin 2x$

40. $\sin 2x + \sqrt{2} \cos x = 0$

41. $\cos 2x - 3 \sin x - 2 = 0$

42. $\sin 2x - 2 \cos x + \sin x - 1 = 0$

43. $\sin \frac{x}{2} + \cos x = 1$

44. $\cos 2x = 1 - \sin x$

45. $\tan 2x - 2 \cos x = 0$

46. $\tan 2x + \sec 2x = 1$

47. $2 - \sin^2 x = 2 \cos^2 \frac{x}{2}$

48. $\cos \frac{x}{2} + \cos x = 0$

For Problems 49–66 verify each identity.

49. $\dfrac{\sin 2\theta}{1 - \cos 2\theta} = \cot \theta$

50. $(\sin \theta + \cos \theta)^2 - \sin 2\theta = 1$

51. $\dfrac{\sin 2\theta \sin \theta}{2 \cos \theta} + \cos^2\theta = 1$

52. $\csc 2\theta = \frac{1}{2} \sec \theta \csc \theta$

53. $2 \sin^2 x = \tan x \sin 2x$

54. $\dfrac{1 - \tan^2 x}{1 + \tan^2 x} = \cos 2x$

55. $2 \cos^2 \frac{x}{2} \tan x = \tan x + \sin x$

56. $\dfrac{\tan x}{1 + \tan^2 x} = \frac{1}{2} \sin 2x$

57. $\cot \theta \sin 2\theta = 1 + \cos 2\theta$

58. $\dfrac{\sin 2\theta}{\sin \theta} - \dfrac{\cos 2\theta}{\cos \theta} = \sec \theta$

59. $\sin 4\theta = 4 \cos \theta \sin \theta (1 - 2 \sin^2\theta)$

60. $\cos^4\theta - \sin^4\theta = \cos 2\theta$

61. $\sec 2\theta = \dfrac{\sec^2\theta}{2 - \sec^2\theta}$

62. $\cot 2\theta = \dfrac{\cot^2\theta - 1}{2 \cot \theta}$

63. $2 \sin^2 2\theta + \cos 4\theta = 1$

64. $\cos^2\theta \tan^2\theta = \frac{1}{2} - \frac{1}{2} \cos 2\theta$

65. $\sin^2\theta \cos^2\theta = \frac{1}{8} - \frac{1}{8} \cos 4\theta$

66. $\cos^4\theta = \frac{3}{8} + \frac{1}{2} \cos 2\theta + \frac{1}{8} \cos 4\theta$

67. Express $\cos 3\theta$ in terms of $\cos \theta$.

68. Express $\cos 4\theta$ in terms of $\cos \theta$.

69. Express $\cos 6\theta$ in terms of $\cos \theta$.

THOUGHTS into WORDS

70. How would you convince someone that $\sin \frac{1}{2}x = \frac{1}{2} \sin x$ is not an identity? Does $\sin \frac{1}{2}x = \frac{1}{2} \sin x$ for any values of x? Defend your answer.

71. Describe how you would solve the equation $\sin \frac{1}{2}\theta = \frac{1}{2}$, where $0° \le \theta < 360°$.

 GRAPHICS CALCULATOR ACTIVITIES

Use a graphics calculator to help solve each of the following equations. Express your answers to the nearest tenth.

72. $\sin \frac{1}{2}x = x + 1$ **73.** $\cos \frac{1}{2}x = x$

74. $\sin 2x = x - 1$ **75.** $\cos \frac{1}{2}x = -2x$

6.10   PRODUCT-TO-SUM AND SUM-TO-PRODUCT FORMULAS

For certain types of problems in calculus it is helpful to be able to change an indicated product of trigonometric functions to an indicated sum. We can use some basic identities to accomplish this objective. We can use the sum and difference formulas of Section 6.8 to develop these identities. For example, consider the formulas for $\sin(\alpha + \beta)$ and $\sin(\alpha - \beta)$.

$$\sin(\alpha + \beta) = \sin \alpha \cos \beta + \cos \alpha \sin \beta$$

$$\sin(\alpha - \beta) = \sin \alpha \cos \beta - \cos \alpha \sin \beta$$

By adding these two equations we obtain

$$\sin(\alpha + \beta) + \sin(\alpha - \beta) = 2 \sin \alpha \cos \beta.$$

Now by multiplying both sides of this equation by $\frac{1}{2}$ we obtain the following identity.

$$\sin \alpha \cos \beta = \tfrac{1}{2}[\sin(\alpha + \beta) + \sin(\alpha - \beta)]$$

Let's use this identity to change from an indicated product to an indicated sum.

EXAMPLE 1

Express $\sin 3\theta \cos 2\theta$ as an indicated sum.

Solution

Let $\alpha = 3\theta$ and $\beta = 2\theta$. The identity

$$\sin \alpha \cos \beta = \tfrac{1}{2}[\sin(\alpha + \beta) + \sin(\alpha - \beta)]$$

becomes

$$\sin 3\theta \cos 2\theta = \tfrac{1}{2}[\sin(3\theta + 2\theta) + \sin(3\theta - 2\theta)]$$

$$= \tfrac{1}{2}\sin 5\theta + \tfrac{1}{2} \sin \theta.$$

By subtracting the formula for $\sin(\alpha - \beta)$ from the formula for $\sin(\alpha + \beta)$ we obtain the following identity.

$$\cos \alpha \sin \beta = \tfrac{1}{2}[\sin(\alpha + \beta) - \sin(\alpha - \beta)]$$

In a similar fashion we can add and subtract the formulas for $\cos(\alpha + \beta)$ and $\cos(\alpha - \beta)$ to produce the following identities.

$$\cos \alpha \cos \beta = \tfrac{1}{2}[\cos(\alpha + \beta) + \cos(\alpha - \beta)]$$

$$\sin \alpha \sin \beta = \tfrac{1}{2}[\cos(\alpha - \beta) - \cos(\alpha + \beta)]$$

EXAMPLE 2

Express $\sin 4\theta \sin 2\theta$ as an indicated difference.

Solution

Let $\alpha = 4\theta$ and $\beta = 2\theta$. The identity

$$\sin \alpha \sin \beta = \tfrac{1}{2}[\cos(\alpha - \beta) - \cos(\alpha + \beta)]$$

becomes

$$\sin 4\theta \sin 2\theta = \tfrac{1}{2}[\cos(4\theta - 2\theta) - \cos(4\theta + 2\theta)]$$

$$= \tfrac{1}{2}\cos 2\theta - \tfrac{1}{2}\cos 6\theta.$$

In trigonometry, as in algebra, we sometimes need to change from an indicated sum form to an indicated product. We can use the previous identities of this section to develop four additional identities that will accomplish this objective. If we let $\alpha + \beta = A$ and $\alpha - \beta = B$, then $(\alpha + \beta) + (\alpha - \beta) = A + B$, which simplifies to $2\alpha = A + B$ or $\alpha = (A + B)/2$. Similarly, $(\alpha + \beta) - (\alpha - \beta) = A - B$, which simplifies to $2\beta = A - B$ or $\beta = (A - B)/2$. Now we can substitute A for $\alpha + \beta$, B for $\alpha - \beta$, $(A + B)/2$ for α, and $(A - B)/2$ for β in the previous four identities to produce the following four identities.

$$\sin A + \sin B = 2 \sin \frac{A + B}{2} \cos \frac{A - B}{2}$$

$$\sin A - \sin B = 2 \cos \frac{A + B}{2} \sin \frac{A - B}{2}$$

$$\cos A + \cos B = 2 \cos \frac{A + B}{2} \cos \frac{A - B}{2}$$

$$\cos A - \cos B = -2 \sin \frac{A + B}{2} \sin \frac{A - B}{2}$$

EXAMPLE 3

Express the indicated sum $\sin 3\theta + \sin \theta$ as an indicated product.

Solution

Let $A = 3\theta$ and $B = \theta$. The identity

$$\sin A + \sin B = 2 \sin \frac{A + B}{2} \cos \frac{A - B}{2}$$

becomes

$$\sin 3\theta + \sin \theta = 2 \sin \frac{3\theta + \theta}{2} \cos \frac{3\theta - \theta}{2}$$

$$= 2 \sin 2\theta \cos \theta.$$

You should realize that the previous example could also be handled by using the sum and difference formulas from Section 6.8 as follows.

$$\sin 3\theta + \sin \theta = \sin(2\theta + \theta) + \sin(2\theta - \theta)$$

$$= \sin 2\theta \cos \theta + \cos 2\theta \sin \theta + \sin 2\theta \cos \theta - \cos 2\theta \sin \theta$$

$$= 2 \sin 2\theta \cos \theta$$

EXAMPLE 4

Solve the equation $\sin 3x + \sin x = 0$ for $0 \le x < 2\pi$.

Solution

From Example 3 we know that $\sin 3x + \sin x$ can be expressed as $2 \sin 2x \cos x$. Therefore, we can solve this equation as follows.

$$\sin 3x + \sin x = 0$$

$$2 \sin 2x \cos x = 0$$

$$\sin 2x = 0 \quad \text{or} \quad \cos x = 0$$

$$2 \sin x \cos x = 0 \quad \text{or} \quad \cos x = 0$$

$$\sin x = 0 \quad \text{or} \quad \cos x = 0 \quad \text{or} \quad \cos x = 0$$

If $\sin x = 0$, then $x = 0$ or π. If $\cos x = 0$, then $x = \pi/2$ or $3\pi/2$. The solutions are 0, $\pi/2$, π, and $3\pi/2$. ▬▬▬

Another approach to Example 4 would be to use a graphing utility to predict the exact solutions; to check the predictions you would substitute them into the given equation. In Figure 6.73 we graphed the function

$$y = \sin 3x + \sin x \quad \text{for } 0 \le x < 2\pi$$

using a scale of $\pi/4$ on the x-axis. It looks as if the x-intercepts (which are the solutions to the equation $\sin 3x + \sin x = 0$) are 0, $\pi/2$, π, $3\pi/2$.

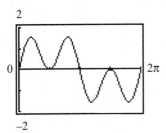

FIGURE 6.73

The sum-to-product identities can also be used to evaluate certain trigonometric expressions without using a calculator or table.

EXAMPLE 5

Find an exact value for $\cos 75° - \cos 15°$.

Solution

Let $A = 75°$ and $B = 15°$. The identity

$$\cos A - \cos B = -2 \sin \frac{A+B}{2} \sin \frac{A-B}{2}$$

becomes

$$\cos 75° - \cos 15° = -2 \sin \frac{75° + 15°}{2} \sin \frac{75° - 15°}{2}$$

$$= -2 \sin 45° \sin 30°.$$

We know that $\sin 45° = \frac{\sqrt{2}}{2}$ and $\sin° = \frac{1}{2}$. Therefore,

$$-2 \sin 45° \sin 30° = -2\left(\frac{\sqrt{2}}{2}\right)\left(\frac{1}{2}\right) = -\frac{\sqrt{2}}{2}.$$

Thus,

$$\cos 75° - \cos 15° = -\frac{\sqrt{2}}{2}.$$

E X A M P L E 6   Verify the identity $\dfrac{\sin 4\theta + \sin 2\theta}{\cos 4\theta + \cos 2\theta} = \tan 3\theta.$

Solution

Let's apply the formula for $\sin A + \sin B$ to the numerator of the left side and also apply the formula for $\cos A + \cos B$ to the denominator. Let $A = 4\theta$ and $B = 2\theta.$

$$\frac{\sin 4\theta + \sin 2\theta}{\cos 4\theta + \cos 2\theta} = \frac{2 \sin \dfrac{4\theta + 2\theta}{2} \cos \dfrac{4\theta - 2\theta}{2}}{2 \cos \dfrac{4\theta + 2\theta}{2} \cos \dfrac{4\theta - 2\theta}{2}}$$

$$= \frac{2 \sin 3\theta \cos \theta}{2 \cos 3\theta \cos \theta}$$

$$= \frac{\sin 3\theta}{\cos 3\theta}$$

$$= \tan 3\theta$$

P R O B L E M   S E T   6 . 10

For Problems 1–12, express each product as a sum or difference.

1. $\sin 5\theta \cos 3\theta$

2. $\sin 7\theta \cos 5\theta$

3. $\cos 4\theta \sin 2\theta$

4. $\cos 6\theta \sin 3\theta$

5. $\sin 3\theta \sin 2\theta$

6. $\sin 5\theta \sin 3\theta$

7. $\cos 2x \cos x$

8. $\cos 4x \cos x$

9. $2 \sin 9\theta \cos 3\theta$

10. $3 \cos 3\theta \sin 2\theta$

11. $3 \cos x \sin 2x$

12. $4 \sin 2x \cos 3x$

For Problems 13–24, express each sum or difference as a product.

13. $\cos 4\theta + \cos 2\theta$

14. $\cos 5\theta + \cos 3\theta$

15. $\sin 5\theta + \sin 3\theta$

16. $\sin 7\theta + \sin \theta$

17. $\sin 6x - \sin 2x$

18. $\sin 5x - \sin 3x$

19. $\cos 7x - \cos 3x$

20. $\cos 6x - \cos 2x$

21. $\sin 2\theta - \sin 4\theta$ **22.** $\cos 5\theta - \cos 9\theta$

23. $\cos \theta + \cos 3\theta$ **24.** $\sin \theta + \sin 5\theta$

For Problems 25–34, evaluate each expression without using a calculator or a table.

25. $\cos 75° + \cos 15°$ **26.** $\sin 75° + \sin 15°$

27. $\sin 15° - \sin 75°$ **28.** $\sin 75° - \sin 15°$

29. $\cos 105° - \cos 15°$ **30.** $\cos 15° + \cos 105°$

31. $\sin 75° \sin 15°$ **32.** $\cos 15° \sin 75°$

33. $\cos 15° \cos 75°$ **34.** $\sin 15° \cos 15°$

For Problems 35–40, solve each equation for $0 \le x < 2\pi$.

35. $\sin 3x - \sin x = 0$ **36.** $\sin x - \sin 3x = 0$

37. $\cos x - \cos 3x = 0$ **38.** $\cos 3x + \cos x = 0$

39. $\cos x - \cos 3x - \sin 2x = 0$

40. $\sin x + \sin 3x + \sin 2x = 0$

For Problems 41–46, verify each identity.

41. $\dfrac{\sin 3\theta + \sin 5\theta}{\cos 3\theta - \cos 5\theta} = \cot \theta$

42. $\dfrac{\cos 2\theta + \cos 4\theta}{\sin 2\theta - \sin 4\theta} = -\cot \theta$

43. $\tan \dfrac{x + y}{2} = \dfrac{\sin x + \sin y}{\cos x + \cos y}$

44. $\cot 2x = \dfrac{\cos 3x + \cos x}{\sin 3x + \sin x}$

45. $4 \cos x \cos 2x \sin 3x = \sin 2x + \sin 4x + \sin 6x$

46. $\dfrac{\sin(x + y) + \sin(x - y)}{\sin(x + y) - \sin(x - y)} = \tan x \cot y$

 GRAPHICS CALCULATOR ACTIVITIES

47. Use your graphics calculator to verify your answers for Problems 35–40.

48. Use your graphics calculator to graphically verify the identities in Problems 41, 42, 44, and 45.

49. Use your graphics calculator to help determine the exact solutions for each of the following equations in the interval $0 \le x < 2\pi$. [*Hint:* Use a scale of $\pi/6$ on the x-axis.]

    a. $\sin 4x + \sin 2x = 0$ **b.** $\sin 4x - \sin 2x = 0$

    c. $\cos 4x + \cos 2x = 0$ **d.** $\cos 4x - \cos 2x = 0$

50. Use your graphics calculator to help solve each of the following equations in the interval $0 \le x < 2\pi$. Express your solutions to the nearest tenth of a radian.

    a. $\sin 3x + \sin 2x = 0$ **b.** $\sin 3x - \sin 2x = 0$

    c. $\cos 3x + \cos 2x = 0$ **d.** $\cos 3x - \cos 2x = 0$

CHAPTER 6 SUMMARY

The following geometric concepts form a basis for the study of trigonometry: Plane angle, vertex, initial side, terminal side, positive angle, negative angle, coterminal angles, degree measure, complementary angles, supplementary angles, radian measure, acute angle, right angle, obtuse angle, central angle, and arc length.

Be sure that you can use the following geometric relationships.

    1 radian = $180/\pi$ degrees; therefore, to change from radians to degrees, multiply by $180/\pi$.

    1 degree = $\pi/180$ radians; therefore, to change from degrees to radians, multiply by $\pi/180$.

    The length of an arc s intercepted by a central angle θ in a circle of radius r is given by $s = r\theta$, where we express θ in radians.

If θ is an angle in standard position and $P(x, y)$ is *any point* (except the origin) on the terminal side of θ, then the six basic trigonometric functions are defined as follows (Figure 6.74).

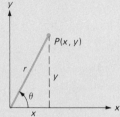

$$\sin \theta = \frac{y}{r} \qquad \csc \theta = \frac{r}{y}$$

$$\cos \theta = \frac{x}{r} \qquad \sec \theta = \frac{r}{x}$$

$$\tan \theta = \frac{y}{x} \qquad \cot \theta = \frac{x}{y}$$

If $r = 1$, then $\sin \theta = y$ and $\cos \theta = x$.

F I G U R E   6 . 7 4

If θ is any angle in standard position with its terminal side in one of the four quadrants, then the **reference angle** of θ (we have called it θ') is the acute angle formed by the terminal side of θ and the x-axis.

The trigonometric functions of any angle θ are equal to those of the reference angle associated with θ, except possibly for the sign. You can determine the sign by considering the quadrant in which the terminal side of θ lies.

You should be able to find, without a calculator or a table, the exact trigonometric functional values of any angle that has a reference angle of 30°, 45°, or 60°.

The basic trigonometric functions can also be interpreted as **circular functions**. Perhaps another reading of the first part of Section 6.3 would help your understanding of the circular functions.

The following ideas that pertain to the sine and cosine functions are helpful for graphing purposes.

1. Both $\sin x$ and $\cos x$ are bounded above by 1 and below by -1.
2. Both $\sin x$ and $\cos x$ have periods of 2π.
3. Through one period of 2π the sine and cosine functions vary as follows.

AS x INCREASES	SINE FUNCTION	COSINE FUNCTION
From 0 to $\dfrac{\pi}{2}$	Increases from 0 to 1	Decreases from 1 to 0
From $\dfrac{\pi}{2}$ to π	Decreases from 1 to 0	Decreases from 0 to -1
From π to $\dfrac{3\pi}{2}$	Decreases from 0 to -1	Increases from -1 to 0
From $\dfrac{3\pi}{2}$ to 2π	Increases from -1 to 0	Increases from 0 to 1

A function f is called periodic if there exists a positive real number p such that $f(x + p) = f(x)$, for all x in the domain of f. The smallest value for p is called the **period** of the function.

The following information about equations of the form $f(x) = a \sin b(x - c)$ or $f(x) = a \cos b(x - c)$, where $b > 0$, is very useful for sketching their graphs.

1. The period of both curves is $2\pi/b$.
2. The amplitude of both curves is $|a|$.
3. The phase shift of both curves is $|c|$. The shift is to the right if c is positive and to the left if c is negative.

The tangent curve has vertical asymptotes at $x = \pm\pi/2$, $\pm 3\pi/2$, $\pm 5\pi/2$, and so on. Refer back to Figure 6.45 to review the shape of the tangent curve. It has a period of π.

The cotangent curve has vertical asymptotes at $x = 0$, $\pm\pi$, $\pm 2\pi$, and so on. Refer back to Figure 6.46 to review the shape of the cotangent curve. It has a period of π.

The following information about equations of the form $f(x) = a \tan b(x - c)$ or $f(x) = a \cot b(x - c)$, where $b > 0$, is very useful for sketching their graphs.

1. The number a affects ordinate values but has no significance in terms of amplitude.
2. The period of both curves is π/b.
3. The phase shift of both curves is $|c|$.

The graphs of $f(x) = \csc x$ and $f(x) = \sec x$ are shown in Figure 6.50 and Figure 6.51, respectively. Both curves have a period of 2π.

The following information about equations of the form $f(x) = a \csc b(x - c)$ or $f(x) = a \sec b(x - c)$, where $b > 0$, is very useful for sketching their graphs.

1. The number a affects ordinate values but has no significance in terms of amplitude.
2. The period of both curves is $2\pi/b$.
3. The phase shift of both curves is $|c|$.

Definitions 6.4–6.6 form the basis for working with the inverse sine, inverse cosine, and inverse tangent functions. Know those definitions.

You should have the following basic trigonometric identities at your fingertips.

$$\csc\theta = \frac{1}{\sin\theta} \qquad \sec\theta = \frac{1}{\cos\theta} \qquad \cot\theta = \frac{1}{\tan\theta}$$

$$\tan\theta = \frac{\sin\theta}{\cos\theta} \qquad \cot\theta = \frac{\cos\theta}{\sin\theta}$$

$$\sin^2\theta + \cos^2\theta = 1 \qquad 1 + \tan^2\theta = \sec^2\theta \qquad 1 + \cot^2\theta = \csc^2\theta$$

These identities can be used to (1) determine other functional values from a given value, (2) simplify trigonometric expressions, (3) verify additional identities (formulas), and (4) help solve trigonometric equations.

Many of the techniques used to solve algebraic equations (such as factoring and applying the property *if ab = 0, then a = 0 or b = 0*) also apply to the solving of trigonometric equations.

The following important identities were verified in this chapter.

$$\sin(-\theta) = -\sin \theta$$

$$\cos(-\theta) = \cos \theta$$

$$\tan(-\theta) = -\tan \theta$$

$$\cos(\alpha - \beta) = \cos \alpha \cos \beta + \sin \alpha \sin \beta$$

$$\cos(\alpha + \beta) = \cos \alpha \cos \beta - \sin \alpha \sin \beta$$

$$\cos(90° - \alpha) = \sin \alpha$$

$$\sin(90° - \alpha) = \cos \alpha$$

$$\tan(90° - \alpha) = \cot \alpha$$

$$\sin(\alpha + \beta) = \sin \alpha \cos \beta + \cos \alpha \sin \beta$$

$$\sin(\alpha - \beta) = \sin \alpha \cos \beta - \cos \alpha \sin \beta$$

$$\tan(\alpha + \beta) = \frac{\tan \alpha + \tan \beta}{1 - \tan \alpha \tan \beta}$$

$$\tan(\alpha - \beta) = \frac{\tan \alpha - \tan \beta}{1 + \tan \alpha \tan \beta}$$

$$\sin 2\alpha = 2 \sin \alpha \cos \alpha$$

$$\cos 2\alpha = \cos^2\alpha - \sin^2\alpha = 1 - 2 \sin^2\alpha = 2 \cos^2\alpha - 1$$

$$\tan 2\alpha = \frac{2 \tan \alpha}{1 - \tan^2\alpha}$$

$$\sin^2\alpha = \frac{1 - \cos 2\alpha}{2}$$

$$\cos^2\alpha = \frac{1 + \cos 2\alpha}{2}$$

$$\tan^2\alpha = \frac{1 - \cos 2\alpha}{1 + \cos 2\alpha}$$

$$\sin \frac{\alpha}{2} = \pm \sqrt{\frac{1 - \cos \alpha}{2}}$$

$$\cos \frac{\alpha}{2} = \pm \sqrt{\frac{1 + \cos \alpha}{2}}$$

$$\tan \frac{\alpha}{2} = \frac{1 - \cos \alpha}{\sin \alpha} = \frac{\sin \alpha}{1 + \cos \alpha}$$

$$\sin \alpha \cos \beta = \tfrac{1}{2}[\sin(\alpha + \beta) + \sin(\alpha - \beta)]$$

$$\cos \alpha \sin \beta = \tfrac{1}{2}[\sin(\alpha + \beta) - \sin(\alpha - \beta)]$$

$$\cos \alpha \cos \beta = \tfrac{1}{2}[\cos(\alpha + \beta) - \cos(\alpha - \beta)]$$

$$\sin \alpha \sin \beta = \tfrac{1}{2}[\cos(\alpha - \beta) - \cos(\alpha + \beta)]$$

$$\sin A + \sin B = 2 \sin \frac{A + B}{2} \cos \frac{A - B}{2}$$

$$\sin A - \sin B = 2 \cos \frac{A + B}{2} \sin \frac{A - B}{2}$$

$$\cos A + \cos B = 2 \cos \frac{A + B}{2} \cos \frac{A - B}{2}$$

$$\cos A - \cos B = -2 \sin \frac{A + B}{2} \sin \frac{A - B}{2}$$

CHAPTER 6 REVIEW PROBLEM SET

1. The measures of two complementary angles are in the ratio of 7 to 11. How large is each angle?

2. Change $35°17'$ and $82°15'36''$ to decimal form and express each of them to the nearest one-hundredth of a degree.

3. Change $93.35°$ and $163.27°$ to degree-minute-second form.

4. Without using a calculator, change each of the following to radians.

   a. $420°$ **b.** $570°$ **c.** $-45°$

5. Without using a calculator, change each of the following to degrees.

   a. $\frac{7\pi}{6}$ **b.** $-\frac{4\pi}{3}$ **c.** $\frac{17\pi}{4}$

6. Find, to the nearest tenth of a centimeter, the length of the arc intercepted by a central angle of $4\pi/3$ radians if a radius of the circle is 17 centimeters long.

7. Find, to the nearest tenth of an inch, the length of the arc intercepted by a central angle of $130°$ if a radius of the circle is 14 inches long.

For Problems 8–11, point P is a point on the terminal side of θ and θ is in standard position. Find $\sin \theta$, $\cos \theta$, and $\tan \theta$.

8. $P(-6, 8)$ 9. $P(1, -3)$

10. $P(-2, -4)$ 11. $P(-5, -12)$

For Problems 12–23, find exact values without using a calculator or a table.

12. $\cos(-150°)$ 13. $\sin(-330°)$

14. csc 45°   **15.** sec 120°

16. tan 675°   **17.** cot 480°

18. $\sin \frac{7\pi}{3}$ **19.** $\cos \frac{13\pi}{3}$

20. $\sec\left(-\frac{3\pi}{2}\right)$ **21.** $\csc(-\pi)$

22. $\cot \frac{7\pi}{4}$ **23.** $\tan \frac{5\pi}{4}$

24. If $\sin \theta > 0$ and $\tan \theta < 0$, what quadrant contains the terminal side of θ?

25. If $\sec \theta > 0$ and $\csc \theta < 0$, what quadrant contains the terminal side of θ?

26. Find $\tan \theta$ if the terminal side of θ lies on the line $y = -5x$ in the fourth quadrant.

27. If $\sin \theta = -\frac{5}{13}$ and θ is a fourth-quadrant angle, find $\cos \theta$.

For Problems 28–41, find the period, amplitude (if it exists), and phase shift for each graph. Do not graph the functions.

28. $f(x) = 4 \sin\left(x + \frac{\pi}{4}\right)$

29. $f(x) = -3 \cos 2\left(x - \frac{\pi}{3}\right)$

30. $f(x) = 2 \tan 2(x + \pi)$

31. $f(x) = \sin(3x - \pi)$

32. $f(x) = -2 \sin(\pi x + \pi)$

33. $f(x) = 2 \cos\left(\pi x - \frac{\pi}{2}\right)$

34. $f(x) = -4 \cos(-3x)$

35. $f(x) = 5 \sin(-2x)$

36. $f(x) = 5 \cot(3x - \pi)$

37. $f(x) = -4 \cot(4x + \pi)$

38. $f(x) = \csc\left(4x + \frac{\pi}{2}\right)$

39. $f(x) = 2 \csc\left(3x - \frac{\pi}{4}\right)$

40. $f(x) = 2 \sec 3(x - 2)$

41. $f(x) = 3 \sec(2x - \pi)$

For Problems 42–55, graph the given function in the indicated interval.

42. $f(x) = -\sin 2x, \quad -2\pi \le x \le 2\pi$

43. $f(x) = -1 + \cos x, \quad -2\pi \le x \le 2\pi$

44. $f(x) = \tan \pi x, \quad -\frac{3}{2} \le x \le \frac{3}{2}$

45. $f(x) = 1 + \cos(x - \pi), \quad -\pi \le x \le 3\pi$

46. $f(x) = \csc \frac{1}{2}x, \quad 0 \le x \le 4\pi$

47. $f(x) = 1 - \sec x, \quad -\frac{\pi}{2} \le x \le \frac{3\pi}{2}$

48. $f(x) = 2 \sin\left(x - \frac{\pi}{2}\right), \quad -\frac{\pi}{2} \le x \le \frac{5\pi}{2}$

49. $f(x) = \cos\left(2x + \frac{\pi}{2}\right), \quad -\pi \le x \le \pi$

50. $f(x) = \tan\left(x - \frac{\pi}{4}\right), \quad -\frac{\pi}{4} \le x \le \frac{7\pi}{4}$

51. $f(x) = 1 + \cot 2x, \quad 0 \le x \le \pi$

52. $f(x) = 2 - \csc 2x, \quad 0 \le x \le 2\pi$

53. $f(x) = \sec \pi\left(x - \frac{1}{2}\right), \quad 0 \le x \le 2$

54. $f(x) = -\cot \pi(x + 1), \quad -2 \le x \le 0$

55. $f(x) = \cot \frac{1}{2}\left(x - \frac{\pi}{4}\right), \quad \frac{\pi}{4} \le x \le \frac{9\pi}{4}$

For Problems 56–59, find exact values without using a calculator or a table.

56. $\sin\left(\cos^{-1} \frac{\sqrt{2}}{2}\right)$ **57.** $\cos\left(\sin^{-1}\left(-\frac{12}{13}\right)\right)$

58. $\tan\left(\arcsin \frac{1}{2}\right)$ **59.** $\sin\left(\arctan\left(-\frac{2}{3}\right)\right)$

For Problems 60–63, solve for y and express y in radians. Do not use a calculator or a table.

60. $y = \tan^{-1}\left(-\frac{\sqrt{3}}{3}\right)$ **61.** $y = \cos^{-1}\left(-\frac{\sqrt{3}}{2}\right)$

62. $y = \arcsin\left(-\frac{1}{2}\right)$ **63.** $y = \arctan(-\sqrt{3})$

For Problems 64–67, solve for y and express y in degrees. Do not use a calculator or a table.

64. $y = \sin^{-1} \frac{\sqrt{3}}{2}$ **65.** $y = \cos^{-1}\left(-\frac{1}{2}\right)$

66. $y = \tan^{-1}(-1)$ **67.** $y = \sin^{-1}\left(-\frac{1}{2}\right)$

For Problems 68–71, use a calculator or the table in the back of the book to solve for y. Express y in radians to three decimal places.

68. $y = \cos^{-1}(-.5724)$ **69.** $y = \sin^{-1}(-.7219)$

70. $y = \arctan(-71.2134)$ **71.** $y = \arcsin(.9417)$

For Problems 72–75, use a calculator or the table in the back of the book to solve for y. Express y to the nearest tenth of a degree.

72. $y = \cos^{-1}(.2479)$ **73.** $y = \sin^{-1}(-.4100)$

74. $y = \tan^{-1}(-9.2147)$ **75.** $y = \cos^{-1}(-.5628)$

76. If $\cos \alpha = -\frac{3}{5}$ and $\tan \beta = \frac{5}{12}$, where α is a third-quadrant angle and β is a first-quadrant angle, find $\sin(\alpha + \beta)$, $\cos(\alpha - \beta)$, and $\tan(\alpha + \beta)$.

77. If $\sin \theta = \frac{5}{13}$ and $90° < \theta < 180°$, find $\sin 2\theta$, $\cos 2\theta$, and $\tan 2\theta$.

78. If $\cos x = \frac{4}{5}$ and $(3\pi/2) \le x < 2\pi$, find $\sin(x/2)$, $\cos(x/2)$, and $\tan(x/2)$.

For Problems 79–84, find exact values. Do not use a calculator or a table.

79. $\sin 165°$ **80.** $\cos 75°$

81. $\sin \frac{7\pi}{12}$ **82.** $\tan \frac{\pi}{8}$

83. $\cos\left[\sin^{-1}\frac{3}{5} + \tan^{-1}\left(-\frac{4}{3}\right)\right]$

84. $\tan\left(\arcsin\frac{4}{5} - \arccos\frac{12}{13}\right)$

For Problems 85–98, solve each of the equations. If the variable is θ, find all solutions such that $0° \le \theta < 360°$. If the variable is x, find all solutions such that $0 \le x < 2\pi$. Do not use a calculator or a table.

85. $\sin^2\theta - \sin \theta = 0$

86. $2 \cos^2\theta + 5 \sin \theta - 4 = 0$

87. $4 \sin^2\theta - 4 \sin \theta + 1 = 0$

88. $\tan \theta = 2 \cos \theta \tan \theta$

89. $\cos 2\theta + 3 \cos \theta + 2 = 0$

90. $2 \cos^2 \frac{\theta}{2} - 3 \cos \theta = 0$

91. $\cos \theta - \sqrt{3} \sin \theta = 1$

92. $\tan 2\theta + 2 \sin \theta = 0$

93. $2 \cos x + \tan x = \sec x$

94. $\cos 2x \sin x - \cos 2x = 0$

95. $2 \sec x \sin x + 2 = 4 \sin x + \sec x$

96. $\sin 2x = \cos 2x$

97. $\cos \frac{x}{2} = \frac{\sqrt{3}}{2}$

98. $\cos 3x - \cos x = 0$

99. Find *all* solutions of $\sec x - 1 = \tan x$ using radian measure.

100. Find *all* solutions of $2 \sin \theta \tan \theta + \tan \theta - 2 \sin \theta - 1 = 0$ using degree measure.

101. Solve $8 \sin^2\theta + 13 \sin \theta - 6 = 0$ for θ, where $0° \le \theta < 360°$. Express the solutions to the nearest tenth of a degree.

102. Solve $2 \sin^2\theta - 3 \sin \theta - 1 = 0$ for θ, where $0° \le \theta < 360°$. Express the solutions to the nearest tenth of a degree.

103. Solve $2 \tan^2 x + 5 \tan x - 12 = 0$ for x, where $0 \le x < 2\pi$. Express the solutions to the nearest hundredth of a radian.

104. Solve $2 \cos^2 \frac{x}{2} = \cos^2 x$, where $0 \le x < 2\pi$. Express the solutions to the nearest hundredth of a radian.

For Problems 105–120, verify each of the identities.

105. $(\cot^2 x + 1)(1 - \cos^2 x) = 1$

106. $\tan x = \dfrac{\tan x - 1}{1 - \cot x}$

107. $\dfrac{1}{1 - \sin x} + \dfrac{1}{1 + \sin x} = 2 \sec^2 x$

108. $\sin(\theta + 270°) = -\cos \theta$

109. $\tan(x + \pi) = \tan x$

110. $\cos\left(x + \frac{\pi}{4}\right) = \frac{\sqrt{2}}{2}(\cos x - \sin x)$

111. $\dfrac{\sin(\alpha - \beta)}{\cos(\alpha + \beta)} = \dfrac{\tan \alpha - \tan \beta}{1 - \tan \alpha \tan \beta}$

112. $4 \sin^2 \frac{\theta}{2} \cos^2 \frac{\theta}{2} = \sin^2\theta$

113. $\dfrac{\cos x}{1 + \sin x} = \sec x - \tan x$

114. $\sin x + \cos x = \dfrac{1 + \cot x}{\csc x}$

115. $2 \cot 2\theta = \cot \theta - \tan \theta$

116. $\cos \theta \sin 2\theta = 2 \sin \theta - 2 \sin^3\theta$

117. $1 - \frac{1}{2}\sin 2x = \dfrac{\sin^3 x + \cos^3 x}{\sin x + \cos x}$

118. $\tan \frac{\theta}{2} = \csc \theta - \cot \theta$

119. $\dfrac{\sin x + \sin y}{\cos x - \cos y} = -\cot \dfrac{x - y}{2}$

120. $\dfrac{\cos x + \cos 4x + \cos 7x}{\sin x + \sin 4x + \sin 7x} = \cot 4x$

121. Find an exact value for $\sin 105° - \sin 15°$ without using a calculator or a table.

122. Express the product $\cos 2x \cos 4x$ as an indicated sum or difference.

TRIGONOMETRY AND PROBLEM SOLVING

F or safety purposes, a manufacturer recommends that the maximum angle made by a ladder with the ground as it leans against a building be 70°. What is the maximum height that the top of a 24-foot ladder can reach?

Suppose that the centerfielder is standing in center field 375 feet from home plate. How far is it from where he is standing to third base?

How much would it cost to shape a 4-inch slab of concrete into a triangle whose sides are 18, 24, and 27 feet long if the cost of the concrete is $42.50 per cubic yard?

A small car weighing 1750 pounds is parked on a ramp that makes a 27° angle with the horizontal. How much force must be applied parallel to the ramp to keep the car from rolling down the ramp?

These problems illustrate the large variety of problems that can be solved by using trigonometric concepts. Chapter 7 is devoted primarily to the problem solving aspects of trigonometry.

Vectors can be used to determine the amount of parallel force needed to keep a tractor from rolling backwards down an incline.

7.1   RIGHT TRIANGLE TRIGONOMETRY

When we use triangles to solve problems, we often designate the vertices and corresponding angles by capital letters, such as A, B, and C. Then we designate the sides opposite the angles A, B, and C by the lowercase letters a, b, and c, respectively, as in Figure 7.1. If triangle ACB is a right triangle, then we use C to denote the right angle as in Figure 7.1(b). Furthermore, we often refer to the sides of a right triangle

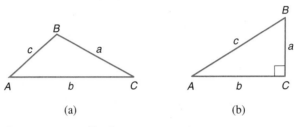

(a)   (b)

FIGURE 7.1

in terms of the acute angles. For example, we call side a the **side opposite** angle A, side b the **side adjacent** to angle A, and side c the **hypotenuse**. We summarize this terminology in Figure 7.2.

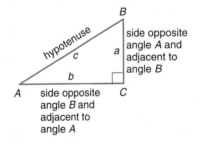

FIGURE 7.2

In Section 6.1 we defined the six basic trigonometric functions in terms of an angle θ in standard position on a Cartesian coordinate system. Now let's consider a special case of this definition, namely, when $\theta = A$ is an acute angle of a right triangle as indicated in Figure 7.3. We define the six trigonometric functions as:

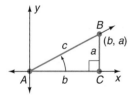

FIGURE 7.3

$$\sin A = \frac{a}{c} = \frac{\text{Side opposite } A}{\text{Hypotenuse}} \qquad \csc A = \frac{c}{a} = \frac{\text{Hypotenuse}}{\text{Side opposite } A}$$

$$\cos A = \frac{b}{c} = \frac{\text{Side adjacent } A}{\text{Hypotenuse}} \qquad \sec A = \frac{c}{b} = \frac{\text{Hypotenuse}}{\text{Side adjacent } A}$$

$$\tan A = \frac{a}{b} = \frac{\text{Side opposite } A}{\text{Side adjacent } A} \qquad \cot A = \frac{b}{a} = \frac{\text{Side adjacent } A}{\text{Side opposite } A}$$

We could also place right triangle ACB so that angle B is in standard position and the six trigonometric functions of angle B could be defined in a similar manner. For example, $\sin B = b/c =$ (side opposite B)/hypotenuse. Furthermore, once we have the definitions in terms of the ratios of sides of the right triangle, we no longer need to consider the coordinate system. Thus, in right triangle ACB, where C is the right angle, the following statements can be made.

$$\sin A = \frac{a}{c} = \cos B \qquad \tan A = \frac{a}{b} = \cot B \qquad \sec A = \frac{c}{b} = \csc B$$

$$\cos A = \frac{b}{c} = \sin B \qquad \cot A = \frac{b}{a} = \tan B \qquad \csc A = \frac{c}{a} = \sec B$$

Note also that A and B are complementary angles. Thus, the sine and cosine functions are called **cofunctions**. Likewise, the tangent and cotangent functions are cofunctions as are the secant and cosecant functions. In general, if θ is an acute angle, any trigonometric function of θ is equal to the cofunction of the complement of θ. Thus, we have the following relationships or identities.

$$\sin \theta = \cos(90° - \theta) \qquad \text{and} \qquad \cos \theta = \sin(90° - \theta)$$

$$\tan \theta = \cot(90° - \theta) \qquad \text{and} \qquad \cot \theta = \tan(90° - \theta)$$

$$\sec \theta = \csc(90° - \theta) \qquad \text{and} \qquad \csc \theta = \sec(90° - \theta)$$

REMARK   The previous identities are actually true for any angle θ. They can be verified by using the appropriate difference formula from Chapter 6. For example, $\cos(90° - \theta) = \cos 90° \cos \theta + \sin 90° \sin \theta = 0(\cos \theta) + 1(\sin \theta) = \sin \theta$.

We say that a triangle has six parts—three sides and three angles. The phrase *solving a triangle* refers to finding the values of all six parts. Solving a right triangle can be analyzed as follows.

1. If we know an acute angle and the length of one of the sides, then the other acute angle is the complement of the one given. We can determine the lengths of the other sides from equations that involve the appropriate trigonometric functions.

2. If the lengths of two sides are given, we can find the third side by using the Pythagorean theorem. We can determine the two acute angles from equations that involve the appropriate trigonometric functions.

Let's consider two examples of solving right triangles.

EXAMPLE 1

Solve the right triangle in Figure 7.4.

Solution

Because A and B are complementary angles, $B = 90° - 34° = 56°$. Use the tangent function to determine a as follows.

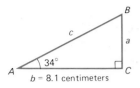

FIGURE 7.4

$$\tan 34° = \frac{a}{8.1}$$

$$a = 8.1 \tan 34° = 5.5 \text{ centimeters,} \quad \text{to the nearest tenth}$$

Use the cosine function to determine c as follows.

$$\cos 34° = \frac{8.1}{c}$$

$$c \cos 34° = 8.1$$

$$c = \frac{8.1}{\cos 34°} = 9.8 \text{ centimeters,} \quad \text{to the nearest tenth} \quad \blacksquare$$

EXAMPLE 2

Solve right triangle ACB where $C = 90°$, $a = 9.4$ meters, and $b = 12.6$ meters.

Solution

Let's sketch the figure and record the known facts (Figure 7.5).

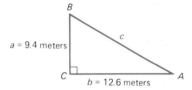

FIGURE 7.5

Using the Pythagorean theorem, c can be obtained as follows.

$$c = \sqrt{a^2 + b^2}$$

$$= \sqrt{(9.4)^2 + (12.6)^2}$$

$$= \sqrt{247.2} = 15.7 \text{ meters,} \quad \text{to the nearest tenth of a meter}$$

Angles A and B can be found as follows.

$$\tan A = \frac{9.4}{12.6} = .7460$$

$$A = 36.7°, \quad \text{to the nearest tenth of a degree}$$

$$\tan B = \frac{12.6}{9.4} = 1.3404$$

$$B = 53.3°, \quad \text{to the nearest tenth of a degree} \quad \blacksquare$$

Notice in Example 2 that after finding angle A to be 36.7°, we did not subtract this value from 90° to find angle B. In so doing, an error in calculating angle A

would produce a corresponding error in angle B. Instead, we would suggest finding A and B from the given information and then using the complementary relationship for checking purposes.

Applications

Right triangle trigonometry has a variety of applications. Before we consider some of these, let's restate some *problem solving suggestions* that are especially appropriate at this time.

1. Read the problem carefully and make sure that you understand the meanings of all of the words. Be alert for any technical terms used in the statement of the problem.

2. Read the problem a second time (perhaps even a third time) to get an overview of the situation being described and to determine the known facts, as well as what is to be found.

3. Sketch a meaningful figure that can be used to record the given information and what is to be found. (Our sketches have been done by professional artists for aesthetic purposes. Your sketches can be roughly drawn as long as they depict the situation in a way that helps you analyze the problem.)

4. Choose a trigonometric function that can be used to set up an equation involving the known and unknown parts.

5. Solve the equation and be sure that you have supplied the answer to the problem.

EXAMPLE 3

Position of a ladder   Suppose that a 20-foot ladder is placed against a building so that its lower end is 5 feet from the base of the building. What angle does the ladder make with the ground?

Solution

Let's sketch a figure and record the given information (Figure 7.6). Use the cosine function to determine angle A as follows.

$$\cos A = \frac{5}{20} = .2500$$

$$A = 75.5°, \quad \text{to the nearest tenth of a degree}$$

In Figure 7.7 we indicated some terminology that is commonly used in **line-of-sight** type problems, where angles of elevation and depression are measured with reference to a horizontal line. If the object being sighted is above the observer, then the angle formed by the line of sight and the horizontal line is called an **angle of elevation** (Figure 7.7(a)). If the object being sighted is below the observer, then the angle formed by the line of sight and the horizontal line is called an **angle of depression** (Figure 7.7(b)).

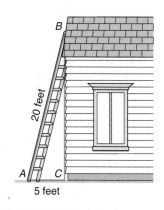

FIGURE   7.6

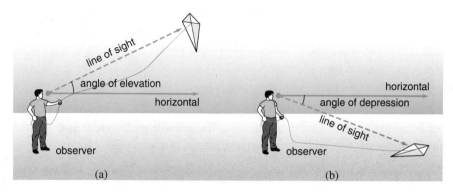

FIGURE 7.7

EXAMPLE 4

Height of a smokestack   At a point 42 meters from the base of a smokestack, the angle of elevation of the top of the stack is 47°. Find the height of the smokestack to the nearest meter.

Solution

Let's sketch a figure and record the given information (Figure 7.8). Let *h* represent the height of the stack and use the tangent function to find *h* as follows.

$$\tan 47° = \frac{h}{42}$$

$$h = 42 \tan 47° = 45 \text{ meters}, \quad \text{to the nearest meter}$$

The height of the smokestack is approximately 45 meters.

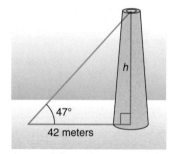

FIGURE 7.8

REMARK   Sometimes it is helpful to estimate the final answer before carrying out all of the computations. This provides a check for *reasonableness* of the answer. In Example 4, because the given acute angle has a measure of 47°, the triangle is close to being isosceles and the leg opposite the 47° angle should be a little longer than the given leg. Thus, our answer of 45 meters is reasonable.

EXAMPLE 5

Distance from a landmark   From the top of a building 350 feet tall, the angle of depression of a special landmark is 71.5°. How far from the base of the building is the landmark?

Solution

Figure 7.9 depicts the situation we described in the problem. Angle *θ* and the given angle of depression are alternate interior angles; thus, *θ* = 71.5°. Using the tangent function of *θ* we can find *x* as follows.

$$\tan 71.5° = \frac{350}{x}$$

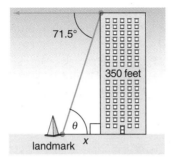

FIGURE 7.9

$$x \tan 71.5° = 350$$

$$x = \frac{350}{\tan 71.5°} = 117 \text{ feet,} \quad \text{to the nearest foot}$$

The landmark is approximately 117 feet from the base of the building. ▬▬▬

EXAMPLE 6

Height of a TV tower   A TV tower stands on the top of the One Shell Plaza building in Houston, Texas. From a point 3000 feet from the base of the building, the angle of elevation of the top of the TV tower is 18.4°. If the building itself is 714 feet tall, how tall is the TV tower?

Solution

Figure 7.10 depicts the situation we described in the problem. Using the tangent function we can proceed as follows.

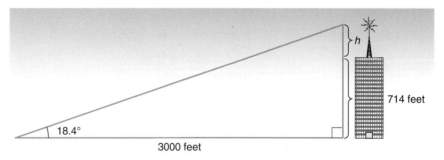

FIGURE 7.10

$$\tan 18.4° = \frac{h + 714}{3000}$$

$$h + 714 = 3000 \tan 18.4°$$

$$h = 3000 \tan 18.4° - 714 = 284 \text{ feet,} \quad \text{to the nearest foot}$$

The TV tower is approximately 284 feet tall. ▬▬▬

Our final example of this section illustrates a situation where two overlapping right triangles are used to generate a system of two equations and two unknowns.

EXAMPLE 7

Height of a tree   In Figure 7.11 a tree is located on the opposite side of a pond from points *A* and *B*. From point *B*, the angle of elevation to the top of the tree is 35°. From point *A*, the angle of elevation to the top of the tree is 25°. If points *A* and *B* are 30 meters apart, find the height of the tree to the nearest tenth of a meter.

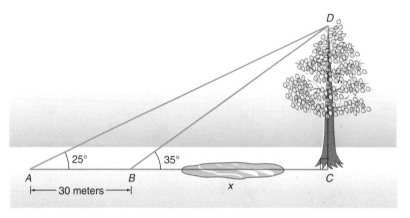

F I G U R E   7 . 11

Solution

Let *x* represent the distance between *B* and *C*. Using right triangle *BCD* we have

$$\tan 35° = \frac{h}{x} \quad \text{from which} \quad h = x \tan 35°.$$

Using right triangle *ACD* we have $\tan 25° = h/(x + 30)$ from which

$$h = (x + 30) \tan 25°.$$

Equating the two values for *h* and solving for *x* produces

$$x \tan 35° = (x + 30) \tan 25°$$

$$x \tan 35° = x \tan 25° + 30 \tan 25°$$

$$x \tan 35° - x \tan 25° = 30 \tan 25°$$

$$x(\tan 35° - \tan 25°) = 30 \tan 25°$$

$$x = \frac{30 \tan 25°}{\tan 35° - \tan 25°} = 59.81, \quad \text{to the nearest hundredth.}$$

Substituting 59.81 for *x* in $h = x \tan 35°$ produces

$$h = 59.81 \tan 35° = 41.9, \quad \text{to the nearest tenth.}$$

The tree is approximately 41.9 meters tall.

PROBLEM SET 7.1

For Problems 1–10, refer to the right triangle labeled Figure 7.12. Solve each of the right triangles and express lengths to the nearest unit, angles to the nearest degree.

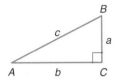

FIGURE 7.12

1. $A = 37°$ and $b = 14$

2. $A = 58°$ and $a = 19$

3. $B = 23°$ and $b = 12$

4. $B = 42°$ and $a = 9$

5. $A = 67°$ and $c = 26$

6. $B = 19°$ and $c = 34$

7. $a = 5$ and $b = 12$

8. $a = 24$ and $c = 25$

9. $b = 12$ and $c = 29$

10. $a = 18$ and $b = 14$

11. *Height of a ladder* A 30-foot ladder, leaning against the side of a building, makes a 50° angle with the ground. How far up on the building does the top of the ladder reach? Express your answer to the nearest tenth of a foot.

12. *Maximum angle of a ladder* For safety purposes, a manufacturer recommends that the maximum angle made by a ladder with the ground as it leans against a building be 70°. What is the maximum height, to the nearest tenth of a foot, that the top of a 24-foot ladder can reach? How far, to the nearest tenth of a foot, is the bottom of the ladder from the base of the building?

13. *Height of a tree* From a point 50 meters from the base of a fir tree, the angle of elevation to the top of the tree is 61.5°. Find the height of the tree to the nearest tenth of a meter.

14. *Angle of depression* Bill is standing on top of a 175-foot cliff overlooking a lake. The measurement of the angle of depression to a boat on the lake is 29°. How far is the boat from the base of the cliff? Express your answer to the nearest foot.

15. *Height of Sears Tower* From a point 2156 feet from the base of the Sears Tower in Chicago, Illinois, the angle of elevation to the top of the tower is 34°. Find, to the nearest foot, the height of the Sears Tower.

16. *Horizontal range of a missile* A radar station is tracking a missile. The angle of elevation is 22.6° and the line of sight distance is 36.8 kilometers (see Figure 7.13). Find the altitude and the horizontal range of the missile to the nearest tenth of a kilometer.

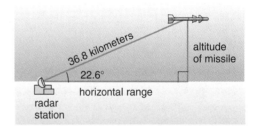

FIGURE 7.13

17. *Finding width of a river* A person wishing to know the width of a river walks 50 yards downstream from a point directly across from a tree on the opposite bank. The angle between the riverbank and the line of sight to the tree at this point is 40°. Find the width of the river to the nearest yard.

18. *Dimensions of a rectangle* A diagonal of a rectangle is 17 centimeters long and makes an angle of 27° with a side of the rectangle. Find the length and width of the rectangle to the nearest centimeter.

19. *Height of Gateway Arch* Use the information in Figure 7.14 to compute, to the nearest foot, the height of the Gateway Arch in St. Louis, Missouri.

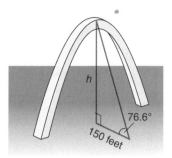

F I G U R E   7 . 1 4

20. *Angle of depression* From the top of the Ala Moana Hotel in Honolulu, Hawaii the angle of depression of a landmark on the ground is 57.3°. If the height of the hotel is 390 feet, determine, to the nearest foot, the distance that the landmark is from the hotel.

21. *Distance between floors* An upward moving escalator, 35 feet long, has an angle of elevation of 34°. What is the vertical distance between the floors traveled by the escalator? Express your answer to the nearest tenth of a foot.

22. *Finding measures of angles* The lengths of the three sides of an isosceles triangle are 18 centimeters, 18 centimeters, and 12 centimeters. Find the measure of each of the three angles to the nearest tenth of a degree.

23. *Height of TV Tower* A TV tower stands on top of the Empire State building in New York City. From a point 1150 feet from the base of the building, the angle of elevation of the top of the TV tower is 52°. If the building itself is 1250 feet tall, find the height of the TV tower to the nearest foot.

24. *Length of a side* In Figure 7.15, find the length of x to the nearest tenth of a meter.

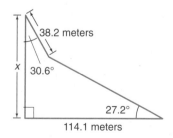

F I G U R E   7 . 1 5

25. *Angle between blades* The length of each blade of a pair of shears from the pivot to the point is 8 inches. Find, to the nearest tenth of a degree, what angle the blades make with each other when the points of the open shears are 6 inches apart.

26. *Angle of elevation* Two people 200 feet apart are in line with the base of a tower. The angle of elevation of the top of the tower from one person is 30° and from the other person is 60°. How far is the tower from each person? (Since the angles are 30° and 60°, try doing this problem without your calculator.)

27. *Height of a building* Two buildings, building A and building B, are separated by an alley that is 15 feet wide. From a second floor window in building A, it can be determined that the angle of elevation of the top of building B is 75° and the angle of depression of the bottom of building B is 50°. Find the height, to the nearest foot, of building B.

28. *Height of a building* Two buildings, building A and building B, are separated by an alley. From a window 66 feet above the ground in building B, it can be observed that the angle of elevation of the top of building A is 52°, and the angle of depression of the bottom of building A is 68°. Find the height, to the nearest foot, of building A.

29. *Height of an antenna* A TV antenna sits on top of a building. From a point on the ground at a distance of 75 feet from the base of the building, a person determines the angle of elevation of the bottom of the antenna to be 48°, and the angle of elevation of the top of the antenna to be 54°. Find the height of the antenna to the nearest foot.

30. *Altitude of a triangle* Find h, to the nearest tenth of a meter, in Figure 7.16.

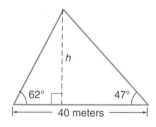

F I G U R E   7 . 1 6

31. *Right circular cone* The right circular cone in Figure 7.17 has a radius of 3 feet and a volume of 50 cubic feet.

Find the measure of angle θ, to the nearest tenth of a degree. The volume of a right circular cone is given by the formula $V = \frac{1}{3}\pi r^2 h$.

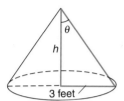

FIGURE 7.17

32. *Altitude of a jet* A jet takes off at a 15° angle traveling 200 feet per second. Find, to the nearest second, how long it takes to reach an altitude of 12,000 feet.

33. *Radius of earth* Suppose that a spacelab is circling the earth at an altitude of 400 miles as shown in Figure 7.18. The angle θ in the figure is 65.5°. Use this information to estimate the radius of the earth to the nearest mile.

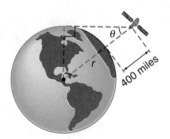

FIGURE 7.18

34. *Angle between diagonals* The rectangular box in Figure 7.19 is 20 inches long, 12 inches wide, and 10 inches

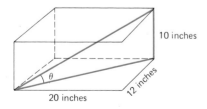

FIGURE 7.19

deep. Find the angle θ, to the nearest tenth of a degree, formed by a diagonal of the base and a diagonal of the box.

35. *Drawbridge problem* A drawbridge is 160 feet long. As shown in Figure 7.20, the two sections of the bridge can be lifted upward to an angle of 40°. If the water level is 20 feet below the bridge, find the distance d between the end of a section and the water level when the bridge is fully open. Express your answer to the nearest foot.

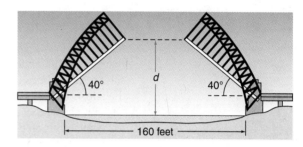

FIGURE 7.20

36. *Guy-wire problem* The length of a guy-wire to a pole is 60 feet as indicated in Figure 7.21; the guy-wire makes an angle of 72° with the ground. How high above the ground is it attached to the pole? Express the answer to the nearest tenth of a foot.

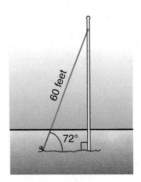

FIGURE 7.21

37. *Area of a triangular plot* Two sides of a triangular plot of ground are 75 yards and 90 yards long, and the angle included by those two sides is 65°. Find the area of the plot to the nearest square yard.

38. Explain the concept of cofunctions.

39. Suppose that someone wants you to find the length of the hypotenuse of a right triangle if the measure of one acute

angle is known to be 46.3°. How would you react to the problem?

7.2   SOLVING OBLIQUE TRIANGLES: LAW OF COSINES

In the previous section we solved a variety of problems using the trigonometric functions of the acute angles of right triangles. Now we want to expand our problem solving capabilities to include any kind of triangle. Any triangle that is not a right triangle is called an **oblique triangle**.

In elementary geometry you studied the concept of congruence as it pertains to geometric figures. Two geometric figures are said to be congruent if they have exactly the same shape and size; that is to say, they can be made to coincide. You also discovered that there are certain conditions that determine the **congruence of triangles**. For example, the SAS condition states that if two sides and the included angle of one triangle are equal in measure, respectively, to two sides and the included angle of another triangle, then the triangles are congruent. In other words, by knowing the lengths of two sides and the measure of the included angle you can determine the exact shape and size of the triangle. Let's solve an example to illustrate this idea.

EXAMPLE 1

Using the information given in Figure 7.22, find the length of $\overline{BC}$.

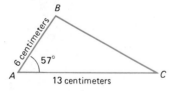

F I G U R E   7 . 22

Solution

By drawing a line segment $\overline{BD}$ perpendicular to $\overline{AC}$, we can form two right triangles as indicated in Figure 7.23. From triangle ADB, the values of x and h can be found as follows.

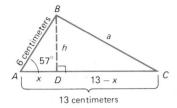

FIGURE 7.23

$$\cos 57° = \frac{x}{6} \qquad\qquad \sin 57° = \frac{h}{6}$$

$$x = 6 \cos 57° = 3.3 \qquad h = 6 \sin 57° = 5.0$$

Now apply the Pythagorean theorem to triangle CDB to obtain

$$a^2 = h^2 + (13 - x)^2$$

$$= (5.0)^2 + (9.7)^2 \qquad 13 - x = 13 - 3.3 = 9.7$$

$$= 25.0 + 94.09 = 110.09.$$

Thus,

$$a = \sqrt{119.09} = 11 \text{ centimeters,} \quad \text{to the nearest centimeter.}$$

Without carrying out the details, it should be evident that the measures of angles B and C in Figure 7.22 are also determined by the given information. In other words, knowing the lengths of two sides and the measure of the angle included by those two sides does determine the remaining parts of the triangle.

Our experience in solving the previous problem should give us some direction as to how to develop a general formula for solving such problems. Let's consider a triangle labeled as in Figure 7.24. By drawing BD perpendicular to AC, we can form two right triangles. From triangle ADB we obtain

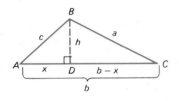

FIGURE 7.24

$$\cos A = \frac{x}{c} \qquad\qquad \sin A = \frac{h}{c}$$

$$x = c \cos A \qquad h = c \sin A.$$

Using the Pythagorean theorem and triangle CDB we obtain

$$a^2 = h^2 + (b - x)^2 = h^2 + b^2 - 2bx + x^2.$$

Now we can substitute $c \cos A$ for x and $c \sin A$ for h and simplify.

$$a^2 = h^2 + b^2 - 2bx + x^2$$

$$= (c \sin A)^2 + b^2 - 2b(c \cos A) + (c \cos A)^2$$

$$= c^2\sin^2 A + b^2 - 2bc \cos A + c^2\cos^2 A$$

$$= c^2\sin^2 A + c^2\cos^2 A + b^2 - 2bc \cos A$$

$$= c^2(\sin^2 A + \cos^2 A) + b^2 - 2bc \cos A \qquad \text{Remember that}$$
$$\qquad\qquad\qquad\qquad\qquad\qquad\qquad\qquad\qquad \sin^2 A + \cos^2 A = 1$$
$$= c^2 + b^2 - 2bc \cos A$$

We could use a similar type of development to show that $b^2 = a^2 + c^2 - 2ac \cos B$ and $c^2 = a^2 + b^2 - 2ab \cos C$. We refer to these three relationships as the **law of cosines**, which can be formally stated as follows.

Law of Cosines

In any triangle ABC that has sides of length a, b, and c, the following relationships are true.

$$a^2 = b^2 + c^2 - 2bc \cos A$$
$$b^2 = a^2 + c^2 - 2ac \cos B$$
$$c^2 = a^2 + b^2 - 2ab \cos C$$

REMARK   You should realize that the development based on Figure 7.24 assumes angle A to be an acute angle. A similar type of development does follow if A is an obtuse angle, and we will have you carry out the details in the next set of problems.

Use the appropriate part of the law of cosines and problems like Example 1 are easy to solve. Let's consider another example of that type.

E X A M P L E 2

Use the information given in Figure 7.25 to find the value of c to the nearest tenth of a meter.

Solution

Use $c^2 = a^2 + b^2 - 2ab \cos C$, to obtain

$$c^2 = (12.3)^2 + (17.6)^2 - 2(12.3)(17.6) \cos 28.1°$$

$$= 79.12.$$

Therefore,

$$c = \sqrt{79.12} = 8.9 \text{ meters}, \quad \text{to the nearest tenth of a meter.}$$

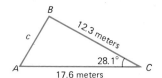

F I G U R E   7 . 2 5

SSS Condition from Elementary Geometry

Refer back again to elementary geometry and you may recall the SSS property of congruence. It stated that if the lengths of three sides of one triangle are equal to the lengths of three sides of another triangle, then the triangles are congruent. In other words, knowing the lengths of three sides of a triangle determines that triangle's exact shape and size. Furthermore, from the law of cosines we see that $\cos A$, $\cos B$, and $\cos C$ can each be expressed in terms of the lengths of the sides as follows.

$$\cos A = \frac{b^2 + c^2 - a^2}{2bc}, \qquad \cos B = \frac{a^2 + c^2 - b^2}{2ac},$$

$$\cos C = \frac{a^2 + b^2 - c^2}{2ab}$$

Therefore, it also becomes evident that we can use the law of cosines to find the size of the angles of a triangle when given the lengths of the three sides. Let's consider an example.

EXAMPLE 3

Measures of angles   Find the measure of each angle of a triangle that has sides of length 9 feet, 15 feet, and 19 feet.

Solution

Let's sketch and label a triangle to organize our use of the law of cosines (Figure 7.26).

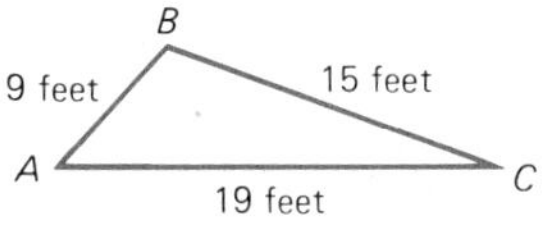

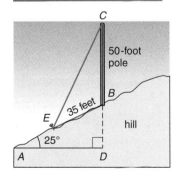

FIGURE 7.26

$$\cos A = \frac{b^2 + c^2 - a^2}{2bc} = \frac{19^2 + 9^2 - 15^2}{2(19)(9)} = \frac{217}{342}$$

Therefore, $A = 50.6°$, to the nearest tenth of a degree.

$$\cos B = \frac{a^2 + c^2 - b^2}{2ac}$$

$$= \frac{15^2 + 9^2 - 19^2}{2(15)(9)} = -\frac{55}{270}$$

Therefore, $B = 101.8°$, to the nearest tenth of a degree.

$$\cos C = \frac{a^2 + b^2 - c^2}{2ab}$$

$$= \frac{15^2 + 19^2 - 9^2}{2(15)(19)} = \frac{505}{570}$$

Therefore, $C = 27.6°$, to the nearest tenth of a degree. As a partial check, we see that $A + B + C = 50.6° + 101.8° + 27.6° = 180°$.

EXAMPLE 4

Length of a guy-wire   A vertical pole 50 feet tall stands on a hillside that makes an angle of 25° with the horizontal. A guy-wire is attached to the top of the pole and to a point on the hillside 35 feet down from the base of the pole. Find the length of the guy-wire.

Solution

First, let's sketch and record the data from the problem (Figure 7.27). From the figure we see that $\angle ABD = 90° - 25° = 65°$. Therefore, $\angle CBE = 180° - 65° = 115°$. Now use triangle EBC and the law of cosines to find the length of the guy-wire (EC).

$$(EC)^2 = (35)^2 + (50)^2 - 2(35)(50) \cos 115°$$

$$= 1225 + 2500 - (-1479.16)$$

$$= 5204.16, \quad \text{to the nearest hundredth}$$

FIGURE 7.27

Therefore,

$$EC = \sqrt{5204.16}$$

$$= 72.1, \quad \text{to the nearest tenth of a foot.}$$

EXAMPLE 5

Measure of an angle   A triangular plot of ground has sides of lengths 300 yards, 275 yards, and 250 yards. Find the measure, to the nearest tenth of a degree, of the smallest angle of the triangle.

Solution

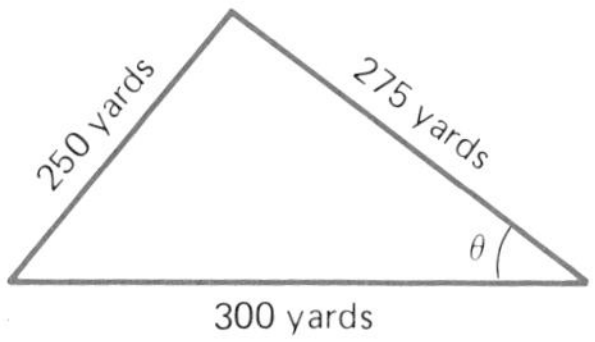

Let's sketch the triangular plot and record the given information (Figure 7.28). Since the smallest angle will be opposite the smallest side, we are looking for the angle opposite the side that is 250 yards long. Therefore,

$$\cos\theta = \frac{(300)^2 + (275)^2 - (250)^2}{2(300)(275)}$$

$$= \frac{103125}{165000}$$

FIGURE   7.28

and

$$\theta = 51.3°, \quad \text{to the nearest tenth of a degree.}$$

One final comment needs to be made about the material in this section. Keep in mind that the law of cosines was developed by partitioning an oblique triangle into two right triangles and then using our knowledge of right triangles. Therefore, if we should forget the law of cosines, all is not lost. We can solve a specific problem by forming right triangles and using our knowledge of right triangle trigonometry as we did in Example 1 of this section.

PROBLEM SET 7.2

Each of Problems 1–10 refers to triangle *ABC*. Express measures of angles to the nearest tenth of a degree and lengths of sides to the nearest tenth of a unit.

1. If $b = 8$ centimeters, $c = 12$ centimeters, and $A = 53°$, find *a*.

2. If $c = 13$ meters, $a = 10$ meters, and $B = 22°$, find *b*.

3. If $a = 11.6$ feet, $b = 5.1$ feet, and $C = 85°$, find *c*.

4. If $b = 21.4$ yards, $c = 15.1$ yards, and $A = 74°$, find *a*.

5. If $a = 27$ centimeters, $c = 21$ centimeters, and $B = 112°$, find *b*.

6. If $a = 14$ centimeters, $b = 18$ centimeters, and $c = 12$ centimeters, find *A*.

7. If $a = 17$ feet, $b = 25$ feet, and $c = 17$ feet, find *B*.

8. If $a = 14.6$ meters, $b = 11.2$ meters, and $c = 4.1$ meters, find *C*.

9. If $a = 8.3$ centimeters, $b = 16.4$ centimeters, and $c = 11.8$ centimeters, find A.

10. If $a = 7.2$ feet, $b = 11.4$ feet, and $c = 5.1$ feet, find B.

11. In triangle ABC, if $a = 7$ yards, $b = 10$ yards, and $c = 4$ yards, find A, B, and C to the nearest tenth of a degree.

12. In triangle ABC, if $a = 7.1$ centimeters, $b = 17.8$ centimeters, and $c = 12.5$ centimeters, find A, B, and C to the nearest tenth of a degree.

13. In triangle ABC, if $a = 41$ feet, $c = 32$ feet, and $B = 100°$, find b to the nearest tenth of a foot and A and C to the nearest tenth of a degree.

14. In triangle ABC, if $a = 8.1$ inches, $b = 14.3$ inches, and $C = 12°$, find c to the nearest tenth of an inch, and A and B to the nearest tenth of a degree.

15. In triangle ACB, if $a = 24$ centimeters, $b = 7$ centimeters, and $c = 25$ centimeters, find C.

16. *Lengths of sides of a parallelogram*   The diagonals of a parallelogram are of lengths 30 centimeters and 22 centimeters, and intersect at an angle of 67°. Find the lengths of the sides of the parallelogram to the nearest tenth of a centimeter. (Remember that the diagonals of a parallelogram bisect each other.)

17. *Angle of a triangle*   A triangular plot of ground measures 50 meters by 65 meters by 80 meters. Find, to the nearest tenth of a degree, the size of the angle opposite the longest side.

18. *Distance between cities*   City A is located 14 miles due north of city B. City C is located 17 miles from city B on a line that is 13° north of west from B. Find the distance between city A and city C, to the nearest mile.

19. *Distance from airport*   A plane travels 250 miles due east after takeoff, then adjusts its course 15° southward and flies another 175 miles. How far is it from the point of departure? Express your answer to the nearest tenth of a mile.

20. *Length of a pond*   To measure the length of a pond, a surveyor determines the measurements indicated in Figure 7.29. Find the length of the pond to the nearest meter.

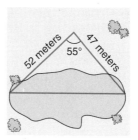

F I G U R E   7 . 2 9

Problems 21–23 refer to an official baseball field, with a 90-foot square diamond and the surrounding outfield, as indicated in Figure 7.30.

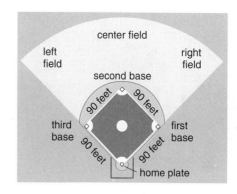

F I G U R E   7 . 3 0

21. *Distance on a baseball field*   The pitcher's mound on a baseball diamond is located 60.5 feet from home plate on the diagonal connecting home plate to second base. Find the distance, to the nearest tenth of a foot, between the pitcher's mound and first base.

22. *Distance on a baseball field*   Suppose that the center-fielder is standing in center field 375 feet from home plate. How far is it from where he is standing to third base? Express your answer to the nearest foot.

23. *Distance on a baseball field*   Suppose the leftfielder is standing 320 feet from home plate and the line segment that connects him to home plate bisects the line segment connecting second base and third base. How far is he from second base? Express your answer to the nearest foot.

24. *Measurements of a rooftop*   Figure 7.31 shows a roof-top with some indicated measurements. Find, to the nearest tenth of a degree, the size of angle θ.

F I G U R E   7 . 3 I

25. *Length of a collector*   A solar collector is attached to a roof as indicated in Figure 7.32. Find the length of the collector to the nearest tenth of a foot.

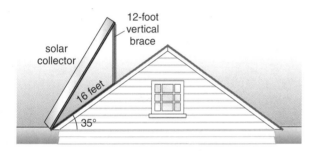

F I G U R E   7 . 3 2

26. *Distance between airplanes*   Two airplanes leave an airport at the same time, one going west at 375 miles per hour and the other going northeast at 425 miles per hour. How far apart are they 2 hours after leaving? Express your answer to the nearest mile.

27. *Distance between two points*   Two points, A and B, are on opposite sides of a building. In order to find the distance between the points, Bob chooses a point C that is 200 feet from A and 175 feet from B, and then determines that angle ACB has a measure of $110°$. Find, to the nearest foot, the distance between A and B.

28. *Angle between diagonals*   The rectangular box in Figure 7.33 is 20 inches long, 12 inches wide, and 10 inches deep. Find the angle θ, to the nearest tenth of a degree, formed by a diagonal of the base and a diagonal of the 12-inch-by-10-inch side.

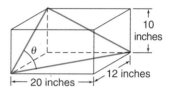

F I G U R E   7 . 3 3

29. *Lengths of diagonals*   A parallelogram has sides of lengths 25 centimeters and 40 centimeters and one of the angles has measure $62°$. Find the length of each diagonal to the nearest tenth of a centimeter.

30. *Area of parallelogram*   A parallelogram has sides of lengths 14 inches and 18 inches and one angle of measure $50°$. Find the area of the parallelogram to the nearest square inch.

31. Verify that $a^2 = b^2 + c^2 - 2bc \cos A$ for a triangle in which angle A is an obtuse angle (Figure 7.34).

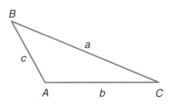

F I G U R E   7 . 3 4

THOUGHTS into WORDS

32. Suppose that the lengths of the sides of a triangle are given as $a = 7.3$ inches, $b = 14.1$ inches, and $c = 5.2$ inches. When we use a calculator to find the measure of angle A, we keep getting an error message. Explain the reason for this.

33. One form of the law of cosines is symbolically stated as
$$\cos A = \frac{b^2 + c^2 - a^2}{2bc}.$$

Express this form in your own words.

7.3 LAW OF SINES

From elementary geometry you may recall the ASA property of congruence. It states that if two angles and the included side of one triangle are equal in measure, respectively, to two angles and the included side of another triangle, then the triangles are congruent. That is to say, knowing the measures of two angles and the included side determines the exact shape and size of the triangle. Furthermore, knowing the size of two angles of a triangle determines the size of the third angle. Therefore, the ASA property can also be stated as an AAS property.

In the previous section we found that the law of cosines can be used to solve triangles when the given information fits the SAS or SSS properties. However, the law of cosines is not useful in ASA or AAS situations. Instead, we need another set of properties, which we refer to as the **law of sines**.

Let's consider triangle ACB in Figure 7.35 with $\overline{BD}$ drawn perpendicular to $\overline{AC}$. Using right triangle ADB we have

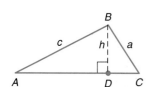

FIGURE 7.35

$$\sin A = \frac{h}{c}$$

$$h = c \sin A.$$

Using right triangle CDB, we obtain

$$\sin C = \frac{h}{a}$$

$$h = a \sin C.$$

Equating the two expressions for h produces

$$a \sin C = c \sin A,$$

which can be written as

$$\frac{a}{\sin A} = \frac{c}{\sin C}.$$

Returning to triangle ACB in Figure 7.35, we could also draw a line segment from vertex C perpendicular to $\overline{AB}$. A similar line of reasoning would produce the relationship

$$\frac{a}{\sin A} = \frac{b}{\sin B}.$$

Therefore, the law of sines can be stated as follows.

Law of Sines

In any triangle ABC, having sides of length a, b, and c, the following relationships are true.

$$\frac{a}{\sin A} = \frac{b}{\sin B} = \frac{c}{\sin C}$$

REMARK   The previous development of the law of sines was based on Figure 7.35 in which angle A is an acute angle. A similar type of development does follow if A is an obtuse angle. We will have you carry out the details in the next set of problems.

EXAMPLE 1

Suppose that in triangle ACB, $A = 71°$, $C = 40°$, and $a = 19$ centimeters. Find c to the nearest tenth of a centimeter.

Solution

Let's sketch a triangle and record the given information (Figure 7.36). Using $a/\sin A = c/\sin C$ from the law of sines, we can substitute 19 for a, 71° for A, 40° for C, and solve for c.

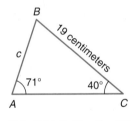

FIGURE 7.36

$$\frac{a}{\sin A} = \frac{c}{\sin C}$$

$$\frac{19}{\sin 71°} = \frac{c}{\sin 40°}$$

$$c \sin 71° = 19 \sin 40°$$

$$c = \frac{19 \sin 40°}{\sin 71°} = 12.9 \text{ centimeters,} \quad \text{to the nearest tenth of a centimeter}$$

EXAMPLE 2

Distance across a river   Two points A and B are on opposite sides of a river. Point C is located 350 feet from A on the same side of the river as A. In triangle ACB, $C = 52°$ and $A = 67°$. Find the distance between A and B to the nearest foot. (See Figure 7.37)

Solution

Because $A + B + C = 180°$, $A = 67°$, and $C = 52°$, we know that

$$67° + B + 52° = 180°$$

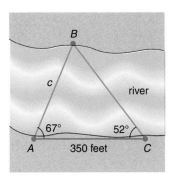

FIGURE 7.37

$$B + 119° = 180°$$

$$B = 61°.$$

Now using $b/\sin B = c/\sin C$, we obtain

$$\frac{350}{\sin 61°} = \frac{c}{\sin 52°}$$

$$c \sin 61° = 350 \sin 52°$$

$$c = \frac{350 \sin 52°}{\sin 61°} = 315 \text{ feet}, \quad \text{to the nearest foot.}$$

EXAMPLE 3

Distance from a helicopter   In Figure 7.38 a straight road makes an angle of 19° with the horizontal. At a certain point A on the road, the angle of elevation of a helicopter hovering in the air is 48°. At this same time, from another point B, 150 meters farther up the road, the angle of elevation is 55°. Find the distance from point A to the helicopter.

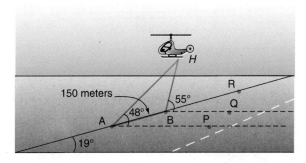

FIGURE 7.38

Solution

Since the three horizontal lines are parallel, we know that $\angle RBQ$ and $\angle BAP$ each have a measure of 19°. Thus, the measure of $\angle HAB$ is $48° - 19° = 29°$ and the measure of $\angle HBR$ is $55° - 19° = 36°$. Therefore, the measure of $\angle ABH$ is $180° - 36° = 144°$. Finally, we can determine that the measure of $\angle AHB$ is $180° - (29° + 144°) = 180° - 173° = 7°$. Now we can use the law of sines to find the length of $\overline{AH}$ in Figure 7.39.

$$\frac{AH}{\sin 144°} = \frac{150}{\sin 7°}$$

$$AH = \frac{150 \sin 144°}{\sin 7°} = 723.5 \text{ meters}, \quad \text{to the nearest tenth}$$

Therefore, from point A to the helicopter is approximately 723.5 meters.

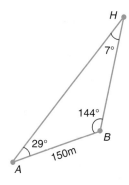

FIGURE 7.39

The next example illustrates a situation where both the law of cosines and the law of sines can be used to find the size of an angle, but one approach may be preferable to the other. Let's solve the problem both ways to illustrate our point.

E X A M P L E   4

In Figure 7.40, $A = 23.1°$, $a = 14$ yards, $b = 21$ yards, and $c = 8$ yards. Find B to the nearest tenth of a degree.

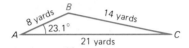

F I G U R E   7 . 40

Solution A

Using the law of cosines we obtain

$$\cos B = \frac{a^2 + c^2 - b^2}{2ac}$$

$$= \frac{14^2 + 8^2 - 21^2}{2(14)(8)}$$

$$= -\frac{181}{224}.$$

Therefore,

$$B = 143.9°, \quad \text{to the nearest tenth of a degree.}$$

Solution B

Using the law of sines we obtain

$$\frac{a}{\sin A} = \frac{b}{\sin B}$$

$$\frac{14}{\sin 23.1°} = \frac{21}{\sin B}$$

$$14 \sin B = 21 \sin 23.1°$$

$$\sin B = \frac{21 \sin 23.1°}{14}.$$

Using our calculator we obtain $B = 36.1°$, to the nearest tenth of a degree. But remember that the sine function is also positive in the second quadrant. Therefore, B might be an obtuse angle with a measure of $180° - 36.1° = 143.9°$. Note that the law of sines does not indicate which value of B should be used for a particular problem. However, in this problem our sketch of the triangle in Figure 7.40 clearly indicates that B is an obtuse angle and thus we need to use $B = 143.9°$.

Relative to Solution B, we should realize that situations do arise where a rough sketch of the triangle may not be sufficient to decide which value of an angle determined by the law of sines is to be used. Therefore, in general we suggest that you use the law of cosines whenever possible.

PROBLEM SET 7.3

Each of the Problems 1–10 refers to triangle ABC. Express measures of angles to the nearest tenth of a degree and lengths of sides to the nearest tenth of a unit.

1. If $A = 64°$, $C = 47°$, and $a = 17$ centimeters, find c.

2. If $A = 28°$, $C = 61°$, and $a = 6$ feet, find c.

3. If $A = 20.4°$, $B = 31.2°$, and $b = 25$ meters, find a.

4. If $B = 115°$, $C = 32°$, and $c = 6.1$ yards, find b.

5. If $A = 41°$, $C = 37°$, and $a = 14$ centimeters, find B; then find b.

6. If $A = 26.3°$, $B = 94.5°$, and $a = 9.2$ feet, find C; then find c.

7. If $A = 132°$, $C = 17°$, and $a = 75$ miles, find B; then find b.

8. If $A = 34.1°$, $a = 23$ feet, $b = 35$ feet, and $c = 17$ feet, find B and C.

9. If $B = 71.7°$, $a = 15$ miles, $b = 17$ miles, and $c = 14$ miles, find A and C.

10. If $C = 136°$, $a = 6$ kilometers, $b = 8$ kilometers, and $c = 13$ kilometers, find A and B.

11. In triangle ABC, if $A = 54°$, $C = 33°$, and $a = 28$ feet, find b and c to the nearest tenth of a foot.

12. In triangle ABC, if $A = 144°$, $B = 19°$, and $b = 12$ yards, find a and c to the nearest tenth of a yard.

13. *Distance between points* Two points A and B are located on opposite sides of a river (Figure 7.41). Point C is located 275 meters from B, on the same side of the river as B. In triangle ABC, $B = 71°$ and $C = 46°$. Find the distance between A and B to the nearest meter.

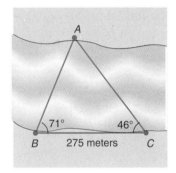

F I G U R E   7 . 4 1

14. *Lining up points* In Figure 7.42 a surveyor standing at point A wants to locate point C such that A, B, and C are on a straight line. However, his line of sight toward C is blocked by a building. Therefore, he determines angle ABP to be 140°, the distance from B to P to be 75 feet, and angle BPC to be 58°. Find the distance from P to C to the nearest tenth of a foot.

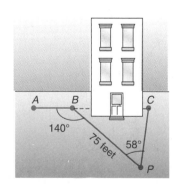

F I G U R E   7 . 4 2

15. *Plank on an incline* One end of a 20-foot plane is placed on the ground at a point 8 feet from the start of a

41° incline (Figure 7.43). The other end of the plank rests on the incline. How far up the incline does the plank extend? Express the answer to the nearest tenth of a foot.

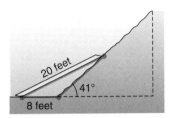

F I G U R E   7 . 4 3

16. *Antenna problem*   A 200-foot TV antenna stands on the top of a hill that has an incline of 23° with the horizontal. How far down the hill will a 150-foot support cable extend if it is attached halfway up the antenna? Express the answer to the nearest foot.

17. *Angle of elevation*   In Figure 7.44, a building 55 feet tall is on top of a hill that has an incline of 19°. A surveyor, standing at a point on the hillside, determines that the angle of elevation to the top of the building is 42°. (Remember that an angle of elevation is measured with reference to a horizontal line.) How far is the surveyor from the bottom of the building? Express the answer to the nearest tenth of a foot.

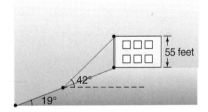

F I G U R E   7 . 4 4

18. *Length of side of triangular lot*   A triangular lot faces two streets that meet at an angle of 82° (Figure 7.45). The two sides of the lot facing the streets are each 175 feet long. Find the length of the third side to the nearest tenth of a foot.

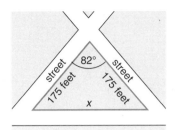

F I G U R E   7 . 4 5

19. *Height of a tower*   Two people 75 feet apart are in line with the base of a tower. The angle of elevation of the top of the tower from one person is 41.2° and from the other person is 32.6°. Find the height of the tower to the nearest tenth of a foot.

20. *Length of vertical brace*   A solar collector that is 10 feet wide is attached to a roof as indicated in Figure 7.46. The roof makes an angle of 35° with the horizontal and the collector makes an angle of 50° with the horizontal. Find the length of the vertical brace to the nearest tenth of a foot.

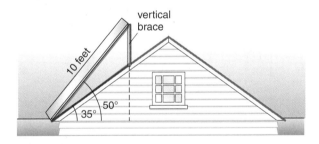

F I G U R E   7 . 4 6

21. *Height of building*   An office building is located at the top of a hill (Figure 7.47). From the base of the hill to the top of the office building, the angle of elevation is 40°. From a point 150 feet from the base of the hill, the angle of elevation to the top of the building is 32°. The hill rises at a 25° angle with the horizontal. Find the height of the office building to the nearest tenth of a foot.

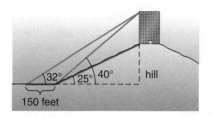

FIGURE 7.47

22. *Suspended weight*   A weight is suspended between two vertical poles of the same height as indicated in Figure 7.48. If $\theta = 39°$, $\alpha = 72°$, and the distance between the poles is 20 feet, find the distance between the weight and

the left pole. Express your answer to the nearest tenth of a foot.

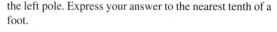

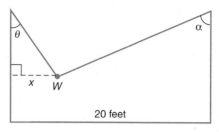

FIGURE 7.48

23. Verify $a/\sin A = c/\sin C$ for a triangle in which angle A is an obtuse angle.

THOUGHTS into WORDS

24. Express the law of sines in words using the concepts of ratio and proportion.

25. How do you know when to use the law of sines and when to use the law of cosines?

7.4   SSA SITUATON (AMBIGUOUS CASE) AND AREA FORMULAS

Thus far, the law of cosines and the law of sines have provided us with methods for solving triangles when the given information fits the SAS, SSS, ASA, or AAS patterns. But what happens if the given information fits the SSA pattern? In other words, how do we solve a triangle if we know the lengths of two sides and the measure of an angle opposite one of those two sides? This question is a little more difficult to answer because the given information of *the lengths of two sides and the measure of an angle opposite one of those sides* may determine two triangles, one triangle , or no triangle at all. Thus, we refer to this situation as the **ambiguous case**.

Let's look at the ambiguous case from both an analytic and geometric viewpoint. Using the law of sines, we can find an expression for sin C as follows.

$$\frac{a}{\sin A} = \frac{c}{\sin C}$$

$$a \sin C = c \sin A$$

$$\sin C = \frac{c \sin A}{a}$$

If $\sin C = 1$, then $C = 90°$. If $\sin C < 1$, then C could be an acute or an obtuse angle. If a number greater than one is obtained for sin C, then there is no triangle, since $-1 \leq \sin \theta \leq 1$ for all θ. Now let's link these ideas to a geometric interpretation of the possible situations. Consider triangle ACB and assume that we are given A, a, and c. The following situations may exist.

Suppose A is an acute angle.

If $h < a < c$, then two possible triangles exist and sin $C < 1$ (Figure 7.49).

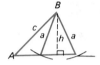

FIGURE 7.49

If $a > c$, then one triangle exists and sin $C < 1$ (Figure 7.50).

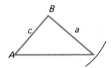

FIGURE 7.50

If $a = h$, then one triangle exists and sin $C = 1$ (Figure 7.51).

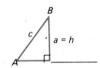

FIGURE 7.5I

If $a < h$, then no triangle is determined and an erroneous value greater than 1 will be obtained for sin C (Figure 7.52).

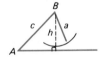

FIGURE 7.52

Suppose A is an obtuse angle.

(The possibilities are easily recognized from a geometric viewpoint.) If $a > c$, then one triangle exists (Figure 7.53).

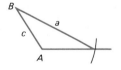

FIGURE 7.53

If $a \leq c$, then no triangle is determined (Figure 7.54).

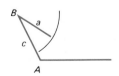

FIGURE 7.54

Fortunately, it is not necessary to memorize all of the possibilities in the previous list. Instead, you can analyze each problem individually. Frequently, by making a careful sketch and using some common sense, you can determine which situation exists. The important issue is that you are alert to the fact that when the given information is of the SSA pattern, then various possibilities might exist. Let's analyze a few problems.

EXAMPLE 1

Suppose we are given $A = 57°$, $a = 17$ feet, and $c = 14$ feet. How many triangles exist that satisfy these conditions? Find C for each triangle.

Solution

Let's make a careful sketch (Figure 7.55). Because $17 > 14$ there is only one possible triangle determined. We can use the law of sines to determine C.

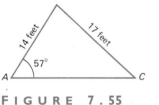

FIGURE 7.55

$$\frac{a}{\sin A} = \frac{c}{\sin C}$$

$$\frac{17}{\sin 57°} = \frac{14}{\sin C}$$

$$17 \sin C = 14 \sin 57°$$

$$\sin C = \frac{14 \sin 57°}{17}$$

Therefore

$$C = 43.7° \quad \text{or} \quad C = 136.3°, \quad \text{to the nearest tenth of a degree.}$$

Either from the figure or from the fact that $57° + 136.3° > 180°$, we know that the answer of $136.3°$ must be discarded and $C = 43.7°$.

EXAMPLE 2

Suppose we are given $A = 43.2°$, $a = 7.7$ meters, and $c = 9.1$ meters. How many triangles exist that satisfy these conditions? Find C for each triangle.

Solution

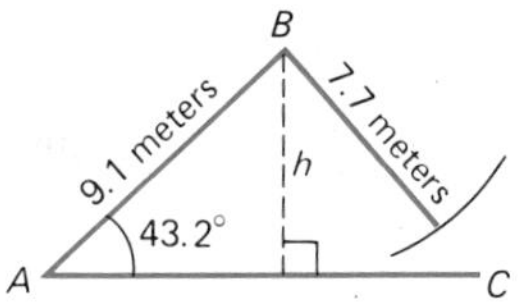

As we attempt to sketch a triangle for this situation (Figure 7.56), we might not be able to tell whether two, one, or no triangles exist. Therefore, let's find an approximate value for h.

$$\sin 43.2° = \frac{h}{9.1}$$

$$h = 9.1 \sin 43.2°$$

$$= 6.2 \text{ meters}, \quad \text{to the nearest tenth of a meter}$$

FIGURE 7.56

Now, because $h < a < c$, we know that two triangles exist, as indicated in Figure 7.57. Using the law of sines, we can find the two possible values for C as follows.

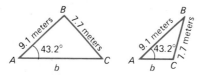

$$\frac{a}{\sin A} = \frac{c}{\sin C}$$

$$\frac{7.7}{\sin 43.2°} = \frac{9.1}{\sin C}$$

$$7.7 \sin C = 9.1 \sin 43.2°$$

$$\sin C = \frac{9.1 \sin 43.2°}{7.7}$$

Therefore

$$C = 54.0° \quad \text{or} \quad C = 180° - 54.0°$$
$$= 126.0°, \quad \text{to the nearest tenth of a degree.}$$

Each of the two values for angle C in Example 2 produces a different value for the length of side b, as indicated by the two triangles in Figure 7.57. If $C = 54.0°$, then $B = 180° - (43.2° + 54.0°) = 82.8°$. Then we can use the law of sines to determine b.

$$\frac{b}{\sin 82.8°} = \frac{7.7}{\sin 43.2°}$$

$$b \sin 43.2° = 7.7 \sin 82.8°$$

$$b = \frac{7.7 \sin 82.8°}{\sin 43.2°}$$

$$b = 11.2 \text{ meters}, \quad \text{to the nearest tenth of a meter}$$

If $C = 126.0°$, then $B = 180° - (43.2° + 126.0°) = 10.8°$. Then we can determine b as follows.

$$\frac{b}{\sin 10.8°} = \frac{7.7}{\sin 43.2°}$$

$$b \sin 43.2° = 7.7 \sin 10.8°$$

$$b = \frac{7.7 \sin 10.8°}{\sin 43.2°}$$

$$b = 2.1 \text{ meters}, \quad \text{to the nearest tenth of a meter}$$

EXAMPLE 3

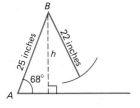

FIGURE 7.58

Suppose we are given $A = 68°$, $a = 22$ inches, and $c = 25$ inches. How many triangles exist that satisfy these conditions? Find C for each triangle.

Solution

As we attempt to sketch a triangle for the situation (Figure 7.58), we might not be able to tell whether two, one, or no triangles exist. Therefore, let's find an approximate value for h.

$$\sin 68° = \frac{h}{25}$$

$$h = 25 \sin 68° = 23.2 \text{ inches}$$

Because $a < h$, no triangle exists that satisfies these conditions.

In Example 3, had we attempted to find C using the law of sines, the following situation would have arisen.

$$\frac{a}{\sin A} = \frac{c}{\sin C}$$

$$\frac{22}{\sin 68°} = \frac{25}{\sin C}$$

$$22 \sin C = 25 \sin 68°$$

$$\sin C = \frac{25 \sin 68°}{22} = 1.053$$

At this stage, we should recognize that because the sine of an angle cannot exceed 1, the set of conditions given in this problem does not determine a triangle.

Areas of Triangles

The basic geometric formula for finding the area (K) of a triangle is $K = \frac{1}{2}bh$, where b represents the length of a side and h represents the length of the altitude to that side. (We are using K to represent area because A is being used to name a vertex of a triangle.) The area formula and sine function can be used to find the area of a triangle if the lengths of two sides and the measure of the included angle are known. The following example clarifies this procedure.

> **REMARK** Technically, the phrase, *area of triangle* should be *area of triangular region.* However, we will at times use the *area of triangle* vocabulary and assume that you understand the intended meaning.

EXAMPLE 4

Find the area of the triangular region in Figure 7.59.

Solution

First, let's draw the altitude from B perpendicular to $\overline{AC}$ (Figure 7.60). Its length can be found by using $\triangle ADB$ and the sine function.

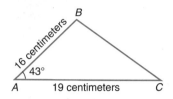

FIGURE 7.59

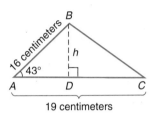

FIGURE 7.60

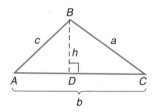

FIGURE 7.61

$$\sin 43° = \frac{h}{16}$$

$$h = 16 \sin 43°$$

$$h = 10.91, \quad \text{to the nearest hundredth}$$

Now we can use the basic area formula for a triangle.

$$K = \frac{1}{2} bh$$

$$K = \frac{1}{2}(19)(10.91)$$

$$K = 103.6, \quad \text{to the nearest tenth}$$

The area of the triangular region is approximately 103.6 square centimeters.

The approach we used in Example 4 can be generalized to obtain an area formula. Consider $\triangle ABC$ and the altitude h in Figure 7.61. Using $\triangle ADB$ and the sine function we can determine h.

$$\sin A = \frac{h}{c}$$

$$h = c \sin A$$

Now we can substitute $c \sin A$ for h in the basic area formula.

$$K = \frac{1}{2} bh$$

$$\boxed{K = \frac{1}{2} bc \sin A}$$

$$K = \frac{1}{2} b(c \sin A)$$

It is possible to develop equivalent formulas using each vertex. Therefore, in general, *the area of a triangle is equal to one-half of the product of the lengths of any two sides and the sine of the included angle.* Now let's use this formula to find the area of the triangle in Example 4.

$$K = \frac{1}{2}(16)(19)(\sin 43°)$$

$$K = 103.7, \quad \text{to the nearest tenth}$$

Thus, the area is approximately 103.7 square centimeters. (In Example 4 our answer was 103.6 square centimeters but we rounded the value of h to the nearest hundredth.)

If the measures of two angles and the included side of a triangle are known, then we can use a formula derived from the previous formula and the law of sines as follows. From the law of sines we obtain

$$\frac{c}{\sin C} = \frac{b}{\sin B}$$

$$c \sin B = b \sin C$$

$$c = \frac{b \sin C}{\sin B}.$$

Now we can substitute this expression for c into the area formula $K = \frac{1}{2}bc \sin A$.

$$K = \frac{1}{2}b\left(\frac{b \sin C}{\sin B}\right) \sin A$$

$$K = \frac{b^2 \sin C \sin A}{2 \sin B}$$

Note that the numerator of the expression for K is the product of the square of the length of a side and the sines of the angles that include the side. The denominator is twice the sine of the angle opposite the given side.

In a similar fashion, two other equivalent formulas could be developed. Thus, *the area of a triangle can be determined if the length of one side and the measures of any two of its angles are known.* (If the measures of two angles are known, the measure of the third angle is easily obtained.)

EXAMPLE 5

Find the area of the triangular region in Figure 7.62.

Solution

The measure of the third angle is

$$180° - (22° + 132°) = 180° - 154° = 26°.$$

Therefore, the area of the triangle is

$$K = \frac{(14^2)(\sin 22°)(\sin 26°)}{(2)(\sin 132°)}$$

$$K = 21.7, \quad \text{to the nearest tenth.}$$

Thus, the area of the triangle is approximately 21.7 square inches.   ▬▬▬

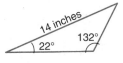

F I G U R E   7 . 62

Finally, we can also find the area of a triangle if the lengths of all three sides are known. For this purpose, a formula known as Heron's formula can be developed by using the law of cosines, the area formula $K = \frac{1}{2}bc \sin A$, and a substantial amount of algebraic manipulation. We will simply state the formula without showing all of the details of its development.

REMARK   Consider a triangle for which the lengths of the three sides are known. The law of cosines can be used to determine the measure of an angle. Then the area can be computed by using $K = \frac{1}{2}bc \sin A$. It should seem reasonable that a general formula can be developed using this procedure.

Heron's Formula

If a, b, and c are the three sides of a triangle and

$$s = \frac{a + b + c}{2},$$ s represents the semiperimeter

then the area of the triangle is given by

$$K = \sqrt{s(s - a)(s - b)(s - c)}.$$

EXAMPLE 6

Find the area of a triangular piece of sheet metal that has sides of length 17 inches, 19 inches, and 26 inches.

Solution

First, let's find the value of s.

$$s = \frac{17 + 19 + 26}{2} = 31$$

Now we can use Heron's formula.

$$K = \sqrt{s(s - a)(s - b)(s - c)}$$
$$= \sqrt{31(31 - 17)(31 - 19)(31 - 26)}$$
$$= \sqrt{31(14)(12)(5)}$$
$$= \sqrt{26040}$$
$$= 161.4, \quad \text{to the nearest tenth}$$

Thus, the area of the piece of sheet metal is approximately 161.4 square inches.

PROBLEM SET 7.4

In Problems 1–8, first decide whether two, one, or no triangles are determined by the given information. If one or two triangles are determined, calculate all possible values for the indicated part.

1. $A = 59°$, $a = 14$ centimeters, $c = 9$ centimeters; find C to the nearest tenth of a degree.

2. $A = 17°$, $a = 7$ feet, $c = 22$ feet; find C to the nearest tenth of a degree.

3. $A = 53.1°$, $a = 10$ meters, $c = 14$ meters; find C to the nearest tenth of a degree.

4. $A = 119°$, $a = 25$ yards, $c = 12$ yards; find C to the nearest tenth of a degree.

5. $A = 28°$, $a = 19$ miles, $c = 32$ miles; find B and C to the nearest tenth of a degree, and find b to the nearest tenth of a mile.

6. $A = 55°$, $a = 31$ feet, $c = 34$ feet; find B and C to the nearest tenth of a degree.

7. $A = 30°$, $a = 21$ centimeters, $c = 42$ centimeters; find C to the nearest degree and b to the nearest tenth of a centimeter.

8. $A = 124°$, $a = 21$ yards, $c = 27$ yards; find C to the nearest tenth of a degree and b to the nearest tenth of a yard.

For Problems 9–16, find the area of each triangular region to the nearest tenth of a square unit.

9. $A = 39°$, $c = 14$ inches, and $b = 27$ inches

10. $C = 18°$, $b = 31$ centimeters, and $a = 23$ centimeters

11. $A = 46°$, $C = 21°$, and $b = 18$ meters

12. $A = 55°$, $B = 45°$, and $c = 12$ feet

13. $a = 35$ yards, $b = 53$ yards, and $c = 27$ yards

14. $a = 21.2$ centimeters, $b = 19.4$ centimeters, and $c = 32.8$ centimeters

15. $A = 35.6°$, $B = 92.3°$, and $b = 63.4$ inches

16. $A = 108.3°$, $C = 31.4°$, and $a = 2.4$ meters

17. *Length of side of triangular lot* A triangular lot is bounded by three straight streets, Washington, Jefferson, and Monroe. Washington and Monroe Streets intersect at an angle of 65°. The side of the lot along Washington is 250 meters long and the side along Jefferson is 235 meters long. Find the length of the side of the lot along Monroe Street. Express the length to the nearest meter.

18. *Distance between points* Two landmarks, A and B, are on the same side of a river and 750 yards apart. A surveyor stands at point C on the opposite side of the river, thus forming triangle ABC. If $C = 57.2°$ and the distance between A and C is 600 yards, find the distance between B and C, to the nearest yard.

19. *Area of a triangular region* Find the area of a triangle if two sides are 18 meters and 24 meters long, and the included angle has a measure of 47°. Express the area to the nearest square meter.

20. *Area of a triangular region* Find the area of a triangle if two angles have measures of 43° and 61°, and the included side is 14 centimeters long. Express the area to the nearest square centimeter.

21. *Area of a triangular plot* Two sides of a triangular plot of ground are 75 yards and 90 yards long, and the angle included by those two sides is 65°. Find the area of the plot to the nearest square yard.

22. *Area of a triangular plot* A triangular plot of ground has two angles that measure 50° each. The side included between the two angles is 80 feet long. Find the area of the plot to the nearest square foot.

23. *Area of a triangular region* The dimensions of a triangle are indicated in Figure 7.63. Find the area to the nearest square inch.

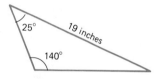

F I G U R E 7 . 63

24. *Area of a triangle* Find the area, to the nearest square centimeter, of a triangle that measures 14 centimeters by 16 centimeters by 18 centimeters.

25. *Area of a triangular plot* Find the area, to the nearest square yard, of a triangular plot of ground that measures 45 yards by 60 yards by 75 yards.

26. *Area of gable of house* The gable end of a house is shown in Figure 7.64. Find the area of the shaded triangle to the nearest square foot.

F I G U R E 7 . 64

27. *Area of equilateral triangle* Find the area of an equilateral triangle, whose sides are each 18 inches long. Express the area to the nearest square inch.

28. *Area of a quadrilateral* Find the area, to the nearest square inch, of the following quadrilateral (Figure 7.65).

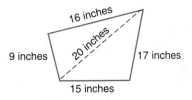

F I G U R E   7 . 65

29. *Area of a parallelogram* Find the area of a parallelogram that has sides 11 centimeters and 17 centimeters long, and the angle included by those sides has a measure of 39°. Express the answer to the nearest square centimeter.

30. *Cost of concrete* How much would it cost to shape a 4-inch slab of concrete into a triangle whose sides are 18, 24, and 27 feet long if the cost of the concrete is $42.50 per cubic yard? Express your answer to the nearest dollar.

THOUGHTS into WORDS

31. How would you describe the *ambiguous case* to a fellow student who was absent from class when it was discussed?

32. Use Heron's formula to find the area of a triangle with sides of lengths 8, 12, and 22 inches. Explain your result.

33. Explain how to find the area of a triangle with sides of lengths 7, 13, and 17 centimeters without using Heron's formula.

7.5   VECTORS

In the previous three sections we solved numerous problems that involved the lengths of sides of triangles. We did not specify any direction in which the measurements were made; in other words, the sides of the triangles had magnitude (length), but no direction. Many quantities, however, can be described completely by specifying both magnitude and direction only. For example, we speak of a car traveling north at 55 miles per hour or an airplane flying east at 350 miles per hour. Another example is force that is exerted with a given magnitude and in a given direction—30 pounds exerted at a 30° angle to the horizontal. Quantitites having both magnitude and direction are called **vector quantities**.

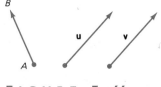

F I G U R E   7 . 66

Geometrically, vector quantities can be represented by directed line segments, called **vectors**. In Figure 7.66, a vector was drawn from point A (called the **initial point**) to the point B (called the **terminal point**) and is denoted by $\overrightarrow{AB}$. Boldface letters are also commonly used to name vectors. For example, vectors **u** and **v** are also represented in Figure 7.66. (Since boldface letters are hard to write, you might use $\vec{u}$ and $\vec{v}$). The length of a directed line segment represents the **magnitude** of the vector and is denoted by $\|\overrightarrow{AB}\|$ or $\|\mathbf{v}\|$. Vectors that have the same magnitude and same direction are considered **equal vectors**. In Figure 7.66, **u** and **v** are equal vectors and we write **u** = **v**. The vector quantities (car traveling north at 55 miles per hour, airplane flying east at 350 miles per hour, and a force of 30 pounds acting at a 30° angle to the horizontal) are represented in Figure 7.67.

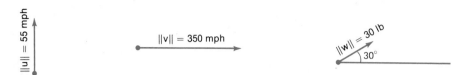

FIGURE 7.67

Vector Addition

The **sum** (also called the **resultant**) of two vectors **u** and **v** is pictured in Figure 7.68. The initial point of **v** is placed at the terminal point of **u** and the vector from the initial point of **u** to the terminal point of **v** is the sum **u** + **v**.

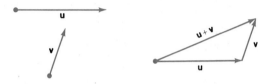

FIGURE 7.68

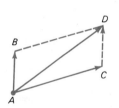

FIGURE 7.69

Another way to describe the addition of vectors is known as the **parallelogram law**. Consider two vectors $\overrightarrow{AB}$ and $\overrightarrow{AC}$ having a common initial point as in Figure 7.69. Complete the parallelogram $ACDB$. Since $\overrightarrow{AB} = \overrightarrow{CD}$, the diagonal vector $\overrightarrow{AD}$ represents the sum of $\overrightarrow{AC}$ and $\overrightarrow{AB}$. So we can write $\overrightarrow{AC} + \overrightarrow{AB} = \overrightarrow{AD}$. (If $\overrightarrow{AC}$ and $\overrightarrow{AB}$ are perpendicular, then $\overrightarrow{AD}$ will be the diagonal of a rectangle.) If $\overrightarrow{AC}$ and $\overrightarrow{AB}$ represent two physical forces acting on some object at A, then it can be shown by physical experiments that $\overrightarrow{AD}$ represents the **resultant force**, that is, the single force that produces the same effect as the two combined forces. In other words, vector addition is consistent with the action of the vector quantities that are being added.

Scalar Multiplication and Vector Subtraction

If **u** is a vector, then 2**u** is the vector in the same direction as **u**, but twice as long; -3**u** is three times as long as **u**, but in the opposite direction (Figure 7.70). In general, if k is a real number (called a **scalar**) and **u** is any vector, then k**u** (called the

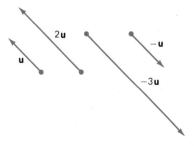

FIGURE 7.70

scalar multiple of **u**) is a vector whose magnitude is $|k|$ times the magnitude of **u** and whose direction is the same as **u** if $k > 0$ and opposite to that of **u** if $k < 0$. In particular, (-1)**u** (usually written as $-$**u**) has the same magnitude as **u** but it is directed in the opposite direction of **u**, as indicated in Figure 7.70. The vector $-$**u** is called the **opposite of** or the **negative of u** and when added to **u** produces the **zero vector** denoted by **0**. So we can write **u** $+$ $(-$**u**$)$ $=$ **0**. (The zero vector is interpreted as a point that has a magnitude of 0 and no direction.) The zero vector is the identity element for vector addition, that is, **u** $+$ **0** $=$ **0** $+$ **u** $=$ **u**. Finally, vector subtraction is defined by **u** $-$ **v** $=$ **u** $+$ $(-$**v**$)$.

EXAMPLE I

Use the two vectors in Figure 7.71 to draw the vectors 3**u** $+ 2$**v** and **u** $- 3$**v**.

Solution

FIGURE 7.71

Place 3**u** (a vector in the same direction as **u** but three times as long) and 2**v** (a vector in the same direction as **v** but twice as long) with their initial points in common. Then complete the parallelogram and draw 3**u** $+ 2$**v**. Place **u** and -3**v** (a vector in the opposite direction of **v** and three times as long) with their initial points in common. Then complete the parallelogram and draw **u** $- 3$**v** (Figure 7.72).

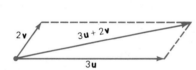
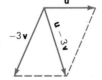

FIGURE 7.72

Vectors and Problem Solving

Vectors can be used to solve a large variety of problems. In this brief introduction to vectors, we want to show you a few such applications. Some of these problems can be solved using only right triangle trigonometry, but others require the law of cosines and the law of sines.

PROBLEM I

Ground speed of an airplane Suppose that an airplane flying at 300 miles per hour is headed due north but is blown off course by the wind blowing at 30 miles per hour from the west. By what angle is the plane blown off of its intended path and what is its actual ground speed?

Solution

The velocity of the plane and the wind velocity can be represented by two vectors, as shown in Figure 7.73. The actual path of the plane is represented by the resultant $\overrightarrow{AC}$, the diagonal of the rectangle. Angle θ is the angle that the plane is blown off of its intended course. Because DC is also 30, we can find θ by using the tangent function.

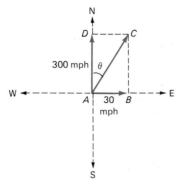

F I G U R E   7 . 73

$$\tan \theta = \frac{30}{300} = .1$$

Therefore,

$\theta = 5.7°$,   to the nearest tenth of a degree.

The magnitude of $\overrightarrow{AC}$ represents the ground speed of the plane.

$$\|\overrightarrow{AC}\|^2 = 300^2 + 30^2 = 90,900$$

Therefore,

$$\|\overrightarrow{AC}\| = 301.5 \text{ miles per hour.}$$

Instead of adding two vectors to form a resultant vector, it is sometimes necessary to reverse the process and to find two vectors whose sum is a given vector. The two vectors that we find are called **components** of the given vector. The components are especially easy to find if they are to be perpendicular.

PROBLEM 2

Forces acting when pulling a sled   Using a rope to pull a sled with a child on it, a man applies a force of 90 pounds. If the rope makes a 40° angle with the horizontal (Figure 7.74), find the horizontal force that tends to move the sled along the ground and the vertical force that tends to lift the sled vertically.

Solution

The vectors **u** and **v** in Figure 7.74 represent the horizontal and vertical components, respectively, of the given force of 90 pounds.

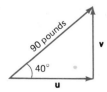

F I G U R E   7 . 74

$$\cos 40° = \frac{\|\mathbf{u}\|}{90}$$

$$\|\mathbf{u}\| = 90 \cos 40° = 68.9,   \text{to the nearest tenth of a pound}$$

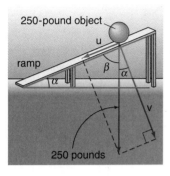

FIGURE 7.75

$$\sin 40° = \frac{\|\mathbf{v}\|}{90}$$

$$\|\mathbf{v}\| = 90 \sin 40° = 57.9, \quad \text{to the nearest tenth of a pound} \quad \blacksquare$$

Suppose that a spherical object weighing 250 pounds is placed on an inclined ramp, as indicated in Figure 7.75. Gravity pulls directly downward with a force of 250 pounds. Part of this force (represented by **u**) tends to pull the object down the ramp, and another part (represented by **v**) presses the object against the ramp on a line perpendicular to the ramp. The angle of the ramp, α, is also the angle between two of the vectors since they are both complementary to angle β. Therefore, if the angle of the ramp is known, then the 250-pound resultant vector, which is a diagonal of the rectangle, can be **resolved into two components**—one directed down the ramp and the other directed perpendicular to the ramp. Let's consider a specific problem.

PROBLEM 3

Components of a force   A 250-pound spherical lead ball is placed on a ramp that has an incline of 22° with the horizontal. How much force is pulling down the ramp and how much force is pressing on a line perpendicular to the ramp?

Solution

We can use Figure 7.75 with $\alpha = 22°$.

$$\cos 22° = \frac{\|\mathbf{v}\|}{250}$$

$$\|\mathbf{v}\| = 250 \cos 22°$$

$$= 231.8, \quad \text{to the nearest tenth}$$

$$\sin 22° = \frac{\|\mathbf{u}\|}{250}$$

$$\|\mathbf{u}\| = 250 \sin 22°$$

$$= 93.7, \quad \text{to the nearest tenth}$$

Therefore, there is a force of approximately 93.7 pounds acting down the ramp and 231.8 pounds acting against the ramp.   ▬▬▬

In certain navigation problems, the **direction** or **bearing** of a ship may be given by stating the size of an acute angle that is measured with respect to a north-south line. For example, a bearing of N40°E denotes an angle whose one side points north and whose other side points 40° east of north, as indicated in Figure 7.76. In the same figure, we have indicated a bearing of S70°W, that is, 70° west of south.

In air navigation, directions and bearings are often specified by measuring from a north line in a **clockwise** direction. (The angles are stated as positive angles even though they are measured in a clockwise direction.) Thus, in Figure 7.76 the bearing of S70°W could also be expressed as a bearing or direction of 250°.

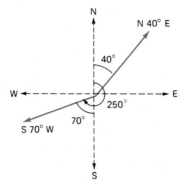

F I G U R E   7 . 7 6

PROBLEM 4

Bearing of a ship   If a ship sails 25 miles in the direction N40°E and then 60 miles straight east, find its distance and bearing with respect to its starting point.

Solution

The route of the ship is indicated in Figure 7.77. The measure of $\angle ABD$ is $90° - 40° = 50°$. Therefore, the measure of $\angle ABC$ is $180° - 50° = 130°$. Then the magnitude of $\overrightarrow{AC}$ can be found by using the law of cosines.

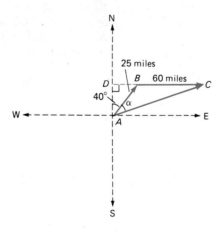

F I G U R E   7 . 7 7

$$\|\overrightarrow{AC}\|^2 = 25^2 + 60^2 - 2(25)(60) \cos 130°$$

$$= 6153.36, \quad \text{to the nearest hundredth}$$

Therefore,

$$\|\overrightarrow{AC}\| = 78.4 \text{ miles}, \quad \text{to the nearest tenth of a mile.}$$

Then the measure of angle α can be found by the law of sines.

$$\frac{\sin \alpha}{60} = \frac{\sin 130°}{78.4}$$

$$78.4 \sin \alpha = 60 \sin 130°$$

$$\sin \alpha = \frac{60 \sin 130°}{78.4}$$

$$\alpha = 35.9°, \quad \text{to the nearest tenth of a degree}$$

From Figure 7.77 we see that the bearing of $\overrightarrow{AC}$ is stated in terms of $\alpha + 40°$ and, therefore, is N75.9°E. ▬▬▬

PROBLEM SET 7.5

For Problems 1–4, use the vectors **u** and **v** in Figure 7.78 to draw the indicated vectors.

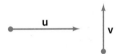

FIGURE 7.78

  1. u + v   **2. u − v**   **3. 2u + 3v**   **4. u − 2v**

For Problems 5–10, use the vectors **u** and **v** in Figure 7.79 to draw the indicated vectors.

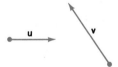

FIGURE 7.79

  5. u − v   **6. u + v**   **7. v + 2u**

  8. 2u + v   **9. 2u − v**   **10. 2v − u**

11. Ground speed of an airplane   Suppose that an airplane flying at 250 miles per hour is headed due south but is blown off course by the wind blowing at 40 miles per hour from the east. By what angle is the plane blown off of its intended path and what is its actual ground speed?

12. Path of a boat   A boat that can travel 15 miles per hour in still water attempts to go directly across a river that is

flowing at 4 miles per hour. By what angle is the boat pushed off of its intended path?

13. Path of a motorboat   A river flows due south at 125 feet per minute. In what direction must a motorboat, that can travel 500 feet per minute, be headed so that it actually travels due east?

14. Path of a balloon   A balloon is rising at 5 feet per second while a wind is blowing at 15 feet per second. Find the speed of the balloon and the angle that it makes with the horizontal.

15. Magnitude of forces   Two forces of 50 pounds and 75 pounds act on an object at right angles. Find the magnitude of the resultant force and the angle it makes with the larger force.

16. Magnitude of resultant force   Two forces of 4 kilograms and 9 kilograms act on an object at right angles. Find the magnitude of the resultant force and the angle it makes with the smaller force.

17. Wind speed   An airplane heads in a direction of 80° at 200 kilometers per hour. A wind blowing in the direction of 170° forces the plane onto a course that is due west. Find the speed of the wind.

18. Wind speed   An airplane heads in a direction of 265° at 330 miles per hour. A wind blowing in the direction of 355° forces the plane onto a course that is due west. Find the speed of the wind.

19. *Components of a force* A force of 45 pounds is acting on an object at a 20° angle to the horizontal. Find the horizontal and vertical components of the force.

20. *Components of velocity* An airplane is flying at 275 miles per hour in a direction of 235°. Find the westerly and southerly components of its velocity.

21. *Components of a force* A boy exerts a force of 20 pounds to pull a wagon with some toys in it (Figure 7.80). The handle of the wagon makes a 35° angle with the horizontal. Find the horizontal and vertical components of the 20-pound force.

FIGURE 7.80

22. *Measuring force* An automobile weighing 3200 pounds is parked on a ramp that makes a 15° angle with the horizontal. How much force is exerted parallel to the ramp and how much force is exerted perpendicular to the ramp?

23. *Force parallel to a ramp* A small car that weighs 1750 pounds is parked on a ramp that makes a 27° angle with the horizontal. How much force must be applied parallel to the ramp to keep the car from rolling down the ramp?

24. *Weight of a barrel* A force of 30 pounds is needed to hold a barrel in place on a ramp that makes an angle of 32° with the horizontal. Find the weight of the barrel.

25. *Angle of a ramp* A force of 52.1 pounds is needed to keep a 75-pound lead ball from rolling down a ramp. Find the angle that the ramp makes with the horizontal.

33. Explain the difference between a vector and a scalar.

26. *Horizontal component* A weight of 60 pounds is held by two wires as indicated in Figure 7.81. Find the horizontal component of force F_1.

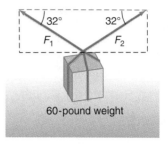

60-pound weight

FIGURE 7.81

27. *Magnitude of resultant* Forces of 220 kilograms and 175 kilograms act on an object. The angle between the forces is 65°. Find the magnitude of the resultant of the two forces and also find the angle that the resultant makes with the larger force.

28. *Magnitude of resultant* Forces of 105 pounds and 85 pounds act on an object. The angle between the forces is 42°. Find the magnitude of the resultant of the two forces and also find the angle that the resultant makes with the smaller force.

29. *Distance of a ship* If a ship sails 35 miles in the direction N32°W and then 70 miles straight west, find its distance and bearing with respect to its starting point.

30. *Bearing of a ship* If a ship sails 50 miles in the direction S47°E and then 80 miles straight east, find its distance and bearing with respect to its starting point.

31. *Bearing of a boat* Suppose that a boat travels 70 miles in the direction N50°E and then travels 85 miles in the direction S65°E. Find its distance and bearing with respect to its starting point.

32. *Bearing of a boat* Suppose that a boat travels 40 miles in the direction S27°W and then 90 miles straight east. Find its distance and bearing with respect to its starting point.

34. Describe how to add two vectors using the parallelogram law.

FURTHER INVESTIGATIONS

35. Present a geometric argument that vector addition is a commutative operation.

36. Present a geometric argument that vector addition is an associative operation.

37. Present a geometric argument that $k(\mathbf{u} + \mathbf{v}) = k\mathbf{u} + k\mathbf{v}$ for any vectors $\mathbf{u}$ and $\mathbf{v}$, and any real number k.

7.6   TRIGONOMETRIC FORM OF COMPLEX NUMBERS

Recall that any number of the form $a + bi$, where a and b are real numbers and i is the imaginary unit with the property $i^2 = -1$, is called a **complex number**. As we have seen, real numbers can be represented geometrically by points on a coordinate line. Complex numbers can also be represented geometrically, but by points in a plane. Every complex number $a + bi$ determines an ordered pair of real numbers (a, b), where a is called the **real part** and b the **imaginary part** of the complex number. Therefore, using a rectangular coordinate system with the horizontal axis as the **real axis** and the vertical axis as the **imaginary axis**, we can associate points of the plane with complex numbers as illustrated in Figure 7.82. Note that the complex number $5 + 2i$ is represented by the point $(5, 2)$, the number $-6 + i$ is represented by the point $(-6, 1)$, and so on. A coordinate plane with complex numbers assigned to the points in this manner is called a **complex plane**. In this context, we refer to the form $a + bi$ of a complex number as the **rectangular form** of the number.

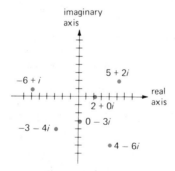

F I G U R E   7 . 82

The absolute value of a real number can be geometrically interpreted as the distance between 0 and the number on the real number line. It is natural, therefore, to interpret the absolute value of a complex number to be the distance between the origin and the point representing the complex number in the complex plane. Specifically, the absolute value of a complex number is defined as follows.

DEFINITION 7.1

The **absolute value** of a complex number $a + bi$ is denoted by $|a + bi|$ and is defined by

$$|a + bi| = \sqrt{a^2 + b^2}.$$

EXAMPLE 1

Compute (a) $|-5 + 12i|$, (b) $|2 - 4i|$, and (c) $|3i|$.

Solution

a. $|-5 + 12i| = \sqrt{(-5)^2 + 12^2} = \sqrt{25 + 144} = \sqrt{169} = 13$

b. $|2 - 4i| = \sqrt{2^2 + (-4)^2} = \sqrt{4 + 16} = \sqrt{20} = 2\sqrt{5}$

c. $|3i| = |0 + 3i| = \sqrt{0^2 + 3^2} = \sqrt{0 + 9} = 3$

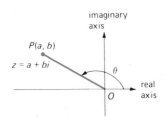

FIGURE 7.83

The geometric representation of a complex number as a point in a coordinate plane provides the basis for representing a complex number using trigonometric functions. Consider the complex number $z = a + bi$ as illustrated in Figure 7.83. Let θ be an angle in standard position whose terminal side is OP and let $r = |z|$, that is, $r = \sqrt{a^2 + b^2}$. By the definition of the sine and cosine functions we have

$$\sin \theta = \frac{b}{r} \quad \text{or} \quad b = r \sin \theta$$

and

$$\cos \theta = \frac{a}{r} \quad \text{or} \quad a = r \cos \theta.$$

Therefore, the complex number $a + bi$ can be expressed as

$$a + bi = (r \cos \theta) + (r \sin \theta)i,$$

which can be written in **trigonometric form** as

$$z = a + bi = r(\cos \theta + i \sin \theta).$$

The form $r(\cos \theta + i \sin \theta)$ is also called the **polar form** of a complex number. Remember that r is the absolute value of the complex number and therefore it is always nonnegative. Angle θ can be expressed in either radian or degree measure. Furthermore, θ is not uniquely determined since $\theta \pm 2k\pi$ will also do for k any integer. We will usually take the smallest positive angle for θ when writing complex numbers in trigonometric form.

REMARK   Traditionally, the number r in the trigonometric form of a complex number is also called the **modulus** of the number, and angle θ is called the **argument**. Also, the expression $r(\cos\theta + i\sin\theta)$ can be abbreviated as r cis θ. However, we will not use this terminology or symbolism in this brief introduction of complex numbers in trigonometric form.

Since a complex number can be written in either rectangular form $(a + bi)$ or trigonometric form $(r(\cos\theta + i\sin\theta))$, we need to be able to switch back and forth between the two forms. Let's consider some examples.

EXAMPLE 2

Express the following complex numbers in trigonometric form, where $0 \le \theta < 2\pi$.

a. $3 + 3i$ 　　　　　　　　　　**b.** $-2\sqrt{3} - 2i$

Solution

a. The complex number $3 + 3i$ is represented geometrically in Figure 7.84. Since the right triangle indicated in the figure is isosceles, $\theta = \pi/4$. Then using either the Pythagorean theorem or the distance formula, we can find the value of r.

$$r = \sqrt{3^2 + 3^2} = \sqrt{18} = 3\sqrt{2}.$$

Therefore,

$$3 + 3i = 3\sqrt{2}\left(\cos\frac{\pi}{4} + i\sin\frac{\pi}{4}\right).$$

b. The complex number $-2\sqrt{3} - 2i$ is graphed in Figure 7.85.

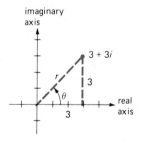

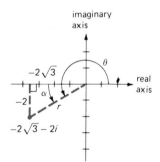

FIGURE 7.84 　　　　　　**FIGURE 7.85**

$$r = \sqrt{(-2\sqrt{3})^2 + (-2)^2} = \sqrt{12 + 4} = \sqrt{16} = 4.$$

Now we should recognize that $\alpha = \pi/6$ and thus $\theta = \pi + \pi/6 = 7\pi/6$. Therefore,

$$-2\sqrt{3} - 2i = 4\left(\cos\frac{7\pi}{6} + i\sin\frac{7\pi}{6}\right).$$

EXAMPLE 3

Express the following complex numbers in trigonometric form, where $0° \leq \theta < 360°$.

a. $0 - 4i$ *b.* $5 + 2i$

Solution

a. The complex number $0 - 4i$ is graphed in Figure 7.86. It is evident from the figure that $r = 4$ and $\theta = 270°$. Therefore,

$$0 - 4i = 4(\cos 270° + i \sin 270°).$$

b. The complex number $5 + 2i$ is represented in Figure 7.87.

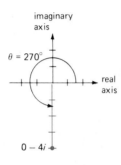

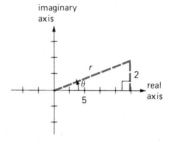

FIGURE 7.86   **FIGURE 7.87**

$$r = \sqrt{5^2 + 2^2} = \sqrt{29}$$

From the figure we see that $\tan \theta = \frac{2}{5} = .4$. Using a calculator or the table in Appendix C, we can find that $\theta = 21.8°$, to the nearest tenth of a degree. Therefore,

$$5 + 2i = \sqrt{29}(\cos 21.8° + i \sin 21.8°).$$

EXAMPLE 4

Change the complex number $8(\cos 60° + i \sin 60°)$ to $a + bi$ form.

Solution

$$8(\cos 60° + i \sin 60°) = 8\left(\frac{1}{2} + i\frac{\sqrt{3}}{2}\right) = 4 + 4\sqrt{3}\,i$$

Multiplying Complex Numbers in Trigonometric Form

In Section 1.6 we discussed the multiplication of complex numbers in the form $a + bi$. For example, the product of $2 + 2i$ and $-3 + 3i$ was handled as follows.

$$(2 + 2i)(-3 + 3i) = 2(-3 + 3i) + 2i(-3 + 3i)$$

$$= -6 + 6i - 6i + 6i^2$$

$$= -6 + 6(-1)$$

$$= -12 + 0i$$

Let's consider the product of two complex numbers using their trigonometric forms. Let $z_1 = r_1(\cos \theta_1 + i \sin \theta_1)$ and $z_2 = r_2(\cos \theta_2 + i \sin \theta_2)$ be the two numbers. Therefore,

$$z_1 z_2 = [r_1(\cos \theta_1 + i \sin \theta_1)][r_2(\cos \theta_2 + i \sin \theta_2)]$$

$$= r_1 r_2[\cos \theta_1 \cos \theta_2 + i \cos \theta_1 \sin \theta_2 + i \sin \theta_1 \cos \theta_2 + i^2 \sin \theta_1 \sin \theta_2]$$

$$= r_1 r_2[\cos \theta_1 \cos \theta_2 - \sin \theta_1 \sin \theta_2 + i(\cos \theta_1 \sin \theta_2 + \sin \theta_1 \cos \theta_2)].$$

Now applying the sum formulas for $\cos(\theta_1 + \theta_2)$ and $\sin(\theta_1 + \theta_2)$, we obtain the following description for multiplying complex numbers in trigonometric form.

$$z_1 z_2 = r_1 r_2[\cos(\theta_1 + \theta_2) + i \sin(\theta_1 + \theta_2)]$$

EXAMPLE 5

Use their trigonometric forms to find the product of $(2 + 2i)$ and $(-3 + 3i)$.

Solution

Let $z_1 = 2 + 2i$ and $z_2 = -3 + 3i$. Their trigonometric forms are as follows.

$$z_1 = 2 + 2i = 2\sqrt{2}\left(\cos\frac{\pi}{4} + i \sin\frac{\pi}{4}\right)$$

$$z_2 = -3 + 3i = 3\sqrt{2}\left(\cos\frac{3\pi}{4} + i \sin\frac{3\pi}{4}\right)$$

Therefore,

$$z_1 z_2 = (2\sqrt{2})(3\sqrt{2})\left[\cos\left(\frac{\pi}{4} + \frac{3\pi}{4}\right) + i \sin\left(\frac{\pi}{4} + \frac{3\pi}{4}\right)\right]$$

$$= 12[\cos \pi + i \sin \pi]$$

$$= 12[-1 + i(0)]$$

$$= -12 + 0i. \qquad \text{This agrees with our earlier result.}$$

As illustrated in Example 5, multiplying complex numbers in trigonometric form is quite easy. Basically, we multiply absolute values and add angles. Most of us would probably agree that multiplying complex numbers in the $a + bi$ form is not very difficult. Therefore, it may seem as if the trigonometric form has not provided us with much extra fire power. That is true at this time; however, in the next section we will find the trigonometric form very convenient for finding powers and roots of complex numbers.

PROBLEM SET 7.6

For Problems 1–12, plot each complex number and find its absolute value.

1. $3 + 4i$

2. $-4 + 3i$

3. $-5 - 12i$

4. $12 - 5i$

5. $0 - 5i$

6. $-4 + 0i$

7. $1 - 2i$

8. $-1 - i$

9. $-2 + 3i$

10. $3 - 2i$

11. $\dfrac{3}{5} - \dfrac{4}{5}i$

12. $-\dfrac{5}{13} - \dfrac{12}{13}i$

For Problems 13–22, express each complex number in trigonometric form, where $0 \le \theta < 2\pi$.

13. $-2 + 2i$

14. $-4 - 4i$

15. $0 - 3i$

16. $-4 + 0i$

17. $2\sqrt{3} - 2i$

18. $-3\sqrt{3} + 3i$

19. $-1 - i$

20. $1 - i$

21. $-1 + \sqrt{3}\,i$

22. $2 - 2\sqrt{3}\,i$

For Problems 23–32, express each complex number in trigonometric form, where $0 \le \theta < 360°$.

23. $5 - 5i$

24. $6 + 6i$

25. $-2 + 0i$

26. $0 + 7i$

27. $\sqrt{3} + i$

28. $-\sqrt{3} - i$

29. $-4 - 4\sqrt{3}\,i$

30. $5 - 5\sqrt{3}\,i$

31. $6\sqrt{3} - 6i$

32. $-7\sqrt{3} + 7i$

For Problems 33–40, express each complex number in trigonometric form, where $0° \le \theta < 360°$. Express θ to the nearest tenth of a degree.

33. $2 + 3i$

34. $4 - 3i$

35. $-2 - i$

36. $-5 + 3i$

37. $4 - i$

38. $2 + i$

39. $-2 + 4i$

40. $-6 - 3i$

For Problems 41–50, change the given complex number from trigonometric form to $a + bi$ form.

41. $4(\cos 30° + i \sin 30°)$

42. $5(\cos 120° + i \sin 120°)$

43. $3\left(\cos \dfrac{5\pi}{4} + i \sin \dfrac{5\pi}{4}\right)$

44. $1\left(\cos \dfrac{11\pi}{6} + i \sin \dfrac{11\pi}{6}\right)$

45. $2\left(\cos \dfrac{4\pi}{3} + i \sin \dfrac{4\pi}{3}\right)$

46. $\dfrac{1}{2}\left(\cos \dfrac{5\pi}{6} + i \sin \dfrac{5\pi}{6}\right)$

47. $\dfrac{2}{3}\left(\cos \dfrac{5\pi}{3} + i \sin \dfrac{5\pi}{3}\right)$

48. $7(\cos \pi + i \sin \pi)$

49. $6(\cos 0° + i \sin 0°)$

50. $8(\cos 60° + i \sin 60°)$

For Problems 51–60, find the product $z_1 z_2$ by using the trigonometric forms of the numbers. Express the final results in $a + bi$ form. Check each product using the methods of Section 1.6.

51. $z_1 = \sqrt{3} + i, \quad z_2 = -2\sqrt{3} - 2i$

52. $z_1 = -3\sqrt{3} - 3i, \quad z_2 = 2\sqrt{3} + 2i$

53. $z_1 = 5\sqrt{3} + 5i, \quad z_2 = 6\sqrt{3} + 6i$

54. $z_1 = 1 + \sqrt{3}\,i, \quad z_2 = -\dfrac{1}{2} - \dfrac{\sqrt{3}}{2}i$

55. $z_1 = \dfrac{1}{2} + \dfrac{\sqrt{3}}{2}i, \quad z_2 = -\dfrac{3}{2} - \dfrac{3\sqrt{3}}{2}i$

56. $z_1 = -1 + i, \quad z_2 = 1 + i$

57. $z_1 = -2 - 2\sqrt{3}\,i, \quad z_2 = 0 + 5i$

58. $z_1 = 0 + 4i, \quad z_2 = 0 - 7i$

59. $z_1 = 8 + 0i, \quad z_2 = 0 - 3i$

60. $z_1 = -\dfrac{5\sqrt{2}}{2} + \dfrac{5\sqrt{2}}{2}i, \quad z_2 = -3 + 0i$

For Problems 61–66, find the product $z_1 z_2$ by using the trigonometric forms of the numbers. Express the final results in trigonometric form.

61. $z_1 = 5(\cos 20° + i \sin 20°), \quad z_2 = 4(\cos 55° + i \sin 55°)$

62. $z_1 = 3(\cos 110° + i \sin 110°),$
$z_2 = (\cos 28° + i \sin 28°)$

63. $z_1 = \sqrt{2}(\cos 120° + i \sin 120°),$
$z_2 = 3\sqrt{2}(\cos 310° + i \sin 310°)$

64. $z_1 = 2\sqrt{3}(\cos 260° + i \sin 260°),$
$z_2 = 4\sqrt{3}(\cos 320° + i \sin 320°)$

65. $z_1 = 5\left(\cos\dfrac{3\pi}{5} + i \sin\dfrac{3\pi}{5}\right),$
$z_2 = 7\left(\cos\dfrac{\pi}{2} + i \sin\dfrac{\pi}{2}\right)$

66. $z_1 = 6\left(\cos\dfrac{3\pi}{4} + i \sin\dfrac{3\pi}{4}\right),$
$z_2 = 4\left(\cos\dfrac{2\pi}{3} + i \sin\dfrac{2\pi}{3}\right)$

THOUGHTS into WORDS

67. Describe how to change a complex number from rectangular form to trigonometric form.

68. Describe how to multiply complex numbers in trigonometric form.

FURTHER INVESTIGATIONS

69. If $z_1 = r_1(\cos \theta_1 + i \sin \theta_1)$ and $z_2 = r_2(\cos \theta_2 + i \sin \theta_2)$, then verify that

$$\frac{z_1}{z_2} = \frac{r_1}{r_2}[\cos(\theta_1 - \theta_2) + i \sin(\theta_1 - \theta_2)].$$

For Problems 70–75, find the quotient z_1/z_2 using the trigonometric forms of the numbers (see Problem 69). Express the final quotient in $a + bi$ form.

70. $z_1 = 1 + i, \quad z_2 = 0 + i$

71. $z_1 = 2 - 2i, \quad z_2 = 0 + 3i$

72. $z_1 = -1 + i, \quad z_2 = 1 + i$

73. $z_1 = 1 - i, \quad z_2 = -1 - i$

74. $z_1 = -1 + \sqrt{3}\,i, \quad z_2 = -1 - \sqrt{3}\,i$

75. $z_1 = 3 + 3\sqrt{3}\,i, \quad z_2 = -\dfrac{3\sqrt{3}}{2} - \dfrac{3}{2}i$

7.7   POWERS AND ROOTS OF COMPLEX NUMBERS

By repeated application of the principle for multiplying complex numbers in trigonometric form, the powers of a complex number $z = r(\cos \theta + i \sin \theta)$ can be easily obtained.

$$z^2 = z \cdot z = [r(\cos \theta + i \sin \theta)][r(\cos \theta + i \sin \theta)] = r^2(\cos 2\theta + i \sin 2\theta)$$

$$z^3 = z^2 \cdot z = [r^2(\cos 2\theta + i \sin 2\theta)][r(\cos \theta + i \sin \theta)] = r^3(\cos 3\theta + i \sin 3\theta)$$

$$z^4 = z^3 \cdot z = [r^3(\cos 3\theta + i \sin 3\theta)][r(\cos \theta + i \sin \theta)] = r^4(\cos 4\theta + i \sin 4\theta)$$

In general, the following result, named for the French mathematician Abraham De Moivre (1667–1754), can be stated.

> ### De Moivre's Theorem
>
> For every positive integer n,
> $$[r(\cos \theta + i \sin \theta)]^n = r^n(\cos n\theta + i \sin n\theta).$$

A complete proof of De Moivre's theorem can be given by using the principle of mathematical induction we discuss in Chapter 11.

EXAMPLE 1

Find $(1 + i)^{16}$.

Solution

First, let's change $1 + i$ to trigonometric form.

$$1 + i = \sqrt{2}\left(\cos\frac{\pi}{4} + i \sin\frac{\pi}{4}\right)$$

Next, we can apply De Moivre's theorem.

$$(1 + i)^{16} = (2^{1/2})^{16}\left[\cos 16\left(\frac{\pi}{4}\right) + i \sin 16\left(\frac{\pi}{4}\right)\right]$$
$$= 2^8[\cos 4\pi + i \sin 4\pi]$$
$$= 256[\cos 4\pi + i \sin 4\pi]$$

Finally, we can change back to $a + bi$ form.

$$(1 + i)^{16} = 256[\cos 4\pi + i \sin 4\pi]$$
$$= 256(1) + 256(i)(0) = 256 + 0i$$

EXAMPLE 2

Find
$$\left(-\frac{\sqrt{3}}{2} - \frac{1}{2}i\right)^{20}.$$

Solution

$$-\frac{\sqrt{3}}{2} - \frac{1}{2}i = 1(\cos 210° + i \sin 210°)$$

Therefore

$$\left(-\frac{\sqrt{3}}{2} - \frac{1}{2}i\right)^{20} = 1^{20}[\cos 20(210°) + i \sin 20(210°)]$$

$$= 1[\cos 4200° + i \sin 4200°]$$

$$= 1[\cos 240° + i \sin 240°]$$

$$= 1\left(-\tfrac{1}{2}\right) + (1)(i)\left(-\tfrac{\sqrt{3}}{2}\right)$$

$$= -\tfrac{1}{2} - \tfrac{\sqrt{3}}{2}i.$$

Finding Roots of Complex Numbers

If the complex number w is an nth root of the complex number z, then $w^n = z$. Substituting the trigonometric forms $s(\cos \alpha + i \sin \alpha)$ for w and $r(\cos \theta + i \sin \theta)$ for z, we obtain

$$[s(\cos \alpha + i \sin \alpha)]^n = r(\cos \theta + i \sin \theta).$$

Now applying De Moivre's theorem to the left side produces

$$s^n(\cos n\alpha + i \sin n\alpha) = r(\cos \theta + i \sin \theta). \tag{1}$$

Equal complex numbers have equal absolute values. Therefore, $s^n = r$ and because s and r are nonnegative

$$s = \sqrt[n]{r}.$$

Furthermore, for equation (1) to hold,

$$\cos n\alpha + i \sin n\alpha = \cos \theta + i \sin \theta.$$

It follows that

$$\cos n\alpha = \cos \theta \quad \text{and} \quad \sin n\alpha = \sin \theta.$$

Since both the sine and cosine functions have a period of 2π, the last two equations are true if and only if $n\alpha$ and θ differ by a multiple of 2π. Therefore,

$$n\alpha = \theta + 2\pi k, \quad \text{where } k \text{ is an integer.}$$

Solving for α produces

$$\alpha = \frac{\theta + 2\pi k}{n}.$$

Substituting $\sqrt[n]{r}$ for s and $(\theta + 2\pi k)/n$ for α in the trigonometric form for w produces

$$w = \sqrt[n]{r}\left[\cos\left(\frac{\theta + 2\pi k}{n}\right) + i \sin\left(\frac{\theta + 2\pi k}{n}\right)\right].$$

If we let $k = 0, 1, 2, \ldots, n - 1$ successively, we obtain n distinct values for w, that is, n distinct nth roots of z. Furthermore, no other value of k will produce a new value for w. For example, if $k = n$, then $\alpha = (\theta + 2\pi n)/n = (\theta/n) + 2\pi$, which produces the same value for w as when $k = 0$. Similarly, $k = n + 1$ yields the same value for w as $k = 1$, and so on. Likewise, negative values of k will merely produce repeat values for w. This discussion has verified the following property.

> ## PROPERTY 7.1
>
> If $z = r(\cos \theta + i \sin \theta)$ is any nonzero complex number and n is any positive integer, then z has precisely n distinct nth roots that are given by
>
> $$\sqrt[n]{r}\left[\cos\left(\frac{\theta + 2\pi k}{n}\right) + i \sin\left(\frac{\theta + 2\pi k}{n}\right)\right]$$
>
> where $k = 0, 1, 2, \ldots, n - 1$.

Property 7.1 can also be stated in terms of degree measure. It then becomes

$$\sqrt[n]{r}\left[\cos\left(\frac{\theta + k \cdot 360°}{n}\right) + i \sin\left(\frac{\theta + k \cdot 360°}{n}\right)\right]$$
$$\text{where } k = 0, 1, 2, \ldots, n - 1.$$

EXAMPLE 3

Find the four fourth roots of $-8 - 8\sqrt{3}\, i$.

Solution

First, let's express the given number in trigonometric form.

$$-8 - 8\sqrt{3}\, i = 16(\cos 240° + i \sin 240°)$$

With $n = 4$, the fourth roots are given by

$$\sqrt[4]{16}\left[\cos\left(\frac{240° + k \cdot 360°}{4}\right) + i \sin\left(\frac{240° + k \cdot 360°}{4}\right)\right],$$

which simplifies to

$$2[\cos(60° + k \cdot 90°) + i \sin(60° + k \cdot 90°)].$$

Substituting 0, 1, 2, and 3 for k yields the following fourth roots.

$$2(\cos 60° + i \sin 60°) = 2\left(\tfrac{1}{2}\right) + 2i\left(\tfrac{\sqrt{3}}{2}\right) = 1 + \sqrt{3}\, i$$

$$2(\cos 150° + i \sin 150°) = 2\left(-\tfrac{\sqrt{3}}{2}\right) + 2i\left(\tfrac{1}{2}\right) = -\sqrt{3} + i.$$

$$2(\cos 240° + i \sin 240°) = 2\left(-\tfrac{1}{2}\right) + 2i\left(-\tfrac{\sqrt{3}}{2}\right) = -1 - \sqrt{3}\, i$$

$$2(\cos 330° + i \sin 330°) = 2\left(\tfrac{\sqrt{3}}{2}\right) + 2i\left(-\tfrac{1}{2}\right) = \sqrt{3} - i$$

Note in Example 3 that each root has an absolute value of 2. Therefore, geometrically they are all located on a circle with its center at the origin and a radius of length 2 units, as illustrated in Figure 7.88. Furthermore, the points associated with the roots are equally spaced around the circle. In general, the nth roots of a complex number $z = r(\cos \theta + i \sin \theta)$ are equally spaced around a circle with a radius of length $\sqrt[n]{r}$ and its center at the origin.

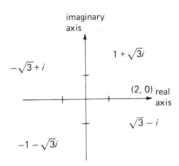

F I G U R E   7 . 88

EXAMPLE 4

Find the three cube roots of $8i$.

Solution

In trigonometric form $0 + 8i = 8\left(\cos\dfrac{\pi}{2} + i \sin\dfrac{\pi}{2}\right)$. With $n = 3$, the cube roots are given by

$$\sqrt[3]{8}\left[\cos\left(\frac{\frac{\pi}{2} + 2\pi k}{3}\right) + i \sin\left(\frac{\frac{\pi}{2} + 2\pi k}{3}\right)\right],$$

which simplifies to

$$2\left[\cos\left(\frac{\pi}{6} + \frac{2\pi k}{3}\right) + i \sin\left(\frac{\pi}{6} + \frac{2\pi k}{3}\right)\right].$$

Substituting 0, 1, and 2 for k yields the following cube roots.

$$2\left(\cos\frac{\pi}{6} + i \sin\frac{\pi}{6}\right) = 2\left(\frac{\sqrt{3}}{2}\right) + 2i\left(\frac{1}{2}\right) = \sqrt{3} + i$$

$$2\left(\cos\frac{5\pi}{6} + i \sin\frac{5\pi}{6}\right) = 2\left(-\frac{\sqrt{3}}{2}\right) + 2i\left(\frac{1}{2}\right) = -\sqrt{3} + i$$

$$2\left(\cos\frac{3\pi}{2} + i \sin\frac{3\pi}{2}\right) = 2(0) + 2i(-1) = 0 - 2i$$

EXAMPLE 5

Find the five fifth roots of -243.

Solution

In trigonometric form, $-243 + 0i = 243(\cos 180° + i \sin 180°)$. With $n = 5$, the fifth roots are given by

$$\sqrt[5]{243}\left[\cos\left(\frac{180° + k \cdot 360°}{5}\right) + i \sin\left(\frac{180° + k \cdot 360°}{5}\right)\right],$$

which simplifies to

$$3[\cos 36° + k \cdot 72°) + i \sin(36° + k \cdot 72°)].$$

Substituting 0, 1, 2, 3, and 4 for k produces the following fifth roots.

$$3(\cos 36° + i \sin 36°)$$

$$3(\cos 108° + i \sin 108°)$$

$$3(\cos 180° + i \sin 180°) = -3 + 0i$$

$$3(\cos 252° + i \sin 252°)$$

$$3(\cos 324° + i \sin 324°)$$

There is one exact root, namely, $-3 + 0i$. Approximations for the other four roots could be obtained by using a calculator or a table. We will leave them in trigonometric form.

PROBLEM SET 7.7

For Problems 1–16, use De Moivre's theorem to find the indicated powers. Express results in $a + bi$ form.

1. $(1 + i)^{20}$

2. $(1 - i)^{12}$

3. $(-1 + i)^{10}$

4. $(-2 - 2i)^4$

5. $(3 + 3i)^5$

6. $(\sqrt{3} + i)^7$

7. $(-1 + \sqrt{3}\,i)^4$

8. $(-2\sqrt{3} + 2i)^5$

9. $\left(\dfrac{\sqrt{3}}{2} - \dfrac{1}{2}i\right)^{14}$

10. $\left(\dfrac{1}{2} - \dfrac{\sqrt{3}}{2}i\right)^{11}$

11. $\left(-\dfrac{\sqrt{2}}{2} + \dfrac{\sqrt{2}}{2}i\right)^{15}$

12. $\left(-\dfrac{\sqrt{2}}{2} - \dfrac{\sqrt{2}}{2}i\right)^{13}$

13. $[2(\cos 15° + i \sin 15°)]^4$

14. $[2(\cos 50° + i \sin 50°)]^6$

15. $\left(\cos\dfrac{\pi}{8} + i \sin\dfrac{\pi}{8}\right)^{10}$

16. $\left(\cos\dfrac{\pi}{12} + i \sin\dfrac{\pi}{12}\right)^8$

For Problems 17–32, find the indicated roots. Express the roots in $a + bi$ form if they are exact. Otherwise, leave them in trigonometric form.

17. The three cube roots of 8

18. The three cube roots of -27

19. The two square roots of $-16i$

20. The two square roots of $9i$

21. The four fourth roots of $-8 + 8\sqrt{3}\,i$

22. The four fourth roots of $-8 - 8\sqrt{3}\,i$

23. The five fifth roots of $1 + i$

24. The five fifth roots of $1 - i$

25. The six sixth roots of 1

26. The eight eighth roots of 1

27. The three cube roots of $-1 + \sqrt{3}\,i$

28. The three cube roots of $1 - \sqrt{3}\,i$

29. The five fifth roots of $-\sqrt{2} + \sqrt{2}\,i$

30. The five fifth roots of $\sqrt{2} - \sqrt{2}\,i$

31. The two square roots of $\dfrac{9}{2} + \dfrac{9\sqrt{3}}{2}i$

32. The two square roots of $-2 - 2\sqrt{3}\,i$

FURTHER INVESTIGATIONS

For Problems 33–40, solve each of the equations using any approach that you think is appropriate.

33. $x^4 - 16 = 0$ **34.** $x^3 - 27 = 0$

35. $x^4 + 16 = 0$ **36.** $x^3 + 27 = 0$

37. $x^5 - 1 = 0$ **38.** $x^5 + 1 = 0$

39. $x^6 + 1 = 0$ **40.** $x^6 - 1 = 0$

CHAPTER 7 SUMMARY

Problem solving is the central theme of Sections 7.1–7.5.

Solving a right triangle can be analyzed as follows.

1. If an acute angle and the length of one side are known, then the other acute angle is the complement of the given one. You can find the lengths of the other two sides by solving an equation involving the appropriate trigonometric functions.

2. If the lengths of two sides are given, the third side can be found by using the Pythagorean theorem. You can determine the two acute angles from equations involving the appropriate trigonometric functions.

The following relationships are referred to as the **law of cosines**.

$$a^2 = b^2 + c^2 - 2bc \cos A$$

$$b^2 = a^2 + c^2 - 2ac \cos B$$

$$c^2 = a^2 + b^2 - 2ab \cos C$$

If two sides and the included angle (SAS) of a triangle are known or if three sides (SSS) are known, then the law of cosines can be used to solve the triangle.

The following relationships are referred to as the **law of sines**.

$$\frac{a}{\sin A} = \frac{b}{\sin B} = \frac{c}{\sin C}$$

If two angles and a side of a triangle are known, then the law of sines can be used to solve the triangle.

If, in a triangle, two sides and an angle opposite one of them are known, then two, one, or no triangles may be determined.

If two sides and the included angle (SAS) of a triangle are known, then the formula $K = \dfrac{1}{2} bc \sin A$ can be used to find the area.

If two angles and the included side (ASA) of a triangle are known, then the formula $K = \dfrac{b^2 \sin A \sin C}{2 \sin B}$ can be used to find the area.

If three sides (SSS) of a triangle are known, then Heron's formula $K = \sqrt{s(s-a)(s-b)(s-c)}$ can be used to find the area.

Vectors, as directed line segments, play an important role in many applications because they can be used to represent quantities that have both magnitude and direction. Problems 1–4 of Section 7.4 provide a good review of some of the applications of vectors presented in this chapter.

The following relationships are apparent from Figure 7.89.

$$b = r \sin \theta$$

$$a = r \cos \theta$$

$$r = \sqrt{a^2 + b^2}$$

$$a + bi = r(\cos \theta + i \sin \theta)$$

$\uparrow$

Trigonometric form
of a complex number

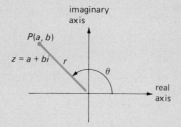

F I G U R E   7 . 8 9

The product of two complex numbers z_1 and z_2, expressed in trigonometric form, is given by

$$z_1 z_2 = r_1 r_2 [\cos(\theta_1 + \theta_2) + i \sin(\theta_1 + \theta_2)].$$

De Moivre's theorem is the basis for raising a complex number to a power.

$$[r(\cos \theta + i \sin \theta)]^n = r^n(\cos n\theta + i \sin n\theta)$$

The nth roots of a complex number $z = r(\cos \theta + i \sin \theta)$ are given by

$$\sqrt[n]{r}\left[\cos\left(\frac{\theta + 2\pi k}{n}\right) + i \sin\left(\frac{\theta + 2\pi k}{n}\right)\right]$$

where $k = 0, 1, 2, \ldots , n - 1$.

CHAPTER 7 REVIEW PROBLEM SET

1. *Measure of an angle*   The sides of a right triangle are of length 8 feet, 15 feet, and 17 feet. Find the size of the angle, to the nearest tenth of a degree, opposite the 15-foot side.

2. *Height of a tree*   From a point 80 feet from the base of a tree, the angle of elevation to the top of the tree is 28°. Find the height of the tree to the nearest tenth of a foot.

3. *Height of a building*   A 50-foot antenna stands on top of a building. From a point on the ground away from the base of the building, the angle of elevation to the top of the antenna is 51° and the angle of elevation to the bottom of the antenna is 42°. Find the height of the building to the nearest foot.

4. In triangle ABC, if $A = 74°$, $c = 19$ miles, and $b = 27$ miles, find a to the nearest tenth of a mile.

5. In triangle ABC, if $A = 118.2°$, $C = 17.3°$, and $c = 56$ yards, find b to the nearest tenth of a yard.

6. If $A = 29°$, $a = 19$ meters, and $c = 37$ meters, how many triangles are determined?

7. In Figure 7.90, find x to the nearest tenth of a foot.

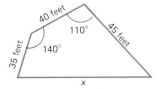

FIGURE   7.90

8. *Angle of a triangle*   A triangular lot measures 52 yards by 47 yards by 85 yards. Find, to the nearest tenth of a degree, the size of the angle opposite the longest side. Also find the area of the lot to the nearest square yard.

9. *Distance of an airplane*   A plane travels 350 miles due east after take-off, then adjusts its course 20° northward and flies another 175 miles. How far is it from its point of departure? Express your answer to the nearest mile.

10. *Distance between two points*   Two points A and B are located on opposite sides of a river. Point C is located 350 yards from B on the same side of the river as B. In $\triangle ABC$, $B = 69°$, and $C = 43°$. Find the distance between A and B to the nearest yard.

11. *Height of a tower*   Two people 60 feet apart are in line with the base of a tower. The angle of elevation to the top of the tower from one person is 39.6° and from the other person is 27.4°. Find the height of the tower to the nearest tenth of a foot.

12. Find the area of triangle ABC if $A = 34.6°$, $c = 13.1$ centimeters, and $b = 17.4$ centimeters. Express your answer to the nearest tenth of a square centimeter.

13. Find the area of triangle ABC if $B = 101°$, $C = 33°$, and $c = 18$ inches. Express your answer to the nearest square inch.

Use vectors to help solve Problems 14–17.

14. *Forces acting when pushing lawn mower*   A lawn mower is being pushed by applying a force of 45 pounds. The handle of the mower makes an angle of 40° with the horizontal. How much force is being applied horizontally and how much force is being applied downward?

15. *Forces on a ramp*   A car weighing 2750 pounds is parked on a ramp that makes a 32° angle with the horizontal. How much force must be applied to keep the car from rolling down the ramp?

16. *Resultant of two forces*   Forces of 130 pounds and 165 pounds act on an object. The angle between the forces is 28°. Find the magnitude of the resultant of the two forces and also find the angle that the resultant makes with the larger force.

17. *Bearing of a ship*   A ship sails 70 miles straight west and then 110 miles in the direction N20°W. Find its distance and bearing with respect to its starting point.

18. Plot the complex number $2 - 4i$ and find its absolute value.

19. Express the complex number $\sqrt{3} - i$ in trigonometric form, where $0 \le \theta < 2\pi$.

20. Express the complex number $-3\sqrt{2} - 3\sqrt{2}i$ in trigonometric form, where $0° \le \theta < 360°$.

21. Express the complex number $5\left(\cos\dfrac{3\pi}{2} + i\sin\dfrac{3\pi}{2}\right)$ in $a + bi$ form.

22. Express the complex number $8(\cos 300° + i \sin 300°)$ in $a + bi$ form.

For Problems 23–25, use De Moivre's theorem to find the indicated powers. Express results in $a + bi$ form.

23. $(-1 - i)^8$ 24. $(1 - \sqrt{3}i)^{10}$

25. $\left(\dfrac{\sqrt{2}}{2} + \dfrac{\sqrt{2}}{2}i\right)^{17}$

For Problems 26–28, find the indicated roots and express them in $a + bi$ form.

26. The three cube roots of $-27i$

27. The four fourth roots of $-2 + 2\sqrt{3}i$

28. The two square roots of $8 - 8\sqrt{3}i$

For Problems 1–16, find exact values without using a calculator or a table.

1. $\sin 120°$

2. $\cos 330°$

3. $\tan \dfrac{5\pi}{4}$

4. $\sec 570°$

5. $\csc \dfrac{11\pi}{3}$

6. $\cot(-300°)$

7. $\cos\left(-\dfrac{5\pi}{6}\right)$

8. $\sin\left[\cos^{-1}\left(-\dfrac{\sqrt{3}}{2}\right)\right]$

9. $\cos\left[\sin^{-1}\left(-\dfrac{1}{2}\right)\right]$

10. $\cos[\tan^{-1}(-\sqrt{3})]$

11. $\sin\left(\arccos\left(-\dfrac{3}{5}\right)\right)$

12. $\tan\left[\arcsin\left(-\dfrac{4}{5}\right)\right]$

13. $\sin 75°$

14. $\cos 22.5°$

15. $\tan\left[\cos^{-1}\left(-\dfrac{3}{5}\right) + \sin^{-1}\left(-\dfrac{12}{13}\right)\right]$

16. $\cos\left[\sin^{-1}\left(-\dfrac{5}{13}\right) - \tan^{-1}\left(\dfrac{3}{4}\right)\right]$

17. Find $\sec \theta$ if $\sin \theta = -\dfrac{7}{25}$ and θ is a third-quadrant angle.

18. Find $\csc \theta$ if the terminal side of θ lies in the second quadrant on the line $y = -\dfrac{1}{2}x$.

For Problems 19–26, solve each of the equations. If the variable is θ, find all solutions such that $0° \le \theta < 360°$. If the variable is x, find all solutions such that $0 \le x < 2\pi$. Do not use a calculator or a table.

19. $2 \sin^2 \theta + 7 \sin \theta - 4 = 0$

20. $\cos x \tan x - \cos x + 2 \tan x - 2 = 0$

21. $2 \cos^2 x + \sin x - 2 = 0$

22. $\tan \theta + 1 = \sec \theta$

23. $\cos 2x + \cos x = 0$

24. $\cos \dfrac{x}{2} + \cos x = 0$

25. $\tan 2\theta - \sqrt{3} = 0$

26. $\sin \dfrac{\theta}{2} + \cos \theta = 1$

27. Solve $12 \sin^2 \theta + \sin \theta - 6 = 0$, where $0° \le \theta < 360°$. Express solutions to the nearest tenth of a degree.

28. Solve $\cos^2 x + 3 \cos x - 3 = 0$, where $0 \le x < 2\pi$. Express solutions to the nearest hundredth of a radian.

29. From a point 65 feet from the base of a building, the angle of elevation to the top of the building is $51°$. Find the height of the building to the nearest foot.

30. One leg of a right triangle is 5 centimeters long and the hypotenuse is 9 centimeters long. Find the measure, to the nearest tenth of a degree, of the angle opposite the 5-foot leg.

31. The lengths of the three sides of a triangle are 13 feet, 17 feet, and 25 feet. Find, to the nearest tenth of a degree, the measure of the angle opposite the longest side. Also find the area of the triangle to the nearest square foot.

32. In $\triangle ABC$, $B = 67°$, $C = 53°$, and $b = 23$ meters. Find a to the nearest tenth of a meter. Also find the area of the triangle to the nearest square meter.

33. In $\triangle ABC$, $B = 73°$, $c = 31$ centimeters, and $a = 38$ centimeters. Find b to the nearest tenth of a centimeter. Also find the area of the triangle to the nearest square centimeter.

34. Two people standing 35 feet apart are in line with the base of a tower. The angle of elevation to the top of the tower from one person is 47° and from the other person is 27°. Find the height of the tower to the nearest foot.

35. A plane flies 265 miles due east after take-off, then adjusts its course 25° southward and flies another 450 miles. How far is it from its point of departure? Express the answer to the nearest mile.

36. A car weighing 3200 pounds is parked on a ramp that makes a 25° angle with the horizontal. How much force must be applied to keep the car from rolling down the ramp? Express the answer to the nearest pound.

37. Suppose we are given $A = 38°$, $c = 32$ inches, and $a = 17$ inches. How many triangles exist that satisfy these conditions?

38. Find, to the nearest tenth of a centimeter, the length of the arc intercepted by a central angle of 210° if a radius of the circle is 12.3 centimeters long.

39. Find the absolute value of the complex number $6 - 2i$.

40. Express the complex number $3 - 3i\sqrt{3}$ in trigonometric form where $0 \le \theta < 2\pi$.

41. Change the complex number $12(\cos 225° + i \sin 225°)$ to $a + bi$ form.

42. Find the indicated power $(1 - i)^6$ and express the result in $a + bi$ form.

43. Find the four fourth roots of $-8 - 8\sqrt{3}\,i$.

44. Find the period, amplitude, and phase shift for $f(x) = -2 \sin(3x - 2\pi)$.

45. Find the period, amplitude, and phase shift for $f(x) = -\cos(\pi x + \pi)$.

46. Find the period and phase shift for $f(x) = 3 \tan\left(2x + \dfrac{\pi}{2}\right)$.

For Problems 47–53 graph each function in the indicated interval.

47. $f(x) = -2 - \sin x, \quad 0 \le x \le 2\pi$

48. $f(x) = -\cos 2x, \quad 0 \le x \le 2\pi$

49. $f(x) = 2 \sin\left(x + \dfrac{\pi}{2}\right), \quad -\dfrac{\pi}{2} \le x \le \dfrac{3\pi}{2}$

50. $f(x) = \dfrac{1}{2}\cos\left(2x - \dfrac{\pi}{2}\right), \quad \dfrac{\pi}{4} \le x \le \dfrac{9\pi}{4}$

51. $f(x) = \tan\left(x + \dfrac{\pi}{4}\right), \quad -\dfrac{3\pi}{4} \le x \le \dfrac{\pi}{4}$

52. $f(x) = 1 + \csc 2x, \quad 0 \le x \le \pi$

53. $f(x) = -\tan\left(x - \dfrac{\pi}{2}\right), \quad 0 \le x \le \pi$

54. Graph the function $f(x) = -\sin^{-1}x$.

For Problems 55–60, verify each of the identities.

55. $\sin x \tan x = \sec x - \cos x$

56. $\dfrac{\tan x}{\sec x - 1} = \dfrac{\sec x + 1}{\tan x}$

57. $\tan^4 x - \sec^4 x = 1 - 2\sec^2 x$

58. $\tan(x + \pi) = \tan x$

59. $\sin 3x = -4\sin^3 x + 3\sin x$

60. $\dfrac{\sin 2x}{\sin x} - \dfrac{\cos 2x}{\cos x} = \sec x$

TOPICS IN ANALYTIC GEOMETRY

S uppose that you paint a dot on the tire of a bicycle wheel that has a radius of 15 inches. If the wheel rolls along a flat surface, can you mentally picture the path of the moving dot? (Turn to page 533 to see if your mental image of the path resembles Figure 8.10.) Using the rectangular coordinate system, the path of the moving dot can be represented by the two equations $x = 15t - 15 \sin t$ and $y = 15 - 15 \cos t$. These two equations are called **parametric equations** and the third variable t in this problem represents the measure (in radians) of the angle formed by a radius perpendicular to the x-axis and a radius drawn to a location of the painted dot.

In this chapter—in addition to introducing parametric equations—we will use an algebraic approach to continue our study of vectors. You will have the opportunity to make some more connections between algebra and geometry. Furthermore, in this chapter, we will introduce another coordinate system (the polar coordinate system) which will allow you to make even more connections between algebra, geometry, and trigonometry. Finally, we will extend the rectangular coordinate system to 3-space.

8

The path of a dot on the tire of a bicycle wheel that has a radius of 15 inches can be represented by the parametric equations $x = 15t - 15 \sin t$ and $y = 15 - 15 \cos t$.

521

8.1 VECTORS AS ORDERED PAIRS OF REAL NUMBERS

We can enhance the study of vectors by introducing a rectangular coordinate system. To each vector **u** that has its initial point at the origin of a rectangular coordinate system, we can assign an ordered pair of real numbers (u_1, u_2) to its terminal point, as indicated in Figure 8.1. Likewise, to each ordered pair of real numbers (u_1, u_2), we can associate a vector that has its initial point at the origin and its terminal point at (u_1, u_2). Thus, we obtain a one-to-one correspondence between vectors and ordered pairs of real numbers. This allows us to regard a vector in a plane as an ordered pair of real numbers.

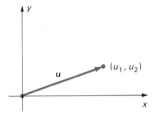

FIGURE 8.1

We will use the symbol $\langle u_1, u_2 \rangle$ for an ordered pair of real numbers that represents a vector **u**. Thus, we can write $\mathbf{u} = \langle u_1, u_2 \rangle$ and the numbers u_1 and u_2 are called the **components** of the vector. Two vectors $\mathbf{u} = \langle u_1, u_2 \rangle$ and $\mathbf{v} = \langle v_1, v_2 \rangle$ are equal if and only if $u_1 = v_1$ and $u_2 = v_2$. It should also be evident from Figure 8.1 and the distance formula that the magnitude $\|\mathbf{u}\|$ of the vector $\mathbf{u} = \langle u_1, u_2 \rangle$ is given by

$$\|\mathbf{u}\| = \sqrt{(u_1)^2 + (u_2)^2}.$$

EXAMPLE 1

Sketch the vector $\mathbf{u} = \langle -2, 4 \rangle$ and find its magnitude.

Solution

The initial point of **u** is at the origin and the terminal point is at $(-2, 4)$ as shown in Figure 8.2. The magnitude of **u** is

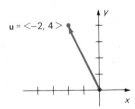

FIGURE 8.2

$$\|\mathbf{u}\| = \sqrt{(-2)^2 + 4^2}$$
$$= \sqrt{20}$$
$$= 2\sqrt{5}.$$

One advantage of considering vectors as ordered pairs becomes evident immediately. The basic operations of vector addition and multiplication by scalars are easy to define and perform in terms of components. If $\mathbf{u} = \langle u_1, u_2 \rangle$ and $\mathbf{v} = \langle v_1, v_2 \rangle$ and k is any scalar (real number), then

$$\mathbf{u} + \mathbf{v} = \langle u_1 + v_1, u_2 + v_2 \rangle \qquad \text{Vector addition}$$
$$k\mathbf{u} = \langle ku_1, ku_2 \rangle. \qquad \text{Scalar multiplication}$$

We use Figure 8.3 to show that these definitions for vector addition and scalar multiplication are consistent with those given in Section 7.5. We will leave the details of this argument for you to complete in the next problem set.

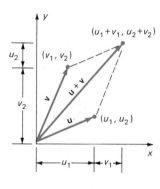 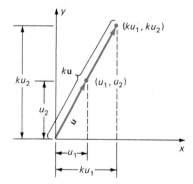

FIGURE   8.3

Since $\mathbf{u} - \mathbf{v} = \mathbf{u} + (-1)\mathbf{v}$, vector subtraction can be defined as follows.

$$\mathbf{u} - \mathbf{v} = \langle u_1 - v_1, u_2 - v_2 \rangle$$

EXAMPLE 2

If $\mathbf{u} = \langle 3, 5 \rangle$ and $\mathbf{v} = \langle -1, -4 \rangle$, determine

a. $\mathbf{u} + \mathbf{v}$ **b.** $\mathbf{u} - \mathbf{v}$ **c.** $-4\mathbf{u}$ **d.** $2\mathbf{v} - 3\mathbf{u}$.

Solution

a. $\mathbf{u} + \mathbf{v} = \langle 3, 5 \rangle + \langle -1, -4 \rangle = \langle 2, 1 \rangle$

b. $\mathbf{u} - \mathbf{v} = \langle 3, 5 \rangle - \langle -1, -4 \rangle = \langle 4, 9 \rangle$

c. $-4\mathbf{u} = (-4)\langle 3, 5 \rangle = \langle -12, -20 \rangle$

d. $2\mathbf{v} - 3\mathbf{u} = (2)\langle -1, -4 \rangle - (3)\langle 3, 5 \rangle$

$$= \langle -2, -8 \rangle - \langle 9, 15 \rangle = \langle -11, -23 \rangle$$

Sometimes a vector may be positioned so that its initial point is not at the origin. If the coordinates of the initial and terminal points of a vector are known, then we can determine a vector that has its initial point at the origin and has the same magnitude and same direction as the given vector. For example, in Figure 8.4 consider the vector that has an initial point at (4, 1) and a terminal point at (2, 4). By subtracting the coordinates of the initial point from the coordinates of the terminal point we obtain $(2 - 4, 4 - 1) = (-2, 3)$. The vector $\langle -2, 3 \rangle$ in Figure 8.4 has the same magnitude and direction as the given vector.

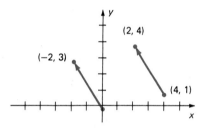

F I G U R E   8 . 4

By defining vectors as ordered pairs of real numbers, some of the basic properties of vector addition and scalar multiplication can be easily verified using the properties of real numbers. For example, to verify that vector addition is a commutative operation, we can reason as follows.

$$\mathbf{u} + \mathbf{v} = \langle u_1, u_2 \rangle + \langle v_1, v_2 \rangle$$

$$= \langle u_1 + v_1, u_2 + v_2 \rangle$$

$$= \langle v_1 + u_1, v_2 + u_2 \rangle$$

$$= \langle v_1, v_2 \rangle + \langle u_1, u_2 \rangle$$

$$= \mathbf{v} + \mathbf{u}$$

For any vectors $\mathbf{u}$, $\mathbf{v}$, and $\mathbf{w}$ and any scalars k and l, the following properties hold.

1. $\mathbf{u} + \mathbf{v} = \mathbf{v} + \mathbf{u}$
2. $(\mathbf{u} + \mathbf{v}) + \mathbf{w} = \mathbf{u} + (\mathbf{v} + \mathbf{w})$
3. $\mathbf{u} + \mathbf{0} = \mathbf{0} + \mathbf{u} = \mathbf{u}$
4. $\mathbf{u} + (-\mathbf{u}) = \mathbf{0}$
5. $k(l\mathbf{u}) = (kl)\mathbf{u}$
6. $k(\mathbf{u} + \mathbf{v}) = k\mathbf{u} + k\mathbf{v}$

7. $(k + l)\mathbf{u} = k\mathbf{u} + l\mathbf{u}$

8. $1(\mathbf{u}) = \mathbf{u}$

Dot Product

To motivate a definition for another operation involving vectors, consider two vectors $\mathbf{u} = \langle u_1, u_2 \rangle$, $\mathbf{v} = \langle v_1, v_2 \rangle$, and the difference vector

$$\mathbf{u} - \mathbf{v} = \langle u_1 - v_1, u_2 - v_2 \rangle$$

as shown in Figure 8.5. Let θ be the smallest positive angle between $\mathbf{u}$ and $\mathbf{v}$. Apply the law of cosines to obtain

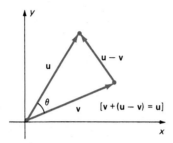

F I G U R E 8 . 5

$$(\|\mathbf{u} - \mathbf{v}\|)^2 = (\|\mathbf{u}\|)^2 + (\|\mathbf{v}\|)^2 - 2\|\mathbf{u}\|\,\|\mathbf{v}\| \cos \theta$$

$$(u_1 - v_1)^2 + (u_2 - v_2)^2 = (u_1)^2 + (u_2)^2 + (v_1)^2 + (v_2)^2 - 2\|\mathbf{u}\|\,\|\mathbf{v}\| \cos \theta$$

$$(u_1)^2 - 2u_1v_1 + (v_1)^2 + (u_2)^2 - 2u_2v_2 + (v_2)^2 =$$
$$(u_1)^2 + (u_2)^2 + (v_1)^2 + (v_2)^2 - 2\|\mathbf{u}\|\,\|\mathbf{v}\| \cos \theta$$

$$-2u_1v_1 - 2u_2v_2 = -2\|\mathbf{u}\|\,\|\mathbf{v}\| \cos \theta$$

$$u_1v_1 + u_2v_2 = \|\mathbf{u}\|\,\|\mathbf{v}\| \cos \theta.$$

Now let's define an operation, called the **dot product**, on two vectors $\mathbf{u}$ and $\mathbf{v}$ as follows.

$$\mathbf{u} \cdot \mathbf{v} = u_1v_1 + u_2v_2 = \|\mathbf{u}\|\,\|\mathbf{v}\| \cos \theta$$

E X A M P L E 3

Find the dot product of $\langle -4, -2 \rangle$ and $\langle 3, 7 \rangle$.

Solution

Using $\mathbf{u} \cdot \mathbf{v} = u_1v_1 + u_2v_2$, we obtain

$$\langle -4, -2 \rangle \cdot \langle 3, 7 \rangle = -4(3) + (-2)(7)$$

$$= -12 - 14 = -26.$$

Note that the dot product of two vectors is a real number (scalar), not another vector. Furthermore, it should be evident that the expression $u_1v_1 + u_2v_2$ provides a convenient way of computing the dot product when the components of the two vectors are known. However, the equation $\mathbf{u} \cdot \mathbf{v} = \|\mathbf{u}\| \|\mathbf{v}\| \cos \theta$ gives a geometric interpretation to the operation of dot product. Solving for $\cos \theta$, we obtain

$$\cos \theta = \frac{\mathbf{u} \cdot \mathbf{v}}{\|\mathbf{u}\| \|\mathbf{v}\|}.$$

In other words, the cosine of the angle of intersection of two vectors is the quotient of the dot product and the product of the magnitudes of the two vectors. Let's consider some examples.

EXAMPLE 4

Find the angle of intersection of the two vectors $\langle -3, 2 \rangle$ and $\langle 2, 3 \rangle$.

Solution

$$\cos \theta = \frac{(-3)(2) + 2(3)}{\sqrt{(-3)^2 + 2^2} \sqrt{2^2 + 3^2}} = \frac{0}{\sqrt{13}\sqrt{13}} = 0$$

Therefore, $\theta = 90°$, and the vectors are perpendicular.

Example 4 illustrates that the dot product is very convenient for determining perpendicular vectors. **In general, two nonzero vectors are perpendicular if and only if their dot product is zero.**

EXAMPLE 5

Find the angle of intersection of the two vectors $\langle -3, 1 \rangle$ and $\langle 5, 2 \rangle$.

Solution

$$\cos \theta = \frac{-3(5) + 1(2)}{\sqrt{(-3)^2 + 1^2} \sqrt{5^2 + 2^2}} = \frac{-13}{\sqrt{10}\sqrt{29}} = -0.7634$$

Therefore,

$$\theta = 139.8°, \quad \text{to the nearest tenth of a degree.}$$

PROBLEM SET 8.1

In Problems 1–8, sketch the vector and find its magnitude.

1. $\langle 3, 4 \rangle$ **2.** $\langle -4, 3 \rangle$ **5.** $\langle 6, -2 \rangle$ **6.** $\langle -2, -4 \rangle$

3. $\langle -1, -3 \rangle$ **4.** $\langle 4, -1 \rangle$ **7.** $\langle -6, 4 \rangle$ **8.** $\langle 2, 6 \rangle$

In Problems 9–16, find $\mathbf{u} + \mathbf{v}$, $\mathbf{u} - \mathbf{v}$, $3\mathbf{u} + 4\mathbf{v}$, and $2\mathbf{u} - 5\mathbf{v}$.

9. $\mathbf{u} = \langle 1, 2 \rangle$, $\mathbf{v} = \langle 3, 5 \rangle$

10. $\mathbf{u} = \langle 5, 6 \rangle$, $\mathbf{v} = \langle 4, -2 \rangle$

11. $\mathbf{u} = \langle -4, -3 \rangle$, $\mathbf{v} = \langle -1, 6 \rangle$

12. $\mathbf{u} = \langle 0, -4 \rangle$, $\mathbf{v} = \langle -3, -7 \rangle$

13. $\mathbf{u} = \langle 7, -1 \rangle$, $\mathbf{v} = \langle -4, 0 \rangle$

14. $\mathbf{u} = \langle -2, 8 \rangle$, $\mathbf{v} = \langle -1, -6 \rangle$

15. $\mathbf{u} = \langle -3, -6 \rangle$, $\mathbf{v} = \langle -2, -4 \rangle$

16. $\mathbf{u} = \langle 4, -4 \rangle$, $\mathbf{v} = \langle -4, 4 \rangle$

In Problems 17–24, (a) sketch the vector that has its initial point at P and its terminal point at Q, (b) determine a vector $\mathbf{u}$ that has its initial point at the origin and has the same magnitude and direction as $\overrightarrow{PQ}$, and (c) sketch the vector $\mathbf{u}$.

17. $P(2, 3)$ and $Q(4, 9)$

18. $P(4, 9)$ and $Q(2, 3)$

19. $P(-1, 3)$ and $Q(-5, 6)$

20. $P(-2, 4)$ and $Q(1, -3)$

21. $P(-1, -5)$ and $Q(-1, 4)$

22. $P(3, -2)$ and $Q(-4, -1)$

23. $P(2, -1)$ and $Q(5, -7)$

24. $P(-3, -4)$ and $Q(1, 2)$

In Problems 25–30, find the dot product of the two given vectors.

25. $\langle 4, 3 \rangle$ and $\langle -2, 6 \rangle$

26. $\langle -1, 2 \rangle$ and $\langle 3, -4 \rangle$

27. $\langle -4, -2 \rangle$ and $\langle -1, -6 \rangle$

28. $\langle 3, -4 \rangle$ and $\langle 5, 4 \rangle$

29. $\langle -2, 7 \rangle$ and $\langle -6, 1 \rangle$

30. $\langle 0, 4 \rangle$ and $\langle 3, -6 \rangle$

In Problems 31–36, determine if the two vectors are perpendicular.

31. $\langle -1, -3 \rangle$ and $\langle 3, -1 \rangle$

32. $\langle 4, 3 \rangle$ and $\langle 3, -4 \rangle$

33. $\langle 4, 5 \rangle$ and $\langle -4, 5 \rangle$

34. $\langle -2, 7 \rangle$ and $\langle -2, -7 \rangle$

35. $\langle -2, -6 \rangle$ and $\langle 6, -2 \rangle$

36. $\langle 5, -4 \rangle$ and $\langle 2, 5 \rangle$

In Problems 37–46, find the angle of intersection of the two vectors. Express your answers to the nearest tenth of a degree.

37. $\langle 2, 5 \rangle$ and $\langle 6, 2 \rangle$

38. $\langle 4, 4 \rangle$ and $\langle 5, 2 \rangle$

39. $\langle -5, 2 \rangle$ and $\langle -6, -1 \rangle$

40. $\langle -2, -7 \rangle$ and $\langle 2, -1 \rangle$

41. $\langle -5, 1 \rangle$ and $\langle 5, 1 \rangle$

42. $\langle -2, 6 \rangle$ and $\langle -2, -6 \rangle$

43. $\langle -1, \sqrt{3} \rangle$ and $\langle 3, 3 \rangle$

44. $\langle \sqrt{3}, 1 \rangle$ and $\langle \sqrt{3}, -1 \rangle$

45. $\langle -4, -1 \rangle$ and $\langle 3, -6 \rangle$

46. $\langle -3, 5 \rangle$ and $\langle 7, -2 \rangle$

47. Show that $k(\mathbf{u} + \mathbf{v}) = k\mathbf{u} + k\mathbf{v}$ for $k = 3$, $\mathbf{u} = \langle 4, 6 \rangle$, and $\mathbf{v} = \langle -3, 9 \rangle$.

48. Show that $(k + l)\mathbf{u} = k\mathbf{u} + l\mathbf{u}$ for $k = -2$, $l = 5$, and $\mathbf{u} = \langle -3, -6 \rangle$.

49. Show that $\mathbf{u} \cdot (\mathbf{v} + \mathbf{w}) = \mathbf{u} \cdot \mathbf{v} + \mathbf{u} \cdot \mathbf{w}$ for $\mathbf{u} = \langle 3, -2 \rangle$, $\mathbf{v} = \langle -4, 5 \rangle$, and $\mathbf{w} = \langle -1, -4 \rangle$.

50. Show that $k(\mathbf{u} \cdot \mathbf{v}) = (k\mathbf{u}) \cdot \mathbf{v} = \mathbf{u} \cdot (k\mathbf{v})$ for $k = 5$, $\mathbf{u} = \langle 2, 7 \rangle$, and $\mathbf{v} = \langle -3, -5 \rangle$.

THOUGHTS into WORDS

51. How would you explain the concept of a vector to an elementary geometry student?

52. Is the concept of *components of a vector* used in this section consistent with the way we used it in Section 7.5? Explain your answer.

53. Prove Properties (2) through (8) on pages 524–525.

54. Prove that $\mathbf{u} \cdot \mathbf{v} = \mathbf{v} \cdot \mathbf{u}$.

55. Prove that $\mathbf{u} \cdot (\mathbf{v} + \mathbf{w}) = \mathbf{u} \cdot \mathbf{v} + \mathbf{u} \cdot \mathbf{w}$.

56. Using Figure 8.3, verify that the definitions for vector addition and scalar multiplication given in this section are consistent with those given in Section 7.5.

8.2   PARAMETRIC EQUATIONS

Sometimes when using the rectangular coordinate system, the xy-coordinates of points on a curve are difficult to specify if we use only one equation involving x and y. It may be easier to express both x and y in terms of a third variable. For example, the x- and y-coordinates may be related to a time element t; so both x and y can be expressed as functions of t. In general, the equations

$$x = f(t) \qquad \text{and} \qquad y = g(t)$$

are called **parametric equations** with a parameter t.

To graph a curve represented by parametric equations, we can allow the parameter to vary within the boundaries set by the problem and determine a set of ordered pairs (x, y). Consider the following example.

EXAMPLE 1

Graph the curve represented by the parametric equations $x = t - 1$ and $y = t^2 - 6t + 8$, where t is any real number between 0 and 5, inclusive.

Solution

Let's set up a table of values that allows t to vary from 0 to 5, inclusive. Plot the points associated with the ordered pairs (x, y) and connect them with a smooth curve to produce Figure 8.6.

t	x	y
0	−1	8
1	0	3
2	1	0
3	2	−1
4	3	0
5	4	3

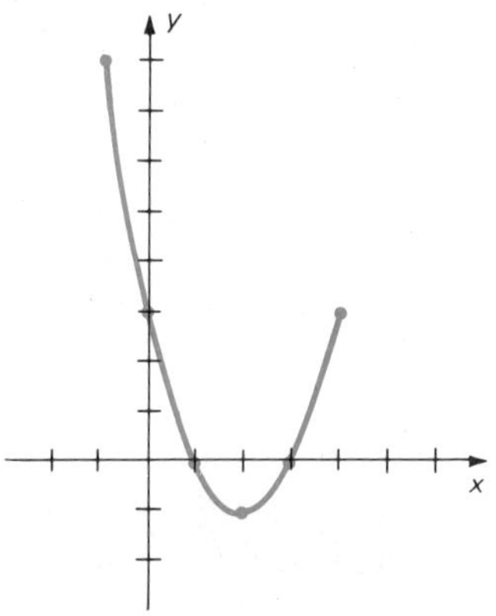

FIGURE   8.6

The curve in Figure 8.6 appears to be a portion of a parabola. We can verify that this is the case by **eliminating the parameter** t as follows. Solve the equation $x = t - 1$ for t.

$$x = t - 1$$
$$x + 1 = t$$

Now substitute $x + 1$ for t in the equation $y = t^2 - 6t + 8$.

$$y = t^2 - 6t + 8$$
$$= (x + 1)^2 - 6(x + 1) + 8$$
$$= x^2 + 2x + 1 - 6x - 6 + 8$$
$$= x^2 - 4x + 3$$

From our previous experiences, we know that $y = x^2 - 4x + 3$ does indeed represent a parabola. So the curve in Figure 8.6 is a portion of a parabola.

E X A M P L E   2

Graph the curve represented by the parametric equations $x = 4 \cos t$ and $y = 2 \sin t$, where $0 \le t \le 2\pi$.

Solution

Again, let's set up a table of values that allows the parameter t to vary. We will choose special values for t to avoid using a calculator or a table of trigonometric values. Plotting the points associated with the ordered pairs (x, y) and connecting them with a smooth curve produces Figure 8.7.

t	x	y
0	4	0
$\frac{\pi}{6}$	$2\sqrt{3}$	1
$\frac{\pi}{3}$	2	$\sqrt{3}$
$\frac{\pi}{2}$	0	2
$\frac{2\pi}{3}$	-2	$\sqrt{3}$
$\frac{5\pi}{6}$	$-2\sqrt{3}$	1
π	-4	0
$\frac{7\pi}{6}$	$-2\sqrt{3}$	-1
$\frac{4\pi}{3}$	-2	$-\sqrt{3}$
$\frac{3\pi}{2}$	0	-2
$\frac{5\pi}{3}$	2	$-\sqrt{3}$
$\frac{11\pi}{6}$	$2\sqrt{3}$	-1
2π	4	0

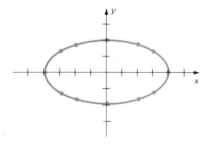

F I G U R E   8 . 7

Figure 8.7 certainly appears to be an ellipse. Again, by eliminating the parameter t, we can verify that this is true. Let's solve the first equation for $\cos t$ and the second equation for $\sin t$.

$$\cos t = \frac{x}{4} \quad \text{and} \quad \sin t = \frac{y}{2}$$

Squaring both sides of each equation produces

$$\cos^2 t = \frac{x^2}{16} \quad \text{and} \quad \sin^2 t = \frac{y^2}{4}.$$

Now adding these two equations produces

$$\cos^2 t + \sin^2 t = \frac{x^2}{16} + \frac{y^2}{4}.$$

Since $\sin^2 t + \cos^2 t = 1$, we have

$$\frac{x^2}{16} + \frac{y^2}{4} = 1,$$

which is the equation of an ellipse with x-intercepts of ± 4 and y-intercepts of ± 2.

How are parametric equations formed? This is a logical question with several answers. First, we should realize that it is sometimes possible to artificially create parametric equations. For example, consider the equation $y = x^2 - x + 5$. Suppose that we arbitrarily let $x = t + 2$, where t is any real number. Then by substituting $t + 2$ for x in the given equation, we obtain $y = t^2 + 3t + 7$. So we can use the pair of equations $x = t + 2$ and $y = t^2 + 3t + 7$ as parametric equations with a parameter t. It should be evident from this approach that the parametric equations for a particular curve are not unique. We arbitrarily chose the relationship between x and t, which in turn determined the relationship between y and t.

The parametric equations may also be determined by a mathematical analysis of a problem. For example, suppose that in Figure 8.8 we want to use a vector

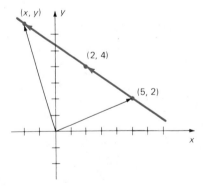

F I G U R E   8 . 8

approach to determine parametric equations for the line that contains the points $(2, 4)$ and $(5, 2)$. The vector from $(5, 2)$ to any point (x, y) is a scalar multiple of the vector from $(5, 2)$ to $(2, 4)$. Therefore, since the vector $\langle x, y \rangle$ is the sum of the vector $\langle 5, 2 \rangle$ and a scalar multiple of $\langle 2 - 5, 4 - 2 \rangle = \langle -3, 2 \rangle$, we can write

$$\langle x, y \rangle = \langle 5, 2 \rangle + k\langle -3, 2 \rangle.$$

The right side can be simplified as follows.

$$\langle x, y \rangle = \langle 5, 2 \rangle + \langle -3k, 2k \rangle = \langle 5 - 3k, 2 + 2k \rangle$$

Equating components we obtain

$$x = 5 - 3k \quad \text{and} \quad y = 2 + 2k.$$

Therefore, the equations $x = 5 - 3k$ and $y = 2 + 2k$, where k is any real number, are a pair of parametric equations for the indicated line. Eliminating the parameter k produces $2x + 3y = 16$, which is the equation of the line in terms of x and y.

Parametric equations may also be the result of the combined efforts of a law of physics and a mathematical analysis of a problem. For example, it can be shown using Newton's laws of motion and some advanced mathematics that the path of a projectile is given by the following equations. (Air resistance is being neglected.)

$$x = (v_0 \cos \alpha)t$$
$$y = (v_0 \sin \alpha)t - 16t^2$$

The constant v_0 is the initial speed of the projectile and α is the angle indicating the direction of flight with respect to a horizontal line, as indicated in Figure 8.9. The parameter t represents time in seconds, and x and y are expressed in feet. Let's consider an example using these general parametric equations.

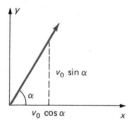

F I G U R E   8 . 9

E X A M P L E 3

Firing a projectile   A projectile is fired at an initial velocity of 64 feet per second at an angle of $60°$ with the horizontal.

a. Find the parametric equations of the path of the projectile.

b. Find the total time of the flight of the projectile.

c. Find the range, that is, the value of x where the projectile strikes the ground.

d. Determine an equation in terms of x and y that describes the path of the projectile.

e. Find the greatest height reached by the projectile.

Solution

a. We can substitute 64 for v_0, $\frac{1}{2}$ for $\cos \alpha$, and $\frac{\sqrt{3}}{2}$ for $\sin \alpha$ in the general parametric equations.

$$x = 64\left(\tfrac{1}{2}\right)t = 32t$$
$$y = 64\left(\tfrac{\sqrt{3}}{2}\right)t - 16t^2 = 32\sqrt{3}t - 16t^2$$

b. To find the total time of the flight we can find the values of t for which $y = 0$.

$$32\sqrt{3}t - 16t^2 = 0$$
$$16t(2\sqrt{3} - t) = 0$$

$$16t = 0 \quad \text{or} \quad 2\sqrt{3} - t = 0$$
$$t = 0 \quad \text{or} \quad t = 2\sqrt{3}$$

Therefore, $y = 0$ when $t = 0$ (time of firing) and when $t = 2\sqrt{3}$ (time of landing). The time of the flight is $2\sqrt{3}$ seconds.

c. The range is given by

$$x = 32t = 32(2\sqrt{3}) = 64\sqrt{3}.$$

Thus, the range is $64\sqrt{3}$ feet.

d. Solving $x = 32t$ for t produces $t = x/32$. Now we can substitute $x/32$ for t in $y = 32\sqrt{3}t - 16t^2$.

$$y = 32\sqrt{3}\left(\frac{x}{32}\right) - 16\left(\frac{x}{32}\right)^2$$

$$y = \sqrt{3}x - \frac{x^2}{64}$$

Therefore, the equation

$$y = -\frac{1}{64}x^2 + \sqrt{3}x,$$

which is a parabola, describes the path of the projectile.

e. The maximum height is reached at one-half of the flight time, that is, when $t = \frac{1}{2}(2\sqrt{3}) = \sqrt{3}$. Therefore, the maximum height the projectile reaches is

$$y = 32\sqrt{3}(\sqrt{3}) - 16(\sqrt{3})^2 = 96 - 48 = 48 \text{ feet.}$$

As a final example illustrating the origin of some parametric equations, let's consider the curve traced by a fixed point P on the circumference of a circle as the circle rolls along a line in a plane. In Figure 8.10 a circle of radius r is shown rolling along the x-axis. Assume P is initially at the origin and let C, A, and B be as indicated in the figure, with t denoting the radian measure of $\angle PCB$. Arc PB is the same length as $\overline{OB}$, namely, rt. Furthermore, $PA = r \sin t$ and $AC = r \cos t$. Therefore, the following parametric equations can be formed.

$$x = OB - PA = rt - r \sin t$$

$$y = BC - CA = r - r \cos t$$

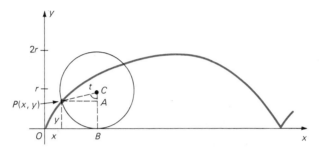

FIGURE 8.10

Even though this development using Figure 8.10 restricts t so that $0 \le t \le \pi/2$, it can be shown that the derived parametric equations generate a complete **cycloid** of period $2\pi r$ by allowing t to be any real number.

E X A M P L E 4

Use a graphing utility to graph the cycloid determined by the parametric equations $x = t - \sin t$ and $y = 1 - \cos t$. (These are the parametric equations of a cycloid with $r = 1$.)

Solution

First, we need to put our graphing utility in the parametric mode. (You may need to consult your user's manual for specific instructions.) Let's set the range values so that $0 \le t \le 4\pi$, $0 \le x \le 4\pi$, and $-1 \le y \le 5$. The graph of two periods of the cycloid determined by the parametric equations $x = t - \sin t$ and $y = 1 - \cos t$ is shown in Figure 8.11.

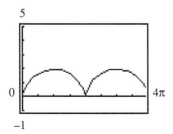

FIGURE 8.11

The cycloid is a good example of a curve that would be very difficult to represent without the use of parametric equations. It is also a curve with many interesting properties. One of these properties is illustrated in Figure 8.12. A bead, sliding without friction on a wire from point A to a point B lower than A, but not on the same vertical line as A, will arrive at B in a shorter time traveling along an inverted cycloid than along any other path.

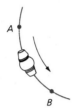

FIGURE 8.12

Many variations of the cycloid exist. For example, if a circle is rolled along a line, the path of a fixed point on a radius is a type of cycloid that does not intersect the horizontal line (Figure 8.13).

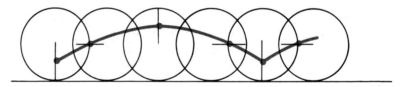

FIGURE 8.13

A **hypocycloid** is formed by tracing the path of a fixed point on the circumference of a circle as it rolls around the inside of the circumference of a larger circle. If the smaller circle has a radius that is one-fourth of the radius of the larger circle, then the hypocycloid is formed as in Figure 8.14. An **epicycloid** is formed by tracing the path of a fixed point on a circle as it rolls around the outside of another circle. If the circle that rolls around the outside has a radius of one-third the length of the radius of the other circle, then the epicycloid is formed as in Figure 8.15.

FIGURE 8.14

FIGURE 8.15

PROBLEM SET 8.2

For Problems 1–22, (a) graph the curve represented by the parametric equations, and (b) eliminate the parameter to form an equation in terms of x and y.

1. $x = 2 + 3t, y = 3 - 2t; \quad -\infty < t < \infty.$

2. $x = -1 - 4t, y = -2 + t; \quad -\infty < t < \infty$

3. $x = t - 2, y = 3t + 1; \quad 0 \le t \le 4$

4. $x = t + 1, y = -2t + 2; \quad -2 \le t \le 3$

5. $x = 2 \cos t, y = 2 \sin t; \quad 0 \le t \le 2\pi$

6. $x = 4 \cos t, y = 4 \sin t; \quad 0 \le t \le 2\pi$

7. $x = \cos t, y = \sin t; \quad 0 \le t \le \pi$

8. $x = \cos t; \quad y = \sin t; \quad -\dfrac{\pi}{2} \le t \le \dfrac{\pi}{2}$

9. $x = t - 1, y = t^2 + 2; \quad -\infty < t < \infty$

10. $x = t + 3, y = t^2 - 2; \quad -\infty < t < \infty$

11. $x = t + 2, y = t^2 + 4; \quad -3 \le t \le 2$

12. $x = t - 1, y = -t^2 + 2; \quad -2 \le t \le 3$

13. $x = 2 \cos t, y = 4 \sin t; \quad 0 \le t \le 2\pi$

14. $x = 2 \cos t, y = 6 \sin t; \quad 0 \le t \le 2\pi$

15. $x = 2 \sec t, y = \tan t; \quad 0 \le t \le 2\pi$

16. $x = 3 \tan t, y = 2 \sec t; \quad 0 \le t \le 2\pi$

17. $x = \sec t, y = \tan t; \quad -\dfrac{\pi}{2} < t < \dfrac{\pi}{2}$

18. $x = 4 \sec t, y = 8 \tan t; \quad -\dfrac{\pi}{2} < t < \dfrac{\pi}{2}$

19. $x = 2t, y = \dfrac{4}{t}; \quad -\infty < t < \infty$

20. $x = \dfrac{-2}{t}, y = 3t; \quad -\infty < t < \infty$

21. $x = e^t, y = e^{-2t}; \quad -\infty < t < \infty$

22. $x = e^t, y = e^{-t}; \quad -\infty < t < \infty$

For Problems 23–28, graph the curve represented by the parametric equations.

23. $x = t^3, y = t^2; \quad -\infty < t < \infty$

24. $x = t^2, y = t^3; \quad -\infty < t < \infty$

25. $x = 2t - 2 \sin t, y = 2 - 2 \cos t; \qquad$ Cycloid
$0 \le t \le 2\pi$

26. $x = 2t - \sin t, y = 2 - \cos t; \qquad$ Curtate cycloid
$0 \le t \le 2\pi$

27. $x = t - 2 \sin t, y = 1 - 2 \cos t; \qquad$ Prolate cycloid
$0 \le t \le 3\pi$

28. $x = 4 \cos^3 t, y = 4 \sin^3 t; \qquad$ Hypocycloid
$0 \le t \le 2\pi$

For Problems 29–32, find parametric equations for the line that contains the two given points. Check your answers by eliminating the parameter.

29. $(-3, 5)$ and $(7, 3)$

30. $(2, -1)$ and $(-1, 7)$

31. $(4, 2)$ and $(-1, -6)$

32. $(5, 6)$ and $(0, 4)$

For Problems 33–36, a projectile is fired with an initial velocity v_0 at an angle α with the horizontal. For each problem, (a) find the parametric equations of the path of the projectile, (b) find the total time of the flight of the projectile, (c) find the range, that is, the value of x where the projectile strikes the ground, (d) determine an equation in terms of x and y that describes the path of the projectile, and (e) find the greatest height reached by the projectile.

33. $v_0 = 48$ feet per second and $\alpha = 60°$

34. $v_0 = 64$ feet per second and $\alpha = 30°$

35. $v_0 = 100$ feet per second and $\alpha = 45°$

36. $v_0 = 500$ feet per second and $\alpha = 45°$

THOUGHTS into WORDS

37. How would you explain the concept of parametric equations to an elementary algebra student?

38. What does it mean to say that the parametric equations for a particular curve are not unique? Give an example.

 GRAPHICS CALCULATOR ACTIVITIES

For Problems 39–46, (a) use your graphics calculator to graph the curve represented by the given parametric equations, (b) eliminate the parameter to form an equation in terms of x and y, and (c) identify the curve.

39. $x = t - 2$, $y = 3t + 1$; $\quad 0 \le t \le 4$

40. $x = t + 1$, $y = -2t + 2$; $\quad -2 \le t \le 3$

41. $x = t + 2$, $y = t^2 + 4$; $\quad -3 \le t \le 2$

42. $x = t - 1$, $y = -t^2 + 2$; $\quad -2 \le t \le 3$

43. $x = 2 \cos t$, $y = 2 \sin t$; $\quad 0 \le t \le 2\pi$

44. $x = 4 \cos t$, $y = 2 \sin t$; $\quad 0 \le t \le 2\pi$

45. $x = 2 \sec t$, $y = \tan t$; $\quad 0 \le t \le 2\pi$

46. $x = e^t$, $y = e^{-2t}$; $\quad -10 \le t \le 10$

For Problems 47–52, use a graphics calculator to graph the curve represented by the parametric equations.

47. $x = t^3$, $y = t^2$, $\quad -10 \le t \le 10$

48. $x = t^2$, $y = t^3$, $\quad -10 \le t \le 10$

49. $x = 2t - 2 \sin t$, $y = 2 - 2 \cos t$, $\qquad$ Cycloid
$\quad 0 \le t \le 4\pi$

50. $x = 2t - \sin t$, $y = 2 - \cos t$, $\qquad$ Curtate cycloid
$\quad 0 \le t \le 4\pi$

51. $x = t - 2 \sin t$, $y = 1 - 2 \cos t$, $\qquad$ Prolate cycloid
$\quad -3 \le t \le 4\pi$

52. $x = 4 \cos^3 t$, $y = 4 \sin^3 t$, $\qquad$ Hypocycloid
$\quad -\pi \le t \le \pi$

For Problems 53–58, first predict the type and location of the curve produced by the given parametric equations, and then use a graphics calculator to check your prediction.

53. $x = t - 2$ and $y = t^2$

54. $x = t + 2$ and $y = t^2$

55. $x = -t$ and $y = t^2 + 2t + 4$

56. $x = t - 3$ and $y = t^2 + 4$

57. $x = t + 3$ and $y = t^3$

58. $x = 2t$ and $y = t^2$

8.3 POLAR COORDINATE SYSTEM

Some problems in analytic geometry, especially those involving motion about a point, are difficult to solve using the rectangular coordinate system. In fact, unwieldy equations such as $x^2 + y^2 - 2x = 2\sqrt{x^2 + y^2}$ are generated from relatively simple motion problems. However, this same equation can be transformed into a much more workable form using the variables r and θ of a plotting system called the **polar coordinate system**.

To set up the polar coordinate system in a plane, we begin with a fixed point O (called the **origin** or **pole**) and a directed half-line (called the **polar axis**) with its endpoint at O (Figure 8.16). The polar axis is usually drawn horizontal and directed to the right. To each point P in the plane we assign the **polar coordinates** (r, θ) as indicated in Figure 8.16. The angle θ has the polar axis as its initial side and the

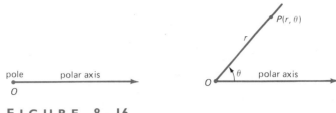

FIGURE   8 . I6

half-line OP as its terminal side. As usual, θ is considered positive if the angle is generated by a counterclockwise rotation of the polar axis and negative if the rotation is clockwise. Either radians or degrees can be used to express the measure of θ. The number r indicates the distance from the pole to the point P. If r is positive, then the distance is measured along the terminal side of θ. If r is negative, then the distance is measured along the half-line from O in the opposite direction of the terminal side of θ. The points associated with the ordered pairs $(5, \pi/3)$, $(-5, \pi/3)$, $(4, -30°)$, and $(-4, -135°)$ are plotted in Figure 8.17.

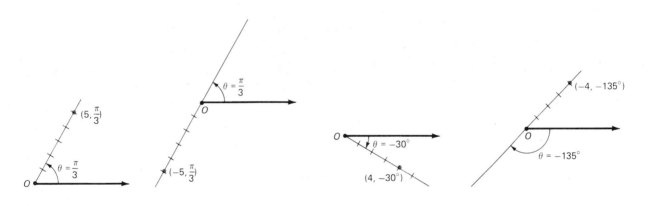

FIGURE   8 . I7

In Figure 8.18 we have a model of polar coordinate paper. Some possible coordinates of point P are $(4, \pi/6)$, $(4, -11\pi/6)$, $(-4, 7\pi/6)$, $(-4, -5\pi/6)$, and $(4, 13\pi/6)$. The concentric circles with O as a common center and the rays emanating from O at intervals corresponding to some special angles facilitate the plotting of points. It should be evident that the polar coordinates of a point are not unique. Note in Figure 8.18 that we have assigned five different ordered pairs to the point P. Actually, every point has infinitely many ordered pairs that can be assigned to it. The pole has polar coordinates $(0, \theta)$ for any angle θ.

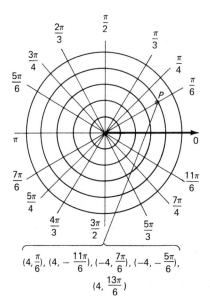

$$\left(4, \frac{\pi}{6}\right), \left(4, -\frac{11\pi}{6}\right), \left(-4, \frac{7\pi}{6}\right), \left(-4, -\frac{5\pi}{6}\right),$$
$$\left(4, \frac{13\pi}{6}\right)$$

FIGURE 8.18

Relationships Between Rectangular and Polar Coordinates

In Figure 8.19 we superimposed an xy-plane on an $r\theta$-plane so that the positive x-axis coincides with the polar axis. The following polar-rectangular relationships can be easily deduced.

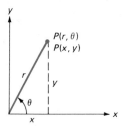

FIGURE 8.19

$$x = r\cos\theta \qquad y = r\sin\theta$$

$$\tan\theta = \frac{y}{x} \qquad r^2 = x^2 + y^2$$

EXAMPLE I

Find the rectangular coordinates of the point P whose polar coordinates are $(4, 210°)$.

Solution

Let's substitute 4 for r and $210°$ for θ in the equations $x = r \cos \theta$ and $y = r \sin \theta$.

$$x = 4 \cos 210° = 4\left(-\frac{\sqrt{3}}{2}\right) = -2\sqrt{3}$$

$$y = 4 \sin 210° = 4\left(-\frac{1}{2}\right) = -2$$

Thus, the rectangular coordinates of point P are $(-2\sqrt{3}, -2)$.

EXAMPLE 2

Suppose that point P has rectangular coordinates $(3, -3)$. Find polar coordinates (r, θ), such that $r > 0$ and $0 \leq \theta < 2\pi$, for point P.

Solution

Since r is to be positive, we can use $r = \sqrt{x^2 + y^2}$.

$$r = \sqrt{3^2 + (-3)^2} = \sqrt{9 + 9} = \sqrt{18} = 3\sqrt{2}$$

Also, we can use the equation $\tan \theta = y/x$.

$$\tan \theta = \frac{-3}{3} = -1$$

From this and the fact that $(3, -3)$ lies in the fourth quadrant, it follows that

$$\theta = \frac{7\pi}{4}.$$

Thus, $(3\sqrt{2}, 7\pi/4)$ are polar coordinates for point P.

> **REMARK** Note in Example 2 we included the restrictions $r > 0$ and $0 \leq \theta < 2\pi$. This is necessary because the polar coordinates of a point are not unique.

The polar-rectangular relationships also provide the basis for changing polar equations to equations in rectangular form and vice versa. The next two examples illustrate this process.

EXAMPLE 3

Change $x^2 + y^2 - 2x = 2\sqrt{x^2 + y^2}$ to polar form.

Solution

Substituting r^2 for $x^2 + y^2$, $r \cos \theta$ for x, and r for $\sqrt{x^2 + y^2}$, the equation $x^2 + y^2 - 2x = 2\sqrt{x^2 + y^2}$ becomes

$$r^2 - 2r \cos \theta = 2r.$$

This equation simplifies to

$$r^2 - 2r \cos \theta - 2r = 0$$

$$r(r - 2 \cos \theta - 2) = 0$$

$$r = 0 \quad \text{or} \quad r - 2 \cos \theta - 2 = 0.$$

The graph of $r = 0$ is the pole and since the pole is also included in the graph of $r - 2 \cos \theta - 2 = 0$ (let $\theta = \pi$), we can discard $r = 0$ and keep only

$$r - 2 \cos \theta - 2 = 0.$$

This could also be written as

$$r = 2 + 2 \cos \theta.$$

Notice in Example 3 that the original complicated equation in rectangular form produced a fairly simple polar equation. Furthermore, in the next section we will see that the polar equation $r = 2 + 2 \cos \theta$ is easy to graph. So in a case like this, changing from rectangular form to polar form can be very beneficial.

E X A M P L E 4

Change $r = \cos \theta + \sin \theta$ to rectangular form.

Solution

Substituting x/r for $\cos \theta$ and y/r for $\sin \theta$, the given equation $r = \cos \theta + \sin \theta$ becomes

$$r = \frac{x}{r} + \frac{y}{r}.$$

Now we can multiply both sides by r. This, in effect, adds $r = 0$ (the pole) to the graph. But the pole is already a part of the graph of $r = \cos \theta + \sin \theta$ (let $\theta = 3\pi/4$), so an equivalent equation

$$r^2 = x + y$$

is produced. Finally, by substituting $x^2 + y^2$ for r^2, we obtain

$$x^2 + y^2 = x + y,$$

which can be written as

$$x^2 + y^2 - x - y = 0.$$

In Example 4, the switch from polar form to rectangular form produced an equation ($x^2 + y^2 - x - y = 0$) that should look familiar to you. Its graph is a circle, and by completing the square we could find its center and the length of a radius. In other words, in this case the switch from polar to rectangular form was beneficial.

Together Examples 3 and 4 illustrate that for some problems the rectangular system is more appropriate; for other problems it may be easier to use the polar coordinate system. Having both systems provides us with more flexibility to solve problems.

Graphing Polar Equations

In Chapter 2 when introducing the rectangular coordinate system, we remarked that there are basically two kinds of problems to solve in analytic geometry, namely, (1) given an algebraic equation, find its geometric graph, and (2) given a set of conditions pertaining to a geometric figure, find its algebraic equation. The polar coordinate system provides another basis for solving those same two kinds of problems. However, in this brief introduction to the polar coordinate system, we will limit our study to problems of type (1), that is, sketching the graph of a given polar equation.

A **polar equation** is an equation involving the variables r and θ. An ordered pair (a, b) is said to be a **solution** of a polar equation if a substituted for r and b substituted for θ produces a true numerical statement. For example $(1, \pi/6)$ is a solution of $r = 2 \sin \theta$ because 1 substituted for r and $\pi/6$ substituted for θ produces the true numerical statement $1 = 2\left(\frac{1}{2}\right)$. The **graph** of a polar equation is the set of all points (in the $r\theta$-plane) that correspond to the set of all solutions of the equation.

EXAMPLE 5

Graph the polar equation $r \cos \theta = 2$.

Solution

Let's change the form of the given equation by solving for r.

$$r \cos \theta = 2$$

$$r = \frac{2}{\cos \theta}, \qquad \cos \theta \neq 0$$

For each value assigned to θ, starting with 0 and using special positive angles, r takes on a corresponding value. (Since $\cos \theta$ cannot equal zero, θ cannot equal $\pi/2$.) The accompanying table contains eight solutions of the equation. Plotting the points associated with the ordered pairs (r, θ) and connecting them produces the line in Figure 8.20.

r	θ
2	0
$\frac{4\sqrt{3}}{3} \approx 2.3$	$\pi/6$
$2\sqrt{2} \approx 2.8$	$\pi/4$
4	$\pi/3$
-4	$2\pi/3$
$-2\sqrt{2} \approx -2.8$	$3\pi/4$
$\frac{-4\sqrt{3}}{3} \approx -2.3$	$5\pi/6$
-2	π

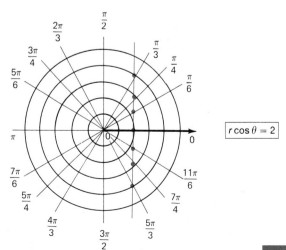

FIGURE 8.20

Notice that the last entry in the table for Example 5, $(-2, \pi)$, determines the same point as the first entry $(2, 0)$. This fact alerted us to the realization that in this case there was no need to allow θ to vary from π to 2π because the same points would be determined again. For example, if $\theta = 7\pi/6$ we get the ordered pair $(-4\sqrt{3}/3, 7\pi/6)$ that determines the same point as $(4\sqrt{3}/3, \pi/6)$. In other words, by paying special attention to the nature of the trigonometric functions, you can often circumvent the need for a large table of values.

EXAMPLE 6

Graph the polar equation $r = 4 \sin \theta$.

Solution

Let's set up a table of values, plot the points associated with the ordered pairs, and draw the graph (Figure 8.21).

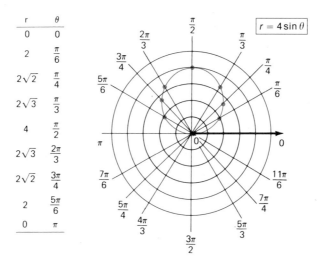

r	θ
0	0
2	$\frac{\pi}{6}$
$2\sqrt{2}$	$\frac{\pi}{4}$
$2\sqrt{3}$	$\frac{\pi}{3}$
4	$\frac{\pi}{2}$
$2\sqrt{3}$	$\frac{2\pi}{3}$
$2\sqrt{2}$	$\frac{3\pi}{4}$
2	$\frac{5\pi}{6}$
0	π

FIGURE 8.21

Examples 5 and 6 illustrate the fact that the graphs of some polar equations are familiar geometric figures. In fact, the polar equation $r \cos \theta = 2$ of Example 5 can be easily changed to the rectangular form $x = 2$, where the graph in Figure 8.20 is obvious. Likewise, the polar equation $r = 4 \sin \theta$ of Example 6 can be changed to the rectangular form $x^2 + y^2 = 4y$ that is equivalent to $x^2 + (y - 2)^2 = 4$. So in the xy-plane it is a circle with its center at $(0, 2)$ that has a radius of 2 units. This agrees with our graph in Figure 8.21. However, at this time our primary objective is to give you some practice graphing polar equations by plotting a sufficient number of points to determine the figures. This will help you in the next section when we encounter some *not so familiar* geometric figures.

Many graphing utilities are designed to graph polar equations, but their methods vary. For example, some graphing utilities have a special mode whereby polar equations can be handled in much the same way as polynomial equations.

Some graphing utilities use parametric equations to graph polar equations. Since $x = r \cos \theta$ and $y = r \sin \theta$, the polar equation $r = f(\theta)$ can be defined by the parametric equations $x = f(\theta) \cos \theta$ and $y = f(\theta) \sin \theta$. Your graphing utility may use the variable t instead of θ; so the parametric equations are $x = f(t) \cos t$ and $y = f(t) \sin t$. Thus, the polar equation $r = 4 \sin \theta$ in Example 6 can be defined by the parametric equations $x = 4 \sin t \cos t$ and $y = 4 \sin^2 t$. Figure 8.22 shows the graph of these equations by using a viewing rectangle such that $-\pi \leq x \leq \pi$ and $0 \leq y \leq 5$. We set the t-values to vary from 0 to π and the t-interval at .1 so that enough points are plotted to determine the circle.

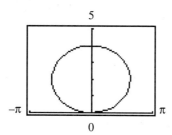

F I G U R E   8 . 22

PROBLEM SET 8.3

For Problems 1–12, plot the indicated ordered pairs as points in a polar coordinate system.

1. $A\left(3, \dfrac{\pi}{4}\right)$

2. $B\left(4, \dfrac{\pi}{3}\right)$

3. $C\left(-2, \dfrac{2\pi}{3}\right)$

4. $D\left(-3, \dfrac{5\pi}{6}\right)$

5. $E\left(5, -\dfrac{3\pi}{4}\right)$

6. $F\left(5, -\dfrac{5\pi}{4}\right)$

7. $G\left(-4, -\dfrac{\pi}{6}\right)$

8. $H\left(-4, -\dfrac{23\pi}{6}\right)$

9. $I(5, 270°)$

10. $J(4, -180°)$

11. $K(-2, -510°)$

12. $L(-2, 150°)$

For Problems 13–30, find the rectangular coordinates of the points whose polar coordinates are given.

13. $(3, 30°)$

14. $(6, 150°)$

15. $(-4, 225°)$

16. $(-2, 315°)$

17. $(2, 420°)$

18. $(5, 570°)$

19. $\left(-3, \dfrac{\pi}{3}\right)$

20. $\left(-7, \dfrac{5\pi}{6}\right)$

21. $\left(4, \dfrac{4\pi}{3}\right)$

22. $\left(6, \dfrac{5\pi}{3}\right)$

23. $\left(1, -\dfrac{2\pi}{3}\right)$

24. $\left(3, -\dfrac{11\pi}{6}\right)$

25. $\left(-7, \dfrac{9\pi}{4}\right)$

26. $\left(-4, \dfrac{11\pi}{4}\right)$

27. $\left(-2, -\dfrac{17\pi}{6}\right)$

28. $\left(-1, -\dfrac{11\pi}{3}\right)$

29. $\left(-3, -\dfrac{3\pi}{2}\right)$

30. $\left(8, -\dfrac{5\pi}{2}\right)$

For Problems 31–40, the rectangular coordinates of a point P are given. Find a pair of polar coordinates (r, θ) for P such that $r > 0$ and $0 \le \theta < 2\pi$.

31. $(-\sqrt{2}, \sqrt{2})$

32. $(2\sqrt{2}, -2\sqrt{2})$

33. $\left(-\dfrac{5\sqrt{3}}{2}, -\dfrac{5}{2}\right)$

34. $(-3\sqrt{3}, 3)$

35. $(3, -3\sqrt{3})$

36. $\left(-\dfrac{1}{2}, -\dfrac{\sqrt{3}}{2}\right)$

37. $(-4, 0)$

38. $(0, -3)$

39. $\left(\dfrac{3\sqrt{3}}{2}, \dfrac{3}{2}\right)$

40. $(\sqrt{3}, 1)$

For Problems 41–46, the rectangular coordinates of a point P are given. Find a pair of polar coordinates (r, θ) for P such that $r < 0$ and $0 \le \theta < 2\pi$.

41. $(\sqrt{2}, \sqrt{2})$

42. $\left(-\dfrac{3\sqrt{2}}{2}, \dfrac{3\sqrt{2}}{2}\right)$

43. $(2, -2\sqrt{3})$

44. $\left(\dfrac{1}{2}, \dfrac{\sqrt{3}}{2}\right)$

45. $\left(-\dfrac{5\sqrt{3}}{2}, \dfrac{5}{2}\right)$

46. $(-\sqrt{3}, -1)$

For Problems 47–52, the rectangular coordinates of a point P are given. Find a pair of polar coordinates (r, θ) for P such that $r > 0$ and $0° \le \theta < 360°$. Express θ to the nearest tenth of a degree.

47. $(3, 2)$

48. $(2, 5)$

49. $(-4, 3)$

50. $(6, -2)$

51. $(-4, -1)$

52. $(-3, -4)$

For Problems 53–64, change each equation to polar form.

53. $y = 2$

54. $x = 7$

55. $3x - 2y = 4$

56. $5x + 4y = 10$

57. $y = x$

58. $y = -2x$

59. $x^2 + y^2 - 8x = 0$

60. $x^2 + y^2 + 6y = 0$

61. $x^2 + y^2 + x = \sqrt{x^2 + y^2}$

62. $x^2 + y^2 - 2y = 2\sqrt{x^2 + y^2}$

63. $x^2 = 4y$

64. $y^2 = x$

For Problems 65–76, change each polar equation to rectangular form.

65. $r \sin \theta = -4$

66. $r \cos \theta = 6$

67. $r - 3 \cos \theta = 0$

68. $r = 2 \sin \theta$

69. $r = 2 \cos \theta + 3 \sin \theta$

70. $r = 3 \cos \theta - 4 \sin \theta$

71. $r(\sin \theta + 4 \cos \theta) = 5$

72. $r(2 \sin \theta - 3 \cos \theta) = -4$

73. $r = \dfrac{4}{2 + \cos \theta}$

74. $r = \dfrac{5}{2 - 3 \sin \theta}$

75. $r = 2 + 3 \sin \theta$

76. $r = -3 - 2 \cos \theta$

For Problems 77–92, sketch the graph of each of the polar equations. These graphs should be the familiar figures: straight line, circle, parabola, ellipse, or hyperbola.

77. $r = 4$

78. $r = -3$

79. $\theta = \dfrac{\pi}{6}$

80. $\theta = -\dfrac{\pi}{4}$

81. $r = 4 \sin \theta$

82. $r = -3 \cos \theta$

83. $r \sin \theta = 3$

84. $r \cos \theta = -2$

85. $r = 3 \cos \theta + 4 \sin \theta$

86. $r = 2 \cos \theta - 3 \sin \theta$

87. $r = \dfrac{4}{1 + \sin \theta}$

88. $r = \dfrac{3}{1 - \sin \theta}$

89. $r = \dfrac{5}{3 + 2 \cos \theta}$

90. $r = \dfrac{5}{3 - 2 \cos \theta}$

91. $r = \dfrac{5}{2 + 3 \sin \theta}$

92. $r = \dfrac{5}{2 - 3 \cos \theta}$

93. What does it mean to say that the polar coordinates of a point are not unique?

94. Explain why the graph of the equation $r = 2$ and the graph of $r = -2$ are identical.

FURTHER INVESTIGATIONS

95. The formula $d = \sqrt{(r_1)^2 + (r_2)^2 - 2r_1r_2\cos(\theta_2 - \theta_1)}$ can be used to find the distance between two points (r_1, θ_1) and (r_2, θ_2) in the polar coordinate system. Use Figure 8.23 and the law of cosines to develop the formula.

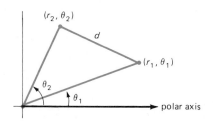

F I G U R E   8 . 23

96. Use the distance formula from Problem 95 to find the distance between each of the following pairs of points.

a. $\left(4, \dfrac{\pi}{2}\right)$ and $\left(3, \dfrac{\pi}{6}\right)$

b. $\left(6, \dfrac{3\pi}{4}\right)$ and $\left(8, \dfrac{\pi}{4}\right)$

c. $\left(10, \dfrac{7\pi}{6}\right)$ and $\left(2, \dfrac{2\pi}{3}\right)$

d. $\left(3, \dfrac{5\pi}{6}\right)$ and $\left(6, \dfrac{\pi}{6}\right)$

 GRAPHICS CALCULATOR ACTIVITIES

97. Use your graphics calculator to graph the polar equations in Problems 81–92. Check these results against what you obtained without using a graphics calculator.

8.4   MORE ON GRAPHING POLAR EQUATIONS

In the previous section we graphed some polar equations by plotting a sufficient number of points to determine the curve. Now let's discuss how the concept of **symmetry** can decrease the number of points that we need to plot and increase our efficiency in graphing polar equations.

In Figure 8.24(a) we indicated that the polar axis reflection of point (r, θ) can be named $(r, -\theta)$ or $(-r, \pi - \theta)$. Likewise, in parts (b) and (c) of Figure 8.24 we indicated the $(\pi/2)$-axis reflection and the pole reflection of (r, θ). From this information the following tests for symmetry can be stated.

Polar axis: A polar equation exhibits polar-axis symmetry if replacing θ by $-\theta$ or replacing r by $-r$ and θ by $\pi - \theta$ produces an equivalent equation.

$\pi/2$-axis: A polar equation exhibits $(\pi/2)$-axis symmetry if replacing r by $-r$ and θ by $-\theta$ or replacing θ by $\pi - \theta$ produces an equivalent equation.

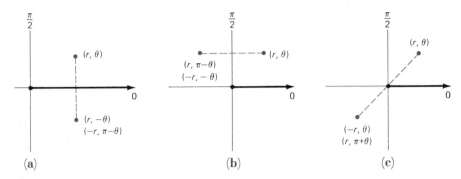

F I G U R E   8 . 24

Pole: A polar equation exhibits pole symmetry if replacing r by $-r$ or replacing θ by $\pi + \theta$ produces an equivalent equation.

A few comments about the tests for symmetry should be made. We refer to polar-axis symmetry, but technically we mean symmetry with respect to the line determined by the polar axis. Likewise, $(\pi/2)$-axis symmetry means symmetry with respect to the line determined by the $(\pi/2)$-axis. Also, note that we have stated more than one test for each kind of symmetry. This is due to the fact that different polar equations produce the same set of points. For example, $r = 2$ and $r = -2$ would both produce a circle of radius 2 with the center at the pole. Finally, we suggest that as you begin to use the tests for symmetry you retain a mental picture of Figure 8.24; it may help you recall the specific tests.

Cardioids

In Chapter 2 we stated that one valuable graphing technique is the ability to recognize the kind of graph produced by a specific type of equation. This ability to link graphs to their corresponding equations is also very helpful when working with polar equations. Let's begin with an example and then state some generalizations.

E X A M P L E I

Graph $r = 2 + 2 \cos \theta$.

Solution

First, since $\cos(-\theta) = \cos \theta$, we know that replacing θ by $-\theta$ will produce an equivalent equation. Thus, this curve is symmetric with respect to the polar axis. So in our table of values we can let θ vary from 0 to π. Then $\cos \theta$ decreases from 1 to -1 and $2 + 2 \cos \theta$ decreases from 4 to 0. Plotting the points represented in the table and connecting them with a smooth curve produces the upper half of Figure 8.25. Then reflecting this curve across the polar axis completes the figure.

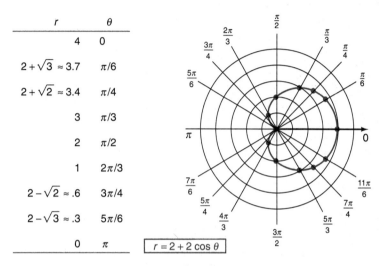

r	θ
4	0
$2 + \sqrt{3} \approx 3.7$	$\pi/6$
$2 + \sqrt{2} \approx 3.4$	$\pi/4$
3	$\pi/3$
2	$\pi/2$
1	$2\pi/3$
$2 - \sqrt{2} \approx .6$	$3\pi/4$
$2 - \sqrt{3} \approx .3$	$5\pi/6$
0	π

$$r = 2 + 2 \cos \theta$$

F I G U R E   8 . 25

The heart-shaped graph in Figure 8.25 is called a **cardioid**. In general, the graph of a polar equation of the form

$$r = a(1 \pm \cos \theta) \qquad \text{or} \qquad r = a(1 \pm \sin \theta),$$

where a is a nonzero real number, is called a cardioid. Therefore, by recognizing the general form of the equation of a cardioid, we can sketch a rough graph of one by simply plotting points determined by $\theta = 0$, $\pi/2$, π, and $3\pi/2$. It is also helpful to recognize that a cardioid involving the cosine function is symmetric with respect to the polar axis because $\cos(-\theta) = \cos \theta$. Likewise, we know that a cardioid involving the sine function is symmetric with respect to the $(\pi/2)$-axis because $\sin(\pi - \theta) = \sin \theta$. Let's consider another example.

E X A M P L E   2

Sketch the graph of $r = 2 - 2 \sin \theta$.

Solution

Letting $\theta = 0$, $\pi/2$, π, and $3\pi/2$ produces the ordered pairs $(2, 0)$, $(0, \pi/2)$, $(2, \pi)$, and $(4, 3\pi/2)$. These points along with the knowledge that the graph is a cardioid allow us to sketch a rough graph, as in Figure 8.26. Note that the graph is symmetric with respect to the $(\pi/2)$-axis.

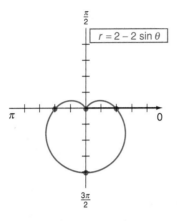

FIGURE 8.26

Limacons

The graph of a polar equation of the form

$$r = a \pm b \cos \theta \qquad \text{or} \qquad r = a \pm b \sin \theta,$$

where $a \neq b$, is called a **limacon**. The graph of a limacon is similar in shape to a cardioid, but depending upon the relative sizes of a and b, it may contain an additional *loop,* as illustrated by the next example.

EXAMPLE 3

Graph $r = 2 + 4 \cos \theta$.

Solution

r	θ
6	0
$2 + 2\sqrt{3} \approx 5.4$	$\pi/6$
$2 + 2\sqrt{2} \approx 4.8$	$\pi/4$
4	$\pi/3$
2	$\pi/2$
0	$2\pi/3$
$2 - 2\sqrt{2} \approx -.8$	$3\pi/4$
$2 - 2\sqrt{3} \approx -1.4$	$5\pi/6$
-2	π

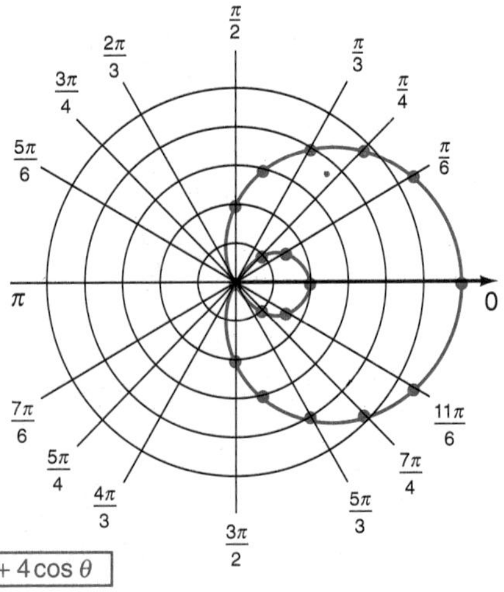

$r = 2 + 4\cos \theta$

FIGURE 8.27

Again, since $\cos(-\theta) = \cos\theta$, this equation exhibits polar axis symmetry. So in the table we allowed θ to vary from 0 to π. Notice in the table that $r = 0$ when $\theta = 2\pi/3$. Then r becomes negative for $2\pi/3 < \theta \le \pi$. So the points from the table determine the upper half of the large loop and the lower half of the small loop in Figure 8.27. Then because of symmetry, the complete figure is determined.

Other Polar Graphs

EXAMPLE 4

Graph $r = 5 \sin 2\theta$.

Solution

To test for symmetry, it might be easier to replace $\sin 2\theta$ by $2 \sin\theta \cos\theta$. Then the given equation becomes $r = 10 \sin\theta \cos\theta$. Using the identities $\sin(\pi - \theta) = \sin\theta$, $\cos(\pi - \theta) = -\cos\theta$, $\sin(\pi + \theta) = -\sin\theta$, and $\cos(\pi + \theta) = -\cos\theta$, we can verify that this curve is symmetric with respect to the polar axis, $(\pi/2)$-axis, and the pole. (We shall leave the details of applying the tests for symmetry for you to complete.) Thus, we can concentrate on values of θ from 0 to $\pi/2$. As θ increases from 0 to $\pi/4$, the value of r increases from 0 to 5. Then as θ continues to increase from $\pi/4$ to $\pi/2$, the value of r decreases from 5 to 0. By keeping these facts in mind and plotting the points $(5\sqrt{3}/2, \pi/6)$, $(5, \pi/4)$, and $(5\sqrt{3}/2, \pi/3)$, we can sketch the upper right-hand part of Figure 8.28. Then the concept of symmetry allows us to complete the figure. It is called a **four-leafed rose**.

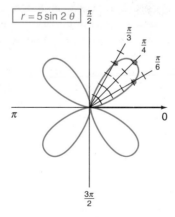

F I G U R E   8 . 28

Another interesting type of curve is produced by equations of the form $r = a\theta$. These curves *wind around the pole* infinitely many times in such a way that r increases (or decreases) steadily as θ increases (or decreases). They are called **Archimedean spirals**. Let's consider one specific example.

EXAMPLE 5

Sketch the curve $r = \theta$ for $\theta \geq 0$.

Solution

A reasonably accurate sketch can be obtained by plotting some points on the axes and using the fact that r increases steadily as θ increases. In Figure 8.29 we plotted the points $(0, 0)$, $(\pi/2, \pi/2)$, (π, π), $(3\pi/2, 3\pi/2)$, $(2\pi, 2\pi)$, $(5\pi/2, 5\pi/2)$, $(3\pi, 3\pi)$, $(7\pi/2, 7\pi/2)$, and $(4\pi, 4\pi)$ and sketched the curve.

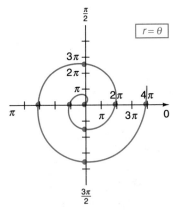

FIGURE 8.29

A graphing utility provides us with an efficient way to study many variations of cardioids, limacons, and other polar curves. The graphics calculator activities in the next problem set are designed to give you the opportunity to investigate some of these ideas.

As demonstrated previously, watching your graphing utility produce a particular curve can give you a very dynamic view of graphing. Watch as your graphing utility produces the graph of $r = \theta$. We used the parametric equations $x = t \cos t$ and $y = t \sin t$ to graph this polar equation in Figure 8.30.

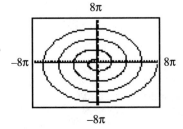

FIGURE 8.30

The spiral in Figure 8.30 was produced from the pole outward in a counter-clockwise direction as we let t vary from 0 to 8π. Now suppose that we graph these same parametric equations for $-8\pi \leq t \leq 0$. This curve, as shown in Figure 8.31, can be considered a clockwise spiral as t varies from 0 to -8π. (Using a graphing utility the curve was actually produced in a counterclockwise direction starting at -8π and spiraling inward toward the pole.)

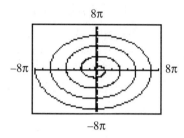

FIGURE 8.31

PROBLEM SET 8.4

Determine the symmetry (polar axis, $\pi/2$-axis, pole, or none) that each of the following equations exhibits. Do not sketch the graphs.

1. $r \cos \theta = -6$

2. $r \sin \theta = 8$

3. $r = \dfrac{3}{1 - \sin \theta}$

4. $r = \dfrac{2}{1 + \cos \theta}$

5. $r = \dfrac{4}{2 + 3 \cos \theta}$

6. $r = \dfrac{3}{3 - 2 \sin \theta}$

7. $r = 4 \sin \theta$

8. $r = 6 \cos \theta$

9. $r = 3 \cos \theta + 2 \sin \theta$

10. $r = 5 \sin \theta + 3 \cos \theta$

11. $r = \sec \theta + 2$

12. $r = \csc \theta - 3$

13. $r = 10 \tan \theta \sin \theta$

14. $r = 4 \cot \theta \cos \theta$

15. $r^2 = \sin 2\theta$

16. $r^2 = \cos 2\theta$

Graph each of the following polar equations.

17. $r = 3 + 3 \sin \theta$

18. $r = 2 - 2 \cos \theta$

19. $r = 1 - \cos \theta$

20. $r = 3 - 3 \sin \theta$

21. $r = 2 + 4 \sin \theta$

22. $r = 3 - 4 \sin \theta$

23. $r = 4 - 2 \cos \theta$

24. $r = 4 + 2 \cos \theta$

25. $r = 2 - 4 \cos \theta$

26. $r = 1 - 3 \cos \theta$

27. $r = 3 + \sin \theta$

28. $r = 3 - \sin \theta$

29. $r = 4 \cos 2\theta$

30. $r = 3 \sin 2\theta$

31. $r = 3 \sin 3\theta$

32. $r = 3 \cos 2\theta$

33. $r^2 = 9 \cos 2\theta$

34. $r^2 = -16 \cos 2\theta$

35. $r^2 = -16 \sin 2\theta$

36. $r^2 = 9 \sin 2\theta$

37. $r = 3 \sin \theta \tan \theta$

38. $r = 2 \cos \theta \cot \theta$

39. $r = \theta, \quad \theta \leq 0$

40. $r = 2\theta, \quad \theta \geq 0$

GRAPHICS CALCULATOR ACTIVITIES

41. Use your graphics calculator and be sure that you agree with the graphs in Examples 1–5 of this section.

42. Use your graphics calculator to check your graphs for Problems 17–40.

43. Graph $r = 1 + 2 \cos t$, $r = 2 + 4 \cos t$, and $r = 3 + 7 \cos t$ on the same set of axes. Then predict the graph of $r = 1 + 5 \cos t$ and check your prediction.

44. Graph $r = 1 + \sin t$, $r = 1 - \sin t$, and $r = 2 + 2 \sin t$ on the same set of axes. Then predict the graph of $r = 4 - 4 \sin t$ and check your prediction.

45. Set your calculator so that $-2 \le x \le 2$ and $-2 \le y \le 2$. Graph $r = \sin 2t$ and $r = \sin 3t$ on the same set of axes. Then predict the graphs of $r = \sin 4t$ and $r = \sin 5t$ and check your predictions.

46. Keep your calculator set so that the $-2 \le x \le 2$ and $-2 \le y \le 2$. Graph $r = \cos 2t$ and $r = \cos 3t$ on the

same set of axes. Then predict the graphs of $r = \cos 4t$ and $r = \cos 5t$ and check your predictions.

47. Set your calculator so that $-5 \le x \le 5$ and $-10 \le y \le 10$. Graph $r = \sin t \tan t$ and $r = 2 \sin t \tan t$ on the same set of axes. Then predict the graphs of $r = 3 \sin t \tan t$ and $r = -2 \sin t \tan t$ and check your predictions.

48. For each of the following polar equations, first try to predict what its graph will look like and then use your graphics calculator to check your prediction.

a. $r = 5 \sin 3\theta$ **b.** $r = 5 \sin 4\theta$

c. $r = 5 \sin 5\theta$ **d.** $r = 5 \sin 6\theta$

e. $r = -5 \sin 2\theta$ **f.** $r = 5 \cos 2\theta$

g. $r = -5 \cos 2\theta$

8.5   3-SPACE COORDINATE GEOMETRY

Just as points on a line can be placed in one-to-one correspondence with real numbers, and points in a plane can be placed in one-to-one correspondence with pairs of real numbers, so points in three-dimensional space can be placed in one-to-one correspondence with triples of real numbers. To form this correspondence let's consider three mutually perpendicular number lines (called the **x-axis**, **y-axis**, and **z-axis**) that have a common point of intersection at zero on each line, as indicated in Figure 8.32.

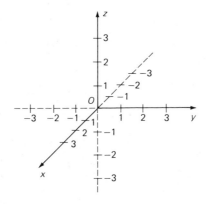

F I G U R E   8 . 3 2

Each pair of axes determines a plane called a **coordinate plane**. We refer to these as the *xy*-**plane**, the *xz*-**plane**, and the *yz*-**plane**. The three coordinate planes partition space into eight parts, called **octants**. To each point P in space we assign a triple of real numbers (a, b, c) called the coordinates of point P. The first number a is the *x*-coordinate and it is the distance that P is from the *yz*-plane measured parallel to the *x*-axis. The second number b is the *y*-coordinate and it is the distance that P is from the *xz*-plane measured parallel to the *y*-axis. The third number c is the *z*-coordinate and it is the distance that P is from the *xy*-plane measured parallel to the *z*-axis. In Figure 8.33, we plotted the point $A(2, 3, -2)$ by moving 2 units along the positive *x*-axis, 3 units to the right parallel to the *y*-axis, and then 2 units down parallel to the *z*-axis. The point $B(-2, -3, 1)$ is located by moving 2 units in the negative direction along the *x*-axis, 3 units to the left parallel to the *y*-axis, and then 1 unit up parallel to the *z*-axis.

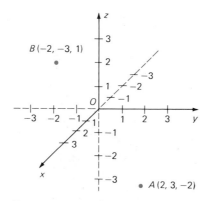

F I G U R E   8 . 3 3

REMARK   The coordinate system that we are using in this text is called a **right-handed** coordinate system. If the *x*- and *y*-axes are interchanged, then the system is said to be left-handed.

It would be helpful for you to recognize the location of some special points as follows.

REGION	DESCRIPTION
xy-plane	All points of the form $(a, b, 0)$
xz-plane	All points of the form $(a, 0, c)$
yz-plane	All points of the form $(0, b, c)$
x-axis	All points of the form $(a, 0, 0)$
y-axis	All points of the form $(0, b, 0)$
z-axis	All points of the form $(0, 0, c)$

Distance Formula

In coordinate geometry, several concepts extend from 2-space to 3-space in a rather easy manner. For example, to find the distance between two points $P_1(x_1, y_1, z_1)$ and $P_2(x_2, y_2, z_2)$ in 3-space, we can use the following formula.

$$d = \sqrt{(x_2 - x_1)^2 + (y_2 - y_1)^2 + (z_2 - z_1)^2}$$

To see the validity of this formula, consider Figure 8.34. The length $\overline{P_1P_2}$ is determined as follows: Applying the Pythagorean theorem to right triangle ABP_1, we find that the length $\overline{P_1A}$ is $\sqrt{(x_2 - x_1)^2 + (y_2 - y_1)^2}$. Then applying the Pythagorean theorem to right triangle P_1AP_2, we find that the length of $\overline{P_1P_2}$ is

$$\sqrt{(P_1A)^2 + (z_2 - z_1)^2} = \sqrt{(x_2 - x_1)^2 + (y_2 - y_1)^2 + (z_2 - z_1)^2}.$$

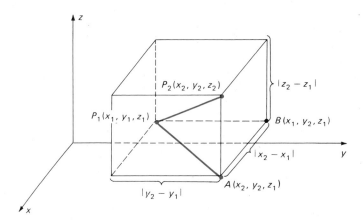

FIGURE 8.34

EXAMPLE I

Find the distance between $A(2, 3, -1)$ and $B(-1, 2, 4)$.

Solution

Using the distance formula we obtain

$$AB = \sqrt{[2 - (-1)]^2 + [3 - 2]^2 + [-1 - 4]^2}$$
$$= \sqrt{3^2 + 1^2 + (-5)^2} = \sqrt{35}.$$

A **sphere** is the set of all points in 3-space equidistant from a given fixed point called the center. A line segment determined by the center and any point on the sphere is called a **radius**. Now consider a sphere in a 3-space coordinate system with its center C at (h, k, l) and a radius of length r (Figure 8.35). If $P(x, y, z)$ is any point on the sphere, then the length of a radius is given by $r =$

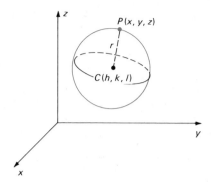

F I G U R E   8 . 35

$\sqrt{(x-h)^2 + (y-k)^2 + (z-l)^2}$. Thus, the standard equation of a sphere of radius r with center $C(h, k, l)$ is

$$(x - h)^2 + (y - k)^2 + (z - l)^2 = r^2.$$

E X A M P L E 2

Find the equation of a sphere with its center at $(3, -4, 5)$ and a radius of length 6 units.

Solution

Let's substitute 3 for h, -4 for k, 5 for l, and 6 for r in the standard equation, and simplify.

$$(x - h)^2 + (y - k)^2 + (z - l)^2 = r^2$$
$$(x - 3)^2 + (y + 4)^2 + (z - 5)^2 = 6^2$$
$$x^2 - 6x + 9 + y^2 + 8y + 16 + z^2 - 10z + 25 = 36$$
$$x^2 - 6x + y^2 + 8y + z^2 - 10z + 14 = 0$$

E X A M P L E 3

Find the center and the length of a radius of the sphere $x^2 + 4x + y^2 - 8y + z^2 + 2z + 12 = 0$.

Solution

We can put the equation in the standard form of a sphere by completing the square on x, y, and z.

$$x^2 + 4x + \underline{\quad\quad} + y^2 - 8y + \underline{\quad\quad} + z^2 + 2z + \underline{\quad\quad} = -12$$
$$x^2 + 4x + 4 + y^2 - 8y + 16 + z^2 + 2z + 1 = -12 + 4 + 16 + 1$$
$$(x + 2)^2 + (y - 4)^2 + (z + 1)^2 = 3^2$$

Therefore, the center of the sphere is at $(-2, 4, -1)$ and the length of a radius is 3 units.

3-Space Vectors

In Section 8.1 we stated that a study of vectors (2-space vectors at that time) can be enhanced by introducing a rectangular coordinate system. At this time, having a three-dimensional rectangular coordinate system allows us to move from 2-space vectors to 3-space vectors in a very logical manner. To begin, let $\mathbf{u}$ be a vector in 3-space positioned with its initial point at the origin and its terminal point at (u_1, u_2, u_3) as in Figure 8.36. The numbers u_1, u_2, and u_3 are called the components of $\mathbf{u}$ and we write

$$\mathbf{u} = \langle u_1, u_2, u_3 \rangle$$

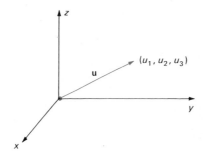

F I G U R E   8 . 36

By applying the 3-space distance formula, it should be evident that the magnitude of $\mathbf{u}$, denoted by $\|\mathbf{u}\|$ is given by

$$\|\mathbf{u}\| = \sqrt{(u_1)^2 + (u_2)^2 + (u_3)^2}.$$

The operations of **vector addition** and **multiplication by a scalar** can be extended from 2-space vectors to 3-space vectors in a very natural way. If $\mathbf{u} = \langle u_1, u_2, u_3 \rangle$, $\mathbf{v} = \langle v_1, v_2, v_3 \rangle$, and k is any scalar (real number), then

$$\mathbf{u} + \mathbf{v} = \langle u_1 + v_1, u_2 + v_2, u_3 + v_3 \rangle$$

and

$$k\mathbf{u} = \langle ku_1, ku_2, ku_3 \rangle.$$

The zero vector $(\mathbf{0})$ and the negative of $\mathbf{u}(-\mathbf{u})$ are

$$\mathbf{0} = \langle 0, 0, 0 \rangle \qquad \text{and} \qquad -\mathbf{u} = \langle -u_1, -u_2, -u_3 \rangle.$$

Subtraction is defined by

$$\mathbf{u} - \mathbf{v} = \langle u_1 - v_1, u_2 - v_2, u_3 - v_3 \rangle.$$

EXAMPLE 4

If $\mathbf{u} = \langle 3, -2, -6 \rangle$ and $\mathbf{v} = \langle 4, 5, -1 \rangle$, find $2\mathbf{u} + 3\mathbf{v}$, $\mathbf{u} - 4\mathbf{v}$, $\|\mathbf{u}\|$, and $\|\mathbf{v}\|$.

Solution

$$2\mathbf{u} + 3\mathbf{v} = 2\langle 3, -2, -6 \rangle + 3\langle 4, 5, -1 \rangle$$
$$= \langle 6, -4, -12 \rangle + \langle 12, 15, -3 \rangle = \langle 18, 11, -15 \rangle$$

$$\mathbf{u} - 4\mathbf{v} = \langle 3, -2, -6 \rangle - 4\langle 4, 5, -1 \rangle$$
$$= \langle 3, -2, -6 \rangle - \langle 16, 20, -4 \rangle$$
$$= \langle -13, -22, -2 \rangle$$

$$\|\mathbf{u}\| = \sqrt{(3)^2 + (-2)^2 + (-6)^2}$$
$$= \sqrt{9 + 4 + 36}$$
$$= \sqrt{49} = 7$$

$$\|\mathbf{v}\| = \sqrt{(4)^2 + (5)^2 + (-1)^2}$$
$$= \sqrt{16 + 25 + 1} = \sqrt{42}$$

The basic properties of vector addition and scalar multiplication that were listed in Section 8.1 extend from 2-space to 3-space vectors. We will not repeat those properties here but simply refer you to Section 8.1 if you need to refresh your memory. The operation of **dot product** also extends to 3-space vectors as follows.

$$\mathbf{u} \cdot \mathbf{v} = u_1 v_1 + u_2 v_2 + u_3 v_3 = \|\mathbf{u}\| \|\mathbf{v}\| \cos \theta$$

Again the expression $u_1 v_1 + u_2 v_2 + u_3 v_3$ provides a convenient form for computing the dot product and the expression $\|\mathbf{u}\| \|\mathbf{v}\| \cos \theta$ provides a geometric interpretation. As before, solving $\mathbf{u} \cdot \mathbf{v} = \|\mathbf{u}\| \|\mathbf{v}\| \cos \theta$ for $\cos \theta$ produces

$$\cos \theta = \frac{\mathbf{u} \cdot \mathbf{v}}{\|\mathbf{u}\| \|\mathbf{v}\|}.$$

EXAMPLE 5

Find the dot product of $\langle 4, 2, -1 \rangle$ and $\langle 3, -5, 2 \rangle$.

Solution

Let's use $\mathbf{u} \cdot \mathbf{v} = u_1 v_1 + u_2 v_2 + u_3 v_3$.

$$\langle 4, 2, -1 \rangle \cdot \langle 3, -5, 2 \rangle = 4(3) + 2(-5) + (-1)(2)$$

$$= 12 - 10 - 2$$

$$= 0$$

A dot product of 0 means that the vectors are perpendicular.   ▬▬▬

EXAMPLE 6

Find the angle of intersection of the two vectors $\langle -2, 1, -3 \rangle$ and $\langle 4, -2, -1 \rangle$.

Solution

We can use $\cos \theta = \dfrac{\mathbf{u} \cdot \mathbf{v}}{\|\mathbf{u}\| \|\mathbf{v}\|}$.

$$\cos \theta = \frac{-2(4) + 1(-2) + (-3)(-1)}{\sqrt{(-2)^2 + 1^2 + (-3)^2} \sqrt{4^2 + (-2)^2 + (-1)^2}}$$

$$= \frac{-8 - 2 + 3}{\sqrt{14}\sqrt{21}} = \frac{-7}{\sqrt{14}\sqrt{21}} = -.4082$$

Therefore, $\theta = 114.1°$ to the nearest tenth of a degree.   ▬▬▬

PROBLEM SET 8.5

For Problems 1–6, plot the points A and B and find the length of $\overline{AB}$.

1. $A(2, 1, 3)$, $B(4, 3, 6)$

2. $A(-3, 2, -1)$, $B(-2, 2, 6)$

3. $A(4, -1, -2)$, $B(-1, 1, 2)$

4. $A(0, -2, -1)$, $B(3, 2, 0)$

5. $A(-2, -3, -4)$, $B(0, 4, -2)$

6. $A(-1, -3, -2)$, $B(2, 0, -4)$

For Problems 7–10, find an equation of the sphere with center at C and a radius of length r.

7. $C(2, -1, 4)$, $r = 2$

8. $C(-1, 3, -2)$, $r = 4$

9. $C(-1, -2, -3)$, $r = 3$

10. $C(2, 5, -3)$, $r = 1$

For Problems 11–16, find the center and the length of a radius of each of the given spheres.

11. $x^2 - 2x + y^2 - 4y + z^2 - 8z + 20 = 0$

12. $x^2 + 2x + y^2 - 6y + z^2 + 8z + 17 = 0$

13. $x^2 + 4x + y^2 + 6y + z^2 - 14z + 46 = 0$

14. $x^2 - 4x + y^2 + 10y + z^2 + 12z + 57 = 0$

15. $x^2 + 8x + y^2 + z^2 - 2z - 1 = 0$

16. $x^2 + y^2 + 6y + z^2 - 16z + 48 = 0$

17. Find an equation of the sphere with its center at $(-2, -3, 4)$ if it is tangent to the xy-plane.

18. Find an equation of the sphere with its center at $(3, -2, -5)$ if it is tangent to the yz-plane.

For Problems 19–24, sketch the vector and find its magnitude.

19. $\langle -3, 4, 0 \rangle$ 20. $\langle 4, 0, -3 \rangle$

21. $\langle 2, -2, 3 \rangle$ **22.** $\langle -3, 4, 2 \rangle$

23. $\langle 6, -3, -2 \rangle$ **24.** $\langle -2, -6, 3 \rangle$

For Problems 25–30, find $2\mathbf{u} + 3\mathbf{v}$, $\mathbf{u} - 2\mathbf{v}$, $3\mathbf{u} - 4\mathbf{v}$, and $\|\mathbf{u} - \mathbf{v}\|$.

25. $\mathbf{u} = \langle -2, 1, -1 \rangle$ and $\mathbf{v} = \langle -1, -2, -3 \rangle$

26. $\mathbf{u} = \langle 3, 0, -2 \rangle$ and $\mathbf{v} = \langle -3, 4, -1 \rangle$

27. $\mathbf{u} = \langle 4, 3, -3 \rangle$ and $\mathbf{v} = \langle 2, 2, -2 \rangle$

28. $\mathbf{u} = \langle -1, 4, -5 \rangle$ and $\mathbf{v} = \langle 2, -4, 6 \rangle$

29. $\mathbf{u} = \langle 1, -3, -1 \rangle$ and $\mathbf{v} = \langle -5, 1, 0 \rangle$

30. $\mathbf{u} = \langle 0, -3, -6 \rangle$ and $\mathbf{v} = \langle 4, 0, 1 \rangle$

For Problems 31–38, if $\mathbf{u} = \langle -1, 2, -3 \rangle$, $\mathbf{v} = \langle 2, -1, 4 \rangle$, and $\mathbf{w}\langle -2, 5, -1 \rangle$, find each of the indicated dot products.

31. $\mathbf{u} \cdot \mathbf{v}$ **32.** $\mathbf{u} \cdot \mathbf{w}$

33. $\mathbf{v} \cdot \mathbf{w}$ **34.** $\mathbf{u} \cdot (\mathbf{v} + \mathbf{w})$

35. $\mathbf{v} \cdot (\mathbf{u} - \mathbf{w})$ **36.** $\mathbf{w} \cdot (\mathbf{v} - \mathbf{u})$

37. $(2\mathbf{u} + \mathbf{v}) \cdot \mathbf{w}$ **38.** $(2\mathbf{v} + \mathbf{u}) \cdot \mathbf{w}$

For Problems 39–46, find the angle of intersection of the two vectors. Express answers to the nearest tenth of a degree.

39. $\langle 1, 3, 4 \rangle$ and $\langle 2, 4, 6 \rangle$

40. $\langle 2, 0, 5 \rangle$ and $\langle 3, 0, 7 \rangle$

41. $\langle -2, 3, -1 \rangle$ and $\langle 3, 2, 0 \rangle$

42. $\langle -1, -2, -3 \rangle$ and $\langle 4, -2, -2 \rangle$

43. $\langle 4, -3, -2 \rangle$ and $\langle 1, -1, 1 \rangle$

44. $\langle 4, -2, -3 \rangle$ and $\langle 3, 6, 0 \rangle$

45. $\langle 5, -1, -1 \rangle$ and $\langle -2, -3, -1 \rangle$

46. $\langle -3, 0, 2 \rangle$ and $\langle 0, -2, -6 \rangle$

47. Show that $k(\mathbf{u} + \mathbf{v}) = k\mathbf{u} + k\mathbf{v}$ for $k = -4$, $\mathbf{u} = \langle 2, 1, -3 \rangle$, and $\mathbf{v} = \langle 3, 2, -4 \rangle$.

48. Show that $(k + l)\mathbf{u} = k\mathbf{u} + l\mathbf{u}$ for $k = 3$, $l = -5$, and $\mathbf{u} = \langle -2, -3, 4 \rangle$.

49. Show that $\mathbf{u} \cdot (\mathbf{v} + \mathbf{w}) = \mathbf{u} \cdot \mathbf{v} + \mathbf{u} \cdot \mathbf{w}$ for $\mathbf{u} = \langle 5, -1, 2 \rangle$, $\mathbf{v} = \langle -4, -1, -3 \rangle$, and $\mathbf{w} = \langle -3, -2, 6 \rangle$.

50. Show that $k(\mathbf{u} \cdot \mathbf{v}) = (k\mathbf{u}) \cdot \mathbf{v} = \mathbf{u} \cdot (k\mathbf{v})$ for $k = 4$, $\mathbf{u} = \langle 4, -2, -6 \rangle$, and $\mathbf{v} = \langle -1, 1, -1 \rangle$.

8.6   GRAPHING IN 3-SPACE

The graph of an equation in three variables, x, y, z is the set of all points (x, y, z) whose coordinates satisfy the equation. Usually, such graphs are **surfaces** of some kind. For example, in the previous section we found that the graph of $x^2 - 6x + y^2 + 8y + z^2 - 10z + 14 = 0$ is a sphere with its center at $(3, -4, 5)$ that has a radius of length 6 units. In this section we want to consider the graphs of other types of surfaces.

Let's begin by considering the graph of $z = 3$. Since we are graphing in 3-space, the equation $z = 3$ means $0(x) + 0(y) + z = 3$. This equation is satisfied by all ordered triples of the form $(x, y, 3)$, where x and y are any real numbers. Thus, the graph is the plane parallel to the xy-plane and 3 units above it, as shown in Figure 8.37. In general, the graphs of $x = a$, $y = b$, and $z = c$ are planes parallel to the yz-plane, xz-plane, and xy-plane, respectively.

Now let's consider a linear equation in three variables, that has just one of the variables missing. For example, let's graph $3x + 2y = 6$. Again, in three variables this equation can be written as $3x + 2y + 0(z) = 6$. So the equation is satisfied by ordered triples of the form (x, y, z), where $3x + 2y = 6$ and z is any real number. An

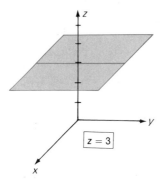

FIGURE   8.37

easy way to picture this situation is to first graph the line $3x + 2y = 6$ in the xy-plane. Then since z can be any real number, think of the line as a window shade that can be drawn both upward and downward infinitely. Thus, the graph of $3x + 2y = 6$ in 3-space is the plane that is parallel to the z-axis as shown in Figure 8.38.

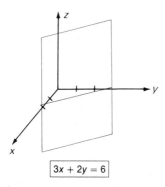

FIGURE   8.38

In general, any equation of the form $Ax + By + Cz = D$ is a plane. If all three variables are present, then the plane can be sketched once you determine the x-, y-, and z-intercepts. Let's consider an example of this type.

EXAMPLE I

Graph $2x + 3y + z = 6$.

Solution

If $x = 0$ and $y = 0$, then $z = 6$; so the plane intersects the z-axis at $(0, 0, 6)$. If $x = 0$ and $z = 0$, then $y = 2$; so the plane intersects the y-axis at $(0, 2, 0)$. If $y = 0$ and $z = 0$, then $x = 3$; so the plane intersects the x-axis at $(3, 0, 0)$. The plane can be sketched as in Figure 8.39.

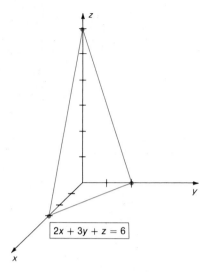

FIGURE   8.39

Now let's consider another equation that is missing one of the three variables.

EXAMPLE 2

Graph $y = x^2$.

Solution

This equation in three variables is satisfied by ordered triples (x, y, z), where $y = x^2$ and z is any real number. So, if $z = 0$ we have the parabola $y = x^2$ in the xy-plane. If $z = 5$, we have the parabola $y = x^2$ in the plane parallel to the xy-plane and 5 units above it as shown in Figure 8.40. If $z = -3$, we have the parabola in the plane parallel to the xy-plane and 3 units below it. The surface generated by the equation $y = x^2$ is shown in Figure 8.40.

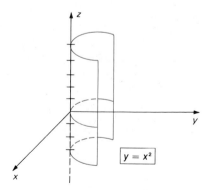

FIGURE   8.40

The surface shown in Figure 8.40 is sometimes called a **cylindrical surface**. In general, any equation containing only two of the three variables x, y, and z represents a cylindrical surface in 3-space. Let's consider another example.

EXAMPLE 3

Sketch the graph of $x^2 + z^2 = 4$.

Solution

This equation is satisfied by ordered triples (x, y, z), where $x^2 + z^2 = 4$ and y is any real number. If $y = 0$, we obtain the circle $x^2 + z^2 = 4$ in the xz-plane. Likewise, for nonzero values for y, we obtain circles in planes parallel to the xz-plane. The cylindrical surface represented by $x^2 + z^2 = 4$ is shown in Figure 8.41.

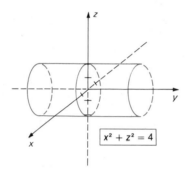

$$x^2 + z^2 = 4$$

FIGURE 8.41

Quadric Surfaces

In general, the graph of a **second-degree equation** in x, y, and z is called a **quadric surface**. Many types of quadric surfaces exist and some of them become quite tedious to graph. In this brief introduction, we will discuss a few basic quadric surfaces and introduce a graphing technique that will be helpful to use in subsequent courses.

When graphing *new* equations in 2-space, we often rely on plotting enough points to determine the curve. However, for surfaces in 3-space, point plotting is in general not very helpful because too many points are needed to get even a crude sketch of the surface. Instead, it is more effective to "build the surface" by studying curves of intersection made by planes intersecting the surface. The curve of intersection of a plane and a surface is called a **trace** of the surface in the plane. Let's illustrate how traces can be used to graph surfaces.

EXAMPLE 4

Sketch the graph of $4x^2 + 4y^2 + z^2 = 4$.

Solution

To find the trace in the xy-plane, let $z = 0$. Thus, the circle $4x^2 + 4y^2 = 4$ or $x^2 + y^2 = 1$ is formed.

To find the trace in the xz-plane, let $y = 0$. Thus, the ellipse $4x^2 + z^2 = 4$ is formed.

To find the trace in the yz-plane, let $x = 0$. Thus, the ellipse $4y^2 + z^2 = 4$ is formed.

The three traces can be used to sketch the graph as in Figure 8.42.

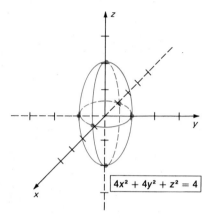

$$4x^2 + 4y^2 + z^2 = 4$$

FIGURE   8.42

EXAMPLE 5

Sketch the graph of $x^2 + 4z^2 = y$.

Solution

In Figure 8.43 we determined the surface by sketching the parabolic traces in the xy-plane and yz-plane, and the elliptic trace formed by the plane $y = 4$.

To find the trace in the xy-plane, let $z = 0$. Thus, the parabola $y = x^2$ is formed.

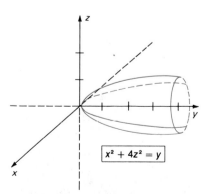

$$x^2 + 4z^2 = y$$

FIGURE   8.43

To find the trace in the yz-plane, let $x = 0$. Thus, the parabola $y = 4z^2$ is formed.

To find the trace in the xz-plane, let $y = 0$. Thus, the equation $x^2 + 4z^2 = 0$ is formed and this equation is satisfied only by the origin. So let's find a trace parallel to the xz-plane by letting $y = 4$. Then $x^2 + 4z^2 = y$ becomes $x^2 + 4z^2 = 4$, which is the equation of an ellipse.

PROBLEM SET 8.6

Sketch a graph of each of the following equations in three variables.

1. $y = 4$

2. $z = -3$

3. $x = -2$

4. $x + y = 4$

5. $2x - z = 6$

6. $y + 3z = 6$

7. $x - 2y - 3z = 6$

8. $2x - y + z = 4$

9. $-2x + y - z = -6$

10. $4x + 3y - 6z = 12$

11. $y = z^2$

12. $y = -2x^2$

13. $x^2 + y^2 = 4$

14. $y^2 + z^2 = 4$

15. $x^2 + 4y^2 = 4$

16. $4x^2 + 9z^2 = 36$

17. $9y^2 + 4z^2 = 36$

18. $xy = 4$

19. $z = 2^y$

20. $y = e^x$

21. $4x^2 + y^2 + 4z^2 = 4$

22. $x^2 + y^2 + z^2 = 4$

23. $4x^2 + y^2 + z^2 = 4$

24. $4x^2 + z^2 = y$

25. $4x^2 + y^2 = z$

26. $4y^2 + z^2 = x$

THOUGHTS into WORDS

27. Is the graph of the equation $x = 2$ a point, a line, or a plane? Explain your answer.

28. What is the graph of $x^2 + y^2 = 0$ when graphing ordered pairs in two-space? What is the graph of $x^2 + y^2 = 0$ when graphing ordered triples in three-space? Explain your answers.

29. What is the graph of $x^2 - y^2 = 0$ when graphing ordered pairs in two-space? What is the graph of $x^2 - y^2 = 0$ when graphing ordered triples in three-space? Explain your answers.

 ### GRAPHICS CALCULATOR ACTIVITIES

30. If you have access to a graphing utility that produces three-dimensional graphs, use it to check your graphs for Problems 1–26.

CHAPTER 8 SUMMARY

Treating 2-space vectors as ordered pairs of real numbers and 3-space vectors as ordered triples provides an algebraic setting for the study of vectors. Some basic operations with vectors can be defined in terms of real numbers.

2-space vector addition: $\mathbf{u} + \mathbf{v} = \langle u_1 + v_1, u_2 + v_2 \rangle$

3-space vector addition: $\mathbf{u} + \mathbf{v} = \langle u_1 + v_1, u_2 + v_2, u_3 + v_3 \rangle$

2-space scalar multiplication: $k\mathbf{u} = \langle ku_1, ku_2 \rangle$

3-space scalar multiplication: $k\mathbf{u} = \langle ku_1, ku_2, ku_3 \rangle$

The basic properties of vector addition and scalar multiplication can be reviewed in Section 8.1. They hold true for both 2-space and 3-space vectors.

The magnitude or length of a vector is denoted by $\|\mathbf{u}\|$ and is given by

$$\|\mathbf{u}\| = \sqrt{(u_1)^2 + (u_2)^2} \quad \text{for 2-space vectors}$$

and

$$\|\mathbf{u}\| = \sqrt{(u_1)^2 + (u_2)^2 + (u_3)^2} \quad \text{for 3-space vectors.}$$

The operation of dot product is defined as follows:

2-space: $\mathbf{u} \cdot \mathbf{v} = u_1 v_1 + u_2 v_2 = \|\mathbf{u}\| \|\mathbf{v}\| \cos \theta$

3-space: $\mathbf{u} \cdot \mathbf{v} = u_1 v_1 + u_2 v_2 + u_3 v_3 = \|\mathbf{u}\| \|\mathbf{v}\| \cos \theta$

From the equation $\mathbf{u} \cdot \mathbf{v} = \|\mathbf{u}\| \|\mathbf{v}\| \cos \theta$ we get

$$\cos \theta = \frac{\mathbf{u} \cdot \mathbf{v}}{\|\mathbf{u}\| \|\mathbf{v}\|},$$

which provides a form for finding the angle of intersection, θ, of two vectors. In a special case, two vectors are perpendicular if and only if their dot product is zero.

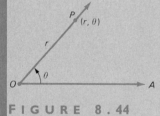

The polar coordinate system provides another way of naming points in a coordinatized plane. The polar coordinates (r, θ) of a point P measure its distance r from a fixed point O and the angle θ that ray OP makes with a horizontal ray OA directed to the right. The point O is called the **pole** and the ray OA is called the **polar axis** (Figure 8.44).

FIGURE   8.44

The following equations express relationships between the polar coordinates (r, θ) and the rectangular coordinates (x, y).

$$x = r \cos \theta \qquad y = r \sin \theta$$

$$\tan \theta = \frac{y}{x} \qquad r^2 = x^2 + y^2$$

The graph of a polar equation of the form

$$r = a(1 + \cos \theta), \qquad r = a(1 - \cos \theta),$$

$$r = a(1 + \sin \theta), \qquad \text{or} \qquad r = a(1 - \sin \theta)$$

is a **cardioid**. The graph of a polar equation of the form

$$r = a \pm b \cos \theta \qquad \text{or} \qquad r = a \pm b \sin \theta,$$

where $a \neq b$, is a limacon. Symmetry tests for polar equations are discussed at the beginning of Section 8.4.

The equations $x = f(t)$ and $y = g(t)$, where x and y are expressed as functions of a third variable t, are called parametric equations. The variable t is called the parameter. To graph a curve represented by parametric equations, we can allow the parameter to vary within the boundaries set by the problem and determine a set of ordered pairs (x, y). Sometimes it is possible to eliminate the parameter t and form a single equation in terms of x and y.

A 3-space rectangular coordinate system sets up a one-to-one correspondence between points in a three-dimensional space and ordered triples of real numbers.

To find the distance between two points $P_1(x_1, y_1, z_1)$ and $P_2(x_2, y_2, z_2)$ in 3-space, we can use the formula

$$d = \sqrt{(x_2 - x_1)^2 + (y_2 - y_1)^2 + (z_2 - z_1)^2}.$$

The equation of a sphere having its center at (h, k, l) and a radius of length r is

$$(x - h)^2 + (y - k)^2 + (z - l)^2 = r^2.$$

A 3-space coordinate system provides the framework for graphing equations in three variables. The following is a list of some equations and the types of surfaces they produce when graphed in 3-space coordinate geometry.

$x = a$	A plane parallel to the yz-plane
$y = b$	A plane parallel to the xz-plane
$z = c$	A plane parallel to the xy-plane
$Ax + By = D$	A plane parallel to the z-axis
$Ax + Cz = D$	A plane parallel to the y-axis
$By + Cz = D$	A plane parallel to the x-axis
$Ax + By + Cz = D$	A plane intersecting the x-axis at $(D/A, 0, 0)$ the y-axis at $(0, D/B, 0)$, and the z-axis at $(0, 0, D/C)$

In general, any equation containing only two of the variables, x, y, and z, represents a cylindrical surface. Look back at Examples 2 and 3 on pgs 561–562 to review graphing cylindrical surfaces.

The curve of intersection of a plane and a surface is called a trace of the surface in the plane. Sketching the traces of a surface in the coordinate planes often helps to graph the surface.

CHAPTER 8 REVIEW PROBLEM SET

Problems 1–14 involve a mixture of 2-space and 3-space vectors. For Problems 1–6, sketch the vector and find its magnitude.

1. $\langle -3, 3 \rangle$　　　**2.** $\langle -2, -4 \rangle$

3. $\langle 1, 3, 4 \rangle$　　　**4.** $\langle -2, -1, 4 \rangle$

5. $\langle 2, 3, -1 \rangle$　　　**6.** $\langle -3, 4, 4 \rangle$

For Problems 7–10, find $\mathbf{v} - \mathbf{u}$, $2\mathbf{u} + 5\mathbf{v}$, and $3\mathbf{u} - 2\mathbf{v}$.

7. $\mathbf{u} = \langle -5, 4 \rangle$, $\mathbf{v} = \langle -3, -2 \rangle$

8. $\mathbf{u} = \langle 2, -6 \rangle$, $\mathbf{v} = \langle 4, 6 \rangle$

9. $\mathbf{u} = \langle 5, -4, -3 \rangle$, $\mathbf{v} = \langle -1, 2, -3 \rangle$

10. $\mathbf{u} = \langle -2, 1, -4 \rangle$, $\mathbf{v} = \langle -3, 6, -1 \rangle$

For Problems 11–14, find the angle of intersection of the two vectors. Express your answers to the nearest tenth of a degree.

11. $\langle 4, 1 \rangle$ and $\langle 5, -3 \rangle$

12. $\langle -3, -4 \rangle$ and $\langle -1, 6 \rangle$

13. $\langle 2, 1, -3 \rangle$ and $\langle -3, 2, 5 \rangle$

14. $\langle -1, 2, -4 \rangle$ and $\langle -2, -1, -6 \rangle$

For Problems 15–20, sketch the graph of each of the polar equations.

15. $r = \dfrac{2}{1 + \cos \theta}$

16. $r = 2 \cos \theta$

17. $r = 1 + \cos \theta$

18. $r = 1 - \sin \theta$

19. $r = 2 - 4 \sin \theta$

20. $r = 3 - 2 \cos \theta$

For Problems 21–24, if the equation is given in rectangular form, change it to polar form. If the equation is given in polar form, change it to rectangular form. Also identify each curve using either of the two forms.

21. $r = 1 - \cos \theta$

22. $y = -\frac{1}{3}x^2$

23. $r = 3 \sin \theta$

24. $x^2 + y^2 - 3y = 2\sqrt{x^2 + y^2}$

For Problems 25–30, (a) graph the curve represented by the parametric equations, and (b) eliminate the parameter to form an equation in terms of x and y.

25. $x = -3 - 2t$, $y = 2 + 5t$; $-\infty < t < \infty$

26. $x = 3 \cos t$, $y = 3 \sin t$; $0 \le t \le 2\pi$

27. $x = \cos t$, $y = 4 \sin t$; $0 \le t \le 2\pi$

28. $x = t - 3$, $y = t^2 + 2$; $-1 \le t \le 4$

29. $x = 2 \sec t$, $y = 3 \tan t$; $0 \le t \le 2\pi$

30. $x = -\dfrac{1}{t}$, $y = 5t$; $-\infty < t < \infty$

31. If a projectile is fired at an initial velocity of 72 feet per second at an angle of $60°$ to the horizontal, find (a) the parametric equations of the path of the projectile, (b) the total time of the flight of the projectile, and (c) the range of the flight.

32. Find the distance between $A(2, 1, -3)$ and $B(-1, 2, -1)$.

33. Find an equation of the sphere that has its center $(4, -1, 5)$ and a radius of length 3 units.

34. Find the center and the length of a radius of the sphere $x^2 + 10x + y^2 + 4y + z^2 - 6z + 6 = 0$.

For Problems 35–40, sketch a graph of each of the equations in three variables.

35. $y = -3$　　　**36.** $2x - 5y = 10$

37. $3x - 2y - 3z = 6$　　　**38.** $z = 4x^2$

39. $y^2 + 4z^2 = 4$　　　**40.** $x^2 + y^2 = z$

CONIC SECTIONS

If a **parabola** is rotated about its axis, a parabolic surface is generated. Parabolic surfaces possess a property that is useful in the design of a large variety of items such as microphones, telescopes, satellite dishes, automobile headlights, solar furnaces, and searchlights. If an **ellipse** is rotated about its major axis, an elliptical surface is generated. Elliptical surfaces also possess a special property that is useful in the design of gears and cams, some airplane wings, domes in buildings, and the modern-day lithotripter (a device that disintegrates kidney stones). If a **hyperbola** is rotated about its major axis, a hyperbolic surface is generated. Hyperbolic surfaces possess a property, analogous to that of elliptical surfaces, that is useful in the design of glasses, nuclear cooling systems, cameras, telescopes, and contemporary architectural structures. Parabolas, circles, ellipses, and hyperbolas can be formed by intersecting a right circular conical surface with a plane, as shown in Figure 9.1. Hence, these figures are often referred to as **conic sections**.

 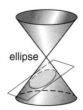  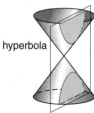

circle   ellipse   parabola   hyperbola

FIGURE 9.1

9

Parabolic surfaces are used in the construction of satellite dishes.

The conic sections are not new to you. You did some graphing of circles and parabolas in Chapters 2 and 3. However, at that time, we gave only a formal definition of a circle and we used that definition to develop a standard form for the equation of a circle. It is now time to study the other conic sections in the same manner. We will define each one and derive a standard form of an equation from the definition. Then in the last section of this chapter we will take another look at the conic sections, using the polar coordinate system.

9.1   PARABOLAS AND TRANSLATION OF AXES

Parabolas were discussed in Section 3.2 as the graphs of quadratic functions. As graphs of functions, all parabolas in those sections had vertical lines as axes of symmetry. Furthermore, the definition for a parabola was not stated at that time. We shall now define a parabola and derive standard forms of equations for those that have either vertical or horizontal axes of symmetry.

DEFINITION 9.1

A **parabola** is the set of all points in a plane such that its distance from a fixed point F (the **focus**) is equal to its distance from a fixed line d (the **directrix**) in the plane.

Using Definition 9.1 we can sketch a parabola by starting with a fixed line d and a fixed point F, not on d. Then a point P is on the parabola if and only if $PF = PP'$, where PP' is perpendicular to d (Figure 9.2). The dashed curved line in Figure 9.2 indicates the possible positions of P; it is the parabola. The line l, through F and perpendicular to the directrix d, is called the **axis of symmetry**. The point V, on the axis of symmetry halfway from F to the directrix d, is the **vertex** of the parabola.

A standard form for the equation of a parabola can be derived by coordinatizing the plane so that the origin is at the vertex of the parabola and the y-axis is the axis of symmetry, as indicated in Figure 9.3. If the focus is at $(0, p)$, where $p \neq 0$, then the equation of the directrix is $y = -p$. Therefore, for any point P on the parabola, $PF = PP'$ and using the distance formula we obtain

$$\sqrt{(x - 0)^2 + (y - p)^2} = \sqrt{(x - x)^2 + (y + p)^2}.$$

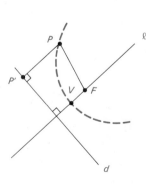

FIGURE 9.2

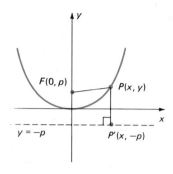

FIGURE 9.3

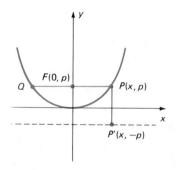

FIGURE 9.4

Squaring both sides and simplifying produces

$$(x - 0)^2 + (y - p)^2 = (x - x)^2 + (y + p)^2$$
$$x^2 + y^2 - 2py + p^2 = y^2 + 2py + p^2$$
$$x^2 = 4py.$$

Thus, the standard form for the equation of a parabola with its vertex at the origin that has the y-axis as its axis of symmetry is

$$x^2 = 4py.$$

If $p > 0$, the parabola opens upward and if $p < 0$, then the parabola opens downward.

In Figure 9.4 the line segment $\overline{QP}$ is called the latus rectum. It contains the focus and is parallel to the directrix. Since $FP = PP' = |2p|$, the entire length of the latus rectum is $|4p|$ units. We will use this fact in a moment when we graph parabolas.

The standard form for the equation of a parabola with its vertex at the origin that has the x-axis as its axis of symmetry can be developed in a similar fashion. By choosing a focus at $F(p, 0)$, a directrix with an equation of $x = -p$ (see Figure 9.5), and applying the definition of a parabola we obtain the standard form

$$y^2 = 4px.$$

If $p > 0$, the parabola opens to the right, as in Figure 9.5, and if $p < 0$, it opens to the left.

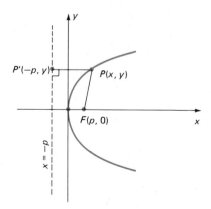

FIGURE 9.5

The concept of symmetry can help us to decide which of the two equations, $x^2 = 4py$ or $y^2 = 4px$, we should use. The graph of $x^2 = 4py$ is symmetric with respect to the y-axis because replacing x with $-x$ does not change the equation. Likewise, the graph of $y^2 = 4px$ is symmetric with respect to the x-axis because replacing y with $-y$ leaves the equation unchanged. The following property summarizes this discussion.

PROPERTY 9.1

The graph of each of the following equations is a parabola that has its vertex at the origin and has the indicated focus, directrix, and symmetry.

a. $x^2 = 4py$:   focus $(0, p)$, directrix $y = -p$, y-axis symmetry

b. $y^2 = 4px$:   focus $(p, 0)$, directrix $x = -p$, x-axis symmetry

Now let's illustrate some uses of the equations $x^2 = 4py$ and $y^2 = 4px$.

EXAMPLE 1

Find the focus and directrix of the parabola $x^2 = -8y$ and sketch its graph.

Solution

Comparing $x^2 = -8y$ to the standard form $x^2 = 4py$, we have $4p = -8$, and therefore $p = -2$. So the focus is at $(0, -2)$ and the equation of the directrix is $y = -(-2) = 2$. The latus rectum is $|4p| = |-8| = 8$ units long. Therefore, the endpoints of the latus rectum are 4 units on both sides of the focus. So the endpoints are at $(4, -2)$ and $(-4, -2)$. Figure 9.6 is the sketch of the graph.

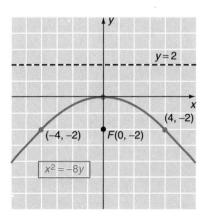

FIGURE   9.6

EXAMPLE 2

Find the focus and directrix of the parabola $y^2 = 6x$ and sketch its graph.

Solution

Comparing $x^2 = -8y$ to the standard form $x^2 = 4py$, we have $4p = -8$, and therefore $p = \frac{3}{2}$. So the focus is at $\left(\frac{3}{2}, 0\right)$ and the equation of the directrix is $x = -\frac{3}{2}$. The latus rectum is $|4p| = |6| = 6$ units long. Thus, the endpoints of the latus rectum are at $\left(\frac{3}{2}, 3\right)$ and $\left(\frac{3}{2}, -3\right)$. Figure 9.7 is a sketch of the graph.

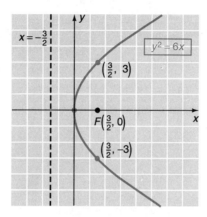

FIGURE 9.7

EXAMPLE 3

Write the equation of the parabola that is symmetric with respect to the y-axis, has its vertex at the origin, and contains the point $P(6, 3)$.

Solution

The standard form of the parabola is $x^2 = 4py$. Since P is on the parabola, the ordered pair $(6, 3)$ must satisfy the equation. Therefore,

$$6^2 = 4p(3)$$

$$36 = 12p$$

$$3 = p.$$

If $p = 3$, the equation becomes

$$x^2 = 4(3)y$$

$$x^2 = 12y.$$

Translation of Axes

In Section 3.2 we translated parabolas horizontally and vertically. For example, the parabola $f(x) = (x - 2)^2 + 3$ was considered to be a translation of the parabola $f(x) = x^2$ two units to the right and three units up. Another way to study a parabola that does not have its vertex at the origin is to translate the origin to the vertex. In other words, we can construct another coordinate system so that its origin is at the vertex of the parabola. Then, using relationships between the origins of the two systems, we can study the parabola with reference to either system. We can describe this technique, called **translation of axes**, as follows.

Consider a point $C(h, k)$ in the xy-coordinate plane. Let's introduce a new $x'y'$-coordinate system that has its origin O' at C. The x'- and y'-axes are parallel to, and have the same unit lengths and positive directions as the x- and y-axis, respectively. Figure 9.8 illustrates this situation with point C, which we chose in the first quadrant of the xy-plane.

We will use primes on letters to denote coordinates of points in the $x'y'$-system. Thus, in Figure 9.9 the point $P(x, y)$ in the xy-system is denoted by $P'(x', y')$ in the $x'y'$-system. Using directed distances the following statements can be made.

$$x = OE = OH + HE = OH + O'D = h + x'$$

$$y = OA = OG + GA = OG + O'B = k + y'$$

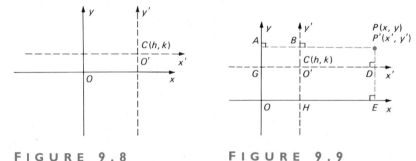

FIGURE 9.8   FIGURE 9.9

Therefore, the following formulas link the xy- and $x'y'$-coordinate systems.

> ### Translation of Axes
>
> If (x, y) are the coordinates of a point P in the xy-system, and (x', y') are the coordinates of the same point P in the $x'y'$-system that has its origin at (h, k) of the xy-system, then
>
> $$x = x' + h \qquad \text{and} \qquad y = y' + k$$
>
> or
>
> $$x' = x - h \qquad \text{and} \qquad y' = y - k.$$

The translation of axes formulas provide the basis for changing equations of graphs from one system to the other. For example, the equation $(x')^2 + (y')^2 = r^2$ represents a circle of radius r with its center at O' of the $x'y'$-plane. Substituting $x - h$ for

x' and $y - k$ for y' produces $(x - h)^2 + (y - k)^2 = r^2$, which is the equation of the same circle relative to the xy-plane. (Recall that in Section 2.4 the equation $(x - h)^2 + (y - k)^2 = r^2$ was developed directly from the definition of a circle.)

Now let's use the translation of axes formulas to expand our work with parabolas. We know that

$$(x')^2 = 4py'$$

is an equation of a parabola with its vertex at the origin O' and is symmetric with respect to the y'-axis of the $x'y'$-system. Therefore, substituting $x - h$ for x' and $y - k$ for y' produces

$$(x - h)^2 = 4p(y - k),$$

which is the equation of the same parabola with its vertex at (h, k) of the xy-system (Figure 9.10). In a similar fashion, the equation $(y')^2 = 4px'$ produces $(y - k)^2 = 4p(x - h)$, as indicated in Figure 9.11. The following property summarizes these ideas.

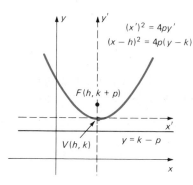

FIGURE 9.10

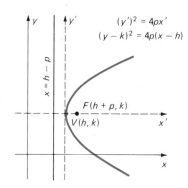

FIGURE 9.11

PROPERTY 9.2

The graph of each of the following equations is a parabola that has its vertex at (h, k) and has the indicated focus, directrix, and symmetry.

a. $(x - h)^2 = 4p(y - k)$: Focus $(h, k + p)$, directrix $y = k - p$, $x = h$ line of symmetry

b. $(y - k)^2 = 4p(x - h)$: Focus $(h + p, k)$, directrix $x = h - p$, $y = k$ line of symmetry

In Property 9.2(a), if $p > 0$ the parabola opens upward, and if $p < 0$ it opens downward. Likewise, in part (b) if $p > 0$ the parabola opens to the right, and if $p < 0$ it opens to the left. Let's illustrate the use of Property 9.2.

EXAMPLE 4

Find the vertex, focus, and directrix of the parabola $y^2 + 4y - 4x + 16 = 0$, and sketch its graph.

Solution

Writing the given equation as $y^2 + 4y = 4x - 16$, we can complete the square on the left side by adding 4 to both sides.

$$y^2 + 4y + 4 = 4x - 16 + 4$$

$$(y + 2)^2 = 4x - 12$$

$$(y - (-2))^2 = 4(x - 3)$$

Now let's compare this final equation to the form $(y - k)^2 = 4p(x - h)$.

$$(y - (-2))^2 = 4(x - 3)$$

$$k = -2 \qquad 4p = 4 \qquad h = 3$$
$$p = 1$$

Since $h = 3$ and $k = -2$, the vertex is at $(3, -2)$. Because $p > 0$, the parabola opens to the right and the focus $(h + p, k)$ is at $(4, -2)$. The equation of the directrix is $x = h - p$ or $x = 2$. The latus rectum is $|4p| = |4| = 4$ units long and its endpoints are at $(4, 0)$ and $(4, -4)$. Figure 9.12 is a sketch of the parabola.

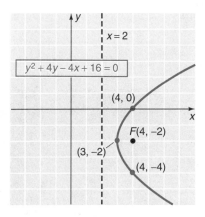

FIGURE 9.12

EXAMPLE 5

Find the vertex, focus, and directrix of the parabola $x^2 + 2x + 6y - 11 = 0$, and sketch its graph.

Solution

Let's complete the square on x.

$$x^2 + 2x = -6y + 11$$

$$x^2 + 2x + 1 = -6y + 11 + 1$$

$$(x + 1)^2 = -6y + 12$$

$$(x - (-1))^2 = -6(y - 2)$$

Now we can compare this final equation to the form $(x - h)^2 = 4p(y - k)$.

$$(x - (-1))^2 = -6(y - 2)$$

$$h = -1 \qquad 4p = -6 \qquad k = 2$$

$$p = -\frac{3}{2}$$

The vertex is at $(-1, 2)$ and because $p < 0$, the parabola opens downward. The focus $(h, k + p)$ is at $\left(-1, \frac{1}{2}\right)$ and the equation of the directrix is $y = k - p$ or $y = \frac{7}{2}$. The latus rectum is $|4p| = |-6| = 6$ units long and its endpoints are at $\left(-4, \frac{1}{2}\right)$ and $\left(2, \frac{1}{2}\right)$. The parabola is depicted in Figure 9.13.

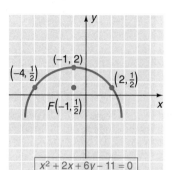

FIGURE 9.13

REMARK Certainly a graphing utility could be used to graph the conic sections presented in this chapter. However, for some equations a significant amount of preliminary work has to be done to change the equations into a proper form for the utility. We discuss these issues in the Graphics Calculator Activities of this chapter.

EXAMPLE 6

Write the equation of the parabola if its focus is at $(-4, 1)$ and the equation of its directrix is $y = 5$.

Solution

Since the directrix is a horizontal line, we know that the equation of the parabola is of the form $(x - h)^2 = 4p(y - k)$. The vertex is halfway between the focus and directrix; so the vertex is at $(-4, 3)$. This means that $h = -4$ and $k = 3$. The parabola opens downward because the focus is below the directrix and the distance between the focus and the vertex is 2 units; so $p = -2$. Substituting -4 for h, 3 for k, and -2 for p in the equation $(x - h)^2 = 4p(y - k)$, we obtain

$$(x - (-4))^2 = 4(-2)(y - 3).$$

This simplifies to

$$(x + 4)^2 = -8(y - 3)$$

$$x^2 + 8x + 16 = -8y + 24$$

$$x^2 + 8x + 8y - 8 = 0.$$

REMARK For a problem such as Example 6, you may find it helpful to put the given information on a set of axes and draw a rough sketch of the parabola to help with the analysis of the problem.

Parabolas possess various properties that make them very useful. For example, if a parabola is rotated about its axis, a parabolic surface is formed. The rays from a source of light placed at the focus will reflect from the surface parallel to the axis. Likewise, rays of light, parallel to the axis, coming into the parabolic surface will be reflected through the focus. It is for this reason that parabolic reflectors such as those on searchlights are used. This same property is useful in the design of mirrors for telescopes and in the construction of radar antennae (Figure 9.14).

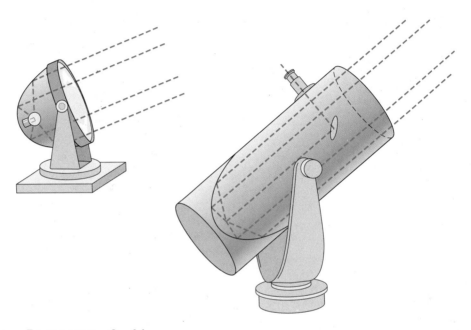

FIGURE 9.14

A bullet fired into the air will follow the curvature of a parabola if only the force of gravity is considered; in other words, if air resistance and other outside factors are ignored (Figure 9.15).

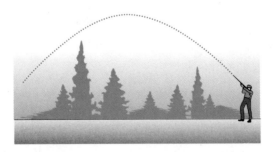

FIGURE 9.15

Different types of bridges are constructed based on the concept of a parabola. One example is shown in Figure 9.16.

PROBLEM SET 9.1

For Problems 1–22, find the vertex, focus, and directrix of the given parabola and sketch its graph.

1. $y^2 = 8x$ **2.** $y^2 = -4x$

3. $x^2 = -12y$ **4.** $x^2 = 8y$

5. $y^2 = -2x$ **6.** $y^2 = 6x$

7. $x^2 = 6y$ **8.** $x^2 = -7y$

9. $x^2 - 4y + 8 = 0$

10. $x^2 - 8y - 24 = 0$

11. $x^2 + 8y + 16 = 0$

12. $x^2 + 4y - 4 = 0$

13. $y^2 - 12x + 24 = 0$

14. $y^2 + 8x - 24 = 0$

15. $x^2 - 2x - 4y + 9 = 0$

16. $x^2 + 4x - 8y - 4 = 0$

17. $x^2 + 6x + 8y + 1 = 0$

18. $x^2 - 4x + 4y - 4 = 0$

19. $y^2 - 2y + 12x - 35 = 0$

20. $y^2 + 4y + 8x - 4 = 0$

21. $y^2 + 6y - 4x + 1 = 0$

22. $y^2 - 6y - 12x + 21 = 0$

For Problems 23–42, find an equation of the parabola that satisfies the given conditions.

23. Focus $(0, 3)$, directrix $y = -3$

24. Focus $\left(0, -\frac{1}{2}\right)$, directrix $y = \frac{1}{2}$

25. Focus $(-1, 0)$, directrix $x = 1$

26. Focus $(5, 0)$, directrix $x = 1$

27. Focus $(0, 1)$, directrix $y = 7$

28. Focus $(0, -2)$, directrix $y = -10$

29. Focus $(3, 4)$, directrix $y = -2$

30. Focus $(-3, -1)$, directrix $y = 7$

31. Focus $(-4, 5)$, directrix $x = 0$

32. Focus $(5, -2)$, directrix $x = -1$

33. Vertex $(0, 0)$, symmetric with respect to the x-axis, and contains the point $(-3, 5)$

34. Vertex $(0, 0)$, symmetric with respect to the y-axis, and contains the point $(-2, -4)$

35. Vertex $(0, 0)$, focus $\left(\frac{5}{2}, 0\right)$

36. Vertex $(0, 0)$, focus $\left(0, -\frac{7}{2}\right)$

37. Vertex $(7, 3)$, focus $(7, 5)$, and symmetric with respect to the line $x = 7$

38. Vertex $(-4, -6)$, focus $(-7, -6)$, and symmetric with respect to the line $y = -6$

39. Vertex $(8, -3)$, focus $(11, -3)$, and symmetric with respect to the line $y = -3$

40. Vertex $(-2, 9)$, focus $(-2, 5)$, and symmetric with respect to the line $x = -2$

41. Vertex $(-9, 1)$, symmetric with respect to the line $x = -9$, and contains the point $(-8, 0)$

42. Vertex $(6, -4)$, symmetric with respect to the line $y = -4$, and contains the point $(8, -3)$

43. One section of a suspension bridge hangs between two towers that are 40 feet above the surface and 300 feet apart as in Figure 9.16. A cable strung between the tops

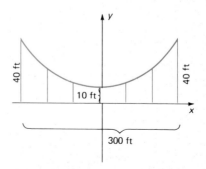

FIGURE 9.16

of the two towers is in the shape of a parabola with its vertex 10 feet above the surface. With axes drawn as indicated in the figure, find the equation of the parabola.

44. In Figure 9.16, suppose that 5 equally spaced vertical cables are used to support the bridge. Find the total length of these supports.

45. Suppose that an arch is shaped like a parabola. It is 20 feet wide at the base and 100 feet high. How wide is the arch 50 feet above the ground?

46. A parabolic arch 27 feet high spans a parkway. How wide is the arch if the center section of the parkway 50 feet wide has a minimum clearance of 15 feet?

47. A parabolic arch spans a stream 200 feet wide. How high must the arch be above the stream to give a minimum clearance of 40 feet over a channel in the center that is 120 feet wide?

THOUGHTS into WORDS

48. How would you explain to an elementary algebra student what is accomplished by developing formulas for the translation of axes?

49. Suppose that someone graphed the equation $y^2 - 6y - 2x + 11 = 0$ and obtained the graph in Figure 9.17. How do you know by looking at the equation that this graph is incorrect?

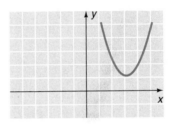

F I G U R E   9 . 17

GRAPHICS CALCULATOR ACTIVITIES

50. The parabola determined by the equation $x^2 + 2x + 6y - 11 = 0$ (Example 5 of this section) is easy to graph using a graphics calculator because it can be expressed as a function of x without much computation. Solving the equation for y produces

$$6y = -x^2 - 2x + 11$$

$$y = \frac{-x^2 - 2x + 11}{6}.$$

Use your graphics calculator to graph this function and compare your result with Figure 9.13.

   The equation $y^2 + 4y - 4x + 16 = 0$ (Example 4) requires a little more effort to change it to proper form for the graphics calculator. Let's solve for y by using the quadratic formula where the coefficient of y^2 is 1, the coefficient of y is 4, and the constant term is $-4x + 16$.

$$y = \frac{-4 \pm \sqrt{16 - 4(-4x + 16)}}{2}$$

At this step *you* (the user of the graphics calculator) have to decide whether to enter this expression or to simplify it first. Simplifying produces

$$y = \frac{-4 \pm \sqrt{16 + 16x - 64}}{2}$$

$$= \frac{-4 \pm \sqrt{16x - 48}}{2}$$

$$= \frac{-4 \pm \sqrt{16(x - 3)}}{2}$$

$$= \frac{-4 \pm 4\sqrt{x - 3}}{2}$$

$$= -2 \pm 2\sqrt{x - 3}$$

Now we can let $Y_1 = 2\sqrt{x - 3}$, $Y_2 = -2 + Y_1$, $Y_3 = -2 - Y_1$, and activate only Y_2 and Y_3. Use your graphics calculator to graph these functions and compare your result with Figure 9.12. Then use your graphics calculator to check your graphs for Problems 1–22.

9.2 ELLIPSES

Let's begin by defining the concept of an ellipse.

> ### DEFINITION 9.2
>
> An **ellipse** is the set of all points in a plane such that the sum of its distances from two fixed points F and F' in the plane (the **foci**) is a constant.

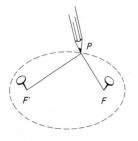

FIGURE 9.18

Using two thumbtacks, a piece of string, and a pencil, it is easy to draw an ellipse by satisfying the conditions of Definition 9.2. First insert two thumbtacks in a piece of cardboard at points F and F' and fasten the ends of the piece of string to the thumbtacks, as in Figure 9.18. Then loop the string around the point of a pencil and hold the pencil so that the string is taut. Finally, by moving the pencil around the points, always keeping the string taut, an ellipse is drawn. The two points F and F' are the foci referred to in Definition 9.2 and the sum of the distances FP and $F'P$ is constant, since it represents the length of the piece of string. With the same piece of string, you could vary the shape of the ellipse by changing the positions of the foci. By moving F and F' further apart, the ellipse would become flatter. Likewise, by moving F and F' closer together, the ellipse would more resemble a circle. In fact, if $F = F'$, a circle is obtained.

A standard form for the equation of an ellipse can be derived by coordinatizing the plane so that the foci are on the x-axis, equidistant from the origin (Figure 9.19). If F has coordinates $(c, 0)$, where $c > 0$, then F' has coordinates $(-c, 0)$, and

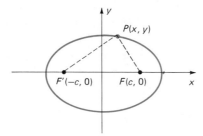

FIGURE 9.19

the distance between F and F' is $2c$ units. We will let $2a$ represent the constant sum of $FP + F'P$. Note that $2a > 2c$ and therefore $a > c$. For any point P on the ellipse,

$$FP + F'P = 2a.$$

Using the distance formula, we can write this as

$$\sqrt{(x - c)^2 + (y - 0)^2} + \sqrt{(x + c)^2 + (y - 0)^2} = 2a.$$

Let's change the form of this equation to

$$\sqrt{(x - c)^2 + y^2} = 2a - \sqrt{(x + c)^2 + y^2}$$

and square both sides

$$(x - c)^2 + y^2 = 4a^2 - 4a\sqrt{(x + c)^2 + y^2} + (x + c)^2 + y^2$$

which can be simplified to

$$a^2 + cx = a\sqrt{(x + c)^2 + y^2}.$$

Again squaring both sides produces

$$a^4 + 2a^2cx + c^2x^2 = a^2[(x + c)^2 + y^2],$$

which can be written in the form

$$x^2(a^2 - c^2) + a^2y^2 = a^2(a^2 - c^2).$$

Dividing both sides by $a^2(a^2 - c^2)$ leads to the form

$$\frac{x^2}{a^2} + \frac{y^2}{a^2 - c^2} = 1.$$

Letting $b^2 = a^2 - c^2$, where $b > 0$, produces the equation

$$\frac{x^2}{a^2} + \frac{y^2}{b^2} = 1. \tag{1}$$

Since $c > 0$, $a > c$, and $b^2 = a^2 - c^2$, it follows that $a^2 > b^2$ and hence $a > b$. This equation that we have derived is called the **standard form** for the equation of an ellipse with its foci on the x-axis and its center at the origin.

The x-intercepts of equation (1) can be found by letting $y = 0$. This produces $x^2/a^2 = 1$ or $x^2 = a^2$, and, consequently, the x-intercepts are a and $-a$. The corresponding points on the graph (see Figure 9.20) are $A(a, 0)$ and $A'(-a, 0)$, and the line segment $\overline{A'A}$, which is of length $2a$, is called the **major axis** of the ellipse. The

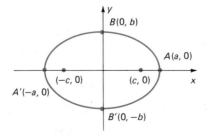

F I G U R E   9 . 2 0

endpoints of the major axis are also referred to as the **vertices** of the ellipse. Similarly, letting $x = 0$ produces $y^2/b^2 = 1$ or $y^2 = b^2$, and, consequently, the y-intercepts are b and $-b$. The corresponding points on the graph are $B(0, b)$ and $B'(0, -b)$, and the line segment $\overline{BB'}$, which is of length $2b$, is called the **minor axis**. Since $a > b$, the major axis is longer than the minor axis. The point of intersection of the major and minor axis is called the **center** of the ellipse.

Let's summarize this discussion by stating the following property.

PROPERTY 9.3

The graph of the equation

$$\frac{x^2}{a^2} + \frac{y^2}{b^2} = 1,$$

for $a^2 > b^2$, is an ellipse with the endpoints of its major axis (vertices) at $(a, 0)$ and $(-a, 0)$, and the endpoints of its minor axis at $(0, b)$ and $(0, -b)$. The foci are at $(c, 0)$ and $(-c, 0)$, where $c^2 = a^2 - b^2$.

Since replacing y with $-y$, or replacing x with $-x$, or replacing both x and y with $-x$ and $-y$ leaves the equation unchanged, the graph of $x^2/a^2 + y^2/b^2 = 1$ is symmetric with respect to the x-axis, the y-axis, and the origin.

EXAMPLE 1

Find the vertices, endpoints of the minor axis, foci, and sketch the ellipse $4x^2 + 9y^2 = 36$.

Solution

You can change the given equation to standard form by dividing both sides by 36.

$$\frac{4x^2}{36} + \frac{9y^2}{36} = \frac{36}{36}$$

$$\frac{x^2}{9} + \frac{y^2}{4} = 1$$

Therefore, $a^2 = 9$ and $b^2 = 4$; hence, the vertices are at $(3, 0)$ and $(-3, 0)$, and the ends of the minor axis are at $(0, 2)$ and $(0, -2)$. Since $c^2 = a^2 - b^2$, we have

$$c^2 = 9 - 4$$

$$= 5.$$

So the foci are at $(\sqrt{5}, 0)$ and $(-\sqrt{5}, 0)$. Figure 9.21 is a sketch of the ellipse.

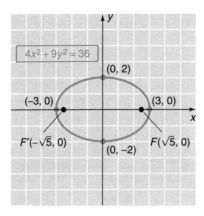

$4x^2 + 9y^2 = 36$

$(0, 2)$

$(-3, 0)$

$(3, 0)$

$F'(-\sqrt{5}, 0)$

$(0, -2)$

$F(\sqrt{5}, 0)$

FIGURE   9.21

REMARK   For a problem such as Example 1, it is not necessary to change to standard form to find the values for a and b. After all, $\pm a$ are the x-intercepts and $\pm b$ are the y-intercepts. These values can be found quite easily from the given form of the equation.

EXAMPLE 2

Find the equation of the ellipse with vertices $(\pm 6, 0)$ and foci at $(\pm 4, 0)$.

Solution

From the given information we know that $a = 6$ and $c = 4$. Therefore,

$$b^2 = a^2 - c^2$$

$$= 36 - 16 = 20.$$

Substituting 36 for a^2 and 20 for b^2 in the standard form produces

$$\frac{x^2}{36} + \frac{y^2}{20} = 1.$$

Multiplying both sides by 180 leads to

$$5x^2 + 9y^2 = 180.$$

Ellipses with Foci on the y-Axis

A standard form for the equation of an ellipse with foci on the y-axis can be developed in a similar fashion. The following property summarizes the results of such a development with the foci at $(0, c)$ and $(0, -c)$, where $c > 0$.

PROPERTY 9.4

The graph of the equation

$$\frac{x^2}{b^2} + \frac{y^2}{a^2} = 1,$$

for $a^2 > b^2$, is an ellipse with the endpoints of its major axis (vertices) at $(0, a)$ and $(0, -a)$, and the endpoints of its minor axis at $(b, 0)$ and $(-b, 0)$. The foci are at $(0, c)$ and $(0, -c)$, where $c^2 = a^2 - b^2$.

From Properties 9.3 and 9.4 it is evident that an equation of an ellipse with its center at the origin and foci on a coordinate axis can be written in the form

$$\frac{x^2}{p} + \frac{y^2}{q} = 1 \qquad \text{or} \qquad qx^2 + py^2 = pq$$

where p and q are positive. If $p > q$, the major axis lies on the x-axis, but if $q > p$, the major axis is on the y-axis. It is not necessary to memorize these facts since for any specific problem the endpoints of the major and minor axes are determined by the x- and y-intercepts. However, it is necessary to remember the relationship $c^2 = a^2 - b^2$.

EXAMPLE 3

Find the vertices, endpoints of the minor axis, foci, and sketch the ellipse $18x^2 + 4y^2 = 36$.

Solution

To find the x-intercepts we let $y = 0$, to obtain

$$18x^2 = 36$$

$$x^2 = 2$$

$$x = \pm\sqrt{2}.$$

Similarly, to find the y-intercepts we let $x = 0$, to obtain

$$4y^2 = 36$$

$$y^2 = 9$$

$$y = \pm 3.$$

Since $3 > \sqrt{2}$, $a = 3$ and $b = \sqrt{2}$. Therefore, the vertices are at $(0, 3)$ and $(0, -3)$, and the endpoints of the minor axis are at $(\sqrt{2}, 0)$ and $(-\sqrt{2}, 0)$. From the relationship $c^2 = a^2 - b^2$ we get

$$c^2 = 9 - 2 = 7.$$

So the foci are at $(0, \sqrt{7})$ and $(0, -7)$. The ellipse is sketched in Figure 9.22.

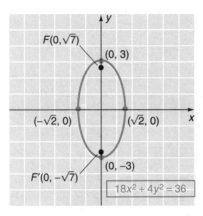

FIGURE 9.22

Other Ellipses

By using the translation of axes formulas we can extend our work to an ellipse with its center at any point (h, k) of the xy-plane. For example, we know that

$$\frac{(x')^2}{a^2} + \frac{(y')^2}{b^2} = 1 \tag{1}$$

is an ellipse with its center at O' of the $x'y'$-plane and its major axis is a portion of the x'-axis. Therefore, substituting $x - h$ for x' and $y - k$ for y' produces

$$\frac{(x - h)^2}{a^2} + \frac{(y - k)^2}{b^2} = 1, \tag{2}$$

which is the equation of the same ellipse with its center at (h, k) of the xy-system. In a similar fashion the equation

$$\frac{(x')^2}{b^2} + \frac{(y')^2}{a^2} = 1$$

produces

$$\frac{(x - h)^2}{b^2} + \frac{(y - k)^2}{a^2} = 1. \tag{3}$$

Figure 9.23 and Figure 9.24 indicate the basic facts associated with equations (2) and (3), respectively. In each case, the physical significance of a, b, and c is the same as before. However, these values are used relative to the center (h, k) to find the endpoints of the major and minor axis, and the foci. Let's see how this works in a specific example.

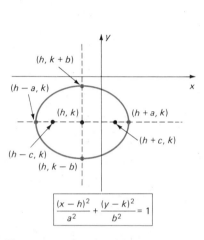

FIGURE   9 . 23   FIGURE   9 . 24

EXAMPLE 4

Find the vertices, endpoints of the minor axis, foci, and sketch the ellipse $9x^2 + 54x + 4y^2 - 8y + 49 = 0$.

Solution

First, we need to change to a standard form by completing the square on both x and y.

$$9(x^2 + 6x + \underline{\hphantom{00}}) + 4(y^2 - 2y + \underline{\hphantom{00}}) = -49$$

$$9(x^2 + 6x + 9) + 4(y^2 - 2y + 1) = -49 + 81 + 4$$

$$9(x + 3)^2 + 4(y - 1)^2 = 36$$

$$\frac{(x + 3)^2}{4} + \frac{(y - 1)^2}{9} = 1$$

Since $a > b$, this last equation is of the form

$$\frac{(x - h)^2}{b^2} + \frac{(y - k)^2}{a^2} = 1,$$

where $h = -3$, $k = 1$, $a = 3$, and $b = 2$. Thus, the endpoints of the major axis (vertices) are up 3 units and down 3 units from the center $(-3, 1)$. So they are at $(-3, 4)$ and $(-3, -2)$. Likewise, the endpoints of the minor axis are 2 units to the right and 2 units to the left of the center. Thus, they are at $(-1, 1)$ and $(-5, 1)$. From the relationship $c^2 = a^2 - b^2$, we get

$$c^2 = 9 - 4 = 5.$$

Thus, the foci are at $(-3, 1 + \sqrt{5})$ and $(-3, 1 - \sqrt{5})$. The ellipse is shown in Figure 9.25.

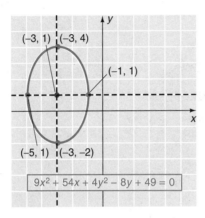

(-3, 1) (-3, 4)

(-1, 1)

(-5, 1) (-3, -2)

$9x^2 + 54x + 4y^2 - 8y + 49 = 0$

FIGURE 9.25

EXAMPLE 5

Write the equation of the ellipse that has vertices at $(-3, -5)$ and $(7, -5)$, and foci at $(-1, -5)$ and $(5, -5)$.

Solution

Since the vertices and foci are on the same horizontal line ($y = -5$) this ellipse has an equation of the form

$$\frac{(x - h)^2}{a^2} + \frac{(y - k)^2}{b^2} = 1.$$

The center of the ellipse is at the midpoint of the major axis. Therefore,

$$h = \frac{-3 + 7}{2} = 2 \quad \text{and} \quad k = \frac{-5 + (-5)}{2} = -5.$$

The distance between the center $(2, -5)$ and a vertex $(7, -5)$ is 5 units; thus, $a = 5$. The distance between the center $(2, -5)$ and a focus $(5, -5)$ is 3 units; thus, $c = 3$. Using the relationship $c^2 = a^2 - b^2$, we obtain

$$b^2 = a^2 - c^2 = 25 - 9 = 16.$$

Now let's substitute 2 for h, -5 for k, 25 for a^2, and 16 for b^2 in the general form and simplify.

$$\frac{(x-2)^2}{25} + \frac{(y+5)^2}{16} = 1$$

$$16(x-2)^2 + 25(y+5)^2 = 400$$

$$16(x^2 - 4x + 4) + 25(y^2 + 10y + 25) = 400$$

$$16x^2 - 64x + 64 + 25y^2 + 250y + 625 = 400$$

$$16x^2 - 64x + 25y^2 + 250y + 289 = 0$$

As with parabolas, ellipses also possess properties that make them very useful. For example, the elliptical surface formed by rotating an ellipse about its major axis has a property that forces light or sound waves emitted at one focus to reflect off of the surface and converge at the other focus. This is the principle behind "whispering galleries," such as the Rotunda of the Capitol Building in Washington, D.C. In such buildings, two people standing at two specific spots that are the foci of the elliptical ceiling can whisper and yet hear each other clearly even though they are quite far apart.

Ellipses also play an important role in astronomy. Johannes Kepler (1571–1630) showed that the orbit of a planet is an ellipse with the sun at one focus. For example, the orbit of the earth around the sun is elliptical but nearly circular, and at the same time the moon's orbit around the earth is an elliptical path (Figure 9.26).

The arches for concrete bridges are sometimes elliptical. One example is shown in Figure 9.28. Also, elliptical gears are used in certain kinds of machinery that require a slow but powerful force at impact, such as a heavy duty punch (Figure 9.27).

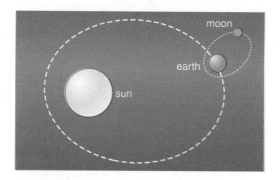

FIGURE 9.26

FIGURE 9.27

PROBLEM SET 9.2

For Problems 1–22, find the vertices, endpoints of minor axis, and foci of the given ellipse, and sketch its graph.

1. $\dfrac{x^2}{4} + \dfrac{y^2}{1} = 1$

2. $\dfrac{x^2}{16} + \dfrac{y^2}{1} = 1$

3. $\dfrac{x^2}{4} + \dfrac{y^2}{9} = 1$ **4.** $\dfrac{x^2}{4} + \dfrac{y^2}{16} = 1$

5. $9x^2 + 3y^2 = 27$ **6.** $4x^2 + 3y^2 = 36$

7. $2x^2 + 5y^2 = 50$ **8.** $5x^2 + 36y^2 = 180$

9. $12x^2 + y^2 = 36$ **10.** $8x^2 + y^2 = 16$

11. $7x^2 + 11y^2 = 77$ **12.** $4x^2 + y^2 = 12$

13. $4x^2 - 8x + 9y^2 - 36y + 4 = 0$

14. $x^2 + 6x + 9y^2 - 36y + 36 = 0$

15. $4x^2 + 16x + y^2 + 2y + 1 = 0$

16. $9x^2 - 36x + 4y^2 + 16y + 16 = 0$

17. $x^2 - 6x + 4y^2 + 5 = 0$

18. $16x^2 + 9y^2 + 36y - 108 = 0$

19. $9x^2 - 72x + 2y^2 + 4y + 128 = 0$

20. $5x^2 + 10x + 16y^2 + 160y + 325 = 0$

21. $2x^2 + 12x + 11y^2 - 88y + 172 = 0$

22. $9x^2 + 72x + y^2 + 6y + 135 = 0$

For Problems 23–36, find an equation of the ellipse that satisfies the given conditions.

23. Vertices $(\pm 5, 0)$, foci $(\pm 3, 0)$

24. Vertices $(\pm 4, 0)$, foci $(\pm 2, 0)$

25. Vertices $(0, \pm 6)$, foci $(0, \pm 5)$

26. Vertices $(0, \pm 3)$, foci $(0, \pm 2)$

27. Vertices $(\pm 3, 0)$, length of minor axis is 2

28. Vertices $(0, \pm 5)$, length of minor axis is 4

29. Foci $(0, \pm 2)$, length of minor axis is 3

30. Foci $(\pm 1, 0)$, length of minor axis is 2

31. Vertices $(0, \pm 5)$, contains the point $(3, 2)$

32. Vertices $(\pm 6, 0)$, contains the point $(5, 1)$

33. Vertices $(5, 1)$ and $(-3, 1)$, foci $(3, 1)$ and $(-1, 1)$

34. Vertices $(2, 4)$ and $(2, -6)$, foci $(2, 3)$ and $(2, -5)$

35. Center $(0, 1)$, one focus at $(-4, 1)$, length of minor axis is 6

36. Center $(3, 0)$, one focus at $(3, 2)$, length of minor axis is 4

37. Find an equation of the set of points in a plane such that the sum of the distances between each point of the set and the points $(2, 0)$ and $(-2, 0)$ is 8 units.

38. Find an equation of the set of points in a plane such that the sum of the distances between each point of the set and the points $(0, 3)$ and $(0, -3)$ is 10 units.

39. An arch of a bridge is semi-elliptical and its major axis is horizontal (see Figure 9.28). The arch is 30 feet wide and 10 feet high. Find the height of the arch 10 feet from the center of the base.

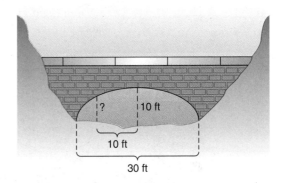

F I G U R E   9 . 2 8

40. In Figure 9.28, how much clearance is there 10 feet from the bank?

THOUGHTS into WORDS

41. What type of figure is the graph of the equation $x^2 + 6x + 2y^2 - 20y + 59 = 0$? Explain your answer. [*Hint:*

You may need to complete the square before you can decide.]

42. Suppose that someone graphed the equation $4x^2 - 16x + 9y^2 + 18y - 11 = 0$ and obtained the graph shown in Figure 9.29. How do you know by looking at the equation that this is an incorrect graph?

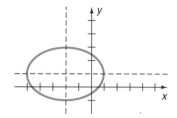

FIGURE 9.29

 GRAPHICS CALCULATOR ACTIVITIES

43. Use your graphics calculator to check your graphs for Problems 13–22.

44. Use your graphics calculator to graph each of the following ellipses.

　a. $2x^2 - 40x + y^2 + 2y + 185 = 0$

　b. $x^2 - 4x + 2y^2 - 48y + 272 = 0$

　c. $4x^2 - 8x + y^2 - 4y - 136 = 0$

　d. $x^2 + 6x + 2y^2 + 56y + 301 = 0$

9.3　HYPERBOLAS

The definition of a hyperbola resembles that of an ellipse except that it involves the **difference of distances** from two fixed points instead of the **sum of distances**.

> ### DEFINITION 9.3
>
> A **hyperbola** is the set of all points in a plane such that the difference of its distances from two fixed points F and F' in the plane (the **foci**) is a positive constant.

Use Definition 9.3 and sketch a hyperbola by starting with two fixed points F and F' (see Figure 9.30). Then locate all points P so that $PF' - PF$ is a positive constant. Likewise, locate all points Q so that $QF - QF'$ is the same positive constant. The two dashed curved lines in Figure 9.30 make up the **hyperbola**. The two curves are called the **branches** of the hyperbola.

To develop a standard form for the equation of a hyperbola, let's coordinatize the plane so that the foci are located at $F(c, 0)$, and $F'(-c, 0)$ as indicated in Figure 9.31. Using the distance formula and setting the difference of distances from any point P on the hyperbola to the foci equal to $2a$, we have the following equation.

$$\left| \sqrt{(x - c)^2 + (y - 0)^2} - \sqrt{(x + c)^2 + (y - 0)^2} \right| = 2a$$

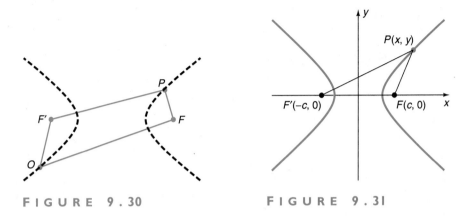

FIGURE 9.30   FIGURE 9.31

(The absolute value sign is used to allow the point P to be on either branch of the hyperbola.) Using the same type of simplification procedure that we used for deriving the standard form for the equation of an ellipse, this equation simplifies to

$$\frac{x^2}{a^2} - \frac{y^2}{c^2 - a^2} = 1.$$

Letting $b^2 = c^2 - a^2$, where $b > 0$, we obtain the standard form

$$\frac{x^2}{a^2} - \frac{y^2}{b^2} = 1. \tag{1}$$

Equation (1) indicates that this hyperbola is symmetric with respect to both axes and the origin. Furthermore, by letting $y = 0$, we obtain $x^2/a^2 = 1$ or $x^2 = a^2$, and therefore the x-intercepts are a and $-a$. The corresponding points $A(a, 0)$ and $A'(-a, 0)$ are the **vertices** of the hyperbola and the line segment $\overline{AA'}$ is called the **focal axis** (or transverse axis) and is of length $2a$ (see Figure 9.32). The origin is the

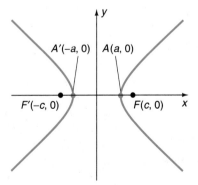

FIGURE 9.32

midpoint of the focal axis and is called the **center** of the hyperbola. By letting $x = 0$ in equation (1), we obtain $-(y^2/b^2) = 1$ or $y^2 = -b^2$. This implies that there are no y-intercepts, as indicated in Figure 9.32. The following property summarizes this discussion.

PROPERTY 9.5

The graph of the equation

$$\frac{x^2}{a^2} - \frac{y^2}{b^2} = 1$$

is a hyperbola with vertices at $(a, 0)$ and $(-a, 0)$. The foci are at $(c, 0)$ and $(-c, 0)$, where $c^2 = a^2 + b^2$.

In conjunction with every hyperbola there are two intersecting lines that pass through the center of the hyperbola. These lines, referred to as **asymptotes**, are very helpful when sketching a hyperbola. Their equations are easily determined based on the following type of reasoning: Solving the equation $(x^2/a^2) - (y^2/b^2) = 1$ for y produces $y = (\pm b/a)\sqrt{x^2 - a^2}$. From this form it is evident that there are no points on the graph for $x^2 - a^2 < 0$, that is, if $-a < x < a$. However, there are points on the graph if $x \geq a$ or $x \leq -a$. If $x \geq a$, then

$$y = \pm(b/a)\sqrt{x^2 - a^2} \text{ can be written as}$$

$$y = \pm\frac{b}{a}\sqrt{x^2\left(1 - \frac{a^2}{x^2}\right)}$$

$$= \pm\frac{b}{a}\sqrt{x^2}\sqrt{1 - \frac{a^2}{x^2}}$$

$$= \pm\frac{b}{a}x\sqrt{1 - \frac{a^2}{x^2}}.$$

Now suppose that we are going to determine some y-values for very large values of x. (Remember that a and b are arbitrary constants; they have specific values for a particular hyperbola). Because a^2/x^2 will be close to zero, the radicand will be close to one. Therefore, the y-value will be close to either $(b/a)x$ or $-(b/a)x$. In other words, as x becomes larger and larger, the point $P(x, y)$ gets closer and closer to either the line $y = (b/a)x$ or the line $y = -(b/a)x$. A corresponding situation occurs when $x \leq a$. The lines with equations

$$y = \pm\frac{b}{a}x$$

are called the **asymptotes** of the hyperbola.

As we mentioned earlier, the asymptotes are very helpful for sketching hyperbolas. An easy way to sketch the asymptotes is to first plot the vertices $A(a, 0)$ and $A'(-a, 0)$, and the points $B(0, b)$ and $B'(0, -b)$, as in Figure 9.33. The line segment $\overline{BB'}$ is of length $2b$ and is called the **conjugate axis** of the hyperbola. The horizontal line segments drawn through the endpoints of the conjugate axis, along with the vertical line segments drawn through the endpoints of the focal axis, form a rectangle. The diagonals of this rectangle have slopes of b/a and $-(b/a)$. Therefore, by extending the diagonals we obtain the asymptotes $y = (b/a)x$ and $y = -(b/a)x$. We can sketch the two branches of the hyperbola using the asymptotes as guidelines, as shown in Figure 9.33.

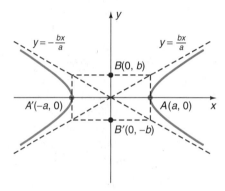

FIGURE 9.33

EXAMPLE 1

Find the vertices, foci, equations of asymptotes, and sketch the hyperbola $9x^2 - 4y^2 = 36$.

Solution

Dividing both sides of the given equation by 36 and simplifying changes the equation to the standard form

$$\frac{x^2}{4} - \frac{y^2}{9} = 1,$$

where $a^2 = 4$ and $b^2 = 9$. Hence, $a = 2$ and $b = 3$. The vertices $(\pm 2, 0)$ and the endpoints $(0, \pm 3)$ of the conjugate axis determine the rectangle whose diagonals extended are the asymptotes. Using $a = 2$ and $b = 3$, the equations of the asymptotes are $y = \frac{3}{2}x$ and $y = -\frac{3}{2}x$. Then using the relationship $c^2 = a^2 + b^2$, we obtain $c^2 = 4 + 9 = 13$. So the foci are at $(\sqrt{13}, 0)$ and $(-\sqrt{13}, 0)$. Using the vertices and the asymptotes, sketch the hyperbola as in Figure 9.34.

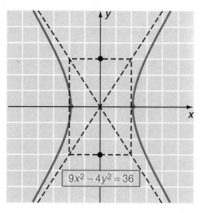

$9x^2 - 4y^2 = 36$

F I G U R E   9 . 3 4

E X A M P L E   2

Find the equation of the hyperbola with vertices at $(\pm 4, 0)$ and foci at $(\pm 2\sqrt{5}, 0)$.

Solution

From the given information we know that $a = 4$ and $c = 2\sqrt{5}$. Then using the relationship $b^2 = c^2 - a^2$, we obtain

$$b^2 = (2\sqrt{5})^2 - 4^2 = 20 - 16 = 4.$$

Substituting 16 for a^2 and 4 for b^2 in the standard form produces

$$\frac{x^2}{16} - \frac{y^2}{4} = 1.$$

Multiplying both sides of this equation by 16 produces

$$x^2 - 4y^2 = 16.$$

Hyperbolas with Foci on the y-Axis

A standard form for the equation of a hyperbola with foci on the y-axis can be developed in a similar fashion. The following property summarizes the results of such a development with the foci at $(0, c)$ and $(0, -c)$.

P R O P E R T Y   9 . 6

The graph of the equation

$$\frac{y^2}{a^2} - \frac{x^2}{b^2} = 1$$

is a hyperbola with vertices at $(0, a)$ and $(0, -a)$. The foci are at $(0, c)$ and $(0, -c)$, where $c^2 = a^2 + b^2$.

For this type of hyperbola, the endpoints of the conjugate axis are at $(b, 0)$ and $(-b, 0)$. Again, you can find the asymptotes by extending the diagonals of the rectangle determined by the horizontal lines through the vertices and the vertical lines through the endpoints of the conjugate axis. The slopes of these diagonals are a/b and $-(a/b)$; thus, the equations of these asymptotes are $y = (a/b)x$ and $y = -(a/b)x$.

EXAMPLE 3

Find the vertices, foci, equations of asymptotes, and sketch the hyperbola $4y^2 - x^2 = 12$.

Solution

Divide both sides of the given equation by 12 to change the equation to the standard form

$$\frac{y^2}{3} - \frac{x^2}{12} = 1,$$

where $a^2 = 3$ and $b^2 = 12$. Hence, $a = \sqrt{3}$ and $b = 2\sqrt{3}$. The vertices $(0, \pm\sqrt{3})$ and the endpoints $(\pm 2\sqrt{3}, 0)$ of the conjugate axis determine the rectangle whose diagonals extended are the asymptotes. Using $a = \sqrt{3}$ and $b = 2\sqrt{3}$, the equations of the asymptotes are $y = (\sqrt{3}/2\sqrt{3})x = \frac{1}{2}x$ and $y = -\frac{1}{2}x$. Then using the relationship $c^2 = a^2 + b^2$, we obtain $c^2 = 3 + 12 = 15$. So the foci are at $(0, \sqrt{15})$ and $(0, -\sqrt{15})$. A sketch of the hyperbola is in Figure 9.35.

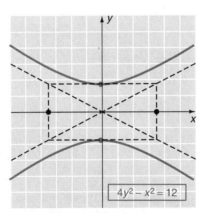

$$4y^2 - x^2 = 12$$

F I G U R E   9 . 35

Other Hyperbolas

As with parabolas and ellipses, the translation of axes formulas can be used to expand our work with hyperbolas. From our previous work in this section we know that

$$\frac{(x')^2}{a^2} - \frac{(y')^2}{b^2} = 1$$

represents a hyperbola with its center at O' of the $x'y'$-plane. Therefore, substituting $x - h$ for x' and $y - k$ for y' produces

$$\frac{(x - h)^2}{a^2} - \frac{(y - k)^2}{b^2} = 1,$$

which is the equation of the same hyperbola with its center at (h, k) of the xy-system. The focal axis of this hyperbola is on the horizontal line $y = k$. In a similar fashion the equation

$$\frac{(y')^2}{a^2} - \frac{(x')^2}{b^2} = 1$$

produces

$$\frac{(y - k)^2}{a^2} - \frac{(x - h)^2}{b^2} = 1,$$

which is the equation of the hyperbola that has its focal axis on the vertical line $x = h$.

The relationship $c^2 = a^2 + b^2$ holds for both of these hyperbolas and the physical significance of a, b, and c remains the same. However, these values are used relative to the center (h, k) to find the endpoints of the focal and conjugate axes, and the foci. Furthermore, the slopes of the asymptotes are as before, but these lines now contain the center (h, k). Let's see how all of this works in a specific example.

E X A M P L E   4

Find the vertices, foci, equations of asymptotes, and sketch the hyperbola $9x^2 - 36x - 16y^2 + 96y - 252 = 0$.

Solution

First, we need to change to a standard form by completing the square on both x and y.

$$9(x^2 - 4x + \underline{\quad}) - 16(h^2 - 6y + \underline{\quad}) = 252$$

$$9(x^2 - 4x + 4) - 16(y^2 - 6y + 9) = 252 + 36 - 144$$

$$9(x - 2)^2 - 16(y - 3)^2 = 144$$

$$\frac{(x - 2)^2}{16} - \frac{(y - 3)^2}{9} = 1$$

The center is at $(2, 3)$ and the focal axis is on the line $y = 3$. Since $a^2 = 16$, we know that $a = 4$. Therefore, the vertices are 4 units to the right and 4 units to the left of the center $(2, 3)$. So they are at $(6, 3)$ and $(-2, 3)$. Likewise, since $b^2 = 9$ or $b = 3$, the endpoints of the conjugate axis are 3 units up and 3 units down from the center. So they are at $(2, 6)$ and $(2, 0)$. Using $a = 4$ and $b = 3$, the slopes of the asymptotes are $\frac{3}{4}$ and $-\frac{3}{4}$. Then using these slopes, the center $(2, 3)$, and the point-slope form for writing the equation of a line, we determine the equations of the asymptotes to be $3x - 4y = -6$ and $3x + 4y = 18$. From the relationship $c^2 = a^2 + b^2$ we can obtain $c^2 = 16 + 9 = 25$. Thus, the foci are at $(7, 3)$ and $(-3, 3)$. Figure 9.36 is a sketch of the hyperbola.

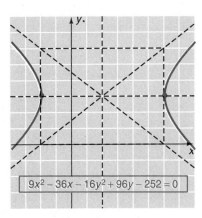

$$9x^2 - 36x - 16y^2 + 96y - 252 = 0$$

FIGURE 9.36

EXAMPLE 5

Find the equation of the hyperbola with vertices at $(-4, 2)$ and $(-4, -4)$, and foci at $(-4, 3)$ and $(-4, -5)$.

Solution

Since the vertices and foci are on the same vertical line ($x = -4$), this hyperbola has an equation of the form

$$\frac{(y - k)^2}{a^2} - \frac{(x - h)^2}{b^2} = 1.$$

The center of the hyperbola is at the midpoint of the focal axis. Therefore,

$$h = \frac{-4 + (-4)}{2} = -4 \qquad \text{and} \qquad k = \frac{2 + (-4)}{2} = -1.$$

The distance between the center $(-4, -1)$ and a vertex $(-4, 2)$ is 3 units; so $a = 3$. The distance between the center $(-4, -1)$ and a focus $(-4, 3)$ is 4 units; so $c = 4$. Then using the relationship $c^2 = a^2 + b^2$, we obtain

$$b^2 = c^2 - a^2 = 16 - 9 = 7.$$

Now we can substitute -4 for h, -1 for k, 9 for a^2, and 7 for b^2 in the general form and simplify.

$$\frac{(y + 1)^2}{9} - \frac{(x + 4)^2}{7} = 1$$

$$7(y + 1)^2 - 9(x + 4)^2 = 63$$

$$7(y^2 + 2y + 1) - 9(x^2 + 8x + 16) = 63$$

$$7y^2 + 14y + 7 - 9x^2 - 72x - 144 = 63$$

$$7y^2 + 14y - 9x^2 - 72x - 200 = 0$$

The hyperbola also has numerous applications, many you may not be aware of. For example, one method of artillery range-finding is based on the concept of a hyperbola. If each of two listening posts, P_1 and P_2 in Figure 9.37 records the time that an artillery blast is heard, then the difference between the times multiplied by the speed of sound gives the difference of the distances of the gun from the two fixed points. Thus, the gun is located somewhere on the hyperbola whose foci are the two listening posts. Now by bringing in a third listening post, P_3, another hyperbola can be formed with foci at P_2 and P_3. Then the location of the gun must be at one of the intersections of the two hyperbolas.

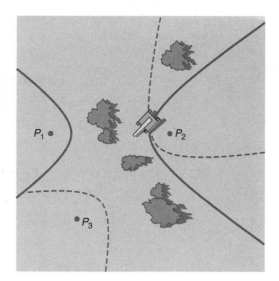

F I G U R E 9 . 37

This same principle of intersecting hyperbolas is used in a long range navigation system known as LORAN. Radar stations serve as the foci of the hyperbolas and of course computers are used for the many calculations that are necessary to fix the location of a plane or ship. At the present time, LORAN is probably used mostly for coastal navigation in connection with small pleasure boats.

Some rather unique architectural creations have used the concept of a hyperbolic paraboloid pictured in Figure 9.38. For example, the TWA building at Kennedy Airport is so designed. Some comets upon entering the sun's gravitational field will follow a hyperbolic path, with the sun as one of the foci (see Figure 9.39).

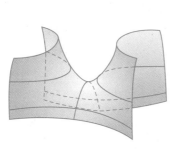

FIGURE   9.38

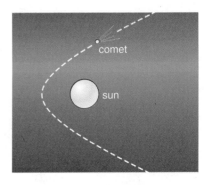

FIGURE   9.39

PROBLEM SET 9.3

For Problems 1–22, find the vertices, foci, equations of asymptotes, and sketch each of the hyperbolas.

1. $\dfrac{x^2}{9} - \dfrac{y^2}{4} = 1$

2. $\dfrac{x^2}{4} - \dfrac{y^2}{16} = 1$

3. $\dfrac{y^2}{4} - \dfrac{x^2}{9} = 1$

4. $\dfrac{y^2}{16} - \dfrac{x^2}{4} = 1$

5. $9y^2 - 16x^2 = 144$

6. $4y^2 - x^2 = 4$

7. $x^2 - y^2 = 9$

8. $x^2 - y^2 = 1$

9. $5y^2 - x^2 = 25$

10. $y^2 - 2x^2 = 8$

11. $y^2 - 9x^2 = -9$

12. $16y^2 - x^2 = -16$

13. $4x^2 - 24x - 9y^2 - 18y - 9 = 0$

14. $9x^2 + 72x - 4y^2 - 16y + 92 = 0$

15. $y^2 - 4y - 4x^2 - 24x - 36 = 0$

16. $9y^2 + 54y - x^2 + 6x + 63 = 0$

17. $2x^2 - 8x - y^2 + 4 = 0$

18. $x^2 + 6x - 3y^2 = 0$

19. $y^2 + 10y - 9x^2 + 16 = 0$

20. $4y^2 - 16y - x^2 + 12 = 0$

21. $x^2 + 4x - y^2 - 4y - 1 = 0$

22. $y^2 + 8y - x^2 + 2x + 14 = 0$

For Problems 23–28, find an equation of the hyperbola that satisfies the given conditions.

23. Vertices $(\pm 2, 0)$, foci $(\pm 3, 0)$

24. Vertices $(\pm 1, 0)$, foci $(\pm 4, 0)$

25. Vertices $(0, \pm 3)$, foci $(0, \pm 5)$

26. Vertices $(0, \pm 2)$, foci $(0, \pm 6)$

27. Vertices $(\pm 1, 0)$, contains the point $(2, 3)$

28. Vertices $(0, \pm 1)$, contains the point $(-3, 5)$

29. Vertices $(0, \pm \sqrt{3})$, length of conjugate axis is 4

30. Vertices $(\pm \sqrt{5}, 0)$, length of conjugate axis is 6

31. Foci $(\pm \sqrt{23}, 0)$, length of focal axis is 8

32. Foci $(0, \pm 3\sqrt{2})$, length of conjugate axis is 4

33. Vertices $(6, -3)$ and $(2, -3)$, foci $(7, -3)$ and $(1, -3)$

34. Vertices $(-7, -4)$ and $(-5, -4)$, foci $(-8, -4)$ and $(-4, -4)$

35. Vertices $(-3, 7)$ and $(-3, 3)$, foci $(-3, 9)$ and $(-3, 1)$

36. Vertices $(7, 5)$ and $(7, -1)$, foci $(7, 7)$ and $(7, -3)$

37. Vertices $(0, 0)$ and $(4, 0)$, foci $(5, 0)$ and $(-1, 0)$

38. Vertices $(0, 0)$ and $(0, -6)$, foci $(0, 2)$ and $(0, -8)$

For Problems 39–48, identify the graph of each of the equations as a straight line, circle, parabola, ellipse, or hyperbola. Do not sketch the graphs.

39. $x^2 - 7x + y^2 + 8y - 2 = 0$

40. $x^2 - 7x - y^2 + 8y - 2 = 0$

41. $5x - 7y = 9$

42. $4x^2 - x + y^2 + 2y - 3 = 0$

43. $10x^2 + y^2 = 8$

44. $-3x - 2y = 9$

45. $5x^2 + 3x - 2y^2 - 3y - 1 = 0$

46. $x^2 + y^2 - 3y - 6 = 0$

47. $x^2 - 3x + y - 4 = 0$

48. $5x + y^2 - 2y - 1 = 0$

49. What is the difference between the graphs of the equations $x^2 + y^2 = 0$ and $x^2 - y^2 = 0$?

50. What is the difference between the graphs of the equations $4x^2 + 9y^2 = 0$ and $9x^2 + 4y^2 = 0$?

51. A flashlight produces a "cone of light" that can be cut by the plane of a wall to illustrate the conic sections. Try

shining a flashlight against a wall (stand within a couple feet of the wall) at different angles to produce a circle, an ellipse, a parabola, and one branch of a hyperbola. (You may find it difficult to distinguish between a parabola and a branch of a hyperbola.) Write a paragraph explaining this experiment to someone else.

 GRAPHICS CALCULATOR ACTIVITIES

52. Use a graphics calculator to check your graphs for Problems 13–22. Be sure to graph the asymptotes for each hyperbola.

53. Use a graphics calculator to check your answers for Problems 39–48.

9.4 ROTATION OF AXES

Each of the standard equations developed in the previous three sections represents a conic section with its axes parallel to the coordinate axes of the xy-plane. For example, the equation

$$\frac{(x - h)^2}{a^2} + \frac{(y - k)^2}{b^2} = 1$$

represents an ellipse with its major axis a part of the horizontal line $y = k$ and its minor axis a part of the vertical line $x = h$. Likewise, each of those standard equations expanded produces a second-degree equation of the form

$$Ax^2 + Cy^2 + Dx + Ey + F = 0.$$

If a conic section is *tilted* so that its axes are not parallel to the x- and y-axis, then its equation contains an xy-term and is of the form

$$Ax^2 + Bxy + Cy^2 + Dx + Ey + F = 0.$$

Such an equation, in which A, B, and C are not all zero, is called a **second-degree equation** in x and y. As an illustration of such a conic section, consider the following example.

EXAMPLE I

Find the equation of the ellipse that has its foci at $(1, 2)$ and $(-1, -2)$ such that the sum of the distances from each point $P(x, y)$ on the ellipse to the foci is 6 units.

Solution

The ellipse is sketched in Figure 9.40. Use the distance formula to express the fact that the sum of the distances from any point P to the foci is 6 units.

$$\sqrt{(x - 1)^2 + (y - 2)^2} + \sqrt{(x + 1)^2 + (y + 2)^2} = 6$$

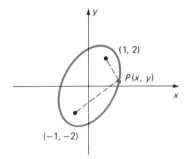

F I G U R E   9 . 40

This equation can be expressed as

$$\sqrt{(x - 1)^2 + (y - 2)^2} = 6 - \sqrt{(x + 1)^2 + (y + 2)^2}.$$

Square both sides, then isolate the remaining radical, then square again and simplify to produce the equation

$$8x^2 - 4xy + 5y^2 - 36 = 0.$$

Rotation of Axes Formulas

To study conics that are *tilted* relative to the coordinate axes it is often helpful to rotate the coordinate axes so that they are parallel to the axes of the conic. In Figure 9.41 we rotated the axes of the xy-system about the origin through an angle θ to produce the $x'y'$-coordinate system. Thus, each point P in the plane has coordinates (x, y) and (x', y'). To see how the two sets of coordinates are related, consider Figure 9.42. In this figure, r represents the distance from the common origin O to the point P, and α is the angle between the x'-axis and $\overline{OP}$. It follows that

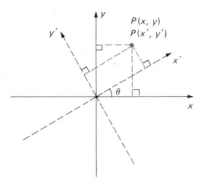

FIGURE 9.41

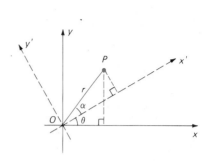

FIGURE 9.42

$$x' = r \cos \alpha, \qquad y' = r \sin \alpha \tag{1}$$

and

$$x = r \cos(\theta + \alpha), \qquad y = r \sin(\theta + \alpha). \tag{2}$$

Using the trigonometric identities for $\sin(\theta + \alpha)$ and $\cos(\theta + \alpha)$, the relationships in (2) can be written as

$$x = r \cos \theta \cos \alpha - r \sin \theta \sin \alpha$$

and

$$y = r \sin \theta \cos \alpha + r \cos \theta \sin \alpha.$$

Now by substituting x' for $r \cos \alpha$ and y' for $r \sin \alpha$, we obtain the following equations for rotating axes.

Rotation
equations

$$x = x' \cos \theta - y' \sin \theta$$
$$y = x' \sin \theta + y' \cos \theta$$

The rotation equations can be used to simplify an equation by eliminating the xy-term. For example, the equation $8x^2 - 4xy + 5y^2 - 36 = 0$ of Example 1 can be simplified by rotating the axes so that they coincide with the axes of the ellipse. From Figure 9.40 we see that this can be accomplished by letting θ be an acute angle such that $\theta = \arctan 2$. The values for $\sin \theta$ and $\cos \theta$ can be determined from Figure 9.43. Therefore,

$$\sin \theta = \frac{2}{\sqrt{5}} = \frac{2\sqrt{5}}{5}$$

and

$$\cos \theta = \frac{1}{\sqrt{5}} = \frac{\sqrt{5}}{5}.$$

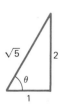

FIGURE 9.43

Using these values for $\sin \theta$ and $\cos \theta$ in the general rotation equations yields the following rotation equations for this problem.

$$x = \frac{\sqrt{5}}{5}x' - \frac{2\sqrt{5}}{5}y' = \frac{\sqrt{5}}{5}(x' - 2y')$$

$$y = \frac{2\sqrt{5}}{5}x' + \frac{\sqrt{5}}{5}y' = \frac{\sqrt{5}}{5}(2x' + y')$$

Substituting these values for x and y into the given equation yields

$$8x^2 - 4xy + 5y^2 - 36 = 0$$

$$8\left[\frac{\sqrt{5}}{5}(x' - 2y')\right]^2 - 4\left[\frac{\sqrt{5}}{5}(x' - 2y')\right]\left[\frac{\sqrt{5}}{5}(2x' + y')\right]$$

$$+ 5\left[\frac{\sqrt{5}}{5}(2x' + y')\right]^2 - 36 = 0,$$

which simplifies to

$$\frac{(x')^2}{9} + \frac{(y')^2}{4} = 1.$$

If $\theta = \arctan 2$, then $\theta = 63.4°$, to the nearest tenth of a degree. Therefore, we can rotate the xy-system $63.4°$ to form the $x'y'$-system and then graph the ellipse as in Figure 9.44. (Remember that Figure 9.40 was a rough sketch based on the given information.)

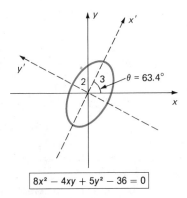

8x² − 4xy + 5y² − 36 = 0

FIGURE 9.44

How to Choose θ

In general, to eliminate the xy-term of any second-degree equation in x and y we can reason as follows: Substitute $x = x' \cos \theta - y' \sin \theta$ and $y = x' \sin \theta + y' \cos \theta$ in the equation $Ax^2 + Bxy + Cy^2 + Dx + Ey + F = 0$.

$$A(x' \cos \theta - y' \sin \theta)^2 + B(x' \cos \theta - y' \sin \theta)(x' \sin \theta + y' \cos \theta)$$
$$+ \; C(x' \sin \theta + y' \cos \theta)^2 + D(x' \cos \theta - y' \sin \theta)$$
$$+ \; E(x' \sin \theta + y' \cos \theta) + F = 0$$

This equation is of the form

$$A'(x')^2 + B'x'y' + C'(y')^2 + D'x' + E'y' + F' = 0$$

where the coefficient B' of the $x'y'$-term is

$$B' = 2(C - A) \sin \theta \cos \theta + B(\cos^2 \theta - \sin^2 \theta).$$

Using the double angle identities, this can be written as

$$B' = (C - A) \sin 2\theta + B \cos 2\theta.$$

To eliminate the $x'y'$-term we can set B' equal to zero. Thus,

$$(C - A) \sin 2\theta + B \cos 2\theta = 0,$$

which is equivalent to

$$\cot 2\theta = \frac{A - C}{B}.$$

The following property summarizes this discussion.

PROPERTY 9.7

The xy-term of the equation $Ax^2 + Bxy + Cy^2 + Dx + Ey + F = 0$, where $B \neq 0$, can be eliminated by using the rotation equations with θ chosen as an acute angle to satisfy the condition

$$\cot 2\theta = \frac{A - C}{B}$$

EXAMPLE 2

Identify and sketch the curve $4x^2 - 24xy + 11y^2 + 20 = 0$.

Solution

From the given equation we have $A = 4$, $B = -24$, and $C = 11$. Therefore,

$$\cot 2\theta = \frac{A - C}{B} = \frac{4 - 11}{-24} = \frac{-7}{-24} = \frac{7}{24}.$$

Then using the following reference right triangle (Figure 9.45), we obtain $\cos 2\theta = \frac{7}{25}$. Now we can use the half-angle formulas to determine $\sin \theta$ and $\cos \theta$.

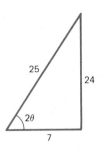

FIGURE 9.45

$$\sin\theta = \sqrt{\frac{1 - \cos 2\theta}{2}} = \sqrt{\frac{1 - \dfrac{7}{25}}{2}} = \frac{3}{5}$$

$$\cos\theta = \sqrt{\frac{1 + \cos 2\theta}{2}} = \sqrt{\frac{1 + \dfrac{7}{25}}{2}} = \frac{4}{5}$$

Substituting these values in the rotation equations produces

$$x = \frac{4}{5}x' - \frac{3}{5}y' = \frac{1}{5}(4x' - 3y')$$

and

$$y = \frac{3}{5}x' + \frac{4}{5}y' = \frac{1}{5}(3x' + 4y').$$

Finally, we can substitute these values for x and y in the original equation and simplify. (We will leave the algebraic details of this process for you to complete.) The resulting equation in the $x'y'$-system is

$$\frac{(x')^2}{4} - \frac{(y')^2}{1} = 1,$$

which is a hyperbola that has its vertices 2 units from the origin on the x'-axis. Since $\sin\theta = \frac{3}{5}$, we obtain $\theta = 36.9°$, to the nearest tenth of a degree. The hyperbola is depicted in Figure 9.46.

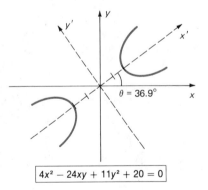

$$4x^2 - 24xy + 11y^2 + 20 = 0$$

FIGURE 9.46

EXAMPLE 3

Identify and sketch the curve

$$3x^2 + 2\sqrt{3}xy + y^2 + 8x - 8\sqrt{3}y = 0.$$

Solution

From the given equation we have $A = 3$, $B = 2\sqrt{3}$, and $C = 1$.

$$\cot 2\theta = \frac{3 - 1}{2\sqrt{3}} = \frac{2}{2\sqrt{3}} = \frac{1}{\sqrt{3}} = \frac{\sqrt{3}}{3}$$

Therefore, $2\theta = 60°$ or $\theta = 30°$; consequently, $\sin 30° = \frac{1}{2}$ and $\cos 30° = \frac{\sqrt{3}}{2}$. Substituting these values in the rotation equations produces

$$x = \frac{\sqrt{3}}{2}x' - \frac{1}{2}y' \qquad \text{and} \qquad y = \frac{1}{2}x' + \frac{\sqrt{3}}{2}y'.$$

Finally, we can substitute these values for x and y in the original equation and simplify. (Again we will leave the algebraic details of this process for you to complete.) The resulting equation in the $x'y'$-system is

$$(x')^2 = 4y',$$

which is a parabola with its vertex at the origin, opening upward, that has the y'-axis as an axis of symmetry. A sketch of the parabola is in Figure 9.47.

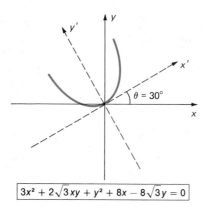

$$\boxed{3x^2 + 2\sqrt{3}\,xy + y^2 + 8x - 8\sqrt{3}\,y = 0}$$

FIGURE 9.47

EXAMPLE 4

Identify and sketch the curve

$$40x^2 - 36xy + 25y^2 - 8\sqrt{13}x - 12\sqrt{13}y = 0.$$

Solution

From the given equation we have $A = 40$, $B = -36$, and $C = 25$.

$$\cot 2\theta = \frac{40 - 25}{-36} = -\frac{15}{36} = -\frac{5}{12}$$

Then using the reference right triangle in Figure 9.48, we obtain $\cos 2\theta = -\frac{5}{13}$. Now the half-angle formulas can be used to determine $\sin \theta$ and $\cos \theta$.

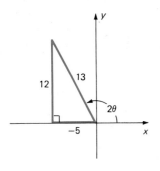

FIGURE 9.48

$$\sin\theta = \sqrt{\frac{1-\cos 2\theta}{2}} = \sqrt{\frac{1+\frac{5}{13}}{2}} = \frac{3\sqrt{13}}{13}$$

$$\cos\theta = \sqrt{\frac{1+\cos 2\theta}{2}} = \sqrt{\frac{1-\frac{5}{13}}{2}} = \frac{2\sqrt{13}}{13}$$

Substituting these values in the rotation equations produces

$$x = \frac{2\sqrt{13}}{13}x' - \frac{3\sqrt{13}}{13}y' = \frac{\sqrt{13}}{13}(2x' - 3y')$$

and

$$y = \frac{3\sqrt{13}}{13}x' + \frac{2\sqrt{13}}{13}y' = \frac{\sqrt{13}}{13}(3x' + 2y').$$

Finally, we can substitute these values for x and y in the original equation and simplify. (Again we will leave the details of this process for you to complete.) The resulting equation in the $x'y'$-system is

$$(x')^2 - 4x' + 4(y')^2 = 0.$$

This is an ellipse translated along the x'-axis. Thus, we can fit a standard form by completing the square on x'.

$$(x')^2 - 4x' + 4 + 4(y') = 4$$

$$(x' - 2)^2 + 4(y')^2 = 4$$

$$\frac{(x' - 2)^2}{4} + \frac{(y')^2}{1} = 1$$

So the ellipse has a major axis 4 units long and a minor axis 2 units long. It is translated 2 units in a positive direction along the x'-axis. The ellipse is sketched in Figure 9.49, where $\theta = 56.3°$, to the nearest tenth of a degree.

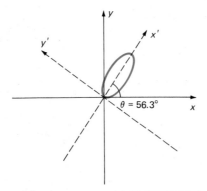

$$\boxed{40x^2 - 36xy + 25y^2 - 8\sqrt{13}x - 12\sqrt{13}y = 0}$$

FIGURE 9.49

E X A M P L E 5

Find the $x'y'$-coordinates of the point $(4, 2)$ if the xy-axes are rotated through an angle of $\theta = 45°$.

Solution

Since $\theta = 45°$, we have $\sin \theta = \sqrt{2}/2$ and $\cos \theta = \sqrt{2}/2$. Now we can substitute 4 for x and 2 for y in the rotation equations to form the following system of equations.

$$\left(\begin{array}{l} 4 = \dfrac{\sqrt{2}}{2}x' - \dfrac{\sqrt{2}}{2}y' \\[2mm] 2 = \dfrac{\sqrt{2}}{2}x' + \dfrac{\sqrt{2}}{2}y' \end{array} \right)$$

Solving this equation for x' and y' produces

$$x' = 3\sqrt{2} \quad \text{and} \quad y' = -\sqrt{2}.$$

So the $x'y'$-coordinates of the point $(4, 2)$ are $(3\sqrt{2}, -\sqrt{2})$ if the xy-axes are rotated $45°$.

P R O B L E M S E T 9 . 4

For Problems 1–10, the xy-system is to be rotated through the given angle θ. Find the equation of the given curve in terms of x' and y'. Then sketch the curve.

1. $xy = 1$, $\quad \theta = 45°$

2. $xy = -2$, $\quad \theta = 45°$

3. $3x^2 - 2xy + 3y^2 = 18$, $\quad \theta = 45°$

4. $5x^2 + 6xy + 5y^2 = 8$, $\quad \theta = 45°$

5. $x^2 - 4xy + y^2 + 9 = 0$, $\quad \theta = 45°$

6. $x^2 - 6xy + y^2 + 18 = 0$, $\quad \theta = 45°$

7. $41x^2 - 24xy + 34y^2 - 25 = 0$ $\quad \theta = \arcsin \dfrac{4}{5}$

8. $31x^2 + 10\sqrt{3}xy + 21y^2 = 144$, $\quad \theta = \arccos \dfrac{\sqrt{3}}{2}$

9. $9x^2 - 24xy + 16y^2 = 100$, $\quad \theta = \arcsin \dfrac{3}{5}$

10. $9x^2 + 24xy + 16y^2 = 225$, $\quad \theta = \arccos \dfrac{3}{5}$

For Problems 11–28, rotate the coordinate axes to remove the xy-term. Then sketch the graph of the curve.

11. $3x^2 + 2\sqrt{3}xy + y^2 - x + \sqrt{3}y = 0$

12. $2x^2 + 4\sqrt{3}xy + 6y^2 - \sqrt{3}x + y = 0$

13. $x^2 + 2xy + y^2 + \sqrt{2}x - \sqrt{2}y + 4 = 0$

14. $x^2 - 2xy + y^2 - \sqrt{2}x - \sqrt{2}y - 2 = 0$

15. $7x^2 + 2\sqrt{3}xy + 5y^2 - 32 = 0$

16. $x^2 + 4xy + y^2 + 9 = 0$

17. $11x^2 + 10\sqrt{3}xy + y^2 = 4$

18. $32x^2 - 72xy + 53y^2 = 80$

19. $16x^2 - 24xy + 9y^2 - 60x - 80y + 100 = 0$

20. $x^2 + 4xy + 4y^2 + 6\sqrt{5}x - 18\sqrt{5}y + 45 = 0$

21. $73x^2 - 72xy + 52y^2 - 60x - 80y = 0$

22. $57x^2 + 48xy + 43y^2 - 60x + 80y + 25 = 0$

23. $5x^2 + 6\sqrt{3}xy - y^2 - 24\sqrt{3}x - 24y + 64 = 0$

24. $7x^2 - 10\sqrt{3}xy - 3y^2 - 12\sqrt{3}x + 12y - 12 = 0$

25. $59x^2 + 24xy + 66y^2 + 170x + 60y - 25 = 0$

26. $7x^2 - 48xy - 7y^2 = 0$

27. $34x^2 - 24xy + 41y^2 = 0$

28. $43x^2 + 48xy + 57y^2 + 25 = 0$

29. Find the $x'y'$-coordinates of the points $(-6, -4)$ and $(2, 8)$ if the xy-axes are rotated through an angle $\theta = 30°$.

30. Find the $x'y'$-coordinates of the points $(-4, -6)$ and $(2, -10)$ if the xy-axes are rotated through an angle $\theta = 60°$.

FURTHER INVESTIGATIONS

31. Solve the system $\begin{pmatrix} x = x' \cos\theta - y' \sin\theta \\ y = x' \sin\theta + y' \cos\theta \end{pmatrix}$ for x' and y'.

32. Use your results from Problem 31 to redo Problems 29 and 30.

GRAPHICS CALCULATOR ACTIVITIES

33. Use your graphics calculator to check your graphs for Problems 1–28.

9.5   POLAR EQUATIONS OF CONICS

We introduced polar coordinates in Section 8.3. Recall that the polar coordinate system provides another way of naming points in a coordinatized plane. The polar coordinates (r, θ) of a point P measure its distance r from a fixed point O and the angle θ that ray OP makes with a horizontal ray OA directed to the right (Figure 9.50). The point O is called the pole and the ray OA is called the polar axis. The following equations summarize the relationships between polar coordinates (r, θ) and rectangular coordinates (x, y).

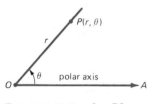

$$x = r \cos\theta \qquad\qquad y = r \sin\theta$$

$$r^2 = x^2 + y^2 \qquad \tan\theta = \frac{y}{x}$$

FIGURE   9.50

Also recall that the polar equation $r \cos\theta = a$ represents a line perpendicular to the polar axis a units from the pole and the equation $r \sin\theta = b$ represents a line parallel to the polar axis b units from the pole.

Now let's use the polar coordinate system to take another look at conic sections. In addition to being able to define each conic section separately, it is also possible to give one general definition that includes all of the conics. Definition 9.4 accomplishes that objective.

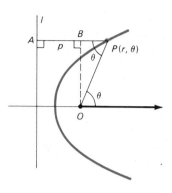

F I G U R E 9 . 5 I

DEFINITION 9.4

A **conic** is the set of all points whose distance from a fixed point is equal to the product of a positive constant e and the distance to a fixed line, not through the fixed point.

The fixed point is called a **focus**, the fixed constant e the **eccentricity**, and the fixed line the **directrix**. The conic is an ellipse if $0 < e < 1$, a parabola if $e = 1$, and a hyperbola if $e > 1$.

Using Definition 9.4 and the polar coordinate system we can derive a general polar equation of conics as follows: In Figure 9.51, the focus is at the pole and the directrix l is perpendicular to the polar axis extended. Let p represent the distance between the focus and the directrix. Now using Definition 9.4 and Figure 9.51 we see that

$$OP = e(AP)$$
$$r = e(AB + BP)$$
$$r = e(p + r\cos\theta)$$
$$r = ep + er\cos\theta$$
$$r - er\cos\theta = ep$$
$$r(1 - e\cos\theta) = ep$$
$$r = \frac{ep}{1 - e\cos\theta}.$$

If we had chosen the directrix to the right of the focus, as in Figure 9.52 then the equation $r = (ep)/(1 + e\cos\theta)$ would have resulted. Likewise, by choosing the directrix parallel to the polar axis, either above or below it, the forms $r = (ep)/(1 + e\sin\theta)$ and $r = (ep)/(1 - e\sin\theta)$ are produced as illustrated in Figures 9.53 and 9.54.

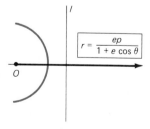

F I G U R E 9 . 5 2

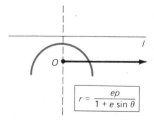

F I G U R E 9 . 5 3

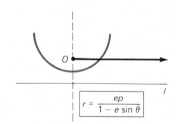

F I G U R E 9 . 5 4

The following property summarizes our previous discussion.

PROPERTY 9.8

A polar equation that has one of the four forms

$$r = \frac{ep}{1 \pm e \cos \theta}, \qquad r = \frac{ep}{1 \pm e \sin \theta}$$

is a conic section. The conic is an ellipse if $0 < e < 1$, a parabola if $e = 1$, and a hyperbola if $e > 1$.

EXAMPLE I

Find the polar equation of the parabola that has its focus at the pole and its vertex at $(3, \pi/2)$. Also sketch its graph.

Solution

Since it is a parabola, we know that $e = 1$. Furthermore, because the vertex is on the 90°-axis and above the focus, the equation is of the form $r = (ep)/(1 + e \sin \theta)$. The distance between the focus and the vertex is 3 units; thus, because it is a parabola the total distance between its focus and directrix is $p = 2(3) = 6$ units. Therefore, using $e = 1$ and $p = 6$, we can write the equation of the parabola.

$$r = \frac{ep}{1 + e \sin \theta} = \frac{6}{1 + \sin \theta}$$

By locating the intercepts, you can easily sketch the parabola (Figure 9.55).

r	θ
6	0
3	$\frac{\pi}{2}$
6	π
undefined	$\frac{3\pi}{2}$

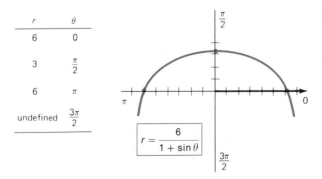

$$r = \frac{6}{1 + \sin \theta}$$

FIGURE   9.55

EXAMPLE 2

Find the polar equation of the conic that has a focus at the pole, $e = \frac{1}{3}$, and the equation of a directrix is $r \cos \theta = 4$, and sketch its graph.

Solution

Since $e = \frac{1}{3}$, we know it is an ellipse. The equation $r \cos \theta = 4$ ($x = 4$ in rectangular form) indicates that a directrix is perpendicular to the polar axis four units to the right of the pole. Thus, the equation of the ellipse is of the form $r = (ep)/(1 + e \cos \theta)$. The distance between a focus and a directrix is 4 units, that is, $p = 4$. Therefore, using $e = \frac{1}{3}$ and $p = 4$, we can write its equation.

$$r = \frac{\frac{1}{3}(4)}{1 + \frac{1}{3} \cos \theta},$$

which can be simplified to

$$r = \frac{4}{3 + \cos \theta}.$$

Locate the intercepts and sketch the ellipse in Figure 9.56.

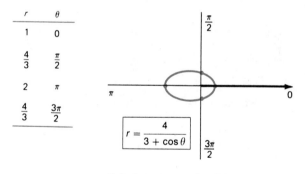

r	θ
1	0
$\frac{4}{3}$	$\frac{\pi}{2}$
2	π
$\frac{4}{3}$	$\frac{3\pi}{2}$

$$r = \frac{4}{3 + \cos \theta}$$

FIGURE 9.56

EXAMPLE 3

Sketch the graph of the polar equation

$$r = \frac{8}{2 - 3 \sin \theta}.$$

Solution

The equation can be changed to a standard form by dividing the numerator and denominator of the fraction by 2.

$$r = \frac{\frac{8}{2}}{\frac{2}{2} - \frac{3 \sin \theta}{2}} = \frac{4}{1 - \frac{3}{2} \sin \theta}$$

Thus, $e = \frac{3}{2}$ and the graph is a hyperbola with a focus at the pole. The expression $\sin \theta$ indicates that the focal axis is a part of the $\frac{\pi}{2}$-axis of the polar system. By plotting the intercepts, one branch can be sketched and then the concept of symmetry allows us to complete the other branch as in Figure 9.57.

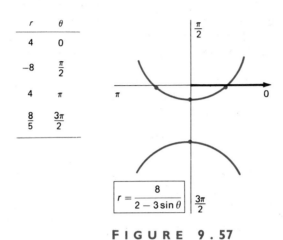

r	θ
4	0
-8	$\frac{\pi}{2}$
4	π
$\frac{8}{5}$	$\frac{3\pi}{2}$

$$r = \frac{8}{2 - 3\sin\theta}$$

FIGURE 9.57

EXAMPLE 4

Sketch the graph of the polar equation

$$r = \frac{10}{5 - 2\cos\theta}.$$

Solution

Let's change the given equation to a standard form by dividing the numerator and denominator of the fraction by 5.

$$r = \frac{\frac{10}{5}}{\frac{5}{5} - \frac{2\cos\theta}{5}} = \frac{2}{1 - \frac{2}{5}\cos\theta}$$

Thus, $e = \frac{2}{5}$ and the graph is an ellipse with a focus at the pole. The expression $\cos \theta$ indicates that the major axis is along the polar axis. By plotting the intercepts you can sketch the ellipse as in Figure 9.58.

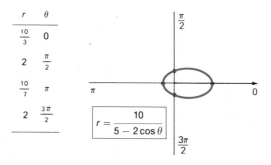

FIGURE 9.58

We can use a graphing utility to study variations of the polar equations that produce the conic sections. For example, we know that an equation of the form $r = \dfrac{3}{1 + e \cos \theta}$, where $0 < e < 1$, produces an ellipse. Now let's use a graphing utility to graph four specific ellipses for which $e = .1$, $e = .5$, $e = .7$, and $e = .8$ (Figure 9.59). Note that when e is close to zero, the ellipse closely resembles a circle.

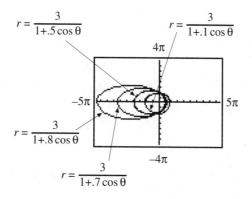

FIGURE 9.59

PROBLEM SET 9.5

For Problems 1–18, sketch the graph of each polar equation.

1. $r = \dfrac{4}{1 - \cos \theta}$

2. $r = \dfrac{3}{1 - \sin \theta}$

3. $r = \dfrac{6}{2 + \sin \theta}$

4. $r = \dfrac{8}{2 - \sin \theta}$

5. $r = \dfrac{6}{3 + 4 \sin \theta}$

6. $r = \dfrac{4}{2 + 3 \cos \theta}$

7. $r = \dfrac{5}{\cos \theta - 2}$

8. $r = \dfrac{6}{\cos \theta - 3}$

9. $r = \dfrac{3}{1 + 2 \sin \theta}$

10. $r = \dfrac{3}{1 - 2 \sin \theta}$

11. $r = \dfrac{6}{3 + 3 \sin \theta}$

12. $r = \dfrac{5}{2 + 2 \cos \theta}$

13. $r = \dfrac{10}{5 + 4 \sin \theta}$

14. $r = \dfrac{10}{5 - 4 \cos \theta}$

15. $r = \dfrac{2}{2 - 8 \cos \theta}$

16. $r = \dfrac{5}{5 + 20 \sin \theta}$

17. $r = \dfrac{1}{2 - 2 \cos \theta}$

18. $r = \dfrac{1}{2 + 2 \sin \theta}$

19. Find the polar equation of the parabola that has its focus at the pole and its vertex at $(2, 0)$. Also sketch its graph.

20. Find the polar equation of the parabola that has its focus at the pole and its vertex at $(1, 3\pi/2)$. Also sketch its graph.

21. Find the polar equation of the ellipse with $e = \frac{2}{3}$, one end of the major axis at $(1, 3\pi/2)$, and a focus at the pole. Also sketch its graph.

22. Find the polar equation of the ellipse with $e = \frac{1}{4}$, one end of the major axis at $(2, \pi)$, and a focus at the pole. Also sketch its graph.

For Problems 23–30, find a polar equation of the conic with a focus at the pole and the given eccentricity and equation of a directrix.

23. $e = 2,\ r \sin \theta = 3$

24. $e = 3,\ r \cos \theta = -4$

25. $e = \frac{1}{5},\ r \cos \theta = 1$

26. $e = \frac{2}{5},\ r \sin \theta = 2$

27. $e = 1,\ r \sin \theta = -4$

28. $e = 1,\ r \cos \theta = 5$

29. $e = \frac{2}{7},\ r = 2 \sec \theta$

30. $e = \frac{4}{3},\ r = -2 \csc \theta$

 GRAPHICS CALCULATOR ACTIVITIES

31. Graph the polar equation $r = \dfrac{\sec \theta}{\sec \theta - 1}$.

32. Graph the polar equation $r = \dfrac{6 \csc \theta}{2 \csc \theta + 3}$.

33. Use your graphics calculator to check your graphs for Problems 1–18.

34. Graph the polar equations $r = \dfrac{3}{1 - e \sin \theta}$ for $e = .1$, $e = .5$, $e = .7$, and $e = .8$ on the same set of axes. Are these results consistent with our conclusion earlier that when e is close to zero the ellipse resembles a circle?

35. Graph the polar equation $r = \dfrac{10}{1 + \sin \theta}$. Then predict the graph of $r = \dfrac{-10}{1 + \sin \theta}$ and check your prediction with your graphics calculator.

36. Graph the polar equation $r = \dfrac{5}{1 - .5 \sin \theta}$. Then predict the graph of $r = \dfrac{-5}{1 - .5 \sin \theta}$ and check your prediction with your graphics calculator.

CHAPTER 9 SUMMARY

The following standard forms in the rectangular coordinate system for the equations of conic sections were developed in this chapter.

Parabolas

1. $x^2 = 4py$: Focus $(0, p)$, directrix $y = -p$, y-axis symmetry

2. $y^2 = 4px$:

Focus $(p, 0)$, directrix $x = -p$, x-axis symmetry

3. $(x - h)^2 = 4p(y - k)$:

Focus $(h, k + p)$, directrix $y = k - p$, symmetric with respect to line $x = h$

4. $(y - k)^2 = 4p(x - h)$:

Focus $(h + p, k)$, directrix $x = h - p$, symmetric with respect to line $y = k$

Ellipses

5. $\dfrac{x^2}{a^2} + \dfrac{y^2}{b^2} = 1$:

Center $(0, 0)$, vertices $(\pm a, 0)$, endpoints of minor axis $(0, \pm b)$, foci $(\pm c, 0)$, $c^2 = a^2 - b^2$, $a^2 > b^2$

6. $\dfrac{x^2}{b^2} + \dfrac{y^2}{a^2} = 1$:

Center $(0, 0)$, vertices $(0, \pm a)$, endpoints of minor axis $(\pm b, 0)$, foci $(0, \pm c)$, $c^2 = a^2 - b^2$, $a^2 > b^2$

7. $\dfrac{(x - h)^2}{a^2} + \dfrac{(y - k)^2}{b^2} = 1$:

Center (h, k), vertices $(h \pm a, k)$, endpoints of minor axis $(h, k \pm b)$, foci $(h \pm c, k)$, $c^2 = a^2 - b^2$, $a^2 > b^2$

8. $\dfrac{(x - h)^2}{b^2} + \dfrac{(y - k)^2}{a^2} = 1$:

Center (h, k), vertices $(h, k \pm a)$, endpoints of minor axis $(h \pm b, k)$, foci $(h, k \pm c)$, $c^2 = a^2 - b^2$, $a^2 > b^2$

Hyperbolas

9. $\dfrac{x^2}{a^2} - \dfrac{y^2}{b^2} = 1$:

Center $(0, 0)$, vertices $(\pm a, 0)$, endpoints of conjugate axis $(0, \pm b)$, foci $(\pm c, 0)$, $c^2 = a^2 + b^2$, asymptotes $y = \pm \dfrac{b}{a} x$

10. $\dfrac{y^2}{a^2} - \dfrac{x^2}{b^2} = 1$:

Center $(0, 0)$, vertices $(0, \pm a)$, endpoints of conjugate axis $(\pm b, 0)$, foci $(0, \pm c)$, $c^2 = a^2 + b^2$, asymptotes $y = \pm \dfrac{a}{b} x$

11. $\dfrac{(x - h)^2}{a^2} - \dfrac{(y - k)^2}{b^2} = 1$:

Center (h, k), vertices $(h \pm a, k)$, endpoints of conjugate axis $(h, k \pm b)$, foci $(h \pm c, k)$, $c^2 = a^2 + b^2$, asymptotes $y - k = \pm \dfrac{b}{a}(x - h)$

12. $\dfrac{(y-k)^2}{a^2} - \dfrac{(x-h)^2}{b^2} = 1$: Center (h, k), vertices $(h, k \pm a)$, end-points of conjugate axis $(h \pm b, k)$, foci $(h, k \pm c)$, $c^2 = a^2 + b^2$, asymptotes

$$y - k = \pm \frac{a}{b}(x - h)$$

Translation of Axes

If (x, y) are the coordinates of a point P in the xy-system, and (x', y') are the coordinates of the same point P in the $x'y'$-system that has its origin at (h, k) of the xy-system, then

$$x = x' + h \quad \text{and} \quad y = y' + k$$

or

$$x' = x - h \quad \text{and} \quad y' = y - k.$$

Rotation of Axes

If (x, y) are the coordinates of a point P in the xy-system, and (x', y') are the coordinates of the same point P in the $x'y'$-system that has the same origin but is rotated through an angle θ, then

$$x = x' \cos \theta - y' \sin \theta$$

and

$$y = x' \sin \theta + y' \cos \theta.$$

The xy-term of the general second-degree equation $Ax^2 + Bxy + Cy^2 + Dx + Ey + F = 0$, where $B \neq 0$, can be eliminated by using the rotation equations with θ chosen as an acute angle to satisfy the condition

$$\cot 2\theta = \frac{A - C}{B}.$$

Polar Equations of Conics

A polar equation that has one of the four forms

$$r = \frac{ep}{1 \pm e \cos \theta}, \qquad r = \frac{ep}{1 \pm e \sin \theta}$$

is a conic section. The conic is an ellipse if $0 < e < 1$, a parabola if $e = 1$, and a hyperbola if $e > 1$.

CHAPTER 9 REVIEW PROBLEM SET

For Problems 1–12, (a) identify the conic section as a parabola, ellipse, or hyperbola, (b) if it is a parabola, find its vertex, focus, and directrix; if it is an ellipse, find its vertices, endpoints of minor axis, and foci; if it is a hyperbola, find its vertices, endpoints of conjugate axis, foci, and asymptotes, and (c) sketch each of the curves.

1. $x^2 + 2y^2 = 32$

2. $y^2 = -12x$

3. $3y^2 - x^2 = 9$

4. $2x^2 - 3y^2 = 18$

5. $5x^2 + 2y^2 = 20$

6. $x^2 = 2y$

7. $x^2 - 8x - 2y^2 + 4y + 10 = 0$

8. $9x^2 - 54x + 2y^2 + 8y + 71 = 0$

9. $y^2 - 2y + 4x + 9 = 0$

10. $x^2 + 2x + 8y + 25 = 0$

11. $x^2 + 10x + 4y^2 - 16y + 25 = 0$

12. $3y^2 + 12y - 2x^2 - 8x - 8 = 0$

For Problems 13–24, find the equation of the indicated conic section that satisfies the given conditions.

13. Parabola, vertex $(0, 0)$, focus $(-5, 0)$, directrix $x = 5$

14. Ellipse, vertices $(0, \pm 4)$, foci $(0, \pm\sqrt{15})$

15. Hyperbola, vertices $(\pm\sqrt{2}, 0)$, length of conjugate axis is 10

16. Ellipse, vertices $(\pm 2, 0)$, contains the point $(1, -2)$

17. Parabola, vertex $(0, 0)$, symmetric with respect to y-axis, contains the point $(2, 6)$

18. Hyperbola, vertices $(0, \pm 1)$, foci $(0, \pm\sqrt{10})$

19. Ellipse, vertices $(6, 1)$ and $(6, 7)$, length of minor axis is 2 units

20. Parabola, vertex $(4, -2)$, focus $(6, -2)$

21. Hyperbola, vertices $(-5, -3)$ and $(-5, -5)$, foci $(-5, -2)$ and $(-5, -6)$

22. Parabola, vertex $(-6, -3)$, symmetric with respect to the line $x = -6$, contains the point $(-5, -2)$

23. Ellipse, endpoints of minor axis $(-5, 2)$ and $(-5, -2)$, length of major axis is 10 units

24. Hyperbola, vertices $(2, 0)$ and $(6, 0)$, length of conjugate axis is 8 units

For Problems 25–30, rotate the coordinate axes to remove the xy-term. Then sketch the graph of the curve.

25. $x^2 + 2\sqrt{3}xy + 3y^2 + 2\sqrt{3}x - 2y = 0$

26. $6x^2 - 4\sqrt{3}xy + 10y^2 - 24 = 0$

27. $5x^2 - 6\sqrt{3}xy - y^2 - 32 = 0$

28. $16x^2 + 24xy + 9y^2 = 100$

29. $x^2 + 2xy + y^2 - \sqrt{2}x + \sqrt{2}y - 4 = 0$

30. $153x^2 - 192xy + 97y^2 - 390x + 230y + 25 = 0$

31. Find the $x'y'$-coordinates of the point $(8, -10)$ if the xy-axes are rotated through an angle $\theta = 60°$.

For Problems 32–35, sketch the graph of each polar equation.

32. $r = \dfrac{7}{3 - 2\sin\theta}$

33. $r = \dfrac{5}{2 + 2\cos\theta}$

34. $r = \dfrac{8}{2 + 3\cos\theta}$

35. $r = \dfrac{6}{1 + 3\sin\theta}$

36. Find the polar equation of the parabola that has its focus at the pole and its vertex at $(3, 3\pi/2)$.

37. Find the polar equation of the ellipse with $e = \frac{1}{5}$, one end of the major axis at $(2, \pi/2)$, and a focus at the pole.

38. Find the polar equation of the conic with $e = \frac{5}{2}$, a focus at the pole, and $r\cos\theta = -4$ as the equation of a directrix.

SEQUENCES AND MATHEMATICAL INDUCTION

Suppose that an auditorium has 35 seats in the first row, 40 seats in the second row, 45 seats in the third row, and so on for 10 rows. The numbers

35, 40, 45, 50, . . . , 80

represent the numbers of seats per row from row 1 through row 10. This list of numbers, for which there is a constant difference of 5 between successive numbers in the list, is called an *arithmetic sequence.*

Suppose that a fungus culture growing under controlled conditions doubles in size each day. If today the size of the culture is 6 units, then the numbers

12, 24, 48, 96, 192

represent the size of the culture for the next five days. This list of numbers, for which each number after the first one is two times the previous number, is called a *geometric sequence.*

Arithmetic and geometric sequences are the focus of this chapter.

10

If you could get a job that pays only a penny the first day of your employment, but then doubles each succeeding day, by the 31st working day your salary would be $10,737,418.24.

10.1   ARITHMETIC SEQUENCES

An **infinite sequence** is a function whose domain is the set of positive integers. For example, consider the function defined by the equation

$$f(n) = 5n + 1,$$

where the domain is the set of positive integers. Furthermore, let's substitute the numbers of the domain, in order, starting with 1. The resulting ordered pairs can be listed as

$$(1, 6), \quad (2, 11), \quad (3, 16), \quad (4, 21), \quad (5, 26),$$

and so on. Since we have agreed to use the domain of positive integers, in order, starting with 1, there is no need to use ordered pairs. We can simply express the infinite sequence as

$$6, \ 11, \ 16, \ 21, \ 26, \ \ldots .$$

Frequently, the letter a is used to represent sequential functions and the functional value at n is written as a_n (read, *a sub n*) instead of $a(n)$. We then express the sequence as

$$a_1, \ a_2, \ a_3, \ a_4, \ \ldots ,$$

where a_1 is the **first term**, a_2 the **second term**, a_3 the **third term**, and so on. The expression a_n, which defines the sequence, is called the **general term** of the sequence. Knowing the general term of a sequence allows us to find as many terms of the sequence as needed and also to find any specific terms. Consider the following example.

EXAMPLE 1

Find the first five terms of the sequence for which $a_n = 2n^2 - 3$, and also find the 20th term.

Solution

The first five terms are generated by replacing n with 1, 2, 3, 4, and 5.

$$a_1 = 2(1)^2 - 3 = -1 \qquad a_2 = 2(2)^2 - 3 = 5$$
$$a_3 = 2(3)^2 - 3 = 15 \qquad a_4 = 2(4)^2 - 3 = 29$$
$$a_5 = 2(5)^2 - 3 = 47$$

The first five terms are -1, 5, 15, 29, and 47. The 20th term is

$$a_{20} = 2(20)^2 - 3 = 797.$$

Arithmetic Sequences

An arithmetic sequence (also called an arithmetic progression) is a sequence where there is a common difference between successive terms. The following are examples of arithmetic sequences.

$$1, 8, 15, 22, 29, \ldots \tag{1}$$
$$4, 7, 10, 13, 16, \ldots \tag{2}$$
$$4, 1, -2, -5, -8, \ldots \tag{3}$$
$$-1, -6, -11, -16, -21, \ldots \tag{4}$$

The common difference in (1) is 7. That is to say, $8 - 1 = 7$, $15 - 8 = 7$, $22 - 15 = 7$, $29 - 22 = 7$, and so on. The common differences for (2), (3), and (4) are 3, -3, and -5, respectively.

In a more general setting we say that the sequence

$$a_1, a_2, a_3, a_4, \ldots, a_n, \ldots$$

is an arithmetic sequence if and only if there is a real number d such that

$$a_{k+1} - a_k = d$$

for every positive integer k. The number d is called the common difference.

From the previous equation we see that $a_{k+1} = a_k + d$. In other words, we can generate an arithmetic sequence that has a common difference of d by starting with a first term of a_1 and then simply adding d to each successive term as follows.

First term:	a_1
Second term:	$a_1 + d$
Third term:	$a_1 + 2d$ $(a_1 + d) + d = a_1 + 2d$
Fourth term:	$a_1 + 3d$
$\vdots$	
nth term:	$a_1 + (n - 1)d$

Thus, the general term of an arithmetic sequence is given by

$$a_n = a_1 + (n - 1)d$$

where a_1 is the first term and d the common difference. This general term formula can be used to solve a variety of problems involving arithmetic sequences.

EXAMPLE 2

Find the general term expression for the arithmetic sequence $6, 2, -2, -6, \ldots$.

Solution

The common difference, d, is $2 - 6 = -4$ and the first term, a_1, is 6. Substituting these values into $a_n = a_1 + (n - 1)d$ and simplifying, we obtain

$$a_n = a_1 + (n - 1)d = 6 + (n - 1)(-4)$$
$$= 6 - 4n + 4 = -4n + 10.$$

EXAMPLE 3

Find the 40th term of the arithmetic sequence 1, 5, 9, 13, ...

Solution

Using $a_n = a_1 + (n - 1)d$, we obtain

$$a_{40} = 1 + (40 - 1)4 = 1 + (39)(4) = 157.$$

EXAMPLE 4

Find the first term of the arithmetic sequence where the 4th term is 26 and the 9th term is 61.

Solution

Using $a_n = a_1 + (n - 1)d$ with $a_4 = 26$ (the 4th term is 26) and $a_9 = 61$ (the 9th term is 61), we have

$$26 = a_1 + (4 - 1)d = a_1 + 3d$$
$$61 = a_1 + (9 - 1)d = a_1 + 8d.$$

Solving the system of equations

$$\begin{pmatrix} a_1 + 3d = 26 \\ a_1 + 8d = 61 \end{pmatrix}$$

yields $a_1 = 5$ and $d = 7$. Thus, the first term is 5.

Sums of Arithmetic Sequences

Often as we use sequences to solve problems we need to be able to find the sum of a certain number of terms of the sequence. Before we develop a general sum formula for arithmetic sequences, let's consider an approach to a specific problem that we can then apply generally.

EXAMPLE 5

Find the sum of the first one hundred positive integers.

Solution

We are being asked to find the sum of $1 + 2 + 3 + 4 + \cdots + 100$. Rather than adding in the usual way, let's find the sum in the following manner.

$$
\begin{array}{c}
1 + \quad 2 + \quad 3 + \quad 4 + \cdots + 100 \\
\underline{100 + \quad 99 + \quad 98 + \quad 97 + \cdots + \quad 1} \\
101 + 101 + 101 + 101 + \cdots + 101
\end{array}
$$

$$\frac{\overset{50}{\cancel{100}}(101)}{\cancel{2}} = 5050$$

Note that we simply wrote the indicated sum *forward and backward* and then added the results. In so doing, 100 sums of 101 are produced, but one-half of them are "repeats." For example, $(100 + 1)$ and $(1 + 100)$ are both counted in this process. Thus, we divide the product $(100)(101)$ by 2, which yields the final result of 5050.

The *forward-backward* approach of Example 5 can be used to develop a formula for finding the sum of the first n terms of any arithmetic sequence. Consider the arithmetic sequence $a_1, a_2, a_3, a_4, \ldots, a_n$ that has a common difference of d. Use S_n to represent the sum of the first n terms and we can proceed as follows.

$$S_n = a_1 + (a_1 + d) + (a_1 + 2d) + \cdots + (a_n - 2d) + (a_n - d) + a_n$$

Now write this sum in reverse as

$$S_n = a_n + (a_n - d) + (a_n - 2d) + \cdots + (a_1 + 2d) + (a_1 + d) + a_1.$$

Adding the two equations produces

$$2S_n = (a_1 + a_n) + (a_1 + a_n) + (a_1 + a_n) + \cdots + (a_1 + a_n) + (a_1 + a_n) + (a_1 + a_n);$$

that is, we have n sums of $(a_1 + a_n)$, so

$$2S_n = n(a_1 + a_n)$$

from which we obtain a **sum formula**

$$S_n = \frac{n(a_1 + a_n)}{2}$$

Using the nth term formula and/or the sum formula, we can solve a variety of problems involving arithmetic sequences.

EXAMPLE 6

Find the sum of the first thirty terms of the arithmetic sequence 3, 7, 11, 15, ...

Solution

Using $a_n = a_1 + (n - 1)d$, we can find the 30th term.

$$a_{30} = 3 + (30 - 1)4 = 3 + 29(4) = 119$$

Now we can use the sum formula.

$$S_{30} = \frac{30(3 + 119)}{2} = 1830$$

EXAMPLE 7

Find the sum of $7 + 10 + 13 + \cdots + 157$.

Solution

To use the sum formula we need to know the number of terms. The nth term formula will do that for us.

$$a_n = a_1 + (n - 1)d$$

$$157 = 7 + (n - 1)3$$

$$157 = 7 + 3n - 3$$

$$157 = 3n + 4$$

$$153 = 3n$$

$$51 = n$$

Now we can use the sum formula.

$$S_{51} = \frac{51(7 + 157)}{2} = 4182$$

—

Keep in mind that the sum formula for an arithmetic sequence was developed using the forward-backward technique that we previously used on a specific problem. Now that we have the sum formula, we have two choices as we meet problems where the formula applies. We can either memorize the formula and use it or disregard the formula and use the forward-backward technique. However, we should emphasize that even if you choose to use the formula and some day your memory fails you, don't panic, simply use the forward-backward technique. In other words, when you understand the development of a formula you often can do problems even though the formula itself is forgotten.

Summation Notation

Sometimes a special notation is used to indicate the sum of a certain number of terms of a sequence. The capital Greek letter sigma, Σ, is used as a summation symbol. For example,

$$\sum_{i=1}^{5} a_i$$

represents the sum $a_1 + a_2 + a_3 + a_4 + a_5$. The letter i is frequently used as the **index of summation** and takes on all integer values from the lower limit to the upper limit, inclusive. Thus, we can write

$$\sum_{i=1}^{4} b_i = b_1 + b_2 + b_3 + b_4$$

$$\sum_{i=3}^{7} a_i = a_3 + a_4 + a_5 + a_6 + a_7$$

$$\sum_{i=1}^{15} i^2 = 1^2 + 2^2 + 3^2 + \cdots + 15^2$$

$$\sum_{i=1}^{n} a_i = a_1 + a_2 + a_3 + \cdots + a_n.$$

If $a_1, a_2, a_3, \ldots$ represents an arithmetic sequence then the sum formula developed earlier can be written as

$$\sum_{i=1}^{n} a_i = \frac{n}{2}(a_1 + a_n).$$

EXAMPLE 8

Find the sum $\displaystyle\sum_{i=1}^{50} (3i + 4)$.

Solution

This indicated sum means

$$\sum_{i=1}^{50} (3i + 4) = [3(1) + 4] + [3(2) + 4] + [3(3) + 4] + \cdots + [3(50) + 4]$$

$$= 7 + 10 + 13 + \cdots + 154.$$

Since this is an indicated sum of an arithmetic sequence, we can use our sum formula.

$$S_{50} = \frac{50}{2}(7 + 154) = 4025$$

EXAMPLE 9

Find the sum $\displaystyle\sum_{i=2}^{7} 2i^2$.

Solution

This indicated sum means

$$\sum_{i=2}^{7} 2i^2 = 2(2)^2 + 2(3)^2 + 2(4)^2 + 2(5)^2 + 2(6)^2 + 2(7)^2$$

$$= 8 + 18 + 32 + 50 + 72 + 98.$$

This is *not* the indicated sum of an arithmetic sequence; therefore, let's simply add the numbers in the usual way. The sum is 278.   ▬▬▬

Example 9 illustrates an important point. Be sure that you analyze the sequence of numbers being represented by the summation symbol. You may or may not be able to use a formula for adding the numbers.

PROBLEM SET 10.1

For Problems 1–10, write the first five terms of the sequence that has the indicated general term.

1. $a_n = 3n - 7$

2. $a_n = 5n - 2$

3. $a_n = -2n + 4$

4. $a_n = -4n + 7$

5. $a_n = 3n^2 - 1$

6. $a_n = 2n^2 - 6$

7. $a_n = n(n - 1)$

8. $a_n = (n + 1)(n + 2)$

9. $a_n = 2^{n+1}$

10. $a_n = 3^{n-1}$

11. Find the 15th and 30th terms of the sequence for which $a_n = -5n - 4$.

12. Find the 20th and 50th terms of the sequence for which $a_n = -n - 3$.

13. Find the 25th and 50th terms of the sequence for which $a_n = (-1)^{n+1}$.

14. Find the 10th and 15th terms of the sequence for which $a_n = -n^2 - 10$.

For Problems 15–24, find the general term (*n*th term) for each of the arithmetic sequences.

15. 11, 13, 15, 17, 19, . . .

16. 7, 10, 13, 16, 19, . . .

17. 2, −1, −4, −7, −10, . . .

18. 4, 2, 0, −2, −4, . . .

19. $\frac{3}{2}$, 2, $\frac{5}{2}$, 3, $\frac{7}{2}$, . . .

20. 0, $\frac{1}{2}$, 1, $\frac{3}{2}$, 2, . . .

21. 2, 6, 10, 14, 18, . . .

22. 2, 7, 12, 17, 22, . . .

23. −3, −6, −9, −12, −15, . . .

24. −4, −8, −12, −16, −20, . . .

For Problems 25–30, find the indicated term for each of the arithmetic sequences.

25. The 15th term of 3, 8, 13, 18, . . .

26. The 20th term of 4, 11, 18, 25, . . .

27. The 30th term of 15, 26, 37, 48, . . .

28. The 35th term of 9, 17, 25, 33, . . .

29. The 52nd term of 1, $\frac{5}{3}$, $\frac{7}{3}$, 3, . . .

30. The 47th term of $\frac{1}{2}$, $\frac{5}{4}$, 2, $\frac{11}{4}$, . . .

31. If the 6th term of an arithmetic sequence is 12 and the 10th term is 16, find the first term.

32. If the 5th term of an arithmetic sequence is 14 and the 12th term is 42, find the first term.

33. If the 3rd term of an arithmetic sequence is 20 and the 7th term is 32, find the 25th term.

34. If the 5th term of an arithmetic sequence is −5 and the 15th term is −25, find the 50th term.

35. Find the sum of the first 50 terms of the arithmetic sequence 5, 7, 9, 11, 13, ...

36. Find the sum of the first 30 terms of the arithmetic sequence 0, 2, 4, 6, 8, ...

37. Find the sum of the first 40 terms of the arithmetic sequence 2, 6, 10, 14, 18, ...

38. Find the sum of the first 60 terms of the arithmetic sequence −2, 3, 8, 13, 18, ...

39. Find the sum of the first 75 terms of the arithmetic sequence 5, 2, −1, −4, −7, ...

40. Find the sum of the first 80 terms of the arithmetic sequence 7, 3, −1, −5, −9, ...

41. Find the sum of the first 50 terms of the arithmetic sequence $\frac{1}{2}$, 1, $\frac{3}{2}$, 2, $\frac{5}{2}$, ...

42. Find the sum of the first 100 terms of the arithmetic sequence $-\frac{1}{3}$, $\frac{1}{3}$, 1, $\frac{5}{3}$, $\frac{7}{3}$, ...

For Problems 43–50, find each of the indicated sums.

43. $1 + 5 + 9 + 13 + \cdots + 197$

44. $3 + 8 + 13 + 18 + \cdots + 398$

45. $2 + 8 + 14 + 20 + \cdots + 146$

46. $6 + 9 + 12 + 15 + \cdots + 93$

47. $(-7) + (-10) + (-13) + (-16) + \cdots + (-109)$

48. $(-5) + (-9) + (-13) + (-17) + \cdots + (-169)$

49. $(-5) + (-3) + (-1) + 1 + \cdots + 119$

50. $(-7) + (-4) + (-1) + 2 + \cdots + 131$

51. Find the sum of the first 200 odd whole numbers.

52. Find the sum of the first 175 positive even whole numbers.

53. Find the sum of all even numbers between 18 and 482, inclusive.

54. Find the sum of all odd numbers between 17 and 379, inclusive.

55. Find the sum of the first 30 terms of the arithmetic sequence that has a general term of $a_n = 5n - 4$.

56. Find the sum of the first 40 terms of the arithmetic sequence that has a general term of $a_n = 4n - 7$.

57. Find the sum of the first 25 terms of the arithmetic sequence that has a general term of $a_n = -4n - 1$.

58. Find the sum of the first 35 terms of the arithmetic sequence that has a general term of $a_n = -5n - 3$.

For Problems 59–70, find each of the following sums.

59. $\sum_{i=1}^{45} (5i + 2)$

60. $\sum_{i=1}^{38} (3i + 6)$

61. $\sum_{i=1}^{30} (-2i + 4)$

62. $\sum_{i=1}^{40} (-3i + 3)$

63. $\sum_{i=4}^{32} (3i - 10)$

64. $\sum_{i=6}^{47} (4i - 9)$

65. $\sum_{i=10}^{20} (4i)$

66. $\sum_{i=15}^{30} (-5i)$

67. $\sum_{i=1}^{5} i^2$

68. $\sum_{i=1}^{6} (i^2 + 1)$

69. $\sum_{i=3}^{8} (2i^2 + i)$

70. $\sum_{i=4}^{7} (3i^2 - 2)$

FURTHER INVESTIGATIONS

The general term of a sequence can consist of one expression for certain values of n and another expression (or expressions) for other values of n. That is to say, a **multiple description** of the sequence can be given. For example,

$$a_n = \begin{cases} 2n + 3 & \text{for } n \text{ odd} \\ 3n - 2 & \text{for } n \text{ even} \end{cases}$$

means that we use $a_n = 2n + 3$ for $n = 1, 3, 5, 7, \ldots$ and we use $a_n = 3n - 2$ for $n = 2, 4, 6, 8, \ldots$. The first six terms of this sequence are 5, 4, 9, 10, 13, and 16.

For Problems 71–74, write the first six terms of each sequence.

71. $a_n = \begin{cases} 2n + 1 & \text{for } n \text{ odd} \\ 2n - 1 & \text{for } n \text{ even} \end{cases}$

72. $a_n = \begin{cases} \dfrac{1}{n} & \text{for } n \text{ odd} \\ n^2 & \text{for } n \text{ even} \end{cases}$

73. $a_n = \begin{cases} 3n + 1 & \text{for } n \le 3 \\ 4n - 3 & \text{for } n > 3 \end{cases}$

74. $a_n = \begin{cases} 5n - 1 & \text{for } n \text{ a multiple of } 3 \\ 2n & \text{otherwise} \end{cases}$

The multiple description approach can also be used to give a **recursive description** for a sequence. A sequence is said to be **described recursively** if the first n terms are stated and then each succeeding term is defined as a function of one or more of the preceding terms. For example,

$$\begin{cases} a_1 = 2 \\ a_n = 2a_{n-1} & \text{for } n \ge 2 \end{cases}$$

means that the first term, a_1, is 2 and each succeeding term is 2 times the previous term. Thus, the first six terms are 2, 4, 8, 16, 32, and 64.

For Problems 75–80, write the first six terms of each sequence.

75. $\begin{cases} a_1 = 4 \\ a_n = 3a_{n-1} & \text{for } n \ge 2 \end{cases}$

76. $\begin{cases} a_1 = 3 \\ a_n = a_{n-1} + 2 & \text{for } n \ge 2 \end{cases}$

77. $\begin{cases} a_1 = 1 \\ a_2 = 1 \\ a_n = a_{n-2} + a_{n-1} & \text{for } n \ge 3 \end{cases}$

78. $\begin{cases} a_1 = 2 \\ a_2 = 3 \\ a_n = 2a_{n-2} + 3a_{n-1} & \text{for } n \ge 3 \end{cases}$

79. $\begin{cases} a_1 = 3 \\ a_2 = 1 \\ a_n = (a_{n-1} - a_{n-2})^2 & \text{for } n \ge 3 \end{cases}$

80. $\begin{cases} a_1 = 1 \\ a_2 = 2 \\ a_3 = 3 \\ a_n = a_{n-1} + a_{n-2} + a_{n-3} & \text{for } n \ge 4 \end{cases}$

10.2   GEOMETRIC SEQUENCES

A **geometric sequence** or **geometric progression** is a sequence in which each term after the first is obtained by multiplying the preceding term by a common multiplier. The common multiplier is called the **common ratio** of the sequence. The common ratio of a geometric sequence can be found by dividing a term (other than the first term) by the preceding term. The following geometric sequences have common ratios of 3, 2, $\frac{1}{2}$, and -4, respectively.

$$1, 3, 9, 27, 81, \ldots, \qquad 3, 6, 12, 24, 48, \ldots,$$

$$16, 8, 4, 2, 1, \ldots, \qquad -1, 4, -16, 64, -256, \ldots$$

In a more general setting we say that the sequence $a_1, a_2, a_3, \ldots, a_n, \ldots$ is a geometric sequence if and only if there is a nonzero real number r such that

$$a_{k+1} = ra_k$$

for every positive integer k. The nonzero real number r is called the common ratio of the sequence.

The previous equation can be used to generate a general geometric sequence that has a_1 as a first term and r as a common ratio. We can proceed as follows.

$$
\begin{aligned}
\text{First term:} \quad & a_1 \\
\text{Second term:} \quad & a_1 r \\
\text{Third term:} \quad & a_1 r^2 \qquad (a_1 r)(r) = a_1 r^2 \\
\text{Fourth term:} \quad & a_1 r^3 \\
& \vdots \\
n\text{th term:} \quad & a_1 r^{n-1}
\end{aligned}
$$

Thus, the general term of a geometric sequence is given by

$$a_n = a_1 r^{n-1}$$

where a_1 is the first term and r is the common ratio.

EXAMPLE 1

Find the general term for the geometric sequence 8, 16, 32, 64, ...

Solution

Using $a_n = a_1 r^{n-1}$ we obtain

$$a_n = 8(2)^{n-1}.$$
$$= (2^3)(2)^{n-1} = 2^{n+2}.$$

EXAMPLE 2

Find the 9th term of the geometric sequence 27, 9, 3, 1, ...

Solution

Using $a_n = a_1 r^{n-1}$ we can find the 9th term as follows.

$$a_9 = 27\left(\tfrac{1}{3}\right)^{9-1}$$
$$= (27)\left(\tfrac{1}{3}\right)^8 = \frac{3^3}{3^8} = \frac{1}{3^5} = \frac{1}{243}.$$

Sums of Geometric Sequences

As with arithmetic sequences, we often need to find the sum of a certain number of terms of a geometric sequence. Before we develop a general sum formula for geometric sequences, let's consider an approach to a specific problem that we can then use in a general setting.

EXAMPLE 3

Find the sum $1 + 3 + 9 + 27 + \cdots + 6561$.

Solution

Letting S represent the sum we can proceed as follows.

$$S = 1 + 3 + 9 + 27 + \cdots + 6561 \tag{1}$$

$$3S = \qquad 3 + 9 + 27 + \cdots + 6561 + 19683 \tag{2}$$

Equation (2) is the result of multiplying equation (1) by the common ratio, 3. Subtracting equation (1) from equation (2) produces

$$2S = 19683 - 1$$

$$2S = 19682$$

$$S = 9841.$$

Now let's consider the general geometric sequence $a_1, a_1r, a_1r^2, \ldots, a_1r^{n-1}$. By applying a procedure similar to the one used in Example 3 we can develop a formula for finding the sum of the first n terms of any geometric sequence. Let S_n represent the sum of the first n terms.

$$S_n = a_1 + a_1r + a_1r^2 + \cdots + a_1r^{n-1} \tag{3}$$

Multiplying both sides of equation (3) by the common ratio r produces

$$rS_n = a_1r + a_1r^2 + a_1r^3 + \cdots + a_1r^n. \tag{4}$$

Subtracting equation (3) from equation (4) yields

$$rS_n - S_n = a_1r^n - a_1.$$

Applying the distributive property on the left side and then solving for S_n, we obtain

$$S_n(r - 1) = a_1r^n - a_1$$

$$S_n = \frac{a_1r^n - a_1}{r - 1}, \qquad r \neq 1.$$

Therefore, the sum of the first n terms of a geometric sequence having a first term of a_1 and a common ratio of r is given by

$$S_n = \frac{a_1r^n - a}{r - 1}, \qquad r \neq 1.$$

EXAMPLE 4

Find the sum of the first 8 terms of the geometric sequence, $1, 2, 4, 8, \ldots$.

Solution

Using the sum formula we obtain

$$S_8 = \frac{1(2)^8 - 1}{2 - 1} = \frac{2^8 - 1}{1} = 255.$$

If the common ratio of a geometric sequence is less than 1, it may be more convenient to change the form of the sum formula. That is, the fraction $(a_1r^n - a_1)/(r - 1)$ can be changed to $(a_1 - a_1r^n)/(1 - r)$ by multiplying both the numerator and denominator by -1. Thus, using $S_n = (a_1 - a_1 r^n)/(1 - r)$ when $r < 1$ can sometimes avoid unnecessary work with negative numbers, as the next example illustrates.

EXAMPLE 5

Find the sum of $1 + \frac{1}{2} + \frac{1}{4} + \cdots + \frac{1}{256}$.

Solution A

To use the sum formula we need to know the number of terms, which can be found by counting them or applying the nth-term formula as follows.

$$a_n = a_1 r^{n-1}$$
$$\frac{1}{256} = 1\left(\frac{1}{2}\right)^{n-1}$$
$$\left(\frac{1}{2}\right)^8 = \left(\frac{1}{2}\right)^{n-1}$$
$$8 = n - 1 \qquad \text{Remember that if } b^n = b^m, \text{ then } n = m$$
$$9 = n$$

Now using $n = 9$, $a_1 = 1$, and $r = \frac{1}{2}$ in the form of the sum formula $S_n = (a_1 - a_1 r^n)/(1 - r)$ we obtain

$$S_9 = \frac{1 - 1\left(\frac{1}{2}\right)^9}{1 - \frac{1}{2}} = \frac{1 - \frac{1}{512}}{\frac{1}{2}} = \frac{\frac{511}{512}}{\frac{1}{2}} = 1\frac{255}{256}.$$

You should realize that a problem such as Example 5 can be done without finding the number of terms when you use the general approach followed in Example 3. Solution B illustrates this idea.

Solution B

Let S represent the desired sum.

$$S = 1 + \frac{1}{2} + \frac{1}{4} + \cdots + \frac{1}{256}.$$

Multiply both sides by the common ratio of $\frac{1}{2}$.

$$\frac{1}{2}S = \frac{1}{2} + \frac{1}{4} + \frac{1}{8} + \cdots + \frac{1}{256} + \frac{1}{512}.$$

Subtract the second equation from the first equation and solve for S.

$$\frac{1}{2}S = 1 - \frac{1}{512} = \frac{511}{512}$$

Therefore,

$$S = \frac{511}{256} = 1\frac{255}{256}.$$

Summation notation can also be used to indicate the sum of a certain number of terms of a geometric sequence.

EXAMPLE 6

Find the sum $\displaystyle\sum_{i=1}^{10} 2^i$.

Solution

This indicated sum means

$$\sum_{i=i}^{10} 2^i = 2^1 + 2^2 + 2^3 + \cdots + 2^{10}$$

$$= 2 + 4 + 8 + \cdots + 1024.$$

Since this is the indicated sum of a geometric sequence, we can use the sum formula with $a_1 = 2$, $r = 2$, and $n = 10$.

$$S_{10} = \frac{2(2)^{10} - 2}{2 - 1} = \frac{2(2^{10} - 1)}{1} = 2046$$

Sum of Infinite Geometric Sequence

Let's take the formula $S_n = (a_1 - a_1 r^n)/(1 - r)$ and rewrite the right side by applying the property $(a - b)/c = (a/c) - (b/c)$. Thus, we obtain

$$S_n = \frac{a_1}{1 - r} - \frac{a_1 r^n}{1 - r}. \tag{1}$$

Now let's examine the behavior of r^n for $|r| < 1$, that is, for $-1 < r < 1$. For example, suppose that $r = \frac{1}{2}$; then

$$r^2 = \left(\tfrac{1}{2}\right)^2 = \tfrac{1}{4}, \qquad r^3 = \left(\tfrac{1}{2}\right)^3 = \tfrac{1}{8},$$

$$r^4 = \left(\tfrac{1}{2}\right)^4 = \tfrac{1}{16}, \qquad r^5 = \left(\tfrac{1}{2}\right)^5 = \tfrac{1}{32},$$

and so on. We can make $\left(\tfrac{1}{2}\right)^n$ as close to 0 as we please by choosing sufficiently large values for n. In general, for values of r such that $|r| < 1$, the expression r^n will approach 0 as n gets larger and larger. Therefore, in equation (1) the fraction, $(a_1 r^n)/(1 - r)$, will approach 0 as n increases and we say that the **sum of the infinite geometric sequence** is given by

$$S_\infty = \frac{a_1}{1 - r}, \qquad |r| < 1.$$

EXAMPLE 7

Find the sum of the infinite geometric sequence

$$1, \frac{1}{2}, \frac{1}{4}, \frac{1}{8}, \ldots.$$

Solution

Since $a_1 = 1$ and $r = \frac{1}{2}$, we obtain

$$S_\infty = \frac{1}{1 - \frac{1}{2}} = \frac{1}{\frac{1}{2}} = 2.$$

In Example 7, by stating that $S_\infty = 2$ we mean that as we add more and more terms, the sum approaches 2, as follows.

First term:	1
Sum of first two terms:	$1 + \frac{1}{2} = 1\frac{1}{2}$
Sum of first three terms:	$1 + \frac{1}{2} + \frac{1}{4} = 1\frac{3}{4}$
Sum of first four terms:	$1 + \frac{1}{2} + \frac{1}{4} + \frac{1}{8} = 1\frac{7}{8}$
Sum of first five terms:	$1 + \frac{1}{2} + \frac{1}{4} + \frac{1}{8} + \frac{1}{16} = 1\frac{15}{16}$
	etc.

If $|r| > 1$, the absolute value of r^n increases without bound as n increases. Consider the following two examples and notice the unbounded growth of the absolute value of r^n.

Let $r = 3$	**Let $r = -2$**
$r^2 = 3^2 = 9$	$r^2 = (-2)^2 = 4$
$r^3 = 3^3 = 27$	$r^3 = (-2)^3 = -8$ and $|-8| = 8$
$r^4 = 3^4 = 81$	$r^4 = (-2)^4 = 16$
$r^5 = 3^5 = 243$	$r^5 = (-2)^5 = -32$ and $|-32| = 32$
etc.	etc.

If $r = 1$, then $S_n = na_1$, and as n increases without bound, $|S_n|$ also increases without bound. If $r = -1$, then S_n will either be a_1 or 0. Therefore, we say that the sum of any infinite geometric sequence where $|r| \geq 1$ *does not exist.*

Repeating Decimals As Sums of Infinite Geometric Sequences

Per our review in Section 1.1, rational numbers are numbers that have either a terminating or repeating decimal representation. For example,

$$.23, \quad .147, \quad .\overline{3}, \quad .\overline{14}, \quad \text{and} \quad .5\overline{6}$$

are examples of rational numbers. (Remember that $.\overline{3}$ means .3333. . . .) Place value provides the basis for changing terminating decimals such as .23 and .147 to a/b form, where a and b are integers, $b \neq 0$.

$$.23 = \frac{23}{100} \quad \text{and} \quad .147 = \frac{147}{1000}$$

However, changing repeating decimals to a/b form requires a different technique and our work with sums of infinite geometric sequences provides the basis for one such approach. Consider the following examples.

EXAMPLE 8

Change $.\overline{14}$ to a/b form, where a and b are integers, $b \neq 0$.

Solution

The repeating decimal $.\overline{14}$ can be written as the indicated sum of an infinite geometric sequence that has a first term of .14 and a common ratio of .01.

$$.14 + .0014 + .000014 + \ldots$$

Using $S_\infty = a_1/(1 - r)$ we obtain

$$S_\infty = \frac{.14}{1 - .01} = \frac{.14}{.99} = \frac{14}{99}.$$

Thus, $.\overline{14} = \frac{14}{99}$.

If the repeating block of digits does not begin immediately after the decimal point, as with $.5\overline{6}$, we can make a slight adjustment in the technique we used in Example 8.

EXAMPLE 9

Change $.5\overline{6}$ to a/b form, where a and b are integers, $b \neq 0$.

Solution

The repeating decimal $.5\overline{6}$ can be written as

$$[.5] + [.06 + .006 + .0006 + \ldots]$$

where

$$.06 + .006 + .0006 + \ldots$$

is the indicated sum of an infinite geometric sequence with $a_1 = .06$ and $r = .1$. Therefore,

$$S_\infty = \frac{.06}{1 - .1} = \frac{.06}{.9} = \frac{6}{90} = \frac{1}{15}.$$

Now we can add .5 and $\frac{1}{15}$.

$$.5\overline{6} = .5 + \frac{1}{15} = \frac{1}{2} + \frac{1}{15} = \frac{15}{30} + \frac{2}{30} = \frac{17}{30}$$

PROBLEM SET 10.2

For Problems 1–12, find the general term (nth term) for each of the geometric sequences.

1. 3, 6, 12, 24, . . .

2. 2, 6, 18, 54, . . .

3. 3, 9, 27, 81, . . .

4. 2, 4, 8, 16, . . .

5. $\frac{1}{4}$, $\frac{1}{8}$, $\frac{1}{16}$, $\frac{1}{32}$, . . .

6. 8, 4, 2, 1, . . .

7. 4, 16, 64, 256, . . .

8. 6, 2, $\frac{2}{3}$, $\frac{2}{9}$, . . .

9. 1, .3, .09, .027, . . .

10. .2, .04, .008, .0016, . . .

11. 1, −2, 4, −8, . . .

12. −3, 9, −27, 81, . . .

For Problems 13–20, find the indicated term for each of the geometric sequences.

13. The 8th term of $\frac{1}{2}$, 1, 2, 4, . . .

14. The 7th term of 2, 6, 18, 54, . . .

15. The 9th term of 729, 243, 81, 27, . . .

16. The 11th term of 768, 384, 192, 96, . . .

17. The 10th term of 1, −2, 4, −8, . . .

18. The 8th term of −1, $-\frac{3}{2}$, $-\frac{9}{4}$, $-\frac{27}{8}$, . . .

19. The 8th term of $\frac{1}{2}$, $\frac{1}{6}$, $\frac{1}{18}$, $\frac{1}{54}$, . . .

20. The 9th term of $\frac{16}{81}$, $\frac{8}{27}$, $\frac{4}{9}$, $\frac{2}{3}$, . . .

21. Find the first term of a geometric sequence if the 5th term is $\frac{32}{3}$ and the common ratio is 2.

22. Find the first term of a geometric sequence if the 4th term is $\frac{27}{128}$ and the common ratio is $\frac{3}{4}$.

23. Find the common ratio of a geometric sequence if the 3rd term is 12 and the 6th term is 96.

24. Find the common ratio of a geometric sequence if the 2nd term is $\frac{8}{3}$ and the 5th term is $\frac{64}{81}$.

25. Find the sum of the first 10 terms of the geometric sequence, 1, 2, 4, 8, . . .

26. Find the sum of the first 7 terms of the geometric sequence 3, 9, 27, 81, . . .

27. Find the sum of the first 9 terms of the geometric sequence 2, 6, 18, 54, . . .

28. Find the sum of the first 10 terms of the geometric sequence 5, 10, 20, 40, . . .

29. Find the sum of the first 8 terms of the geometric sequence 8, 12, 18, 27, . . .

30. Find the sum of the first 8 terms of the geometric sequence 9, 12, 16, $\frac{64}{3}$, . . .

31. Find the sum of the first 10 terms of the geometric sequence −4, 8, −16, 32, . . .

32. Find the sum of the first 9 terms of the geometric sequence −2, 6, −18, 54, . . .

For Problems 33–38, find each of the indicated sums.

33. $9 + 27 + 81 + \cdots + 729$

34. $2 + 8 + 32 + \cdots + 8192$

35. $4 + 2 + 1 + \cdots + \frac{1}{512}$

36. $1 + (-2) + 4 + \cdots + 256$

37. $(-1) + 3 + (-9) + \cdots + (-729)$

38. $16 + 8 + 4 + \cdots + \frac{1}{32}$

For Problems 39–44, find each of the indicated sums.

39. $\sum_{i=1}^{9} 2^{i-3}$

40. $\sum_{i=1}^{6} 3^i$

41. $\sum_{i=2}^{5} (-3)^{i+1}$

42. $\sum_{i=3}^{8} (-2)^{i-1}$

43. $\sum_{i=1}^{6} 3\left(\frac{1}{2}\right)^i$

44. $\sum_{i=1}^{5} 2\left(\frac{1}{3}\right)^i$

For Problems 45–56, find the sum of each infinite geometric sequence. If the sequence has no sum, so state.

45. 2, 1, $\frac{1}{2}$, $\frac{1}{4}$, . . .

46. 9, 3, 1, $\frac{1}{3}$, . . .

47. $1, \frac{2}{3}, \frac{4}{9}, \frac{8}{27}, \ldots$

48. $5, 3, \frac{9}{5}, \frac{27}{25}, \ldots$

49. $4, 8, 16, 32, \ldots$

50. $32, 16, 8, 4, \ldots$

51. $9, -3, 1, -\frac{1}{3}, \ldots$

52. $2, -6, 18, -54, \ldots$

53. $\frac{1}{2}, \frac{3}{8}, \frac{9}{32}, \frac{27}{128}, \ldots$

54. $4, -\frac{4}{3}, \frac{4}{9}, -\frac{4}{27}, \ldots$

55. $8, -4, 2, -1, \ldots$

56. $7, \frac{14}{5}, \frac{28}{25}, \frac{56}{125}, \ldots$

59. $.\overline{26}$

60. $.\overline{18}$

61. $.\overline{123}$

62. $.\overline{273}$

63. $.2\overline{6}$

64. $.4\overline{3}$

65. $.2\overline{14}$

66. $.3\overline{71}$

67. $2.\overline{3}$

68. $3.\overline{7}$

For Problems 57–68, change each repeating decimal to a/b form, where a and b are integers, $b \neq 0$. Express a/b in reduced form.

57. $.\overline{3}$ **58.** $.\overline{4}$

THOUGHTS into WORDS

69. Explain the difference between an arithmetic sequence and a geometric sequence.

70. What does it mean to say that the sum of the infinite geometric sequence $1, \frac{1}{2}, \frac{1}{4}, \frac{1}{8}, \ldots$ is 2?

71. What do we mean when we state that the infinite geometric sequence 1, 2, 4, 8, . . . has no sum?

10.3 ANOTHER LOOK AT PROBLEM SOLVING

In the previous two sections many of the exercises fell into one of the following four categories.

1. Finding the nth term of an arithmetic sequence ($a_n = a_1 + (n - 1)d$);

2. Finding the sum of the first n terms of an arithmetic sequence ($S_n = n(a_1 + a_n)/2$);

3. Finding the nth term of a geometric sequence ($a_n = a_1 r^{n-1}$);

4. Finding the sum of the first n terms of a geometric sequence $\left(S_n = \dfrac{a_1 r^n - a_1}{r - 1} \right).$

In this section we want to use this knowledge of arithmetic and geometric sequences to expand our problem solving capabilities. Let's begin by restating some *old* problem solving suggestions that continue to apply here, and also to consider some other suggestions that are directly related to problems involving sequences of numbers. (We will indicate these *new* suggestions with an asterisk.)

Suggestions for Solving Word Problems

1. Read the problem carefully and make sure that you understand the meanings of all of the words. Be especially alert for any technical terms used in the statement of the problem.

2. Read the problem a second time (perhaps even a third time) to get an overview of the situation being described and to determine the known facts, as well as what is to be found.

3. Sketch a figure, diagram, or chart that might be helpful in analyzing the problem.

*4. Write down the first few terms of the sequence that describe what is taking place in the problem. Be sure that you understand term by term what the sequence represents in the problem.

*5. Determine whether the sequence is arithmetic or geometric.

*6. Determine whether the problem is asking for a specific term of the sequence or whether it is asking for the sum of a certain number of terms.

*7. Carry out the necessary calculations and check your answer for ''reasonableness.''

As we solve some problems, these suggestions should become even more meaningful to you.

PROBLEM 1

Salary increases   Domenica started to work in 1975 at an annual salary of $14,500. She received a $1050 raise each year. How much was her annual salary in 1984?

Solution

The following sequence represents her annual salary beginning in 1975.

   14500, 15550, 16600, 17650, . . .

This is an arithmetic sequence with $a_1 = 14500$ and $d = 1050$. Since each term of the sequence represents her annual salary, we are looking for the 10th term.

$$a_{10} = 14500 + (10 - 1)1050$$
$$= 14500 + 9(1050)$$
$$= 23950$$

Her annual salary in 1984 was $23,950.   ▬▬▬

PROBLEM 2

Seats in an auditorium   An auditorium has 20 seats in the front row, 24 seats in the second row, 28 seats in the third row, and so on, for 15 rows. How many seats are there in the auditorium?

Solution

The following sequence represents the number of seats per row starting with the first row.

   20, 24, 28, 32, . . .

This is an arithmetic sequence with $a_1 = 20$ and $d = 4$; therefore, the 15th term, which represents the number of seats in the 15th row, is given by

$$a_{15} = 20 + (15 - 1)4$$
$$= 20 + 14(4)$$
$$= 76.$$

The total number of seats in the auditorium is represented by

$$20 + 24 + 28 + \cdots + 76.$$

Using the sum formula for an arithmetic sequence we obtain

$$S_{15} = \frac{15}{2}(20 + 76) = 720.$$

There are 720 seats in the auditorium.

PROBLEM 3

Double your savings   Suppose that you save 25 cents the first day of a week, 50 cents the second day, one dollar the third day, and continue to double your savings each day. How much will you save on the 7th day? What will be your total savings for the week?

Solution

The following sequence represents your savings per day, expressed in cents.

25, 50, 100, . . .

This is a geometric sequence with $a_1 = 25$ and $r = 2$. Your savings on the 7th day is the 7th term of this sequence. Therefore, using $a_n = a_1 r^{n-1}$ we obtain

$$a_7 = 25(2)^6 = 1600.$$

So you will save $16 on the 7th day. Your total savings for the 7 days is given by

$$25 + 50 + 100 + \cdots + 1600.$$

Using the sum formula for a geometric sequence we obtain

$$S_7 = \frac{25(2)^7 - 25}{2 - 1} = \frac{25(2^7 - 1)}{1}$$
$$= 3175.$$

So your savings for the entire week is $31.75.

PROBLEM 4

Vacuum pump   A pump is attached to a container for the purpose of creating a vacuum. For each stroke of the pump, $\frac{1}{4}$ of the air remaining in the container is removed. To the nearest tenth of a percent, how much of the air remains in the container after 6 strokes?

Solution

Let's draw a diagram to help with the analysis of this problem.

| | First stroke: | $\frac{1}{4}$ of the air is removed | $1 - \frac{1}{4} = \frac{3}{4}$ of the air remains |

First stroke: $\frac{1}{4}$ of the air is removed $1 - \frac{1}{4} = \frac{3}{4}$ of the air remains

Second stroke: $\frac{1}{4}\left(\frac{3}{4}\right) = \frac{3}{16}$ of the air is removed $\frac{3}{4} - \frac{3}{16} = \frac{9}{16}$ of the air remains

Third stroke: $\frac{1}{4}\left(\frac{9}{16}\right) = \frac{9}{64}$ of the air is removed $\frac{9}{16} - \frac{9}{64} = \frac{27}{64}$ of the air remains

From the diagram we see two approaches to the problem as follows.

Approach A

The sequence

$$\frac{1}{4}, \frac{3}{16}, \frac{9}{64}, \dots$$

represents term by term the fractional amount of air being removed with each stroke. Therefore, we can find the total amount removed and subtract from 100%. The sequence is geometric with $a_1 = \frac{1}{4}$ and $r = \frac{3}{4}$.

Using the sum formula we obtain

$$S_6 = \frac{\frac{1}{4} - \frac{1}{4}\left(\frac{3}{4}\right)^6}{1 - \frac{3}{4}} = \frac{\frac{1}{4}\left(1 - \left(\frac{3}{4}\right)^6\right)}{\frac{1}{4}}$$

$$= 1 - \frac{729}{4096} = \frac{3367}{4096}$$

$$= 82.2\%.$$

Therefore,

$$100\% - 82.2\% = 17.8\%$$

of the air remains.

Approach B

The sequence

$$\frac{3}{4}, \frac{9}{16}, \frac{27}{64}, \dots$$

represents term by term the amount of air that remains in the container after each stroke. Therefore, if we find the 6th term of this geometric sequence we should have the answer to the problem. Since $a_1 = \frac{3}{4}$ and $r = \frac{3}{4}$, we obtain

$$a_6 = \frac{3}{4}\left(\frac{3}{4}\right)^{6-1} = \left(\frac{3}{4}\right)^6$$

$$= \frac{729}{4096} = 17.8\%.$$

Therefore, 17.8% of the air remains after 6 strokes.

Perhaps it would be helpful for you to take another look at the two approaches we used to solve Problem 4. Notice in Approach B that finding the 6th term of a sequence produced the answer to the problem without any further calculations. In Approach A, however, we had to find the sum of 6 terms of a sequence and then subtract that amount from 100%. Obviously, Approach B requires less computation, but both approaches are meaningful. As we solve problems involving sequences it is necessary that we understand what a particular sequence physically represents on a term-by-term basis.

PROBLEM SET 10.3

Use your knowledge of arithmetic and geometric sequences to help solve each of the following problems.

1. **Annual salary**   A man started to work in 1960 at an annual salary of $9500. He received a $700 raise each year. How much was his annual salary in 1981?

2. **Annual salary**   A woman started to work in 1970 at an annual salary of $13,400. She received a $900 raise per year. How much was her annual salary in 1985?

3. **University enrollment**   State University had an enrollment of 9600 students in 1960. Each year the enrollment increased by 150 students. What was the enrollment in 1973?

4. **University enrollment**   Math University had an enrollment of 12,800 students in 1977. Each year the enrollment decreased by 75 students. What was the enrollment in 1984?

5. **Predicted increase in enrollment**   The enrollment at University X is predicted to increase at the rate of 10% per year. If the enrollment for 1990 was 5000, find the predicted enrollment for 1994. Express your answer to the nearest whole number.

6. **Depreciation on a car**   If you pay $12,000 for a car and its value depreciates 20% per year, how much will it be worth in 5 years? Express your answer to the nearest dollar.

7. **Emptying a tank**   A tank contains 16,000 liters of water. Each day one-half of the water in the tank is removed and not replaced. How much water remains in the tank at the end of 7 days?

8. **Predicted price of coffee**   If the price of a pound of coffee is $3.20 and the projected rate of inflation is 5% per year, how much per pound will coffee cost in 5 years? Express your answer to the nearest cent.

9. **Emptying a tank**   A tank contains 5832 gallons of water. Each day one-third of the water in the tank is removed and not replaced. How much water remains in the tank at the end of 6 days?

10. **Growth of a fungus culture**   A fungus culture growing under controlled conditions doubles in size each day. How many units will the culture contain after 7 days if it originally contains 4 units?

11. **Saving quarters**   Sue is saving quarters. She saves 1 quarter the first day, 2 quarters the second day, 3 quarters the third day, and so on for 30 days. How much money will she have saved in 30 days?

12. **Saving pennies**   Suppose you save a penny the first day

of a month, 2 cents the second day, 3 cents the third day, and so on for 31 days. What will be your total savings for the 31 days?

13. *Saving pennies*   Suppose you save a penny the first day of a month, 2 cents the second day, 4 cents the third day, and continue to double your savings per day. How much will you save on the 15th day of the month? How much will your total savings be for the 15 days?

14. *Doubling your savings*   Eric saved a nickel the first day of a month, a dime the second day, 20 cents the third day, and continued to double his daily savings each day for 14 days. What were his daily savings on the 14th day? What were his total savings for the 14 days?

15. *Investments*   Ms. Bryan invested $1500 at 12% simple interest at the beginning of each year for a period of 10 years. Find the total accumulated value of all the investments at the end of the 10-year period.

16. *Investments*   Mr. Woodley invested $1200 at 11% simple interest at the beginning of each year for a period of 8 years. Find the total accumulated value of all the investments at the end of the 8-year period.

17. *Falling object*   An object falling from rest in a vacuum falls approximately 16 feet the first second, 48 feet the second second, 80 feet the third second, 112 feet the fourth second, and so on. How far will it fall in 11 seconds?

18. *Raffle tickets*   A raffle is organized so that the amount paid for each ticket is determined by the number on the ticket. The tickets are numbered with the consecutive odd whole numbers 1, 3, 5, 7, ... Each contestant pays as many cents as the number on the ticket that he draws. How much money will the raffle take in if 1000 tickets are sold?

19. *Half-life*   Suppose an element has a half-life of 4 hours. This means that if n grams of it exist at a specific time, then only $\frac{1}{2}n$ remains 4 hours later. If at a particular moment we have 60 grams of the element, how much of it remains 24 hours later?

20. *Half-life*   Suppose an element has a half-life of 3 hours. (See Problem 19 for a definition of half-life.) If at a particular moment we have 768 grams of the element, how much of it remains 24 hours later?

21. *Bouncing ball*   A rubber ball is dropped from a height of 1458 feet and each time it rebounds one-third of the height from which it last fell. How far has the ball traveled by the time it strikes the ground for the 6th time?

22. *Bouncing ball*   A rubber ball is dropped from a height of 100 feet and each time it rebounds one-half of the height from which it last fell. What distance has the ball traveled up to the instant it hits the ground for the 8th time?

23. *Pile of logs*   A pile of logs has 25 logs in the bottom layer, 24 logs in the next layer, 23 logs in the next layer, and so on until the top layer has 1 log. How many logs are in the pile?

24. *Drilling a well*   A ''well-driller'' charges $9.00 per foot for the first 10 feet, $9.10 per foot for the next 10 feet, $9.20 per foot for the next 10 feet, and so on, continuing to increase the price by $.10 per foot for succeeding intervals of 10 feet. How much would it cost to drill a well with a depth of 150 feet?

25. *Vacuum pump*   A pump is attached to a container for the purpose of creating a vacuum. For each stroke of the pump, $\frac{1}{3}$ of the air remaining in the container is removed. To the nearest tenth of a percent, how much of the air remains in the container after 7 strokes?

26. *Vacuum pump*   Suppose that in Problem 25 each stroke of the pump removed $\frac{1}{2}$ of the air remaining in the container. What fractional part of the air has been removed after 6 strokes?

27. *Adding antifreeze*   A tank contains 20 gallons of water. One-half of the water is removed and replaced with antifreeze. Then one-half of this mixture is removed and replaced with antifreeze. This process is continued 8 times. How much water remains in the tank after the 8th replacement process?

28. *Adding antifreeze*   The radiator of a truck contains 10 gallons of water. Suppose we remove 1 gallon of water and replace it with antifreeze. Then we remove 1 gallon of this mixture and replace it with antifreeze. This process is continued 7 times. To the nearest tenth of a gallon, how much antifreeze is in the final mixture?

10.4   MATHEMATICAL INDUCTION

Is $2^n > n$ for all positive integer values of n? In an attempt to answer this question we might proceed as follows.

If $n = 1$, then $2^n > n$ becomes $2^1 > 1$, a true statement.

If $n = 2$, then $2^n > n$ becomes $2^2 > 2$, a true statement.

If $n = 3$, then $2^n > n$ becomes $2^3 > 3$, a true statement.

We could continue in this way as long as we wanted, but obviously we could never show that $2^n > n$ for *every* positive integer n in this manner. However, we do have a form of proof called **proof by mathematical induction** that can be used to verify the truth of many mathematical statements involving positive integers. This form of proof is based on the following principle.

> ### Principle of Mathematical Induction
>
> Let P_n be a statement in terms of n, where n is a positive integer. If
>
> 1. P_1 is true, and
> 2. The truth of P_k implies the truth of P_{k+1} for every positive integer k, then P_n is true for every positive integer n.

A proof based on the principle of mathematical induction consists of two parts. First, we must show that the statement is true for the positive integer 1. Then we must show that if the statement is true for some positive integer, then it follows that it is also true for the next positive integer. Let's illustrate what this means.

EXAMPLE 1

Prove that $2^n > n$ for all positive integer values of n.

Proof

Part I   If $n = 1$, then $2^n > n$ becomes $2^1 > 1$, which is a true statement.

Part 2   We must prove the statement, *if $2^k > k$, then $2^{k+1} > k + 1$ for all positive integer values of k.* In other words, we should be able to start with $2^k > k$ and from that deduce $2^{k+1} > k + 1$. This can be done as follows.

$$2^k > k$$

$$2(2^k) > 2(k) \qquad \text{Multiply both sides by 2}$$

$$2^{k+1} > 2k$$

We know that $k \geq 1$ because we are working with positive integers. Therefore,

$k + k \geq k + 1$ Add k to both sides

$2k \geq k + 1$.

Since $2^{k+1} > 2k$ and $2k \geq k + 1$, by transitivity we conclude that

$2^{k+1} > k + 1$. ▬▬▬▬

Perhaps it would be helpful for you to look back over the proof in Example 1. Notice that in part 1 we established that $2^n > n$ is true for $n = 1$. Then in part 2 we established that if $2^n > n$ is true for any positive integer, then it must be true for the next consecutive positive integer. Therefore, since $2^n > n$ is true for $n = 1$, then it must be true for $n = 2$. Likewise, if $2^n > n$ is true for $n = 2$, then it must be true for $n = 3$, and so on for *all* positive integers.

Proof by mathematical induction can be physically illustrated with dominoes. Suppose that in Figure 10.1 we have infinitely many dominoes lined up. If we can push the first domino over (part 1 of a mathematical induction proof) and if the dominoes are so spaced that each time one falls over it causes the next one to fall over (part 2 of a mathematical induction proof), then by pushing the first one over we should cause a chain reaction that will topple all of the dominoes (Figure 10.2).

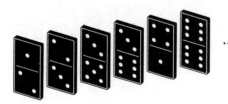

FIGURE 10.1

FIGURE 10.2

Now let's consider another proof by mathematical induction.

EXAMPLE 2

Prove that for all positive integers n, $3^{2n} - 1$ is divisible by 8.

Proof

Part 1   If $n = 1$, then $3^{2n} - 1$ becomes $3^{2(1)} - 1 = 3^2 - 1 = 8$, and of course 8 is divisible by 8.

Part 2   We need to prove the statement, *if $3^{2k} - 1$ is divisible by 8, then $3^{2k+2} - 1$ is divisible by 8 for all integer values of k.* This can be verified as follows: If $3^{2k} - 1$ is divisible by 8, then this means that for some integer x, $3^{2k} - 1 = 8x$. Therefore,

$3^{2k} - 1 = 8x$

$3^{2k} = 1 + 8x$

$$3^2(3^{2k}) = 3^2(1 + 8x)$$ Multiply both sides by 3^2 (or 9)

$$3^{2k+2} = 9(1 + 8x)$$

$$3^{2k+2} = 9 + 9(8x)$$

$$3^{2k+2} = 1 + 8 + 9(8x)$$ $9 = 1 + 8$

$$3^{2k+2} = 1 + 8(1 + 9x)$$ Apply distributive property to $8 + 9(8x)$

$$3^{2k+2} - 1 = 8(1 + 9x).$$

Therefore, $3^{2k+2} - 1$ is divisible by 8.   ▬▬▬▬

Recall that in the first three sections of this chapter we used a_n to represent the nth term of a sequence and S_n to represent the sum of the first n terms of a sequence. For example, if $a_n = 2n$, then the first three terms of the sequence are $a_1 = 2(1) = 2$, $a_2 = 2(2) = 4$, and $a_3 = 2(3) = 6$. Furthermore, the kth term is $a_k = 2(k) = 2k$ and the $(k + 1)$ term is $a_{k+1} = 2(k + 1) = 2k + 2$. Relative to this same sequence we can state that $S_1 = 2$, $S_2 = 2 + 4 = 6$, and $S_3 = 2 + 4 + 6 = 12$.

There are numerous sum formulas for sequences that can be verified by mathematical induction. For such proofs, the following property of sequences is used.

$$S_{k+1} = S_k + a_{k+1}$$

This property states that **the sum of the first $(k + 1)$ terms is equal to the sum of the first k terms plus the $(k + 1)$ term.** Let's see how this can be used in a specific example.

EXAMPLE 3

Prove that $S_n = n(n + 1)$ for the sequence $a_n = 2n$, where n is any positive integer.

Proof

Part 1   If $n = 1$, $S_1 = 1(1 + 1) = 2$ and 2 is the first term of the sequence $a_n = 2n$.

Part 2   We need to prove that if $S_k = k(k + 1)$, then $S_{k+1} = (k + 1)/(k + 2)$. Using the property $S_{k+1} = S_k + a_{k+1}$, we can proceed as follows.

$$S_{k+1} = S_k + a_{k+1}$$

$$= k(k + 1) + 2(k + 1)$$

$$= (k + 1)(k + 2)$$ ▬▬▬▬

EXAMPLE 4

Prove that $S_n = (5n(n + 1))/2$ for the sequence $a_n = 5n$, where n is any positive integer.

Proof

Part I $S_1 = (5(1)(1 + 1))/2 = 5$ and 5 is the first term of the sequence $a_n = 5n$.

Part 2 We need to prove that if $S_k = (5k(k + 1))/2$, then

$$S_{k+1} = (5(k + 1)(k + 2))/2.$$

$$S_{k+1} = S_k + a_{k+1}$$

$$= \frac{5k(k + 1)}{2} + 5(k + 1)$$

$$= \frac{5k(k + 1)}{2} + 5k + 5$$

$$= \frac{5k(k + 1) + 2(5k + 5)}{2}$$

$$= \frac{5k^2 + 5k + 10k + 10}{2}$$

$$= \frac{5k^2 + 15k + 10}{2} = \frac{5(k^2 + 3k + 2)}{2}$$

$$= \frac{5(k + 1)(k + 2)}{2}$$

EXAMPLE 5

Prove that $S_n = (4^n - 1)/3$ for the sequence $a_n = 4^{n-1}$, where n is any positive integer.

Proof

Part I Since $(4^1 - 1)/3 = 1$ and 1 is the first term of the sequence $a_n = 4^{n-1}$, we have $S_1 = a_1 = 1$.

Part 2 We need to prove that if $S_k = (4^k - 1)/3$, then $S_{k+1} = (4^{k+1} - 1)/3$.

$$S_{k+1} = S_k + a_{k+1}$$

$$= \frac{4^k - 1}{3} + 4^k$$

$$= \frac{4^k - 1 + 3(4^k)}{3}$$

$$= \frac{4^k + 3(4^k) - 1}{3}$$

$$= \frac{4^k(1 + 3) - 1}{3}$$

$$= \frac{4^k(4) - 1}{3}$$

$$= \frac{4^{k+1} - 1}{3}.$$

Therefore, using part 1 and part 2 we proved that $S_n = (4^n - 1)/3$ yields the correct sum for any number of terms of the sequence $a_n = 4^{n-1}$.

Let's conclude this section with a few final comments about proof by mathematical induction. Every mathematical induction proof is a two-part proof and both parts are absolutely necessary. There are mathematical statements that hold for one or the other of the two parts but not for both. For example, $(a + b)^n = a^n + b^n$ is true for $n = 1$, but is false for any positive integer greater than 1. Therefore, if one were to attempt a mathematical induction proof for $(a + b)^n = a^n + b^n$, part 1 could be established but part 2 would break down. Another example of this type is the statement, $n^2 - n + 41$ *produces a prime number for all positive integer values of n.* This statement is true for $n = 1, 2, 3, 4, \ldots, 40$, but is false when $n = 41$. ($41^2 - 41 + 41 = 41^2$, which is not a prime number.)

It is also possible that part 2 of a mathematical induction proof can be established, but part 1 breaks down. For example, consider the sequence $a_n = n$ and a sum formula of $S_n = [(n + 3)(n - 2)]/2$. If $n = 1$, then $a_1 = 1$ but $S_1 = [(4)(-1)]/2 = -2$; so part 1 does not hold. However, it is possible to show that

$$S_k = \frac{(k + 3)(k - 2)}{2} \quad \text{implies} \quad S_{k+1} = \frac{(k + 4)(k - 1)}{2}.$$

We will leave the details of this for you to do.

Finally, we need to realize that some mathematical statements are true for all positive integers greater than some fixed positive integer other than 1. (Back in Figure 10.1, perhaps we cannot knock down the first four dominoes, but we can knock down the fifth domino and every one thereafter.) For example, we can prove by mathematical induction that $2^n > n^2$ for all positive integers $n > 4$. It does require a slight variation in the statement of the principle of mathematical induction. We will not concern ourselves with such problems in this text, but we did want you to be aware of their existence.

PROBLEM SET 10.4

In Problems 1–10, use mathematical induction to prove that each statement is true for all positive integers n.

1. $3^n \geq 2n + 1$ **2.** $4^n \geq 4n$

3. $n^2 \geq n$ **4.** $2^n \geq n + 1$

5. $4^n - 1$ is divisible by 3

6. $5^n - 1$ is divisible by 4

7. $6^n - 1$ is divisible by 5

8. $9^n - 1$ is divisible by 4

9. $n^2 + n$ is divisible by 2

10. $n^2 - n$ is divisible by 2

In Problems 11–20, use mathematical induction to prove each of the sum formulas for the indicated sequences. They are to hold for all positive integers n.

11. $S_n = \dfrac{n(n + 1)}{2}$ for $a_n = n$

12. $S_n = n^2$ for $a_n = 2n - 1$

13. $S_n = \dfrac{n(3n + 1)}{2}$ for $a_n = 3n - 1$

14. $S_n = \dfrac{n(5n + 9)}{2}$ for $a_n = 5n + 2$

15. $S_n = 2(2^n - 1)$ for $a_n = 2^n$

16. $S_n = \dfrac{3(3^n - 1)}{2}$ for $a_n = 3^n$

17. $S_n = \dfrac{n(n + 1)(2n + 1)}{6}$ for $a_n = n^2$

18. $S_n = \dfrac{n^2(n + 1)^2}{4}$ for $a_n = n^3$

19. $S_n = \dfrac{n}{n + 1}$ for $a_n = \dfrac{1}{n(n + 1)}$

20. $S_n = \dfrac{n(n + 1)(n + 2)}{3}$ for $a_n = n(n + 1)$

THOUGHTS into WORDS

21. How would you describe *proof by mathematical induction?*

22. Compare *inductive reasoning* to *proof by mathematical induction.*

CHAPTER 10 SUMMARY

Four topics were discussed in this chapter, namely, (1) arithmetic sequences, (2) geometric sequences, (3) problem solving, and (4) mathematical induction.

Arithmetic Sequences

The sequence $a_1, a_2, a_3, a_4, \ldots$ is called **arithmetic** if and only if

$$a_{k+1} - a_k = d$$

for every positive integer k. In other words, there is a common difference, d, between successive terms. The general term of an arithmetic sequence is given by the formula

$$a_n = a_1 + (n - 1)d,$$

where a_1 is the first term, n is the number of terms, and d is the common difference. The sum of the first n terms of an arithmetic sequence is given by the formula

$$S_n = \frac{n(a_1 + a_n)}{2}.$$

Summation notation can be used to indicate the sum of a certain number of terms of a sequence. For example,

$$\sum_{i=1}^{5} 4^i = 4^1 + 4^2 + 4^3 + 4^4 + 4^5.$$

Geometric Sequences

The sequence $a_1, a_2, a_3, a_4, \ldots$ is called geometric if and only if

$$a_{k+1} = ra_k$$

for every positive integer k. There is a common ratio, r, between successive terms. The general term of a geometric sequence is given by the formula

$$a_n = a_1 r^{n-1}$$

where a_1 is the first term, n the number of terms, and r the common ratio. The sum of the first n terms of a geometric sequence is given by the formula

$$S_n = \frac{a_1 r^n - a_1}{r - 1}, \qquad r \neq 1.$$

The sum of an infinite geometric sequence is given by the formula

$$S_\infty = \frac{a_1}{1 - r} \quad \text{for } |r| < 1.$$

If $|r| \geq 1$, the sequence has no sum. Repeating decimals such as .4 can be changed to a/b form, where a and b are integers, $b \neq 0$, by treating them as the sum of an infinite geometric sequence. The repeating decimal .4 can be written as $.4 + .04 + .004 + .0004 + \ldots$.

Problem Solving

Many of the problem solving suggestions offered earlier in this text are still appropriate when solving problems that deal with sequences. However, there are also some special suggestions pertaining to sequence problems.

1. Write down the first few terms of the sequence that describe what is taking place in the problem. A picture or diagram may help with this step.

2. Be sure that you understand term by term what the sequence represents in the problem.

3. Determine whether the sequence is arithmetic or geometric. (Those are the only kinds of sequences that we are working with in this text.)

4. Determine whether the problem is asking for a specific term or whether it is asking for the sum of a certain number of terms.

Mathematical Induction

Proof by mathematical induction relies on the following principle of induction: Let P_n be a statement in terms of n, where n is a positive integer. If

1. P_1 is true, and

2. The truth of P_k implies the truth of P_{k+1} for every positive integer k, then P_n is true for every positive integer n.

CHAPTER 10 REVIEW PROBLEM SET

For Problems 1–10, find the general term (nth term) for each of the following sequences. These problems contain a mixture of arithmetic and geometric sequences.

1. 3, 9, 15, 21, . . .

2. $\frac{1}{3}$, 1, 3, 9, . . .

3. 10, 20, 40, 80, . . .

4. 5, 2, -1, -4, . . .

5. -5, -3, -1, 1, . . .

6. 9, 3, 1, $\frac{1}{3}$, . . .

7. -1, 2, -4, 8, . . .

8. 12, 15, 18, 21, . . .

9. $\frac{2}{3}$, 1, $\frac{4}{3}$, $\frac{5}{3}$, . . .

10. 1, 4, 16, 64, . . .

For Problems 11–16, find the indicated term of each of the sequences.

11. The 19th term of 1, 5, 9, 13, . . .

12. The 28th term of -2, 2, 6, 10, . . .

13. The 9th term of 8, 4, 2, 1, . . .

14. The 8th term of $\frac{243}{32}$, $\frac{81}{16}$, $\frac{27}{8}$, $\frac{9}{4}$, . . .

15. The 34th term of 7, 4, 1, -2, . . .

16. The 10th term of -32, 16, -8, 4, . . .

17. If the 5th term of an arithmetic sequence is -19 and the 8th term is -34, find the common difference of the sequence.

18. If the 8th term of an arithmetic sequence is 37 and the 13th term is 57, find the 20th term.

19. Find the first term of a geometric sequence if the 3rd term is 5 and the 6th term is 135.

20. Find the common ratio of a geometric sequence if the 2nd term is $\frac{1}{2}$ and the 6th term is 8.

21. Find the sum of the first 9 terms of the sequence 81, 27, 9, 3, . . .

22. Find the sum of the first 70 terms of the sequence -3, 0, 3, 6, . . .

23. Find the sum of the first 75 terms of the sequence 5, 1, -3, -7, . . .

24. Find the sum of the first 10 terms of the sequence for which $a_n = 2^{5-n}$.

25. Find the sum of the first 95 terms of the sequence for which $a_n = 7n + 1$.

26. Find the sum $5 + 7 + 9 + \cdots + 137$.

27. Find the sum $64 + 16 + 4 + \cdots + \frac{1}{64}$.

28. Find the sum of all even numbers between 8 and 384, inclusive.

29. Find the sum of all multiples of 3 between 27 and 276, inclusive.

For Problems 30–33, find each of the indicated sums.

30. $\displaystyle\sum_{i=1}^{45} (-2i + 5)$ **31.** $\displaystyle\sum_{i=1}^{5} i^3$

32. $\displaystyle\sum_{i=1}^{8} 2^{8-i}$ **33.** $\displaystyle\sum_{i=4}^{75} (3i - 4)$

34. Find the sum of the infinite geometric sequence 64, 16, 4, 1, . . .

35. Change $.\overline{36}$ to reduced a/b form, where a and b are integers, $b \neq 0$.

36. Change $.4\overline{5}$ to reduced a/b form, where a and b are integers, $b \neq 0$.

Solve each of the Problems 37–40 by using your knowledge of arithmetic and geometric sequences.

37. *Withdrawing from a savings account*   Suppose that at the beginning of a year your savings account contains $3750. If you withdraw $250 per month from the account, how much will it contain at the end of the year?

38. *Saving dimes*   Sonya decides to start saving dimes. She plans to save 1 dime the first day of April, 2 dimes the second day, 3 dimes the third day, 4 dimes the fourth day, and so on for the 30 days of April. How much money will she save in April?

39. *Saving dimes*   Nancy decides to start saving dimes. She plans to save 1 dime the first day of April, 2 dimes the second day, 4 dimes the third day, 8 dimes the fourth day, and so on for the first 15 days of April. How much will she save in 15 days?

40. *Draining a tank*   A tank contains 61,440 gallons of water. Each day one-fourth of the water is drained out. How much remains in the tank at the end of 6 days?

For Problems 41–43, show a mathematical induction proof.

41. Prove that $5^n > 5n - 1$ for all positive integer values of n.

42. Prove that $n^3 - n + 3$ is divisible by 3 for all positive integer values of n.

43. Prove that

$$S_n = \frac{n(n + 3)}{4(n + 1)(n + 2)}$$

is the sum formula for the sequence

$$a_n = \frac{1}{n(n + 1)(n + 2)}, \quad \text{where } n \text{ is any positive integer.}$$

SYSTEMS OF EQUATIONS AND INEQUALITIES

In Section 2.3 we reviewed the substitution and elimination-by-addition methods of solving systems of linear equations. Many applications of mathematics require the use of large numbers of variables and equations; in this chapter we will introduce some additional techniques for solving such systems of linear equations. These same techniques also form a basis for solving systems by using a computer. In the final section of the chapter, we will use systems of inequalities to set up and solve a few basic linear programming problems.

11

A matrix is a very old mathematical concept but in terms of applications it is becoming more and more useful with the advent of the computer.

11.1 MATRIX APPROACH TO SOLVING SYSTEMS

In Section 2.3 we found that the techniques of substitution and elimination-by-addition worked effectively with two equations and two unknowns, but they started to become a bit cumbersome with three equations and three unknowns. Therefore, we will begin to analyze some techniques that lend themselves to use with larger systems of equations; some of these techniques form the basis for solving systems using a computer. Even though these techniques are primarily designed for large systems of equations, we will study them in the context of small systems so that we don't become too bogged down with the computational aspects of the techniques.

Matrices

A **matrix** is simply an array of numbers arranged in horizontal rows and vertical columns enclosed in brackets. For example, the matrix

$$2 \text{ rows} \longrightarrow \begin{bmatrix} 2 & 3 & -1 \\ -4 & 7 & 12 \end{bmatrix}$$

$$\uparrow \quad \uparrow \quad \uparrow$$
$$3 \text{ columns}$$

has 2 rows and 3 columns and is called a 2×3 (read *two by three*) matrix. Each number in a matrix is called an **element** of the matrix. Some additional examples of matrices (''matrices'' is the plural of matrix) are as follows.

$$\begin{array}{cccc} 3 \times 2 & 2 \times 2 & 1 \times 2 & 4 \times 1 \end{array}$$

$$\begin{bmatrix} 2 & 1 \\ 1 & -4 \\ \frac{1}{2} & \frac{2}{3} \end{bmatrix} \quad \begin{bmatrix} 17 & 18 \\ -14 & 16 \end{bmatrix} \quad \begin{bmatrix} 7 & 14 \end{bmatrix} \quad \begin{bmatrix} 3 \\ -2 \\ 1 \\ 19 \end{bmatrix}$$

In general, a matrix of m rows and n columns is called a matrix of **dimension** $m \times n$ or **order** $m \times n$.

With every system of linear equations we can associate a matrix that consists of the coefficients and constant terms. For example, with the system

$$\begin{pmatrix} a_1x + b_1y + c_1z = d_1 \\ a_2x + b_2y + c_2z = d_2 \\ a_3x + b_3y + c_3z = d_3 \end{pmatrix}$$

we can associate the matrix

$$\begin{bmatrix} a_1 & b_1 & c_1 & \vdots & d_1 \\ a_2 & b_2 & c_2 & \vdots & d_2 \\ a_3 & b_3 & c_3 & \vdots & d_3 \end{bmatrix}$$

that is commonly called the **augmented matrix** of the system. The dashed line simply separates the coefficients from the constant terms and reminds us that we are working with an augmented matrix.

On page 123 we listed the operations or the transformations that can be applied to a system of equations which will produce an equivalent system. Since augmented matrices are nothing more than abbreviated forms of systems of linear equations, there are analogous transformations that can be applied to augmented matrices. We usually refer to these transformations as **elementary row operations** which we state as follows.

> For any augmented matrix of a system of linear equations, the following elementary row operations will produce a matrix of an equivalent system:
>
> **1.** Any two rows of the matrix can be interchanged.
>
> **2.** Any row of the matrix can be multiplied by a nonzero real number.
>
> **3.** Any row of the matrix can be replaced by adding a nonzero multiple of another row to that row.

Let's illustrate the use of augmented matrices and elementary row operations to solve a system of two linear equations in two variables.

EXAMPLE 1

Solve the system

$$\begin{pmatrix} x - 3y = -17 \\ 2x + 7y = 31 \end{pmatrix}.$$

Solution

The augmented matrix of the system is

$$\begin{bmatrix} 1 & -3 & \vdots & -17 \\ 2 & 7 & \vdots & 31 \end{bmatrix}.$$

We would like to change this matrix to a matrix of the form

$$\begin{bmatrix} 1 & 0 & \vdots & a \\ 0 & 1 & \vdots & b \end{bmatrix}$$

from which the solution $x = a$ and $y = b$ could be readily determined. Let's begin by multiplying row 1 by -2; adding this result to row 2, we get a new row 2.

$$\begin{bmatrix} 1 & -3 & \vdots & -17 \\ 0 & 13 & \vdots & 65 \end{bmatrix}$$

Now we can multiply row 2 by $\frac{1}{13}$.

$$\begin{bmatrix} 1 & -3 & | & -17 \\ 0 & 1 & | & 5 \end{bmatrix}$$

Finally, we can multiply row 2 by 3 and add this result to row 1 to produce a new row 1.

$$\begin{bmatrix} 1 & 0 & | & -2 \\ 0 & 1 & | & 5 \end{bmatrix}$$

From this last matrix we see that $x = -2$ and $y = 5$. In other words, the solution set of the original system is $\{(-2, 5)\}$. ▬▬▬

Already from Example 1 it should be evident that the matrix approach does not provide us with much extra power for solving systems of two linear equations in two unknowns. However, as the systems become larger, the compactness of the matrix approach becomes more convenient. Let's consider a system of three equations in three variables.

EXAMPLE 2

Solve the system

$$\begin{pmatrix} x + 2y - 3z = 15 \\ -2x - 3y + z = -15 \\ 4x + 9y - 4z = 49 \end{pmatrix}.$$

Solution

The augmented matrix of this system is

$$\begin{bmatrix} 1 & 2 & -3 & | & 15 \\ -2 & -3 & 1 & | & -15 \\ 4 & 9 & -4 & | & 49 \end{bmatrix}.$$

If this system has a unique solution, then we should be able to change the augmented matrix to the form

$$\begin{bmatrix} 1 & 0 & 0 & | & a \\ 0 & 1 & 0 & | & b \\ 0 & 0 & 1 & | & c \end{bmatrix}$$

where the solution $x = a$, $y = b$, and $z = c$ can be easily determined. Multiplying row 1 by 2 and adding this result to row 2 produces a new row 2. Likewise, multiplying row 1 by -4 and adding this result to row 3 produces a new row 3.

$$\begin{bmatrix} 1 & 2 & -3 & | & 15 \\ 0 & 1 & -5 & | & 15 \\ 0 & 1 & 8 & | & -11 \end{bmatrix}$$

Now multiplying row 2 by -2 and adding to row 1 produces a new row 1. Also, multiplying row 2 by -1 and adding to row 3 produces a new row 3.

$$\begin{bmatrix} 1 & 0 & 7 & | & -15 \\ 0 & 1 & -5 & | & 15 \\ 0 & 0 & 13 & | & -26 \end{bmatrix}$$

Now let's multiply row 3 by $\frac{1}{13}$.

$$\begin{bmatrix} 1 & 0 & 7 & | & -15 \\ 0 & 1 & -5 & | & 15 \\ 0 & 0 & 1 & | & -2 \end{bmatrix}$$

Finally, we can multiply row 3 by -7 and add to row 1 to produce a new row 1, and multiply row 3 by 5 and add to row 2 for a new row 2.

$$\begin{bmatrix} 1 & 0 & 0 & | & -1 \\ 0 & 1 & 0 & | & 5 \\ 0 & 0 & 1 & | & -2 \end{bmatrix}$$

From this last matrix we can see that the solution set of the original system is $\{(-1, 5, -2)\}$. ■

The final matrices of Examples 1 and 2,

$$\begin{bmatrix} 1 & 0 & | & -2 \\ 0 & 1 & | & 5 \end{bmatrix} \quad \text{and} \quad \begin{bmatrix} 1 & 0 & 0 & | & -1 \\ 0 & 1 & 0 & | & 5 \\ 0 & 0 & 1 & | & -2 \end{bmatrix},$$

are said to be in **reduced echelon form**. In general, a matrix is in reduced echelon form if the following conditions are satisfied.

1. The first (reading from left to right) nonzero entry of each row is 1.

2. The remaining entries in the **column** containing the leftmost 1 of a row are all 0s.

3. The leftmost 1 of any row is to the right of the leftmost 1 of the preceding row.

4. Rows containing only 0s are below rows containing nonzero entries.

In addition to the final matrices of Examples 1 and 2, the following are also in reduced echelon form.

$$\begin{bmatrix} 1 & 2 & | & -3 \\ 0 & 0 & | & 0 \end{bmatrix} \quad \begin{bmatrix} 1 & 0 & -2 & | & 5 \\ 0 & 1 & 4 & | & 7 \\ 0 & 0 & 0 & | & 0 \end{bmatrix} \quad \begin{bmatrix} 1 & 0 & 0 & 0 & | & 8 \\ 0 & 1 & 0 & 0 & | & -9 \\ 0 & 0 & 1 & 0 & | & -2 \\ 0 & 0 & 0 & 1 & | & 12 \end{bmatrix}$$

In contrast, the following matrices are not in reduced echelon form for the reason indicated below each matrix.

$$\begin{bmatrix} 1 & 0 & 0 & \vdots & 11 \\ 0 & 3 & 0 & \vdots & -1 \\ 0 & 0 & 1 & \vdots & -2 \end{bmatrix} \qquad \begin{bmatrix} 1 & 2 & -3 & \vdots & 5 \\ 0 & 1 & 7 & \vdots & 9 \\ 0 & 0 & 1 & \vdots & -6 \end{bmatrix}$$

Violates 1   Violates 2

$$\begin{bmatrix} 1 & 0 & 0 & \vdots & 7 \\ 0 & 0 & 1 & \vdots & -8 \\ 0 & 1 & 0 & \vdots & 14 \end{bmatrix} \qquad \begin{bmatrix} 1 & 0 & 0 & 0 & \vdots & -1 \\ 0 & 0 & 0 & 0 & \vdots & 0 \\ 0 & 0 & 1 & 0 & \vdots & 7 \\ 0 & 0 & 0 & 0 & \vdots & 0 \end{bmatrix}$$

Violates 3   Violates 4

Once we have an augmented matrix in reduced echelon form, the solution set of the system is easily determined. Furthermore, the procedure for changing a given augmented matrix to reduced echelon form can be described in a very systematic way. For example, the augmented matrix of a system of three linear equations in three unknowns that has a unique solution can be changed to reduced echelon form as follows.

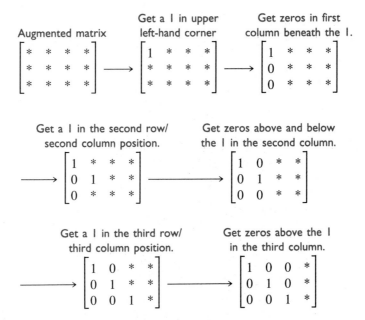

Inconsistent and dependent systems can be identified during the process of changing a matrix to reduced echelon form. We will show some examples of such cases in a moment, but first let's consider another example of a system of three linear equations in three unknowns that has a unique solution.

EXAMPLE 3

Solve the system
$$\begin{pmatrix} 2x + 4y - 5z = 37 \\ x + 3y - 4z = 29 \\ 5x - y + 3z = -20 \end{pmatrix}.$$

Solution

The augmented matrix
$$\begin{bmatrix} 2 & 4 & -5 & | & 37 \\ 1 & 3 & -4 & | & 29 \\ 5 & -1 & 3 & | & -20 \end{bmatrix}$$

does not have a 1 in the upper left-hand corner, but this can be remedied by exchanging rows 1 and 2.

$$\begin{bmatrix} 1 & 3 & -4 & | & 29 \\ 2 & 4 & -5 & | & 37 \\ 5 & -1 & 3 & | & -20 \end{bmatrix}$$

Now we can get 0s in the first column beneath the 1 by multiplying -2 times row 1 and adding to row 2, and by multiplying -5 times row 1 and adding to row 3.

$$\begin{bmatrix} 1 & 3 & -4 & | & 29 \\ 0 & -2 & 3 & | & -21 \\ 0 & -16 & 23 & | & -165 \end{bmatrix}$$

Next, we can get a 1 as the first nonzero entry of the second row by multiplying the second row by $-\frac{1}{2}$.

$$\begin{bmatrix} 1 & 3 & -4 & | & 29 \\ 0 & 1 & -\frac{3}{2} & | & \frac{21}{2} \\ 0 & -16 & 23 & | & -165 \end{bmatrix}$$

Now we can get 0s above and below the 1 in the second column by multiplying -3 times row 2 and adding to row 1; and by multiplying 16 times row 2 and adding to row 3.

$$\begin{bmatrix} 1 & 0 & \frac{1}{2} & | & -\frac{5}{2} \\ 0 & 1 & -\frac{3}{2} & | & \frac{21}{2} \\ 0 & 0 & -1 & | & 3 \end{bmatrix}$$

Next, we can get a 1 as the first nonzero entry of the third row by multiplying the third row by -1.

$$\begin{bmatrix} 1 & 0 & \frac{1}{2} & | & -\frac{5}{2} \\ 0 & 1 & -\frac{3}{2} & | & \frac{21}{2} \\ 0 & 0 & 1 & | & -3 \end{bmatrix}$$

Finally, we can get 0s above the 1 in the third column by multiplying $-\frac{1}{2}$ times row 3 and adding to row 1; and by multiplying $\frac{3}{2}$ times row 3 and adding to row 2.

$$\begin{bmatrix} 1 & 0 & 0 & | & -1 \\ 0 & 1 & 0 & | & 6 \\ 0 & 0 & 1 & | & -3 \end{bmatrix}.$$

From the last matrix, we can see that the solution set of the original system is $\{(-1, 6, -3)\}$.

Example 3 illustrates that even though the process of changing to reduced echelon form can be systematically described, it can involve some rather messy calculations. However, with the aid of a computer such calculations are not troublesome. For our purposes in this text, we have chosen as examples and problems those systems that minimize messy calculations. This should allow you to concentrate on developing an understanding of the procedures we are discussing.

We want to call your attention to another issue in the solution for Example 3. Consider the matrix

$$\begin{bmatrix} 1 & 3 & -4 & | & 29 \\ 0 & 1 & -\frac{3}{2} & | & \frac{21}{2} \\ 0 & -16 & 23 & | & -165 \end{bmatrix},$$

which is obtained about halfway through the solution. At this step it seems evident that the calculations are getting a little messy. Therefore, instead of continuing toward the reduced echelon form, let's multiply row 2 by 16 and add to row 3 to produce a new row 3.

$$\begin{bmatrix} 1 & 3 & -4 & | & 29 \\ 0 & 1 & -\frac{3}{2} & | & \frac{21}{2} \\ 0 & 0 & -1 & | & 3 \end{bmatrix}$$

The system represented by this matrix is

$$\left(\begin{array}{r} x + 3y - 4z = 29 \\ y - \frac{3}{2}z = \frac{21}{2} \\ -z = 3 \end{array} \right)$$

and it is said to be in **triangular form**. The last equation determines the value for z and then we can use the process of back-substitution to determine the values for y and x.

Finally, let's consider two examples to illustrate what happens as we use the matrix approach on inconsistent and dependent systems.

EXAMPLE 4

Solve the system

$$\left(\begin{array}{r} x - 2y + 3z = 3 \\ 5x - 9y + 4z = 2 \\ 2x - 4y + 6z = -1 \end{array} \right).$$

Solution

The augmented matrix of the system is

$$\left[\begin{array}{rrr|r} 1 & -2 & 3 & 3 \\ 5 & -9 & 4 & 2 \\ 2 & -4 & 6 & -1 \end{array}\right].$$

We can get 0s below the 1 in the first column by multiplying -5 times row 1 and adding to row 2, and by multiplying -2 times row 1 and adding to row 3.

$$\left[\begin{array}{rrr|r} 1 & -2 & 3 & 3 \\ 0 & 1 & -11 & -13 \\ 0 & 0 & 0 & -7 \end{array}\right]$$

At this step we can stop because the bottom row of the matrix represents the statement $0(x) + 0(y) + 0(z) = -7$, which is obviously a false statement for all values of x, y, and z. Thus, the original system is inconsistent; its solution set is $\varnothing$.

EXAMPLE 5

Solve the system

$$\begin{pmatrix} x + 2y + 2z = 9 \\ x + 3y - 4z = 5 \\ 2x + 5y - 2z = 14 \end{pmatrix}.$$

Solution

The augmented matrix of the system is

$$\left[\begin{array}{rrr|r} 1 & 2 & 2 & 9 \\ 1 & 3 & -4 & 5 \\ 2 & 5 & -2 & 14 \end{array}\right].$$

We can get 0s in the first column below the 1 in the upper left-hand corner by multiplying -1 times row 1 and adding to row 2; and by multiplying -2 times row 1 and adding to row 3.

$$\left[\begin{array}{rrr|r} 1 & 2 & 2 & 9 \\ 0 & 1 & -6 & -4 \\ 0 & 1 & -6 & -4 \end{array}\right]$$

Now we can get 0s in the second column above and below the 1 in the second row by multiplying -2 times row 2 and adding to row 1, and by multiplying -1 times row 2 and adding to row 3.

$$\left[\begin{array}{rrr|r} 1 & 0 & 14 & 17 \\ 0 & 1 & -6 & -4 \\ 0 & 0 & 0 & 0 \end{array}\right]$$

The bottom row of 0s represents the statement $0(x) + 0(y) + 0(z) = 0$, which is true for all values of x, y, and z. The second row represents the statement $y - 6z = -4$, which can be written as $y = 6z - 4$. The top row represents the statement $x + 14z = 17$, which can be written as $x = -14z + 17$. Therefore, if we let $z = k$, where k is any real number, the solution set of infinitely many ordered triples can be represented by $\{(-14k + 17, 6k - 4, k)\}$. Specific solutions can be generated by letting k take on a value. For example, if $k = 2$, then $6k - 4$ becomes $6(2) - 4 = 8$ and $-14k + 17$ becomes $-14(2) + 17 = -11$. Thus, the ordered triple $(-11, 8, 2)$ is a member of the solution set.

PROBLEM SET 11.1

For Problems 1–10, indicate whether each matrix is in reduced echelon form.

1. $\begin{bmatrix} 1 & 0 & | & -4 \\ 0 & 1 & | & 14 \end{bmatrix}$

2. $\begin{bmatrix} 1 & 2 & | & 8 \\ 0 & 0 & | & 0 \end{bmatrix}$

3. $\begin{bmatrix} 1 & 0 & 2 & | & 5 \\ 0 & 1 & 3 & | & 7 \\ 0 & 0 & 0 & | & 0 \end{bmatrix}$

4. $\begin{bmatrix} 1 & 0 & 0 & | & 5 \\ 0 & 3 & 0 & | & 8 \\ 0 & 0 & 1 & | & -11 \end{bmatrix}$

5. $\begin{bmatrix} 1 & 0 & 0 & | & 17 \\ 0 & 0 & 0 & | & 0 \\ 0 & 1 & 0 & | & -14 \end{bmatrix}$

6. $\begin{bmatrix} 1 & 0 & 0 & | & -7 \\ 0 & 1 & 0 & | & 0 \\ 0 & 0 & 1 & | & 9 \end{bmatrix}$

7. $\begin{bmatrix} 1 & 1 & 0 & | & -3 \\ 0 & 1 & 2 & | & 5 \\ 0 & 0 & 1 & | & 7 \end{bmatrix}$

8. $\begin{bmatrix} 1 & 0 & 3 & | & 8 \\ 0 & 1 & 2 & | & -6 \\ 0 & 0 & 0 & | & 0 \end{bmatrix}$

9. $\begin{bmatrix} 1 & 0 & 0 & 3 & | & 4 \\ 0 & 1 & 0 & 5 & | & -3 \\ 0 & 0 & 1 & -1 & | & 7 \\ 0 & 0 & 0 & 0 & | & 0 \end{bmatrix}$

10. $\begin{bmatrix} 1 & 0 & 0 & 0 & | & 2 \\ 0 & 0 & 1 & 0 & | & 4 \\ 0 & 1 & 0 & 0 & | & -3 \\ 0 & 0 & 0 & 1 & | & 9 \end{bmatrix}$

Use a matrix approach of this section to solve each of the following systems.

11. $\begin{pmatrix} x - 3y = 14 \\ 3x + 2y = -13 \end{pmatrix}$

12. $\begin{pmatrix} x + 5y = -18 \\ -2x + 3y = -16 \end{pmatrix}$

13. $\begin{pmatrix} 3x - 4y = 33 \\ x + 7y = -39 \end{pmatrix}$

14. $\begin{pmatrix} 2x + 7y = -55 \\ x - 4y = 25 \end{pmatrix}$

15. $\begin{pmatrix} x - 6y = -2 \\ 2x - 12y = 5 \end{pmatrix}$

16. $\begin{pmatrix} 2x - 3y = -12 \\ 3x + 2y = 8 \end{pmatrix}$

17. $\begin{pmatrix} 3x - 5y = 39 \\ 2x + 7y = -67 \end{pmatrix}$

18. $\begin{pmatrix} 3x + 9y = -1 \\ x + 3y = 10 \end{pmatrix}$

19. $\begin{pmatrix} x - 2y - 3z = -6 \\ 3x - 5y - z = 4 \\ 2x + y + 2z = 2 \end{pmatrix}$

20. $\begin{pmatrix} x + 3y - 4z = 13 \\ 2x + 7y - 3z = 11 \\ -2x - y + 2z = -8 \end{pmatrix}$

21. $\begin{pmatrix} -2x - 5y + 3z = 11 \\ x + 3y - 3z = -12 \\ 3x - 2y + 5z = 31 \end{pmatrix}$

22. $\begin{pmatrix} -3x + 2y + z = 17 \\ x - y + 5z = -2 \\ 4x - 5y - 3z = -36 \end{pmatrix}$

23. $\begin{pmatrix} x - 3y - z = 2 \\ 3x + y - 4z = -18 \\ -2x + 5y + 3z = 2 \end{pmatrix}$

24. $\begin{pmatrix} x - 4y + 3z = 16 \\ 2x + 3y - 4z = -22 \\ -3x + 11y - z = -36 \end{pmatrix}$

25. $\begin{pmatrix} x - y + 2z = 1 \\ -3x + 4y - z = 4 \\ -x + 2y + 3z = 6 \end{pmatrix}$

26. $\begin{pmatrix} x + 2y - 5z = -1 \\ 2x + 3y - 2z = 2 \\ 3x + 5y - 7z = 4 \end{pmatrix}$

27. $\begin{pmatrix} -2x + y + 5z = -5 \\ 3x + 8y - z = -34 \\ x + 2y + z = -12 \end{pmatrix}$

28. $\begin{pmatrix} 4x - 10y + 3z = -19 \\ 2x + 5y - z = -7 \\ x - 3y - 2z = -2 \end{pmatrix}$

29. $\begin{pmatrix} 2x + 3y - z = 7 \\ 3x + 4y + 5z = -2 \\ 5x + y + 3z = 13 \end{pmatrix}$ **30.** $\begin{pmatrix} 4x + 3y - z = 0 \\ 3x + 2y + 5z = 6 \\ 5x - y - 3z = 3 \end{pmatrix}$

Subscript notation is frequently used when working with large systems of equations. Use a matrix approach to solve each of the following systems. Express the solutions as 4-tuples of the form (x_1, x_2, x_3, x_4).

31. $\begin{pmatrix} x_1 - 3x_2 - 2x_3 + x_4 = -3 \\ -2x_1 + 7x_2 + x_3 - 2x_4 = -1 \\ 3x_1 - 7x_2 - 3x_3 + 3x_4 = -5 \\ 5x_1 + x_2 + 4x_3 - 2x_4 = 18 \end{pmatrix}$

32. $\begin{pmatrix} x_1 - 2x_2 + 2x_3 - x_4 = -2 \\ -3x_1 + 5x_2 - x_3 - 3x_4 = 2 \\ 2x_1 + 3x_2 + 3x_3 + 5x_4 = -9 \\ 4x_1 - x_2 - x_3 - 2x_4 = 8 \end{pmatrix}$

33. $\begin{pmatrix} x_1 + 3x_2 - x_3 + 2x_4 = -2 \\ 2x_1 + 7x_2 + 2x_3 - x_4 = 19 \\ -3x_1 - 8x_2 + 3x_3 + x_4 = -7 \\ 4x_1 + 11x_2 - 2x_3 - 3x_4 = 19 \end{pmatrix}$

34. $\begin{pmatrix} x_1 + 2x_2 - 3x_3 + x_4 = -2 \\ -2x_1 - 3x_2 + x_3 - x_4 = 5 \\ 4x_1 + 9x_2 - 2x_3 - 2x_4 = -28 \\ -5x_1 - 9x_2 + 2x_3 - 3x_4 = 14 \end{pmatrix}$

Each matrix in Problems 35–42 is the reduced matrix for a system with variables x_1, x_2, x_3, and x_4. Find the solution set of each system.

35. $\begin{bmatrix} 1 & 0 & 0 & 0 & | & -2 \\ 0 & 1 & 0 & 0 & | & 4 \\ 0 & 0 & 1 & 0 & | & -3 \\ 0 & 0 & 0 & 1 & | & 0 \end{bmatrix}$

36. $\begin{bmatrix} 1 & 0 & 0 & 0 & | & 0 \\ 0 & 1 & 0 & 0 & | & -5 \\ 0 & 0 & 1 & 0 & | & 0 \\ 0 & 0 & 0 & 1 & | & 4 \end{bmatrix}$

37. $\begin{bmatrix} 1 & 0 & 0 & 0 & | & -8 \\ 0 & 1 & 0 & 0 & | & 5 \\ 0 & 0 & 1 & 0 & | & -2 \\ 0 & 0 & 0 & 0 & | & 1 \end{bmatrix}$

38. $\begin{bmatrix} 1 & 0 & 0 & 0 & | & 2 \\ 0 & 1 & 0 & 2 & | & -3 \\ 0 & 0 & 1 & 3 & | & 4 \\ 0 & 0 & 0 & 0 & | & 0 \end{bmatrix}$

39. $\begin{bmatrix} 1 & 0 & 0 & 3 & | & 5 \\ 0 & 1 & 0 & 0 & | & -1 \\ 0 & 0 & 1 & 4 & | & 2 \\ 0 & 0 & 0 & 0 & | & 0 \end{bmatrix}$

40. $\begin{bmatrix} 1 & 3 & 0 & 0 & | & 0 \\ 0 & 0 & 1 & 0 & | & 0 \\ 0 & 0 & 0 & 0 & | & 1 \\ 0 & 0 & 0 & 0 & | & 0 \end{bmatrix}$

41. $\begin{bmatrix} 1 & 3 & 0 & 0 & | & 9 \\ 0 & 0 & 1 & 0 & | & 2 \\ 0 & 0 & 0 & 1 & | & -3 \\ 0 & 0 & 0 & 0 & | & 0 \end{bmatrix}$

42. $\begin{bmatrix} 1 & 0 & 0 & 0 & | & 7 \\ 0 & 1 & 0 & 0 & | & -3 \\ 0 & 0 & 1 & -2 & | & 5 \\ 0 & 0 & 0 & 0 & | & 0 \end{bmatrix}$

FURTHER INVESTIGATIONS

For Problems 43–48, change each augmented matrix of the system to reduced echelon form and then indicate the solutions of the system.

43. $\begin{pmatrix} x - 2y + 3z = 4 \\ 3x - 5y - z = 7 \end{pmatrix}$

44. $\begin{pmatrix} x + 3y - 2z = -1 \\ -2x - 5y + 7z = 4 \end{pmatrix}$

45. $\begin{pmatrix} 2x - 4y + 3z = 8 \\ 3x + 5y - z = 7 \end{pmatrix}$ **46.** $\begin{pmatrix} 3x + 6y - z = 9 \\ 2x - 3y + 4z = 1 \end{pmatrix}$

47. $\begin{pmatrix} x - 2y + 4z = 9 \\ 2x - 4y + 8z = 3 \end{pmatrix}$

48. $\begin{pmatrix} x + y - 2z = -1 \\ 3x + 3y - 6z = -3 \end{pmatrix}$

GRAPHICS CALCULATOR ACTIVITIES

49. If your graphics calculator has the capability to manipulate matrices, this is a good time to become familiar with that procedure. You may need to refer to your calculator manual for the technical instructions. To begin, load your calculator with the three augmented matrices in Examples 1, 2, and 3. Then for each one carry out the row operations as described in the text.

11.2   DETERMINANTS

Before we introduce the concept of a determinant, let's agree on some new symbolism that is convenient to use at this time. A general $m \times n$ (m by n) matrix can be represented by

$$A = \begin{bmatrix} a_{11} & a_{12} & a_{13} & \cdots & a_{1n} \\ a_{21} & a_{22} & a_{23} & \cdots & a_{2n} \\ \vdots & & & & \vdots \\ a_{m1} & a_{m2} & a_{m3} & \cdots & a_{mn} \end{bmatrix},$$

where the double subscripts are used to identify the number of the row and the number of the column in that order. For example, a_{23} is the entry at the intersection of the second row and third column. In general, the entry at the intersection of row i and column j is denoted by a_{ij}.

A **square matrix** is one that has the same number of rows as columns. Associated with each square matrix having real number entries is a real number called the **determinant** of the matrix. The determinant of a matrix A is denoted by $|A|$. Let's first define $|A|$ for a 2×2 matrix.

DEFINITION 11.1

If $A = \begin{bmatrix} a_{11} & a_{12} \\ a_{21} & a_{22} \end{bmatrix}$, then $|A| = \begin{vmatrix} a_{11} & a_{12} \\ a_{21} & a_{22} \end{vmatrix} = a_{11}a_{22} - a_{12}a_{21}.$

EXAMPLE 1

If $A = \begin{bmatrix} 3 & -2 \\ 5 & 8 \end{bmatrix}$, find $|A|$.

Solution

Using Definition 11.1, we obtain

$$|A| = \begin{vmatrix} 3 & -2 \\ 5 & 8 \end{vmatrix} = 3(8) - (-2)(5)$$
$$= 24 + 10$$
$$= 34.$$

Finding the determinant of a square matrix is commonly called **evaluating the determinant** and the matrix notation is often omitted.

EXAMPLE 2

Evaluate $\begin{vmatrix} -3 & 6 \\ 2 & 8 \end{vmatrix}$.

Solution

$$\begin{vmatrix} -3 & 6 \\ 2 & 8 \end{vmatrix} = (-3)(8) - (6)(2)$$
$$= -24 - 12$$
$$= -36$$

To define determinants of 3×3 and larger square matrices, it is convenient to introduce some additional terminology.

DEFINITION 11.2

If A is a 3×3 matrix, then the **minor** (denoted by M_{ij}) of the a_{ij} element is the determinant of the 2×2 matrix obtained by deleting row i and column j of A.

EXAMPLE 3

If $A = \begin{bmatrix} 2 & 1 & 4 \\ -6 & 3 & -2 \\ 4 & 2 & 5 \end{bmatrix}$, find **a.** M_{11} and **b.** M_{23}.

Solution

a. To find M_{11} we first delete row 1 and column 1 of A.

$$\begin{bmatrix} 2 & 1 & 4 \\ -6 & 3 & -2 \\ 4 & 2 & 5 \end{bmatrix}$$

Thus,

$$M_{11} = \begin{vmatrix} 3 & -2 \\ 2 & 5 \end{vmatrix} = 3(5) - (-2)(2) = 19.$$

b. To find M_{23} we first delete row 2 and column 3 of A.

$$\begin{bmatrix} 2 & 1 & 4 \\ -6 & 3 & -2 \\ 4 & 2 & 5 \end{bmatrix}$$

Thus,

$$M_{23} = \begin{vmatrix} 2 & 1 \\ 4 & 2 \end{vmatrix} = 2(2) - (1)(4) = 0.$$

The following definition will also be used.

DEFINITION 11.3

If A is a 3×3 matrix, then the **cofactor** (denoted by C_{ij}) of the element a_{ij} is defined by

$$C_{ij} = (-1)^{i+j} M_{ij}.$$

According to Definition 11.3, to find the cofactor of any element a_{ij} of a square matrix A, we find the minor of a_{ij} and multiply it by 1 if $(i + j)$ is even, or multiply it by -1 if $(i + j)$ is odd.

EXAMPLE 4

If $A = \begin{bmatrix} 3 & 2 & -4 \\ 1 & 5 & 4 \\ 2 & -3 & 1 \end{bmatrix}$, find C_{32}.

Solution

First, let's find M_{32} by deleting row 3 and column 2 of A.

$$\begin{bmatrix} 3 & 2 & -4 \\ 1 & 5 & 4 \\ 2 & -3 & 1 \end{bmatrix}$$

Thus,

$$M_{32} = \begin{vmatrix} 3 & -4 \\ 1 & 4 \end{vmatrix}$$
$$= 3(4) - (-4)(1) = 16.$$

Therefore,

$$C_{32} = (-1)^{3+2} M_{32}$$
$$= (-1)^5 (16) = -16.$$

The concept of cofactor can be used to define the determinant of a 3×3 matrix as follows.

DEFINITION 11.4

If $A = \begin{bmatrix} a_{11} & a_{12} & a_{13} \\ a_{21} & a_{22} & a_{23} \\ a_{31} & a_{32} & a_{33} \end{bmatrix}$, then

$$|A| = a_{11}C_{11} + a_{21}C_{21} + a_{31}C_{31}.$$

Definition 11.4 simply states that the determinant of a 3×3 matrix can be found by multiplying each element of the first column by its corresponding cofactor and then adding the three results. Let's illustrate this procedure.

EXAMPLE 5

Find $|A|$ if $A = \begin{bmatrix} -2 & 1 & 4 \\ 3 & 0 & 5 \\ 1 & -4 & -6 \end{bmatrix}$.

Solution

$$|A| = a_{11}C_{11} + a_{21}C_{21} + a_{31}C_{31}$$

$$= (-2)(-1)^{1+1}\begin{vmatrix} 0 & 5 \\ -4 & -6 \end{vmatrix} + (3)(-1)^{2+1}\begin{vmatrix} 1 & 4 \\ -4 & -6 \end{vmatrix} + (1)(-1)^{3+1}\begin{vmatrix} 1 & 4 \\ 0 & 5 \end{vmatrix}$$

$$= (-2)(1)(20) + (3)(-1)(10) + (1)(1)(5)$$

$$= -40 - 30 + 5$$

$$= -65$$

From Definition 11.4, we say that *the determinant is being expanded about the first column.* It can be shown that **any row or column can be used to expand a determinant**. For example, the expansion of the determinant of matrix A in Example 5 about the second row is as follows.

$$\begin{vmatrix} -2 & 1 & 4 \\ 3 & 0 & 5 \\ 1 & -4 & -6 \end{vmatrix} = (3)(-1)^{2+1}\begin{vmatrix} 1 & 4 \\ -4 & -6 \end{vmatrix} + (0)(-1)^{2+2}\begin{vmatrix} -2 & 4 \\ 1 & -6 \end{vmatrix} + (5)(-1)^{2+3}\begin{vmatrix} -2 & 1 \\ 1 & -4 \end{vmatrix}$$

$$= (3)(-1)(10) + (0)(1)(8) + (5)(-1)(7)$$
$$= -30 + 0 - 35$$
$$= -65$$

Notice that when expanding about the second row, the computation was simplified by the presence of a zero. In general, it is helpful to expand about a row or column that contains the most zeros.

The concepts of minor and cofactor were defined in terms of 3×3 matrices. Analogous definitions can be given for any square matrix ($n \times n$ matrix with $n \geq 2$) and the determinant of any such matrix can be expanded about any row or column. Certainly as the matrices become larger than 3×3, the computation gets more and more tedious. We will concentrate most of our efforts in this text on 2×2 and 3×3 matrices.

Properties of Determinants

There are several properties of determinants; some are primarily important from a theoretical standpoint, but some are also very useful when evaluating determinants. We will state these properties for square matrices in general but we will use 2×2 or 3×3 matrices as examples. Proofs of these properties can be shown by evaluating the determinants involved. We will have you show some of these proofs for 3×3 matrices in the next problem set.

PROPERTY II.1

If any row (or column) of a square matrix A contains only 0s, then $|A| = 0$.

If every element of a row (or column) of a square matrix A is 0, then it should be evident that expanding the determinant about that row (or column) of 0s will produce 0.

PROPERTY II.2

If square matrix B is obtained from square matrix A by interchanging two rows (or two columns), then $|B| = -|A|$.

Property 11.2 states, *interchanging two rows (or columns) changes the sign of the determinant.* As an example of this property suppose that

$$A = \begin{bmatrix} 2 & 5 \\ -1 & 6 \end{bmatrix}$$

and that rows 1 and 2 are interchanged to form

$$B = \begin{bmatrix} -1 & 6 \\ 2 & 5 \end{bmatrix}.$$

Calculating $|A|$ and $|B|$ we obtain

$$|A| = \begin{vmatrix} 2 & 5 \\ -1 & 6 \end{vmatrix} = 2(6) - (5)(-1) = 17$$

and

$$|B| = \begin{vmatrix} -1 & 6 \\ 2 & 5 \end{vmatrix} = (-1)(5) - (6)(2) = -17.$$

PROPERTY 11.3

If square matrix B is obtained from square matrix A by multiplying each element of any row (or column) of A by some real number k, then $|B| = k|A|$.

Property 11.3 states, *multiplying any row (or column) by a factor of k affects the value of the determinant by a factor of k.* As an example of this property, suppose that

$$A = \begin{bmatrix} 1 & -2 & 8 \\ 2 & 1 & 12 \\ 3 & 2 & -16 \end{bmatrix}$$

and that B is formed by multiplying each element of the third column by $\frac{1}{4}$.

$$B = \begin{bmatrix} 1 & -2 & 2 \\ 2 & 1 & 3 \\ 3 & 2 & -4 \end{bmatrix}$$

Now let's calculate $|A|$ and $|B|$ by expanding about the third column in each case.

$$|A| = \begin{vmatrix} 1 & -2 & 8 \\ 2 & 1 & 12 \\ 3 & 2 & -16 \end{vmatrix}$$

$$= (8)(-1)^{1+3}\begin{vmatrix} 2 & 1 \\ 3 & 2 \end{vmatrix} + (12)(-1)^{2+3}\begin{vmatrix} 1 & -2 \\ 3 & 2 \end{vmatrix} + (-16)(-1)^{3+3}\begin{vmatrix} 1 & -2 \\ 2 & 1 \end{vmatrix}$$

$$= (8)(1)(1) + (12)(-1)(8) + (-16)(1)(5)$$

$$= -168$$

$$|B| = \begin{vmatrix} 1 & -2 & 2 \\ 2 & 1 & 3 \\ 3 & 2 & -4 \end{vmatrix}$$

$$= (2)(-1)^{1+3}\begin{vmatrix} 2 & 1 \\ 3 & 2 \end{vmatrix} + (3)(-1)^{2+3}\begin{vmatrix} 1 & -2 \\ 3 & 2 \end{vmatrix} + (-4)(-1)^{3+3}\begin{vmatrix} 1 & -2 \\ 2 & 1 \end{vmatrix}$$

$$= (2)(1)(1) + (3)(-1)(8) + (-4)(1)(5)$$

$$= -42$$

We see that $|B| = \frac{1}{4}|A|$. This example also illustrates the usual computational use of Property 11.3; that is, we factor out a common factor from a row or column and then adjust the value of the determinant by that factor. For example,

$$\begin{vmatrix} 2 & 6 & 8 \\ -1 & 2 & 7 \\ 5 & 2 & 1 \end{vmatrix} = 2\begin{vmatrix} 1 & 3 & 4 \\ -1 & 2 & 7 \\ 5 & 2 & 1 \end{vmatrix}.$$

Factor a 2 from
the top row

PROPERTY 11.4

If square matrix B is obtained from square matrix A by adding k times a row (or column) of A to another row (or column) of A, then $|B| = |A|$.

Property 11.4 states, *adding the product of k times a row (or column) to another row (or column) does not affect the value of the determinant.* As an example of this property suppose that

$$A = \begin{bmatrix} 1 & 2 & 4 \\ 2 & 4 & 7 \\ -1 & 3 & 5 \end{bmatrix}.$$

Now let's form B by replacing row 2 with the result of multiplying row 1 by -2 and adding to row 2.

$$B = \begin{bmatrix} 1 & 2 & 4 \\ 0 & 0 & -1 \\ -1 & 3 & 5 \end{bmatrix}.$$

Next, let's evaluate $|A|$ and $|B|$ by expanding about the second row in each case.

$$|A| = \begin{vmatrix} 1 & 2 & 4 \\ 2 & 4 & 7 \\ -1 & 3 & 5 \end{vmatrix}$$

$$= (2)(-1)^{2+1}\begin{vmatrix} 2 & 4 \\ 3 & 5 \end{vmatrix} + (4)(-1)^{2+2}\begin{vmatrix} 1 & 4 \\ -1 & 5 \end{vmatrix} + (7)(-1)^{2+3}\begin{vmatrix} 1 & 2 \\ -1 & 3 \end{vmatrix}$$

$$= (2)(-1)(-2) + (4)(1)(9) + (7)(-1)(5)$$

$$= 5$$

$$|B| = \begin{vmatrix} 1 & 2 & 4 \\ 0 & 0 & -1 \\ -1 & 3 & 5 \end{vmatrix}$$

$$= (0)(-1)^{2+1}\begin{vmatrix} 2 & 4 \\ 3 & 5 \end{vmatrix} + (0)(-1)^{2+2}\begin{vmatrix} 1 & 4 \\ -1 & 5 \end{vmatrix} + (-1)(-1)^{2+3}\begin{vmatrix} 1 & 2 \\ -1 & 3 \end{vmatrix}$$

$$= (0) + (0) + (-1)(-1)(5)$$

$$= 5$$

Notice that $|B| = |A|$. Furthermore, notice that evaluating $|B|$, because of the 0s in the second row, is much easier than evaluating $|A|$. Property 11.4 can often be used to obtain some 0s before evaluating a determinant.

A word of caution is in order at this time. Be careful not to confuse Properties 11.2, 11.3, and 11.4 with the three elementary row transformations of augmented matrices that were used in Section 11.3. The statements of the two sets of properties do resemble each other, but the properties pertain to **two different concepts**. So be sure to keep them separate.

One final property of determinants should be mentioned.

PROPERTY 11.5

If the two rows (or columns) of a square matrix A are identical, then $|A| = 0$.

Property 11.5 is a direct consequence of Property 11.2. Suppose that A is a square matrix (any size) with two identical rows. Square matrix B can be formed from A by interchanging the two identical rows. Since identical rows were interchanged, $|B| = |A|$ and by Property 11.2, $|B| = -|A|$. For both of these statements to be true, $|A| = 0$.

Let's conclude this section by evaluating a 4×4 determinant using Properties 11.3 and 11.4 to facilitate the computation.

E X A M P L E 6

Evaluate $\begin{vmatrix} 6 & 2 & 1 & -2 \\ 9 & -1 & 4 & 1 \\ 12 & -2 & 3 & -1 \\ 0 & 0 & 9 & 3 \end{vmatrix}$.

Solution

First, let's multiply the 4th column by -3 and add that result to the 3rd column.

$$\begin{vmatrix} 6 & 2 & 7 & -2 \\ 9 & -1 & 1 & 1 \\ 12 & -2 & 6 & -1 \\ 0 & 0 & 0 & 3 \end{vmatrix}$$

Now evaluating by expanding about the 4th row produces only one nonzero product.

$$(3)(-1)^{4+4} \begin{vmatrix} 6 & 2 & 7 \\ 9 & -1 & 1 \\ 12 & -2 & 6 \end{vmatrix}$$

Factoring a 3 out of the first column of the 3×3 determinant we obtain

$$(3)(-1)^8(3) \begin{vmatrix} 2 & 2 & 7 \\ 3 & -1 & 1 \\ 4 & -2 & 6 \end{vmatrix}.$$

Now working with this 3×3 determinant we can first add column 3 to column 2 and then add -3 times column 3 to column 1.

$$(3)(-1)^8(3) \begin{vmatrix} -19 & 9 & 7 \\ 0 & 0 & 1 \\ -14 & 4 & 6 \end{vmatrix}$$

Finally, by expanding this 3×3 determinant about the second row we obtain

$$(3)(-1)^8(3)(1)(-1)^{2+3} \begin{vmatrix} -19 & 9 \\ -14 & 4 \end{vmatrix}.$$

Our final result is

$$(3)(-1)^8(3)(1)(-1)^5(50) = -450.$$

PROBLEM SET 11.2

Evaluate each of the following 2×2 determinants by using Definition 11.1.

1. $\begin{vmatrix} 4 & 3 \\ 2 & 7 \end{vmatrix}$ **2.** $\begin{vmatrix} 3 & 5 \\ 6 & 4 \end{vmatrix}$ **3.** $\begin{vmatrix} -3 & 2 \\ 7 & 5 \end{vmatrix}$ **4.** $\begin{vmatrix} 5 & 3 \\ 6 & -1 \end{vmatrix}$ **5.** $\begin{vmatrix} 2 & -3 \\ 8 & -2 \end{vmatrix}$ **6.** $\begin{vmatrix} -5 & 5 \\ -6 & 2 \end{vmatrix}$

7. $\begin{vmatrix} -2 & -3 \\ -1 & -4 \end{vmatrix}$ 8. $\begin{vmatrix} -4 & -3 \\ -5 & -7 \end{vmatrix}$ 9. $\begin{vmatrix} \frac{1}{2} & \frac{1}{3} \\ -3 & -6 \end{vmatrix}$

10. $\begin{vmatrix} \frac{2}{3} & \frac{3}{4} \\ 8 & 6 \end{vmatrix}$ 11. $\begin{vmatrix} \frac{1}{2} & \frac{2}{3} \\ \frac{3}{4} & -\frac{1}{3} \end{vmatrix}$ 12. $\begin{vmatrix} \frac{2}{3} & \frac{1}{5} \\ -\frac{1}{4} & \frac{3}{2} \end{vmatrix}$

Evaluate each of the following 3×3 determinants. Use the properties of determinants to your advantage.

13. $\begin{vmatrix} 1 & 2 & -1 \\ 3 & 1 & 2 \\ 2 & 4 & 3 \end{vmatrix}$ 14. $\begin{vmatrix} 1 & -2 & 1 \\ 2 & 1 & -1 \\ 3 & 2 & 4 \end{vmatrix}$

15. $\begin{vmatrix} 1 & -4 & 1 \\ 2 & 5 & -1 \\ 3 & 3 & 4 \end{vmatrix}$ 16. $\begin{vmatrix} 3 & -2 & 1 \\ 2 & 1 & 4 \\ -1 & 3 & 5 \end{vmatrix}$

17. $\begin{vmatrix} 6 & 12 & 3 \\ -1 & 5 & 1 \\ -3 & 6 & 2 \end{vmatrix}$ 18. $\begin{vmatrix} 2 & 35 & 5 \\ 1 & -5 & 1 \\ -4 & 15 & 2 \end{vmatrix}$

19. $\begin{vmatrix} 2 & -1 & 3 \\ 0 & 3 & 1 \\ 1 & -2 & -1 \end{vmatrix}$ 20. $\begin{vmatrix} 2 & -17 & 3 \\ 0 & 5 & 1 \\ 1 & -3 & -1 \end{vmatrix}$

21. $\begin{vmatrix} -3 & -2 & 1 \\ 5 & 0 & 6 \\ 2 & 1 & -4 \end{vmatrix}$ 22. $\begin{vmatrix} -5 & 1 & -1 \\ 3 & 4 & 2 \\ 0 & 2 & -3 \end{vmatrix}$

23. $\begin{vmatrix} 3 & -4 & -2 \\ 5 & -2 & 1 \\ 1 & 0 & 0 \end{vmatrix}$ 24. $\begin{vmatrix} -6 & 5 & 3 \\ 2 & 0 & -1 \\ 4 & 0 & 7 \end{vmatrix}$

25. $\begin{vmatrix} 24 & -1 & 4 \\ 40 & 2 & 0 \\ -16 & 6 & 0 \end{vmatrix}$ 26. $\begin{vmatrix} 2 & -1 & 3 \\ 0 & 3 & 1 \\ 4 & -8 & -4 \end{vmatrix}$

27. $\begin{vmatrix} 2 & 3 & -4 \\ 4 & 6 & -1 \\ -6 & 1 & -2 \end{vmatrix}$ 28. $\begin{vmatrix} 1 & 2 & -3 \\ -3 & -1 & 1 \\ 4 & 5 & 4 \end{vmatrix}$

Evaluate each of the following 4×4 determinants. Use the properties of determinants to your advantage.

29. $\begin{vmatrix} 1 & -2 & 3 & 2 \\ 2 & -1 & 0 & 4 \\ -3 & 4 & 0 & -2 \\ -1 & 1 & 1 & 5 \end{vmatrix}$ 30. $\begin{vmatrix} 1 & 2 & 5 & 7 \\ -6 & 3 & 0 & 9 \\ -3 & 5 & 2 & 7 \\ 2 & 1 & 4 & 3 \end{vmatrix}$

31. $\begin{vmatrix} 3 & -1 & 2 & 3 \\ 1 & 0 & 2 & 1 \\ 2 & 3 & 0 & 1 \\ 5 & 2 & 4 & -5 \end{vmatrix}$ 32. $\begin{vmatrix} 1 & 2 & 0 & 0 \\ 3 & -1 & 4 & 5 \\ -2 & 4 & 1 & 6 \\ 2 & -1 & -2 & -3 \end{vmatrix}$

Use the appropriate property of determinants from this section to justify each of the following true statements. Do not evaluate the determinants.

33. $(-4)\begin{vmatrix} 2 & 1 & -1 \\ 3 & 2 & 1 \\ 2 & 1 & 3 \end{vmatrix} = \begin{vmatrix} 2 & -4 & -1 \\ 3 & -8 & 1 \\ 2 & -4 & 3 \end{vmatrix}$

34. $\begin{vmatrix} 1 & -2 & 3 \\ 4 & -6 & -8 \\ 0 & 2 & 7 \end{vmatrix} = (-2)\begin{vmatrix} 1 & -2 & 3 \\ -2 & 3 & 4 \\ 0 & 2 & 7 \end{vmatrix}$

35. $\begin{vmatrix} 4 & 7 & 9 \\ 6 & -8 & 2 \\ 4 & 3 & -1 \end{vmatrix} = -\begin{vmatrix} 4 & 9 & 7 \\ 6 & 2 & -8 \\ 4 & -1 & 3 \end{vmatrix}$

36. $\begin{vmatrix} 3 & -1 & 4 \\ 5 & 2 & 7 \\ 3 & -1 & 4 \end{vmatrix} = 0$

37. $\begin{vmatrix} 1 & 3 & 4 \\ -2 & 5 & 7 \\ -3 & -1 & 2 \end{vmatrix} = \begin{vmatrix} 1 & 3 & 4 \\ -2 & 5 & 7 \\ 0 & 8 & 14 \end{vmatrix}$

38. $\begin{vmatrix} 3 & 2 & 0 \\ 1 & 4 & 1 \\ -4 & 9 & 2 \end{vmatrix} = \begin{vmatrix} 3 & 2 & -3 \\ 1 & 4 & 0 \\ -4 & 9 & 6 \end{vmatrix}$

39. $\begin{vmatrix} 6 & 2 & 2 \\ 3 & -1 & 4 \\ 9 & -3 & 6 \end{vmatrix} = 6\begin{vmatrix} 2 & 2 & 1 \\ 1 & -1 & 2 \\ 3 & -3 & 3 \end{vmatrix} = 18\begin{vmatrix} 2 & 2 & 1 \\ 1 & -1 & 2 \\ 1 & -1 & 1 \end{vmatrix}$

40. $\begin{vmatrix} 2 & 1 & -3 \\ 0 & 2 & -4 \\ -5 & 1 & 3 \end{vmatrix} = -\begin{vmatrix} 2 & 1 & -3 \\ -5 & 1 & 3 \\ 0 & 2 & -4 \end{vmatrix}$

41. $\begin{vmatrix} 2 & -3 & 2 \\ 1 & -4 & 1 \\ 7 & 8 & 7 \end{vmatrix} = 0$

42. $\begin{vmatrix} 3 & 1 & 2 \\ -4 & 5 & -1 \\ 2 & -2 & -4 \end{vmatrix} = \begin{vmatrix} 3 & 1 & 0 \\ -4 & 5 & -11 \\ 2 & -2 & 0 \end{vmatrix}$

FURTHER INVESTIGATIONS

For Problems 43–45, use

$$A = \begin{bmatrix} a_{11} & a_{12} & a_{13} \\ a_{21} & a_{22} & a_{23} \\ a_{31} & a_{32} & a_{33} \end{bmatrix}$$

as a general representation for any 3×3 matrix.

43. Verify Property 11.2 for 3×3 matrices.

44. Verify Property 11.3 for 3×3 matrices.

45. Verify Property 11.4 for 3×3 matrices.

46. If

$$A = \begin{bmatrix} a_{11} & a_{12} & a_{13} & a_{14} \\ 0 & a_{22} & a_{23} & a_{24} \\ 0 & 0 & a_{33} & a_{34} \\ 0 & 0 & 0 & a_{44} \end{bmatrix},$$

then show that $|A| = a_{11}a_{22}a_{33}a_{44}$.

GRAPHICS CALCULATOR ACTIVITIES

47. Use a graphics calculator to check your answers for Problems 29–32.

48. Let matrix

$$A = \begin{bmatrix} 2 & 5 & 7 & 9 \\ -4 & 6 & 2 & 4 \\ 6 & 9 & 12 & 3 \\ 5 & 4 & -2 & 8 \end{bmatrix}.$$

Form matrix B by interchanging rows 1 and 3 of matrix A. Now use your calculator to show that $|B| = -|A|$.

49. Let matrix

$$A = \begin{bmatrix} 2 & 1 & 7 & 6 & 8 \\ 3 & -2 & 4 & 5 & -1 \\ 6 & 7 & 9 & 12 & 13 \\ -4 & -7 & 6 & 2 & 1 \\ 9 & 8 & 12 & 14 & 17 \end{bmatrix}.$$

Form matrix B by multiplying each element of the second row of A by 3. Now use your calculator to show that $|B| = 3|A|$.

50. Let matrix

$$A = \begin{bmatrix} 4 & 3 & 2 & 1 & 5 & -3 \\ 5 & 2 & 7 & 8 & 6 & 3 \\ 0 & 9 & 1 & 4 & 7 & 2 \\ 4 & 3 & 2 & 1 & 5 & -3 \\ -4 & -6 & 7 & 12 & 11 & 9 \\ 5 & 8 & 6 & -3 & 2 & -1 \end{bmatrix}.$$

Use your calculator to show that $|A| = 0$.

11.3 CRAMER'S RULE

Determinants provide the basis for another method of solving linear systems. Consider the linear system of two equations and two unknowns

$$\begin{pmatrix} a_1x + b_1y = c_1 \\ a_2x + b_2y = c_2 \end{pmatrix}.$$

The augmented matrix of this system is

$$\begin{bmatrix} a_1 & b_1 & | & c_1 \\ a_2 & b_2 & | & c_2 \end{bmatrix}.$$

Using the elementary row transformations of augmented matrices, this matrix can be changed to the following reduced echelon form. (We will leave the details of this for you to do as an exercise.)

$$\begin{bmatrix} 1 & 0 & \vdots & \dfrac{c_1b_2 - c_2b_1}{a_1b_2 - a_2b_1} \\ 0 & 1 & \vdots & \dfrac{a_1c_2 - a_2c_1}{a_1b_2 - a_2b_1} \end{bmatrix}, \qquad a_1b_2 - a_2b_1 \neq 0$$

The solutions for x and y can be expressed in determinant form as follows.

$$x = \frac{c_1b_2 - c_2b_1}{a_1b_2 - a_2b_1} = \frac{\begin{vmatrix} c_1 & b_1 \\ c_2 & b_2 \end{vmatrix}}{\begin{vmatrix} a_1 & b_1 \\ a_2 & b_2 \end{vmatrix}}$$

$$y = \frac{a_1c_2 - a_2c_1}{a_1b_2 - a_2b_1} = \frac{\begin{vmatrix} a_1 & c_1 \\ a_2 & c_2 \end{vmatrix}}{\begin{vmatrix} a_1 & b_1 \\ a_2 & b_2 \end{vmatrix}}$$

This method of using determinants to solve a system of two linear equations in two variables is called **Cramer's rule** and can be stated as follows.

Cramer's Rule (2 × 2 Case)

Given the system

$$\begin{pmatrix} a_1x + b_1y = c_1 \\ a_2x + b_2y = c_2 \end{pmatrix},$$

we have

$$D = \begin{vmatrix} a_1 & b_1 \\ a_2 & b_2 \end{vmatrix} \neq 0, \qquad D_x = \begin{vmatrix} c_1 & b_1 \\ c_2 & b_2 \end{vmatrix}, \qquad \text{and} \qquad D_y = \begin{vmatrix} a_1 & c_1 \\ a_2 & c_2 \end{vmatrix}.$$

The solution for this system is given by

$$x = \frac{D_x}{D}, \qquad \text{and} \qquad y = \frac{D_y}{D}.$$

Notice that the elements of D are the coefficients of the variables in the given system. In D_x, the coefficients of x are replaced by the respective constants and in D_y the coefficients of y are replaced by the respective constants. Let's illustrate the use of Cramer's rule to solve some systems.

E X A M P L E 1

Solve the system

$$\begin{pmatrix} y = -2x - 2 \\ 4x - 5y = 17 \end{pmatrix}.$$

Solution

First, we must change the form of the first equation so that the system fits the form given in Cramer's rule. The equation $y = -2x - 2$ can be written as $2x + y = -2$. The system now becomes

$$\begin{pmatrix} 2x + y = -2 \\ 4x - 5y = 17 \end{pmatrix}$$

and we can proceed to determine D, D_x, and D_y.

$$D = \begin{vmatrix} 2 & 1 \\ 4 & -5 \end{vmatrix} = -10 - 4 = -14$$

$$D_x = \begin{vmatrix} -2 & 1 \\ 17 & -5 \end{vmatrix} = 10 - 17 = -7$$

$$D_y = \begin{vmatrix} 2 & -2 \\ 4 & 17 \end{vmatrix} = 34 - (-8) = 42$$

Thus,

$$x = \frac{D_x}{D} = \frac{-7}{-14} = \frac{1}{2} \quad \text{and} \quad y = \frac{D_y}{D} = \frac{42}{-14} = -3.$$

The solution set is $\left\{ \left(\frac{1}{2}, -3 \right) \right\}$ which can be verified, as always, by substituting back into the original equations.

E X A M P L E 2

Solve the system

$$\begin{pmatrix} \dfrac{1}{2}x + \dfrac{2}{3}y = -4 \\ \dfrac{1}{4}x - \dfrac{3}{2}y = 20 \end{pmatrix}.$$

Solution

With such a system we can either produce an equivalent system with integral coefficients first before applying Cramer's rule or apply the rule immediately. Let's avoid some work with fractions by multiplying the first equation by 6 and the second equation by 4, to produce the following equivalent system.

$$\begin{pmatrix} 3x + 4y = -24 \\ x - 6y = 80 \end{pmatrix}$$

Now we can proceed as before.

$$D = \begin{vmatrix} 3 & 4 \\ 1 & -6 \end{vmatrix} = -18 - 4 = -22$$

$$D_x = \begin{vmatrix} -24 & 4 \\ 80 & -6 \end{vmatrix} = 144 - 320 = -176$$

$$D_y = \begin{vmatrix} 3 & -24 \\ 1 & 80 \end{vmatrix} = 240 - (-24) = 264$$

Therefore,

$$x = \frac{D_x}{D} = \frac{-176}{-22} = 8 \qquad \text{and} \qquad y = \frac{D_y}{D} = \frac{264}{-22} = -12.$$

The solution set is $\{(8, -12)\}$.

In the statement of Cramer's rule, the condition was imposed that $D \neq 0$. If $D = 0$ and either D_x or D_y (or both) are nonzero, then the system is inconsistent and has no solution. If $D = 0$, $D_x = 0$, and $D_y = 0$, then the equations are dependent and there are infinitely many solutions.

Cramer's Rule Extended

Without elaborating on the details, we will simply state that Cramer's rule also applies to solving systems of three linear equations in three variables. It can be stated as follows.

Cramer's Rule (3 × 3 Case)

Given the system

$$\begin{pmatrix} a_1x + b_1y + c_1z = d_1 \\ a_2x + b_2y + c_2z = d_2 \\ a_3x + b_3y + c_3z = d_3 \end{pmatrix}$$

with

$$D = \begin{vmatrix} a_1 & b_1 & c_1 \\ a_2 & b_2 & c_2 \\ a_3 & b_3 & c_3 \end{vmatrix} \neq 0, \qquad D_x = \begin{vmatrix} d_1 & b_1 & c_1 \\ d_2 & b_2 & c_2 \\ d_3 & b_3 & c_3 \end{vmatrix}$$

$$D_y = \begin{vmatrix} a_1 & d_1 & c_1 \\ a_2 & d_2 & c_2 \\ a_3 & d_3 & c_3 \end{vmatrix}, \qquad D_z = \begin{vmatrix} a_1 & b_1 & d_1 \\ a_2 & b_2 & d_2 \\ a_3 & b_3 & d_3 \end{vmatrix}$$

then

$$x = \frac{D_x}{D}, \qquad y = \frac{D_y}{D}, \qquad \text{and} \qquad z = \frac{D_z}{D}.$$

Again notice the restriction that $D \neq 0$. If $D = 0$ and at least one of D_x, D_y, and D_z is not zero, then the system is inconsistent. If D, D_x, D_y, and D_z are all zero, then the equations are dependent and there are infinitely many solutions.

EXAMPLE 3

Solve the system

$$\begin{pmatrix} x - 2y + z = -4 \\ 2x + y - z = 5 \\ 3x + 2y + 4z = 3 \end{pmatrix}.$$

Solution

We will simply indicate the values of D, D_x, D_y, and D_z, and leave the computation for you to do.

$$D = \begin{vmatrix} 1 & -2 & 1 \\ 2 & 1 & -1 \\ 3 & 2 & 4 \end{vmatrix} = 29$$

$$D_x = \begin{vmatrix} -4 & -2 & 1 \\ 5 & 1 & -1 \\ 3 & 2 & 4 \end{vmatrix} = 29$$

$$D_y = \begin{vmatrix} 1 & -4 & 1 \\ 2 & 5 & -1 \\ 3 & 3 & 4 \end{vmatrix} = 58$$

$$D_z = \begin{vmatrix} 1 & -2 & -4 \\ 2 & 1 & 5 \\ 3 & 2 & 3 \end{vmatrix} = -29$$

Therefore,

$$x = \frac{D_x}{D} = \frac{29}{29} = 1, \qquad y = \frac{D_y}{D} = \frac{58}{29} = 2, \qquad \text{and} \qquad z = \frac{D_z}{D} = \frac{-29}{29} = -1.$$

The solution set is $\{(1, 2, -1)\}$. (Be sure to check it!)

EXAMPLE 4

Solve the system

$$\begin{pmatrix} x + 3y - z = 4 \\ 3x - 2y + z = 7 \\ 2x + 6y - 2z = 1 \end{pmatrix}.$$

Solution

$$D = \begin{vmatrix} 1 & 3 & -1 \\ 3 & -2 & 1 \\ 2 & 6 & -2 \end{vmatrix}$$

and since the third row is twice the first row, we know that $D = 0$. We can also establish that

$$D_x = \begin{vmatrix} 4 & 3 & -1 \\ 7 & -2 & 1 \\ 1 & 6 & -2 \end{vmatrix} = -7.$$

Therefore, since $D = 0$ and at least one of D_x, D_y, and D_z is not zero, the system is inconsistent. The solution set is $\varnothing$.

Example 4 illustrates the reason that D should be determined first. Having found that $D = 0$ and $D_x \neq 0$, we knew that the system was inconsistent and there was no need to find D_y and D_z.

Finally, it should be noted that Cramer's rule can be extended to systems of n linear equations in n variables. However, the method in general is not considered to be a very efficient way of solving a system of linear equations.

PROBLEM SET 11.3

Use Cramer's rule to find the solution set for each of the following systems. If the equations are dependent, simply indicate that there are infinitely many solutions.

1. $\begin{pmatrix} 2x - y = -2 \\ 3x + 2y = 11 \end{pmatrix}$

2. $\begin{pmatrix} 3x + y = -9 \\ 4x - 3y = 1 \end{pmatrix}$

3. $\begin{pmatrix} 5x + 2y = 5 \\ 3x - 4y = 29 \end{pmatrix}$

4. $\begin{pmatrix} 4x - 7y = -23 \\ 2x + 5y = -3 \end{pmatrix}$

5. $\begin{pmatrix} 5x - 4y = 14 \\ -x + 2y = -4 \end{pmatrix}$

6. $\begin{pmatrix} -x + 2y = 10 \\ 3x - y = -10 \end{pmatrix}$

7. $\begin{pmatrix} y = 2x - 4 \\ 6x - 3y = 1 \end{pmatrix}$

8. $\begin{pmatrix} -3x - 4y = 14 \\ -2x + 3y = -19 \end{pmatrix}$

9. $\begin{pmatrix} -4x + 3y = 3 \\ 4x - 6y = -5 \end{pmatrix}$

10. $\begin{pmatrix} x = 4y - 1 \\ 2x - 8y = -2 \end{pmatrix}$

11. $\begin{pmatrix} 9x - y = -2 \\ 8x + y = 4 \end{pmatrix}$

12. $\begin{pmatrix} 6x - 5y = 1 \\ 4x + 7y = 2 \end{pmatrix}$

13. $\begin{pmatrix} -\frac{2}{3}x + \frac{1}{2}y = -7 \\ \frac{1}{3}x - \frac{3}{2}y = 6 \end{pmatrix}$

14. $\begin{pmatrix} \frac{1}{2}x + \frac{2}{3}y = -6 \\ \frac{1}{4}x - \frac{1}{3}y = -1 \end{pmatrix}$

15. $\begin{pmatrix} 2x + 7y = -1 \\ x = 2 \end{pmatrix}$

16. $\begin{pmatrix} 5x - 3y = 2 \\ y = 4 \end{pmatrix}$

17. $\begin{pmatrix} x - y + 2z = -8 \\ 2x + 3y - 4z = 18 \\ -x + 2y - z = 7 \end{pmatrix}$

18. $\begin{pmatrix} x - 2y + z = 3 \\ 3x + 2y + z = -3 \\ 2x - 3y - 3z = -5 \end{pmatrix}$

19. $\begin{pmatrix} 2x - 3y + z = -7 \\ -3x + y - z = -7 \\ x - 2y - 5z = -45 \end{pmatrix}$

20. $\begin{pmatrix} 3x - y - z = 18 \\ 4x + 3y - 2z = 10 \\ -5x - 2y + 3z = -22 \end{pmatrix}$

21. $\begin{pmatrix} 4x + 5y - 2z = -14 \\ 7x - y + 2z = 42 \\ 3x + y + 4z = 28 \end{pmatrix}$

22. $\begin{pmatrix} -5x + 6y + 4z = -4 \\ -7x - 8y + 2z = -2 \\ 2x + 9y - z = 1 \end{pmatrix}$

23. $\begin{pmatrix} 2x - y + 3z = -17 \\ 3y + z = 5 \\ x - 2y - z = -3 \end{pmatrix}$

24. $\begin{pmatrix} 2x - y + 3z = -5 \\ 3x + 4y - 2z = -25 \\ -x + z = 6 \end{pmatrix}$

25. $\begin{pmatrix} x + 3y - 4z = -1 \\ 2x - y + z = 2 \\ 4x + 5y - 7z = 0 \end{pmatrix}$

26. $\begin{pmatrix} x - 2y + z = 1 \\ 3x + y - z = 2 \\ 2x - 4y + 2z = -1 \end{pmatrix}$

27. $\begin{pmatrix} 3x - 2y - 3z = -5 \\ x + 2y + 3z = -3 \\ -x + 4y - 6z = 8 \end{pmatrix}$

28. $\begin{pmatrix} 3x - 2y + z = 11 \\ 5x + 3y = 17 \\ x + y - 2z = 6 \end{pmatrix}$

29. $\begin{pmatrix} x - 2y + 3z = 1 \\ -2x + 4y - 3z = -3 \\ 5x - 6y + 6z = 10 \end{pmatrix}$

30. $\begin{pmatrix} 2x - y + 2z = -1 \\ 4x + 3y - 4z = 2 \\ x + 5y - z = 9 \end{pmatrix}$

31. $\begin{pmatrix} -x - y + 3z = -2 \\ -2x + y + 7z = 14 \\ 3x + 4y - 5z = 12 \end{pmatrix}$

32. $\begin{pmatrix} -2x + y - 3z = -4 \\ x + 5y - 4z = 13 \\ 7x + 2y - z = 37 \end{pmatrix}$

THOUGHTS into WORDS

33. Explain the difference between a matrix and a determinant.

34. Give a step-by-step description of how you would solve the system

$$\begin{pmatrix} 2x - y + 3z = 31 \\ x - 2y - z = 8 \\ 3x + 5y + 8z = 35 \end{pmatrix}.$$

35. Give a step-by-step description of how you would find the value of x in the solution for the system

$$\begin{pmatrix} x + 5y - z = -9 \\ 2x - y + z = 11 \\ -3x - 2y + 4z = 20 \end{pmatrix}.$$

FURTHER INVESTIGATIONS

36. A linear system in which the constant terms are all zero is called a **homogeneous system**.

a. Verify that for a 3×3 homogeneous system, if $D \neq 0$, then $(0, 0, 0)$ is the only solution for the system.

b. Verify that for a 3×3 homogeneous system, if $D = 0$, then the equations are dependent.

For Problems 37–40, solve each of the homogeneous systems (see Problem 36). If the equations are dependent, indicate that the system has infinitely many solutions.

37. $\begin{pmatrix} x - 2y + 5z = 0 \\ 3x + y - 2z = 0 \\ 4x - y + 3z = 0 \end{pmatrix}$

38. $\begin{pmatrix} 2x - y + z = 0 \\ 3x + 2y + 5z = 0 \\ 4x - 7y + z = 0 \end{pmatrix}$

39. $\begin{pmatrix} 3x + y - z = 0 \\ x - y + 2z = 0 \\ 4x - 5y - 2z = 0 \end{pmatrix}$

40. $\begin{pmatrix} 2x - y + 2z = 0 \\ x + 2y + z = 0 \\ x - 3y + z = 0 \end{pmatrix}$

GRAPHICS CALCULATOR ACTIVITIES

41. Use determinants and your calculator to help solve each of the following systems. Be sure to check your answers.

a. $\begin{pmatrix} 4x - 3y + z = 10 \\ 8x + 5y - 2z = -6 \\ -12x - 2y + 3z = -2 \end{pmatrix}$

b. $\begin{pmatrix} 2x + y - z + w = -4 \\ x + 2y + 2z - 3w = 6 \\ 3x - y - z + 2w = 0 \\ 2x + 3y + z + 4w = -5 \end{pmatrix}$

c. $\begin{pmatrix} x - 2y + z - 3w = 4 \\ 2x + 3y - z - 2w = -4 \\ 3x - 4y + 2z - 4w = 12 \\ 2x - y - 3z + 2w = -2 \end{pmatrix}$

d. $\begin{pmatrix} 1.98x + 2.49y + 3.45z = 80.10 \\ 2.15x + 3.20y + 4.19z = 97.16 \\ 1.49x + 4.49y + 2.79z = 83.92 \end{pmatrix}$

11.4   SYSTEMS INVOLVING LINEAR INEQUALITIES AND LINEAR PROGRAMMING

Finding solution sets for **systems of linear inequalities** relies heavily on the graphing approach. The solution set of the system

$$\begin{pmatrix} x + y > 2 \\ x - y < 2 \end{pmatrix}$$

is the intersection of the solution sets of the individual inequalities. In Figure 11.1(a) we indicated the solution set for $x + y > 2$ and in Figure 11.1(b) we indicated the solution set for $x - y < 2$. Then in Figure 11.1(c), the shaded region represents the intersection of the two solution sets and therefore it is the graph of the system. Remember that dashed lines are used to indicate that points on the lines are not included in the solution set. In the next examples we have indicated only the final solution set for the system.

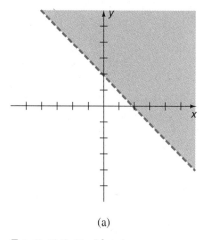
(a)

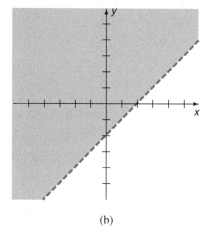
(b)

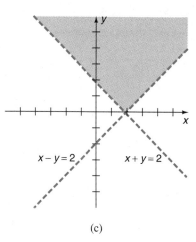
(c)

FIGURE 11.1

EXAMPLE 1

Solve the following system by graphing.

$$\begin{pmatrix} 2x - y \geq 4 \\ x + 2y < 2 \end{pmatrix}$$

Solution

The graph of $2x - y \geq 4$ consists of all points *on or below* the line $2x - y = 4$. The graph of $x + 2y < 2$ consists of all points *below* the line $x + 2y = 2$. The graph of the system is indicated by the shaded region in Figure 11.2. Notice that all points in the shaded region are on or below the line $2x - y = 4$ and below the line $x + 2y = 2$.

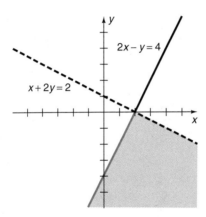

FIGURE 11.2

EXAMPLE 2

Solve the following system by graphing.

$$\begin{pmatrix} x \leq 2 \\ y \geq -1 \end{pmatrix}$$

Solution

Remember that even though each inequality contains only one variable, we are working in a rectangular coordinate system that involves ordered pairs. That is to say, the system could be written as

$$\begin{pmatrix} x + 0(y) \leq 2 \\ 0(x) + y \geq -1 \end{pmatrix}.$$

The graph of this system is the shaded region in Figure 11.3. Notice that all points in the shaded region are on or to the left of the line $x = 2$ and on or above the line $y = -1$.

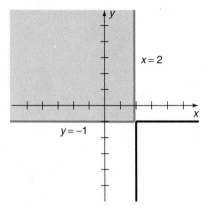

FIGURE 11.3

The system may contain more than two inequalities, as the next example illustrates.

EXAMPLE 3

Solve the following system by graphing.

$$\begin{pmatrix} x \geq 0 \\ y \geq 0 \\ 2x + 3y \leq 12 \\ 3x + y \leq 6 \end{pmatrix}$$

Solution

The solution set for the system is the intersection of the solution sets of the four inequalities. The shaded region in Figure 11.4 indicates the solution set for the system. Notice that all points in the shaded region are on or to the right of the y-axis,

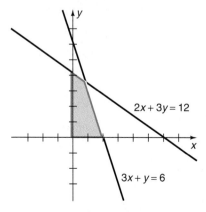

FIGURE 11.4

on or above the *x*-axis, on or below the line $2x + 3y = 12$, and on or below the line $3x + y = 6$.   ▬▬▬

Linear Programming—Another Look at Problem Solving

Throughout this text, problem solving is a unifying theme. Therefore, it seems appropriate at this time to give you a brief glimpse of an area of mathematics that was developed in the 1940s specifically as a problem solving tool. Many applied problems involve the idea of maximizing or minimizing a certain function that is subject to various constraints; these can be expressed as linear inequalities. **Linear programming** was developed as one method for solving such problems.

> **REMARK**   The term *programming* refers to the distribution of limited resources in order to maximize or minimize a certain function such as cost, profit, distance, and so on. Thus, it is not synonymous with its meaning in computer programming. The constraints under which the distribution of resources is to be made are the linear equations; thus, the term *linear programming* is used.

Before introducing a linear programming type of problem, we need to extend one mathematical concept a bit. **A linear function in two variables *x* and *y*** is a function of the form $f(x, y) = ax + by + c$, where *a*, *b*, and *c* are real numbers. In other words, to each ordered pair (x, y) we associate a third number by the rule $ax + by + c$. For example, suppose the function *f* is described by $f(x, y) = 4x + 3y + 5$; then $f(2, 1) = 4(2) + 3(1) + 5 = 16$.

First, let's take a look at some mathematical ideas that form the basis for solving a linear programming problem. Consider the shaded region in Figure 11.5 and the accompanying linear functions in two variables.

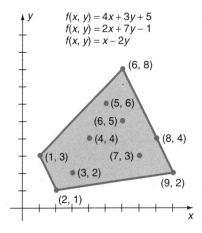

$$f(x, y) = 4x + 3y + 5$$
$$f(x, y) = 2x + 7y - 1$$
$$f(x, y) = x - 2y$$

F I G U R E   11 . 5

Suppose that we need to find the maximum and minimum value achieved by each of the functions in the indicated region. The following chart summarizes the values for the ordered pairs indicated in Figure 11.5. Notice that for each function the maximum and minimum values are obtained at a vertex of the region.

	ORDERED PAIRS	VALUE OF $f(x, y) =$ $4x + 3y + 5$	VALUE OF $f(x, y) =$ $2x + 7y - 1$	VALUE OF $f(x, y) =$ $x - 2y$
Vertex	(2, 1)	16 (minimum)	10 (minimum)	0
	(3, 2)	23	19	−1
Vertex	(9, 2)	47	31	5 (maximum)
Vertex	(1, 3)	18	22	−5
	(7, 3)	42	34	1
	(4, 4)	33	35	−4
	(8, 4)	49	43	0
	(6, 5)	44	46	−4
	(5, 6)	43	51	−7
Vertex	(6, 8)	53 (maximum)	67 (maximum)	−10 (minimum)

To further illustrate the idea that maximum and minimum functional values are attained at a vertex of the region, let's consider the family of lines $x - 2y = k$, where k is an arbitrary constant. (We are now working only with the function $f(x, y) = x - 2y$.) In slope-intercept form, $x - 2y = k$ becomes $y = \frac{1}{2}x - \frac{1}{2}k$; so we have a family of parallel lines that each have a slope of $\frac{1}{2}$. In Figure 11.6 we sketched some of these lines so that each line has at least one point in common with the given region. Note that $x - 2y$ reaches a minimum value of -10 at the vertex (6, 8) and a maximum value of 5 at the vertex (9, 2).

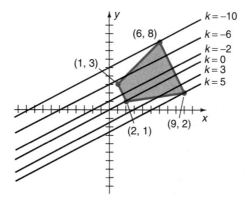

F I G U R E   I I . 6

In general, suppose that f is a linear function in two variables x and y, and S is a region of the xy-plane. If f attains a maximum (minimum) value in S, then that maximum (minimum) value is obtained at a vertex of S.

REMARK   A subset of the xy-plane is said to be **bounded** if there is a circle that contains all of its points; otherwise the subset is said to be **unbounded**. A bounded set will contain a maximum and minimum value for a function, but an unbounded set may not contain such values.

Now we will consider two examples that illustrate a general graphing approach for solving a linear programming problem in two variables. In the first example we will illustrate the general makeup of such a problem without the context. The second example presents the type of setting from which such a problem is extracted.

EXAMPLE 4

Find the maximum value and the minimum value of the function $f(x, y) = 9x + 13y$ in the region determined by the following system of inequalities.

$$\begin{pmatrix} x \geq 0 \\ y \geq 0 \\ 2x + 3y \leq 18 \\ 2x + y \leq 10 \end{pmatrix}$$

Solution

First, let's graph the inequalities to determine the region as indicated in Figure 11.7. (Such a region is called the **set of feasible solutions** and the inequalities are referred to as **constraints**.) The point $(3, 4)$ is determined by solving the system

$$\begin{pmatrix} 2x + 3y = 18 \\ 2x + y = 10 \end{pmatrix}.$$

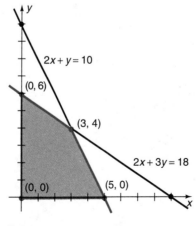

FIGURE 11.7

Secondly, we can determine the values of the given function at the vertices of the region. (Such a function to be maximized or minimized is called the **objective function**.) Therefore, a minimum value of 0 is obtained at (0, 0) and a maximum value of 79 is obtained at (3, 4).

VERTICES	VALUE OF $f(x, y) = 9x + 13y$
(0, 0)	0 (minimum)
(5, 0)	45
(3, 4)	79 (maximum)
(0, 6)	78

EXAMPLE 5

Maximizing profit A company that manufactures gidgets and gadgets has the following production information available.

1. To produce a gidget requires 3 hours of working time on machine A and 1 hour on machine B.

2. To produce a gadget requires 2 hours on machine A and 1 hour on machine B.

3. Machine A is available for no more than 120 hours per week and machine B is available for no more than 50 hours per week.

4. Gidgets can be sold at a profit of $3.75 each while a profit of $3 each can be realized on a gadget.

How many gidgets and how many gadgets should be produced each week to maximize profit? What would the maximum profit be?

Solution

Let x be the number of gidgets and y the number of gadgets. Thus, the profit function is $P(x, y) = 3.75x + 3y$. The constraints for the problem can be represented by the following inequalities.

$$3x + 2y \leq 120 \qquad \text{Machine } A \text{ is available for no more than 120 hours}$$

$$x + y \leq 50 \qquad \text{Machine } B \text{ is available for no more than 50 hours}$$

$$x \geq 0 \qquad \text{The number of gidgets and gadgets must be represented}$$

$$y \geq 0 \qquad \text{by a nonnegative number}$$

Graphing these inequalities produces the set of feasible solutions indicated by the shaded region in Figure 11.8. Finding the value of the profit function at the vertices produces the following chart. Thus, a maximum profit of $165 is realized by producing 20 gidgets and 30 gadgets.

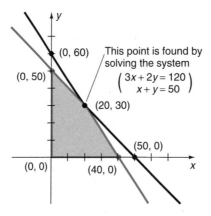

This point is found by solving the system

$$\begin{pmatrix} 3x + 2y = 120 \\ x + y = 50 \end{pmatrix}$$

FIGURE 11.8

VERTICES	VALUE OF $P(x, y) = 3.75x + 3y$
$(0, 0)$	0
$(40, 0)$	150
$(20, 30)$	165 (maximum)
$(0, 50)$	150

PROBLEM SET 11.4

Indicate the solution set for each of the following systems of inequalities by graphing the system and shading the appropriate region.

1. $\begin{pmatrix} x + y > 3 \\ x - y > 1 \end{pmatrix}$ 2. $\begin{pmatrix} x - y < 2 \\ x + y < 1 \end{pmatrix}$

3. $\begin{pmatrix} x - 2y \leq 4 \\ x + 2y > 4 \end{pmatrix}$ 4. $\begin{pmatrix} 3x - y > 6 \\ 2x + y \leq 4 \end{pmatrix}$

5. $\begin{pmatrix} 2x + 3y \leq 6 \\ 3x - 2y \leq 6 \end{pmatrix}$ 6. $\begin{pmatrix} 4x + 3y \geq 12 \\ 3x - 4y \geq 12 \end{pmatrix}$

7. $\begin{pmatrix} 2x - y \geq 4 \\ x + 3y < 3 \end{pmatrix}$ 8. $\begin{pmatrix} 3x - y < 3 \\ x + y \geq 1 \end{pmatrix}$

9. $\begin{pmatrix} x + 2y > -2 \\ x - y < -3 \end{pmatrix}$ 10. $\begin{pmatrix} x - 3y < -3 \\ 2x - 3y > -6 \end{pmatrix}$

11. $\begin{pmatrix} y > x - 4 \\ y < x \end{pmatrix}$ 12. $\begin{pmatrix} y \leq x + 2 \\ y \geq x \end{pmatrix}$

13. $\begin{pmatrix} x - y > 2 \\ x - y > -1 \end{pmatrix}$ 14. $\begin{pmatrix} x + y > 1 \\ x + y > 3 \end{pmatrix}$

15. $\begin{pmatrix} y \geq x \\ x > -1 \end{pmatrix}$ 16. $\begin{pmatrix} y < x \\ y \leq 2 \end{pmatrix}$

17. $\begin{pmatrix} y < x \\ y > x + 3 \end{pmatrix}$ 18. $\begin{pmatrix} x \leq 3 \\ y \leq -1 \end{pmatrix}$

19. $\begin{pmatrix} y > -2 \\ x > 1 \end{pmatrix}$ 20. $\begin{pmatrix} x + 2y > 4 \\ x + 2y < 2 \end{pmatrix}$

21. $\begin{pmatrix} x \geq 0 \\ y \geq 0 \\ x + y \leq 4 \\ 2x + y \leq 6 \end{pmatrix}$ 22. $\begin{pmatrix} x \geq 0 \\ y \geq 0 \\ x - y \leq 5 \\ 4x + 7y \leq 28 \end{pmatrix}$

23. $\begin{pmatrix} x \geq 0 \\ y \geq 0 \\ 2x + y \leq 4 \\ 2x - 3y \leq 6 \end{pmatrix}$ 24. $\begin{pmatrix} x \geq 0 \\ y \geq 0 \\ 3x + 5y \geq 15 \\ 5x + 3y \geq 15 \end{pmatrix}$

For Problems 25–28, find the maximum and minimum values of the given function in the indicated region (Figures 11.9–11.12).

25. $f(x, y) = 3x + 5y$

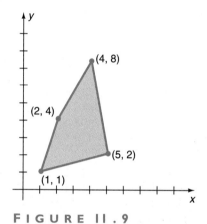

FIGURE 11.9

26. $f(x, y) = 8x + 3y$

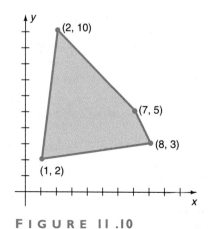

FIGURE 11.10

27. $f(x, y) = x + 4y$

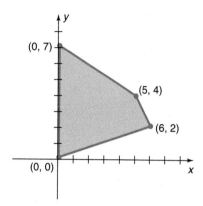

FIGURE 11.11

28. $f(x, y) = 2.5x + 3.5y$

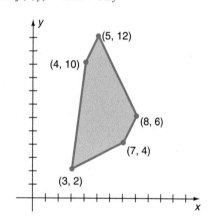

FIGURE 11.12

29. Maximize the function $f(x, y) = 3x + 7y$ in the region determined by the following constraints.

$$\begin{pmatrix} 3x + 2y \leq 18 \\ 3x + 4y \geq 12 \\ x \geq 0 \\ y \geq 0 \end{pmatrix}$$

30. Maximize the function $f(x, y) = 1.5x + 2y$ in the region determined by the following constraints.

$$\begin{pmatrix} 3x + 2y \leq 36 \\ 3x + 10y \leq 60 \\ x \geq 0 \\ y \geq 0 \end{pmatrix}$$

31. Maximize the function $f(x, y) = 40x + 55y$ in the region determined by the following constraints.

$$\begin{cases} 2x + y \le 10 \\ x + y \le 7 \\ 2x + 3y \le 18 \\ x \ge 0 \\ y \ge 0 \end{cases}$$

32. Maximize the function $f(x, y) = .08x + .09y$ in the region determined by the following constraints.

$$\begin{cases} x + y \le 8000 \\ y \le \dfrac{1}{3}x \\ y \ge 500 \\ x \le 7000 \\ x \ge 0 \end{cases}$$

33. Minimize the function $f(x, y) = .2x + .5y$ in the region determined by the following constraints.

$$\begin{cases} 2x + y \ge 12 \\ 2x + 5y \ge 12 \\ x \ge 0 \\ y \ge 0 \end{cases}$$

34. Minimize the function $f(x, y) = 3x + 7y$ in the region determined by the following constraints.

$$\begin{cases} x + y \ge 9 \\ 6x + 11y \ge 84 \\ x \ge 0 \\ y \ge 0 \end{cases}$$

35. Maximize the function $f(x, y) = 9x + 2y$ in the region determined by the following constraints.

$$\begin{cases} 5y - 4x \le 20 \\ 4x + 5y \le 60 \\ x \ge 0 \\ x \le 10 \\ y \ge 0. \end{cases}$$

36. Maximize the function $f(x, y) = 3x + 4y$ in the region determined by the following constraints.

$$\begin{cases} 2y - x \le 6 \\ x + y \le 12 \\ x \ge 2 \\ x \le 8 \\ y \ge 0. \end{cases}$$

Solve each of the following linear programming problems by using the graphing method illustrated in Example 5.

37. *Investing in stocks*   Suppose that an investor wants to invest up to $10,000. She plans to buy one speculative type of stock and one conservative type. The speculative stock is paying a 12% return and the conservative stock is paying a 9% return. She has decided to invest at least $2000 in the conservative stock and no more than $6000 in the speculative stock. Furthermore, she does not want the speculative stock to exceed the conservative investment. How much should she invest at each rate to maximize her return?

38. *Manufacturing golf clubs*   A manufacturer of golf clubs makes a profit of $50 per set on a model A set and $45 per set on a model B set. Daily production of the model A clubs is between 30 and 50 sets, inclusive; for the model B clubs production is between 10 and 20 sets, inclusive. The total daily production is not to exceed 50 sets. How many sets of each model should be manufactured per day to maximize the profit?

39. *Producing calculators*   A company makes two types of calculators. Type A sells for $12 and type B sells for $10. It costs the company $9 to produce one type A calculator and $8 to produce one type B calculator. The company is equipped to produce between 200 and 300, inclusive, of the type A per month and between 100 and 250, inclusive, of the type B calculator, but not more than 500 altogether. How many calculators of each type should be produced per month to maximize the difference between the selling prices and the costs of production?

40. *Manufacturing copiers*   A manufacturer of small copiers makes a profit of $200 on a deluxe model and $250 on a standard model. The company wants to produce at least 50 deluxe models per week and at least 75 standard models per week. However, the weekly production is not to exceed 150 copiers. How many copiers of each kind should be produced in order to maximize the profit?

41. *Production statistics*   Products A and B are produced by a company according to the following production information.

  a. To produce one unit of product A requires 1 hour of working time on machine I, 2 hours on machine II, and 1 hour on machine III.

  b. To produce one unit of product B requires 1 hour of working time on machine I, 1 hour on machine II, and 3 hours on machine III.

c. Machine I is available for no more than 40 hours per week, machine II is available for no more than 40 hours per week, and machine III for no more than 60 hours per week.

d. Product A can be sold at a profit of $2.75 per unit and product B at a profit of $3.50 per unit.

How many units of product A and product B should be produced per week to maximize profit?

42. *Production statistics* Suppose that the company we referred to in Example 5 also manufactures widgets and wadgets and has the following production information available.

a. To produce a widget requires 4 hours of working time on machine A and 2 hours on machine B.

b. To produce a wadget requires 5 hours of working time on machine A and 5 hours on machine B.

c. Machine A is available for no more than 200 hours in a month and machine B is available for no more than 150 hours per month.

d. Widgets can be sold at a profit of $7 each and wadgets at a profit of $8 each.

How many widgets and wadgets should be produced per month in order to maximize profit?

CHAPTER 11 SUMMARY

The primary focus of this chapter is the development of additional techniques for solving systems of linear equations. Remember that we reviewed the substitution method and the elimination-by-addition method in Chapter 2.

Matrix Approach

You can change the augmented matrix of a system to reduced echelon form by applying the following elementary row operations.

   1. Any two rows of the matrix can be interchanged.

   2. Any row of the matrix can be multiplied by a nonzero real number.

   3. Any row of the matrix can be replaced by adding a nonzero multiple of another row to that row.

For example, the augmented matrix of the system

$$\begin{pmatrix} x - 2y + 3z = & 4 \\ 2x + y - 4z = & 3 \\ -3x + 4y - z = & -2 \end{pmatrix}$$

is

$$\begin{bmatrix} 1 & -2 & 3 & \vdots & 4 \\ 2 & 1 & -4 & \vdots & 3 \\ -3 & 4 & -1 & \vdots & -2 \end{bmatrix},$$

which can be changed to the reduced echelon form

$$\begin{bmatrix} 1 & 0 & 0 & \vdots & 4 \\ 0 & 1 & 0 & \vdots & 3 \\ 0 & 0 & 1 & \vdots & 2 \end{bmatrix}$$

where the solution set of $\{(4, 3, 2)\}$ is obvious.

Cramer's Rule

Cramer's rule for solving systems of linear equations involves the use of determinants. It is stated for the 2×2 case on page 677 and for the 3×3 case on page 679. For example, the solution set of the system

$$\begin{pmatrix} 3x - y - z = 2 \\ 2x + y + 3z = 9 \\ -x + 5y - 6z = -29 \end{pmatrix} \text{ is determined by}$$

$$x = \frac{\begin{vmatrix} 2 & -1 & -1 \\ 9 & 1 & 3 \\ -29 & 5 & -6 \end{vmatrix}}{\begin{vmatrix} 3 & -1 & -1 \\ 2 & 1 & 3 \\ -1 & 5 & -6 \end{vmatrix}} = \frac{-83}{-83} = 1$$

$$y = \frac{\begin{vmatrix} 3 & 2 & -1 \\ 2 & 9 & 3 \\ -1 & -29 & -6 \end{vmatrix}}{\begin{vmatrix} 3 & -1 & -1 \\ 2 & 1 & 3 \\ -1 & 5 & -6 \end{vmatrix}} = \frac{166}{-83} = -2$$

$$z = \frac{\begin{vmatrix} 3 & -1 & 2 \\ 2 & 1 & 9 \\ -1 & 5 & -29 \end{vmatrix}}{\begin{vmatrix} 3 & -1 & -1 \\ 2 & 1 & 3 \\ -1 & 5 & -6 \end{vmatrix}} = \frac{-249}{-83} = 3.$$

Linear programming problems deal with the idea of maximizing or minimizing a certain function that is subject to various constraints. The constraints are expressed as linear inequalities. Look over Examples 1–5 of Section 11.4 to help summarize the general approach to linear programming problems of this chapter.

CHAPTER 11 REVIEW PROBLEM SET

Solve each of the following systems by using the *substitution method.*

1. $\begin{pmatrix} 3x - y = 16 \\ 5x + 7y = -34 \end{pmatrix}$

2. $\begin{pmatrix} 6x + 5y = -21 \\ x - 4y = 11 \end{pmatrix}$

3. $\begin{pmatrix} 2x - 3y = 12 \\ 3x + 5y = -20 \end{pmatrix}$

4. $\begin{pmatrix} 5x + 8y = 1 \\ 4x + 7y = -2 \end{pmatrix}$

Solve each of the following systems by using the *elimination-by-addition method.*

5. $\begin{pmatrix} 4x - 3y = 34 \\ 3x + 2y = 0 \end{pmatrix}$ **6.** $\begin{pmatrix} \frac{1}{2}x - \frac{2}{3}y = 1 \\ \frac{3}{4}x + \frac{1}{6}y = -1 \end{pmatrix}$

7. $\begin{pmatrix} 2x - y + 3z = -19 \\ 3x + 2y - 4z = 21 \\ 5x - 4y - z = -8 \end{pmatrix}$ **8.** $\begin{pmatrix} 3x + 2y - 4z = 4 \\ 5x + 3y - z = 2 \\ 4x - 2y + 3z = 11 \end{pmatrix}$

Solve each of the following systems by *changing the augmented matrix to reduced echelon form.*

9. $\begin{pmatrix} x - 3y = 17 \\ -3x + 2y = -23 \end{pmatrix}$ **10.** $\begin{pmatrix} 2x + 3y = 25 \\ 3x - 5y = -29 \end{pmatrix}$

11. $\begin{pmatrix} x - 2y + z = -7 \\ 2x - 3y + 4z = -14 \\ -3x + y - 2z = 10 \end{pmatrix}$

12. $\begin{pmatrix} -2x - 7y + z = 9 \\ x + 3y - 4z = -11 \\ 4x + 5y - 3z = -11 \end{pmatrix}$

Solve each of the following systems by using *Cramer's rule.*

13. $\begin{pmatrix} 5x + 3y = -18 \\ 4x - 9y = -3 \end{pmatrix}$ **14.** $\begin{pmatrix} .2x + .3y = 2.6 \\ .5x + .1y = 1.4 \end{pmatrix}$

15. $\begin{pmatrix} 2x - 3y - 3z = 25 \\ 3x + y + 2z = -5 \\ 5x - 2y - 4z = 32 \end{pmatrix}$ **16.** $\begin{pmatrix} 3x - y + z = -10 \\ 6x - 2y + 5z = -35 \\ 7x + 3y - 4z = 19 \end{pmatrix}$

Solve each of the following systems by using whatever method that you think is most appropriate.

17. $\begin{pmatrix} 4x + 7y = -15 \\ 3x - 2y = 25 \end{pmatrix}$ **18.** $\begin{pmatrix} \frac{3}{4}x - \frac{1}{2}y = -15 \\ \frac{2}{3}x + \frac{1}{4}y = -5 \end{pmatrix}$

19. $\begin{pmatrix} x + 4y = 3 \\ 3x - 2y = 1 \end{pmatrix}$ **20.** $\begin{pmatrix} 7x - 3y = -49 \\ y = \frac{3}{5}x - 1 \end{pmatrix}$

21. $\begin{pmatrix} x - y - z = 4 \\ -3x + 2y + 5z = -21 \\ 5x - 3y - 7z = 30 \end{pmatrix}$

22. $\begin{pmatrix} 2x - y + z = -7 \\ -5x + 2y - 3z = 17 \\ 3x + y + 7z = -5 \end{pmatrix}$

23. $\begin{pmatrix} 3x - 2y - 5z = 2 \\ -4x + 3y + 11z = 3 \\ 2x - y + z = -1 \end{pmatrix}$

24. $\begin{pmatrix} 7x - y + z = -4 \\ -2x + 9y - 3z = -50 \\ x - 5y + 4z = 42 \end{pmatrix}$

Evaluate each of the following determinants.

25. $\begin{vmatrix} -2 & 6 \\ 3 & 8 \end{vmatrix}$ **26.** $\begin{vmatrix} 5 & -4 \\ 7 & -3 \end{vmatrix}$

27. $\begin{vmatrix} 2 & 3 & -1 \\ 3 & 4 & -5 \\ 6 & 4 & 2 \end{vmatrix}$ **28.** $\begin{vmatrix} 3 & -2 & 4 \\ 1 & 0 & 6 \\ 3 & -3 & 5 \end{vmatrix}$

29. $\begin{vmatrix} 5 & 4 & 3 \\ 2 & -7 & 0 \\ 3 & -2 & 0 \end{vmatrix}$ **30.** $\begin{vmatrix} 5 & -4 & 2 & 1 \\ 3 & 7 & 6 & -2 \\ 2 & 1 & -5 & 0 \\ 3 & -2 & 4 & 0 \end{vmatrix}$

For Problems 31–34, indicate the solution set for each of the systems of linear inequalities by graphing the system and shading the appropriate region.

31. $\begin{pmatrix} 3x - 4y \geq 0 \\ 2x + 3y \leq 0 \end{pmatrix}$ **32.** $\begin{pmatrix} 3x - 2y < 6 \\ 2x - 3y < 6 \end{pmatrix}$

33. $\begin{pmatrix} x - 4y < 4 \\ 2x + y \geq 2 \end{pmatrix}$ **34.** $\begin{pmatrix} x \geq 0 \\ y \geq 0 \\ x + 2y \leq 4 \\ 2x - y \leq 4 \end{pmatrix}$

35. Maximize the function $f(x, y) = 8x + 5y$ in the region determined by the following constraints.

$$\begin{cases} y \leq 4x \\ x + y \leq 5 \\ x \geq 0 \\ y \geq 0 \\ x \leq 4 \end{cases}$$

36. Maximize the function $f(x, y) = 2x + 7y$ in the region determined by the following constraints.

$$\begin{cases} x \geq 0 \\ y \geq 0 \\ x + 2y \leq 16 \\ x + y \leq 9 \\ 3x + 2y \leq 24 \end{cases}$$

37. Maximize the function $f(x, y) = 7x + 5y$ in the region determined by the constraints of Problem 36.

38. Maximize the function $f(x, y) = 150x + 200y$ in the region determined by the constraints of Problem 36.

39. *Manufacturing ice cream freezers* A manufacturer of electric ice cream freezers makes a profit of $4.50 on a one-gallon freezer and a profit of $5.25 on a two-gallon freezer. The company wants to produce at least 75 one-gallon and at least 100 two-gallon freezers per week. However, the weekly production is not to exceed a total of 250 freezers. How many freezers of each type should be produced per week in order to maximize the profit?

APPENDIXES

T he appendixes of this text contain a table of natural logarithms, a table of common logarithms, and a table of trigonometric values. Along with each table is a brief discussion regarding the use of that table. When using tables, we often confront the problem of determining values that are in between two values listed in the table. By a process called **linear interpolation** we can approximate such values. We will briefly explain the general process of linear interpolation.

Suppose that for some function f we know $f(a)$ and $f(b)$, but we want to determine $f(c)$, where c is between a and b as indicated in Figure A.1. To determine a reasonable approximation for $f(c)$ we assume that f is a straight line between $f(a)$ and $f(b)$ as indicated in Figure A.2.

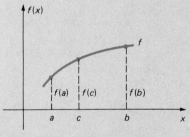

FIGURE A.1   **FIGURE A.2**

From similar right triangles we have the proportion
$$\frac{k}{f(b) - f(a)} = \frac{c - a}{b - a}.$$
Solving for k we obtain
$$k = \left(\frac{c - a}{b - a}\right)(f(b) - f(a)).$$
Therefore, an approximation for $f(c)$ is given by
$$f(c) = f(a) + k.$$
The use of linear interpolation is demonstrated as a part of the discussion for each table in the appendixes.

NATURAL LOGARITHMS

Table A contains the natural logarithms of numbers between .1 and 10, inclusive, at intervals of .1. Reading directly from the table we obtain ln 1.6 = .4700, ln 4.8 = 1.5686, and ln 9.2 = 2.192. When using Table A to find the natural logarithm of a positive number less than .1 or greater than 10, we can use the property ln rs = ln r + ln s and proceed as follows.

$$\begin{aligned} \ln 190 &= \ln(1.9 \cdot 10^2) \\ &= \ln 1.9 + \ln 10^2 \\ &= \ln 1.9 + 2 \ln 10 \\ &= .6419 \; + 2(2.3026) \end{aligned}$$
$$\underset{\text{From Table A}}{\uparrow} \qquad \underset{\text{From Table A}}{\uparrow}$$
$$= 5.2471$$

$$\begin{aligned} \ln .0084 &= \ln(8.4 \cdot 10^{-3}) \\ &= \ln 8.4 + \ln 10^{-3} \\ &= \ln 8.4 - 3 \ln 10 \\ &= 2.1282 \; - 3(2.3026) \end{aligned}$$
$$\underset{\text{From Table A}}{\uparrow} \qquad \underset{\text{From Table A}}{\uparrow}$$
$$= -4.7796$$

To determine an approximation for the natural logarithm of a number such as 6.24, which is in between two numbers in Table A, we can use the process of linear interpolation. The following format can be used to carry out this process.

$$\begin{array}{cc} x & \ln x \\ .04\left\{\begin{matrix} 6.2 \\ 6.24 \\ 6.3 \end{matrix}\right\}.1 & k\left\{\begin{matrix} 1.8245 \\ ? \\ 1.8405 \end{matrix}\right\}.0160 \end{array}$$

Setting up a proportion and solving for k yields

$$\frac{.04}{.1} = \frac{k}{.0160}$$

$$.4 = \frac{k}{.0160}$$

$$k = .4(.0160) = .0064.$$

TABLE A
Natural Logarithms

n	$\ln n$	n	$\ln n$	n	$\ln n$	n	$\ln n$
.1	−2.3026	2.6	.9555	5.1	1.6292	7.6	2.0281
.2	−1.6094	2.7	.9933	5.2	1.6487	7.7	2.0412
.3	−1.2040	2.8	1.0296	5.3	1.6677	7.8	2.0541
.4	−.9163	2.9	1.0647	5.4	1.6864	7.9	2.0669
.5	−.6931	3.0	1.0986	5.5	1.7047	8.0	2.0794
.6	−.5108	3.1	1.1314	5.6	1.7228	8.1	2.0919
.7	−.3567	3.2	1.1632	5.7	1.7405	8.2	2.1041
.8	−.2231	3.3	1.1939	5.8	1.7579	8.3	2.1163
.9	−.1054	3.4	1.2238	5.9	1.7750	8.4	2.1282
1.0	.0000	3.5	1.2528	6.0	1.7918	8.5	2.1401
1.1	.0953	3.6	1.2809	6.1	1.8083	8.6	2.1518
1.2	.1823	3.7	1.3083	6.2	1.8245	8.7	2.1633
1.3	.2624	3.8	1.3350	6.3	1.8405	8.8	2.1748
1.4	.3365	3.9	1.3610	6.4	1.8563	8.9	2.1861
1.5	.4055	4.0	1.3863	6.5	1.8718	9.0	2.1972
1.6	.4700	4.1	1.4110	6.6	1.8871	9.1	2.2083
1.7	.5306	4.2	1.4351	6.7	1.9021	9.2	2.2192
1.8	.5878	4.3	1.4586	6.8	1.9169	9.3	2.2300
1.9	.6419	4.4	1.4816	6.9	1.9315	9.4	2.2407
2.0	.6931	4.5	1.5041	7.0	1.9459	9.5	2.2513
2.1	.7419	4.6	1.5261	7.1	1.9601	9.6	2.2618
2.2	.7885	4.7	1.5476	7.2	1.9741	9.7	2.2721
2.3	.8329	4.8	1.5686	7.3	1.9879	9.8	2.2824
2.4	.8755	4.9	1.5892	7.4	2.0015	9.9	2.2925
2.5	.9163	5.0	1.6094	7.5	2.0149	10	2.3026

Therefore, $\ln 6.24 = 1.8245 + .0064 = 1.8309$.

Table A can also be used to find x when given $\ln x$. For example, if $\ln x = 1.9879$, then reading directly from Table A we obtain $x = 7.3$. To find x if $|\ln x| > 2.3026$, we take into consideration the natural logarithms of powers of 10. For example, if $x = 6.5073$ we can proceed as follows.

$$6.5073 = 4.6052 + 1.9021$$

$2 \ln 10 = \ln 10^2 = \ln 100 \qquad \ln 6.7$

Therefore,

$$x = (100)(6.7) = 670.$$

If $\ln x$ falls between two values in Table A, then we can use linear interpolation. Suppose $\ln x = 1.7310$; then we can interpolate as follows.

$$
\begin{array}{cc}
x & \ln x \\[4pt]
h\left\{\begin{array}{l} 5.6 \\ ? \\ 5.7 \end{array}\right\}.1 & .0082\left\{\begin{array}{l} 1.7228 \\ 1.7310 \\ 1.7405 \end{array}\right\}.0177
\end{array}
$$

Setting up a proportion and solving for h yields

$$\frac{h}{.1} = \frac{.0082}{.0177}$$

$$\frac{h}{.1} = \frac{88}{177}$$

$$177h = 8.2$$

$$h = \frac{8.2}{177}$$

$$= .05, \quad \text{to the nearest hundredth}$$

Therefore, $x = 5.6 + .05 = 5.65$ to the nearest hundredth.

COMMON LOGARITHMS

Table B contains the common logarithms of numbers between 1.00 and 9.99, inclusive, at intervals of .01. To find the common logarithm of a number such as 1.75, we look at the intersection of the row containing 1.7 and the column headed 5. Thus,

log 1.75 = .2430,   to the nearest ten-thousandth

When using Table B to find the common logarithm of a positive number less than 1 or greater than 10, we need to represent the number in scientific notation and apply the property log rs = log r + log s. For example, to find log 1340 we can proceed as follows.

$$
\begin{aligned}
\log 1340 &= \log(1.34 \cdot 10^3) \\
&= \log 1.34 + \log 10^3 \\
&= \log 1.34 + 3 \log 10 \\
&= .1271 + 3
\end{aligned}
$$

↑   ↖
From Table B   By inspection, since log 10 = 1

The decimal part (.1271) of the common logarithm 3.1271 is called the **mantissa**, and the integral part (3) is called the **characteristic**. Thus, we can find the characteristic of a common logarithm by inspection (it is the exponent of 10 when the number is written in scientific notation) and the mantissa by using Table B. Let's consider another example.

$$
\begin{aligned}
\log .192 &= \log(1.92 \cdot 10^{-1}) \\
&= \log 1.92 + \log 10^{-1} \\
&= .2833 + (-1)
\end{aligned}
$$

↑   ↖
From Table B   Exponent of 10

Note that we expressed the common logarithm of .192 as .2833 + (−1); we did not add .2833 and −1. This is normal procedure when using a table of common logarithms because the mantissas given in the table are positive numbers. However, you should recognize that adding .2833 and −1 produces −.7167, which agrees with the result obtained with a calculator.

To determine an approximation for the common logarithm of a number such as 2.744, which is in between two numbers in Table B, we can use linear interpolation. For example, we can approximate log 2.744 as follows.

$$x \qquad\qquad\qquad \log x$$

$$.004 \left\{ \begin{array}{c} 2.740 \\ 2.744 \\ 2.750 \end{array} \right\}.010 \qquad k\left\{ \begin{array}{c} .4378 \\ ? \\ .4393 \end{array} \right\}.0015$$

Setting up a proportion and solving for k yields

$$\frac{.004}{.010} = \frac{k}{.0015}$$

$$\frac{2}{5} = \frac{k}{.0015}$$

$$5k = .0030$$

$$k = .0006.$$

Therefore, log 2.744 = .4378 + .0006 = .4384.

Table B can also be used to find x when given log x. Traditionally in this situation, x is called the **antilogarithm** (abbreviated **antilog**) of log x. Let's consider some examples using Table B to find antilogarithms.

EXAMPLE 1

Determine antilog 1.3365.

Solution

Finding an antilogarithm simply reverses the process we used before when finding a logarithm. Thus, antilog 1.3365 means that 1 is the characteristic and .3365 the mantissa. We look for .3365 in the body of the common logarithm table and we find that it is located at the intersection of the 2.1-row and the 7-column. Therefore, the antilogarithm is

$$2.17 \cdot 10^1 = 21.7.$$

EXAMPLE 2

Determine antilog −2.6038.

Solution

The mantissas given in a table are **positive** numbers. Thus, we need to express −2.6038 in terms of a positive mantissa and this can be done by adding and subtracting 3 as follows.

$$(-2.6038 + 3) - 3 = .3962 + (-3)$$

Now we can look for .3962 and find it at the intersection of the 2.4-row and 9-column. Therefore, the antilogarithm is

$$2.49 \cdot 10^{-3} = .00249.$$

The process of linear interpolation can also be used to approximate an antilogarithm when the mantissa is in between two values in the table. The following example illustrates this procedure.

E X A M P L E 3

Find antilog 1.6157.

Solution

From the table we see that the mantissa, .6157, is between .6149 and .6160. We can carry out the interpolation as follows.

$$h\left\{\begin{bmatrix} 4.120 \\ \\ ? \\ 4.130 \end{bmatrix}\right\}.010 \qquad .0008\left\{\begin{bmatrix} .6149 \\ \\ .6157 \\ .6160 \end{bmatrix}\right\}.0011$$

$$\frac{h}{.010} = \frac{8}{11} \qquad \frac{.0008}{.0011} = \frac{8}{11}$$

$$11h = 8(.010) = .080$$

$$h = \frac{1}{11}(.080) = .007, \quad \text{to the nearest thousandth}$$

Thus, antilog .6157 = 4.120 + .007 = 4.127. Therefore,

$$\text{antilog } 1.6157 = \text{antilog}(.6157 + 1)$$
$$= 4.127 \cdot 10^1 = 41.27.$$

Computation with Common Logarithms

Let's first restate the basic properties of logarithms in terms of **common logarithms**. (Remember that we are writing $\log x$ instead of $\log_{10} x$.) If x and y are positive real numbers, then

1. $\log xy = \log x + \log y$

2. $\log \dfrac{x}{y} = \log x - \log y$

3. $\log x^p = p \log x.$ p is any real number.

The following two properties of equality that pertain to logarithms will also be used.

4. If $x = y$ (x and y are positive), then $\log x = \log y$.

5. If $\log x = \log y$, then $x = y$.

EXAMPLE 4

Find the product $(49.1)(876)$.

Solution

Let $N = (49.1)(876)$; by Property 4,

$$\log N = \log(49.1)(876).$$

By Property 1,

$$\log N = \log 49.1 + \log 876.$$

From the table we find that $\log 49.1 = 1.6911$ and that $\log 876 = 2.9425$. Thus,

$$\log N = 1.6911 + 2.9425$$
$$= 4.6336.$$

Therefore,

$$N = \text{antilog } 4.6336.$$

By using linear interpolation, we can determine antilog .6336 to four significant digits. Thus, we obtain

$$N = \text{antilog}(.6336 + 4)$$
$$= 4.301 \cdot 10^4$$
$$= 43{,}010.$$

 Check   By using a calculator we obtain

$$N = (49.1)(876) = 43011.6.$$

EXAMPLE 5

Find the quotient $\dfrac{942}{64.8}$.

Solution

Let $N = \dfrac{94.2}{64.8}$. Therefore,

$$\log N = \log \dfrac{942}{64.8}$$

$$= \log 942 - \log 64.8$$

$$= 2.9741 - 1.8116 \qquad \log\dfrac{x}{y} = \log x - \log y$$

$$= 1.1625. \qquad\qquad\quad \text{from the table}$$

Therefore,

$$N = \text{antilog } 1.1625$$
$$= \text{antilog}(.01625 + 1)$$
$$= 1.454 \cdot 10^1$$
$$= 14.54$$

Check   By using a calculator we obtain

$$N = \frac{942}{64.8} = 14.537037.$$

EXAMPLE 6

Evaluate $\dfrac{(571.4)(8.236)}{71.68}$.

Solution

Let $N = \dfrac{(571.4)(8.236)}{71.68}$. Therefore,

$$\log N = \log \frac{(571.4)(8.236)}{71.68}$$

$$= \log 571.4 + \log 8.236 - \log 71.68$$

$$= 2.7569 + .9157 - 1.8554 = 1.8172.$$

Therefore,

$$N = \text{antilog } 1.8172$$
$$= \text{antilog}(.8172 + 1)$$
$$= 6.564 \cdot 10^1 = 65.64.$$

Check   By using a calculator we obtain

$$N = \frac{(571.4)(8.236)}{71.68} = 65.653605.$$

EXAMPLE 7

Evaluate $\sqrt[3]{3770}$.

Solution

Let $N = \sqrt[3]{3770} = (3770)^{1/3}$. Therefore,

$$\log N = \log(3770)^{1/3}$$

$$= \frac{1}{3}\log 3770 \qquad \log x^p = p \log x$$

$$= \frac{1}{3}(3.5763)$$

$$= 1.1921.$$

Therefore,

$$N = \text{antilog } 1.1921$$
$$= \text{antilog}(.1921 + 1)$$
$$= 1.556 \cdot 10^1 = 15.56$$

 Check   By using a calculator we obtain

$$N = \sqrt[3]{3370} = 15.563733.$$

When using tables of logarithms, it is sometimes necessary to change the form of writing a logarithm so that the decimal part (mantissa) is positive. The next example illustrates this idea.

EXAMPLE 8   Find the quotient $\dfrac{1.73}{5.08}$.

Solution

Let $N = \dfrac{1.73}{5.08}$. Therefore,

$$\log N = \log \frac{1.73}{5.08}$$

$$= \log 1.73 - \log 5.08$$

$$= .2380 - .7059 = -.4679.$$

Now by adding 1 and subtracting 1, which changes the form but not the value, we obtain

$$\log N = -.4679 + 1 - 1$$
$$= .5321 - 1$$
$$= .5321 + (-1).$$

Therefore,

$$N = \text{antilog}(.5321 + (-1))$$
$$= 3.405 \cdot 10^{-1} = .3405.$$

 Check   By using a calculator we obtain

$$N = \frac{1.73}{5.08} = .34055118.$$

Sometimes it is also necessary to change the form of a logarithm so that a subsequent calculation will produce an **integer for the characteristic part of the logarithm**. Let's consider an example to illustrate this idea.

EXAMPLE 9

Evaluate $\sqrt[4]{.0767}$.

Solution

Let $N = \sqrt[4]{.0767} = (.0767)^{1/4}$. Therefore,

$$\log N = \log(.0767)^{1/4} = \frac{1}{4}\log .0767$$

$$= \frac{1}{4}(.8848 + (-2))$$

$$= \frac{1}{4}(-2 + .8848).$$

At this stage we recognize that applying the distributive property will produce a nonintegral characteristic, namely, $-\frac{1}{2}$. Therefore, let's add 4 and subtract 4 inside the parentheses, which will change the form as follows.

$$\log N = \frac{1}{4}(-2 + .8848 + 4 - 4)$$

$$= \frac{1}{4}(4 - 2 + .8848 - 4)$$

$$= \frac{1}{4}(2.8848 - 4)$$

Now applying the distributive property we obtain

$$\log N = \frac{1}{4}(2.8848) - \frac{1}{4}(4)$$

$$= .7212 - 1 = .7212 + (-1).$$

Therefore,

$$N = \text{antilog}(.7212 + (-1))$$
$$= 5.262 \cdot 10^{-1} = .5262.$$

 Check   By using a calculator we obtain

$$N = \sqrt[4]{.0767} = .5262816.$$

PRACTICE EXERCISES

Use Table B and linear interpolation to find each of the following common logarithms. Check your answers with a calculator.

1. log 4.327

2. log 27.43

3. log 128.9

4. log 3526

5. log .8761

6. log .07692

7. log .005186

8. log .0002558

Use Table B and linear interpolation to find each of the following antilogarithms to four significant digits. Check your answers with a calculator.

9. antilog .4690   **10.** antilog 1.7971

11. antilog 2.1925   **12.** antilog 3.7225

13. antilog(.5026 + (−1))

14. antilog(.9397 + (−2))

Use common logarithms and linear interpolation to help evaluate each of the following. Express your answers with four significant digits. Check your answers with a calculator.

15. (294)(71.2)   **16.** (192.6)(4.017)

17. $\dfrac{23.4}{4.07}$ **18.** $\dfrac{718.5}{8.248}$

19. $(17.3)^5$ **20.** $(48.02)^3$

21. $\dfrac{(108)(76.2)}{13.4}$ **22.** $\dfrac{(126.3)(24.32)}{8.019}$

23. $\sqrt[5]{0.821}$ **24.** $\sqrt[4]{645.3}$

25. $(79.3)^{3/5}$ **26.** $(176.8)^{3/4}$

27. $\sqrt{\dfrac{(7.05)(18.7)}{.521}}$ **28.** $\sqrt[3]{\dfrac{(41.3)(.271)}{8.05}}$

T A B L E   B
Common Logarithms

N	0	1	2	3	4	5	6	7	8	9
1.0	.0000	.0043	.0086	.0128	.0170	.0212	.0253	.0294	.0334	.0374
1.1	.0414	.0453	.0492	.0531	.0569	.0607	.0645	.0682	.0719	.0755
1.2	.0792	.0828	.0864	.0899	.0934	.0969	.1004	.1038	.1072	.1106
1.3	.1139	.1173	.1206	.1239	.1271	.1303	.1335	.1367	.1399	.1430
1.4	.1461	.1492	.1523	.1553	.1584	.1614	.1644	.1673	.1703	.1732
1.5	.1761	.1790	.1818	.1847	.1875	.1903	.1931	.1959	.1987	.2014
1.6	.2041	.2068	.2095	.2122	.2148	.2175	.2201	.2227	.2253	.2279
1.7	.2304	.2330	.2355	.2380	.2405	.2430	.2455	.2480	.2504	.2529
1.8	.2553	.2577	.2601	.2625	.2648	.2672	.2695	.2718	.2742	.2765
1.9	.2788	.2810	.2833	.2856	.2878	.2900	.2923	.2945	.2967	.2989
2.0	.3010	.3032	.3054	.3075	.3096	.3118	.3139	.3160	.3181	.3201
2.1	.3222	.3243	.3263	.3284	.3304	.3324	.3345	.3365	.3385	.3404
2.2	.3424	.3444	.3464	.3483	.3502	.3522	.3541	.3560	.3579	.3598
2.3	.3617	.3636	.3655	.3674	.3692	.3711	.3729	.3747	.3766	.3784
2.4	.3802	.3820	.3838	.3856	.3874	.3892	.3909	.3927	.3945	.3962
2.5	.3979	.3997	.4014	.4031	.4048	.4065	.4082	.4099	.4116	.4133
2.6	.4150	.4166	.4183	.4200	.4216	.4232	.4249	.4265	.4281	.4298
2.7	.4314	.4330	.4346	.4362	.4378	.4393	.4409	.4425	.4440	.4456
2.8	.4472	.4487	.4502	.4518	.4533	.4548	.4564	.4579	.4594	.4609
2.9	.4624	.4639	.4654	.4669	.4683	.4698	.4713	.4728	.4742	.4757
3.0	.4771	.4786	.4800	.4814	.4829	.4843	.4857	.4871	.4886	.4900
3.1	.4914	.4928	.4942	.4955	.4969	.4983	.4997	.5011	.5024	.5038

TABLE B *(continued)*

N	0	1	2	3	4	5	6	7	8	9
3.2	.5051	.5065	.5079	.5092	.5105	.5119	.5132	.5145	.5159	.5172
3.3	.5185	.5198	.5211	.5224	.5237	.5250	.5263	.5276	.5289	.5302
3.4	.5315	.5328	.5340	.5353	.5366	.5378	.5391	.5403	.5416	.5428
3.5	.5441	.5453	.5465	.5478	.5490	.5502	.5514	.5527	.5539	.5551
3.6	.5563	.5575	.5587	.5599	.5611	.5623	.5635	.5647	.5658	.5670
3.7	.5682	.5694	.5705	.5717	.5729	.5740	.5752	.5763	.5775	.5786
3.8	.5798	.5809	.5821	.5832	.5843	.5855	.5866	.5877	.5888	.5899
3.9	.5911	.5922	.5933	.5944	.5955	.5966	.5977	.5988	.5999	.6010
4.0	.6021	.6031	.6042	.6053	.6064	.6075	.6085	.6096	.6107	.6117
4.1	.6128	.6138	.6149	.6160	.6170	.6180	.6191	.6201	.6212	.6222
4.2	.6232	.6243	.6253	.6263	.6274	.6284	.6294	.6304	.6314	.6325
4.3	.6335	.6345	.6355	.6365	.6375	.6385	.6395	.6405	.6415	.6425
4.4	.6435	.6444	.6454	.6464	.6474	.6484	.6493	.6503	.6513	.6522
4.5	.6532	.6542	.6551	.6561	.6571	.6580	.6590	.6599	.6609	.6618
4.6	.6628	.6637	.6646	.6656	.6665	.6675	.6684	.6693	.6702	.6712
4.7	.6721	.6730	.6739	.6749	.6758	.6767	.6776	.6785	.6794	.6803
4.8	.6812	.6821	.6830	.6839	.6848	.6857	.6866	.6875	.6884	.6893
4.9	.6902	.6911	.6920	.6928	.6937	.6946	.6955	.6964	.6972	.6981
5.0	.6990	.6998	.7007	.7016	.7024	.7033	.7042	.7050	.7059	.7067
5.1	.7076	.7084	.7093	.7101	.7110	.7118	.7126	.7135	.7143	.7152
5.2	.7160	.7168	.7177	.7185	.7193	.7202	.7210	.7218	.7226	.7235
5.3	.7243	.7251	.7259	.7267	.7275	.7284	.7292	.7300	.7308	.7316
5.4	.7324	.7332	.7340	.7348	.7356	.7364	.7372	.7380	.7388	.7396
5.5	.7404	.7412	.7419	.7427	.7435	.7443	.7451	.7459	.7466	.7474
5.6	.7482	.7490	.7497	.7505	.7513	.7520	.7528	.7536	.7543	.7551
5.7	.7559	.7566	.7574	.7582	.7589	.7597	.7604	.7612	.7619	.7627
5.8	.7634	.7642	.7649	.7657	.7664	.7672	.7679	.7686	.7694	.7701
5.9	.7709	.7716	.7723	.7731	.7738	.7745	.7752	.7760	.7767	.7774
6.0	.7782	.7789	.7796	.7803	.7810	.7818	.7825	.7832	.7839	.7846
6.1	.7853	.7860	.7868	.7875	.7882	.7889	.7896	.7903	.7910	.7917
6.2	.7924	.7931	.7938	.7945	.7952	.7959	.7966	.7973	.7980	.7987
6.3	.7993	.8000	.8007	.8014	.8021	.8028	.8035	.8041	.8048	.8055
6.4	.8062	.8069	.8075	.8082	.8089	.8096	.8102	.8109	.8116	.8122
6.5	.8129	.8136	.8142	.8149	.8156	.8162	.8169	.8176	.8182	.8189
6.6	.8195	.8202	.8209	.8215	.8222	.8228	.8235	.8241	.8248	.8254
6.7	.8261	.8267	.8274	.8280	.8287	.8293	.8299	.8306	.8312	.8319
6.8	.8325	.8331	.8338	.8344	.8351	.8357	.8363	.8370	.8376	.8382
6.9	.8388	.8395	.8401	.8407	.8414	.8420	.8426	.8432	.8439	.8445
7.0	.8451	.8457	.8463	.8470	.8476	.8482	.8488	.8494	.8500	.8506
7.1	.8513	.8519	.8525	.8531	.8537	.8543	.8549	.8555	.8561	.8567

TABLE B *(continued)*

N	0	1	2	3	4	5	6	7	8	9
7.2	.8573	.8579	.8585	.8591	.8597	.8603	.8609	.8615	.8621	.8627
7.3	.8633	.8639	.8645	.8651	.8657	.8663	.8669	.8675	.8681	.8686
7.4	.8692	.8698	.8704	.8710	.8716	.8722	.8727	.8733	.8739	.8745
7.5	.8751	.8756	.8762	.8768	.8774	.8779	.8785	.8791	.8797	.8802
7.6	.8808	.8814	.8820	.8825	.8831	.8837	.8842	.8848	.8854	.8859
7.7	.8865	.8871	.8876	.8882	.8887	.8893	.8899	.8904	.8910	.8915
7.8	.8921	.8927	.8932	.8938	.8943	.8949	.8954	.8960	.8965	.8971
7.9	.8976	.8982	.8987	.8993	.8998	.9004	.9009	.9015	.9020	.9025
8.0	.9031	.9036	.9042	.9047	.9053	.9058	.9063	.9069	.9074	.9079
8.1	.9085	.9090	.9096	.9101	.9106	.9112	.9117	.9122	.9128	.9133
8.2	.9138	.9143	.9149	.9154	.9159	.9165	.9170	.9175	.9180	.9186
8.3	.9191	.9196	.9201	.9206	.9212	.9217	.9222	.9227	.9232	.9238
8.4	.9243	.9248	.9253	.9258	.9263	.9269	.9274	.9279	.9284	.9289
8.5	.9294	.9299	.9304	.9309	.9315	.9320	.9325	.9330	.9335	.9340
8.6	.9345	.9350	.9355	.9360	.9365	.9370	.9375	.9380	.9385	.9390
8.7	.9395	.9400	.9405	.9410	.9415	.9420	.9425	.9430	.9435	.9440
8.8	.9445	.9450	.9455	.9460	.9465	.9469	.9474	.9479	.9484	.9489
8.9	.9494	.9499	.9504	.9509	.9513	.9518	.9523	.9528	.9533	.9538
9.0	.9542	.9547	.9552	.9557	.9562	.9566	.9571	.9576	.9581	.9586
9.1	.9590	.9595	.9600	.9605	.9609	.9614	.9619	.9624	.9628	.9633
9.2	.9638	.9643	.9647	.9652	.9657	.9661	.9666	.9671	.9675	.9680
9.3	.9685	.9689	.9694	.9699	.9703	.9708	.9713	.9717	.9722	.9727
9.4	.9731	.9736	.9741	.9745	.9750	.9754	.9759	.9763	.9768	.9773
9.5	.9777	.9782	.9786	.9791	.9795	.9800	.9805	.9809	.9814	.9818
9.6	.9823	.9827	.9832	.9836	.9841	.9845	.9850	.9854	.9859	.9863
9.7	.9868	.9872	.9877	.9881	.9886	.9890	.9894	.9899	.9903	.9908
9.8	.9912	.9917	.9921	.9926	.9930	.9934	.9939	.9943	.9948	.9952
9.9	.9956	.9961	.9965	.9969	.9974	.9978	.9983	.9987	.9991	.9996

TRIGONOMETRIC VALUES

Table C contains trigonometric values for angles measured in degrees or radians. Degree measures are given in .1° intervals from .0° to 45.0° in the second column from the left and from 45.0° to 90.0° in the second column from the right. Since .1° ≈ .0017 radians, the radian measures are given in intervals of approximately .0017. The following examples illustrate the use of Table C.

Degree Measure

EXAMPLE 1

Find $\cos 32.4°$.

Solution

Locate 32.4° by reading down in the second column from the left. Then read across to the column labeled **cos** on **top**. Therefore,

$$\cos 32.4° = .8443.$$

EXAMPLE 2

Find $\sin 73.8°$.

Solution

Locate 73.8° by reading up in the second column from the right. Then read across the column labeled **sin** at the **bottom**. Therefore,

$$\sin 73.8° = .9603.$$

EXAMPLE 3

Find θ if $\tan \theta = 1.076$.

Solution

Locate 1.076 in the column labeled **tan** at the **bottom**. (If $0 < \tan \theta < 1$, then it would be located in the column labeled **tan** at the **top**.) Reading across to the *right* in the degree column we obtain

$$\theta = 47.1°$$

EXAMPLE 4

Find θ, to the nearest tenth of a degree, if $\sin \theta = .0562$.

Solution

Reading down in the column labeled **sin** at the **top**, we see that .0562 falls between .0558 and .0576. Since .0562 is closer to .0558, we obtain

$$\theta = 3.2°.$$

Radian Measure

EXAMPLE 5

Find $\cos 1.4556$.

Solution

Locate 1.4556 in the column on the far right labeled **radians** at the **bottom**. Then read across to the column labeled **cos** at the **bottom**. Therefore,

$$\cos 1.4556 = .1149.$$

EXAMPLE 6

Find x, to the nearest hundredth of a radian, if $\cos \theta = .0650$.

Solution

In the column labeled **cos** at the **bottom**, we find that .0650 falls between .0645 and .0663. Since .0650 is closer to .0645 we obtain $x = 1.5062$ by reading across in the far right column. Therefore, to the nearest hundredth of a radian, we obtain

$$x = 1.51.$$

T A B L E   C
Values of the Trigonometric Functions

RADIANS	DEGREES	SIN	COS	TAN	COT		
.0000	.0°	.0000	1.0000	.0000	—	90.0°	1.5708
.0017	.1°	.0017	1.0000	.0017	573.0	89.9°	1.5691
.0035	.2°	.0035	1.0000	.0035	286.5	89.8°	1.5673
.0052	.3°	.0052	1.0000	.0052	191.0	89.7°	1.5656
.0070	.4°	.0070	1.0000	.0070	143.2	89.6°	1.5638
.0087	.5°	.0087	1.0000	.0087	114.6	89.5°	1.5621
.0105	.6°	.0105	.9999	.0105	95.49	89.4°	1.5603
.0122	.7°	.0122	.9999	.0122	81.85	89.3°	1.5586
.0140	.8°	.0140	.9999	.0140	71.62	89.2°	1.5568
.0157	.9°	.0157	.9999	.0157	63.66	89.1°	1.5551
.0175	1.0°	.0175	.9998	.0175	57.29	89.0°	1.5533
.0192	1.1°	.0192	.9998	.0192	52.08	88.9°	1.5516
.0209	1.2°	.0209	.9998	.0209	47.74	88.8°	1.5499
.0227	1.3°	.0227	.9997	.0227	44.07	88.7°	1.5481
.0244	1.4°	.0244	.9997	.0244	40.92	88.6°	1.5464
.0262	1.5°	.0262	.9997	.0262	38.19	88.5°	1.5446
.0279	1.6°	.0279	.9996	.0279	35.80	88.4°	1.5429
.0297	1.7°	.0297	.9996	.0297	33.69	88.3°	1.5411
.0314	1.8°	.0314	.9995	.0314	31.82	88.2°	1.5394
.0332	1.9°	.0332	.9995	.0332	30.14	88.1°	1.5376
.0349	2.0°	.0349	.9994	.0349	28.64	88.0°	1.5359
.0367	2.1°	.0366	.9993	.0367	27.27	87.9°	1.5341
.0384	2.2°	.0384	.9993	.0384	26.03	87.8°	1.5324
.0401	2.3°	.0401	.9992	.0402	24.90	87.7°	1.5307
.0419	2.4°	.0419	.9991	.0419	23.86	87.6°	1.5289
.0436	2.5°	.0436	.9990	.0437	22.90	87.5°	1.5272
.0454	2.6°	.0454	.9990	.0454	22.02	87.4°	1.5254
.0471	2.7°	.0471	.9989	.0472	21.20	87.3°	1.5237
.0489	2.8°	.0488	.9988	.0489	20.45	87.2°	1.5219
.0506	2.9°	.0506	.9987	.0507	19.74	87.1°	1.5202
.0524	3.0°	.0523	.9986	.0524	19.08	87.0°	1.5184
.0541	3.1°	.0541	.9985	.0542	18.46	86.9°	1.5167
.0559	3.2°	.0558	.9984	.0559	17.89	86.8°	1.5149
.0576	3.3°	.0576	.9983	.0577	17.34	86.7°	1.5132
.0593	3.4°	.0593	.9982	.0594	16.83	86.6°	1.5115
		COS	SIN	COT	TAN	DEGREES	RADIANS

T A B L E   C (*continued*)

RADIANS	DEGREES	SIN	COS	TAN	COT		
.0611	3.5°	.0610	.9981	.0612	16.35	86.5°	1.5097
.0628	3.6°	.0628	.9980	.0629	15.89	86.4°	1.5080
.0646	3.7°	.0645	.9979	.0647	15.46	86.3°	1.5062
.0663	3.8°	.0663	.9978	.0664	15.06	86.2°	1.5045
.0681	3.9°	.0680	.9977	.0682	14.67	86.1°	1.5027
.0698	4.0°	.0698	.9976	.0699	14.30	86.0°	1.5010
.0716	4.1°	.0715	.9974	.0717	13.95	85.9°	1.4992
.0733	4.2°	.0732	.9973	.0734	13.62	85.8°	1.4975
.0750	4.3°	.0750	.9972	.0752	13.30	85.7°	1.4957
.0768	4.4°	.0767	.9971	.0769	13.00	85.6°	1.4940
.0785	4.5°	.0785	.9969	.0787	12.71	85.5°	1.4923
.0803	4.6°	.0802	.9968	.0805	12.43	85.4°	1.4905
.0820	4.7°	.0819	.9966	.0822	12.16	85.3°	1.4888
.0838	4.8°	.0837	.9965	.0840	11.91	85.2°	1.4870
.0855	4.9°	.0854	.9963	.0857	11.66	85.1°	1.4853
.0873	5.0°	.0872	.9962	.0875	11.43	85.0°	1.4835
.0890	5.1°	.0889	.9960	.0892	11.20	84.9°	1.4818
.0908	5.2°	.0906	.9959	.0910	10.99	84.8°	1.4800
.0925	5.3°	.0924	.9957	.0928	10.78	84.7°	1.4783
.0942	5.4°	.0941	.9956	.0945	10.58	84.6°	1.4765
.0960	5.5°	.0958	.9954	.0963	10.39	84.5°	1.4748
.0977	5.6°	.0976	.9952	.0981	10.20	84.4°	1.4731
.0995	5.7°	.0993	.9951	.0998	10.02	84.3°	1.4713
.1012	5.8°	.1011	.9949	.1016	9.845	84.2°	1.4696
.1030	5.9°	.1028	.9947	.1033	9.677	84.1°	1.4678
.1047	6.0°	.1045	.9945	.1051	9.514	84.0°	1.4661
.1065	6.1°	.1063	.9943	.1069	9.357	83.9°	1.4643
.1082	6.2°	.1080	.9942	.1086	9.205	83.8°	1.4626
.1100	6.3°	.1097	.9940	.1104	9.058	83.7°	1.4608
.1117	6.4°	.1115	.9938	.1122	8.915	83.6°	1.4591
.1134	6.5°	.1132	.9936	.1139	8.777	83.5°	1.4573
.1152	6.6°	.1149	.9934	.1157	8.643	83.4°	1.4556
.1169	6.7°	.1167	.9932	.1175	8.513	83.3°	1.4539
.1187	6.8°	.1184	.9930	.1192	8.386	83.2°	1.4521
.1204	6.9°	.1201	.9928	.1210	8.264	83.1°	1.4504
.1222	7.0°	.1219	.9925	.1228	8.144	83.0°	1.4486
.1239	7.1°	.1236	.9923	.1246	8.028	82.9°	1.4469
		COS	**SIN**	**COT**	**TAN**	**DEGREES**	**RADIANS**

T A B L E   C (*continued*)

RADIANS	DEGREES	SIN	COS	TAN	COT		
.1257	7.2°	.1253	.9921	.1263	7.916	82.8°	1.4451
.1274	7.3°	.1271	.9919	.1281	7.806	82.7°	1.4434
.1292	7.4°	.1288	.9917	.1299	7.700	82.6°	1.4416
.1309	7.5°	.1305	.9914	.1317	7.596	82.5°	1.4399
.1326	7.6°	.1323	.9912	.1334	7.495	82.4°	1.4382
.1344	7.7°	.1340	.9910	.1352	7.396	82.3°	1.4364
.1361	7.8°	.1357	.9907	.1370	7.300	82.2°	1.4347
.1379	7.9°	.1374	.9905	.1388	7.207	82.1°	1.4329
.1396	8.0°	.1392	.9903	.1405	7.115	82.0°	1.4312
.1414	8.1°	.1409	.9900	.1423	7.026	81.9°	1.4294
.1431	8.2°	.1426	.9898	.1441	6.940	81.8°	1.4277
.1449	8.3°	.1444	.9895	.1459	6.855	81.7°	1.4529
.1466	8.4°	.1461	.9893	.1477	6.772	81.6°	1.4242
.1484	8.5°	.1478	.9890	.1495	6.691	81.5°	1.4224
.1501	8.6°	.1495	.9888	.1512	6.612	81.4°	1.4207
.1518	8.7°	.1513	.9885	.1530	6.535	81.3°	1.4190
.1536	8.8°	.1530	.9882	.1548	6.460	81.2°	1.4172
.1553	8.9°	.1547	.9880	.1566	6.386	81.1°	1.4155
.1571	9.0°	.1564	.9877	.1584	6.314	81.0°	1.4137
.1588	9.1°	.1582	.9874	.1602	6.243	80.9°	1.4120
.1606	9.2°	.1599	.9871	.1620	6.174	80.8°	1.4102
.1623	9.3°	.1616	.9869	.1638	6.107	80.7°	1.4085
.1641	9.4°	.1633	.9866	.1655	6.041	80.6°	1.4067
.1658	9.5°	.1650	.9863	.1673	5.976	80.5°	1.4050
.1676	9.6°	.1668	.9860	.1691	5.912	80.4°	1.4032
.1693	9.7°	.1685	.9857	.1709	5.850	80.3°	1.4015
.1710	9.8°	.1702	.9854	.1727	5.789	80.2°	1.3998
.1728	9.9°	.1719	.9851	.1745	5.730	80.1°	1.3980
.1745	10.0°	.1736	.9848	.1763	5.671	80.0°	1.3963
.1763	10.1°	.1754	.9845	.1781	5.614	79.9°	1.3945
.1780	10.2°	.1771	.9842	.1799	5.558	79.8°	1.3928
.1798	10.3°	.1788	.9839	.1817	5.503	79.7°	1.3910
.1815	10.4°	.1805	.9836	.1835	5.449	79.6°	1.3893
.1833	10.5°	.1822	.9833	.1853	5.396	79.5°	1.3875
.1850	10.6°	.1840	.9829	.1871	5.343	79.4°	1.3858
.1868	10.7°	.1857	.9826	.1890	5.292	79.3°	1.3840
.1885	10.8°	.1874	.9823	.1908	5.242	79.2°	1.3823
		COS	**SIN**	**COT**	**TAN**	**DEGREES**	**RADIANS**

T A B L E C (*continued*)

RADIANS	DEGREES	SIN	COS	TAN	COT		
.1902	10.9°	.1891	.9820	.1926	5.193	79.1°	1.3806
.1920	11.0°	.1908	.9816	.1944	5.145	79.0°	1.3788
.1937	11.1°	.1925	.9813	.1962	5.097	78.9°	1.3771
.1955	11.2°	.1942	.9810	.1980	5.050	78.8°	1.3753
.1972	11.3°	.1959	.9806	.1998	5.005	78.7°	1.3736
.1990	11.4°	.1977	.9803	.2016	4.959	78.6°	1.3718
.2007	11.5°	.1994	.9799	.2035	4.915	78.5°	1.3701
.2025	11.6°	.2011	.9796	.2053	4.872	78.4°	1.3683
.2042	11.7°	.2028	.9792	.2071	4.829	78.3°	1.3666
.2059	11.8°	.2045	.9789	.2089	4.787	78.2°	1.3648
.2077	11.9°	.2062	.9785	.2107	4.745	78.1°	1.3631
.2094	12.0°	.2079	.9789	.2126	4.705	78.0°	1.3614
.2112	12.1°	.2096	.9778	.2144	4.665	77.9°	1.3596
.2129	12.2°	.2113	.9774	.2162	4.625	77.8°	1.3579
.2147	12.3°	.2130	.9770	.2180	4.586	77.7°	1.3561
.2164	12.4°	.2147	.9767	.2199	4.548	77.6°	1.3544
.2182	12.5°	.2164	.9763	.2217	4.511	77.5°	1.3526
.2199	12.6°	.2181	.9759	.2235	4.474	77.4°	1.3509
.2217	12.7°	.2198	.9755	.2254	4.437	77.3°	1.3491
.2234	12.8°	.2215	.9751	.2272	4.402	77.2°	1.3474
.2251	12.9°	.2233	.9748	.2290	4.366	77.1°	1.3456
.2269	13.0°	.2250	.9744	.2309	4.331	77.0°	1.3439
.2286	13.1°	.2267	.9740	.2327	4.297	76.9°	1.3422
.2304	13.2°	.2284	.9736	.2345	4.264	76.8°	1.3404
.2321	13.3°	.2300	.9732	.2364	4.230	76.7°	1.3387
.2339	13.4°	.2317	.9728	.2382	4.198	76.6°	1.3369
.2356	13.5°	.2334	.9724	.2401	4.165	76.5°	1.3352
.2374	13.6°	.2351	.9720	.2419	4.134	76.4°	1.3334
.2391	13.7°	.2368	.9715	.2438	4.102	76.3°	1.3317
.2409	13.8°	.2385	.9711	.2456	4.071	76.2°	1.3299
.2426	13.9°	.2402	.9707	.2475	4.041	76.1°	1.3282
.2443	14.0°	.2419	.9703	.2493	4.011	76.0°	1.3265
.2461	14.1°	.2436	.9699	.2512	3.981	75.9°	1.3247
.2478	14.2°	.2453	.9694	.2530	3.952	75.8°	1.3230
.2496	14.3°	.2470	.9690	.2549	3.923	75.7°	1.3212
.2513	14.4°	.2487	.9686	.2568	3.895	75.6°	1.3195
.2531	14.5°	.2504	.9681	.2586	3.867	75.5°	1.3177
		COS	SIN	COT	TAN	DEGREES	RADIANS

T A B L E C (*continued*)

RADIANS	DEGREES	SIN	COS	TAN	COT		
.2548	14.6°	.2521	.9677	.2605	3.839	75.4°	1.3160
.2566	14.7°	.2538	.9673	.2623	3.812	75.3°	1.3142
.2583	14.8°	.2554	.9668	.2642	3.785	75.2°	1.3125
.2601	14.9°	.2571	.9664	.2661	3.758	75.1°	1.3107
.2618	15.0°	.2588	.9659	.2679	3.732	75.0°	1.3090
.2635	15.1°	.2605	.9655	.2698	3.706	74.9°	1.3073
.2653	15.2°	.2622	.9650	.2717	3.681	74.8°	1.3055
.2670	15.3°	.2639	.9646	.2736	3.655	74.7°	1.3038
.2688	15.4°	.2656	.9641	.2754	3.630	74.6°	1.3020
.2705	15.5°	.2672	.9636	.2773	3.606	74.5°	1.3003
.2723	15.6°	.2689	.9632	.2792	3.582	74.4°	1.2985
.2740	15.7°	.2706	.9627	.2811	3.558	74.3°	1.2968
.2758	15.8°	.2723	.9622	.2830	3.534	74.2°	1.2950
.2775	15.9°	.2740	.9617	.2849	3.511	74.1°	1.2933
.2793	16.0°	.2756	.9613	.2867	3.487	74.0°	1.2915
.2810	16.1°	.2773	.9608	.2886	3.465	73.9°	1.2898
.2827	16.2°	.2790	.9603	.2905	3.442	73.8°	1.2881
.2845	16.3°	.2807	.9598	.2924	3.420	73.7°	1.2863
.2862	16.4°	.2823	.9593	.2943	3.398	73.6°	1.2846
.2880	16.5°	.2840	.9588	.2962	3.376	73.5°	1.2828
.2897	16.6°	.2857	.9583	.2981	3.354	73.4°	1.2811
.2915	16.7°	.2874	.9578	.3000	3.333	73.3°	1.2793
.2932	16.8°	.2890	.9573	.3019	3.312	73.2°	1.2776
.2950	16.9°	.2907	.9568	.3038	3.291	73.1°	1.2758
.2967	17.0°	.2924	.9563	.3057	3.271	73.0°	1.2741
.2985	17.1°	.2940	.9558	.3076	3.251	72.9°	1.2723
.3002	17.2°	.2957	.9553	.3096	3.230	72.8°	1.2706
.3019	17.3°	.2974	.9548	.3115	3.211	72.7°	1.2689
.3037	17.4°	.2990	.9542	.3134	3.191	72.6°	1.2671
.3054	17.5°	.3007	.9537	.3153	3.172	72.5°	1.2654
.3072	17.6°	.3024	.9532	.3172	3.152	72.4°	1.2636
.3089	17.7°	.3040	.9527	.3191	3.133	72.3°	1.2619
.3107	17.8°	.3057	.9521	.3211	3.115	72.2°	1.2601
.3124	17.9°	.3074	.9516	.3230	3.096	72.1°	1.2584
.3142	18.0°	.3090	.9511	.3249	3.078	72.0°	1.2566
.3159	18.1°	.3107	.9505	.3269	3.060	71.9°	1.2549
.3176	18.2°	.3123	.9500	.3288	3.042	71.8°	1.2531
		COS	SIN	COT	TAN	DEGREES	RADIANS

T A B L E   C   (*continued*)

RADIANS	DEGREES	SIN	COS	TAN	COT		
.3194	18.3°	.3140	.9494	.3307	3.024	71.7°	1.2514
.3211	18.4°	.3156	.9489	.3327	3.006	71.6°	1.2497
.3229	18.5°	.3173	.9483	.3346	2.989	71.5°	1.2479
.3246	18.6°	.3190	.9478	.3365	2.971	71.4°	1.2462
.3264	18.7°	.3206	.9472	.3385	2.954	71.3°	1.2444
.3281	18.8°	.3223	.9466	.3404	2.937	71.2°	1.2427
.3299	18.9°	.3239	.9461	.3424	2.921	71.1°	1.2409
.3316	19.0°	.3256	.9455	.3443	2.904	71.0°	1.2392
.3334	19.1°	.3272	.9449	.3463	2.888	70.9°	1.2374
.3351	19.2°	.3289	.9444	.3482	2.872	70.8°	1.2357
.3368	19.3°	.3305	.9438	.3502	2.856	70.7°	1.2339
.3386	19.4°	.3322	.9432	.3522	2.840	70.6°	1.2322
.3403	19.5°	.3338	.9426	.3541	2.824	70.5°	1.2305
.3421	19.6°	.3355	.9421	.3561	2.808	70.4°	1.2287
.3438	19.7°	.3371	.9415	.3581	2.793	70.3°	1.2270
.3456	19.8°	.3387	.9409	.3600	2.778	70.2°	1.2252
.3473	19.9°	.3404	.9403	.3620	2.762	70.1°	1.2235
.3491	20.0°	.3420	.9397	.3640	2.747	70.0°	1.2217
.3508	20.1°	.3437	.9391	.3659	2.733	69.9°	1.2200
.3526	20.2°	.3453	.9385	.3679	2.718	69.8°	1.2182
.3543	20.3°	.3469	.9379	.3699	2.703	69.7°	1.2165
.3560	20.4°	.3486	.9373	.3719	2.689	69.6°	1.2147
.3578	20.5°	.3502	.9367	.3739	2.675	69.5°	1.2130
.3595	20.6°	.3518	.9361	.3759	2.660	69.4°	1.2113
.3613	20.7°	.3535	.9354	.3779	2.466	69.3°	1.2095
.3630	20.8°	.3551	.9348	.3799	2.633	69.2°	1.2078
.3648	20.9°	.3567	.9342	.3819	2.619	69.1°	1.2060
.3665	21.0°	.3584	.9336	.3839	2.605	69.0°	1.2043
.3683	21.1°	.3600	.9330	.3859	2.592	68.9°	1.2025
.3700	21.2°	.3616	.9323	.3879	2.578	68.8°	1.2008
.3718	21.3°	.3633	.9317	.3899	2.565	68.7°	1.1990
.3735	21.4°	.3649	.9311	.3919	2.552	68.6°	1.1973
.3752	21.5°	.3665	.9304	.3939	2.539	68.5°	1.1956
.3770	21.6°	.3681	.9298	.3959	2.526	68.4°	1.1938
.3787	21.7°	.3697	.9291	.3979	2.513	68.3°	1.1921
.3805	21.8°	.3714	.9285	.4000	2.500	68.2°	1.1903
.3822	21.9°	.3730	.9278	.4020	2.488	68.1°	1.1886
		COS	SIN	COT	TAN	DEGREES	RADIANS

TABLE C (continued)

RADIANS	DEGREES	SIN	COS	TAN	COT		
.3840	22.0°	.3746	.9272	.4040	2.475	68.0°	1.1868
.3857	22.1°	.3762	.9265	.4061	2.463	67.9°	1.1851
.3875	22.2°	.3778	.9259	.4081	2.450	67.8°	1.1833
.3892	22.3°	.3795	.9252	.4101	2.438	67.7°	1.1816
.3910	22.4°	.3811	.9245	.4122	2.426	67.6°	1.1798
.3927	22.5°	.3827	.9239	.4142	2.414	67.5°	1.1781
.3944	22.6°	.3843	.9232	.4163	2.402	67.4°	1.1764
.3962	22.7°	.3859	.9225	.4183	2.391	67.3°	1.1746
.3979	22.8°	.3875	.9219	.4204	2.379	67.2°	1.1729
.3997	22.9°	.3891	.9212	.4224	2.367	67.1°	1.1711
.4014	23.0°	.3907	.9205	.4245	2.356	67.0°	1.1694
.4032	23.1°	.3923	.9198	.4265	2.344	66.9°	1.1676
.4049	23.2°	.3939	.9191	.4286	2.333	66.8°	1.1659
.4067	23.3°	.3955	.9184	.4307	2.322	66.7°	1.1641
.4084	23.4°	.3971	.9178	.4327	2.311	66.6°	1.1624
.4102	23.5°	.3987	.9171	.4348	2.300	66.5°	1.1606
.4119	23.6°	.4003	.9164	.4369	2.289	66.4°	1.1589
.4136	23.7°	.4019	.9157	.4390	2.278	66.3°	1.1572
.4154	23.8°	.4035	.9150	.4411	2.267	66.2°	1.1554
.4171	23.9°	.4051	.9143	.4431	2.257	66.1°	1.1537
.4189	24.0°	.4067	.9135	.4452	2.246	66.0°	1.1519
.4206	24.1°	.4083	.9128	.4473	2.236	65.9°	1.1502
.4224	24.2°	.4099	.9121	.4494	2.225	65.8°	1.1484
.4241	24.3°	.4115	.9114	.4515	2.215	65.7°	1.1467
.4259	24.4°	.4131	.9107	.4536	2.204	65.6°	1.1449
.4276	24.5°	.4147	.9100	.4557	2.194	65.6°	1.1432
.4294	24.6°	.4163	.9092	.4578	2.184	65.4°	1.1414
.4311	24.7°	.4179	.9085	.4599	2.174	65.3°	1.1397
.4328	24.8°	.4195	.9078	.4621	2.164	65.2°	1.1380
.4346	24.9°	.4210	.9070	.4642	2.154	65.1°	1.1362
.4363	25.0°	.4226	.9063	.4663	2.145	65.0°	1.1345
.4381	25.1°	.4242	.9056	.4684	2.135	64.9°	1.1327
.4398	25.2°	.4258	.9048	.4706	2.125	64.8°	1.1310
.4416	25.3°	.4274	.9041	.4727	2.116	64.7°	1.1292
.4433	25.4°	.4289	.9033	.4748	2.106	64.6°	1.1275
.4451	25.5°	.4305	.9026	.4770	2.097	64.5°	1.1257
.4468	25.6°	.4321	.9018	.4791	2.087	64.4°	1.1240
		COS	SIN	COT	TAN	DEGREES	RADIANS

T A B L E   C (*continued*)

RADIANS	DEGREES	SIN	COS	TAN	COT		
.4485	25.7°	.4337	.9011	.4813	2.078	64.3°	1.1222
.4503	25.8°	.4352	.9003	.4834	2.069	64.2°	1.1205
.4520	25.9°	.4368	.8996	.4856	2.059	64.1°	1.1188
.4538	26.0°	.4384	.8988	.4877	2.050	64.0°	1.1170
.4555	26.1°	.4399	.8980	.4899	2.041	63.9°	1.1153
.4573	26.2°	.4415	.8973	.4921	2.032	63.8°	1.1135
.4590	26.3°	.4431	.8965	.4942	2.023	63.7°	1.1118
.4608	26.4°	.4446	.8957	.4964	2.014	63.6°	1.1110
.4625	26.5°	.4462	.8949	.4986	2.006	63.5°	1.1083
.4643	26.6°	.4478	.8942	.5008	1.997	63.4°	1.1065
.4660	26.7°	.4493	.8934	.5029	1.988	63.3°	1.1048
.4677	26.8°	.4509	.8926	.5051	1.980	63.2°	1.1030
.4695	26.9°	.4524	.8918	.5073	1.971	63.1°	1.1013
.4712	27.0°	.4540	.8910	.5095	1.963	63.0°	1.0996
.4730	27.1°	.4555	.8902	.5117	1.954	62.9°	1.0978
.4747	27.2°	.4571	.8894	.5139	1.946	62.8°	1.0961
.4765	27.3°	.4586	.8886	.5161	1.937	62.7°	1.0943
.4782	27.4°	.4602	.8878	.5184	1.929	62.6°	1.0926
.4800	27.5°	.4617	.8870	.5206	1.921	62.5°	1.0908
.4817	27.6°	.4633	.8862	.5228	1.913	62.4°	1.0891
.4835	27.7°	.4648	.8854	.5250	1.905	62.3°	1.0873
.4852	27.8°	.4664	.8846	.5272	1.897	62.2°	1.0856
.4869	27.9°	.4679	.8838	.5295	1.889	62.1°	1.0838
.4887	28.0°	.4695	.8829	.5317	1.881	62.0°	1.0821
.4904	28.1°	.4710	.8821	.5340	1.873	61.9°	1.0804
.4922	28.2°	.4726	.8813	.5362	1.865	61.8°	1.0786
.4939	28.3°	.4741	.8805	.5384	1.857	61.7°	1.0769
.4957	28.4°	.4756	.8796	.5407	1.849	61.6°	1.0751
.4974	28.5°	.4772	.8788	.5430	1.842	61.5°	1.0734
.4992	28.6°	.4787	.8780	.5452	1.834	61.4°	1.0716
.5009	28.7°	.4802	.8771	.5475	1.827	61.3°	1.0699
.5027	28.8°	.4818	.8763	.5498	1.819	61.2°	1.0681
.5044	28.9°	.4833	.8755	.5520	1.811	61.1°	1.0664
.5061	29.0°	.4848	.8746	.5543	1.804	61.0°	1.0647
.5079	29.1°	.4863	.8738	.5566	1.797	60.9°	1.0629
.5096	29.2°	.4879	.8729	.5589	1.789	60.8°	1.0612
.5114	29.3°	.4894	.8721	.5612	1.782	60.7°	1.0594
		COS	**SIN**	**COT**	**TAN**	**DEGREES**	**RADIANS**

T A B L E   C (*continued*)

RADIANS	DEGREES	SIN	COS	TAN	COT		
.5131	29.4°	.4909	.8712	.5635	1.775	60.6°	1.0577
.5149	29.5°	.4924	.8704	.5658	1.767	60.5°	1.0559
.5166	29.6°	.4939	.8695	.5681	1.760	60.4°	1.0542
.5184	29.7°	.4955	.8686	.5704	1.753	60.3°	1.0524
.5201	29.8°	.4970	.8678	.5727	1.746	60.2°	1.0507
.5219	29.9°	.4985	.8669	.5750	1.739	60.1°	1.0489
.5236	30.0°	.5000	.8660	.5774	1.732	60.0°	1.0472
.5253	30.1°	.5015	.8652	.5797	1.725	59.9°	1.0455
.5271	30.2°	.5030	.8643	.5820	1.718	59.8°	1.0437
.5288	30.3°	.5045	.8634	.5844	1.711	59.7°	1.0420
.5306	30.4°	.5060	.8625	.5867	1.704	59.6°	1.0402
.5323	30.5°	.5075	.8616	.5890	1.698	59.5°	1.0385
.5341	30.6°	.5090	.8607	.5914	1.691	59.4°	1.0367
.5358	30.7°	.5105	.8599	.5938	1.684	59.3°	1.0350
.5376	30.8°	.5120	.8590	.5961	1.678	59.2°	1.0332
.5393	30.9°	.5135	.8581	.5985	1.671	59.1°	1.0315
.5411	31.0°	.5150	.8572	.6009	1.664	59.0°	1.0297
.5428	31.1°	.5165	.8563	.6032	1.658	58.9°	1.0280
.5445	31.2°	.5180	.8554	.6056	1.651	58.8°	1.0263
.5463	31.3°	.5195	.8545	.6080	1.645	58.7°	1.0245
.5480	31.4°	.5210	.8536	.6104	1.638	58.6°	1.0228
.5498	31.5°	.5225	.8526	.6128	1.632	58.5°	1.0210
.5515	31.6°	.5240	.8517	.6152	1.625	58.4°	1.0193
.5533	31.7°	.5255	.8508	.6176	1.619	58.3°	1.0175
.5550	31.8°	.5270	.8499	.6200	1.613	58.2°	1.0158
.5568	31.9°	.5284	.8490	.6224	1.607	58.1°	1.0140
.5585	32.0°	.5299	.8480	.6249	1.600	58.0°	1.0123
.5603	32.1°	.5314	.8471	.6273	1.594	57.9°	1.0105
.5620	32.2°	.5329	.8462	.6297	1.588	57.8°	1.0088
.5637	32.3°	.5344	.8453	.6322	1.582	57.7°	1.0071
.5655	32.4°	.5358	.8443	.6346	1.576	57.6°	1.0053
.5672	32.5°	.5373	.8434	.6371	1.570	57.5°	1.0036
.5690	32.6°	.5388	.8425	.6395	1.564	57.4°	1.0018
.5707	32.7°	.5402	.8415	.6420	1.558	57.3°	1.0001
.5725	32.8°	.5417	.8406	.6445	1.552	57.2°	.9983
.5742	32.9°	.5432	.8396	.6469	1.546	57.1°	.9966
.5760	33.0°	.5446	.8387	.6494	1.540	57.0°	.9948
		COS	SIN	COT	TAN	DEGREES	RADIANS

T A B L E C (continued)

RADIANS	DEGREES	SIN	COS	TAN	COT		
.5777	33.1°	.5461	.8377	.6519	1.534	56.9°	.9931
.5794	33.2°	.5476	.8368	.6544	1.528	56.8°	.9913
.5812	33.3°	.5490	.8358	.6569	1.522	56.7°	.9896
.5829	33.4°	.5505	.8348	.6594	1.517	56.6°	.9879
.5847	33.5°	.5519	.8339	.6619	1.511	56.5°	.9861
.5864	33.6°	.5534	.8329	.6644	1.505	56.4°	.9844
.5882	33.7°	.5548	.8320	.6669	1.499	56.3°	.9826
.5899	33.8°	.5563	.8310	.6694	1.494	56.2°	.9809
.5917	33.9°	.5577	.8300	.6720	1.488	56.1°	.9791
.5934	34.0°	.5592	.8290	.6745	1.483	56.0°	.9774
.5952	34.1°	.5606	.8281	.6771	1.477	55.9°	.9756
.5969	34.2°	.5621	.8271	.6796	1.471	55.8°	.9739
.5986	34.3°	.5635	.8261	.6822	1.466	55.7°	.9721
.6004	34.4°	.5650	.8251	.6847	1.460	55.6°	.9704
.6021	34.5°	.5664	.8241	.6873	1.455	55.5°	.9687
.6039	34.6°	.5678	.8231	.6899	1.450	55.4°	.9669
.6056	34.7°	.5693	.8221	.6924	1.444	55.3°	.9652
.6074	34.8°	.5707	.8211	.6950	1.439	55.2°	.9634
.6091	34.9°	.5721	.8202	.6976	1.433	55.1°	.9617
.6109	35.0°	.5736	.8192	.7002	1.428	55.0°	.9599
.6126	35.1°	.5750	.8181	.7028	1.423	54.9°	.9582
.6144	35.2°	.5764	.8171	.7054	1.418	54.8°	.9564
.6161	35.3°	.5779	.8161	.7080	1.412	54.7°	.9547
.6178	35.4°	.5793	.8151	.7107	1.407	54.6°	.9530
.6196	35.5°	.5807	.8141	.7133	1.402	54.5°	.9512
.6213	35.6°	.5821	.8131	.7159	1.397	54.4°	.9495
.6231	35.7°	.5835	.8121	.7186	1.392	54.3°	.9477
.6248	35.8°	.5850	.8111	.7212	1.387	54.2°	.9460
.6266	35.9°	.5864	.8100	.7239	1.381	54.1°	.9442
.6283	36.0°	.5878	.8090	.7265	1.376	54.0°	.9425
.6301	36.1°	.5892	.8080	.7292	1.371	53.9°	.9407
.6318	36.2°	.5906	.8070	.7319	1.366	53.8°	.9390
.6336	36.3°	.5920	.8059	.7346	1.361	53.7°	.9372
.6353	36.4°	.5934	.8049	.7373	1.356	53.6°	.9355
.6370	36.5°	.5948	.8039	.7400	1.351	53.5°	.9338
.6388	36.6°	.5962	.8028	.7427	1.347	53.4°	.9320
.6405	36.7°	.5976	.8018	.7454	1.342	53.3°	.9303
		COS	SIN	COT	TAN	DEGREES	RADIANS

TABLE C (*continued*)

RADIANS	DEGREES	SIN	COS	TAN	COT		
.6423	36.8°	.5990	.8007	.7481	1.337	53.2°	.9285
.6440	36.9°	.6004	.7997	.7508	1.332	53.1°	.9268
.6458	37.0°	.6018	.7986	.7536	1.327	53.0°	.9250
.6475	37.1°	.6032	.7976	.7563	1.322	52.9°	.9233
.6493	37.2°	.6046	.7965	.7590	1.317	52.8°	.9215
.6510	37.3°	.6060	.7955	.7618	1.313	52.7°	.9198
.6528	37.4°	.6074	.7944	.7646	1.308	52.6°	.9180
.6545	37.5°	.6088	.7934	.7673	1.303	52.5°	.9163
.6562	37.6°	.6101	.7923	.7701	1.299	52.4°	.9146
.6580	37.7°	.6115	.7912	.7729	1.294	52.3°	.9128
.6597	37.8°	.6129	.7902	.7757	1.289	52.2°	.9111
.6615	37.9°	.6143	.7891	.7785	1.285	52.1°	.9093
.6632	38.0°	.6157	.7880	.7813	1.280	52.0°	.9076
.6650	38.1°	.6170	.7869	.7841	1.275	51.9°	.9058
.6667	38.2°	.6184	.7859	.7869	1.271	51.8°	.9041
.6685	38.3°	.6198	.7848	.7898	1.266	51.7°	.9023
.6702	38.4°	.6211	.7837	.7926	1.262	51.6°	.9006
.6720	38.5°	.6225	.7826	.7954	1.257	51.5°	.8988
.6737	38.6°	.6239	.7815	.7983	1.253	51.4°	.8971
.6754	38.7°	.6252	.7804	.8012	1.248	51.3°	.8954
.6772	38.8°	.6266	.7793	.8040	1.244	51.2°	.8936
.6789	38.9°	.6280	.7782	.8069	1.239	51.1°	.8919
.6807	39.0°	.6293	.7771	.9098	1.235	51.0°	.8901
.6824	39.1°	.6307	.7760	.8127	1.230	50.9°	.8884
.6842	39.2°	.6320	.7749	.8156	1.226	50.8°	.8866
.6859	39.3°	.6334	.7738	.8185	1.222	50.7°	.8849
.6877	39.4°	.6347	.7727	.8214	1.217	50.6°	.8831
.6894	39.5°	.6361	.7716	.8243	1.213	50.5°	.8814
.6912	39.6°	.6374	.7705	.8273	1.209	50.4°	.8796
.6929	39.7°	.6388	.7694	.8302	1.205	50.3°	.8779
.6946	39.8°	.6401	.7683	.8332	1.200	50.2°	.8762
.6964	39.9°	.6414	.7672	.8361	1.196	50.1°	.8744
.6981	40.0°	.6428	.7660	.8391	1.192	50.0°	.8727
.6999	40.1°	.6441	.7649	.8421	1.188	49.9°	.8709
.7016	40.2°	.6455	.7638	.8451	1.183	49.8°	.8692
.7034	40.3°	.6468	.7627	.8481	1.179	49.7°	.8674
.7051	40.4°	.6481	.7615	.8511	1.175	49.6°	.8657
		COS	SIN	COT	TAN	DEGREES	RADIANS

T A B L E C (*continued*)

RADIANS	DEGREES	SIN	COS	TAN	COT		
.7069	40.5°	.6494	.7604	.8541	1.171	49.5°	.8639
.7086	40.6°	.6508	.7593	.8571	1.167	49.4°	.8622
.7103	40.7°	.6521	.7581	.8601	1.163	49.3°	.8604
.7121	40.8°	.6534	.7570	.8632	1.159	49.2°	.8587
.7138	40.9°	.6547	.7559	.8662	1.154	49.1°	.8570
.7156	41.0°	.6561	.7547	.8693	1.150	49.0°	.8552
.7173	41.1°	.6574	.7536	.8724	1.146	48.9°	.8535
.7191	41.2°	.6587	.7524	.8754	1.142	48.8°	.8517
.7208	41.3°	.6600	.7513	.8785	1.138	48.7°	.8500
.7226	41.4°	.6613	.7501	.8816	1.134	48.6°	.8482
.7243	41.5°	.6626	.7490	.8847	1.130	48.5°	.8465
.7261	41.6°	.6639	.7478	.8878	1.126	48.4°	.8447
.7278	41.7°	.6652	.7466	.8910	1.122	48.3°	.8430
.7295	41.8°	.6665	.7455	.8941	1.118	48.2°	.8412
.7313	41.9°	.6678	.7443	.8972	1.115	48.1°	.8395
.7330	42.0°	.6691	.7431	.9004	1.111	48.0°	.8378
.7348	42.1°	.6704	.7420	.9036	1.107	47.9°	.8360
.7365	42.2°	.6717	.7408	.9067	1.103	47.8°	.8343
.7383	42.3°	.6730	.7396	.9099	1.099	47.7°	.8325
.7400	42.4°	.6743	.7385	.9131	1.095	47.6°	.8308
.7418	42.5°	.6756	.7373	.9163	1.091	47.5°	.8290
.7435	42.6°	.6769	.7361	.9195	1.087	47.4°	.8273
.7453	42.7°	.6782	.7349	.9228	1.084	47.3°	.8255
.7470	42.8°	.6794	.7337	.9260	1.080	47.2°	.8238
.7487	42.9°	.6807	.7325	.9293	1.076	47.1°	.8221
.7505	43.0°	.6820	.7314	.9325	1.072	47.0°	.8203
.7522	43.1°	.6833	.7302	.9358	1.069	46.9°	.8186
.7540	43.2°	.6845	.7290	.9391	1.065	46.8°	.8168
.7557	43.3°	.6858	.7278	.9424	1.061	46.7°	.8151
.7575	43.4°	.6871	.7266	.9457	1.057	46.6°	.8133
.7592	43.5°	.6884	.7254	.9490	1.054	46.5°	.8116
.7610	43.6°	.6896	.7242	.9523	1.050	46.4°	.8098
.7627	43.7°	.6909	.7230	.9556	1.046	46.3°	.8081
.7645	43.8°	.6921	.7218	.9590	1.043	46.2°	.8063
.7662	43.9°	.6934	.7206	.9623	1.039	46.1°	.8046
.7679	44.0°	.6947	.7193	.9657	1.036	46.0°	.8029
.7697	44.1°	.6959	.7181	.9691	1.032	45.9°	.8011
		COS	SIN	COT	TAN	DEGREES	RADIANS

T A B L E   C (*continued*)

RADIANS	DEGREES	SIN	COS	TAN	COT		
.7714	44.2°	.6972	.7169	.9725	1.028	45.8°	.7994
.7732	44.3°	.6984	.7157	.9759	1.025	45.7°	.7976
.7749	44.4°	.6997	.7145	.9793	1.021	45.6°	.7959
.7767	44.5°	.7009	.7133	.9827	1.018	45.5°	.7941
.7784	44.6°	.7022	.7120	.9861	1.014	45.4°	.7924
.7802	44.7°	.7034	.7108	.9896	1.011	45.3°	.7906
.7819	44.8°	.7046	.7096	.9930	1.007	45.2°	.7889
.7837	44.9°	.7059	.7083	.9965	1.003	45.1°	.7871
.7854	45.0°	.7071	.7071	1.0000	1.000	45.0°	.7854
		COS	SIN	COT	TAN	DEGREES	RADIANS

ANSWERS TO ODD-NUMBERED PROBLEMS AND ALL REVIEW PROBLEMS

CHAPTER 1

Problem Set 1.1 (page 13)

1. True **3.** False **5.** False **7.** True
9. False **11.** $\subseteq$ **13.** $\subseteq$ **15.** $\nsubseteq$
17. $\subseteq$ **19.** $\nsubseteq$ **21.** -22 **23.** 8
25. 66 **27.** 1 **29.** -8 **31.** -8
33. -22 **35. (a)** 18 **(c)** 39 **(e)** 35
37. $\frac{1}{8}$ **39.** $-\frac{1}{1000}$ **41.** 27 **43.** 4
45. $-\frac{27}{8}$ **47.** 1 **49.** $\frac{16}{25}$ **51.** 4 **53.** 81
55. $\frac{3}{4}$ **57.** $\frac{16}{25}$ **59.** $\frac{17}{72}$ **61.** $\frac{1}{6}$ **63.** $\frac{48}{19}$
65. $\frac{324}{49}$ **67.** $\frac{y^4}{x^3}$ **69.** $\frac{1}{x^3y^{12}}$ **71.** $\frac{9a^2}{4b^4}$
73. $\frac{a^3}{b}$ **75.** $\frac{6}{x^3y}$ **77.** $\frac{6}{a^2y^3}$ **79.** $\frac{4x^3}{y^5}$
81. $-\frac{5}{a^2b}$ **83.** $\frac{1}{4x^2y^4}$ **85.** $12x^{3a+1}$ **87.** 1
89. x^{2a} **91.** $-4y^{6b+2}$ **93.** x^b

Problem Set 1.2 (page 22)

1. $14x^2 + x - 6$ **3.** $-x^2 - 4x - 9$ **5.** $6x - 11$
7. $6x^2 - 5x - 7$ **9.** $12x^3y^2 + 15x^2y^3$
11. $30a^4b^3 - 24a^5b^3 + 18a^4b^4$ **13.** $6x^2 + x - 2$
15. $3n^2 - 23n + 14$ **17.** $20n^2 - 27n - 14$
19. $x^3 + x^2 - 14x - 24$ **21.** $6x^3 - x^2 - 11x + 6$
23. $6t^3 + t^2 - 5t - 2$ **25.** $x^4 + 8x^3 + 15x^2 + 2x - 4$
27. $x^4 - 10x^3 + 21x^2 + 20x + 4$ **29.** $25x^2 - 49$
31. $49 - 4x^2$ **33.** $4x^2 - 16$
35. $-9x^2 + 12x - 4$ **37.** $2n^3 - n^2 - 8n + 4$
39. $4t^2 - 28t + 49$ **41.** $1 - 10x + 25x^2$

43. $x^3 + 12x^2 + 48x + 64$ **45.** $8x^3 + 12x^2 + 6x + 1$
47. $125x^3 - 150x^2y + 60xy^2 - 8y^3$
49. $x^3 + 6x^2 - 32$
51. $a^7 + 7a^6b + 21a^5b^2 + 35a^4b^3 + 35a^3b^4$
$\qquad + 21a^2b^5 + 7ab^6 + b^7$
53. $x^6 - 6x^5y + 15x^4y^2 - 20x^3y^3 + 15x^2y^4 - 6xy^5 + y^6$
55. $n^5 - 5n^4 + 10n^3 - 10n^2 + 5n - 1$
57. $16n^4 + 32n^3 + 24n^2 + 8n + 1$
59. $16a^4 - 32a^3b + 24a^2b^2 - 8ab^3 + b^4$
61. $x^{14} + 7x^{12} + 21x^{10}y^2 + 35x^8y^3 + 35x^6y^4$
$\qquad + 21x^4y^5 + 7x^2y^6 + y^7$
63. $64x^{12} - 192x^{10}y^2 + 240x^8y^4 - 160x^6y^6 + 60x^4y^8$
$\qquad - 12x^2y^{10} + y^{12}$

65. $32 + \dfrac{80}{n} + \dfrac{80}{n^2} + \dfrac{40}{n^3} + \dfrac{10}{n^4} + \dfrac{1}{n^5}$

67. $1 - \dfrac{8}{n} + \dfrac{28}{n^2} - \dfrac{56}{n^3} + \dfrac{70}{n^4} - \dfrac{56}{n^5} + \dfrac{28}{n^6} - \dfrac{8}{n^7} + \dfrac{1}{n^8}$

69. $x^4 - 8x^3y + 24x^2y^2 - 32xy^3 + 16y^4$
71. $x^{12} + 12x^{11}y + 66x^{10}y^2 + 220x^9y^3$
73. $x^{28} - 28x^{26}y^3 + 364x^{24}y^6 - 2912x^{22}y^9$

75. $a^9 + \dfrac{9a^8}{n} + \dfrac{36a^7}{n^2} + \dfrac{84a^6}{n^3}$

77. $x^{10} - 20x^9y + 180x^8y^2 - 960x^7y^3$ **79.** $56x^5y^3$

81. $126x^5y^4$ **83.** $120x^6y^{21}$ **85.** $\dfrac{5005}{n^6}$

87. (a) $3x^2 + 3xh + h^2$
(c) $5x^4 + 10x^3h + 10x^2h^2 + 5xh^3 + h^4$

Problem Set 1.3 (page 30)

1. $2xy(3 - 4y)$ **3.** $(z + 3)(x + y)$
5. $(3x + 5)(3x - 5)$ **7.** $(a + 8)(a - 3)$

A29

9. $(5n - 2)(n + 4)$ **11.** Not factorable

13. $(x + y)(3 + a)$ **15.** $(x + 4 + y)(x + 4 - y)$

17. $(3 - 4x)(4 + 3x)$

19. $(2x + 3y)(4x^2 - 6xy + 9y^2)$

21. $(x^2 + 3)(x^2 - 10)$ **23.** $(3x + 2y)(7x - y)$

25. $3y(x^2 + 7)(x + 2)(x - 2)$ **27.** $(a - b)(2a + 3c)$

29. $3x(x^2 - 7x + 48)$ **31.** Not factorable

33. $(2x^2 - 3)(x + 2)(x - 2)$

35. $(4x - 3y)(16x^2 + 12xy + 9y^2)$

37. $4(n + 2)(n^2 - 2n + 4)$ **39.** $(5t + 1)(2t - 7)$

41. $4(x^2 + 4)$ **43.** $(4n + 9)(3n + 8)$

45. $3n(2n + 5)(3n - 1)$ **47.** Not factorable

49. $(4x - y)(2x + y)$ **51.** $2x(2x - 1)(4x^2 + 2x + 1)$

53. $2y(x + 4)(x - 4)(x^2 + 3)$

55. $(a + b + c + d)(a + b - c - d)$

57. $(x + 4 + y)(x + 4 - y)$

59. $(x + y + 5)(x - y - 5)$

61. $(x + 1)(x - 1)(x + y)$ **63.** $(x^a + 4)(x^a - 4)$

65. $(x^n - y^n)(x^{2n} + x^n y^n + y^{2n})$

67. $(x^a + 4)(x^a - 7)$

69. $(2x^n - 5)(x^n + 6)$

71. $(x^{2n} + y^{2n})(x^n + y^n)(x^n - y^n)$

77. (a) $(x + 32)(x + 3)$ **(c)** $(x - 21)(x - 24)$

   (e) $(x + 28)(x + 32)$ **(g)** $(4x + 3)(8x + 3)$

   (i) $(8x - 5)(2x + 5)$

Problem Set 1.4 (page 40)

1. $\dfrac{2x}{3}$ **3.** $\dfrac{7y^3}{9x}$ **5.** $\dfrac{a + 4}{a - 9}$ **7.** $\dfrac{x(2x + 7)}{y(x + 9)}$

9. $\dfrac{x^2 + xy + y^2}{x + 2y}$ **11.** $-\dfrac{2}{x + 1}$ **13.** $\dfrac{x}{2y^3}$

15. $-\dfrac{8x^3 y^3}{15}$ **17.** $\dfrac{14}{27a}$ **19.** $5y$

21. $\dfrac{5(a + 3)}{a(a - 2)}$ **23.** $\dfrac{(x + 6y)^2(2x + 3y)}{y^3(x + 4y)}$

25. $\dfrac{3xy}{4(x + 6)}$ **27.** $\dfrac{x - 9}{42x^2}$ **29.** $\dfrac{8x + 5}{12}$

31. $\dfrac{7x}{24}$ **33.** $\dfrac{35b + 12a^3}{80a^2 b^2}$ **35.** $\dfrac{12 + 9n - 10n^2}{12n^2}$

37. $\dfrac{9y + 8x - 12xy}{12xy}$ **39.** $\dfrac{13x + 14}{(2x + 1)(3x + 4)}$

41. $\dfrac{7x + 21}{x(x + 7)}$ **43.** $\dfrac{1}{a - 2}$ **45.** $\dfrac{1}{x + 1}$

47. $\dfrac{9x + 73}{(x + 3)(x + 7)(x + 9)}$

49. $\dfrac{3x^2 + 30x - 78}{(x + 1)(x - 1)(x + 8)(x - 2)}$

51. $\dfrac{-x^2 - x + 1}{(x + 1)(x - 1)}$

53. $\dfrac{-8}{(n^2 + 4)(n + 2)(n - 2)}$

55. $\dfrac{5x^2 + 16x + 5}{(x + 1)(x - 4)(x + 7)}$

57. (a) $\dfrac{5}{x - 1}$ **(c)** $\dfrac{5}{a - 3}$ **(e)** $x + 3$

59. $\dfrac{5y^2 - 3xy^2}{x^2 y + 2x^2}$ **61.** $\dfrac{x + 1}{x - 1}$ **63.** $\dfrac{n - 1}{n + 1}$

65. $\dfrac{-6x - 4}{3x + 9}$ **67.** $\dfrac{x^2 + x + 1}{x + 1}$

69. $\dfrac{a^2 + 4a + 1}{4a + 1}$ **71.** $-\dfrac{2x + h}{x^2(x + h)^2}$

73. $-\dfrac{1}{(x + 1)(x + h + 1)}$

75. $-\dfrac{4}{(2x - 1)(2x + 2h - 1)}$

Problem Set 1.5 (page 52)

1. $\{-10\}$ **3.** $\left\{\frac{1}{14}\right\}$ **5.** $\left\{\frac{11}{4}\right\}$ **7.** $\left\{-\frac{2}{3}\right\}$

9. $\left\{\frac{1}{2}\right\}$ **11.** $\{10\}$ **13.** $\{-8\}$ **15.** $\{27\}$

17. $\left\{\frac{25}{9}\right\}$ **19.** $\{9\}$ **21.** $\left\{\frac{10}{3}\right\}$ **23.** $\{4\}$

25. $\left\{\frac{1}{4}\right\}$ **27.** $\left\{\frac{2}{3}\right\}$ **29.** $\{-8\}$ **31.** $\varnothing$

33. $\{300\}$ **35.** $\left\{-\frac{66}{37}\right\}$ **37.** $\{6\}$

39. $b_1 = \dfrac{2A - hb_2}{h}$ **41.** $T = \dfrac{N(C - V)}{C}$

43. $R_n = \dfrac{R_1 R_2}{R_1 + R_2}$ **45.** 18, 19, and 20

47. 6, 7, and 8

49. \$24,000 for Renee, \$20,000 for Kelly, and \$16,000 for Nina

51. 48 pennies, 21 nickels, and 11 dimes

53. Eric is 16 and his father is 42.

55. 50 nickels, 60 dimes, and 120 quarters

57. \$2500 at 8% and \$4000 at 9%

59. \$1500 at 9% and \$2000 at 11%

61. 6 centimeters by 10 centimeters

63. $4\frac{1}{2}$ hours   **65.** 12 minutes   **67.** 3 liters

69. 3.5 liters of the 50% solution and 7 liters of the 80% solution

Problem Set 1.6 (page 59)

1. $13 + 8i$ **3.** $3 + 4i$ **5.** $-11 + i$

7. $-1 - 2i$ **9.** $-\frac{3}{20} + \frac{5}{12}i$ **11.** $\frac{7}{10} - \frac{11}{12}i$

13. $4 + 0i$ **15.** $3i$ **17.** $i\sqrt{19}$ **19.** $\frac{2}{3}i$

21. $2i\sqrt{2}$ **23.** $3i\sqrt{3}$ **25.** $3i\sqrt{6}$ **27.** $18i$

29. $12i\sqrt{2}$ **31.** -8 **33.** $-\sqrt{6}$ **35.** $-2\sqrt{5}$

37. $-2\sqrt{15}$ **39.** $-2\sqrt{14}$ **41.** 3 **43.** $\sqrt{6}$

45. -21 **47.** $8 + 12i$ **49.** $0 + 26i$

51. $53 - 26i$ **53.** $10 - 24i$ **55.** $-14 - 8i$

57. $-7 + 24i$ **59.** $-3 + 4i$ **61.** $113 + 0i$

63. $13 + 0i$ **65.** $-\frac{8}{13} + \frac{12}{13}i$ **67.** $1 - \frac{2}{3}i$

69. $0 - \frac{3}{2}i$ **71.** $\frac{22}{41} - \frac{7}{41}i$ **73.** $-1 + 2i$

75. $-\frac{17}{10} + \frac{1}{10}i$ **77.** $\frac{5}{13} - \frac{1}{13}i$ **79.** $-2 + 2i$

81. $-128 + 128i$ **83.** $-278 - 29i$

Problem Set 1.7 (page 73)

1. $\{-4, 7\}$ **3.** $\left\{-3, \frac{4}{3}\right\}$ **5.** $\left\{\dfrac{-1 \pm 2\sqrt{5}}{2}\right\}$

7. $\{-5 \pm 3\sqrt{3}\}$ **9.** $\left\{\dfrac{-6 \pm \sqrt{46}}{2}\right\}$

11. $\{2 \pm 2i\}$ **13.** $\{-16, 18\}$ **15.** $\left\{-\frac{5}{3}, \frac{2}{5}\right\}$

17. $\left\{\dfrac{3 \pm i\sqrt{19}}{2}\right\}$ **19.** $\left\{\dfrac{3 \pm i\sqrt{47}}{4}\right\}$

21. $\left\{\dfrac{3 \pm \sqrt{7}}{2}\right\}$ **23.** $\left\{-\frac{3}{2}, \frac{1}{4}\right\}$ **25.** $\left\{0, \frac{3}{2}\right\}$

27. $\left\{\frac{3}{5}\right\}$ **29.** $\left\{\dfrac{2 \pm \sqrt{10}}{2}\right\}$

31. One real solution   **33.** One real solution
35. Two complex but nonreal solutions
37. Two unequal real solutions
39. Two complex but nonreal solutions

41. $\{-8, 1\}$ **43.** $\left\{\frac{6}{29}\right\}$

45. $\left\{n \mid n \neq \frac{3}{2} \text{ and } n \neq 3\right\}$ **47.** $\left\{-\frac{1}{4}\right\}$

49. $\{-2, 1\}$ **51.** $\{\pm 1, \pm 2\}$ **53.** $\left\{\pm\frac{\sqrt{2}}{2}, \pm 2\right\}$

55. $\{\pm i\sqrt{5}, \pm\sqrt{7}\}$ **57.** $\{\pm\sqrt{2 + \sqrt{3}}, \pm\sqrt{2 - \sqrt{3}}\}$

59. $\left\{-\frac{1}{6}, \frac{1}{2}\right\}$ **61.** $\left\{\pm\frac{\sqrt{6}}{3}, \pm i\right\}$

63. $\left\{-4, 1, \dfrac{-3 \pm \sqrt{5}}{2}\right\}$ **65.** $\{\pm 1.62, \pm.62\}$

67. $\{\pm 1.78, \pm.56\}$ **69.** $\{\pm 8.00, \pm 6.00\}$
71. 9 rows and 14 trees per row
73. 50 mph for the freight and 70 mph for the express
75. $2\frac{2}{5}$ hours   **77.** 60 minutes
79. 9 minutes for Pat and 18 minutes for Mike
81. 7 golf balls   **83.** 60 hours
85. 10 meters and 24 meters
87. 8 inches by 14 inches
89. 7 meters wide and 18 meters long   **91.** 1 meter
93. 7 inches by 11 inches

Problem Set 1.8 (page 86)

1. $[7, \infty)$ **3.** $\left(-\infty, \frac{17}{5}\right]$ **5.** $\left(-\infty, \frac{7}{3}\right)$

7. $[-20, \infty)$ **9.** $(300, \infty)$ **11.** $\left(\frac{1}{5}, \frac{7}{5}\right)$

13. $[1, 5]$ **15.** $(-\infty, -3) \cup (5, \infty)$

17. $(-\infty, -4) \cup \left(\frac{1}{3}, \infty\right)$ **19.** $\left[\frac{2}{5}, \frac{4}{3}\right]$

21. $\left(-\infty, \frac{1}{2}\right) \cup \left(\frac{1}{2}, \infty\right)$ **23.** $(-2, -1)$

25. $\left(-\infty, \frac{22}{3}\right]$ **27.** $(-4, 1) \cup (2, \infty)$

29. $(-\infty, -2] \cup \left[\frac{1}{2}, 5\right]$ **31.** $[-4, 0] \cup [6, \infty)$

33. $(-3, 2) \cup (2, \infty)$ **35.** $\left(-2, \frac{1}{2}\right)$ **37.** $\left(\frac{1}{3}, 3\right]$

39. $(-\infty, -5) \cup (-2, \infty)$ **41.** $(-\infty, -5)$

43. $(-3, 2)$ **45.** $\{-3, 4\}$ **47.** $\left\{-\frac{7}{2}, \frac{5}{2}\right\}$

49. $\varnothing$ **51.** $\left\{\frac{1}{4}, \frac{7}{4}\right\}$ **53.** $\left\{-\frac{2}{5}, 4\right\}$ **55.** $\{-1\}$

57. $[-3, 4]$ **59.** $\left(-\infty, -\frac{11}{3}\right) \cup \left(\frac{7}{3}, \infty\right)$ **61.** $\varnothing$

63. $(-\infty, -9] \cup [7, \infty)$ **65.** $\left(-\infty, \frac{5}{4}\right) \cup \left(\frac{7}{2}, \infty\right)$

67. $(-\infty, -3) \cup (-3, -1)$ **69.** $\left[-\frac{2}{5}, 0\right) \cup \left(0, \frac{2}{3}\right]$

71. $\left(-\infty, \frac{2}{5}\right] \cup \left[\frac{2}{3}, \infty\right)$ **73.** Greater than 12%

75. 98 or better
77. Between 5°C and 15°C, inclusive
79. $8.8 \leq M \leq 15.4$ **89.** $\{-2, 4\}$

91. $\left(-\infty, -\frac{3}{2}\right)$

Chapter 1 Review Problem Set (page 91)

1. $\frac{1}{125}$ **2.** $-\frac{1}{81}$ **3.** $\frac{16}{9}$ **4.** $\frac{1}{9}$ **5.** 16

6. -8 **7.** $\frac{2}{9}$ **8.** $\frac{9}{16}$ **9.** 144 **10.** $\frac{12}{7}$

11. $12x^2y$ **12.** $-12y^7$ **13.** $-\dfrac{x^3}{13y}$

14. $\dfrac{a^4b^8}{4}$ **15.** $4x - 1$ **16.** $-3x + 8$

17. $12a - 19$ **18.** $20x^2 - 11x - 42$

19. $-12x^2 + 17x - 6$ **20.** $-35x^2 + 22x - 3$

21. $x^3 + x^2 - 19x - 28$ **22.** $6x^3 - x^2 + 10x + 6$

23. $x^4 + 2x^3 - 6x^2 - 22x - 15$

24. $2x^4 + 11x^3 - 16x^2 - 8x + 8$

25. $25x^2 - 30x + 9$ **26.** $9x^2 + 42x + 49$

27. $8x^3 - 12x^2 + 6x - 1$

28. $27x^3 + 135x^2 + 225x + 125$

29. $x^6 + 12x^5 + 60x^4 + 160x^3 + 240x^2 + 192x + 64$

30. $x^5 - 10x^4y + 40x^3y^2 - 80x^2y^3 + 80xy^4 - 32y^5$

31. $462a^6$ **32.** $-15a^3b^7$ **33.** $1120x^8y^4$

34. $495x^{24}y^8$ **35.** $(3x + 2y)(3x - 2y)$

36. $3x(x + 5)(x - 8)$ **37.** $(2x + 5)^2$

38. $(x - y + 3)(x - y - 3)$ **39.** $(x - 2)(x - y)$

40. $(4x - 3y)(16x^2 + 12xy + 9y^2)$

41. $(3x - 4)(5x + 2)$ **42.** $3(x^3 + 12)$

43. Not factorable   **44.** $3(x + 2)(x^2 - 2x + 4)$

45. $(x + 3)(x - 3)(x + 2)(x - 2)$

46. $(2x - 1 - y)(2x - 1 + y)$ **47.** $-11 - 6i$

48. $-1 - 2i$ **49.** $1 - 2i$ **50.** $21 + 0i$

51. $26 - 7i$ **52.** $-25 + 15i$ **53.** $-14 - 12i$

54. $29 + 0i$ **55.** $0 - \frac{5}{3}i$ **56.** $-\frac{6}{25} + \frac{17}{25}i$

57. $0 + i$ **58.** $-\frac{12}{29} - \frac{30}{29}i$ **59.** $\dfrac{2}{3y}$

60. $\dfrac{-5a^2}{3}$ **61.** $\dfrac{3x + 5}{x}$ **62.** $\dfrac{2(3x - 1)}{x^2 + 4}$

63. $\dfrac{29x - 10}{12}$ **64.** $\dfrac{x - 38}{15}$ **65.** $\dfrac{-6n + 15}{5n^2}$

66. $\dfrac{-3x - 16}{x(x + 7)}$ **67.** $\dfrac{3x^2 - 8x - 40}{(x + 4)(x - 4)(x - 10)}$

68. $\dfrac{8x - 4}{x(x + 2)(x - 2)}$ **69.** $\dfrac{3xy - 2x^2}{5y + 7x^2}$

70. $\dfrac{3x - 2}{4x + 3}$ **71.** $-\dfrac{6x + 3h}{x^2(x + h)^2}$ **72.** $\{-14\}$

73. $\{-19\}$ **74.** $\left\{\frac{10}{7}\right\}$ **75.** $\{200\}$

76. $\left\{-1, \frac{5}{3}\right\}$ **77.** $\left\{\frac{5}{4}, 6\right\}$ **78.** $\{3 \pm i\}$

79. $\{-22, 18\}$ **80.** $\left\{-\frac{2}{5}, 0, \frac{1}{3}\right\}$ **81.** $\{-5\}$

82. $\left\{\frac{1}{2}, 6\right\}$ **83.** $\{\pm 3i, \pm\sqrt{5}\}$

84. $\left\{\pm\frac{\sqrt{5}}{5}, \pm\sqrt{2}\right\}$ **85.** $\left\{-1, 2, \dfrac{-5 \pm \sqrt{33}}{2}\right\}$

86. $\left\{-\frac{6}{5}, \frac{8}{5}\right\}$ **87.** $\left\{\frac{2}{5}, 12\right\}$ **88.** $\left\{\frac{1}{4}, \frac{7}{4}\right\}$

89. $(-8, \infty)$ **90.** $\left[-\frac{65}{4}, \infty\right)$ **91.** $\left(-\infty, -\frac{9}{2}\right)$

92. $(-\infty, 400]$ **93.** $[-2, 1]$ **94.** $\left(-\frac{2}{3}, 2\right)$

95. $(-3, 6)$ **96.** $(-\infty, -2] \cup [7, \infty)$

97. $(-\infty, -2) \cup (1, 4)$ **98.** $\left[-4, \frac{3}{2}\right)$

99. $\left(-\infty, \frac{1}{5}\right) \cup (2, \infty)$ **100.** $[-7, -3)$

101. $(-\infty, 4)$ **102.** $\left(-\infty, -\frac{1}{2}\right) \cup (2, \infty)$

103. $\left[-\frac{19}{3}, 3\right]$ **104.** $\left(-\frac{9}{2}, \frac{3}{2}\right)$ **105.** $(-1, 0) \cup \left(0, \frac{1}{3}\right)$

106. $\left(-\frac{3}{2}, \infty\right)$ **107.** 21, 23, and 25

108. 9 and 65   **109.** 7 centimeters by 12 centimeters

110. 13 nickels, 39 dimes, and 36 quarters

111. $20   **112.** 20 gallons

113. Rosie is 14 and her mother is 33.

114. $350 at 9% and $450 at 12%   **115.** 95 or better

116. $10\frac{10}{11}$ minutes   **117.** $26\frac{2}{3}$ minutes

118. 40 shares at $15 per share

119. 54 miles per hour for Mike and 52 miles per hour for Larry

120. Cindy in 4 hours and Bill in 6 hours

CHAPTER 2

Problem Set 2.1 (page 107)

1. 10   **3.** -5 **5.** 6   **7.** 15   **9.** 7

11. $\frac{1}{3}$ **13.** -7 **15.** $(3, 5)$ **17.** $(2, 5)$

19. $\left(\frac{17}{8}, -7\right)$ **21.** 10; $(6, 4)$; $\frac{3}{4}$

23. $\sqrt{13}$; $\left(2, -\frac{5}{2}\right)$; $-\frac{3}{2}$ **25.** $3\sqrt{2}$; $\left(\frac{15}{2}, -\frac{11}{2}\right)$; -1

27. $\frac{\sqrt{74}}{6}$; $\left(\frac{1}{12}, \frac{11}{12}\right)$; $-\frac{7}{5}$ **29.** $\left(4, \frac{25}{4}\right)$ **31.** $x = -2$

33. Answers will vary   **35.** $15 + 9\sqrt{5}$

37. $(8, 9)$, $(-12, 1)$, or $(4, -3)$ **45. (a)** 105.6 feet

47. 1.0 feet

Problem Set 2.2 (page 118)

1.   **3.**

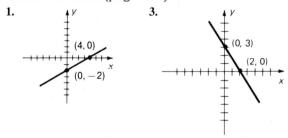

5.

(5, 0)
(0, −4)

7.
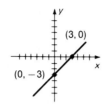
(3, 0)
(0, −3)

9.
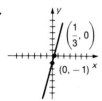
$\left(\frac{1}{3}, 0\right)$
(0, −1)

11.
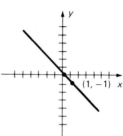
(1, −1)

13. The graph is the y-axis.

15.
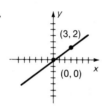
(3, 2)
(0, 0)

17. $x - 3y = -10$　　**19.** $2x + 3y = -1$
21. $5x - 7y = -11$　　**23.** $5x + 6y = 37$
25. $y = -3$　　**27.** $3x + 7y = 14$
29. $8x - 2y = -3$　　**31.** $5x - 4y = 20$
33. $x = -4$　　**35.** $5x + 2y = 14$
37. $4x + y = -2$
39. Parallel　　**41.** Perpendicular
43. Intersecting lines that are not perpendicular
45. Perpendicular　　**47.** $m = \frac{1}{2}$ and $b = -\frac{7}{2}$
49. $m = -3$ and $b = 0$
51. $x - y = -7$, $x + 5y = -19$, $2x + y = 16$
53. $9x + 8y = -2$, $6x - 7y = 11$, $15x + y = 9$

55. $\dfrac{2\sqrt{5}}{5}$ units

57. (a)
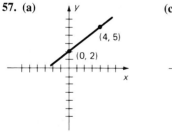
(4, 5)
(0, 2)

(c)
(−5, 5)
(0, 1)

(e)
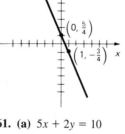
$\left(0, \frac{5}{4}\right)$
$\left(1, -\frac{3}{4}\right)$

59.
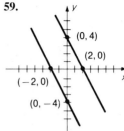
(0, 4)
(2, 0)
(−2, 0)
(0, −4)

61. (a) $5x + 2y = 10$　　**(c)** $2x - 3y = 12$

Problem Set 2.3 (page 131)
1. $\{(-4, 2)\}$　　**3.** $\{(5, 5)\}$　　**5.** $\{(12, -24)\}$
7. $\{(200, 800)\}$　　**9.** $\{(k, 5k - 9)\}$　　**11.** $\left\{\left(-\frac{1}{2}, \frac{1}{3}\right)\right\}$
13. $\left\{\left(\frac{13}{22}, \frac{2}{11}\right)\right\}$　　**15.** $\{(3, 1, 2)\}$　　**17.** $\{(-1, 3, 5)\}$
19. $\{(-2, -1, 3)\}$　　**21.** $\{(0, 2, 4)\}$
23. $\{(4, -1, -2)\}$　　**25.** $\{(-4, 0, -1)\}$
27. $\{(2, 2, -3)$
29. 8 single rooms and 15 double rooms
31. 2500 student tickets and 500 nonstudent tickets
33. \$500 at 9% and \$1500 at 11%
35. \$1.25 per tennis ball and \$1.75 per golf ball
37. 7 nickels, 13 dimes, and 22 quarters
39. 40°, 60°, and 80°
41. \$500 at 12%, \$1000 at 13%, and \$1500 at 14%
43. 50 of type A, 75 of type B, and 150 of type C
51. $\{(4, 6)\}$　　**53.** $\{(2, -3)\}$　　**55.** $\left\{\left(\frac{1}{4}, -\frac{2}{3}\right)\right\}$
57. $\{(-3, 5)\}$　　**59.** $\{(2, 12)\}$　　**61.** $\{(4.2, 7.1)\}$
63. $\{(.4, 3)\}$　　**65.** $\{(18, 32)\}$

Problem Set 2.4 (page 141)
1. $x^2 + y^2 - 4x - 6y - 12 = 0$
3. $x^2 + y^2 + 2x + 10y + 17 = 0$
5. $x^2 + y^2 - 6x = 0$　　**7.** $x^2 + y^2 = 49$
9. $x^2 + y^2 + 6x - 8y + 9 = 0$ and
$$x^2 + y^2 + 6x + 8y + 9 = 0$$
11. $x^2 + y^2 + 12x + 12y + 36 = 0$
13. $x^2 + y^2 - 8x + 4\sqrt{3}y + 12 = 0$ and
$$x^2 + y^2 - 8x - 4\sqrt{3}y + 12 = 0$$
15. $(3, 5)$, $r = 2$　　**17.** $(-5, -7)$, $r = 1$
19. $(5, 0)$, $r = 5$　　**21.** $(0, 0)$, $r = 2\sqrt{2}$
23. $\left(\frac{1}{2}, 1\right)$, $r = 2$　　**25.** $6x + 5y = 29$
27. $x^2 + y^2 + 6x + 8y = 0$
29. $x^2 + y^2 - 4x - 4y + 4 = 0$ and
$$x^2 + y^2 + 20x - 20y + 100 = 0$$
31. $x + 2y = 7$　　**33.** $x^2 + y^2 + 12x + 2y - 21 = 0$

Problem Set 2.5 (page 150)

1. $(4, -3)$; $(-4, 3)$; $(-4, -3)$
3. $(-6, 1)$; $(6, -1)$; $(6, 1)$
5. $(0, -4)$; $(0, 4)$; $(0, -4)$ **7.** y-axis   **9.** x-axis
11. x-axis, y-axis, and origin   **13.** None
15. Origin   **17.** None   **19.** y-axis

21.

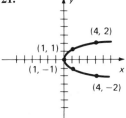

23.

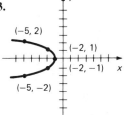

25.

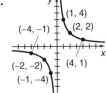

27.

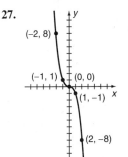

29.

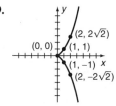

31.

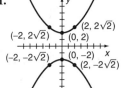

33.

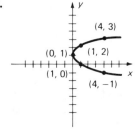

35.

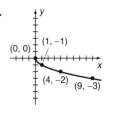

37.

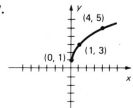

39.

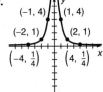

41.

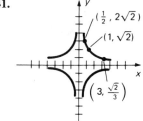

43.

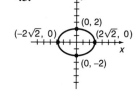

45.

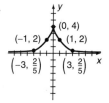

Chapter 2 Review Problem Set (page 154)

1. 5   **2.** -5 **3.** $\left(9, \frac{1}{3}\right)$ **4.** $(-2, 6)$

7. $2\sqrt{34}$; $(1, 1)$ **8.** $-\frac{9}{10}$ **9.** $\frac{2}{7}$

10. $3x + 4y = 29$ **11.** $2x - y = -4$
12. $5x + 6y = -36$ **13.** $7x - 5y = -35$
14. $4x + 3y = -4$ **15.** $x + 2y = 3$
16. $x^2 + y^2 - 10x + 12y + 60 = 0$
17. $x^2 + y^2 - 4x - 6y - 4 = 0$
18. $x^2 + y^2 + 10x - 24y = 0$
19. $x^2 + y^2 + 8x + 8y + 16 = 0$
20. $x^2 + y^2 - 8x - 6y = 0$ **21.** x-axis
22. None   **23.** x-axis, y-axis, and origin
24. y-axis   **25.** Origin   **26.** y-axis

27.

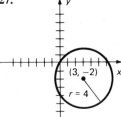

28.

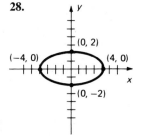

29.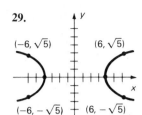

30.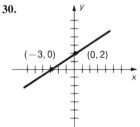

31.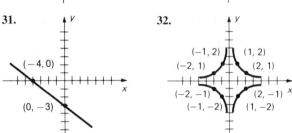

32.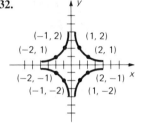

33.

34.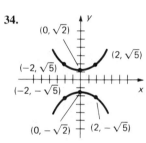

35.

36.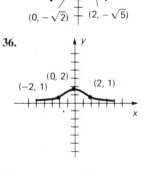

37.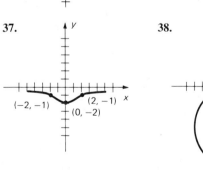

38.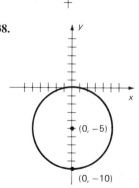

39.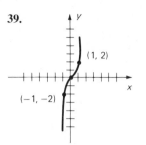

40.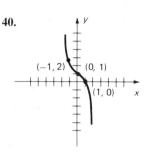

41. $\{(3, -7)\}$ **42.** $\{(-1, -3)\}$ **43.** $\{(4, -6)\}$

44. $\left\{\left(-\frac{6}{7}, -\frac{15}{7}\right)\right\}$ **45.** $\{(-1, 2, -5)\}$

46. $\{(2, -3, -1)\}$ **47.** 72

48. \$900 at 10% and \$1600 at 12%

49. 20 nickels, 32 dimes, and 54 quarters

50. 25°, 45°, and 110°

CHAPTER 3

Problem Set 3.1 (page 166)

1. $f(3) = -1$; $f(5) = -5$; $f(-2) = 9$

3. $g(3) = -20$; $g(-1) = -8$; $g(-4) = -41$

5. $h(3) = \frac{5}{4}$; $h(4) = \frac{23}{12}$; $h\left(-\frac{1}{2}\right) = -\frac{13}{12}$

7. $f(5) = 3$; $f\left(\frac{1}{2}\right) = 0$; $f(23) = 3\sqrt{5}$

9. $f(2) = 8$; $f(6) = 20$; $f(-1) = -6$; $f(-4) = -21$

11. $f(3) = 10$; $f(6) = -1$; $f(0) = 1$; $f(-3) = 2$

13. -6 **15.** $4a + 2h$ **17.** $6a + 3h - 1$

19. $-2a - h - 4$ **21.** $3a^2 + 3ah + h^2$

23. $3a^2 + 3ah + h^2 - 2a - h + 2$

25. $-\dfrac{1}{(a + 1)(a + h + 1)}$ **27.** $\dfrac{1}{(a + 1)(a + h + 1)}$

29. Yes   **31.** No   **33.** Yes   **35.** No

37. $D = \{x \,|\, x \geq 0\}$
$R = \{f(x) \,|\, f(x) \geq 0\}$

39. $D = \{x \,|\, x$ is any real number$\}$
$R = \{f(x) \,|\, f(x) \geq 1\}$

41. The domain and the range each consists of the set of all real numbers.

43. $D = \{x \,|\, x$ is any real number$\}$
$R = \{f(x) \,|\, f(x)$ is any nonnegative real number$\}$

45. $D = \{x \,|\, x \neq 4\}$ **47.** $D = \{x \,|\, x \neq 2$ and $x \neq -3\}$

49. $D = \left\{x \,|\, x \geq -\frac{1}{5}\right\}$

51. $D = \{x \,|\, x \neq -2$ and $x \neq -3\}$

53. $D = \{x \,|\, x \neq 0$ and $x \neq -4\}$

55. $(-\infty, -1] \cup [1, \infty)$ **57.** $(-\infty, \infty)$

59. $(-\infty, -4] \cup [6, \infty)$ **61.** $\left(-\infty, -\frac{3}{4}\right] \cup \left[\frac{2}{3}, \infty\right)$

63. Even   **65.** Even   **67.** Neither   **69.** Odd
71. Odd   **73.** -1500; 600; 1000; 900
75. 97.3; 93.9; 55.8   **77.** $74; $98; $122; $258
79. 8; $4\sqrt{3}$; 0

Problem Set 3.2 (page 180)

1.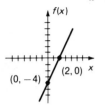

3.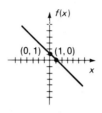

5.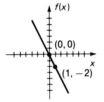

7.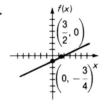

9.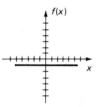

11.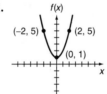

13.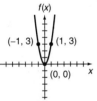

15.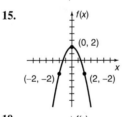

17.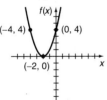

19.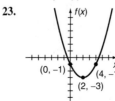

21.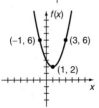

23.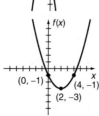

25.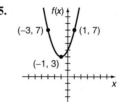

27.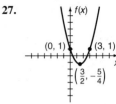

29.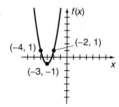

31.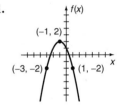

33.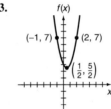

35.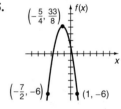

37.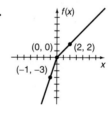

39.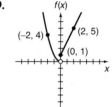

41.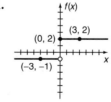

43.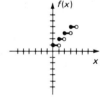

45.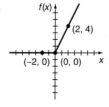

47.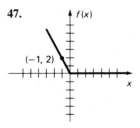

49.

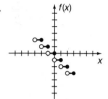

51.

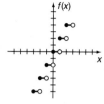

21. 3 and 5; minimum value of -1
23. 6 and 8; minimum value of -2
25. 4 and 6; maximum value of 1
27. $7 \pm \sqrt{5}$; minimum value of -5
29. No x-intercepts; maximum value of $-\frac{3}{4}$
31. $\dfrac{1 \pm \sqrt{5}}{2}$; maximum value of 5

33. 70   **35.** 144   **37.** 25 and 25
39. 60 meters by 60 meters
41. 1100 subscribers at \$13.75 per month
43. **(a)** Vertex at $(1, 11)$, opens upward
    (c) Vertex at $(-6, 8)$, opens upward
    (e) Vertex at $(12, 11)$, opens upward
    (g) Vertex at $(-2, -15)$, opens upward

Problem Set 3.3 (page 189)

1.

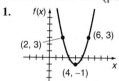

3.

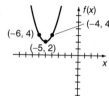

Problem Set 3.4 (page 200)

1.

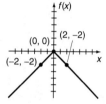

3.

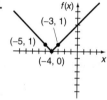

5.

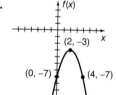

7.

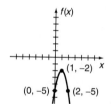

5.

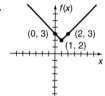

7.

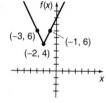

9.

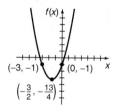

11.

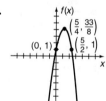

9.

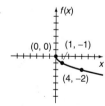

11.

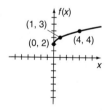

13.

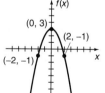

15.

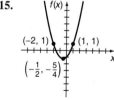

13.

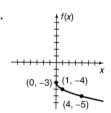

15.

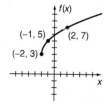

17.

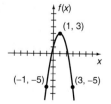

19.

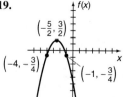

17.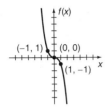

19.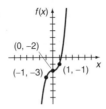

21.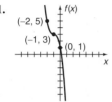

23.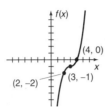

25.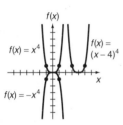

27.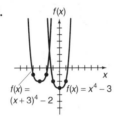

Problem Set 3.5 (page 207)

1. $8x - 2$; $-2x - 6$; $15x^2 - 14x - 8$; $\dfrac{3x - 4}{5x + 2}$

3. $x^2 - 7x + 3$; $x^2 - 5x + 5$; $-x^3 + 5x^2 + 2x - 4$;
$\dfrac{x^2 - 6x + 4}{-x - 1}$

5. $2x^2 + 3x - 6$; $-5x + 4$; $x^4 + 3x^3 - 10x^2 + x + 5$;
$\dfrac{x^2 - x - 1}{x^2 + 4x - 5}$

7. $\sqrt{x - 1} + \sqrt{x}$; $\sqrt{x - 1} - \sqrt{x}$; $\sqrt{x^2 - x}$; $\dfrac{\sqrt{x(x - 1)}}{x}$

9. $(f \circ g)(x) = 6x - 2$, $D = \{\text{all reals}\}$
$(g \circ f)(x) = 6x - 1$, $D = \{\text{all reals}\}$

11. $(f \circ g)(x) = 10x + 2$, $D = \{\text{all reals}\}$
$(g \circ f)(x) = 10x - 5$, $D = \{\text{all reals}\}$

13. $(f \circ g)(x) = 3x^2 + 7$, $D = \{\text{all reals}\}$
$(g \circ f)(x) = 9x^2 + 24x + 17$, $D = \{\text{all reals}\}$

15. $(f \circ g)(x) = 3x^2 + 9x - 16$, $D = \{\text{all reals}\}$
$(g \circ f)(x) = 9x^2 - 15x$, $D = \{\text{all reals}\}$

17. $(f \circ g)(x) = \dfrac{1}{2x + 7}$, $D = \left\{x \mid x \neq -\frac{7}{2}\right\}$

$(g \circ f)(x) = \dfrac{7x + 2}{x}$, $D = \{x \mid x \neq 0\}$

19. $(f \circ g)(x) = \sqrt{3x - 3}$, $D = \{x \mid x \geq 1\}$
$(g \circ f)(x) = 3\sqrt{x - 2} - 1$, $D = \{x \mid x \geq 2\}$

21. $(f \circ g)(x) = \dfrac{x}{2 - x}$, $D = \{x \mid x \neq 0 \text{ and } x \neq 2\}$

$(g \circ f)(x) = 2x - 2$, $D = \{x \mid x \neq 1\}$

23. 4; 50   **25.** 9; 0   **27.** $\sqrt{11}$; 5

35. $g(x) = 3x - 1$ and $f(x) = \sqrt[3]{x}$

37. $g(x) = 5x - 1$ and $f(x) = \dfrac{-2}{x}$

39. $g(x) = 3x - 1$ and $f(x) = x^{2/3}$

Problem Set 3.6 (page 218)

1. Yes   **3.** No   **5.** Yes
7. Yes   **9.** Yes   **11.** No   **13.** No
15. Domain of f: $\{1, 2, 5\}$
Range of f: $\{5, 9, 21\}$
$f^{-1} = \{(5, 1), (9, 2), (21, 5)\}$
Domain of f^{-1}: $\{5, 9, 21\}$
Range of f^{-1}: $\{1, 2, 5\}$

17. Domain of f: $\{0, 2, -1, -2\}$
Range of f: $\{0, 8, -1, -8\}$
$f^{-1} = \{(0, 0), (8, 2), (-1, -1), (-8, -2)\}$
Domain of f^{-1}: $\{0, 8, -1, -8\}$
Range of f^{-1}: $\{0, 2, -1, -2\}$

27. No   **29.** Yes   **31.** No   **33.** Yes

35. Yes   **37.** $f^{-1}(x) = x + 4$

39. $f^{-1}(x) = \dfrac{-x - 4}{3}$

41. $f^{-1}(x) = \dfrac{12x + 10}{9}$ **43.** $f^{-1}(x) = -\frac{3}{2}x$

45. $f^{-1}(x) = x^2$ for $x \geq 0$
47. $f^{-1}(x) = \sqrt{x - 4}$ for $x \geq 4$
49. $f^{-1}(x) = \frac{1}{3}x$ **51.** $f^{-1}(x) = \dfrac{x - 1}{2}$

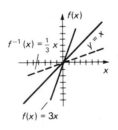

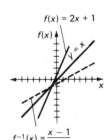

53. $f^{-1}(x) = \dfrac{x + 2}{x}$ for $x > 0$

$f^{-1}(x) = \dfrac{x + 2}{x}$

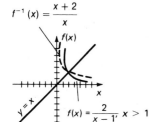

$y = x$

$f(x) = \dfrac{2}{x - 1}, \ x > 1$

55. $f^{-1}(x) = \sqrt{x + 4}$ for $x \geq -4$

$f^{-1}(x) = \sqrt{x + 4}$

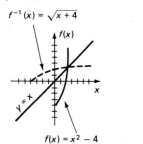

$y = x$

$f(x) = x^2 - 4$

57. Increasing on $[0, \infty)$ and decreasing on $(-\infty, 0]$
59. Decreasing on $(-\infty, \infty)$
61. Increasing on $(-\infty, -2]$ and decreasing on $[-2, \infty)$
63. Increasing on $(-\infty, -4]$ and decreasing on $[-4, \infty)$
69. (a) $f^{-1}(x) = \dfrac{x + 9}{3}$ **(c)** $f^{-1}(x) = -x + 1$

(e) $f^{-1}(x) = -\dfrac{1}{5}x$

Chapter 3 Review Problem Set (page 224)
1. (a) 7; 4; 32   **(b)** 14; 6; -10
2. (a) -5 **(b)** $4a + 2h - 1$
(c) $-6a - 3h + 2$
3. The domain is the set of all real numbers and the range is the set of real numbers greater than or equal to 5.
4. The domain is the set of all real numbers except $\frac{1}{2}$ and -4.
5. $(-\infty, 2] \cup [5, \infty)$
6.

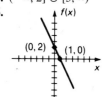

$(0, 2)$ $(1, 0)$

7.

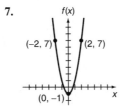

$(-2, 7)$ $(2, 7)$

$(0, -1)$

8.

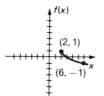

$(2, 1)$

$(6, -1)$

9.

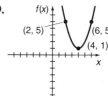

$(2, 5)$ $(6, 5)$

$(4, 1)$

10.

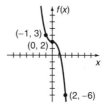

$(-1, 3)$

$(0, 2)$

$(2, -6)$

11.

$(0, 5)$ $(2, 5)$

$(1, 3)$

12.

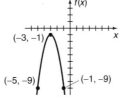

$(-3, -1)$

$(-5, -9)$ $(-1, -9)$

13.

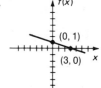

$(0, 1)$

$(3, 0)$

14.

$\left(-4, -\frac{1}{8}\right)$ $\left(4, -\frac{1}{8}\right)$

$(-1, -2)$ $(1, -2)$

$\left(-\frac{1}{2}, -8\right)$ $\left(\frac{1}{2}, -8\right)$

15.

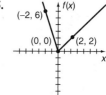

$(-2, 6)$

$(0, 0)$ $(2, 2)$

16. $x^2 - 2x$; $-x^2 + 6x + 6$; $2x^3 - 5x^2 - 18x - 9$;

$\dfrac{2x + 3}{x^2 - 4x - 3}$

17. $(f \circ g)(x) = -6x + 12$, $D = \{\text{all reals}\}$
$(g \circ f)(x) = -6x + 25$, $D = \{\text{all reals}\}$
18. $(f \circ g)(x) = 25x^2 - 40x + 11$, $D = \{\text{all reals}\}$
$(g \circ f)(x) = 5x^2 - 29$, $D = \{\text{all reals}\}$
19. $(f \circ g)(x) = \sqrt{x - 3}$, $D = \{x \mid x \geq 3\}$
$(g \circ f)(x) = \sqrt{x - 5} + 2$, $D = \{x \mid x \geq 5\}$
20. $(f \circ g)(x) = \dfrac{x + 2}{-3x - 5}$,

$D = \left\{x \mid x \neq -2 \text{ and } x \neq -\frac{5}{3}\right\}$

$(g \circ f)(x) = \dfrac{x - 3}{2x - 5}$, $D = \left\{x \mid x \neq 3 \text{ and } x \neq \frac{5}{2}\right\}$

21. 1; 5
22. The domain of f equals the range of g, and the range

of f equals the domain of g. Furthermore, $(f \circ g)(x) = x$
and $(g \circ f)(x) = x$.
23. Yes   **24.** No   **25.** Yes   **26.** Yes
27. $f^{-1}(x) = \dfrac{x - 5}{4}$ **28.** $f^{-1}(x) = \dfrac{-x - 7}{3}$
29. $f^{-1}(x) = \dfrac{6x + 2}{5}$ **30.** $f^{-1}(x) = \sqrt{-2 - x}$

31. 112 students
32. (a) Neither   **(b)** Odd   **(c)** Even   **33.** 14
34. 5   **35.** $g(x) = 5x - 2$ and $f(x) = \sqrt{x}$
36. Increasing on $(-\infty, 4]$ and decreasing on $[4, \infty)$.
37. Increasing on $[3, \infty)$

CHAPTER 4

Problem Set 4.1 (page 237)

1. $\frac{6}{7}$ **3.** 5   **5.** 4   **7.** .3   **9.** .2

11. $6\sqrt{2}$ **13.** $-6\sqrt{11}$ **15.** $\dfrac{3\sqrt{5}}{2}$

17. $2x\sqrt{3}$ **19.** $8x^2y^3\sqrt{y}$ **21.** $\dfrac{9y^3\sqrt{5x}}{7}$

23. $4\sqrt[3]{2}$ **25.** $2x\sqrt[3]{2x}$ **27.** $2x\sqrt[4]{3x}$
29. $\dfrac{2\sqrt{3}}{5}$ **31.** $\dfrac{\sqrt{14}}{4}$ **33.** $\dfrac{4\sqrt{15}}{5}$ **35.** $\dfrac{3\sqrt{2}}{7}$
37. $\dfrac{\sqrt{15}}{6x^2}$ **39.** $\dfrac{2\sqrt{15a}}{5ab}$ **41.** $\dfrac{3\sqrt[3]{2}}{2}$
43. $\dfrac{\sqrt[3]{18x^2y}}{3x}$ **45.** $12\sqrt{3}$ **47.** $3\sqrt{7}$
49. $\dfrac{11\sqrt{3}}{6}$ **51.** $-\dfrac{89\sqrt{2}}{30}$ **53.** $48\sqrt{6}$
55. $10\sqrt{6} + 8\sqrt{30}$ **57.** $3x\sqrt{6y} - 6\sqrt{2xy}$
59. $13 + 7\sqrt{3}$ **61.** $30 + 11\sqrt{6}$ **63.** $3\sqrt{5} - 6$
65. $\dfrac{-2\sqrt{10} + 3\sqrt{14}}{43}$ **67.** $\dfrac{x - \sqrt{xy}}{x - y}$
69. $\dfrac{6x + 7\sqrt{xy} + 2y}{9x - 4y}$ **71.** $\dfrac{1}{\sqrt{x - 1 + h} + \sqrt{x - 1}}$
73. $\dfrac{2}{\sqrt{2(x + h) - 1} + \sqrt{2x - 1}}$ **75.** $\{6\}$
77. $\{3\}$ **79.** $\varnothing$ **81.** $\{-15\}$ **83.** $\left\{\frac{2}{3}, 1\right\}$
85. $\{5\}$ **87.** $\{-2, -1\}$ **89.** $\{0\}$ **91.** $\{6\}$
93. $\{0, 4\}$ **99.** 3, $\dfrac{-3 + 3i\sqrt{3}}{2}$, and $\dfrac{-3 - 3i\sqrt{3}}{2}$

Problem Set 4.2 (page 245)

1. 7   **3.** 8   **5.** -4 **7.** 2   **9.** 64
11. .001   **13.** $\frac{1}{32}$ **15.** 2   **17.** $15x^{7/12}$
19. $y^{5/12}$ **21.** $64x^{3/4}y^{3/2}$ **23.** $4x^{4/15}$
25. $\dfrac{7}{a^{1/12}}$ **27.** $\dfrac{16x^{4/3}}{81y}$ **29.** $\dfrac{y^{3/2}}{x}$
31. $8a^{9/2}x^2$ **33.** $\sqrt[4]{8}$
35. $\sqrt[12]{x^7}$ **37.** $xy\sqrt[4]{xy^3}$
39. $a\sqrt[12]{a^5b^{11}}$ **41.** $4\sqrt[6]{2}$ **43.** $\sqrt[6]{2}$
45. $\sqrt{2}$ **47.** $x\sqrt[12]{x^7}$ **49.** $\dfrac{5\sqrt[3]{x^2}}{x}$
51. $\dfrac{\sqrt[6]{x^3y^4}}{y}$ **53.** $\dfrac{\sqrt[20]{x^{15}y^8}}{y}$ **55.** $\dfrac{5\sqrt[12]{x^9y^8}}{4x}$
57. $\sqrt[6]{2}$ **59.** $\sqrt{x}$ **61.** $\sqrt[9]{x^2}$
63. $\sqrt[8]{x^5}$ **65.** $\{3\}$ **67.** $\{3\}$ **69.** $\{4\}$
71. $\{2\}$ **73.** $\{-2\}$ **75.** $\left\{\frac{5}{3}\right\}$ **77.** $\left\{\frac{3}{2}\right\}$
79. $\left\{\frac{4}{9}\right\}$ **81.** $\left\{\frac{4}{3}\right\}$ **83.** $\left\{\frac{2}{3}\right\}$
85. (a) 12   **(c)** 7   **(e)** 11
87. (a) 1024   **(c)** 512   **(e)** 49
89. $\dfrac{x + 2}{(x + 1)^{3/2}}$ **91.** $\dfrac{6x^2 + 2x}{(4x + 1)^{3/2}}$ **93.** $\dfrac{2x}{(3x)^{4/3}}$

Problem Set 4.3 (page 259)

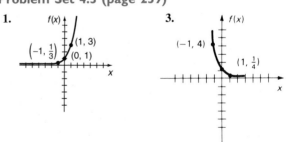

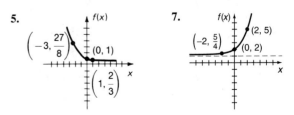

9.

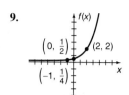

11.

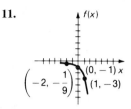

13.

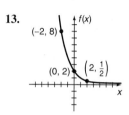

15.

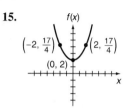

17.

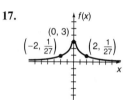

19.

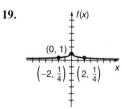

21.

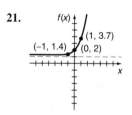

23.

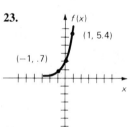

25.

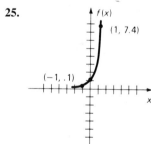

27. (a) \$.61   **(c)** \$2.02   **(e)** \$10,689
(g) \$636
29. \$384.66   **31.** \$480.31   **33.** \$2479.35
35. \$1816.70   **37.** \$1356.59   **39.** \$567.63
41. \$1422.36   **43.** \$8963.38   **45.** \$17547.35
47. \$32558.88   **49.** 5.9%   **51.** 8.06%
53. 8.25% compounded quarterly
55. 50 grams; 37 grams   **57.** 2226; 3320; 7389

59. 2000
61. (a) 6.5 pounds per square inch
(c) 13.6 pounds per square inch
67.

	1 yr	5 yrs	10 yrs	20 yrs
Compounded annually	\$1120	1762	3106	9646
Compounded semiannually	1124	1791	3207	10286
Compounded quarterly	1126	1806	3262	10641
Compounded monthly	1127	1817	3300	10893
Compounded continuously	1127	1822	3320	11023

69.

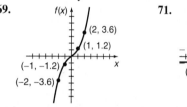

71.

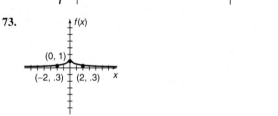

73.

Problem Set 4.4 (page 270)

1. $\log_3 9 = 2$ **3.** $\log_5 125 = 3$ **5.** $\log_2\left(\frac{1}{16}\right) = -4$
7. $\log_{10}.01 = -2$ **9.** $2^6 = 64$ **11.** $10^{-1} = .1$
13. $2^{-4} = \frac{1}{16}$ **15.** 2   **17.** -1 **19.** 1
21. $\frac{1}{2}$ **23.** $\frac{1}{2}$ **25.** $-\frac{1}{8}$ **27.** 7   **29.** 0
31. $\{25\}$ **33.** $\{32\}$ **35.** $\{9\}$ **37.** $\{1\}$
39. 5.1293   **41.** 6.9657   **43.** 1.4037
45. 7.4512   **47.** 6.3219   **49.** $-.3791$
51. .5766   **53.** 2.1531   **55.** .3949
57. $\log_b x + \log_b y + \log_b z$ **59.** $2\log_b x + 3\log_b y$
61. $\frac{1}{2}\log_b x + \frac{1}{2}\log_b y$ **63.** $\frac{1}{2}\log_b x - \frac{1}{2}\log_b y$
65. $\log_b\left(\dfrac{xy}{z}\right)$ **67.** $\log_b\left(\dfrac{x}{yz}\right)$ **69.** $\log_b(x\sqrt{y})$
71. $\log_b\left(\dfrac{x^2\sqrt{x-1}}{(2x+5)^4}\right)$ **73.** $\left\{\frac{9}{4}\right\}$ **75.** $\left\{\frac{7}{5}\right\}$

77. $\{4\}$ **79.** $\left\{\frac{19}{8}\right\}$ **81.** $\{9\}$ **83.** $\{1\}$

Problem Set 4.5 (page 280)

1. .6931   **3.** 3.0634   **5.** 6.0210
7. -1.1394 **9.** -2.6381 **11.** -7.1309
13. .9754   **15.** 1.5393   **17.** 3.6741
19. $-.2132$ **21.** -2.3279 **23.** 4.802
25. 24.996   **27.** .467   **29.** .033   **31.** 16.573
33. 3246.385   **35.** .072

37.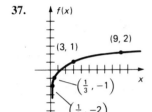

39.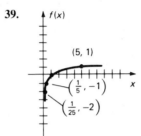

41.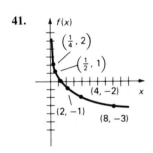

43.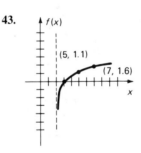

45.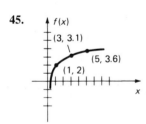

47.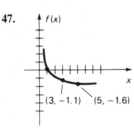

49.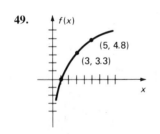

51.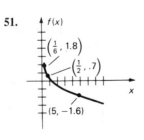

53.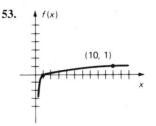

55.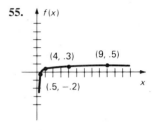

57.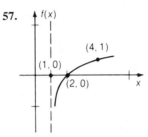

59.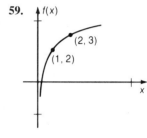

61. Same graph as Problem 41   **63.** $\{2\}$
65. $\left\{\frac{29}{8}\right\}$ **67.** $\left\{\dfrac{-1 + \sqrt{65}}{2}\right\}$ **69.** $\{\sqrt{2}\}$
71. $\{6\}$ **73.** $\{1, 100\}$

Problem Set 4.6 (page 289)

1. $\{3.17\}$ **3.** $\{1.95\}$ **5.** $\{1.81\}$ **7.** $\{1.41\}$
9. $\{1.41\}$ **11.** $\{3.10\}$ **13.** $\{1.82\}$
15. $\{7.84\}$ **17.** $\{10.32\}$ **19.** 2.4022
21. .4610   **23.** 2.6571   **25.** 1.2114
27. 7.9 years   **29.** 12.2 years   **31.** 11.8%
33. 6.6 years   **35.** 1.5 hours   **37.** 34.7 years
39. 6.7   **41.** Approximately 8 times
51. $x = \ln(y + \sqrt{y^2 + 1})$

Chapter 4 Review Problem Set (page 293)

1. 32   **2.** -125 **3.** 81   **4.** 3   **5.** -2
6. $\frac{1}{3}$ **7.** $\frac{1}{4}$ **8.** -5 **9.** 1   **10.** 12
11. $20\sqrt{3}$ **12.** $6x\sqrt{6x}$ **13.** $2xy\sqrt[3]{4xy^2}$
14. $\sqrt{3}$ **15.** $\dfrac{\sqrt{10x}}{2y}$ **16.** $-\dfrac{3(\sqrt{2} - 5)}{23}$
17. $\dfrac{24 - 4\sqrt{6}}{15}$ **18.** $\dfrac{3x + 6\sqrt{xy}}{x - 4y}$ **19.** $\sqrt[6]{5^5}$
20. $\sqrt[12]{x^{11}}$ **21.** $x^2\sqrt[6]{x^5}$ **22.** $x\sqrt[10]{xy^9}$
23. $\sqrt[6]{5}$ **24.** $\dfrac{\sqrt[12]{x^{11}}}{x}$ **25.** $12x^2y$
26. $-30x^{7/6}$ **27.** $\dfrac{48}{a^{1/6}}$ **28.** $\dfrac{27y^{3/5}}{x^2}$

29. $\dfrac{4y^5}{x^5}$ **30.** $\dfrac{8y}{x^{7/12}}$ **31.** $\dfrac{16x^6}{y^6}$

32. $-\dfrac{a^3b}{3}$ **33.** $\{5\}$ **34.** $\left\{\dfrac{1}{9}\right\}$ **35.** $\left\{\dfrac{7}{2}\right\}$

36. $\{3.40\}$ **37.** $\{8\}$

38. $\left\{\dfrac{1}{11}\right\}$ **39.** $\{1.95\}$ **40.** $\{1.41\}$

41. $\{1.56\}$ **42.** $\{20\}$ **43.** $\{10^{100}\}$

44. $\{2\}$ **45.** $\left\{\dfrac{11}{2}\right\}$ **46.** $\{0\}$ **47.** $\{2\}$

48. $\left\{-1, \dfrac{1}{2}\right\}$ **49.** $\{0\}$ **50.** $.3680$

51. 1.3222 **52.** 1.4313 **53.** $.5634$

54. (a) $\log_b x - 2\log_b y$ (b) $\frac{1}{4}\log_b x + \frac{1}{2}\log_b y$

 (c) $\frac{1}{2}\log_b x - 3\log_b y$

55. (a) $\log_b x^3 y^2$ (b) $\log_b\left(\dfrac{\sqrt{y}}{x^4}\right)$

 (c) $\log_b\left(\dfrac{\sqrt{xy}}{z^2}\right)$

56. 1.5850 **57.** $.6309$ **58.** 3.7887
59. -2.1203

60.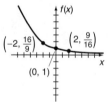

61.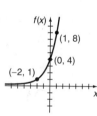

62.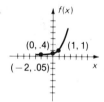

63.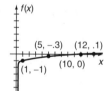

64.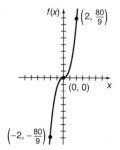

65.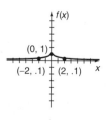

66.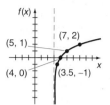

67.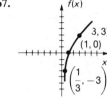

68.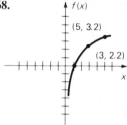

69.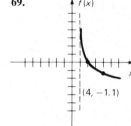

70. $\$2219.91$ **71.** $\$4797.55$ **72.** $\$15999.31$
73. 5.3 years **74.** 12.1 years **75.** 8.7%
76. $61070; 67493; 74591$ **77.** 4.8 hours
78. 133 grams **79.** 8.1

CHAPTER 5

Problem Set 5.1 (page 305)

1. Q: $x^2 + 2x - 4$ **3.** Q: $3x - 4$
 R: 0 R: $3x - 1$

5. Q: $3x + 4y$ **7.** Q: $x^2 + x$ **9** Q: $3x + 4$
 R: 0 R: -1 R: 0

11. Q: $x^2 - 1$ **13.** Q: $3x^3 - 4x^2 + 6x - 13$
 R: 0 R: 12

15. Q: $x^2 - 2x - 3$ **17.** Q: $x^2 + 3x + 2$
 R: 0 R: 0

19. Q: $x^4 + x^3 + x^2 + x + 1$
 R: 0

21. Q: $x^4 + x^3 + x^2 + x + 1$
 R: 2

23. Q: $2x^2 + 2x - 3$

 R: $\dfrac{9}{2}$

25. Q: $4x^3 + 2x^2 - 4x - 2$
 R: 0

27. $f(-1) = -2$ **29.** $f(-2) = 9$ **31.** $f(6) = 74$
33. $f(-1) = 5$ **35.** $f(7) = -5$

37. $f(-2) = -27$ **39.** $f\left(\frac{1}{2}\right) = -2$ **41.** Yes

43. Yes **45.** No **47.** Yes **49.** Yes
51. $(x + 2)(x + 6)(x - 1)$
53. $(x - 3)(2x - 1)(3x + 2)$

55. $(x + 1)^2(x - 4)$ **57.** $k = 6$ **59.** $k = -30$

61. Let $f(x) = x^{12} - 4096$; then $f(-2) = 0$; therefore, $x + 2$ is a factor of $f(x)$.

63. Let $f(x) = x^n - 1$. Since $1^n = 1$ for all positive integral values of n, then $f(1) = 0$ and $x - 1$ is a factor.

65. (a) Let $f(x) = x^n - y^n$. Therefore, $f(y) = y^n - y^n = 0$ and $x - y$ is a factor of $f(x)$.
     (c) Let $f(x) = x^n + y^n$. Therefore, $f(-y) = (-y)^n + y^n = -y^n + y^n = 0$ when n is odd, and $x - (-y) = x + y$ is a factor of $f(x)$.

69. $f(1 + i) = 2 + 6i$

71.
$$2i \overline{\smash{)}\begin{array}{cccccc} 1 & 0 & 6 & 0 & 8 \\ & 2i & -4 & 4i & -8 \\ \hline 1 & 2i & 2 & 4i & 0 \end{array}}$$
Therefore, $(x - 2i)$ is a factor of $x^4 + 6x^2 + 8$.

73. (a) $f(4) = 137$; $f(-5) = 11$; $f(7) = 575$
     (c) $f(4) = -79$; $f(5) = -162$; $f(-3) = 110$

Problem Set 5.2 (page 318)

1. $\{-2, -1, 2\}$ **3.** $\left\{-\frac{3}{2}, \frac{1}{3}, 1\right\}$ **5.** $\left\{-7, \frac{2}{3}, 2\right\}$

7. $\{-1, 4\}$ **9.** $\{-3, 1, 2, 4\}$ **11.** $\{-2, 1 \pm \sqrt{7}\}$

13. $\left\{-\frac{2}{3}, 1, \pm\sqrt{2}\right\}$ **15.** $\left\{-\frac{4}{3}, 0, \frac{1}{2}, 3\right\}$

17. $\{-1, 2, 1 \pm i\}$ **19.** $\left\{-1, \frac{3}{2}, 2, \pm i\right\}$

27. (a) $\{-4, -2, 1\}$ (c) $\left\{-4, -2, \frac{3}{2}\right\}$

29. 2 positives or 2 nonreal complex solutions

31. 1 negative and 2 nonreal complex solutions

33. 1 positive and 2 negative
     or
     1 positive and 2 nonreal complex solutions

35. 1 negative and 2 positive and 2 nonreal complex solutions or
     1 negative and 4 nonreal complex solutions

37. 1 positive and 1 negative and 4 nonreal complex solutions

39. $x^4 + 2x^3 - 9x^2 - 2x + 8 = 0$

41. $12x^3 - 37x^2 - 3x + 18 = 0$

43. $x^4 + 12x^3 + 54x^2 + 108x + 81 = 0$

45. $x^3 + 13x + 34 = 0$

47. $x^4 + 4x^3 + 14x^2 + 4x + 13 = 0$

53. (a) An upper bound of 3 and a lower bound of -1
     (c) An upper bound of 3 and a lower bound of -6
     (e) An upper bound of 5 and a lower bound of -3

55. (a) 1 negative and 2 positive solutions
     (c) 4 nonreal complex solutions

     (e) 1 negative, 1 positive, and 2 nonreal complex solutions
     (g) 1 negative and 3 positive solutions

Problem Set 5.3 (page 328)

1. 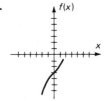   **3.**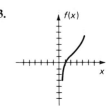

5. 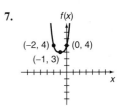   **7.**

9. 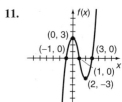   **11.**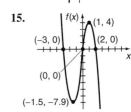

13. 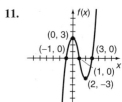   **15.**

17. 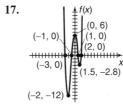   **19.**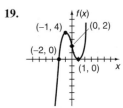

21. 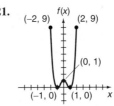   **23.**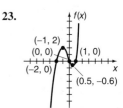

25.

(-

2

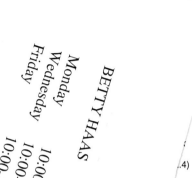

.4)

, 5)
∞)

2, ∞)

∪ (4, ∞)
2)

45. (a) 1.6
51. (a) −2, 1, and 4; ƒ(. . . . . 1) ∪ (4, ∞) and
     $f(x) < 0$ for $(-\infty, -2) \cup$
   (c) 2 and 3; $f(x) > 0$ for $(3, \infty)$ and $f(x) < 0$ for
     $(2, 3) \cup (-\infty, 2)$
   (e) −3, −1, and 2; $f(x) > 0$ for $(-\infty, -3) \cup (2, \infty)$
     and $f(x) < 0$ for $(-3, -1) \cup (-1, 2)$
53. (a) −3.3; (.5, 3.1), (−1.9, 10.1)
   (c) −2.2, 2.2; (−1.4, −8.0), (0.0, −4.0), (1.4, 8.0)
55. 32 units

Problem Set 5.4 (page 340)

1.

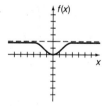

3.

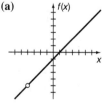

5.

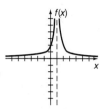

7.

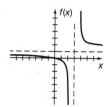

9.

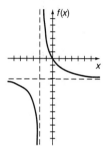

11.

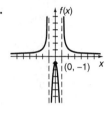

13.

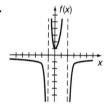

15.

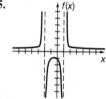

17.

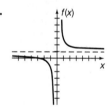

19.

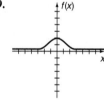

21.

23. (a)

23. (c)

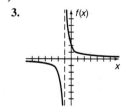

Problem Set 5.5 (page 349)

1.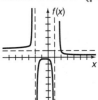

3.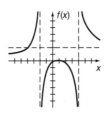

5.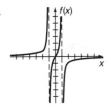

7.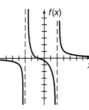

9.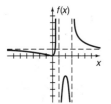

11.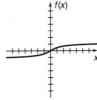

13.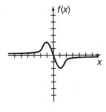

15.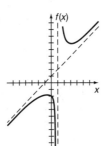

17.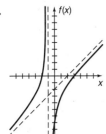

19.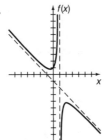

5. $\dfrac{1}{3x-1}+\dfrac{6}{2x+3}$　　　**7.** $\dfrac{2}{x-1}+\dfrac{3}{x+2}-\dfrac{4}{x-3}$

9. $\dfrac{-1}{x}+\dfrac{2}{2x-1}-\dfrac{3}{4x+1}$　　　**11.** $\dfrac{2}{x-2}+\dfrac{5}{(x-2)^2}$

13. $\dfrac{4}{x}+\dfrac{7}{x^2}-\dfrac{10}{x+3}$　　　**15.** $\dfrac{-3}{x^2+1}-\dfrac{2}{x-4}$

17. $\dfrac{3}{x+2}-\dfrac{2}{(x+2)^2}+\dfrac{1}{(x+2)^3}$

19. $\dfrac{2}{x}+\dfrac{3x+5}{x^2-x+3}$　　　**21.** $\dfrac{2x}{x^2+1}+\dfrac{3-x}{(x^2+1)^2}$

Chapter 5 Review Problem Set (page 357)

1. $Q:\ 3x^2-5x+4$　　　**2.** $Q:\ 2a-1$
　　$R:\ 4$　　　　　　　　　$R:\ 5$
3. $Q:\ 3x^2-x+5$　　　**4.** $Q:\ 5x^2-3x-3$
　　$R:\ 3$　　　　　　　　　$R:\ 16$
5. $Q:\ -2x^3+9x^2-38x+151$
　　$R:\ -605$
6. $Q:\ -3x^3-9x^2-32x-96$　　　**7.** $f(1)=1$
　　$R:\ -279$
8. $f(-3)=-197$　　　**9.** $f(-2)=20$　　　**10.** $f(8)=0$
11. Yes　　　**12.** No　　　**13.** Yes　　　**14.** Yes
15. $\{-3,1,5\}$　　　**16.** $\left\{-\frac{7}{2},-1,\frac{5}{4}\right\}$
17. $\{1,2,1\pm5i\}$　　　**18.** $\{-2,3\pm\sqrt{7}\}$
19. 2 positives and 2 negatives
　　or
　　2 positives and 2 nonreal complexes
　　or
　　2 negatives and 2 nonreal complexes
　　or
　　4 nonreal complex solutions
20. 1 negative and 4 nonreal complex solutions
21. $2x^3-x^2-13x-6=0$
22. $x^4-5x^3+6x^2+4x-8=0$
23. $x^3+2x^2+29x+148=0$
24.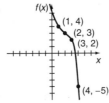

25.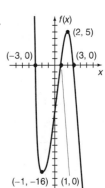

Problem Set 5.6 (page 355)

1. $\dfrac{4}{x-2}+\dfrac{7}{x+1}$　　　**3.** $\dfrac{3}{x+1}-\dfrac{5}{x-1}$

26.

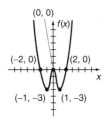

27.

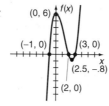

16. $f(9) = 33$ **17.** $3x^4 + 9x^3 + 2x^2 - x - 2$

18. No   **19.** 5.64   **20.** $(-3, 2)$ and $r = 3$

21. $x + 3y = 2$ **22.** $4x + 3y = 5$ **23.** $\{(-2, 9)\}$

24. $\{(2, -4, -1)\}$ **25.** 12   **26.** $\frac{2}{7}$ **27.** \$784

28. 8.7 years

29. 10 nickels, 15 dimes, and 32 quarters   **30.** \$125

31. $1\frac{1}{3}$ quarts   **32.** 45 miles   **33.** 4 hours

34. $\left\{\frac{3}{5}\right\}$ **35.** $\left\{\dfrac{-13 \pm \sqrt{193}}{2}\right\}$ **36.** $\{-7, 0, 2\}$

37. $\left\{-\frac{5}{2}, -1, \frac{2}{3}\right\}$ **38.** $\left\{-1, \frac{5}{2}\right\}$ **39.** $\{0\}$

40. $\{-1\}$ **41.** $\left\{\frac{2}{3}\right\}$ **42.** $\{3\}$

43. $\{\pm 3i, \pm \sqrt{6}\}$ **44.** $\left\{-\frac{13}{2}, 4\right\}$

45. $\left\{1, 2, \dfrac{-1 \pm i\sqrt{11}}{2}\right\}$ **46.** $(-\infty, -5)$

47. $\left[-\frac{11}{17}, \infty\right)$ **48.** $(-3, 6)$ **49.** $[-3, 1] \cup [2, \infty)$

50. $\left(-\infty, -\frac{5}{2}\right) \cup \left(\frac{7}{2}, \infty\right)$ **51.** $\left[-\frac{10}{3}, 2\right]$

52. $\left(-\infty, \frac{3}{4}\right] \cup (2, \infty)$ **53.** $(-\infty, 4) \cup \left(\frac{15}{2}, \infty\right)$

28.

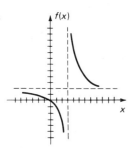

29.

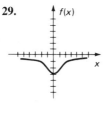

30.

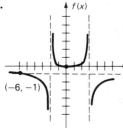

31.

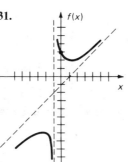

54.

55.

56.

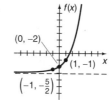

57.

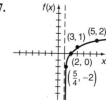

32. $\dfrac{1}{x} - \dfrac{2}{x^2} + \dfrac{4}{x + 2}$ **33.** $\dfrac{3x + 1}{x^2 + 4} - \dfrac{5}{2x - 1}$

Chapters 1–5 Cumulative Review Problem Set (page 358)

1. $\frac{64}{27}$ **2.** $-\frac{2}{3}$ **3.** $-\frac{1}{25}$ **4.** 16   **5.** $\frac{1}{27}$

6. 3   **7.** -4 **8.** -5 **9.** 16   **10.** 3

11. $(-\infty, -6] \cup \left[\frac{1}{2}, \infty\right)$

12. $(f \circ g)(-2) = 26$ and $(g \circ f)(3) = 59$

13. $(f \circ g)(x) = -2x + 8$ and $D = \{x \mid x \neq 4\}$

     $(g \circ f)(x) = -\dfrac{x}{4x + 2}$ and $D = \left\{x \mid x \neq 0 \text{ and}\right.$

     $\left. x \neq -\frac{1}{2}\right\}$

14. $f^{-1}(x) = \dfrac{-x + 7}{2}$ **15.** $2a + h + 7$

58.

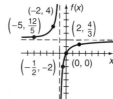

59.

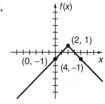

60.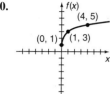

61.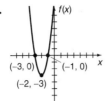

62.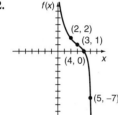

63.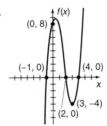

64.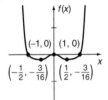

71. $\frac{\sqrt{2}}{2}$, $-\frac{\sqrt{2}}{2}$, -1, $\sqrt{2}$, $-\sqrt{2}$, -1

73. 0, -1, 0, undefined, -1, undefined

75. $\frac{\sqrt{2}}{2}$, $\frac{\sqrt{2}}{2}$, 1, $\sqrt{2}$, $\sqrt{2}$, 1

For Problems 77–93, the answers are given in the order of $\sin\theta$, $\cos\theta$, and $\tan\theta$.

77. $\frac{1}{2}$, $-\frac{\sqrt{3}}{2}$, $-\frac{\sqrt{3}}{3}$ **79.** $-\frac{1}{2}$, $-\frac{\sqrt{3}}{2}$, $\frac{\sqrt{3}}{3}$

81. $-\frac{1}{2}$, $\frac{\sqrt{3}}{2}$, $-\frac{\sqrt{3}}{3}$ **83.** $-\frac{\sqrt{3}}{2}$, $\frac{1}{2}$, $-\sqrt{3}$

85. $\frac{1}{2}$, $-\frac{\sqrt{3}}{2}$, $-\frac{\sqrt{3}}{3}$ **87.** $-\frac{\sqrt{2}}{2}$, $\frac{\sqrt{2}}{2}$, -1

89. $\frac{\sqrt{3}}{2}$, $-\frac{1}{2}$, $-\sqrt{3}$ **91.** $-\frac{\sqrt{3}}{2}$, $\frac{1}{2}$, $-\sqrt{3}$

93. $\frac{\sqrt{2}}{2}$, $-\frac{\sqrt{2}}{2}$, -1 **95.** $-\frac{\sqrt{2}}{2}$ **97.** -2

99. $\cos\theta = \frac{3}{5}$ and $\tan\theta = -\frac{4}{3}$

101. $\sin\theta = \frac{5}{13}$ and $\cos\theta = -\frac{12}{13}$ **103.** I or IV

105. I   **107.** $\theta = 225°$ **109.** $\theta = 120°$

111. $\theta = 240°$

117. **(a)** 3000π radians per minute; 9000π inches per minute

     (c) Approximately 616 revolutions per minute; approximately 3870 radians per minute

CHAPTER 6

Problem Set 6.1 (page 373)

1. $14.50°$ **3.** $22°18'$ **5.** $8.76°$

7. $45°19'12''$ **9.** $150.17°$ **11.** $9°7'48''$

13. $\frac{\pi}{18}$ **15.** $\frac{4\pi}{9}$ **17.** $\frac{5\pi}{6}$ **19.** $\frac{5\pi}{4}$

21. $-\frac{\pi}{6}$ **23.** $-\frac{19\pi}{6}$ **25.** $20°$ **27.** $130°$

29. $240°$ **31.** $390°$ **33.** $-45°$ **35.** $-210°$

37. $114.6°$ **39.** $401.1°$ **41.** $-229.2°$

43. $.5$ **45.** $.3$ **47.** -4.4 **49.** 46.1 inches

51. 17.9 centimeters   **53.** $127.2°$ **55.** $412.5°$

57. $630°$ **59.** 2.8 revolutions

For Problems 61–75, the answers are given in the order of $\sin\theta$, $\cos\theta$, $\tan\theta$, $\csc\theta$, $\sec\theta$, and $\cot\theta$.

61. $-\frac{4}{5}$, $-\frac{3}{5}$, $\frac{4}{3}$, $-\frac{5}{4}$, $-\frac{5}{3}$, $\frac{3}{4}$ **63.** $\frac{5}{13}$, $\frac{12}{13}$, $\frac{5}{12}$, $\frac{13}{5}$, $\frac{13}{12}$, $\frac{12}{5}$

65. $-\frac{\sqrt{2}}{2}$, $-\frac{\sqrt{2}}{2}$, 1, $-\sqrt{2}$, $-\sqrt{2}$, 1

67. $-\frac{2\sqrt{13}}{13}$, $\frac{3\sqrt{13}}{13}$, $-\frac{2}{3}$, $-\frac{\sqrt{13}}{2}$, $\frac{\sqrt{13}}{3}$, $-\frac{3}{2}$

69. $-\frac{3\sqrt{10}}{10}$, $\frac{\sqrt{10}}{10}$, -3, $-\frac{\sqrt{10}}{3}$, $\sqrt{10}$, $-\frac{1}{3}$

Problem Set 6.2 (page 382)

1. I   **3.** IV   **5.** III   **7.** II   **9.** $150°$

11. $240°$ **13.** $300°$ **15.** $240°$ **17.** $\frac{3\pi}{2}$

19. $\frac{7\pi}{6}$ **21.** $\frac{3\pi}{4}$ **23.** $85°$ **25.** $71.8°$

27. $73°$ **29.** $\frac{\pi}{4}$ **31.** $\frac{\pi}{3}$ **33.** $\frac{\pi}{3}$ **35.** $\frac{\sqrt{3}}{2}$

37. $-\frac{\sqrt{3}}{2}$ **39.** $-\sqrt{3}$ **41.** $\sqrt{2}$ **43.** 2

45. $-\frac{1}{2}$ **47.** $\frac{1}{2}$ **49.** $-\sqrt{3}$ **51.** -1

53. $\frac{\sqrt{2}}{2}$ **55.** $\frac{\sqrt{3}}{2}$ **57.** $\sqrt{3}$ **59.** $-\frac{\sqrt{2}}{2}$

61. $\frac{\sqrt{3}}{3}$ **63.** $\frac{1}{2}$ **65.** Undefined   **67.** $.9659$

69. 4.0108 **71.** $.8607$ **73.** $-.9135$

75. 1.0358 **77.** -3.9408 **79.** -1.6003

81. $-\frac{1}{2}$ **83.** $-\frac{2\sqrt{3}}{3}$ **85.** $-.1080$

87. -1.897 **89.** $.8902$ **91.** 2.1642

93. -1.4916

Problem Set 6.3 (page 394)

The answers for Problems 1–11 are given in the order $\sin s$, $\cos s$, $\tan s$, $\csc s$, $\sec s$, and $\cot s$.

1. $\frac{\sqrt{2}}{2}, -\frac{\sqrt{2}}{2}, -1, \sqrt{2}, -\sqrt{2}, -1$

3. $-1, 0,$ undefined, $-1,$ undefined, -1

5. $-\frac{\sqrt{2}}{2}, \frac{\sqrt{2}}{2}, -1, -\sqrt{2}, \sqrt{2}, -1$

7. $-\frac{\sqrt{3}}{2}, -\frac{1}{2}, \sqrt{3}, -\frac{2\sqrt{3}}{3}, -2, \frac{\sqrt{3}}{3}$

9. $1, 0,$ undefined, $1,$ undefined, 0

11. $-\frac{\sqrt{2}}{2}, -\frac{\sqrt{2}}{2}, 1, -\sqrt{2}, -\sqrt{2}, 1$

13.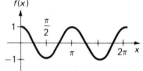

15.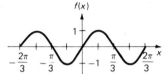

17.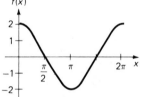

19.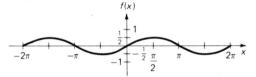

21.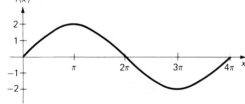

23.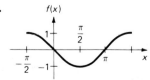

25.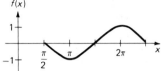

27.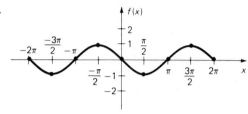

29.

31.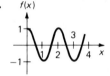

33.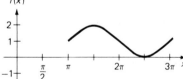

35.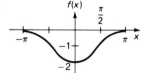

37.

39.

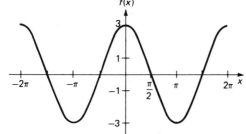

period: 2π
amplitude: 3
phase shift: $\pi/2$ to the left

41.

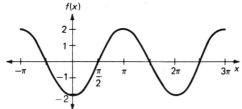

period: 2π
amplitude: 3
phase shift: π to the right

43.

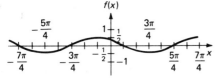

period: 2π
amplitude: 1/2
phase shift: $\pi/4$ to the left

45.

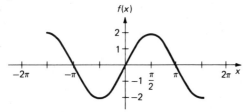

period: 2π
amplitude: 2
phase shift: π to the left

47.

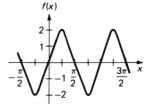

period: π
amplitude: 2
phase shift: π to the right

49.

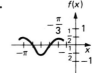

period: $2\pi/3$
amplitude: 1/2
phase shift: π to the
left

51.

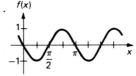

period: π
amplitude: 1
phase shift: $\pi/2$ to
the right

53.

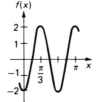

period: $2\pi/3$
amplitude: 2
phase shift: $\pi/3$ to
the right

55.

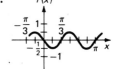

period: $2\pi/3$
amplitude: 1/2
phase shift: $\pi/3$ to
the right

57.

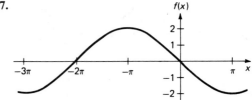

period: 4π
amplitude: 2
phase shift: π to the left

59.

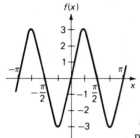

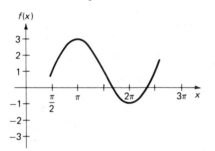

period: π
amplitude: 3
phase shift: $\pi/2$ to the left

61.

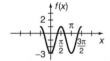

63.

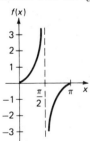

Problem Set 6.4 (page 402)

1.

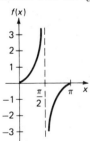

3.

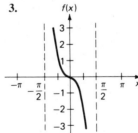

5.

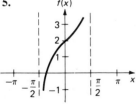

7.

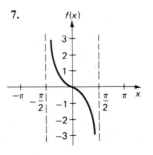

9.

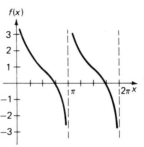

11.

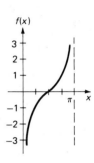

13.

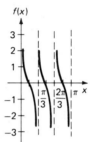

15.

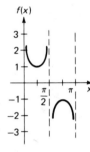

17.

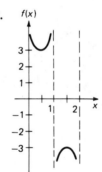

19.

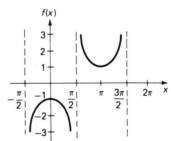

21.

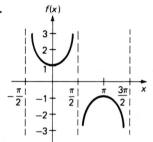

23.

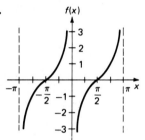

period: π
phase shift: $\pi/2$ to the left

25.

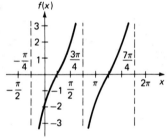

period: π
phase shift: $\pi/4$ to the right

27.

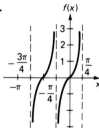

period: $\pi/2$
phase shift: $\pi/2$ to
the left

29.

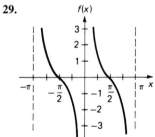

period: π
phase shift: $\pi/2$ to
the right

31.

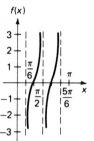

period: $\pi/3$
phase shift: $2\pi/3$ to the right

33.

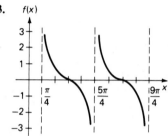

period: π
phase shift: $\pi/4$ to the right

35.

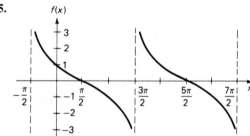

period: 2π
phase shift: $\pi/2$ to the left

37.

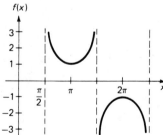

period: 2π
phase shift: $\pi/2$ to the right

39.

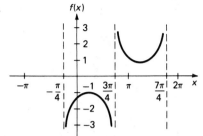

period: 2π

phase shift: $\pi/4$ to the left

41.

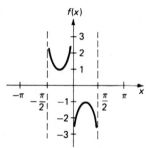

period: π

phase shift: $\pi/2$ to the left

43.

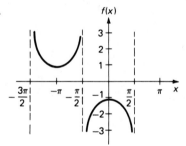

period: 2π

phase shift: π to the left

45.

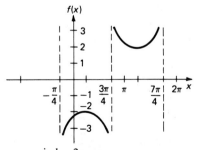

period: 2π

phase shift: $\pi/4$ to the right

Problem Set 6.5 (page 411)

1. $\frac{\pi}{4}$ **3.** $-\frac{\pi}{3}$ **5.** $\frac{\pi}{3}$ **7.** $\frac{\pi}{6}$ **9.** $\frac{\pi}{4}$

11. $\frac{\pi}{3}$ **13.** $-\frac{\pi}{2}$ **15.** $30°$ **17.** $135°$

19. $0°$ **21.** $-45°$ **23.** $.366$ **25.** -1.154

27. $.940$ **29.** 2.000 **31.** 1.455 **33.** $-.196$

35. $25.5°$ **37.** $-55.2°$ **39.** $74.7°$ **41.** $99.3°$

43. $86.0°$ **45.** $-83.1°$ **47.** $\frac{\sqrt{3}}{2}$ **49.** 0

51. 1 **53.** $\frac{\sqrt{3}}{2}$ **55.** $\frac{\sqrt{2}}{2}$ **57.** $\frac{3}{5}$ **59.** $\frac{3}{5}$

61. $-\frac{4}{3}$ **63.** $\frac{\sqrt{5}}{3}$ **65.** $-2\sqrt{2}$ **67.** $\frac{4\sqrt{7}}{7}$

69. $-\frac{3\sqrt{10}}{20}$

71.

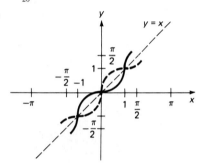

73.

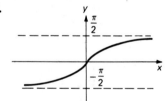

75.

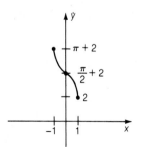

77.

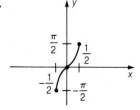

79.

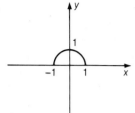

81.

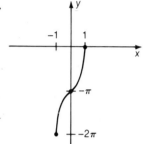

Problem Set 6.6 (page 421)

1. $\sec \theta = \dfrac{r}{x} = \dfrac{1}{\dfrac{x}{r}} = \cos \theta$ $\cot \theta = \dfrac{x}{y} = \dfrac{1}{\dfrac{y}{x}} = \dfrac{1}{\tan \theta}$

For Problems 3–11, the answers are arranged in the order $\sin \theta$, $\cos \theta$, $\tan \theta$, $\csc \theta$, $\sec \theta$, and $\cot \theta$ omitting the value given in the problem.

3. $\dfrac{3}{5}, \dfrac{4}{3}, \dfrac{5}{4}, \dfrac{5}{3}, \dfrac{3}{4}$ **5.** $-\dfrac{12}{13}, -\dfrac{5}{13}, -\dfrac{13}{12}, -\dfrac{13}{5}, \dfrac{5}{12}$

7. $-\dfrac{3}{5}, -\dfrac{4}{3}, \dfrac{5}{4}, -\dfrac{5}{3}, -\dfrac{3}{4}$

9. $-\dfrac{\sqrt{5}}{5}, \dfrac{2\sqrt{5}}{5}, -\sqrt{5}, \dfrac{\sqrt{5}}{2}, -2$

11. $\dfrac{2}{3}, -\dfrac{\sqrt{5}}{3}, -\dfrac{2\sqrt{5}}{5}, -\dfrac{3\sqrt{5}}{5}, -\dfrac{\sqrt{5}}{2}$ **13.** $\sin \theta$

15. $\cot x$ **17.** $-\tan^2 x$ **19.** 1 **21.** $\sec \theta$
23. $\cos x$

Problem Set 6.7 (page 428)

1. $60°$ and $120°$ **3.** $180°$ **5.** $120°$ and $300°$

7. $270°$ **9.** $\dfrac{4\pi}{3}$ and $\dfrac{5\pi}{3}$ **11.** 0

13. $\dfrac{\pi}{4}, \dfrac{7\pi}{6}, \dfrac{5\pi}{4}$, and $\dfrac{11\pi}{6}$ **15.** No solutions

17. $0, \pi, \dfrac{\pi}{6}, \dfrac{5\pi}{6}$ **19.** $0°, 45°, 180°, 225°$

21. $45°, 90°, 135°, 225°, 270°$, and $315°$

23. $\dfrac{2\pi}{3}, \pi$, and $\dfrac{4\pi}{3}$ **25.** $60°, 180°$, and $300°$

27. $\dfrac{\pi}{3}, \pi$, and $\dfrac{5\pi}{3}$ **29.** $0, \dfrac{\pi}{2}$, and $\dfrac{3\pi}{2}$ **31.** 0 and $\dfrac{\pi}{2}$

33. $\dfrac{\pi}{4}, \dfrac{3\pi}{4}, \dfrac{5\pi}{4}$, and $\dfrac{7\pi}{4}$

For Problems 35–45, n is an integer.

35. $30° + n \cdot 360°$ and $330° + n \cdot 360°$

37. $\dfrac{4\pi}{3} + 2\pi n$ and $\dfrac{5\pi}{3} + 2\pi n$ **39.** $\dfrac{3\pi}{4} + \pi n$

41. $60° + n \cdot 180°$ and $120° + n \cdot 180°$

43. $\dfrac{\pi}{4} + \pi n$ and $\dfrac{\pi}{2} + \pi n$

45. $\dfrac{\pi}{6} + 2\pi n$ and $\dfrac{5\pi}{6} + 2\pi n$ and $\dfrac{3\pi}{2} + 2\pi n$

(All of these can be represented by the one expression $\dfrac{\pi}{6} + \dfrac{2\pi n}{3}$.)

47. $347.5°$ and $192.5°$ **49.** $130.0°$ and $230.0°$
51. $287.7°$ and $107.7°$ **53.** $19.5°$ and $160.5°$
55. $48.2°$ and $311.8°$ **57.** $15.5°$ and $164.5°$
59. 3.93 and 5.49 **61.** 2.53 and 3.75
63. 2.23 and 5.37 **65.** $.25$ and 2.89
67. 3.74 and 5.68 **69.** $.90$ and 5.38 **75.** 7

Problem Set 6.8 (page 437)

1. $\dfrac{\sqrt{6} - \sqrt{2}}{4}$ **3.** $2 + \sqrt{3}$ **5.** $\dfrac{\sqrt{6} + \sqrt{2}}{4}$

7. $\dfrac{-\sqrt{6} - \sqrt{2}}{4}$ **9.** $2 + \sqrt{3}$ **11.** $\dfrac{\sqrt{6} + \sqrt{2}}{4}$

13. $\dfrac{\sqrt{6} + \sqrt{2}}{4}$ **15.** $-\dfrac{77}{85}; -\dfrac{13}{84}$ **17.** $-\dfrac{36}{85}, \dfrac{13}{85}$

19. $\dfrac{416}{425}; -\dfrac{87}{425}$ **21.** $\dfrac{4}{5}$ **23.** $-\dfrac{84}{13}$ **25.** $\dfrac{9\sqrt{10}}{170}$

43. **(a)** Conditional equation; 0 and 3.1
     (c) Identity   **(e)** Conditional equation; 1.9 and 4.3
     (g) Conditional equation; $0, 1.8, 3.1$, and 4.5

Problem Set 6.9 (page 446)

1. $\dfrac{24}{25}, \dfrac{7}{25}, \dfrac{24}{7}$ **3.** $-\dfrac{120}{169}, -\dfrac{119}{169}, \dfrac{120}{119}$

5. $-\dfrac{336}{625}, \dfrac{527}{625}, -\dfrac{336}{527}$ **7.** $\dfrac{4}{5}, \dfrac{3}{5}, \dfrac{4}{3}$ **9.** $\dfrac{\sqrt{2 - \sqrt{3}}}{2}$

11. $\sqrt{7 - 4\sqrt{3}}$ **13.** $1 - \sqrt{2}$ **15.** $\dfrac{\sqrt{2 - \sqrt{2}}}{2}$

17. $2 + \sqrt{3}$ **19.** $-\dfrac{\sqrt{2 - \sqrt{3}}}{2}$

21. $\dfrac{\sqrt{10}}{10}, \dfrac{3\sqrt{10}}{10}, \dfrac{1}{3}$ **23.** $\dfrac{2\sqrt{5}}{5}, -\dfrac{\sqrt{5}}{5}, -2$

25. $\dfrac{3\sqrt{13}}{13}, \dfrac{2\sqrt{13}}{13}, \dfrac{3}{2}$ **27.** $\dfrac{\sqrt{6}}{6}, -\dfrac{\sqrt{30}}{6}, -\dfrac{\sqrt{5}}{5}$

29. $0°, 60°, 180°$, and $300°$ **31.** $30°, 90°$, and $150°$
33. $90°$ and $270°$ **35.** $0°$ and $240°$
37. $0°, 30°, 90°, 150°, 180°, 210°, 270°$, and $330°$

39. $\frac{\pi}{6}, \frac{\pi}{2}, \frac{5\pi}{6},$ and $\frac{3\pi}{2}$ **41.** $\frac{7\pi}{6}, \frac{3\pi}{2},$ and $\frac{11\pi}{6}$

43. $0, \frac{\pi}{3},$ and $\frac{5\pi}{3}$ **45.** $\frac{\pi}{6}, \frac{\pi}{2}, \frac{5\pi}{6},$ and $\frac{3\pi}{2}$

47. $0, \frac{\pi}{2},$ and $\frac{3\pi}{2}$ **67.** $\cos 3\theta = 4\cos^3\theta - 3\cos\theta$

69. $\cos 6\theta = 32\cos^6\theta - 48\cos^4\theta + 18\cos^2\theta - 1$

73. $.9$ **75.** $-.5$

Problem Set 6.10 (page 451)

1. $\frac{1}{2}\sin 8\theta + \frac{1}{2}\sin 2\theta$ **3.** $\frac{1}{2}\sin 6\theta + \frac{1}{2}\sin 2\theta$

5. $\frac{1}{2}\cos\theta - \frac{1}{2}\cos 5\theta$ **7.** $\frac{1}{2}\cos 3x + \frac{1}{2}\cos x$

9. $\sin 12\theta + \sin 6\theta$ **11.** $\frac{3}{2}\sin 3x + \frac{3}{2}\sin x$

13. $2\cos 3\theta\cos\theta$ **15.** $2\sin 4\theta\cos\theta$

17. $2\cos 4x\sin 2x$ **19.** $-2\sin 5x\sin 2x$

21. $-2\cos 3\theta\sin\theta$ **23.** $2\cos 2\theta\cos\theta$

25. $\frac{\sqrt{6}}{2}$ **27.** $\frac{\sqrt{6}}{2}$ **29.** $-\frac{\sqrt{6}}{2}$ **31.** $\frac{1}{4}$

33. $\frac{1}{4}$ **35.** $0, \frac{\pi}{4}, \frac{3\pi}{4}, \pi, \frac{5\pi}{4},$ and $\frac{7\pi}{4}$

37. $0, \frac{\pi}{2}, \pi,$ and $\frac{3\pi}{2}$ **39.** $0, \frac{\pi}{6}, \frac{\pi}{2}, \frac{5\pi}{6}, \pi,$ and $\frac{3\pi}{2}$

49. (a) $0, \frac{\pi}{3}, \frac{\pi}{2}, \frac{2\pi}{3}, \pi, \frac{4\pi}{3}, \frac{3\pi}{2},$ and $\frac{5\pi}{3}$

 (c) $\frac{\pi}{6}, \frac{\pi}{2}, \frac{5\pi}{6}, \frac{7\pi}{6}, \frac{3\pi}{2},$ and $\frac{11\pi}{6}$

Chapter 6 Review Problem Set (page 456)

1. $35°$ and $55°$ **2.** $35.28°$ and $82.26°$

3. $93°21'$ and $163°16'12''$

4. (a) $\frac{7\pi}{3}$ **(b)** $\frac{19\pi}{6}$ **(c)** $-\frac{\pi}{4}$

5. (a) $210°$ **(b)** $-240°$ **(c)** $765°$

6. 71.2 centimeters **7.** 31.8 inches

8. $\frac{4}{5}, -\frac{3}{5}, -\frac{4}{3}$ **9.** $-\frac{3\sqrt{10}}{10}, \frac{\sqrt{10}}{10}, -3$

10. $-\frac{2\sqrt{5}}{5}, -\frac{\sqrt{5}}{5}, 2$ **11.** $-\frac{12}{13}, -\frac{5}{13}, \frac{12}{5}$

12. $-\frac{\sqrt{3}}{2}$ **13.** $\frac{1}{2}$ **14.** $\sqrt{2}$ **15.** -2

16. -1 **17.** $-\frac{\sqrt{3}}{3}$ **18.** $\frac{\sqrt{3}}{2}$ **19.** $\frac{1}{2}$

20. Undefined **21.** Undefined **22.** -1

23. 1 **24.** II **25.** IV **26.** -5 **27.** $\frac{12}{13}$

28. Period of 2π, amplitude of 4, phase shift of $\frac{\pi}{4}$ units to the left

29. Period of π, amplitude of 3, phase shift of $\frac{\pi}{3}$ units to the right

30. Period of $\frac{\pi}{2}$, no amplitude, phase shift of π units to the left

31. Period of $\frac{2\pi}{3}$, amplitude of 1, phase shift of $\frac{\pi}{3}$ units to the right

32. Period of 2, amplitude of 2, phase shift of 1 unit to the left

33. Period of 2, amplitude of 2, phase shift of $\frac{1}{2}$ unit to the right

34. Period of $\frac{2\pi}{3}$, amplitude of 4, no phase shift

35. Period of π, amplitude of 5, no phase shift

36. Period of $\frac{\pi}{3}$, no amplitude, phase shift of $\frac{\pi}{3}$ to the right

37. Period of $\frac{\pi}{4}$, no amplitude, phase shift of $\frac{\pi}{4}$ to the left

38. Period of $\frac{\pi}{2}$, no amplitude, phase shift of $\frac{\pi}{8}$ to the left

39. Period of $\frac{2\pi}{3}$, no amplitude, phase shift of $\frac{\pi}{12}$ to the right

40. Period of $\frac{2\pi}{3}$, no amplitude, phase shift of 2 to the right

41. Period of π, no amplitude, phase shift of $\frac{\pi}{2}$ to the right

42.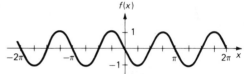

43.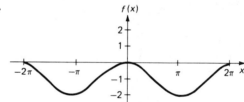

44.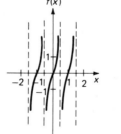

45.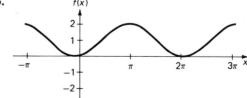

46.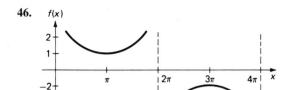

47.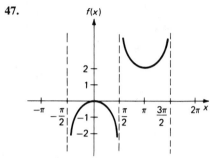

48.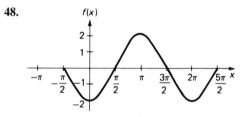

49.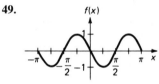

50.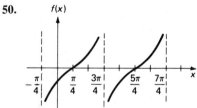

51.   **52.**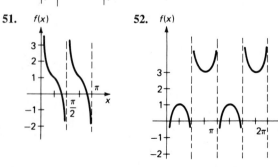

53.   **54.**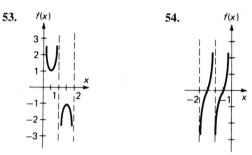

55.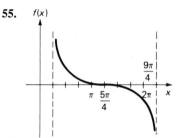

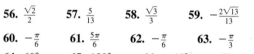

56. $\frac{\sqrt{2}}{2}$ **57.** $\frac{5}{13}$ **58.** $\frac{\sqrt{3}}{3}$ **59.** $-\frac{2\sqrt{13}}{13}$

60. $-\frac{\pi}{6}$ **61.** $\frac{5\pi}{6}$ **62.** $-\frac{\pi}{6}$ **63.** $-\frac{\pi}{3}$

64. $60°$ **65.** $120°$ **66.** $-45°$ **67.** $-30°$

68. 2.180 **69.** $-.807$ **70.** -1.557

71. 1.228 **72.** $75.6°$ **73.** $-24.2°$

74. $-83.8°$ **75.** $124.2°$ **76.** $-\frac{63}{65}, -\frac{56}{65}, \frac{63}{16}$

77. $-\frac{120}{169}, \frac{119}{169}, -\frac{120}{119}$ **78.** $\frac{\sqrt{10}}{10}, -\frac{3\sqrt{10}}{10}, -\frac{1}{3}$

79. $\frac{\sqrt{6} - \sqrt{2}}{4}$ or $\frac{\sqrt{2 - \sqrt{3}}}{2}$

80. $\frac{\sqrt{6} - \sqrt{2}}{4}$ or $\frac{\sqrt{2 - \sqrt{3}}}{2}$

81. $\frac{\sqrt{6} + \sqrt{2}}{4}$ or $\frac{\sqrt{2 + \sqrt{3}}}{2}$ **82.** $\sqrt{2} - 1$

83. $\frac{24}{25}$ **84.** $\frac{33}{56}$ **85.** $0°, 90°,$ and $180°$

86. $30°$ and $150°$ **87.** $30°$ and $150°$

88. $0°, 60°, 180°,$ and $300°$

89. $120°, 180°,$ and $240°$ **90.** $60°$ and $300°$

91. $0°$ and $240°$ **92.** $0°, 60°, 180°,$ and $300°$

93. $\frac{7\pi}{6}$ and $\frac{11\pi}{6}$ **94.** $\frac{\pi}{4}, \frac{\pi}{2}, \frac{3\pi}{4}, \frac{5\pi}{4},$ and $\frac{7\pi}{4}$

95. $\frac{\pi}{6}, \frac{\pi}{3}, \frac{5\pi}{6},$ and $\frac{5\pi}{3}$ **96.** $\frac{\pi}{8}, \frac{5\pi}{8}, \frac{9\pi}{8},$ and $\frac{13\pi}{8}$

97. $\frac{\pi}{3}$ **98.** $0, \frac{\pi}{2}, \pi,$ and $\frac{3\pi}{2}$

99. $2\pi n$, where n in an integer

100. $45° + n \cdot 180°, 210° + n \cdot 360°,$ and $330° + n \cdot 360°$
where n is an integer

101. 22.0° and 158.0°   **102.** 196.3° and 343.7°
103. .98, 1.81, 4.12, and 4.95   **104.** 2.24 and 4.04
121. $\frac{\sqrt{2}}{2}$ **122.** $\frac{1}{2}\cos 6x + \frac{1}{2}\cos 2x$

CHAPTER 7
Problem Set 7.1 (page 469)
1. $B = 53°$, $a = 11$, and $c = 18$
3. $A = 67°$, $a = 28$, and $c = 31$
5. $B = 23°$, $a = 24$, and $b = 10$
7. $c = 13$, $A = 23°$, and $B = 67°$
9. $a = 26$, $A = 66°$, and $B = 24°$
11. 23.0 feet   **13.** 92.1 meters   **15.** 1454 feet
17. 42 yards   **19.** 630 feet   **21.** 19.6 feet
23. 222 feet   **25.** 44.0°   **27.** 74 feet
29. 20 feet   **31.** 29.5°   **33.** 4043 miles
35. 71 feet   **37.** 3059 square yards

Problem Set 7.2 (page 476)
1. 9.6 centimeters   **3.** 12.3 feet
5. 39.9 centimeters   **7.** 94.7°   **9.** 28.8°
11. $A = 33.1°$, $B = 128.7°$, and $C = 18.2°$
13. $b = 56.2$ feet, $A = 45.9°$, and $C = 34.1°$
15. $C = 90°$ **17.** 87.1°   **19.** 421.5 miles
21. 63.7 feet   **23.** 203 feet   **25.** 24.9 feet
27. 308 feet
29. 56.2 centimeters and 35.9 centimeters

Problem Set 7.3 (page 483)
1. $c = 13.8$ centimeters   **3.** $a = 16.8$ meters
5. $B = 102°$ and $b = 20.9$ centimeters
7. $B = 31°$ and $b = 52.0$ miles
9. $A = 56.9°$ and $C = 51.4°$
11. $b = 34.6$ feet and $c = 18.8$ feet
13. 222 meters   **15.** 13.3 feet   **17.** 104.6 feet
19. 178.0 feet   **21.** 163.1 feet

Problem Set 7.4 (page 492)
1. One triangle; $C = 33.4°$
3. No triangle determined
5. Two triangles; $C = 52.2°$, $B = 99.8°$, and $b = 39.9$
     miles or $C = 127.8°$, $B = 24.2°$, and $b = 16.6$ miles
7. One triangle; $C = 90°$ and $b = 36.4$ centimeters
9. 118.9 square inches   **11.** 45.4 square meters
13. 421.4 square yards   **15.** 923.9 square inches
17. 168 meters or 43 meters   **19.** 158 square meters
21. 3059 square yards   **23.** 31 square inches
25. 1350 square yards   **27.** 140 square inches
29. 118 square centimeters

Problem Set 7.5 (page 500)
1.

3.

5.

7.

9.

11. 9.1° and 253.2 miles per hour
13. N75.5°E   **15.** 90.1 pounds and 33.7°
17. 35.3 kilometers per hour
19. 42.3 pounds and 15.4 pounds
21. 16.4 pounds and 11.5 pounds
23. 794.5 pounds   **25.** 44.0°
27. 334.0 kilograms and 28.4°
29. 93.4 miles and N71.5°W
31. 131.0 miles and N86.0°E

Problem Set 7.6 (page 507)
1. 5   **3.** 13   **5.** 5   **7.** $\sqrt{5}$ **9.** $\sqrt{13}$
11. 1   **13.** $2\sqrt{2}\left(\cos\frac{3\pi}{4} + i\sin\frac{3\pi}{4}\right)$
15. $3\left(\cos\frac{3\pi}{2} + i\sin\frac{3\pi}{2}\right)$ **17.** $4\left(\cos\frac{11\pi}{6} + i\sin\frac{11\pi}{6}\right)$
19. $\sqrt{2}\left(\cos\frac{5\pi}{4} + i\sin\frac{5\pi}{4}\right)$ **21.** $2\left(\cos\frac{2\pi}{3} + i\sin\frac{2\pi}{3}\right)$
23. $5\sqrt{2}(\cos 315° + i\sin 315°)$
25. $2(\cos 180° + i\sin 180°)$
27. $2(\cos 30° + i\sin 30°)$ **29.** $8(\cos 240° + i\sin 240°)$
31. $12(\cos 330° + i\sin 330°)$
33. $\sqrt{13}(\cos 56.3° + i\sin 56.3°)$
35. $\sqrt{5}(\cos 206.6° + i\sin 206.6°)$
37. $\sqrt{17}(\cos 346.0° + i\sin 346.0°)$
39. $2\sqrt{5}(\cos 116.6° + i\sin 116.6°)$
41. $2\sqrt{3} + 2i$ **43.** $-\frac{3\sqrt{2}}{2} - \frac{3\sqrt{2}}{2}i$

45. $-1 - \sqrt{3}i$ **47.** $\frac{1}{3} - \frac{\sqrt{3}}{3}i$ **49.** $6 + 0i$

51. $-4 - 4\sqrt{3}i$ **53.** $60 + 60\sqrt{3}i$

55. $\frac{3}{2} - \frac{3\sqrt{3}}{2}i$ **57.** $10\sqrt{3} - 10i$ **59.** $0 - 24i$

61. $20(\cos 75° + i \sin 75°)$ **63.** $6(\cos 70° + i \sin 70°)$

65. $35\left(\cos \frac{11\pi}{10} + i \sin \frac{11\pi}{10}\right)$ **71.** $-\frac{2}{3} - \frac{2}{3}i$

73. $0 + i$ **75.** $-\sqrt{3} - i$

Problem Set 7.7 (page 513)

1. $-1024 + 0i$ **3.** $0 - 32i$ **5.** $-972 - 972i$

7. $-8 + 8\sqrt{3}i$ **9.** $\frac{1}{2} - \frac{\sqrt{3}}{2}i$ **11.** $-\frac{\sqrt{2}}{2} - \frac{\sqrt{2}}{2}i$

13. $8 + 8\sqrt{3}i$ **15.** $-\frac{\sqrt{2}}{2} - \frac{\sqrt{2}}{2}i$

17. $2 + 0i, -1 + \sqrt{3}i,$ and $-1 - \sqrt{3}i$

19. $-2\sqrt{2} + 2\sqrt{2}i$ and $2\sqrt{2} - 2\sqrt{2}i$

21. $\sqrt{3} + i, -1 + \sqrt{3}i, -\sqrt{3} - i,$ and $1 - \sqrt{3}i$

23. $\sqrt[10]{2}(\cos \theta + i \sin \theta)$ where $\theta = 9°, 81°, 153°, 225°,$ and $297°$

25. $1 + 0i, \frac{1}{2} + \frac{\sqrt{3}}{2}i, -\frac{1}{2} + \frac{\sqrt{3}}{2}i, -1 + 0i, -\frac{1}{2} - \frac{\sqrt{3}}{2}i,$ and $\frac{1}{2} - \frac{\sqrt{3}}{2}i$

27. $\sqrt[3]{2}(\cos \theta + i \sin \theta)$ where $\theta = 40°, 160°,$ and $280°$

29. $\sqrt[5]{2}(\cos \theta + i \sin \theta)$ where $\theta = 27°, 99°, 171°, 243°,$ and $315°$

31. $\frac{3\sqrt{3}}{2} + \frac{3}{2}i$ and $-\frac{3\sqrt{3}}{2} - \frac{3}{2}i$ **33.** $\{\pm 2, \pm 2i\}$

35. $\{\sqrt{2} \pm \sqrt{2}i, -\sqrt{2} \pm \sqrt{2}i\}$

37. $(\cos \theta + i \sin \theta)$ where $\theta = 0°, 72°, 144°, 216°,$ and $288°$

39. $\{\pm i, \frac{\sqrt{3}}{2} \pm \frac{1}{2}i, -\frac{\sqrt{3}}{2} \pm \frac{1}{2}i\}$

Chapter 7 Review Problem Set (page 516)

1. $61.9°$ **2.** 42.5 feet   **3.** 135 feet

4. 28.4 miles   **5.** 132.0 yards   **6.** Two

7. 84.5 feet   **8.** $118.2°$; 1077 square yards

9. 518 miles   **10.** 257 yards   **11.** 83.3 feet

12. 64.7 square centimeters   **13.** 210 square inches

14. 34.5 pounds and 28.9 pounds   **15.** 1457.3 pounds

16. 286.4 pounds and $12.3°$

17. 149.2 miles and N46.1°W   **18.** $2\sqrt{5}$

19. $2\left(\cos \frac{11\pi}{6} + i \sin \frac{11\pi}{6}\right)$ **20.** $6(\cos 225° + i \sin 225°)$

21. $0 - 5i$ **22.** $4 - 4\sqrt{3}i$ **23.** $16 + 0i$

24. $-512 + 512\sqrt{3}i$ **25.** $\frac{\sqrt{2}}{2} + \frac{\sqrt{2}}{2}i$

26. $0 + 3i, -\frac{3\sqrt{3}}{2} - \frac{3}{2}i,$ and $\frac{3\sqrt{3}}{2} - \frac{3}{2}i$

27. $\frac{\sqrt{6}}{2} + \frac{\sqrt{2}}{2}i, -\frac{\sqrt{2}}{2} + \frac{\sqrt{6}}{2}i, -\frac{\sqrt{6}}{2} - \frac{\sqrt{2}}{2}i,$ and $\frac{\sqrt{2}}{2} - \frac{\sqrt{6}}{2}i$

28. $-2\sqrt{3} + 2i$ and $2\sqrt{3} - 2i$

Cumulative Review Problem Set (Chapters 6 and 7) (page 518)

1. $\frac{\sqrt{3}}{2}$ **2.** $\frac{\sqrt{3}}{2}$ **3.** 1   **4.** $-\frac{2\sqrt{3}}{3}$ **5.** $-\frac{2\sqrt{3}}{3}$

6. $\frac{\sqrt{3}}{3}$ **7.** $-\frac{\sqrt{3}}{2}$ **8.** $\frac{1}{2}$ **9.** $\frac{\sqrt{3}}{2}$ **10.** $\frac{1}{2}$

11. $\frac{4}{5}$ **12.** $-\frac{4}{3}$ **13.** $\frac{\sqrt{6} + \sqrt{2}}{4}$

14. $\frac{\sqrt{2 + \sqrt{2}}}{2}$ **15.** $\frac{56}{33}$ **16.** $\frac{33}{65}$ **17.** $-\frac{25}{24}$

18. $\sqrt{5}$ **19.** $30°$ and $150°$ **20.** $\frac{\pi}{4}$ and $\frac{5\pi}{4}$

21. $0, \frac{\pi}{6}, \frac{5\pi}{6},$ and π **22.** $0°$ **23.** $\frac{\pi}{3}, \pi,$ and $\frac{5\pi}{3}$

24. $\frac{2\pi}{3}$ and $\frac{4\pi}{3}$ **25.** $30°, 120°, 210°,$ and $300°$

26. $0°, 60°,$ and $300°$

27. $41.8°, 138.2°, 228.6°,$ and $311.4°$

28. .66 and 5.62   **29.** 80 feet   **30.** $33.7°$

31. $112.2°$; 102 square feet

32. 21.6 meters; 199 square meters

33. 41.4 centimeters; 563 square centimeters

34. 34 feet   **35.** 699 miles   **36.** 1352 pounds

37. None   **38.** 45.1 centimeters

39. $2\sqrt{10}$ **40.** $6\left(\cos \frac{5\pi}{3} + i \sin \frac{5\pi}{3}\right)$

41. $-6\sqrt{2} - 6\sqrt{2}i$ **42.** $0 + 8i$

43. $1 + \sqrt{3}i, -\sqrt{3} + i, -1 - \sqrt{3}i,$ and $\sqrt{3} - i$

44. Period of $\frac{2\pi}{3}$, amplitude of 2, and phase shift of $\frac{2\pi}{3}$ units to the right

45. Period of 2, amplitude of 1, and phase shift of 1 unit to the left

46. Period of π, phase shift of $\frac{\pi}{4}$ units to the left

47.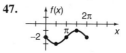

48.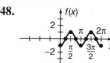

49.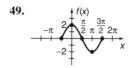

50.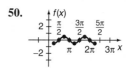

51.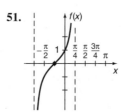

52.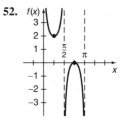

53. 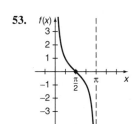　　**54.**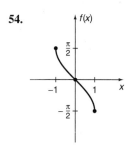

CHAPTER 8

Problem Set 8.1 (page 526)

1. 5　　**3.** $\sqrt{10}$　　**5.** $2\sqrt{10}$　　**7.** $2\sqrt{13}$
9. $\langle 4, 7\rangle$; $\langle -2, -3\rangle$; $\langle 15, 26\rangle$; $\langle -13, -21\rangle$
11. $\langle -5, 3\rangle$; $\langle 3, -9\rangle$; $\langle -16, 15\rangle$; $\langle -3, -36\rangle$
13. $\langle 3, -1\rangle$; $\langle 11, -1\rangle$; $\langle 5, -3\rangle$; $\langle 34, -2\rangle$
15. $\langle -5, -10\rangle$; $\langle -1, -2\rangle$; $\langle -17, -34\rangle$; $\langle 4, 8\rangle$
17. $\langle 2, 6\rangle$　　**19.** $\langle -4, 3\rangle$　　**21.** $\langle 0, 9\rangle$
23. $\langle 3, -6\rangle$　　**25.** 10　　**27.** 16　　**29.** 19
31. Yes　　**33.** No　　**35.** Yes　　**37.** 49.8°
39. 31.3°　　**41.** 157.4°　　**43.** 75.0°　　**45.** 102.5°

Problem Set 8.2 (page 535)

1. The line $2x + 3y = 13$
3. The line segment $3x - y = -7$ with endpoints at
　　$(-2, 1)$ and $(2, 13)$
5. The circle $x^2 + y^2 = 4$
7. The upper half of the circle $x^2 + y^2 = 1$
9. The parabola $y = x^2 + 2x + 3$
11. The portion of the parabola $y = x^2 - 4x + 8$ between
　　and including the points $(-1, 13)$ and $(4, 8)$
13. The ellipse $4x^2 + y^2 = 16$
15. The hyperbola $x^2 - 4y^2 = 4$
17. The right-hand branch of the hyperbola $x^2 - y^2 = 1$
19. The hyperbola $xy = 8$
21. The right-hand branch of the curve $x^2y = 1$
23.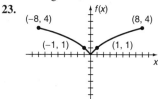

25.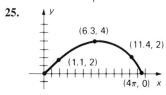

27.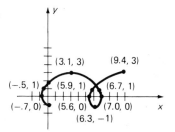

29. and 31. Answers may vary.
33. (a) $x = 24t$ and $y = 24\sqrt{3}t - 16t^2$
　　(c) $36\sqrt{3}$ feet　　**(e)** 27 feet
35. (a) $x = 50\sqrt{2}t$ and $y = 50\sqrt{2}t - 16t^2$
　　(c) 312.5 feet　　**(e)** 78.125 feet
39. The line segment $3x - y = -7$ with endpoints at
　　$(-2, 1)$ and $(2, 13)$
41. The portion of the parabola $y = x^2 - 4x + 8$ between
　　and including the points $(-1, 13)$ and $(4, 8)$
43. The circle $x^2 + y^2 = 4$
45. The hyperbola $x^2 - 4y^2 = 4$

Problem Set 8.3 (page 543)

The points in Problems 1, 3, 5, 7, 9, and 11 are located on
the following figure.

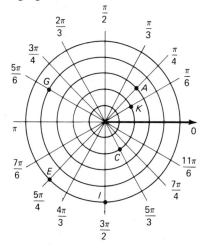

13. $\left(\frac{3\sqrt{3}}{2}, \frac{3}{2}\right)$　　**15.** $(2\sqrt{2}, 2\sqrt{2})$　　**17.** $(1, \sqrt{3})$

19. $\left(-\frac{3}{2}, -\frac{3\sqrt{3}}{2}\right)$　　**21.** $(-2, -2\sqrt{3})$

23. $\left(-\frac{1}{2}, -\frac{\sqrt{3}}{2}\right)$　　**25.** $\left(-\frac{7\sqrt{2}}{2}, -\frac{7\sqrt{2}}{2}\right)$　　**27.** $(\sqrt{3}, 1)$

29. $(0, -3)$　　**31.** $\left(2, \frac{3\pi}{4}\right)$　　**33.** $\left(5, \frac{7\pi}{6}\right)$

35. $\left(6, \frac{5\pi}{3}\right)$　　**37.** $(4, \pi)$　　**39.** $\left(3, \frac{\pi}{6}\right)$

41. $\left(-2, \frac{5\pi}{4}\right)$ **43.** $\left(-4, \frac{2\pi}{3}\right)$ **45.** $\left(-5, \frac{11\pi}{6}\right)$

47. $(\sqrt{13}, 33.7°)$ **49.** $(5, 143.1°)$

51. $(\sqrt{17}, 194.0°)$ **53.** $r \sin \theta = 2$

55. $r(3 \cos \theta - 2 \sin \theta) = 4$ **57.** $\tan \theta = 1$

59. $r = 8 \cos \theta$ **61.** $r = 1 - \cos \theta$

63. $r = 4 \tan \theta \sec \theta$ **65.** $y = -4$

67. $x^2 + y^2 - 3x = 0$ **69.** $x^2 + y^2 - 2x - 3y = 0$

71. $y + 4x = 5$ **73.** $3x^2 + 4y^2 + 8x - 16 = 0$

75. $x^2 + y^2 - 3y = 2\sqrt{x^2 + y^2}$

77.

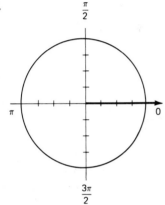

79.

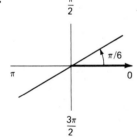

81.

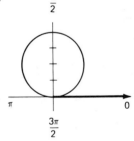

83.

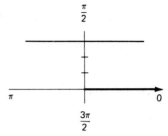

85.

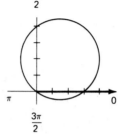

87.

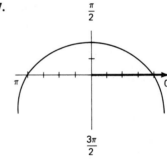

89.

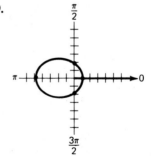

91.

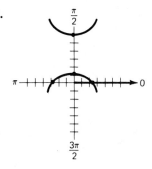

Problem Set 8.4 (page 551)

1. Polar axis **3.** $\frac{\pi}{2}$-axis **5.** Polar axis

7. $\frac{\pi}{2}$-axis **9.** None **11.** Polar axis

13. Polar axis **15.** Pole

17.

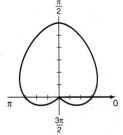

19.

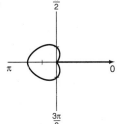

21.

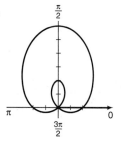

23.

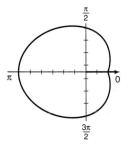

25.

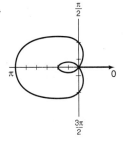

27.

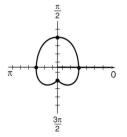

29.

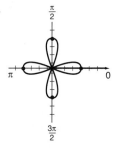

31.

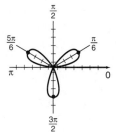

33.

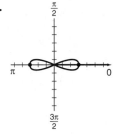

35.

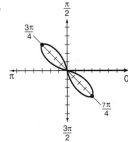

37.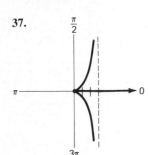

39.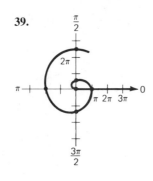

Problem Set 8.5 (page 558)

1. $\sqrt{17}$ **3.** $3\sqrt{5}$ **5.** $\sqrt{57}$
7. $x^2 - 4x + y^2 + 2y + z^2 - 8x + 17 = 0$
9. $x^2 + 2x + y^2 + 4y + z^2 + 6z + 5 = 0$
11. $(1, 2, 4)$, $r = 1$ **13.** $(-2, -3, 7)$, $r = 4$
15. $(-4, 0, 1)$, $r = 3\sqrt{2}$
17. $x^2 + 4x + y^2 + 6y + z^2 - 8z + 13 = 0$
19. 5   **21.** $\sqrt{17}$ **23.** 7
25. $\langle -7, -4, -11 \rangle$, $\langle 0, 5, 5 \rangle$, $\langle -2, 11, 9 \rangle$, $\sqrt{14}$
27. $\langle 14, 12, -12 \rangle$, $\langle 0, -1, 1 \rangle$, $\langle 4, 1, -1 \rangle$, $\sqrt{6}$
29. $\langle -13, -3, -2 \rangle$, $\langle 11, -5, -1 \rangle$, $\langle 23, -13, -3 \rangle$, $\sqrt{53}$
31. -16 **33.** -13 **35.** -3 **37.** 17
39. $5.2°$ **41.** $90.0°$ **43.** $57.6°$ **45.** $108.0°$

Problem Set 8.6 (page 564)

1. A plane parallel to the xz-plane intersecting the y-axis at $(0, 4, 0)$
3. A plane parallel to the yz-plane intersecting the x-axis at $(-2, 0, 0)$
5. A plane parallel to the y-axis intersecting the xz-plane in the line $2x - z = 6$
7. A plane having intercepts at $(6, 0, 0)$, $(0, -3, 0)$, and $(0, 0, -2)$
9. A plane having intercepts at $(3, 0, 0)$, $(0, -6, 0)$, and $(0, 0, 6)$
11. The graph is a cylindrical surface generated by parabolas of the form $y = z^2$ in planes parallel to the yz-plane.
13. The graph is a cylindrical surface generated by circles of the form $x^2 + y^2 = 4$ in planes parallel to the xy-plane.
15. The graph is a cylindrical surface generated by ellipses of the form $x^2 + 4y^2 = 4$ in planes parallel to the xy-plane.
17. The graph is a cylindrical surface generated by ellipses of the form $9y^2 + 4z^2 = 36$ in planes parallel to the yz-plane.

19. The graph is a cylindrical surface generated by exponential curves of the form $z = 2^y$ in planes parallel to the yz-plane.

21.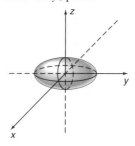

23.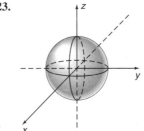

25.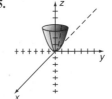

Chapter 8 Review Problem Set (page 567)

1. $3\sqrt{2}$ **2.** $2\sqrt{5}$ **3.** $\sqrt{26}$ **4.** $\sqrt{21}$
5. $\sqrt{14}$ **6.** $\sqrt{41}$
7. $\langle 2, -6 \rangle$, $\langle -25, -2 \rangle$, $\langle -9, 16 \rangle$
8. $\langle 2, 12 \rangle$, $\langle 24, 18 \rangle$, $\langle -2, -30 \rangle$
9. $\langle -6, 6, 0 \rangle$, $\langle 5, 2, -21 \rangle$, $\langle 17, -16, -3 \rangle$
10. $\langle -1, 5, 3 \rangle$, $\langle -19, 32, -13 \rangle$, $\langle 0, -9, -10 \rangle$
11. $45.0°$ **12.** $133.7°$ **13.** $145.5°$ **14.** $35.1°$
15.   **16.**

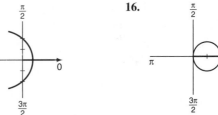

17.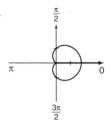

18.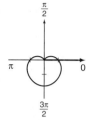

19.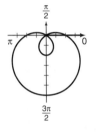

20.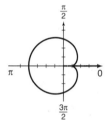

21. $x^2 + y^2 + x = \sqrt{x^2 + y^2}$, cardioid
22. $r = -3 \sec \theta \tan \theta$, parabola
23. $x^2 + y^2 - 3y = 0$, circle
24. $r = 2 + 3 \sin \theta$, limacon
25. The line $5x + 2y = -11$
26. The circle $x^2 + y^2 = 9$
27. The ellipse $16x^2 + y^2 = 16$
28. The portion of the parabola $y = x^2 + 6x + 11$ between and including the points $(-4, 3)$ and $(1, 18)$
29. The hyperbola $9x^2 - 4y^2 = 36$
30. The hyperbola $xy = -5$
31. (a) $x = 36t$ and $y = 36\sqrt{3}t - 16t^2$

    (b) $\frac{9\sqrt{3}}{4}$ seconds   (c) $81\sqrt{3}$ feet

32. $\sqrt{14}$
33. $x^2 - 8x + y^2 + 2y + z^2 - 10z + 33 = 0$
34. $(-5, -2, 3)$ and $r = 4\sqrt{2}$
35. A plane parallel to the xz-plane intersecting the y-axis at $(0, -3, 0)$
36. A plane parallel to the z-axis intersecting the xy-plane in the line $2x - 5y = 10$

37. A plane having intercepts at $(2, 0, 0)$, $(0, -3, 0)$, and $(0, 0, -2)$
38. The graph is a cylindrical surface generated by parabolas of the form $z = 4x^2$ in planes parallel to the xz-plane.
39. The graph is a cylindrical surface generated by ellipses of the form $y^2 + 4z^2 = 4$ in planes parallel to the yz-plane.

40.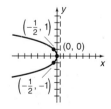

CHAPTER 9

Problem Set 9.1 (page 579)

1. $V(0, 0)$, $F(2, 0)$, $x = -2$

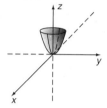

3. $V(0, 0)$, $F(0, -3)$, $y = 3$

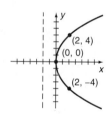

5. $V(0, 0)$, $F\left(-\frac{1}{2}, 0\right)$, $x = \frac{1}{2}$

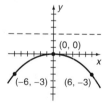

7. $V(0, 0)$, $F\left(0, \frac{3}{2}\right)$, $y = -\frac{3}{2}$

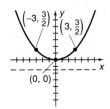

9. $V(0, 2)$, $F(0, 3)$, $y = 1$

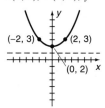

11. $V(0, -2)$, $F(0, -4)$, $y = 0$

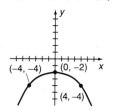

13. $V(2, 0)$, $F(5, 0)$, $x = -1$

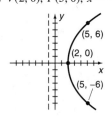

15. $V(1, 2)$, $F(1, 3)$, $y = 1$

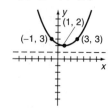

17. $V(-3, 1)$, $F(-3, -1)$, $y = 3$

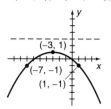

19. $V(3, 1)$, $F(0, 1)$, $x = 6$

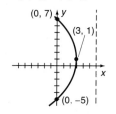

21. $V(-2, -3)$, $F(-1, -3)$, $x = -3$

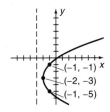

23. $x^2 = 12y$ **25.** $y^2 = -4x$
27. $x^2 + 12y - 48 = 0$ **29.** $x^2 - 6x - 12y + 21 = 0$
31. $y^2 - 10y + 8x + 41 = 0$ **33.** $3y^2 = -25x$
35. $y^2 = 10x$ **37.** $x^2 - 14x - 8y + 73 = 0$
39. $y^2 + 6y - 12x + 105 = 0$
41. $x^2 + 18x + y + 80 = 0$ **43.** $x^2 = 750(y - 10)$
45. $10\sqrt{2}$ feet   **47.** 62.5 feet

Problem Set 9.2 (page 589)

For Problems 1–21, the foci are indicated above the graph, and the vertices and endpoints of the minor axes are indicated on the graph.

1. $f(\sqrt{3}, 0)$, $F'(-\sqrt{3}, 0)$

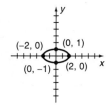

3. $F(0, \sqrt{5})$, $F'(0, -\sqrt{5})$

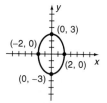

5. $F(0, \sqrt{6})$, $F'(0, -\sqrt{6})$

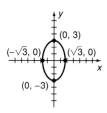

7. $F(\sqrt{15}, 0)$, $F'(-\sqrt{15}, 0)$

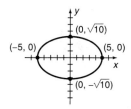

9. $F(0, \sqrt{33})$, $F'(0, -\sqrt{33})$ **11.** $F(2, 0)$, $F'(-2, 0)$

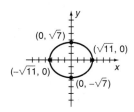

13. $F(1 + \sqrt{5}, 2)$, $F'(1 - \sqrt{5}, 2)$

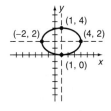

15. $F(-2, -1 + 2\sqrt{3})$, $F'(-2, -1 - 2\sqrt{3})$

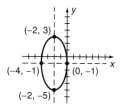

17. $F(3 + \sqrt{3}, 0)$, $F'(3 - \sqrt{3}, 0)$

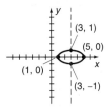

19. $F(4, -1 + \sqrt{7})$, $F'(4, -1 - \sqrt{7})$

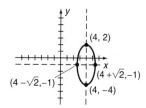

21. $F(0, 4)$, $F'(-6, 4)$

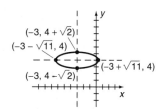

23. $16x^2 + 25y^2 = 400$ **25.** $36x^2 + 11y^2 = 396$
27. $x^2 + 9y^2 = 9$ **29.** $100x^2 + 36y^2 = 225$
31. $7x^2 + 3y^2 = 75$
33. $3x^2 - 6x + 4y^2 - 8y - 41 = 0$
35. $9x^2 + 25y^2 - 50y - 200 = 0$
37. $3x^2 + 4y^2 = 48$ **39.** $\frac{10\sqrt{5}}{3}$ feet

Problem Set 9.3 (page 600)

For Problems 1–21, the foci and equations of the asymptotes are indicated above the graphs. The vertices are given on the graphs.

1. $F(\sqrt{13}, 0)$, $F'(-\sqrt{13}, 0)$

$y = \pm\frac{2}{3}x$

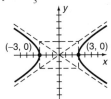

3. $F(0, \sqrt{13})$, $F'(0, -\sqrt{13})$

$y = \pm\frac{2}{3}x$

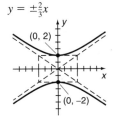

5. $F(0, 5)$, $F'(0, -5)$

$y = \pm\frac{4}{3}x$

7. $F(3\sqrt{2}, 0)$, $F'(-3\sqrt{2}, 0)$

$y = \pm x$

9. $F(0, \sqrt{30})$, $F'(0, -\sqrt{30})$

$y = \pm\frac{\sqrt{5}}{5}x$

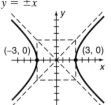

11. $F(\sqrt{10}, 0)$, $F'(-\sqrt{10}, 0)$

$y = \pm 3x$

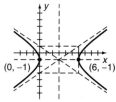

13. $F(3 + \sqrt{13}, -1)$, $F'(3 - \sqrt{13}, -1)$

$2x - 3y = 9$ and $2x + 3y = 3$

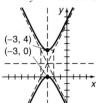

15. $F(-3, 2 + \sqrt{5})$, $F'(-3, 2 - \sqrt{5})$

$2x - y = -8$ and $2x + y = -4$

17. $F(2 + \sqrt{6}, 0)$, $F'(2 - \sqrt{6}, 0)$

$\sqrt{2}x - y = 2\sqrt{2}$ and $\sqrt{2}x + y = 2\sqrt{2}$

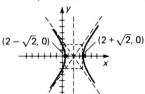

19. $F(0, -5 + \sqrt{10})$, $F'(0, -5 - \sqrt{10})$

$3x - y = 5$ and $3x + y = -5$

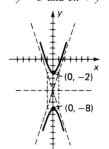

21. $F(-2 + \sqrt{2}, -2)$, $F'(-2 - \sqrt{2}, -2)$
   $x - y = 0$ and $x + y = -4$

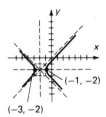

23. $5x^2 - 4y^2 = 20$ **25.** $16y^2 - 9x^2 = 144$
27. $3x^2 - y^2 = 3$ **29.** $4y^2 - 3x^2 = 12$
31. $7x^2 - 16y^2 = 112$
33. $5x^2 - 40x - 4y^2 - 24y + 24 = 0$
35. $3y^2 - 30y - x^2 - 6x + 54 = 0$
37. $5x^2 - 20x - 4y^2 = 0$ **39.** Circle
41. Straight line   **43.** Ellipse   **45.** Hyperbola
47. Parabola

Problem Set 9.4 (page 609)

1. $(x')^2 - (y')^2 = 2$

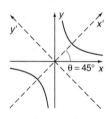

3. $(x')^2 + 2(y')^2 = 9$

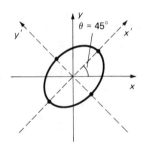

5. $(x')^2 - 3(y')^2 = 9$

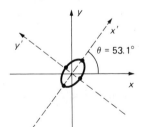

7. $(x')^2 + 2(y')^2 = 1$

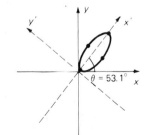

9. $(y')^2 = 4$

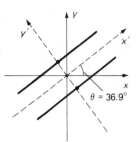

11. $y' = -2(x')^2$

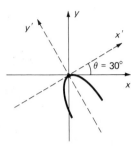

13. $y' = (x')^2 + 2$

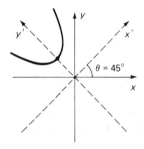

15. $2(x')^2 + (y')^2 = 8$

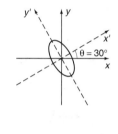

17. $4(x')^2 - (y')^2 = 1$

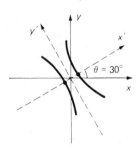

19. $(y')^2 = 4(x' - 1)$

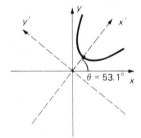

21. $\dfrac{(x' - 2)^2}{4} + \dfrac{(y')^2}{1} = 1$

23. $\dfrac{(x'-3)^2}{1} - \dfrac{(y')^2}{2} = 1$

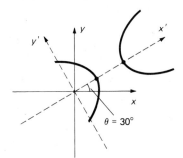

25. $\dfrac{(x'+1)^2}{2} + \dfrac{(y'-1)^2}{3} = 1$

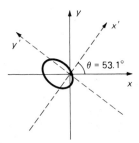

27. $(x')^2 + 2(y')^2 = 0$
The graph contains only one point, the origin.
29. $(-2 - 3\sqrt{3}, 3 - 2\sqrt{3}), (4 + \sqrt{3}, -1 + 4\sqrt{3})$
31. $x' = x\cos\theta + y\sin\theta$
$y' = -x\sin\theta + y\cos\theta$

Problem Set 9.5 (page 615)

1.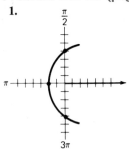

3.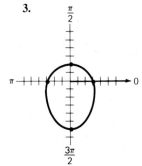

5.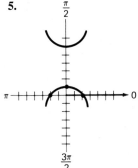

7.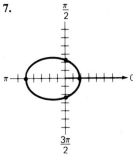

9.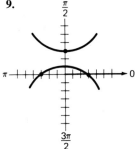

11.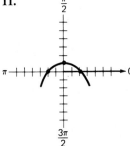

13.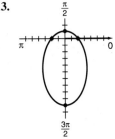

15.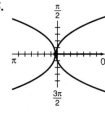

17.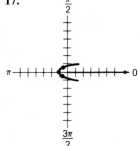

19. $r = \dfrac{4}{1 + \cos\theta}$

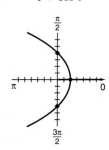

21. $r = \dfrac{5}{3 - 2\sin\theta}$

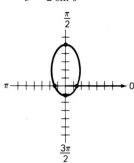

23. $r = \dfrac{6}{1 + 2\sin\theta}$ **25.** $r = \dfrac{1}{5 + \cos\theta}$

27. $r = \dfrac{4}{1 - \sin\theta}$ **29.** $r = \dfrac{4}{7 + 2\cos\theta}$

Chapter 9 Review Problem Set (page 619)

1. $F(4, 0),\ F'(-4, 0)$ **2.** $F(-3, 0)$

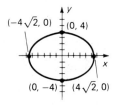   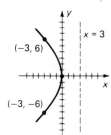

3. $F(0, 2\sqrt{3}),\ F'(0, -2\sqrt{3})$
$y = \pm\dfrac{\sqrt{3}}{3}x$

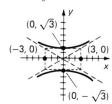

4. $F(\sqrt{15}, 0),\ F'(-\sqrt{15}, 0)$
$y = \pm\dfrac{\sqrt{6}}{3}x$

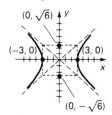

5. $F(0, \sqrt{6}),\ F'(0, -\sqrt{6})$ **6.** $F\left(0, \frac{1}{2}\right)$

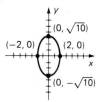   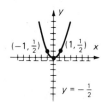

7. $F(4 + \sqrt{6}, 1),\ F'(4 - \sqrt{6}, 1),\ \sqrt{2}x - 2y = 4\sqrt{2} - 2$
and $\sqrt{2}x + 2y = 4\sqrt{2} + 2$

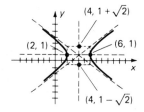

8. $F(3, -2 + \sqrt{7}),\ F'(3, -2 - \sqrt{7})$

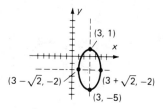

9. $F(-3, 1),\ x = -1$ **10.** $F(-1, -5),\ y = -1$

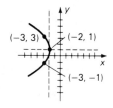   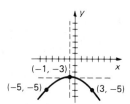

11. $F(-5 + 2\sqrt{3}, 2),\ F'(-5 - 2\sqrt{3}, 2)$

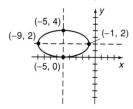

12. $F(-2, -2 + \sqrt{10})$, $F'(-2, -2 - \sqrt{10})$,
$\sqrt{6}x - 3y = 6 - 2\sqrt{6}$ and $\sqrt{6}x + 3y = -6 - 2\sqrt{6}$

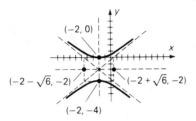

13. $y^2 = -20x$ **14.** $y^2 + 16x^2 = 16$
15. $25x^2 - 2y^2 = 50$ **16.** $4x^2 + 3y^2 = 16$
17. $3x^2 = 2y$ **18.** $9y^2 - x^2 = 9$
19. $9x^2 - 108x + y^2 - 8y + 331 = 0$
20. $y^2 + 4y - 8x + 36 = 0$
21. $3y^2 + 24y - x^2 - 10x + 20 = 0$
22. $x^2 + 12x - y + 33 = 0$
23. $4x^2 + 40x + 25y^2 = 0$
24. $4x^2 - 32x - y^2 + 48 = 0$
25. $y' = (x')^2$ **26.** $(x')^2 + 3(y')^2 = 6$

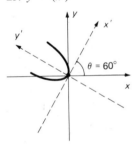

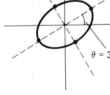

27. $2(y')^2 - (x')^2 = 8$ **28.** $(x')^2 = 4$

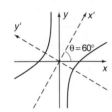

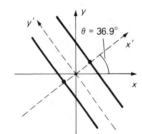

29. $y' = -(x')^2 + 2$

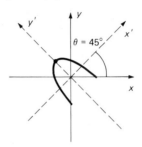

30. $\dfrac{(x' - 1)^2}{9} + \dfrac{(y' + 1)^2}{1} = 1$

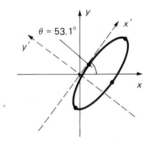

31. $(4 - 5\sqrt{3}, -5 - 4\sqrt{3})$

32.

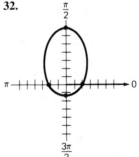

33.

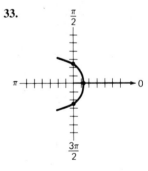

34.

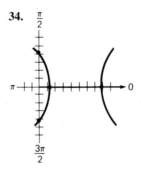

35.

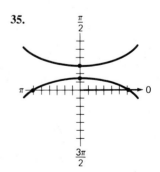

36. $r = \dfrac{6}{1 - \sin\theta}$ **37.** $r = \dfrac{12}{5 + \sin\theta}$

38. $r = \dfrac{20}{2 - 5\cos\theta}$

CHAPTER 10

Problem Set 10.1 (page 628)

1. $-4, -1, 2, 5, 8$ **3.** $2, 0, -2, -4, -6$
5. $2, 11, 26, 47, 74$ **7.** $0, 2, 6, 12, 20$
9. $4, 8, 16, 32, 64$ **11.** $a_{15} = -79; a_{30} = -154$
13. $a_{25} = 1; a_{50} = -1$ **15.** $a_n = 2n + 9$

17. $a_n = -3n + 5$ **19.** $a_n = \dfrac{n + 2}{2}$

21. $a_n = 4n - 2$ **23.** $a_n = -3n$ **25.** 73
27. 334   **29.** 35   **31.** 7   **33.** 86
35. 2700   **37.** 3200   **39.** -7950 **41.** 637.5
43. 4950   **45.** 1850   **47.** -2030 **49.** 3591
51. 40,000   **53.** 58,250   **55.** 2205
57. -1325 **59.** 5265   **61.** -810 **63.** 1276
65. 660   **67.** 55   **69.** 431
71. $3, 3, 7, 7, 11, 11$ **73.** $4, 7, 10, 13, 17, 21$
75. $4, 12, 36, 108, 324, 972$ **77.** $1, 1, 2, 3, 5, 8$
79. $3, 1, 4, 9, 25, 256$

Problem Set 10.2 (page 637)

1. $a_n = 3(2)^{n-1}$ **3.** $a_n = 3^n$ **5.** $a_n = \left(\tfrac{1}{2}\right)^{n+1}$

7. $a_n = 4^n$ **9.** $a_n = (.3)^{n-1}$ **11.** $a_n = (-2)^{n-1}$

13. 64   **15.** $\tfrac{1}{9}$ **17.** -512 **19.** $\tfrac{1}{4374}$

21. $\tfrac{2}{3}$ **23.** 2   **25.** 1023   **27.** 19,682

29. $394\tfrac{1}{16}$ **31.** 1364   **33.** 1089   **35.** $7\tfrac{511}{512}$

37. -547 **39.** $127\tfrac{3}{4}$ **41.** 540   **43.** $2\tfrac{61}{64}$

45. 4   **47.** 3   **49.** No sum   **51.** $\tfrac{27}{4}$

53. 2   **55.** $\tfrac{16}{3}$ **57.** $\tfrac{1}{3}$ **59.** $\tfrac{26}{99}$ **61.** $\tfrac{41}{333}$

63. $\tfrac{4}{15}$ **65.** $\tfrac{106}{495}$ **67.** $\tfrac{7}{3}$

Problem Set 10.3 (page 642)

1. \$24,200   **3.** 11,550   **5.** 7320
7. 125 liters   **9.** 512 gallons   **11.** \$116.25
13. \$163.84; \$327.67   **15.** \$24,900

17. 1936 feet   **19.** $\tfrac{15}{16}$ of a gram   **21.** 2910 feet

23. 325 logs   **25.** 5.9%   **27.** $\tfrac{5}{64}$ of a gallon

Problem Set 10.4 (page 649)

These problems are proofs by mathematical induction and require class discussion.

Chapter 10 Review Problem Set (page 651)

1. $a_n = 6n - 3$ **2.** $a_n = 3^{n-2}$ **3.** $a_n = 5 \cdot 2^n$
4. $a_n = -3n + 8$ **5.** $a_n = 2n - 7$
6. $a_n = 3^{3-n}$ **7.** $a_n = -(-2)^{n-1}$

8. $a_n = 3n + 9$ **9.** $a_n = \dfrac{n + 1}{3}$ **10.** $a_n = 4^{n-1}$

11. 73   **12.** 106   **13.** $\tfrac{1}{32}$ **14.** $\tfrac{4}{9}$

15. -92 **16.** $\tfrac{1}{16}$ **17.** -5 **18.** 85   **19.** $\tfrac{5}{9}$

20. 2 or -2 **21.** $121\tfrac{40}{81}$ **22.** 7035

23. $-10,725$ **24.** $31\tfrac{31}{32}$ **25.** 32,015

26. 4757   **27.** $85\tfrac{21}{64}$ **28.** 37,044   **29.** 12,726

30. -1845 **31.** 225   **32.** 255   **33.** 8244

34. $85\tfrac{1}{3}$ **35.** $\tfrac{4}{11}$ **36.** $\tfrac{41}{90}$ **37.** \$750

38. \$46.50   **39.** \$3276.70   **40.** 10,935 gallons

CHAPTER 11

Problem Set 11.1 (page 664)

1. Yes   **3.** Yes   **5.** No   **7.** No   **9.** Yes
11. $\{(-1, -5)\}$ **13.** $\{(3, -6)\}$ **15.** $\varnothing$
17. $\{(-2, -9)\}$ **19.** $\{(-1, -2, 3)\}$
21. $\{(3, -1, 4)\}$ **23.** $\{(0, -2, 4)\}$
25. $\{(-7k + 8, -5k + 7, k)\}$ **27.** $\{(-4, -3, -2)\}$
29. $\{(4, -1, -2)\}$ **31.** $\{(1, -1, 2, -3)\}$
33. $\{(2, 1, 3, -2)\}$ **35.** $\{(-2, 4, -3, 0)\}$ **37.** $\varnothing$
39. $\{(-3k + 5, -1, -4k + 2, k)\}$
41. $\{(-3k + 9, k, 2, -3)\}$ **43.** $\{(17k - 6, 10k - 5, k)\}$
45. $\left\{\left(-\tfrac{1}{2}k + \tfrac{34}{11}, \tfrac{1}{2}k - \tfrac{5}{11}, k\right)\right\}$ **47.** $\varnothing$

Problem Set 11.2 (page 674)

1. 22   **3.** -29 **5.** 20   **7.** 5   **9.** -2
11. $-\tfrac{2}{3}$ **13.** -25 **15.** 58   **17.** 39
19. -12 **21.** -41 **23.** -8 **25.** 1088
27. -140 **29.** 81   **31.** 146
33. Property 11.3   **35.** Property 11.2
37. Property 11.4   **39.** Property 11.3
41. Property 11.5

Problem Set 11.3 (page 681)

1. $\{(1, 4)\}$ **3.** $\{(3, -5)\}$ **5.** $\{(2, -1)\}$

7. $\varnothing$ **9.** $\left\{\left(-\frac{1}{4}, \frac{2}{3}\right)\right\}$ **11.** $\left\{\left(\frac{2}{17}, \frac{52}{17}\right)\right\}$

13. $\{(9, -2)\}$ **15.** $\left\{\left(2, -\frac{5}{7}\right)\right\}$ **17.** $\{(0, 2, -3)\}$

19. $\{(2, 6, 7)\}$ **21.** $\{(4, -4, 5)\}$

23. $\{(-1, 3, -4)\}$ **25.** Infinitely many solutions

27. $\left\{\left(-2, \frac{1}{2}, -\frac{2}{3}\right)\right\}$ **29.** $\left\{\left(3, \frac{1}{2}, -\frac{1}{3}\right)\right\}$

31. $\{(-4, 6, 0)\}$ **35.** $\{(0, 0, 0)\}$

37. Infinitely many solutions   **39.** $\{(0, 0, 0)\}$

Problem Set 11.4 (page 690)

1.

3.
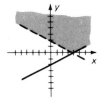

5.
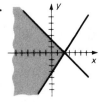

7.
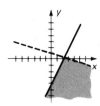

9.
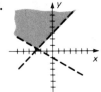

11.
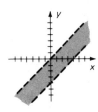

13.
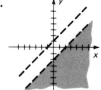

15.
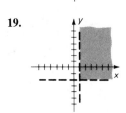

17. $\varnothing$ **19.**

21.
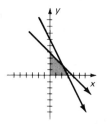

23.
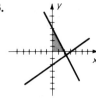

25. Minimum of 8 and maximum of 52

27. Minimum of 0 and maximum of 28

29. 63   **31.** 340   **33.** 2   **35.** 98

37. $5000 at 9% and $5000 at 12%

39. 300 of type A and 200 of type B

41. 12 units of A and 16 units of B

Chapter 11 Review Problem Set (page 694)

1. $\{(3, -7)\}$ **2.** $\{(-1, -3)\}$ **3.** $\{(0, -4)\}$

4. $\left\{\left(\frac{23}{3}, -\frac{14}{3}\right)\right\}$ **5.** $\{(4, -6)\}$ **6.** $\left\{\left(-\frac{6}{7}, -\frac{15}{7}\right)\right\}$

7. $\{(-1, 2, -5)\}$ **8.** $\{(2, -3, -1)\}$ **9.** $\{(5, -4)\}$

10. $\{(2, 7)\}$ **11.** $\{(-2, 2, -1)\}$ **12.** $\{(0, -1, 2)\}$

13. $\{(-3, -1)\}$ **14.** $\{(4, 6)\}$ **15.** $\{(2, -3, -4)\}$

16. $\{(-1, 2, -5)\}$ **17.** $\{(5, -5)\}$ **18.** $\{(-12, 12)\}$

19. $\left\{\left(\frac{5}{7}, \frac{4}{7}\right)\right\}$ **20.** $\{(-10, -7)\}$ **21.** $\{(1, 1, -4)\}$

22. $\{(-4, 0, 1)\}$ **23.** $\varnothing$ **24.** $\{(-2, -4, 6)\}$

25. -34 **26.** 13   **27.** -40 **28.** 16

29. 51   **30.** 125

31.

32.

33.

34.

35. 37   **36.** 56   **37.** 57   **38.** 1700

39. 75 one-gallon and 175 two-gallon freezers

INDEX

area A **width** w **base** b **volume** V
perimeter P **surface area** S **circumference** C **area of base** B
length l **altitude (height)** h **radius** r **slant height** s

RECTANGLE

$$A = lw \qquad P = 2l + 2w$$

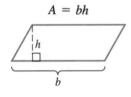

PARALLELOGRAM

$$A = bh$$

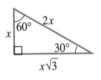

30°–60° RIGHT TRIANGLE

RIGHT CIRCULAR CYLINDER

$$V = \pi r^2 h \qquad S = 2\pi r^2 + 2\pi rh$$

TRIANGLE

$$A = \frac{1}{2} bh$$

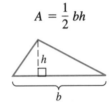

TRAPEZOID

$$A = \frac{1}{2} h(b_1 + b_2)$$

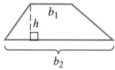

RIGHT TRIANGLE

$$a^2 + b^2 = c^2$$

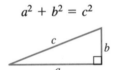

SPHERE

$$S = 4\pi r^2 \qquad V = \frac{4}{3} \pi r^3$$

SQUARE

$$A = s^2 \qquad P = 4s$$

CIRCLE

$$A = \pi r^2 \qquad C = 2\pi r$$

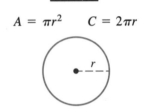

ISOSCELES RIGHT TRIANGLE

RIGHT CIRCULAR CONE

$$V = \frac{1}{3} \pi r^2 h \qquad S = \pi r^2 + \pi rs$$

PYRAMID

$$V = \frac{1}{3} Bh$$

Base

PRISM

$$V = Bh$$

Base